# rigonometry

## Math 102

**College of Canyons**

create.mheducation.com

ISBN-13: 9781308278766

ISBN-10: 1308278764

# Contents

**Most coral reefs in the world are 7000–9000 years old,** but new reefs can fully develop in as few as 20 years. In addition to being home to over 4000 species of tropical or reef fish, coral reefs are immensely beneficial to humans and must be carefully preserved. They buffer coastal regions from strong waves and storms, provide millions of people with food and jobs, and prompt advances in modern medicine.

Similar to the ancient reefs, a course in trigonometry is based on thousands of years of mathematical curiosity, insight, and wisdom. In this one short course, we unravel the celestial mysteries that inspired the study of angles so long ago, as well as develop a more modern vision of periodic phenomena, both of which remain tremendously important. Just as the variety of fish in the sea rely on the coral reefs to survive, students in a trigonometry course rely on mastery of this bedrock of concepts to successfully pursue more advanced courses, as well as their career goals.

## From the Authors

This textbook, while intended for a relatively short course, contains some of humanity's most important discoveries. Within these pages lie the condensed, concentrated, and illuminated collective works of generations of scholars and intellectuals. In reflecting on the works of the ancient astronomers and mathematicians that serve as the foundation for this course, we see an analogy in the great coral reefs, where thousands of years of growth provide the underlying structure for a vibrant, living community. Similarly, trigonometry is a subject that, while ancient, is still teeming with life—colorful, beautiful, and often mysterious.

Long before we began writing a text for this course, our teaching experience left a nagging sense that most texts on the market lacked the ability to connect with so diverse an audience. In addition, they appeared to offer too scant a framework to build concepts, too terse a development to make connections, and insufficient support in their exercise sets to develop long-term retention or foster a love of mathematics. In particular, the applications seemed to lack a sense of realism, curious interest, and/or connections to a student's everyday experience.

With all of this in mind and a strong desire to write a better text, we set about the task of creating what we hoped would become a more engaging tool for students, and a more supportive tool for instructors. We believe drawing on the diversity of our own educational experience and exposure to different cultures, views, and perspectives, has contributed to the text's unique and engaging style, and we hope in the end, to more and better connections with our diverse audience. Having feedback from more than 400 people, including manuscript reviewers, focus group participants, and contributors, was invaluable to helping us hone the connections in this book. As a collateral outgrowth of this experience, there was also a desire to interest and engage ourselves, the instructors—to remind us again and again, why we fell in love with mathematics in the first place.    —John Coburn and J.D. Herdlick

# Making Connections...

**Trigonometry tends to be a challenging course for many students.** They may not see the connections that trigonometry has to their life or why it is so critical that they take and pass this course. Others may enter into this course underprepared or improperly placed and with very little motivation.

Instructors are faced with several challenges as well. They are given the task of improving pass rates and student retention while ensuring the students are adequately prepared for more advanced courses. Furthermore, it can be difficult to distinguish between students who are likely to succeed and students who may struggle until after the first test is given.

The goal of this textbook series is to provide both students and instructors with tools to address these challenges, so that both can experience greater success in trigonometry. For instance, the comprehensive exercise sets have a range of difficulty that provides very strong support for weaker students, while advanced students are challenged to reach even further. The rest of this preface further explains the tools that John Coburn, J.D. Herdlick, and McGraw-Hill have developed and how they can be used to *connect* students to trigonometry and *connect* instructors to their students.

**The Coburn/Herdlick Trigonometry Series provides you with strong tools to achieve better outcomes in your Trigonometry course as follows:**

▶ *Better Student Preparedness*

▶ *Increased Student Engagement*

▶ *Solid Skill Development*

▶ *Strong Connections*

### ▶ Better Student Preparedness

No two students have the same strengths and weaknesses in mathematics. Typically students will enter any math course with different preparedness levels. For most students who have trouble retaining or recalling concepts learned in past courses, basic review is simply not enough to sustain them successfully throughout the course. Moreover, instructors whose main focus is to prepare students for the next course do not have adequate time in or out of class to individually help each student with review material.

ALEKS Prep uniquely assesses each student to determine their individual strengths and weaknesses and informs the student of their capabilities using a personalized pie chart. From there, students begin learning through ALEKS via a personalized learning path uniquely designed for each student. ALEKS Prep interacts with students like a private tutor and provides a safe learning environment to remediate their individual knowledge gaps of the course prerequisite material outside of class.

ALEKS Prep is the only learning tool that empowers students by giving them an opportunity to remediate individual knowledge gaps and improve their chances for success. ALEKS Prep is especially effective when used in conjunction with ALEKS Placement and ALEKS 3.0 course-based software.

### ▶ Increased Student Engagement

What make John Coburn and J.D. Herdlick's applications unique is that they are constantly thinking mathematically. Their applications are spawned during a trip to Chicago, a phone call with a brother or sister, or even while wakeboarding. They literally take notes on things seen in everyday life and connect these situations to math. This truly makes for relevant applications that are born from real-life experiences as opposed to applications that can seem too fictitious or contrived.

### ▶ Solid Skill Development

The Coburn/Herdlick series intentionally relates the examples to the exercise sets so there is a strong connection between what students are learning while working through the examples in each section and the homework exercises that they complete. In turn, students who attempt to work the exercises first can surely rely on the examples to offer support as needed. Because of how well the examples and exercises are connected, key concepts are easily understood and students have plenty of help when using the book outside of class.

There is also an abundance of exercise types to choose from to ensure that homework challenges a wide variety of skills. Furthermore, John and J.D. reconnect students to earlier chapter material with Mid-Chapter Checks; students have praised these exercises for helping them understand what key concepts require additional practice.

### ▶ Strong Connections

John Coburn and J.D. Herdlick's experience in the classroom and their strong connections to how students comprehend the material are evident in their writing style. This is demonstrated by the way they provide a tight weave from topic to topic and foster an environment that doesn't just focus on procedures but illustrates the big picture, which is something that so often is sacrificed in this course. Moreover, they employ a clear and supportive writing style, providing the students with a tool they can depend on when the teacher is not available, when they miss a day of class, or simply when working on their own.

# Better Student Preparedness...

## Experience Student Success!

**ALEKS** ALEKS is a unique online math tool that uses adaptive questioning and artificial intelligence to correctly place, prepare, and remediate students . . . all in one product! Institutional case studies have shown that **ALEKS has improved pass rates by over 20% versus traditional online homework and by over 30% compared to using a text alone.**

By offering each student an individualized learning path, ALEKS directs students to work on the math topics that they are ready to learn. Also, to help students keep pace in their course, instructors can correlate ALEKS to their textbook or syllabus in seconds.

To learn more about how ALEKS can be used to boost student performance, please visit **www.aleks.com/highered/math** or contact your McGraw-Hill representative.

**Easy Graphing Utility!**
Students can answer graphing problems with ease!

**ALEKS Pie**
Each student is given their own individualized learning path.

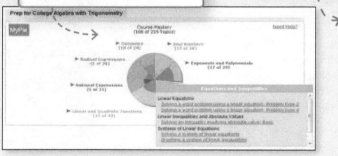

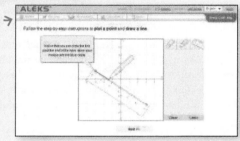

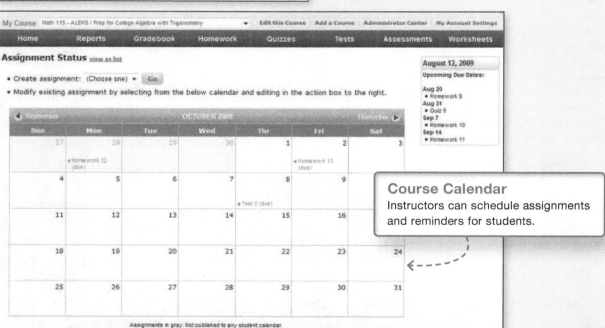

**Course Calendar**
Instructors can schedule assignments and reminders for students.

# ...Through ALEKS®

## New ALEKS Instructor Module

### Enhanced Functionality and Streamlined Interface Help to Save Instructor Time

**ALEKS®** The new ALEKS Instructor Module features enhanced functionality and streamlined interface based on research with ALEKS instructors and homework management instructors. Paired with powerful assignment driven features, textbook integration, and extensive content flexibility, the new ALEKS Instructor Module simplifies administrative tasks and makes ALEKS more powerful than ever.

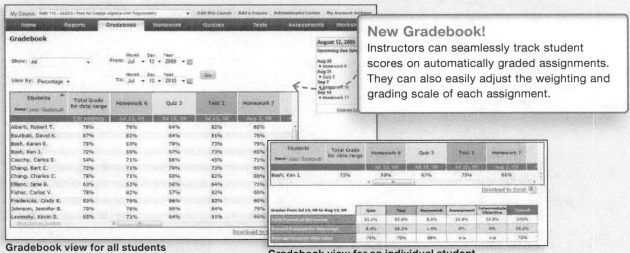

Gradebook view for all students

**New Gradebook!**
Instructors can seamlessly track student scores on automatically graded assignments. They can also easily adjust the weighting and grading scale of each assignment.

Gradebook view for an individual student

**Track Student Progress Through Detailed Reporting**
Instructors can track student progress through automated reports and robust reporting features.

**Automatically Graded Assignments**
Instructors can easily assign homework, quizzes, tests, and assessments to all or select students. Deadline extensions can also be created for select students.

Select topics for each assignment

Learn more about ALEKS by visiting **www.aleks.com/highered/math** or contact your McGraw-Hill representative.

# *Increased Student Engagement...*

## Through Meaningful Applications

Making mathematics meaningful requires that students experience the connection between mathematics and its impact on the world they live in. This text is also the result of a powerful commitment to provide applications of the highest quality, having close ties to the examples, and with carefully monitored levels of difficulty.

Many of these examples were born of our own diverse life experiences, others came from a curious, lucid, and even visionary folly that allows one to seize upon the every day events of life, and see the significant or meaningful mathematics in the background. Our ever-present notebooks were used a thousand times to capture that casual observation, or that sudden burst of inspiration that is the genesis for outstanding applications. These were supported at home by a substantial library of reference and research books, an eye toward both history and current events, and of course our modern marvel of a research tool—the Internet. After a (sometimes long) period of thought, reflection, and research, followed by a wording and a rewording of the exercise so that it would resonate with students while filling the need, a significant and meaningful application was born.  —JC/JD

▶ **Chapter Openers** highlight Chapter Connections, an interesting application exercise from the chapter, and provide a list of other real-world connections to give context for students who wonder how math relates to them.

> **"**I especially like the depth and variety of applications in this textbook. Other Precalculus texts the department considered did not share this strength. In particular, there is a clear effort on the part of the author to include realistic examples showing how such math can be utilized in the real world.**"** —*George Alexander, Madison Area Technical College*

▶ **Examples** throughout the text feature word problems, providing students with a starting point for how to solve these types of problems in their exercise sets.

> **"**One of this text's strongest features is the wide range of applications exercises. As an instructor, I can choose which exercises fit my teaching style as well as the student interest level.**"**
> —*Stephen Toner, Victor Valley College*

▶ **Application Exercises** at the end of each section are the hallmark of the Coburn series. Never contrived, always creative, and born out of the author's life and experiences, each application tells a story and appeals to a variety of teaching styles, disciplines, backgrounds, and interests.

> **"** [The application problems] answered the question, 'When are we ever going to use this?' **"**
> —*Student class tester at Metropolitan Community College–Longview*

▶ **Math in Action Applets,** located online, enable students to work collaboratively as they manipulate applets that apply mathematical concepts in real-world contexts.

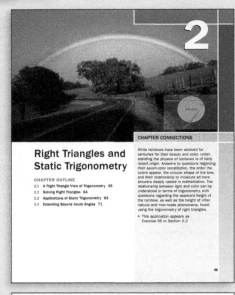

**Right Triangles and Static Trigonometry**

CHAPTER OUTLINE

2.1 A Right Triangle View of Trigonometry  46
2.2 Solving Right Triangles  54
2.3 Applications of Static Trigonometry  63
2.4 Extending Beyond Acute Angles  71

**CHAPTER CONNECTIONS**

While rainbows have been admired for centuries for their beauty and color, understanding the physics of rainbows is of fairly recent origin. Answers to questions regarding their seven-color constitution, the order the colors appear, the circular shape of the bow, and their relationship to moisture all have answers deeply rooted in mathematics. The relationship between light and color can be understood in terms of trigonometry, with questions regarding the apparent height of the rainbow, as well as the height of other natural and man-made phenomena, found using the trigonometry of right triangles.

▶ This application appears as Exercise 55 in Section 2.2

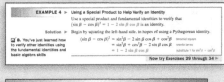

EXAMPLE 4 ▶ Using a Special Product to Help Verify an Identity
Use a special product and fundamental identities to verify that
$(\sin \beta - \cos \beta)^2 = 1 - 2 \sin \beta \cos \beta$ is an identity.

Solution ▶ Begin by squaring the left-hand side, in hopes of using a Pythagorean identity.

$(\sin \beta - \cos \beta)^2 = \sin^2\beta - 2 \sin \beta \cos \beta + \cos^2\beta$
$= \sin^2\beta + \cos^2\beta - 2 \sin \beta \cos \beta$
$= 1 - 2 \sin \beta \cos \beta$

Now try Exercises 29 through 34 ▶

**PC Project 6 –Angles**

xii

# Through Timely Examples

In mathematics, it would be difficult to overstate the importance of examples that set the stage for learning. Not a few educational experiences have faltered due to an example that was too difficult, a poor fit, out of sequence, or had a distracting result. In this series, a careful and deliberate effort was made to select examples that were timely and clear, with a direct focus on the concept or skill at hand. Everywhere possible, they were further designed to link previous concepts to current ideas, and to lay the groundwork for concepts to come. As a trained educator knows, the best time to answer a question is often before it's ever asked, and a timely sequence of carefully constructed examples can go a long way in this regard, making each new idea simply the next logical, even anticipated step. When successful, the mathematical maturity of a student grows in unnoticed increments, as though it was just supposed to be that way. —JC/JD

► **Titles** have been added to Examples in this edition to highlight relevant learning objectives and reinforce the importance of speaking mathematically using vocabulary.

► **Annotations** located to the right of the solution sequence help the student recognize which property or procedure is being applied.

► **"Now Try"** boxes immediately following Examples guide students to specific matched exercises at the end of the section, helping them identify exactly which homework problems coincide with each discussed concept.

► **Graphical Support Boxes,** located after selected examples, visually reinforce algebraic concepts with a corresponding graphing calculator example.

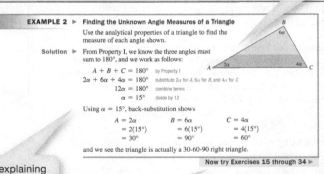

EXAMPLE 2 ► Finding the Unknown Angle Measures of a Triangle

Use the analytical properties of a triangle to find the measure of each angle shown.

Solution ► From Property I, we know the three angles must sum to 180°, and we work as follows:

$A + B + C = 180°$    by Property I

$2\alpha + 6\alpha + 4\alpha = 180°$    substitute $2\alpha$ for $A$, $6\alpha$ for $B$, and $4\alpha$ for $C$

$12\alpha = 180°$    combine terms

$\alpha = 15°$    divide by 12

Using $\alpha = 15°$, back-substitution shows

| | | |
|---|---|---|
| $A = 2\alpha$ | $B = 6\alpha$ | $C = 4\alpha$ |
| $= 2(15°)$ | $= 6(15°)$ | $= 4(15°)$ |
| $= 30°$ | $= 90°$ | $= 60°$ |

and we see the triangle is actually a 30-60-90 right triangle.

Now try Exercises 15 through 34 ►

GRAPHICAL SUPPORT

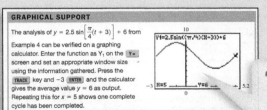

The analysis of $y = 2.5 \sin\left[\frac{\pi}{4}(t + 3)\right] + 6$ from Example 4 can be verified on a graphing calculator. Enter the function as $Y_1$ on the [Y=] screen and set an appropriate window size using the information gathered. Press the [TRACE] key and $-3$ [ENTER] and the calculator gives the average value $y = 6$ as output. Repeating this for $x = 5$ shows one complete cycle has been completed.

# Solid Skill Development...

## Through Exercises

### Mid-Chapter Checks

Mid-Chapter Checks provide students with a good stopping place to assess their knowledge before moving on to the second half of the chapter.

### End-of-Section Exercise Sets

▶ **Concepts and Vocabulary** exercises to help students recall and retain important terms.

▶ **Developing Your Skills** exercises to provide practice of relevant concepts just learned with increasing levels of difficulty.

▶ **Working with Formulas** exercises to demonstrate contextual applications of well-known formulas.

▶ **Extending the Concept** exercises that require communication of topics, synthesis of related concepts, and the use of higher-order thinking skills.

▶ **Maintaining Your Skills** exercises that address skills from previous sections to help students retain previously learning knowledge.

**MID-CHAPTER CHECK**

Verify that the following equations are identities.

1. $\cos^2 x - \cot^2 x = -\cos^2 x \cot^2 x$
2. $1 - \sin^2 t = (1 + \sin^2 t)\cos^2 t$
3. $\dfrac{2\sin x}{\sec x} - \dfrac{\cos x}{\csc x} = \cos x \sin x$
4. $\dfrac{1 - \cos t}{\cos t} + \dfrac{\sec t - 1}{\sec t} = \sec t - \cos t$

8. $\sin\left(\dfrac{\pi}{4}t\right)\cos\left(\dfrac{\pi}{3}t\right) + \cos\left(\dfrac{\pi}{4}t\right)\sin\left(\dfrac{\pi}{3}t\right)$

9. Given $\alpha$ and $\beta$ are acute angles with $\cos \alpha = \dfrac{3}{5}$ and $\cot \beta = \dfrac{5}{12}$, find
   a. $\sin(\alpha + \beta)$   b. $\cos(\alpha - \beta)$

**2.1 EXERCISES**

▶ **CONCEPTS AND VOCABULARY**

Fill in each blank with the appropriate word or phrase. Carefully reread the section if needed.

1. Every right triangle contains two _____ angles. The word _____ is actually a shortened form of "complement of tangent."

2. Given $\sin \theta = \frac{7}{4}$, $\csc \theta =$ _____ because they are _____.

3. The sine of an angle is the ratio of the _____ side to the _____.

4. The cosine of an angle is the ratio of the _____ side to the _____.

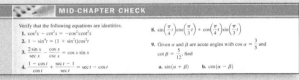

▶ **DEVELOPING YOUR SKILLS**

Given the point is on a unit circle, complete the ordered pair $(x, y)$ for the quadrant indicated. For Exercises 7 to 14, answer in radical form as needed. For Exercises 15 to 18, round results to four decimal places.

7. $(x, -0.8)$; QIII
8. $(-0.6, y)$; QII
9. $\left(\dfrac{5}{13}, y\right)$; QIV
10. $\left(x, -\dfrac{8}{17}\right)$; QIV
11. $\left(\dfrac{\sqrt{11}}{6}, y\right)$; QI
12. $\left(x, -\dfrac{\sqrt{13}}{7}\right)$; QIII
13. $\left(-\dfrac{\sqrt{11}}{4}, y\right)$; QII
14. $\left(x, \dfrac{\sqrt{6}}{5}\right)$; QI

Find the reference angle associated with each rotation, then find the associated point $(x, y)$ on the unit circle.

29. $\theta = \dfrac{5\pi}{4}$
30. $\theta = \dfrac{5\pi}{3}$
31. $\theta = \dfrac{5\pi}{6}$
32. $\theta = \dfrac{7\pi}{4}$
33. $\theta = \dfrac{11\pi}{4}$
34. $\theta = \dfrac{11\pi}{3}$
35. $\theta = \dfrac{25\pi}{6}$
36. $\theta = \dfrac{39\pi}{4}$

▶ **WORKING WITH FORMULAS**

53. Area of a regular polygon inscribed in a circle:
$A = \dfrac{nr^2}{2}\sin\left(\dfrac{2\pi}{n}\right)$

Exercise 53

The formula shown gives the area of a regular polygon inscribed in a circle, where $n$ is the number of sides ($n \geq 3$) and $r$ is the radius of the circle. Given $r = 10$ cm.
a. What is the area of

54. Hydrostatics, surface tension, and contact angles: $y = \dfrac{2y\cos\theta}{kr}$

The height that a liquid will rise in a capillary tube is given by the formula shown, where $r$ is the radius of the tube, $\theta$ is the contact angle of the liquid (the meniscus), $y$ is the surface tension of the liquid-vapor film, and $k$ is a constant that

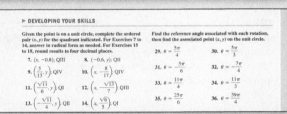

▶ **EXTENDING THE CONCEPT**

79. In this section, we discussed the *domain* of the circular functions, but said very little about their *range*. Review the concepts presented here and determine the range of $y = \cos t$ and $y = \sin t$. In other words, what are the smallest and largest output values we can expect?

Use the radian grid given with Exercises 25–36 to answer Exercises 81 and 82.

81. Given $\cos(2t) = -0.6$ with the terminal side of the arc in QII, (a) what is the value of $2t$? (b) What quadrant is $t$ in? (c) What is the value of $\cos t$? (d) Does $\cos(2t) = 2\cos t$?

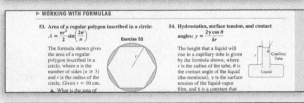

▶ **MAINTAINING YOUR SKILLS**

63. (6.3) Find the primary solution to:
$-3 \sec\theta + 7\sqrt{3} = 5\sqrt{3}$.

64. (3.3) State exact forms for each of the following:
$\sin\dfrac{\pi}{6}$, $\cos\left(\dfrac{7\pi}{6}\right)$, and $\tan\left(\dfrac{\pi}{3}\right)$.

66. (1.4) Use fundamental identities to find the values of all six trig functions that satisfy the conditions $\sin x = -\dfrac{5}{13}$ and $\cos x > 0$.

67. (5.2) Use a sum identity to find the value of $\sin 75°$ in exact form.

## End-of-Chapter Review Material

Exercises located at the end of the chapter provide students with the tools they need to prepare for a quiz or test. Each chapter features the following:

▶ **Chapter Summary and Concept Reviews** that present key concepts with corresponding exercises by section in a format easily used by students.

▶ **Mixed Reviews** that offer more practice on topics from the entire chapter, arranged in random order requiring students to identify problem types and solution strategies on their own.

▶ **Practice Tests** that give students the opportunity to check their knowledge and prepare for classroom quizzes, tests, and other assessments.

> "We always did reviews and a quiz before the actual test; it helped a lot."
> —*Melissa Cowan, student class tester Metropolitan Community College–Longview*

▶ **Cumulative Reviews** that are presented at the end of each chapter help students retain previously learned skills and concepts by revisiting important ideas from earlier chapters (starting with Chapter 2).

> "The cumulative review is very good and is considerably better than some of the books I have reviewed/used. I have found these to be wonderful practice for the final exam."
> —*Sarah Clifton, Southeastern Louisiana University*

▶ 🖩 **Graphing Calculator** icons appear next to exercises where important concepts can be supported by the use of graphing technology.

> "The summary and concept review was very helpful because it breaks down each section. That is what helps me the most."
> —*Brittany Pratt, student class tester at Baton Rouge Community College*

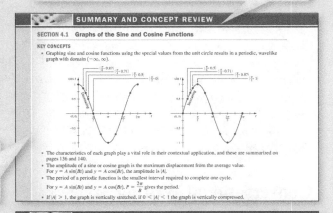

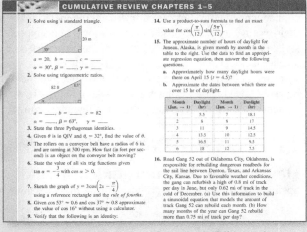

## Homework Selection Guide

A list of suggested homework exercises has been provided for each section of the text (Annotated Instructor's Edition only). This feature may prove especially useful for departments that encourage consistency among many sections, or those having a large adjunct population. The feature was also designed as a convenience to instructors, enabling them to develop an inventory of exercises that is more in tune with the course as they like to teach it. The guide provides prescreened and preselected assignments at four different levels: *Core, Standard, Extended,* and *In Depth.*

- **Core:** These assignments go right to the heart of the material, offering a minimal selection of exercises that cover the primary concepts and solution strategies of the section, along with a small selection of the best applications.

- **Standard:** The assignments at this level include the *Core* exercises, while providing for additional practice without excessive drill. A wider assortment of the possible variations on a theme are included, as well as a greater variety of applications.

- **Extended:** Assignments from the *Extended* category expand on the *Standard* exercises to include more applications, as well as some conceptual or theory-based questions. Exercises may include selected items from the *Concepts and Vocabulary, Working with Formulas,* and the *Extending the Concept* categories of the exercise sets.

- **In Depth:** The *In Depth* assignments represent a more comprehensive look at the material from each section, while attempting to keep the assignment manageable for students. These include a selection of the most popular and highest-quality exercises from each category of the exercise set, with an additional emphasis on *Maintaining Your Skills.*

# *Strong Connections...*

## Through a Conversational Writing Style

While examples and applications are arguably the most prominent features of a mathematics text, it's the writing style and readability that binds them together. It may be true that some students don't read the text, and that others open the text only when looking for an example similar to the exercise they're currently working. But when they do and for those students who do (read the text), it's important they have a text that "speaks to them," relating concepts in a form and at a level they understand and can relate to. Ideally this text will draw students in and keep their interest, becoming a positive experience and bringing them back a second and third time, until it becomes habitual. At this point, students might begin to see the true value of their text (as more than just a source of problems—pun intended), and it becomes a resource for learning on equal footing with any other form of supplemental instruction.     —JC/JD

### Conversational Writing Style

John and J.D.'s experience in the classroom and their strong connections to how students comprehend the material are evident in their writing style. They use a conversational and supportive writing style, providing the students with a tool they can depend on when the teacher is not available, when they miss a day of class, or simply when working on their own. The effort they have put into the writing is representative of John Coburn's unofficial mantra: "If you want more students to reach the top, you gotta put a few more rungs on the ladder."

> " The author does a fine job with his narrative. His explanations are very clear and concise. I really like his explanations better than in my current text."
> —Tammy Potter, Gadsden State College

> " The author does an excellent job of engagement and it is easily seen that he is conscious of student learning styles."
> —Conrad Krueger, San Antonio College

## Through Student Involvement

**How do you design a student-friendly textbook?** We decided to get students involved by hosting two separate focus groups. During these sessions we asked students to advise us on how they use their books,

what pedagogical elements are useful, which elements are distracting and not useful, as well as general feedback on page layout. During this process there were times when we thought, "Now why hasn't anyone ever thought of that before?" Clearly these student focus groups were invaluable. Taking direct student feedback and incorporating what is feasible and doesn't detract from instructor use of the text is the best way to design a truly student-friendly text. The next two pages will highlight what we learned from students so you can see for yourself how their feedback played an important role in the development of the Coburn/Herdlick series.

Students said that **Learning Objectives** should clearly define the goals of each section.

Students asked for **Check Points** throughout each section to alert them when a specific learning objective has been covered and to reinforce the use of correct mathematical terms.

Described by students as one of the most useful features in a math text, **Caution Boxes** signal a student to stop and take note in order to avoid mistakes in problem solving.

Students told us that the color red should only be used for things that are really important. Also, anything significant should be included in the body of the text; marginal readings imply optional.

**Examples** are called out in the margins so they are easy for students to spot.

**Examples** are "boxed" so students can clearly see where they begin and end.

Students told us they liked when the examples were linked to the exercises.

---

### 7.1 | Oblique Triangles and the Law of Sines

**Learning Objectives**

*In Section 7.1 you will learn how to:*

☐ A. Develop the law of sines and use it to solve ASA and AAS triangles

☐ B. Solve SSA triangles (the ambiguous case) using the law of sines

☐ C. Use the law of sines to solve applications

Many applications of trigonometry involve *oblique triangles*, or triangles that do not have a 90° angle. For example, suppose a trolley carries passengers from ground level up to a mountain chateau, as shown in Figure 7.1. Assuming the cable could be held taut, what is its approximate length? Can we also determine the slant height of the mountain? To answer questions like these, we'll develop techniques that enable us to solve acute and obtuse triangles using fundamental trigonometric relationships.

Figure 7.1

**A. The Law of Sines and Unique Solutions**

Consider the oblique triangle $ABC$ pictured in Figure 7.2. Since it is not a right triangle, it seems the trigonometric ratios studied earlier cannot be applied. But if we draw the altitude $h$ (from vertex $B$), two right triangles are formed that *share a common side*. By applying the sine ratio to angles $A$ and $C$, we can develop a relationship that will help

Figure 7.2

---

**WORTHY OF NOTE**

Although not a definitive check, always review the solution table to ensure the smallest side is opposite the smallest angle, the largest side is opposite the largest angle, and so on. If this is not the case, you should go back and check your work.

☑ A. You've just learned how to develop the law of sines and use it to solve ASA and AAS triangles

$$\frac{\sin A}{a} = \frac{\sin B}{b} \qquad \text{law of sines applied to } \angle A \text{ and } \angle B$$

$$\frac{\sin 38°}{39} = \frac{\sin 110°}{b} \qquad \text{substitute given values}$$

$$b \sin 38° = 39 \sin 110° \qquad \text{multiply by } 39b$$

$$b = \frac{39 \sin 110°}{\sin 38°} \qquad \text{divide by } \sin 38°$$

$$b \approx 59.5 \qquad \text{result}$$

Repeating this procedure using $\frac{\sin A}{a} = \frac{\sin C}{c}$ shows side $c \approx 33.6$ cm. In table form we have

| Angles | Sides (cm) |
|--------|-----------|
| $A = 38°$ | $a = 39.0$ |
| $B = 110°$ | $b \approx 59.5$ |
| $C = 32°$ | $c \approx 33.6$ |

Now try Exercises 7 through 24 ▶

---

**b.** $\cos(\alpha + \beta) = \cos\alpha \cos\beta - \sin\alpha \sin\beta \qquad \text{sum identity}$

$\cos(45° + 30°) = \cos 45° \cos 30° - \sin 45° \sin 30° \qquad \alpha = 45°, \beta = 30°$

$= \left(\frac{\sqrt{2}}{2}\right)\left(\frac{\sqrt{3}}{2}\right) - \left(\frac{\sqrt{2}}{2}\right)\left(\frac{1}{2}\right) \qquad \text{standard values}$

$\cos 75° = \frac{\sqrt{6} - \sqrt{2}}{4} \qquad \text{combine terms}$

To 10 decimal places, $\cos 75° = 0.2588190451$.

Now try Exercises 7 through 12 ▶

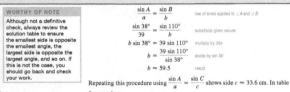

⚠ **CAUTION** ▶ Be sure you clearly understand how these identities work. In particular, note that $\cos(60° + 30°) \neq \cos 60° + \cos 30° \left(0 \neq \frac{1}{2} + \frac{\sqrt{3}}{2}\right)$ and in general $f(a + b) \neq f(a) + f(b)$.

These identities are listed here using the "±" and "∓" notation to avoid needless repetition. In their application, use both upper symbols or both lower symbols depending on whether you're evaluating the cosine of a sum (upper symbols) or difference (lower symbols). As with the other identities, these can be rewritten to form other members of the identity family, as when they are used to consolidate a larger expression. This is shown in Example 2.

---

focus on verifying identities by using algebra. In Section 5.1 we'll introduce some guidelines and ideas that will help you verify a wider range of identities.

**EXAMPLE 2** ▶ Using Algebra to Help Verify an Identity

Use the distributive property to verify that $\sin\theta(\csc\theta - \sin\theta) = \cos^2\theta$ is an identity.

Solution ▶ Use the distributive property to simplify the left-hand side.

$\sin\theta(\csc\theta - \sin\theta) = \sin\theta\csc\theta - \sin^2\theta \qquad \text{distribute}$

$= 1 - \sin^2\theta \qquad \text{substitute 1 for } \sin\theta\csc\theta$

$= \cos^2\theta \qquad 1 - \sin^2\theta = \cos^2\theta$

Since we were able to transform the left-hand side into a duplicate of the right, there can be no doubt the original equation is an identity.

Now try Exercises 11 through 20 ▶

Often we must *factor* an expression, rather than multiply, to begin the verification process.

**EXAMPLE 3** ▶ Using Algebra to Help Verify an Identity

Verify that $1 = \cot^2\alpha \sec^2\alpha - \cot^2\alpha$ is an identity.

Solution ▶ The left side is as simple as it gets. The terms on the right side have a common factor and we begin there.

$\cot^2\alpha \sec^2\alpha - \cot^2\alpha = \cot^2\alpha(\sec^2\alpha - 1) \qquad \text{factor out } \cot^2\alpha$

$= \cot^2\alpha \tan^2\alpha \qquad \text{substitute } \tan^2\alpha \text{ for } \sec^2\alpha - 1$

$= (\cot\alpha \tan\alpha)^2 \qquad \text{power property of exponents}$

$= 1^2 = 1 \qquad \cot\alpha \cdot \tan\alpha = 1$

Now try Exercises 21 through 28 ▶

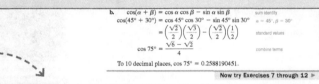

Students told us that directions should be in bold so they are easily distinguishable from the problems.

**Use the formula for arc length to find the value of the unknown quantity:** $s = r\theta$.

**7.** $\theta = 3.5$; $r = 280$ m

**8.** $\theta = 2.3$; $r = 129$ cm

**9.** $s = 2007$ mi; $r = 2676$ mi

**10.** $s = 4435.2$ km; $r = 12{,}320$ km

**11.** $\theta = \frac{3\pi}{4}$; $s = 4146.9$ yd

**12.** $\theta = \frac{11\pi}{6}$; $s = 28.8$ nautical miles

**13.** $\theta = \frac{4\pi}{3}$; $r = 2$ mi

**14.** $\theta = \frac{3\pi}{2}$; $r = 424$ in.

**15.** $s = 252.35$ ft; $r = 980$ ft

**16.** $s = 942.3$ mm; $r = 1800$ mm

**17.** $\theta = 320°$; $s = 52.5$ km

**18.** $\theta = 220.5°$; $s = 7627$ m

**Point $P$ passes through a central angle $\theta$ in time $t$ as it travels around a circle. Find its exact angular velocity in radians per unit time.**

**19.** $\theta = 360°$; $t = 8$ sec  **20.** $\theta = 540°$; $t = 9$ yr

**21.** $\theta = 450°$; $t = 10$ hr  **22.** $\theta = 270°$; $t = 12$ min

**23.** $\theta = 210°$; $t = 7$ days  **24.** $\theta = 690°$; $t = 5$ sec

**25.** $\theta = 420°$; $t = 4$ min  **26.** $\theta = 300°$; $t = 5$ hr

**Point $P$ travels around a circle of radius $r$ as described. Find its linear velocity, rounded to the nearest hundredth as necessary.**

**27.** $\omega = 5$ rad/sec; $r = 8$ in.

**28.** $\omega = 12$ rad/min; $r = 15$ ft

**29.** $\omega = 14\pi$ rad/hr; $r = 3.2$ mi

**30.** $\omega = 2312\pi$ rad/hr; $r = 0.01$ km

**31.** $\theta = 168°$; $t = 0.28$ sec; $r = 3$ mm

**32.** $\theta = 282°$; $t = 4.1$ min; $r = 1.2$ yd

**33.** $\theta = 30$; $t = 6$ hr; $r = 1.2$ km

**34.** $\theta = 45$; $t = 3$ hr; $r = 2$ mi

**Use the formula for area of a circular sector to find the value of the unknown quantity:** $A = \frac{1}{2}r^2\theta$.

**35.** $\theta = 5$; $r = 6.8$ km

**36.** $\theta = 3$; $r = 45$ mi

**37.** $A = 1080$ mi$^2$; $r = 60$ mi

**38.** $A = 437.5$ cm$^2$; $r = 12.5$ cm

**39.** $\theta = \frac{7\pi}{6}$; $A = 16.5$ m$^2$

**40.** $\theta = \frac{19\pi}{12}$; $A = 753$ cm$^2$

---

Because students spend a lot of time in the exercise section of a text, they said that a white background is hard on their eyes...so we used a soft, off-white color for the background.

**As our study of trigonometry progresses, we will learn to find the measure of an angle _based on its trig function values_ (first studied in Section 2.2). Here we practice finding these trig function values.**

**83. Billiards:** In Carolina's attempt to end a pool game by sinking the eight ball, she "scratches," accidentally sending the cue ball into the corner pocket located 60 in. to the west and 40 in. to the north of where it contacted the eight ball. Find tan $\theta$, for the angle $\theta$ shown. For convenience, a coordinate system is shown with the point of contact at the origin.

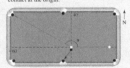

**84. Ice hockey:** Wydonyu Yustrig takes a low slap shot from the blue line, as shown in the figure.

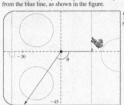

Unfortunately, the puck strikes the skate of a teammate and from there goes to the "boards," 45 ft south and 30 ft west. Find tan $\theta$, where $\theta$ is the angle shown. For convenience, a coordinate system is shown with the point of deflection at the origin.

**For Exercises 85 through 88, find the indicated value by drawing sketches similar to those used in Exercises 83 and 84. Carefully choose the location of the origin so the angle $\theta$ will be in standard position.**

**85. Oil painting:** An aspiring artist begins her latest masterpiece by raising her 10″ Filbert paintbrush to horizontal. Keeping her hand steady, she then raises the tip of the brush 3″. Find sin $\theta$, where $\theta$ is the angle she inclined the brush.

**86. Violin:** When Lucy is practicing her violin, the bow makes contact with both the D and A strings when held horizontally (parallel to the ground). By raising the end of the bow in her hand 13 cm (with the far end resting on the strings), she prepares to make contact with the G string. Given that her bow is 65 cm long, find sin $\theta$, where $\theta$ is the angle she inclined the bow.

**87. Baseball:** After a baseball is struck by a bat, it travels 70 ft through the air, at which time it is directly above the pitcher, 60 ft from the point of contact. Find cos $\theta$, where $\theta$ is the acute angle formed by the path of the ball and a horizontal line.

**88. Golf:** The eighteenth hole at Pebble Beach is a 543-yd, par 5 beauty. A slow-motion review of Kevin's tee shot showed that the ball traveled 9.5 yd through the air as it moved 7.6 yd toward the pin. Find cos $\theta$, where $\theta$ is the acute angle formed by the path of the ball and a horizontal line.

---

Students said having a lot of icons was confusing. The graphing calculator is the only icon used in the exercise sets; no unnecessary icons are used.

▶ **WORKING WITH FORMULAS**

 **85. Supersonic speeds, the sound barrier, and Mach numbers:** $M = \csc\left(\dfrac{\theta}{2}\right)$

The speed of sound varies with temperature and altitude. At 32°F, sound travels about 742 mi/hr at sea level. A jet-plane flying faster than the speed of sound (called supersonic speed) has "broken the sound barrier." The plane projects three-dimensional sound waves about the nose of the craft that form the shape of a cone. The cone intersects the Earth along a hyperbolic path, with a sonic boom being heard by anyone along this path. The ratio of the plane's speed to the speed of sound is

called its Mach number $M$, meaning a plane flying at $M = 3.2$ is traveling 3.2 times the speed of sound. This Mach number can be determined using the formula given here, where $\theta$ is the vertex angle of the cone described. For the following exercises, use the formula to find $M$ or $\theta$ as required. For parts (a) and (b), answer in exact form (using a half-angle identity) and approximate form.

**a.** $\theta = 30°$  **b.** $\theta = 45°$  **c.** $M = 2$

**86. Malus's law:** $I = I_0\cos^2\theta$

When a beam of plane-polarized light with intensity $I_0$ hits an analyzer, the intensity $I$ of the transmitted beam of light can be found using the

# Making Connections...

## Through New and Updated Content

### New to the Second Edition

▶ An extensive reworking of the narrative and refining of advanced concepts enhance the clarity of the exposition and improve the student's experience in the text.

▶ A reordering of the table of contents highlights the different approaches to trigonometry and their respective applications, and helps instructors create a more balanced assessment schedule.

▶ A modified interior design based on student and instructor feedback from focus groups features increased font size, improved exercise and example layout, more white space on the page, and the careful use of color to enhance the presentation of pedagogy.

▶ Chapter Openers based on applications bring awareness to students of the relevance of concepts presented in each chapter.

▶ Checkpoints throughout each section alert students when a specific learning objective has been covered and reinforce the use of correct mathematical terms.

▶ The Homework Selection Guide, appearing in each exercise section in the Annotated Instructor's Edition, provides instructors with suggestions for developing core, standard, extended, and in-depth homework assignments without much prep work.

▶ The *Modeling With Technology* feature after Chapter 4 provides students a detailed exposure to real-world applications of trigonometry, using both critical-point model construction as well as data regression.

### Chapter-by-Chapter Changes

#### CHAPTER 1 Introduction to Trigonometry

• Section 1.1 includes improved DMS to decimal degrees conversion coverage and improved introduction to the standard 45-45-90 and 30-60-90 triangles.
• Section 1.2 classifies triangles by both side length and angle size and contains a more extensive treatment of triangle properties and similar triangles.
• The trigonometric functions are first presented using their coordinate plane definitions in Section 1.3, along with an algebraic analysis of the angle's terminal side.
• Section 1.3 also includes enhanced coverage of the signs of the trigonometric functions and quadrantal angles.
• Section 1.4 offers an introductory exposure to what an identity is (the definition of an identity), as well as an additional example of quadrant and sign analysis.

#### CHAPTER 2 Right Triangles and Static Trigonometry

• Section 2.1 connects the right triangle definition of the trigonometric functions with their coordinate plane counterparts and contains improved coverage of cofunction relationships.
• Section 2.2 isolates and highlights the critical skill of solving right triangles.
• Section 2.3 has better illustrations for angles of elevation and depression, and new applications involving angles of rotation.
• Section 2.4 covers reference angles in greater detail and uses them to extend right triangle trigonometry beyond acute angles.

#### CHAPTER 3 Radian Measure and Dynamic Trigonometry

• Section 3.1 has expanded coverage of finding the radian measure of standard angles and their multiples.
• Section 3.2 includes better illustrations of longitude and latitude applications, and enhanced coverage of angular and linear velocity.
• Section 3.3 offers a dedicated treatment of the unit circle, emphasizing its importance to trigonometry.
• Section 3.4 has a streamlined and improved presentation of the trigonometry of real numbers.

#### CHAPTER 4 Trigonometric Graphs and Models

• Section 4.1 has dedicated and improved coverage of sine and cosine graphs.
• Section 4.2 has improved coverage of secant and cosecant graphs and a strengthened connection between $y = \tan x$ and $y = (\sin x)/(\cos x)$.
• Section 4.3 has an improved introduction to transformations, and a clearer distinction between phase angle and phase shift.
• New and improved applications of trigonometric models have been consolidated in Section 4.4.

# CHAPTER 5 Trigonometric Identities

- Section 5.1 has a better introduction to clarify goals, as well as an improved format for verifying identities.
- Section 5.2 has improved coverage of the cofunction identities, as well as extended coverage of the sum and difference identities.
- The double-angle and half-angle identities in Section 5.3 have been separated from the product-to-sum and sum-to-product identities in Section 5.4 to help students organize and differentiate between these two families.

# CHAPTER 6 Inverse Functions and Trigonometric Equations

- Section 6.1 includes examples of finding inverses of rational functions, as well as better coverage of restricting the domain to find the inverse.
- Section 6.2 has a strengthened connection between inverse trig functions and drawn diagrams, improved coverage on evaluating the inverse trig functions, and more real-world applications of inverse trig functions.
- Parametric equations have been moved to Chapter 8 for an improved flow of topics.

# CHAPTER 7 Applications of Trigonometry

- Section 7.1 has a consolidated coverage of the ambiguous case.
- Section 7.2 has expanded coverage of computing areas using trig, as well as six new contextual applications of triangular area using trig.
- Section 7.3 has improved discussion, coverage, and illustrations of vector subtraction, and stronger connections between solutions using components, and solutions using the law of cosines.
- Complex numbers, DeMoivre's theorem, and the theorem on nth roots have been moved to Chapter 8 for improved flow and a more "connected" arrangement of topics.

# CHAPTER 8 Trigonometric Connections to Algebra

- Section 8.1 contains improved coverage and additional examples of rewriting imaginary numbers of the form $\sqrt{-k}$.
- Section 8.2 has additional real-world applications of complex numbers (AC circuits).
- The examples for the theorem on nth roots in Section 8.3 have been resequenced.
- Additional examples of converting equations between rectangular and polar form have been added to Section 8.4.

# Making Connections...

## Through 360° Development

**McGraw-Hill's 360° Development Process** is an ongoing, never-ending, market-oriented approach to building accurate and innovative print and digital products. It is dedicated to continual large-scale and incremental improvement driven by multiple customer feedback loops and checkpoints. This process is initiated during the early planning stages of our new products, intensifies during the development and production stages, and then begins again on publication, in anticipation of the next edition.

A key principle in the development of any mathematics text is its ability to adapt to teaching specifications in a universal way. The only way to do so is by contacting those universal voices—and learning from their suggestions. We are confident that our book has the most current content the industry has to offer, thus pushing our desire for accuracy to the highest standard possible. In order to accomplish this, we have moved through an arduous road to production. Extensive and open-minded advice is critical in the production of a superior text.

We engaged over 400 instructors and students to provide us guidance in the development of the second edition. By investing in this extensive endeavor, McGraw-Hill delivers to you a product suite that has been created, refined, tested, and validated to be a successful tool in your course.

## Board of Advisors

A hand-picked group of trusted teachers active in the College Algebra, Precalculus, and Trigonometry course areas served as the chief advisors and consultants to the author and editorial team with regards to manuscript development. The Board of Advisors reviewed the manuscript in two drafts; served as a sounding board for pedagogical, media, and design concerns; approved organizational changes; and attended a symposium to confirm the manuscript's readiness for publication.

Bill Forrest, *Baton Rouge Community College*
Marc Grether, *University of North Texas*
Sharon Hamsa, *Metropolitan Community College–Longview*
Max Hibbs, *Blinn College*
Terry Hobbs, *Metropolitan Community College–Maple Woods*
Klay Kruczek, *Western Oregon University*
Nancy Matthews, *University of Oklahoma*

Rebecca Muller, *Southeastern Louisiana University*
Rita Marie O'Brien, *Navarro College*
Jason Pallett, *Metropolitan Community College–Longview*
Kevin Ratliff, *Blue Ridge Community College*
Stephen Toner, *Victor Valley College*

## Student Focus Groups

Two student focus groups were held at Illinois State University and Southeastern Louisiana University to engage students in the development process and provide feedback as to how the design of a textbook impacts homework and study habits in the College Algebra, Precalculus, and Trigonometry course areas.

Francisco Arceo, *Illinois State University*
Candace Banos, *Southeastern Louisiana University*
Dave Cepko, *Illinois State University*
Andrea Connell, *Illinois State University*
Nicholas Curtis, *Southeastern Louisiana University*
M. D. "Boots" Feltenberger, *Southeastern Louisiana University*
Regina Foreman, *Southeastern Louisiana University*
Ashley Lae, *Southeastern Louisiana University*
Brian Lau, *Illinois State University*
Daniel Nathan Mielneczek, *Illinois State University*
Mingaile Orakauskaite, *Illinois State University*
Todd Michael Rapnikas, *Illinois State University*
Bethany Rollet, *Illinois State University*

Teddy Schrishuhn, *Illinois State University*
Josh Schultz, *Illinois State University*
Jessica Smith, *Southeastern Louisiana University*
Andy Thurman, *Illinois State University*
Ashley Youngblood, *Southeastern Louisiana University*

## Special Thanks

Sherry Meier, *Illinois State University*
Rebecca Muller, *Southeastern Louisiana University*
Anne Schmidt, *Illinois State University*

## Instructor Focus Groups

Focus groups held at Baton Rouge Community College and ORMATYC provided feedback on the new Connections to Calculus feature in *Precalculus*, and shed light on the coverage of review material in this course. User focus groups at Southeastern Louisiana University and Madison Area Technical College confirmed the organizational changes planned for the second edition, provided feedback on the interior design, and helped us enhance and refine the strengths of the first edition.

Virginia Adelmann, *Southeastern Louisiana University*
George Alexander, *Madison Area Technical College*
Kenneth R. Anderson, *Chemeketa Community College*
Wayne G. Barber, *Chemeketa Community College*
Thomas Dick, *Oregon State University*
Vickie Flanders, *Baton Rouge Community College*
Bill Forrest, *Baton Rouge Community College*
Susan B. Guidroz, *Southeastern Louisiana University*
Christopher Guillory, *Baton Rouge Community College*
Cynthia Harrison, *Baton Rouge Community College*
Judy Jones, *Madison Area Technical College*
Lucyna Kabza, *Southeastern Louisiana University*
Ann Kirkpatrick, *Southeastern Louisiana University*
Sunmi Ku, *Bellevue Community College*

Pamela Larson, *Madison Area Technical College*
Jennifer Laveglia, *Bellevue Community College*
DeShea Miller, *Southeastern Louisiana University*
Elizabeth Miller, *Southeastern Louisiana University*
Rebecca Muller, *Southeastern Louisiana University*
Donna W. Newman, *Baton Rouge Community College*
Scott L. Peterson, *Oregon State University*
Ronald Posey, *Baton Rouge Community College*
Ronni Settoon, *Southeastern Louisiana University*
Jeganathan Sriskandarajah, *Madison Area Technical College*
Martha Stevens, *Bellevue Community College*
Mark J. Stigge, *Baton Rouge Community College*
Nataliya Svyeshnikova, *Southeastern Louisiana University*

## Developmental Symposia

McGraw-Hill conducted two symposia directly related to the development of the Coburn/Herdlick text. These events were an opportunity for editors from McGraw-Hill to gather information about the needs and challenges of instructors teaching these courses and confirm the direction of the second edition.

## Diary Reviews and Class Tests

Users of the first edition, Said Ngobi and Stephen Toner of Victor Valley College, provided chapter-by chapter feedback in diary form based on their experience using the text. Board of Advisors members facilitated class tests of the manuscript for a given topic. Both instructors and students returned questionnaires detailing their thoughts on the effectiveness of the text's features.

### Class Tests

Hayley Hentzen, *University of North Texas*
Courtney Hodge, *University of North Texas*
Janice Hollaway, *Navarro College*
Weslon Hull, *Baton Rouge Community College*
Sarah James, *Baton Rouge Community College*
Georlin Johnson, *Baton Rouge Community College*
Michael Jones, *Navarro College*
Robert Koon, *Metropolitan Community College–Longview*
Ben Lenfant, *Baton Rouge Community College*
Colin Luke, *Baton Rouge Community College*
Lester Maloney, *Baton Rouge Community College*
Ana Mariscal, *Navarro College*
Tracy Ann Nguyen, *Baton Rouge Community College*
Alexandra Ortiz, *University of North Texas*
Robert T. R. Paine, *Baton Rouge Community College*
Kade Parent, *Baton Rouge Community College*
Brittany Louise Pratt, *Baton Rouge Community College*

Brittney Pruitt, *Metropolitan Community College–Longview*
Paul Rachal, *Baton Rouge Community College*
Matt Rawls, *Baton Rouge Community College*
Adam Reichert, *Metropolitan Community College–Longview*
Ryan Rodney, *Baton Rouge Community College*
Cody Scallan, *Baton Rouge Community College*
Laura Shafer, *University of North Texas*
Natina Simpson, *Navarro College*
Stephanie Sims, *Metropolitan Community College–Longview*
Cassie Snow, *University of North Texas*
Justin Stewart, *Metropolitan Community College–Longview*
Marjorie Tulana, *Navarro College*
Ashleigh Variest, *Baton Rouge Community College*
James A. Wann, *Navarro College*
Amber Wendleton, *Metropolitan Community College–Longview*
Eric Williams, *Metropolitan Community College–Longview*
Katy Wood, *Metropolitan Community College–Longview*

## Developmental Editing

The manuscript has been impacted by numerous developmental reviewers who edited for clarity and consistency. Efforts resulted in cutting length from the manuscript, while retaining a conversational and casual narrative style. Editorial work also ensured the positive visual impact of art and photo placement.

### First Edition Chapter Reviews and Manuscript Reviews

Over 200 instructors participated in postpublication single chapter reviews of the first edition and helped the team build the revision plan for the second edition. Over 100 teachers and academics from across the country reviewed the current edition text, the proposed second edition table of contents, and first-draft second edition manuscript to give feedback on reworked narrative, design changes, pedagogical enhancements, and organizational changes. This feedback was summarized by the book team and used to guide the direction of the second-draft manuscript.

Scott Adamson, *Chandler-Gilbert Community College*
Teresa Adsit, *University of Wisconsin–Green Bay*
Ebrahim Ahmadizadeh, *Northampton Community College*
George M. Alexander, *Madison Area Technical College*
Frances Alvarado, *University of Texas–Pan American*
Deb Anderson, *Antelope Valley College*
Jeff Anderson, *Winona State University*
Michael Anderson, *West Virginia State University*
Philip Anderson, *South Plains College*
Robin Anderson, *Southwestern Illinois College*
Raul Aparicio, *Blinn College*
Judith Barclay, *Cuesta College*
Laurie Battle, *Georgia College and State University*
David Bell, *Florida Community College—Jacksonville*

Annette Benbow, *Tarrant County College–Northwest*
Amy Benvie, *Florida Gulf Coast University*
Sandra Berry, *Hinds Community College*
Scott Berthiaume, *Edison State College*
Wes Black, *Illinois Valley Community College*
Leonard Blackburn, *Parkland College*
Arlene Blasius, *SUNY College of Old Westbury*
Caroline Maher Boulis, *Lee University*
Amin Boumenir, *University of West Georgia*
Terence Brenner, *Hostos Community College*
Gail Brooks, *McLennan Community College*
Nick Bykov, *San Joaquin Delta College*
G. Robert Carlson, *Victor Valley College*
Hope Carr, *East Mississippi Community College*
Denise Chellsen, *Cuesta College*
Kim Christensen, *Metropolitan Community College–Maple Woods*
Lisa Christman, *University of Central Arkansas*
John Church, *Metropolitan Community College–Longview*
Sarah Clifton, *Southeastern Louisiana University*
David Collins, *Southwestern Illinois College*
Sarah V. Cook, *Washburn University*
Rhonda Creech, *Southeast Kentucky Community and Technical College*
Raymond L. Crownover, *Gateway College of Evangelism*
Marc Cullison, *Connors State College*

Steven Cunningham, *San Antonio College*
Callie Daniels, *St. Charles Community College*
John Denney, *Northeast Texas Community College*
Donna Densmore, *Bossier Parish Community College*
Alok Dhital, *University of New Mexico–Gallup*
James Michael Dubrowsky, *Wayne Community College*
Brad Dyer, *Hazzard Community & Technical College*
Sally Edwards, *Johnson County Community College*
John Elliott, *St. Louis Community College–Meramec*
Gay Ellis, *Missouri State University*
Barbara Elzey, *Bluegrass Community College*
Dennis Evans, *Concordia University Wisconsin*
Samantha Fay, *University of Central Arkansas*
Victoria Fischer, *California State University–Monterey Bay*
Dorothy French, *Community College of Philadelphia*
Jennifer Friedenreich, *Diablo Valley College*
Eric Garcia, *South Texas College*
Laurice Garrett, *Edison College*
Ramona Gartman, *Gadsden State Community College–Ayers Campus*
Scott Gaulke, *University of Wisconsin–Eau Claire*
Scott Gordon, *University of West Georgia*
Teri Graville, *Southern Illinois University Edwardsville*
Marc Grether, *University of North Texas*
Shane Griffith, *Lee University*
Barry Griffiths, *University of Central Florida*
Gary Grohs, *Elgin Community College*
Peter Haberman, *Portland Community College*
Todd Hammond, *Truman State University*
Joseph Harris, *Gulf Coast Community College*
Margret Hathaway, *Kansas City Community College*
Tom Hayes, *Montana State University*
Bill Heider, *Hibbling Community College*
Max Hibbs, *Blinn College*
Terry Hobbs, *Metropolitan Community College–Maple Woods*
Michelle Hollis, *Bowling Green CC of WKU*
Sharon Holmes, *Tarrant County College–Southeast*
Jamie Holtin, *Freed-Hardeman University*
Brian Hons, *San Antonio College*
Kevin Hopkins, *Southwest Baptist University*
Teresa Houston, *East Mississippi Community College*
Keith Hubbard, *Stephen F. Austin State University*
Sharon Hudson, *Gulf Coast Community College*
Jeffrey Hughes, *Hinds Community College–Raymond*
Matthew Isom, *Arizona State University*
Dwayne Jennings, *Union University*
Judy Jones, *Madison Area Technical College*
Lucyna Kabza, *Southeastern Louisiana University*
Aida Kadic-Galeb, *University of Tampa*

Cheryl Kane, *University of Nebraska*
Rahim Karimpour, *Southern Illinois University Edwardsville*
Ryan Kasha, *Valencia Community College*
David Kay, *Moorpark College*
Katrina Keating, *Diablo Valley College*
Raja Khoury, *Collin County Community College*
Jong Kim, *Long Beach City College*
Lynette King, *Gadsden State Community College*
William Kirby, *Gadsden State Community College*
Carolyn Kistner, *St. Petersburg College*
Barbara Kniepkamp, *Southern Illinois University Edwardsville*
Susan Knights, *Boise State University*
Louis Kolitsch, *University of Tennessee at Martin*
Stephanie Kolitsch, *University of Tennessee at Martin*
Larry Kropp, *Rich Mountain Community College*
Karl Kruczek, *Northeastern State University*
Conrad Krueger, *San Antonio College*
Marcia Lambert, *Pitt Community College*
Rebecca Lanier, *Bluegrass Community College*
Marie Larsen, *Cuesta College*
Pam Larson, *Madison Area Technical College*
Jennifer Lawhon, *Valencia Community College*
Rebecca Leefers, *Michigan State University*
John Levko, *University of Scranton*
Mitchel Levy, *Broward Community College*
Runchang Lin, *Texas A&M International University*
John Lofberg, *South Dakota School of Mines and Technology*
Mitzi Logan, *Pitt Community College*
Sandra Maldonado, *Florida Gulf Coast University*
Robin C. Manker, *Illinois College*
Manoug Manougian, *University of South Florida*
Nancy Matthews, *University of Oklahoma*
Roger McCoach, *County College of Morris*
James McKinney, *California Polytechnic State University–Pomona*
Jennifer McNeilly, *University of Illinois Urbana Champaign*
Kathleen Miranda, *SUNY College at Old Westbury*
Mary Ann (Molly) Misko, *Gadsden State Community College*
Marianne Morea, *SUNY College of Old Westbury*
Michael Nasab, *Long Beach City College*
Said Ngobi, *Victor Valley College*
Tonie Niblett, *Northeast Alabama Community College*
Gary Nonnemacher, *Bowling Green State University*
Elaine Nye, *Alfred State College*
Rhoda Oden, *Gadsden State Community College*
Jeannette O'Rourke, *Middlesex County College*
Darla Ottman, *Elizabethtown Community & Technical College*
Jason Pallett, *Metropolitan Community College–Longview*

Priti Patel, *Tarrant County College–Southeast*
Judy Pennington-Price, *Midway College*
Susan Pfeifer, *Butler County Community College*
Margaret Poitevint, *North Georgia College & State University*
Tammy Potter, *Gadsden State Community College*
Debra Prescott, *Central Texas College*
Elise Price, *Tarrant County College*
Kevin Ratliff, *Blue Ridge Community College*
Bruce Reid, *Howard Community College*
Edgar Reyes, *Southeastern Louisiana University*
Jolene Rhodes, *Valencia Community College*
Dale Rohm, *University of Wisconsin—Stevens Point*
Karen Rollins, *University of West Georgia*
Randy Ross, *Morehead State University*
Michael Sawyer, *Houston Community College*
Dan Schapiro, *Yakima Valley Community College*
Richard Schnackenberg, *Florida Gulf Coast University*
Bethany Seto, *Horry-Georgetown Technical College*
Delphy Shaulis, *University of Colorado–Boulder*
Jennifer Simonton, *Southwestern Illinois College*
David Slay, *McNeese State University*
David Snyder, *Texas State University at San Marcos*
Larry L. Southard, *Florida Gulf Coast University*
Lee Ann Spahr, *Durham Technical Community College*
Jeganathan Sriskandarajah, *Madison Area Technical College*
Adam Stinchcombe, *Eastern Arizona College*

Pam Stogsdill, *Bossier Parish Community College*
Eleanor Storey, *Front Range Community College*
Kathy Stover, *College of Southern Idaho*
Mary Teel, *University of North Texas*
Carlie Thompson, *Southeast Kentucky Community & Technical College*
Bob Tilidetzke, *Charleston Southern University*
Stephen Toner, *Victor Valley College*
Thomas Tunnell, *Illinois Valley Community College*
Carol Ulsafer, *University of Montana*
K. Vajravelu, *University of Central Florida*
John Van Eps, *California Polytechnic State University–San Luis Obispo*
Andrea Vorwark, *Metropolitan Community College–Maple Woods*
Jim Voss, *Front Range Community College*
Jennifer Walsh, *Daytona State College*
Jiantian Wang, *Kean University*
Sheryl Webb, *Tennessee Technological University*
Bill Weber, *Fort Hays State University*
John Weglarz, *Kirkwood Community College*
Tressa White, *Arkansas State University–Newport*
Cheryl Winter, *Metropolitan Community College–Blue River*
Kenneth Word, *Central Texas College*
Paul Wright, *Austin Community College*
Laurie Yourk, *Dickinson State University*

## Acknowledgments

We first want to express a deep appreciation for the guidance, comments, and suggestions offered by all reviewers of the manuscript. We have once again found their collegial exchange of ideas and experience very refreshing and instructive, and always helping to create a better learning tool for our students.

Vicki Krug has continued to display an uncanny ability to bring innumerable pieces from all directions into a unified whole, in addition to providing spiritual support during some extremely trying times; Patricia Steele's skill as a copy editor is as sharp as ever, and her attention to detail continues to pay great dividends; which helps pay the debt we owe Katie White, Michelle Flomenhoft, and Christina Lane for their useful suggestions, infinite patience, tireless efforts, and art-counting eyes, which helped in bringing the manuscript to completion. We must also thank John Osgood for his ready wit, creative energies, and ability to step into the flow without missing a beat; Laurie Janssen and our magnificent design team, and Dawn Bercier whose influence on this project remains strong although she has moved on, as it was her indefatigable spirit that kept the ship on course through trial and tempest, and her ski-jumper's vision that brought J.D. on board. In truth, our hats are off to all the fine people at McGraw-Hill for their continuing support and belief in this series. A final word of thanks must go to Rick Armstrong, whose depth of knowledge, experience, and mathematical connections seems endless; Anne Marie Mosher for her contributions to various features of the text, Mitch Levy for his consultation on the exercise sets, Stephen Toner for his work on the videos, Rosemary Karr and Brianna Killian for their meticulous work on the solutions manuals, Donna Gerker for her work on the preformatted tests, Jon Booze and his team for their work on the test bank, Carrie Green for her invaluable ability to catch what everyone else misses; and to Rick Pescarino, Kelly Ballard, John Elliot, Jim Frost, Barb Kurt, Lillian Seese, Nate Wilson, and all of our colleagues at St. Louis Community College, whose friendship, encouragement, and love of mathematics makes going to work each day a joy.

# *Making Connections...*

## Through Supplements

*All online supplements are available through the book's website: www.mhhe.com/coburn.

### Instructor Supplements

- **Computerized Test Bank Online:** Utilizing Brownstone Diploma® algorithm-based testing software enables users to create customized exams quickly.
- **Instructor's Solutions Manual:** Provides comprehensive, worked-out solutions to all exercises in the text.
- **Annotated Instructor's Edition:** Contains all answers to exercises in the text, which are printed in a second color, adjacent to corresponding exercises, for ease of use by the instructor.

### Student Supplements

- **Student Solutions Manual** provides comprehensive, worked-out solutions to all of the odd-numbered exercises.
- **Videos**
  - Interactive video lectures are provided for each section in the text, which explain to the students how to do key problem types, as well as highlighting common mistakes to avoid.
  - Exercise videos provide step-by-step instruction for the key exercises which students will most wish to see worked out.
  - Graphing calculator videos help students master the most essential calculator skills used in the college algebra course.
  - The videos are closed-captioned for the hearing impaired, subtitled in Spanish, and meet the Americans with Disabilities Act Standards for Accessible Design.

 www.mhhe.com/coburn

McGraw-Hill's MathZone™ is a complete online homework system for mathematics and statistics. Instructors can assign textbook-specific content from over 40 McGraw-Hill titles as well as customize the level of feedback students receive, including the ability to have students show their work for any given exercise. Assignable content includes an array of videos and other multimedia along with algorithmic exercises, providing study tools for students with many different learning styles.

MathZone also helps ensure consistent assignment delivery across several sections through a course administration function and makes sharing courses with other instructors easy.

In addition, instructors can take advantage of a virtual whiteboard by setting up a Live Classroom for online office hours or a review session with students.

For more information, visit the book's website (www.mhhe.com/coburn) or contact your local McGraw-Hill sales representative (www.mhhe.com/rep).

## ALEKS® www.aleks.com

ALEKS (**A**ssessment and **LE**arning in **K**nowledge **S**paces) is a dynamic online learning system for mathematics education, available over the Web 24/7. ALEKS assesses students, accurately determines their knowledge, and then guides them to the material that they are most ready to learn. With a variety of reports, Textbook Integration Plus, quizzes, and homework assignment capabilities, ALEKS offers flexibility and ease of use for instructors.

- ALEKS uses artificial intelligence to determine exactly what each student knows and is ready to learn. ALEKS remediates student gaps and provides highly efficient learning and improved learning outcomes
- ALEKS is a comprehensive curriculum that aligns with syllabi or specified textbooks. Used in conjunction with McGraw-Hill texts, students also receive links to text-specific videos, multimedia tutorials, and textbook pages.
- ALEKS offers a dynamic classroom management system that enables instructors to monitor and direct student progress toward mastery of course objectives.

### ALEKS Prep/Remediation:

- Helps instructors meet the challenge of remediating underprepared or improperly placed students.
- Assesses students on their prerequisite knowledge needed for the course they are entering (i.e., Calculus students are tested on Precalculus knowledge) and prescribes a unique and efficient learning path specifically to address their strengths and weaknesses.
- Students can address prerequisite knowledge gaps outside of class freeing the instructor to use class time pursuing course outcomes.

### TEGRITY—http://tegritycampus.mhhe.com

McGraw-Hill Tegrity Campus™ is a service that makes class time available all the time by automatically capturing every lecture in a searchable format for students to review when they study and complete assignments. With a simple one-click start and stop process, you capture all computer screens and corresponding audio. Students replay any part of any class with easy-to-use browser-based viewing on a PC or Mac.

Educators know that the more students can see, hear, and experience class resources, the better they learn. With Tegrity, students quickly recall key moments by using Tegrity's unique search feature. This search helps students efficiently find what they need, when they need it across an entire semester of class recordings. Help turn all your students' study time into learning moments immediately supported by your lecture.

To learn more about Tegrity watch a 2-minute Flash demo at **http://tegritycampus.mhhe.com.**

**Electronic Textbook:** CourseSmart is a new way for faculty to find and review eTextbooks. It's also a great option for students who are interested in accessing their course materials digitally and saving money. CourseSmart offers thousands of the most commonly adopted textbooks across hundreds of courses from a wide variety of higher education publishers. It is the only place for faculty to review and compare the full text of a textbook online, providing immediate access without the environmental impact of requesting a print exam copy. At CourseSmart, students can save up to 50% off the cost of a print book, reduce their impact on the environment, and gain access to powerful web tools for learning including full text search, notes and highlighting, and email tools for sharing notes between classmates. **www.CourseSmart.com**

**Primis:** You can customize this text with McGraw-Hill/Primis Online. A digital database offers you the flexibility to customize your course including material from the largest online collection of textbooks, readings, and cases. Visit **www.primisonline.com** to learn more.

# Index of Applications

# Introduction to
# Trigonometry

# Introduction to Trigonometry

## CHAPTER OUTLINE

## CHAPTER CONNECTIONS

From the Egyptian pyramids to the Eiffel Tower, a building's significance has often been tied to its height. Many cities, such as St. Louis, Missouri, Washington, D.C., and others, are trying to preserve the significance of certain buildings by enforcing building codes that effectively prevent new construction from surpassing the height of their national landmarks. In the case of Washington, D.C., the Washington Monument is the tallest building in the greater D.C. area. Since its completion in 1884, the monument's exact height has been found using many different methods, including metal chains, GPS receivers, and of course—trigonometry. One additional method involves using similar triangles and the monument's reflection.

▶ This application appears as Exercise 69 in Section 1.2

## Learning Objectives

*In Section 1.1 you will learn how to:*

☐ **A.** Use the vocabulary associated with a study of angles and triangles

☐ **B.** Find and recognize coterminal angles

☐ **C.** Find fixed ratios of the sides of special triangles

Trigonometry, like her sister science geometry, has its origins deeply rooted in the practical use of measurement and proportion. In this section, we'll look at the fundamental concepts on which trigonometry is based, which we hope will lead to a better understanding and a greater appreciation of the wonderful study that trigonometry has become.

## A. Angle Measure in Degrees

Beginning with the common notion of a straight line, a **ray** is a half line, or all points extending from a single point, in a single direction. An **angle** is the joining of two rays at a common endpoint called the **vertex.** Arrowheads are used to indicate the half lines continue forever and can be extended if necessary. Angles can be named using a single letter at the vertex, the letters from the rays forming the sides, or by a single Greek letter, with the favorites being **alpha** $\alpha$, **beta** $\beta$, **gamma** $\gamma$, and **theta** $\theta$. The symbol $\angle$ is often used to designate an angle (see Figure 1.1).

**Figure 1.1**

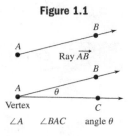

Euclid (325–265 B.C.), often thought of as the *father of geometry,* described an angle as "the inclination of one to another of two lines which meet in a plane." This *amount of inclination* gives rise to the common notion of angle measure in degrees, often measured with a semicircular **protractor** like the one shown in Figure 1.2. The notation for degrees is the ° symbol. By definition 1° is $\frac{1}{360}$ of a full rotation, so this protractor can be used to measure any angle from 0° (where the two rays are coincident), to 180° (where they form a straight line). An angle measuring 180° is called a **straight angle,** while an angle that measures 90° is called a **right angle.** Two angles that sum to 90° are said to be **complementary,** while two that sum to 180° are **supplementary** angles. Recall the "⌐" symbol represents a 90° angle.

**Figure 1.2**

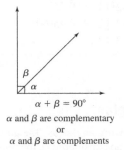

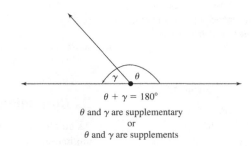

$\alpha + \beta = 90°$
$\alpha$ and $\beta$ are complementary
or
$\alpha$ and $\beta$ are complements

$\theta + \gamma = 180°$
$\theta$ and $\gamma$ are supplementary
or
$\theta$ and $\gamma$ are supplements

---

**EXAMPLE 1 ▶** **Finding the Complement and Supplement of an Angle**

Determine the measure of each angle described.

　**a.** the complement of a 57° angle 　　**b.** the supplement of a 132° angle

　**c.** the measure of angle $\theta$ shown in the figure

**Solution ▶** **a.** The complement of 57° is 33° since
　　$90° - 57° = 33° \Rightarrow 33° + 57° = 90°$.

　**b.** The supplement of 132° is 48° since
　　$180° - 132° = 48° \Rightarrow 48° + 132° = 180°$.

　**c.** Since $\theta$ and 39° are complements,
　　$\theta = 90° - 39° = 51°$.

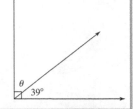

**Now try Exercises 7 through 10 ▶**

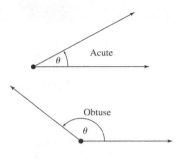

Acute

Obtuse

In the study of trigonometry, it helps to further classify the various angles we encounter. An angle greater than 0° but less than 90° is called an **acute** angle. An angle greater than 90° but less than 180° is called an **obtuse** angle. For very fine measurements, each degree is divided into 60 smaller parts called **minutes,** and each minute into 60 smaller parts called **seconds.** This means that a minute is $\frac{1}{60}$ of a degree, while a second is $\frac{1}{3600}$ of a degree. The angle whose measure is "sixty-one degrees, eighteen minutes, and forty-five seconds" is written as $61°18'45''$. The degrees-minutes-seconds (DMS) method of measuring angles is commonly used in aviation and navigation, while in other areas **decimal degrees** such as $61.3125°$ are preferred. You will sometimes be asked to convert between the two.

**EXAMPLE 2** ▶   Converting Between Decimal Degrees and Degrees/Minutes/Seconds

Convert as indicated.

  **a.** $61°18'45''$ to decimal degrees
  **b.** $142.2075°$ to DMS

Solution ▶   **a.** Since $1' = \frac{1}{60}$ of a degree and $1'' = \frac{1}{3600}$ of a degree, we have

$$61°18'45'' = \left[61 + 18\left(\frac{1}{60}\right) + 45\left(\frac{1}{3600}\right)\right]°$$
$$= 61.3125°$$

**b.** For the conversion to DMS we write the fractional part separate from the whole number part to compute the number of degrees and minutes represented, then repeat the process to find the number of degrees, minutes, and seconds:

$$142.2075° = 142° + 0.2075°$$ separate fractional part from the whole
$$= 142° + 0.2075(60)'$$ $0.2075° = 0.2075 \cdot 1°$; substitute 60' for 1°
$$= 142°12.45'$$ result in degrees and minutes
$$= 142°12' + 0.45'$$ separate fractional part from the whole
$$= 142°12' + 0.45(60)''$$ $0.45' = 0.45 \cdot 1'$; substitute 60'' for 1'
$$= 142°12'27''$$ result in degrees, minutes, and seconds

☑ **A. You've just learned how to use the vocabulary associated with a study of angles and triangles**

Now try Exercises 11 through 26 ▶

**Figure 1.3**

Counter-clockwise

Clockwise

## B. Coterminal Angles

As an alternative to viewing angles as "the amount of inclination" between two rays, angle measure can also be considered as the *amount of rotation* from a fixed ray called the **initial side,** to a rotated ray called the **terminal side.** This allows for positive or negative angles, depending on the direction of rotation. Angles formed by a counter-clockwise rotation are considered **positive angles,** and angles formed by a clockwise rotation are **negative angles** (see Figure 1.3). We can then name an angle of any size, including those greater than 360° where the amount of rotation exceeds one revolution. See Figures 1.4 through 1.8.

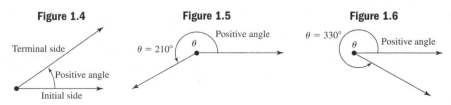

**Figure 1.4**          **Figure 1.5**          **Figure 1.6**

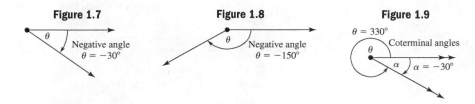

**Figure 1.7**    **Figure 1.8**    **Figure 1.9**

Note in Figure 1.9 that angle $\theta = 330°$ and angle $\alpha = -30°$ share the same initial and terminal sides and are called **coterminal angles.** Coterminal angles will always differ by multiples of 360°, meaning that for any integer $k$, angles $\theta$ and $\theta + 360°k$ will be coterminal.

---

**EXAMPLE 3** ▶ **Finding Coterminal Angles**

Find two positive angles and two negative angles that are coterminal with 60°.

Solution ▶

For $k = -2$, $60° + 360°(-2) = -660°$.
For $k = -1$, $60° + 360°(-1) = -300°$.
For $k = 1$, $60° + 360°(1) = 420°$.
For $k = 2$, $60° + 360°(2) = 780°$.

☑ **B.** You've just learned how to find and recognize coterminal angles

Note that many other answers are possible.

Now try Exercises 35 through 44 ▶

---

## C. Special Triangles

Recall that a triangle is a closed plane figure with three straight sides and three angles. If two of the sides meet at a 90° angle, a **right triangle** is formed. The longest side (opposite the 90° angle) is called the **hypotenuse,** while the other two sides are simply referred to as the **legs** of the triangle. In this section, we investigate two "special" right triangles. These two triangles, and the proportional relationships between their angles and sides, will appear frequently throughout this course of study, and in the courses that follow. Students are strongly urged to commit these relationships to memory.

**Figure 1.10**

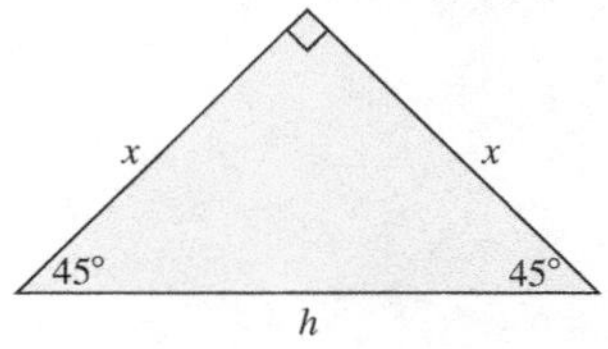

These triangles, commonly called **45-45-90** and **30-60-90** triangles, are *special* because no estimation or interpolation is needed to find the relationships between their sides. For the first, consider a right triangle with two equal sides and two 45° angles (Figure 1.10). After naming the equal sides $x$ and the hypotenuse $h$, we can apply the Pythagorean theorem to find a relationship between the sides and the hypotenuse in terms of $x$.

$$c^2 = a^2 + b^2 \quad \text{Pythagorean theorem}$$
$$h^2 = x^2 + x^2 \quad \text{substitute } x \text{ for } a, x \text{ for } b, \text{ and } h \text{ for } c$$
$$= 2x^2 \quad \text{combine like terms}$$
$$h = \sqrt{2}x \quad \text{solve for } h \, (h > 0)$$

This important result is summarized in the following box.

**WORTHY OF NOTE**

Recall that the Pythagorean theorem states that for any right triangle, the sum of the squares of the two legs, is equal to the square of the hypotenuse: $a^2 + b^2 = c^2$.

## 45-45-90 Triangles

Given a 45-45-90 triangle with one side of length $x$, the relationship between corresponding sides is:

$$1x : 1x : \sqrt{2}\,x.$$

(1) The two legs are equal
(2) The hypotenuse is $\sqrt{2}$ times the length of either leg:

$$a = b \qquad c = \sqrt{2}\,a \qquad c = \sqrt{2}\,b$$

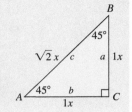

The proportional relationship for a 30-60-90 triangle is developed in **Exercise 76,** and the result is stated here.

## 30-60-90 Triangles

Given a 30-60-90 triangle with the shortest side of length $x$, the relationship between corresponding sides is:

$$1x : \sqrt{3}\,x : 2x.$$

(1) The longer leg is $\sqrt{3}$ times the length of the shorter leg
(2) The hypotenuse is 2 times the length of the shorter leg:

$$b = \sqrt{3}\,a \qquad c = 2a$$

**EXAMPLE 4** ▶ **Finding Exact Lengths of the Unknown Sides of Special Triangles**

Find the unknown side lengths of the following 30-60-90 triangles. Check the results for part a using the Pythagorean theorem.

**a.** The hypotenuse measures 10 m.
**b.** The longer leg measures $4\sqrt{3}$ in.

Solution ▶ **a.** In this first triangle, the hypotenuse measures 10 m.

| | |
|---|---|
| $c = 2a$ | 30-60-90 triangle property (2) |
| $10 = 2a$ | substitute 10 for $c$ |
| $5 = a$ | solve for $a$ |

The shorter leg measures 5 m.

| | |
|---|---|
| $b = \sqrt{3}\,a$ | 30-60-90 triangle property (1) |
| $\quad = \sqrt{3} \cdot 5$ | substitute 5 for $a$ |
| $\quad = 5\sqrt{3}$ | rewrite factors |

The longer leg measures $5\sqrt{3}$ m.

Check:

| | |
|---|---|
| $a^2 + b^2 = c^2$ | Pythagorean theorem |
| $5^2 + (5\sqrt{3})^2 = 10^2$ | substitute 5 for $a$, $5\sqrt{3}$ for $b$, and 10 for $c$ |
| $25 + 75 = 100$ | square |
| $100 = 100\ \checkmark$ | result checks |

**b.** In this triangle, the length $b$ of the longer leg measures $4\sqrt{3}$ in.

$$b = \sqrt{3}\,a \qquad \text{30-60-90 triangle property (1)}$$
$$4\sqrt{3} = \sqrt{3}\,a \qquad \text{substitute } 4\sqrt{3} \text{ for } b$$
$$4 = a \qquad \text{solve for } a$$

The shorter leg measures 4 in.

$$c = 2a \qquad \text{30-60-90 triangle property (2)}$$
$$= 2(4) \qquad \text{substitute 4 for } a$$
$$= 8 \qquad \text{multiply}$$

The hypotenuse measures 8 in.

**Now try Exercises 45 through 58** ▶

---

**EXAMPLE 5** ▶  **Applications of 45-45-90 Triangles: The Height of a Kite**

Seeking to reduce energy consumption and carbon emissions, many shipping companies are harnessing wind power using specialized kites. If such a kite is flying at a 45° angle, and 216 m of cable has been let out, what is the height $h$ of the kite's bridle point $B$ (see illustration)?

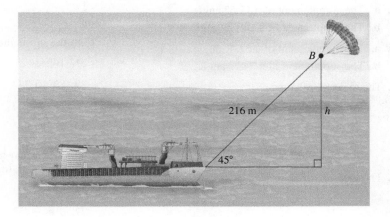

**Solution** ▶  In the 45-45-90 triangle, the hypotenuse is formed by the cable: $c = 216$ m. The height of the kite will be the length of one of the legs.

$$c = \sqrt{2}\,a \qquad \text{45-45-90 triangle property (2)}$$
$$216 = \sqrt{2}\,a \qquad \text{substitute 216 for } c$$
$$\frac{216}{\sqrt{2}} = a \qquad \text{solve for } a$$
$$a = \frac{216\sqrt{2}}{2} \qquad \text{rewrite equation and rationalize denominator}$$
$$= 108\sqrt{2} \qquad \text{simplify: exact form}$$
$$\approx 152.7 \text{ m} \qquad \text{approximate form (rounded to tenths)}$$

☑ **C. You've just learned how to find fixed ratios of the sides of special triangles**

The bridle point of the kite is $108\sqrt{2}$ m (about 152.7 m) higher than the deck of the ship.

**Now try Exercises 59 and 60** ▶

**1.1 EXERCISES**

▶ **CONCEPTS AND VOCABULARY**

**Fill in each blank with the appropriate word or phrase. Carefully reread the section if needed.**

1. _____ angles sum to 90°. Supplementary angles sum to _____°.

2. Acute angles are _____ than 90°, obtuse angles are _____ than 90°, and _____ angles are equal to 90°.

3. Two angles that share the same initial and terminal sides are called _____ angles. These angles always differ by multiples of _____.

4. The _____ of a 45-45-90 triangle is $\sqrt{2}$ times the length of either _____. In a 30-60-90 triangle, the shorter leg is _____ the length of the hypotenuse.

5. Discuss/Explain the difference between a positive angle and a negative angle. Can positive and negative angles be coterminal? Give a specific real-world example.

6. Discuss/Explain a strategy for remembering the relationship between corresponding sides of a 30-60-90 triangle.

▶ **DEVELOPING YOUR SKILLS**

**Determine the measure of the angle described.**

7. **a.** The complement of a 12.5° angle
   **b.** The supplement of a 149.2° angle

8. **a.** The complement of a 62.4° angle
   **b.** The supplement of a 74.7° angle

9. The measure of angle $\alpha$

10. The measure of angle $\beta$

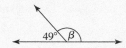

**Convert from DMS (degree/minute/seconds) notation to decimal degrees.**

11. 42°30′               12. 125°45′

13. 67°33′18″            14. 9°15′36″

15. 285°00′09″           16. 312°00′54″

17. 45°45′45″            18. 30°30′27″

**Convert the angles from decimal degrees to DMS (degree/minute/sec) notation.**

19. 20.25°               20. 40.75°

21. 67.307°              22. 83.516°

23. 275.33°              24. 330.45°

25. 5.4525°              26. 12.3275°

**Find the supplements of the following angles.**

27. 102°45′              28. 116°30′

29. 89°10′24″            30. 77°20′39″

31. 179°03′52″           32. 179°59′03″

33. 132°0′01″            34. 62°0′59″

**Find two positive angles and two negative angles that are coterminal with the angle given. Answers may vary.**

35. $\theta = 75°$       36. $\theta = 225°$

37. $\theta = -45°$      38. $\theta = -60°$

**Find the coterminal angle whose measure is between −180° and 180°.**

39. $\theta = 425°$      40. $\theta = 495°$

41. $\theta = 590°$      42. $\theta = 645°$

43. $\theta = 800°$      44. $\theta = 1140°$

**Given a 45-45-90 triangle with the stated measure(s), find the length of the unknown side(s) in exact form.**

45. The legs measure 5 cm.

46. The legs measure 3 m.

**47.** The hypotenuse measures $6\sqrt{2}$ ft.

**48.** The hypotenuse measures $7\sqrt{2}$ in.

**49.** The legs measure $5\sqrt{2}$ mm.

**50.** The legs measure $3\sqrt{2}$ in.

**51.** The hypotenuse measures 8 yd.

**52.** The hypotenuse measures 4 cm.

**Given a 30-60-90 triangle with the stated measure(s), find the length of the unknown sides.**

**53.** The shorter leg measures 3 mm.

**54.** The shorter leg measures 9 ft.

**55.** The hypotenuse measures 7 in.

**56.** The hypotenuse measures 5 m.

**57.** The longer leg measures 6 cm.

**58.** The longer leg measures 9 mi.

**Solve using special triangles. Answer in both exact and approximate form.**

**59. Special triangles:** A ladder-truck arrives at a high-rise apartment complex where a fire has broken out. If the maximum length the ladder extends is 82 ft and the angle of inclination is 45°, how high up the side of the building does the ladder reach? Assume the ladder is mounted atop a 10 ft high truck.

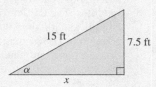

**60. Special triangles:** A heavy-duty ramp is used to winch heavy appliances from street level up to a warehouse loading dock. If the ramp is 7.5 ft high and the incline is 15 ft long, (a) what angle $\alpha$ does the dock make with the street? (b) How long is the base of the ramp?

▶ **WORKING WITH FORMULAS**

**61. Converting from DMS to decimal degrees:**
$$\theta = \frac{3600D + 60M + S}{3600}$$

Convert $67°33'18''$ to decimal degrees using the formula shown. Compare your result to Exercise 13.

**62. The unique coterminal angle in $[0°, 360°)$:**
$$\alpha = 360\left[\frac{\beta}{360} - \text{int}\left(\frac{\beta}{360}\right)\right]$$

For any positive angle $\beta$, the formula shown gives the unique coterminal angle $\alpha \in [0°, 360°)$, where $\text{int}\left(\dfrac{\beta}{360}\right)$ is the integer part of $\dfrac{\beta}{360}$. Use the formula to find the angle in $[0°, 360°)$ that is coterminal with 1140°. Compare your result to Exercise 44.

**63. Area of 30-60-90 triangle:** $A = \dfrac{\sqrt{3}s^2}{2}$

The area of a 30-60-90 triangle can be found using only $s$, the length of the shorter leg. Compute the area of a 30-60-90 triangle given its *hypotenuse* measures 10 cm. Verify your result using the familiar formula $A = \frac{1}{2} \times$ base $\times$ height.

**64. Area of 45-45-90 triangle:** $A = \dfrac{h^2}{4}$

The area of a 45-45-90 triangle can be found using only $h$, the length of the hypotenuse. Compute the area of a 45-45-90 triangle given its hypotenuse measures 10 cm. Verify your result using the familiar formula $A = \frac{1}{2} \times$ base $\times$ height.

▶ **APPLICATIONS**

**65. Fly-swatting:** A *Musca domestica* (common housefly) has been annoying Paula all afternoon and finally landed atop a table. Carefully, she raised her flyswatter and inclined it 34° from vertical, toward the pest (see figure).

  **a.** How many degrees must the flyswatter pass through before it is horizontal?

  **b.** If she covers 8° of the remaining angle in 0.1 sec, how long will it take for the swatter to strike the table? (The pesky fly escaped!)

**66. Orthopedic surgery:** A physical therapist uses a goniometer to measure the range of motion in Javier's knee after an anterior cruciate ligament (ACL) reconstruction. Javi can bend his knee through 132°, but his therapist wants him to acquire a full 180° range of motion.

   **a.** How many degrees of motion does Javi have to recover?

   **b.** If Javi can recover 4° per week, how long will the rehabilitation take?

**67. Global positioning system:** A handheld GPS receiver deciphers information from the U.S. Air Force 50th Space Wing's Navstar system of satellites. The GPS device uses software to convert latitude and longitude readings from decimal notation to DMS notation, which it then displays. Convert the coordinates 35.5575°S, 58.055°W to DMS form.

**68. Geocaching:** Handheld GPS recievers are used in the outdoor "treasure"-hunting game of geocaching. After Donovan inputs a geocache's coordinates in DMS form, software converts them to decimal form. Convert the coordinates 38°37′25″N, 90°11′38″W to decimal form. Round to four decimal places.

**69. Wakeboarding:** In 1999, Parks Bonifay became the first wakeboarder to land a documented 1080° spin in the air. In 2006, Danny Harf collected a $1080 reward when he became the second to do so. In 2008, Harf went bigger when he landed a documented 1260°. Were the angles of Harf's two spins coterminal? Find the two smallest, positive spins (angles) coterminal to Harf's 1260°.

**70. Game shows:** Many game shows use large segmented wheels that contestants must spin during play. All require the wheel to make one complete revolution for the spin to be valid. If the segment for a trip to Hawaii occurs −135° of the prize indicator, find two positive spins (angles) that will send a contestant to the Aloha state. Answers may vary.

On topographical maps, each closed figure represents a fixed elevation (a vertical change) according to a given *contour interval*. The *measured distance* on the map from point *A* to point *B* indicates the horizontal distance or the horizontal change between point *A* and a location directly beneath point *B*, according to a given *scale of distances.*

**Exercise 71 and 72**

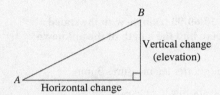

**71. Special triangles:** In the figure shown, the *contour interval* is 1:250 (each figure indicates a change of 250 m in elevation) and the scale of distances is 1 cm = 625 m. (a) Find the change of elevation from *A* to *B*; (b) use a proportion to find the horizontal distance between points *A* and *B* if the measured distance on the map is 1.6 cm; and (c) Draw the corresponding right triangle and use a special triangle relationship to find the length of the trail up the mountain side that connects *A* and *B*.

**Exercise 71**

**72. Special triangles:** As part of park maintenance, the 2 by 4 handrail alongside a mountain trail leading to the summit of Mount Marilyn must be replaced. In the figure, the *contour interval* is 1:200 (each figure indicates a change of 200 m in elevation) and the scale of distances is 1 cm = 400 m. (a) Find the change of elevation from *A* to *B*; (b) use a proportion to find the horizontal distance between *A* and *B* if the measured distance on the map is 4.33 cm; and (c) draw the corresponding right triangle and use a special triangle relationship to find the length needed to replace the handrail (recall that $\sqrt{3} \approx 1.732$).

**Exercise 72**

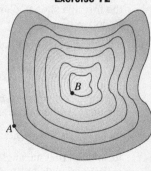

**73. Special triangles:** Two light planes are flying in formation at 100 mph, doing some reconnaissance work. At a designated instant, one pilot breaks to the left at an angle of 90° to the other plane. Assuming they keep the same altitude and continue to fly at 100 mph, use a special triangle to find the distance between them after 0.5 hr.

**74. Special triangles:** Two ships are cruising together on the open ocean at 10 nautical miles per hour. One of them turns to make a 90° angle with the first and increases speed, heading for port. Assuming the first ship continues traveling at 10 knots, use a special triangle to find the speed of the other ship if they are 20 mi apart after 1 hr.

## ► EXTENDING THE CONCEPT

**75.** The figure shown is made up of three 30-60-90 triangles. Use your knowledge of this special triangle and the Pythagorean theorem to find the exact distance from $B$ to $E$.

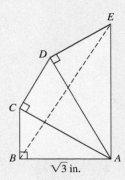

**76.** Ancient geometers knew that a hexagon (six sides) could be inscribed in a circle by laying out six consecutive chords equal in length to the radius ($r = 10$ cm for illustration). After connecting the diagonals of the hexagon, six equilateral triangles are formed with sides of 10 cm. Use the diagram given to develop the fixed ratios for the sides of a 30-60-90 triangle. (*Hint:* Use a perpendicular bisector.)

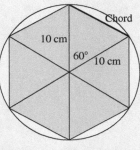

# 1.2 | Properties of Triangles; Similar Triangles

## Learning Objectives

*In Section 1.2 you will learn how to:*

☐ **A.** Recognize and classify different types of triangles

☐ **B.** Analyze triangles using their common properties

☐ **C.** Solve applications using similar triangles

During the period 2000–1600 B.C., the ancient Mesopotamians developed much of the algebra and geometry we take for granted today. In addition, there is a great deal of evidence they understood right triangles and the Pythagorean theorem more than a thousand years before the birth of Pythagoras. In this section, we extend our study of triangles by including additional properties used to identify and classify other triangles. We will also introduce some of the fundamental triangle relationships used to solve applications.

## A. Triangle Classifications

In Section 1.1, we defined three types of angles: right, acute, and obtuse. These same classifications can be applied to triangles as well. We have already been introduced to two special triangles, the 45-45-90 and 30-60-90 **right triangles** (so called because of the 90° angle). Similarly, an **acute triangle** contains three acute angles [Figure 1.11(a)], while an **obtuse triangle** will have exactly one obtuse angle [Figure 1.11(b)].

**Figure 1.11**

(a)                                    (b)

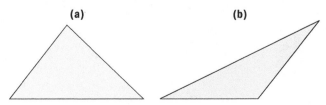

In addition to classifying triangles based on angle size, we can classify them based on their side length. A triangle with three sides of equal length is an **equilateral triangle.** In Figure 1.12(a), a single mark through each side indicates all three sides have equal length. An **isosceles triangle** has two sides of equal length [Figure 1.12(b)], while no two sides of a **scalene triangle** are of the same length [Figure 1.12(c)].

**Figure 1.12**

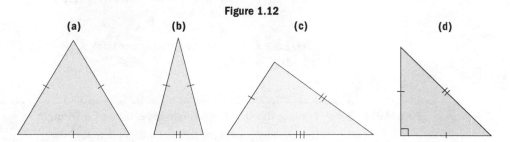

(a)        (b)        (c)        (d)

Using these classifications, we note the triangle in Figure 1.12(d) is both right and isosceles, while the triangle in Figure 1.12(b) is both isosceles and acute. In Exercise 76, you will be asked to show that any equilateral triangle must have three equal acute angles.

---

**EXAMPLE 1** ▶ **Classifying Triangles Based on Angles and Sides**

Match each of the triangles shown to its correct description below. Note there are more descriptions than triangles.

a.                    b.                    c.

**i.** acute and scalene        **ii.** acute and isosceles        **iii.** acute and equilateral
**iv.** right and scalene        **v.** right and isosceles        **vi.** obtuse and scalene
**vii.** obtuse and isosceles

Solution ▶  **a.** The triangle is a right triangle, determined by the "⌐" symbol. Since no two sides have equal length, the correct description is iv, right and scalene.

**b.** By inspection, the top angle of the triangle is obtuse. The single mark through two sides indicates they have equal length, so the correct description is vii, obtuse and isosceles.

☑ **A.** You've just learned how to recognize and classify different types of triangles

**c.** By careful observation, all three angles are acute. The side marks indicate all three sides are of unequal length, and the correct description of this triangle is i, acute and scalene.

Now try Exercises 7 through 14 ▶

## B. Analytical Properties of Triangles

As mentioned previously, a triangle is a closed plane figure with three straight sides and three angles. It is customary to name each angle using a capital letter and the side opposite the angle using the corresponding lowercase letter. Regardless of their size or orientation, triangles have the following properties.

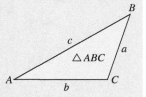

**Properties of Triangles**

Given triangle $ABC$ with sides $a$, $b$, and $c$, respectively,
  **I.** The sum of the angles is 180°:
   $A + B + C = 180°$
  **II.** The combined length of any two sides exceeds
   that of the third side:
   $a + b > c$, $a + c > b$, and $b + c > a$.
  **III.** Larger angles are opposite larger sides:
   If $C > B$, then $c > b$.

---

**EXAMPLE 2** ▶ **Finding the Unknown Angle Measures of a Triangle**

Use the analytical properties of a triangle to find the
measure of each angle shown.

Solution ▶ From Property I, we know the three angles must
sum to 180°, and we work as follows:

$A + B + C = 180°$     by Property I
$2\alpha + 6\alpha + 4\alpha = 180°$     substitute $2\alpha$ for $A$, $6\alpha$ for $B$, and $4\alpha$ for $C$
$12\alpha = 180°$     combine terms
$\alpha = 15°$     divide by 12

Using $\alpha = 15°$, back-substitution shows

| $A = 2\alpha$ | $B = 6\alpha$ | $C = 4\alpha$ |
|---|---|---|
| $= 2(15°)$ | $= 6(15°)$ | $= 4(15°)$ |
| $= 30°$ | $= 90°$ | $= 60°$ |

and we see the triangle is actually a 30-60-90 right triangle.

**Now try Exercises 15 through 34 ▶**

---

**EXAMPLE 3** ▶ **Using Side/Angle Relationships**

The three sides of a given triangle are $a = 156$ cm, $b = 131$ cm, and $c = 147$ cm.
Two of the angles measure 51° and 61°.
  **a.** Find the measure of the third angle.
  **b.** Name each angle using the correct corresponding capital letter.

Solution ▶ **a.** As in Example 2, the sum of the angles must be 180°.

$\angle 1 + \angle 2 + \angle 3 = 180°$     by Property I
$\angle 3 = 180° - \angle 1 - \angle 2$     subtract $\angle 1$ and $\angle 2$
$= 180° - 51° - 61°$     substitute 51° for $\angle 1$, 61° for $\angle 2$
$= 68°$     simplify

The third angle measures 68°.

**b.** Property III states that larger angles are opposite larger sides. This implies
the largest angle will be opposite the largest side, the smallest angle will be
opposite the smallest side, and so on.

$A = 68°$     largest side is $a = 156$ cm; largest angle is 68°
$B = 51°$     smallest side is $b = 131$ cm; smallest angle is 51°
$C = 61°$     remaining angle

☑ **B.** You've just learned how
to analyze triangles using
their common properties

**Now try Exercises 35 through 48 ▶**

## C. Similar Triangles

Two triangles are **similar triangles** if corresponding angles are equal, meaning for $\triangle ABC$ and $\triangle DEF$, $A = D$, $B = E$, and $C = F$. Since antiquity it's been known that *if two triangles are similar, corresponding sides are proportional* (corresponding sides are those opposite the equal angles from each triangle). This relationship, used extensively by the engineers of virtually all ancient civilizations, is very important to our study of trigonometry. Example 4 illustrates how proportions and similar triangles are often used.

---

**EXAMPLE 4** ▶ **Using Similar Triangles to Find Heights**

To estimate the height of a flagpole, Carrie reasons that $\triangle ABC$ formed by her height and shadow must be similar to $\triangle DEF$ formed by the flagpole. She is 5 ft 6 in. tall and casts an 8-ft shadow, while the shadow of the flagpole measures 44 ft. How tall is the pole?

**Solution** ▶ Let $H$ represent the height of the flagpole.

$$\frac{\text{Height}}{\text{Shadow Length}} : \frac{5.5}{8} = \frac{H}{44} \qquad \text{original proportion, } 5'6'' = 5.5 \text{ ft}$$

$$8H = 242 \qquad \text{cross multiply}$$

$$H = 30.25 \qquad \text{result}$$

The flagpole is $30\frac{1}{4}$ ft tall (30 ft 3 in.).

**Now try Exercises 49 through 52** ▶

---

In Example 4, Carrie reasoned that the triangles formed by her shadow and the shadow of the flagpole were similar (assuming the ground was horizontal), and both she and the flagpole were perfectly vertical. As here, many applications use similar triangles that naturally have the same orientation. However, having the same orientation is not a requirement for similarity, only that the three corresponding angles are equal. Consider Example 5.

---

**EXAMPLE 5** ▶ **Finding Unknown Sides of Similar Triangles**

Use properties of similar triangles to find the lengths of all three sides of the smaller triangle.

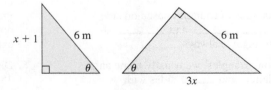

**Solution** ▶ Since both have a 90° angle and the same angle $\theta$, the third angle in both must be $90° - \theta$ and the triangles are similar. While both triangles have a side of length 6, we note 6 is the *hypotenuse* of the smaller triangle but a *leg* of the larger, and the triangles are oriented differently. This means we must take great care in setting up the proportion.

$$\frac{\text{Side Opposite } \theta}{\text{Hypotenuse}} : \frac{x+1}{6} = \frac{6}{3x} \qquad \text{proportion due to similarity}$$

$$3x(x+1) = 6(6) \qquad \text{cross multiply}$$

$$3x^2 + 3x = 36 \qquad \text{distribute}$$

$$3x^2 + 3x - 36 = 0 \qquad \text{subtract 36}$$

$$3(x^2 + x - 12) = 0 \qquad \text{factor GCF} = 3$$

$$3(x-3)(x+4) = 0 \qquad \text{factor trinomial}$$

$$x = 3 \quad \text{or} \quad x = -4 \qquad \text{zero factor property}$$

We discard $x = -4$ as a possibility, since this value would yield negative lengths in both triangles. For $x = 3$, we find the hypotenuse of the larger triangle measures $3(3) = 9$ m, while one of the legs of the smaller triangle measures $3 + 1 = 4$ m. We can now use the Pythagorean theorem to find the length of the remaining leg of the smaller triangle.

$$a^2 + b^2 = c^2 \qquad \text{Pythagorean theorem}$$

$$4^2 + b^2 = 6^2 \qquad \text{substitute 4 for } a, 6 \text{ for } c$$

$$b^2 = 36 - 16 \qquad \text{subtract } 4^2 = 16$$

$$= 20 \qquad \text{simplify}$$

$$b = \sqrt{20} \qquad \text{solve for } b\ (b > 0)$$

$$= 2\sqrt{5} \qquad \text{simplify}$$

 **C.** You've just learned how to solve applications using similar triangles

The two legs of the smaller triangle measure 4 m and $2\sqrt{5}$ m.

**Now try Exercises 53 through 64** ▶

## 1.2 EXERCISES

### ▶ CONCEPTS AND VOCABULARY

**Fill in each blank with the appropriate word or phrase. Carefully reread the section if needed.**

1. Triangles can be classified based on their angles or ____. The classifications based on angles are ____, ____, and ____.

2. The classifications of triangles based on side lengths are ____, ____, and ____. An equilateral triangle is always ____.

3. When labeling triangles, we usually name angles with ____ letters and ____ sides with corresponding ____ letters.

4. The combined length of any ____ ____ of a triangle must exceed the length of the ____ side.

5. Discuss/Explain why Property III of triangles implies that the middle-sized angle must be opposite the middle-sized side. Give a specific example.

6. Discuss/Explain how Section 1.1's treatment of the 45-45-90 and 30-60-90 triangles laid the foundation for a discussion of similar triangles.

## ▶ DEVELOPING YOUR SKILLS

**For Exercises 7–14, match each description with the appropriate choice a–h.**

**7.** acute and scalene      **8.** right and scalene

**9.** obtuse and isosceles    **10.** acute and equilateral

**11.** obtuse and scalene     **12.** acute and isosceles

**13.** right and isosceles     **14.** obtuse and equilateral

**a.**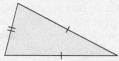

**b.**

**c.**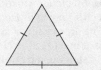

**d.**

**e.**

**f.**

**g.**

**h.** Not possible

**Determine the measure of the angle indicated.**

**15.** angle $\alpha$

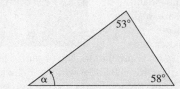

**16.** angle $\beta$

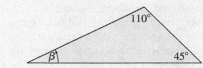

**17.** $\angle A$

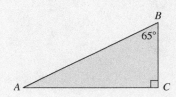

**18.** $\angle B$

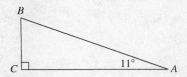

**Find the measure of angle $C$, for each triangle $ABC$ as described.**

**19.** $A = 67°$, $B = 88°$

**20.** $A = 13°$, $B = 59°$

**21.** $A = 23.1°$, $B = 91.4°$

**22.** $A = 37.3°$, $B = 55.8°$

**23.** $A = 98°35'$, $B = 43°15'$

**24.** $A = 9°36'$, $B = 68°21'$

**25.** $A = 44°32'18''$, $B = 92°5'51''$

**26.** $A = 71°35'44''$, $B = 57°41'10''$

**Use properties of triangles to find the actual measure of each angle in triangle $ABC$.**

**27.** $A = (3x - 3)°$, $B = 93°$, $C = 6x°$

**28.** $A = 3x°$, $B = (5x - 3)°$, $C = 47°$

**29.** $A = 51y°$, $B = 7y°$, $C = 32y°$

**30.** $A = 3y°$, $B = 4y°$, $C = (9y + 4)°$

**Use the figure shown and information given to find the measure of all three angles in $\triangle ABC$ for the relationships given.**

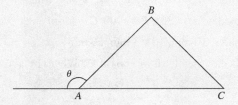

**31.** $\theta = 129°$, $B = (6x - 1)°$ and $C = (8x + 4)°$

**32.** $\theta = 134°$, $B = 7x°$ and $C = (12x + 1)°$

**33.** $\theta = (4x + 10)°$, $B = (2x + 10)°$ and $C = 72°$

**34.** $\theta = (3x + 8)°$, $B = 92°$ and $C = (x + 8)°$

**In Exercises 35–46, three sides and two angles are given.
(a) Find the measure of the third angle, and (b) name
each angle or side using the correct corresponding
lowercase or uppercase letter.**

35. sides: $a = 182$ mi, $b = 206$ mi, $c = 122$ mi

    angles: 83° and 36°

36. sides: $a = 391$ km, $b = 268$ km, $c = 373$ km

    angles: 41° and 73°

37. sides: $a = 3.2$ ft, $b = 4.8$ ft, $c = 3.2$ ft

    angles: 98° and 41°

38. sides: $a = 1.9$ m, $b = 1.6$ m, $c = 1.6$ m

    angles: 54° and 72°

39. sides: $a = 2\sqrt{3}$ cm, $b = 4$ cm, $c = 2$ cm

    angles: 30° and 60°

40. sides: $a = \sqrt{3} + 1$ in., $b = \sqrt{3} - 1$ in.,
    $c = 2\sqrt{2}$ in.

    angles: 15° and 90°

41. angles: $A = 57°$, $B = 38°$, $C =$ third angle

    sides: 121 dm, 144 dm, 89 dm

42. angles: $A = 37°$, $B = 102°$, $C =$ third angle

    sides: 265 yd, 178 yd, 163 yd

43. angles: $A = 104°$, $B = 38°$, $C =$ third angle

    sides: 4.7 ft, 7.4 ft, 4.7 ft

44. angles: $A = 38°$, $B = 71°$, $C =$ third angle

    sides: 13.6 km, 13.6 km, 8.9 km

45. angles: $A = 90°$, $B = 75°$, $C =$ third angle

    sides: $\sqrt{3} + 1$ in., $2\sqrt{2}$ in., $\sqrt{3} - 1$ in.

46. angles: $A = 30°$, $B = 90°$, $C =$ third angle

    sides: 10 mm, $10\sqrt{3}$ mm, 20 mm

47. Is the triangle shown possible? Why/why not?

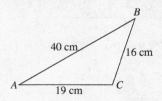

48. Is the triangle below possible? Why/why not?

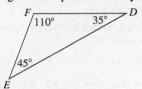

49. **Similar triangles:** A helicopter is hovering over a crowd of people watching a police standoff in a parking garage across the street. Stewart notices the shadow of the helicopter is lagging approximately 50 m behind a point directly below the helicopter. If he is 2 m tall and casts a shadow of 1.6 m at this time, what is the altitude of the helicopter?

50. **Similar triangles:** Near Fort Macloud, Alberta (Canada), there is a famous cliff known as *Head Smashed in Buffalo Jump*. The area is now a Canadian National Park, but at one time the Native Americans hunted buffalo by steering a part of the herd over the cliff. While visiting the park late one afternoon, Denise notices that its shadow reaches 201 ft from the foot of the cliff, at the same time she is casting a shadow of 12′1″. If Denise is 5′4″ tall, what is the height of the cliff?

51. **Similar triangles:** On a recent trip, Jorgelina visited the Mayan ruins of Chichen Itza on the Yucatan Peninsula (Mexico). During the Spring Equinox, the Temple of Kukulkan casts a serpent-like shadow, which appears to slither down the northern staircase. After a few  minutes of quiet appreciation, she observes that the pyramid casts a 40-m shadow while her shadow measured 2.2 m. If Jorgelina is 1.65 m tall, what is the height of the temple?

52. **Similar triangles:** The Osage Beach Fire Department is engaged in a firefight at a local marina. The shadow of the burning boat storage structure is 25 m long. At the same moment, the 3-m-high engine cast a shadow that was 5 m long. Assuming the ground is level, how tall is the structure?

Use properties of similar triangles to find the length of the missing side.

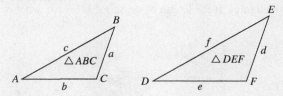

**53.** $b = 6$ m, $e = 18$ m, $f = 33$ m, $c = $ ?

**54.** $c = 3$ ft, $d = 16$ ft, $f = 6$ ft, $a = $ ?

**55.** $a = 3$ in., $b = 10$ in., $e = 6$ in., $d = $ ?

**56.** $a = 12$ ft, $c = 5$ ft, $d = 16$ ft, $f = $ ?

**57.** $a = \dfrac{5}{3}$ in., $b = \dfrac{1}{5}$ in., $d = \dfrac{20}{3}$ in., $e = $ ?

**58.** $b = \dfrac{2}{7}$ cm, $c = \dfrac{3}{4}$ cm, $e = \dfrac{4}{35}$ cm, $f = $ ?

Use properties of similar triangles to find the value of $x$ and the length of the sides involving $x$. Note the figures are not to scale.

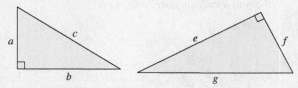

**59.** $a = x$, $c = 18$ m, $f = 2$ m, $g = x$

**60.** $b = x$, $c = 15$ yd, $e = \dfrac{20}{3}$ yd, $g = x$

**61.** $a = 4x$, $b = 14$ ft, $e = x + 1$, $f = 12$ ft

**62.** $a = 5$ in., $b = x + 4$, $e = 18$ in., $f = 2x$

**63.** $a = x - 1$, $b = 2x$, $e = 6x$, $f = 2x - 1$

**64.** $a = 3x$, $b = 4x - 3$, $e = 2x - 2$, $f = x + 1$

▶ **WORKING WITH FORMULAS**

**65. Relationships in a right triangle:**
$$h = \frac{ab}{c}, m = \frac{b^2}{c}, \text{ and } n = \frac{a^2}{c}$$

Given $\angle C$ is a right angle, and $h$ is the altitude of $\triangle ABC$, then $h$, $m$, and $n$ can all be expressed directly in terms of $a$, $b$, and $c$ by the relationships shown here. Compute the value of $h$, $m$, and $n$ for a right triangle with sides of 8, 15, and 17 cm.

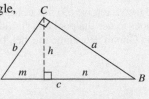

**66. The height of an equilateral triangle:** $H = \dfrac{\sqrt{3}}{2}S$

Given an equilateral triangle with sides of length $S$, the height of the triangle is given by the formula shown. Once the height is known the area of the triangle can easily be found (also see Exercise 65). The Gateway Arch in St. Louis, Missouri, is actually composed of stainless steel sections that are equilateral triangles. At the base of the arch the length of the sides is 54 ft. The smallest cross section at the top of the arch has sides of 17 ft. Find the area of these cross sections.

▶ **APPLICATIONS**

**67. Building height:** An alternative method for measuring the height of a building is known as the **stadia method.** One version of this method relies on a special scope known as a **stadimeter.** At 100 m from the building, the surveyor adjusts the scope until a reference line appears exactly as tall as the building and the properties of similar triangles can be applied. If the reference line is 12 mm tall and 57 mm from the surveyor's eye, how tall is the building (to the nearest meter)?

**Exercise 67**

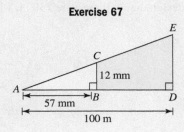

**68. Tank warfare:** In the early days of modern warfare, the stadia method was commonly applied, as similar triangles could be used to determine the distance to a target (for the artillery). Using a *stadiametric range-finding* scope, a 2.7-m-tall enemy tank appears to be 1.2 cm tall (see figure). If the length of the scope is 56 cm, what is the horizontal distance to the tank?

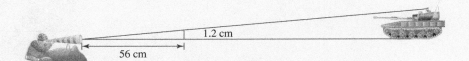

**69. Washington Monument:** The reflecting pool that lies between the Washington Monument and the Lincoln Memorial in Washington, D.C., is one of the most famous in the world. Kiaro is visiting the nation's capitol, and decides to use his handheld GPS receiver, the reflecting pool, and similar triangles to estimate the height of this obelisk. Using the diagram shown, help Kiaro determine this height (to the nearest foot).

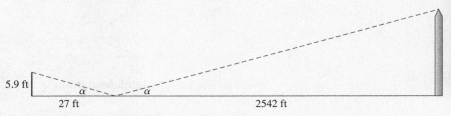

**70. Height of the Taj Majal:** Another famous reflecting pool (see Exercise 69) lies in front of the Taj Majal in Agra, India. Gianni is visiting this famous mausoleum, and decides to use the pool and similar triangles to estimate the height of the central dome. Using the diagram shown, help Gianni determine this height (to the nearest meter).

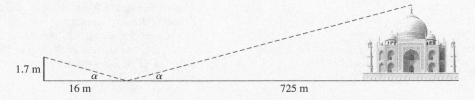

**71. Automotive design:** Before a new car becomes reality, several scale models are built out of clay. On one particular model, a triangular tail light measures 5.3 cm wide by 5.9 cm tall. If the actual tail light is to measure 16.9 cm wide, how tall will it be (to the nearest tenth)?

**72. Experimental aircraft:** On November 16, 2004, the NASA experimental aircraft X-43A used scramjet technology to set a world speed record of Mach 9.6 (nearly 7000 mph). The aircraft is roughly triangular in shape and measures 144 in. long by 60 in. wide at its tail. If the next generation of scramjet-powered aircraft is a similar triangle based on this same design, but will measure 150 in. wide at the tail, how long will it be?

**73. Navigation:** The mysteries of the Bermuda Triangle are well known to ships and their crew. The vertices of the triangle are located near Miami (Florida), San Juan (Puerto Rico), and of course, the island of Bermuda. The captain of a salvage operation has this region marked on her navigational map. On this map, the measured distance from Miami to San Juan is 20.75 cm, and the distance from San Juan to Bermuda is 19.2 cm. If the actual distance from Miami to San Juan is 1037 mi, use similar triangles to determine the distance from San Juan to Bermuda (to the nearest mile).

**74. Architecture:** The construction of the world's first spaceport is currently planned for just outside of Dubai, in the United Arab Emirates. The American developer, Space Adventures, is considering a design that calls for a runway system and adjoining terminals that are similar triangles. Referring to the illustration, how long will the main runway be?

**Exercise 74**

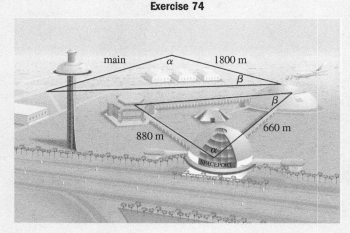

▶ **EXTENDING THE CONCEPT**

**75.** Discuss why the other two angles of a right triangle must be acute.

**76.** The third property of triangles states that larger angles are opposite larger sides. As a result, we find equal length sides are opposite angles with equal measures. Use this relationship to show that all equilateral triangles are acute triangles.

**77.** Recall that a triangle is a closed plane figure with three sides. Using a ruler, try to draw a triangle that does *not* satisfy triangle Property II: the combined length of two sides must exceed the length of the third side. Begin by drawing the base of the triangle 6 cm long. On both sides of this base, carefully draw the two other sides, while attempting to keep their combined length at 6 cm or less. What do you notice?

▶ **MAINTAINING YOUR SKILLS**

**78.** (1.1) Convert $35°15'36''$ from DMS notation to decimal degrees.

**79.** (1.1) Convert $84.275°$ from decimal degrees to DMS notation.

**80.** (1.1) Find the complement of $61°36'51''$.

**81.** (1.1) Find an angle in $[0°, 360°)$ that is coterminal with $-433°$.

**82.** (1.1) Given the longer leg of a 30-60-90 triangle measures 10 ft, find the length of the hypotenuse.

**83.** (1.1) The hypotenuse of a 45-45-90 triangle measures 5 cm. How long is each leg?

1. The city of Las Vegas, Nevada, is located at 36°06′36″ north latitude, 115°04′48″ west longitude. Convert both measures to decimal degrees.

2. Use a special triangle relationship to find the lengths of the remaining sides of the triangle shown.

**Exercise 2**

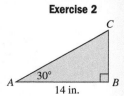

3. Name one positive angle and one negative angle that are coterminal with the angles given. Answers may vary.

   **a.** 18°          **b.** −107°

4. Find the complement of the angles.

   **a.** 39°          **b.** 73.7°

   **c.** 54°15′39″     **d.** $x$

5. A triangle has sides of 95 mm, 100 mm, and 90 mm. Its angles (in random order) measure 65°, 55°, and 60°. If the sides are named $a$, $b$, and $c$, respectively, what are the measures of angles $B$ and $C$?

6. An absent-minded painter leaned her 6-ft roller at a 45° angle against a freshly painted wall. Needless to say, it left a mark at the point of contact. How high above the floor was this mark?

7. In triangle $RST$, $R = (4x − 7)°$, $S = (15x + 6)°$, and $T = (7x − 1)°$. Find the measure of each angle.

8. A jeweler is making a triangular amulet out of three gold rods. If the first two rods measure 10 mm and 14 mm, what must be the minimum length (to the nearest 0.1 mm) of the third rod to ensure that a triangle is formed?

9. Use the properties of similar triangles to find the value of $x$ from the diagram given.

**Exercise 9**

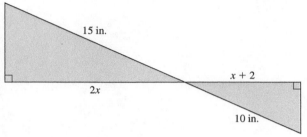

10. The headsail and mainsail of a new sloop are similar right triangles. The base of the mainsail measures 10.3 ft, and its height is 15.8 ft. If the height of the headsail is 13.2 ft, how long is its base (to the nearest tenth of a foot)?

## More on Special Triangles

Many fine buildings and roadways have been constructed using a "carpenters' (right) triangle" with sides having a 3-4-5 ratio. In fact, any three numbers that satisfy the Pythagorean theorem (known as Pythagorean triples) also form a right triangle. Unfortunately, the acute angles in these triangles cannot be expressed in exact form (for a 3-4-5 triangle, the acute angles are approximately 36.87° and 53.13°), and perhaps we begin to appreciate just how "special" the 30-60-90 and 45-45-90 triangles are. It then seems natural to wonder whether there are any other special triangles, with angles and sides that *can* be expressed in exact form.

It turns out that there are many such triangles, but the expressions for the side lengths become somewhat complex. For now, we'll turn our attention to a 15-75-90 triangle, as this triangle can be constructed with a clever diagram involving both 30-60-90 and 45-45-90 triangles. We begin by drawing a 30-60-90 triangle with the right angle at the bottom, inclined 45° from the horizontal (Figure 1.13). For the sake of generality, we will use the side lengths without units of measure.

Next, inscribe this triangle in the smallest rectangle possible and note the angle measure of the three new triangles formed (Figure 1.14). The new triangles beneath the 30-60-90 triangle are 45-45-90 triangles while the triangle above is a 15-75-90 triangle. Now we carefully label the legs of the 45-45-90 triangles using the unknowns $x$ and $y$ ($x > y$), noting that the longer leg of the 15-75-90 triangle

**Figure 1.13**

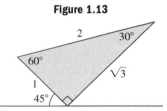

**Figure 1.14**

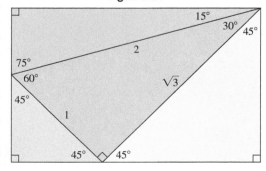

becomes $x + y$, with the shorter leg measuring $x - y$ (see Figure 1.15).

To find expressions for the sides of the 15-75-90 triangle, we must first determine the value of $x$ and $y$. For the 45-45-90 triangles, we know the hypotenuse is $\sqrt{2}$ times the length of a side, giving

$$c = \sqrt{2}a \quad \text{45-45-90 triangle property (3)}$$
$$\sqrt{3} = \sqrt{2}x \quad \text{substitute } \sqrt{3} \text{ for } c, x \text{ for } a$$
$$\frac{\sqrt{3}}{\sqrt{2}} = x \quad \text{solve for } x$$
$$x = \frac{\sqrt{6}}{2} \quad \text{simplify}$$

We can likewise find the value of $y$:

$$c = \sqrt{2}a \quad \text{45-45-90 triangle property (3)}$$
$$1 = \sqrt{2}y \quad \text{substitute 1 for } c, y \text{ for } a$$
$$\frac{1}{\sqrt{2}} = y \quad \text{solve for } y$$
$$y = \frac{\sqrt{2}}{2} \quad \text{simplify}$$

**Figure 1.15**

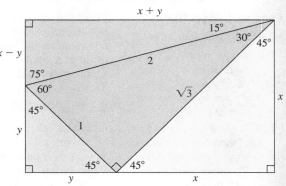

**Figure 1.16**

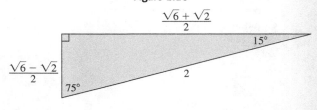

Now that we have exact values for $x$ and $y$, we know the sides of the 15-75-90 triangle must be in the proportion $\frac{\sqrt{6} - \sqrt{2}}{2} : \frac{\sqrt{6} + \sqrt{2}}{2} : 2$ (Figure 1.16). Dividing each expression by 2 (to obtain a hypotenuse of length 1) yields the following result.

## 15-75-90 Triangles

Given a 15-75-90 triangle with hypotenuse of length $x$, the relationships between corresponding sides is

$$\frac{\sqrt{6} - \sqrt{2}}{4}x : \frac{\sqrt{6} + \sqrt{2}}{4}x : 1x$$

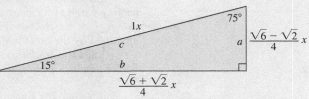

(1) The shorter leg is $\frac{\sqrt{6} - \sqrt{2}}{4}$ times the length of the hypotenuse: $a = \frac{\sqrt{6} - \sqrt{2}}{4}c$;

(2) The longer leg is $\frac{\sqrt{6} + \sqrt{2}}{4}$ times the length of the hypotenuse: $b = \frac{\sqrt{6} + \sqrt{2}}{4}c$.

**Find the length of the indicated side using the information given about the following 15-75-90 triangles.**

**Exercise 1:** $c = 8$ cm, $a = ?$

**Exercise 2:** $c = 12''$, $b = ?$

**Exercise 3:** $b = 5$ ft, $c = ?$

**Exercise 4:** $a = 7$ m, $c = ?$

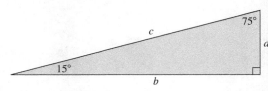

**Exercise 5:** $c = \sqrt{6} - \sqrt{2}$ mm, $b = ?$

**Exercise 6:** $c = \sqrt{6} + \sqrt{2}$ yd, $a = ?$

## 1.3 | Trigonometry: A View from the Coordinate Plane

### Learning Objectives

*In Section 1.3 you will learn how to:*

☐ **A.** Define the six trigonometric functions using the coordinates of a point on the terminal side of an angle

☐ **B.** Analyze the signs of the trigonometric functions of an angle based on the quadrant of the terminal side

☐ **C.** Evaluate the trigonometric functions of quadrantal angles

While definitely important and useful, applying properties of similar triangles requires *two* triangles and at least two side lengths from one of the triangles. Often these minimum requirements are not available and we are forced to search for alternative methods to apply triangle properties. With this goal in mind, we turn our attention to a more detailed study of angles and their properties.

### A. Trigonometric Functions and the Point *P*(*x, y*)

In Section 1.1, our main focus was the measure of an angle. These angles consisted of a fixed ray called the initial side and a rotated ray called the terminal side, with the amount of rotation measured in degrees. In this section, we will graph these same angles in the rectangular coordinate system (Figure 1.17) and look at some new ideas and relationships that are then possible.

**Figure 1.17**

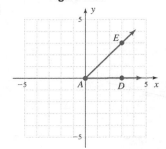

**Figure 1.18**

An angle is said to be in **standard position** if its vertex is at the origin and the initial side is along the positive *x*-axis. Both ∠*BAC* in Figure 1.17 and ∠*DAE* in Figure 1.18 measure 45°, but only ∠*DAE* is in standard position.

For any angle in standard position, identifying the terminal side is done simply by naming a point on the terminal side. However, we also note that *every such terminal side is coincident with a line that passes through the origin* and could alternatively be identified by the equation of this line. The equation of the line must be of the form $y = mx$ and this is *almost* sufficient for our purpose, but here we need to know which *half* of this line is coincident with the terminal side.

---

**EXAMPLE 1** ▶ **Writing the Equation of the Coincident Line**

Identify the terminal side of the angle $\alpha$ by writing an equation for the coincident half line.

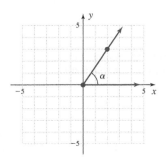

Solution ▶  Noting the terminal side passes through the point (2, 3), we begin by calculating the slope of the line through this point and the origin (0, 0).

$$m = \frac{y_2 - y_1}{x_2 - x_1} \qquad \text{slope formula}$$

$$= \frac{3 - 0}{2 - 0} \qquad \text{substitute (0, 0) for } (x_1, y_1) \text{ and (2, 3) for } (x_2, y_2)$$

$$= \frac{3}{2} \qquad \text{simplify}$$

Since the $y$-intercept is (0, 0), the equation of this line is $y = \frac{3}{2}x$ (from the slope-intercept formula $y = mx + b$). Since the terminal side lies in quadrant I, all the $x$-values must be nonnegative and the needed half of the coincident line is described by $y = \frac{3}{2}x; x \in [0, \infty)$.

Now try Exercises 7 through 14 ▶

By placing the angle in a coordinate system as in Example 1, the similar triangle limitations mentioned at the beginning of this section can be overcome. To this end, one of the most important observations to be made involves ratios of the $x$- and $y$-coordinates of a point on the terminal side of the angle. Largely due to the fact that the slope of a line is constant, these ratios are also constant. See Example 2.

**EXAMPLE 2** ▶  **Evaluating Ratios of the Coordinates of Points**

Consider the angle $\alpha$ and the line $y = \frac{3}{2}x$ from Exercise 1.

**a.** Find two additional points (other than the origin) on the terminal side of $\alpha$.

**b.** Compare the ratios $\frac{y}{x}$ and $\frac{x}{y}$ for both points.

Solution ▶  **a.** From Example 1, we know the point (2, 3) is on the terminal side of $\alpha$. In addition, any point on the terminal side of $\alpha$ is on the line $y = \frac{3}{2}x; x \in [0, \infty)$, so for ease of calculation, we choose a multiple of 2 for the $x$-coordinate. Here we chose $x = 4$.

$$y = \frac{3}{2}x \qquad \text{original equation}$$

$$= \frac{3}{2}(4) \qquad \text{substitute 4 for } x$$

$$= 6 \qquad \text{simplify}$$

The point (4, 6) is also on the terminal side of $\alpha$.

**b.** First evaluate the ratio $\frac{y}{x}$:

at the point (2, 3);           at the point (4, 6)

$$\frac{y}{x} = \frac{3}{2} \qquad\qquad \frac{y}{x} = \frac{6}{4}$$

$$= \frac{3}{2}$$

Note the points yield the same ratio. Now evaluate the ratio $\frac{x}{y}$:

at the point (2, 3);            at the point (4, 6)

$$\frac{x}{y} = \frac{2}{3} \qquad\qquad \frac{x}{y} = \frac{4}{6}$$

$$= \frac{2}{3}$$

We find that although different points on the terminal side were chosen, both possible ratios of $x$ and $y$ were equivalent.

**Now try Exercises 15 through 24 ▶**

While the results from Exercise 2 may not be surprising, they are extremely important. Early mathematicians also realized these types of ratios remained constant, independent of the point chosen on the terminal side. By including the distance $r$ from the origin to the point $P(x, y)$, they were able to consider four more ratios that yielded similar results: $\frac{x}{r}, \frac{r}{x}, \frac{y}{r},$ and $\frac{r}{y}$.

In general, assume $\theta$ is an arbitrary angle whose terminal side is coincident with the line $y = kx$. Now consider *any* two points $(x_1, y_1)$ and $(x_2, y_2)$ on the terminal side, at corresponding distances $r_1$ and $r_2$ from the origin (Figure 1.19). Note the distance $r$ can be found using the Pythagorean theorem: $r = \sqrt{x^2 + y^2}$. Because the triangles formed are similar, we have $\frac{y_1}{x_1} = \frac{y_2}{x_2}, \frac{x_1}{r_1} = \frac{x_2}{r_2}, \frac{y_1}{r_1} = \frac{y_2}{r_2},$ and so on, with the six distinct ratios formed remaining constant, *regardless of the point chosen*. To apply these ratios in context, it was helpful to give each one a special name. Since the point $(x, y)$ is on the terminal side of angle $\theta$, each ratio depends on $\theta$ and we name each ratio as follows:

**Figure 1.19**

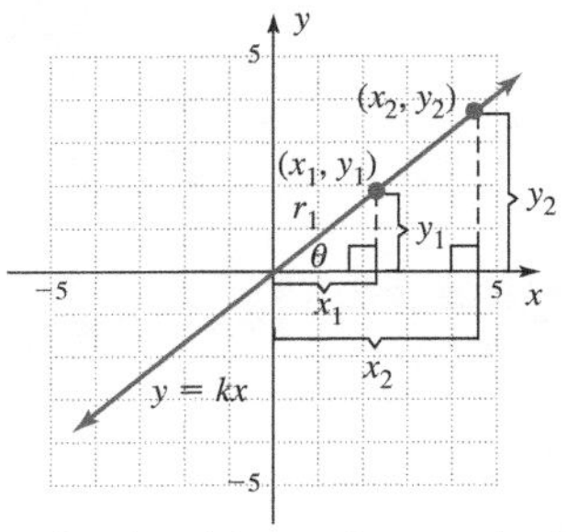

$$\text{sine } \theta = \frac{y}{r} \qquad \text{cosine } \theta = \frac{x}{r} \qquad \text{tangent } \theta = \frac{y}{x}$$

The reciprocal ratios, for example, $\frac{r}{y}$ instead of $\frac{y}{r}$, also play a significant role in trigonometry, and are likewise given a name:

$$\text{cosecant } \theta = \frac{r}{y} \qquad \text{secant } \theta = \frac{r}{x} \qquad \text{cotangent } \theta = \frac{x}{y}$$

In actual use, each function name is written in abbreviated form as sin $\theta$, cos $\theta$, tan $\theta$, csc $\theta$, sec $\theta$, and cot $\theta$, respectively, and are collectively called the trigonometric functions (or simply the trig functions). Over the course of this study, you will see many connections between this view of trigonometry and the alternative approaches that follow. In summary, we have

**WORTHY OF NOTE**

Since the points $(x_1, y_1)$ and $(x_2, y_2)$ lie on the line $y = kx$, we can express them as $(x_1, kx_1)$ and $(x_2, kx_2)$. The proportion $\frac{y_1}{x_1} = \frac{y_2}{x_2}$ then becomes $\frac{kx_1}{x_1} = \frac{kx_2}{x_2}$, or simply $k = k$. Similarly, the other five proportions can be verified algebraically.

## Trigonometric Functions of Any Angle

Given $P(x, y)$ is any point on the terminal side of angle $\theta$ in standard position, with $r = \sqrt{x^2 + y^2}$ $(r > 0)$ the distance from the origin to $(x, y)$. The six trigonometric functions of $\theta$ are

$$\sin \theta = \frac{y}{r} \qquad \cos \theta = \frac{x}{r} \qquad \tan \theta = \frac{y}{x}$$
$$x \neq 0$$

$$\csc \theta = \frac{r}{y} \qquad \sec \theta = \frac{r}{x} \qquad \cot \theta = \frac{x}{y}$$
$$y \neq 0 \qquad\qquad x \neq 0 \qquad\qquad y \neq 0$$

---

**EXAMPLE 3** ▶ **Evaluating Trig Functions Given a Point P**

Find the value of the six trigonometric functions given $P(-5, 5)$ is on the terminal side of angle $\theta$ in standard position.

Solution ▶ For $P(-5, 5)$ we have $x < 0$ and $y > 0$ so the terminal side is in QII. Solving for $r$ yields $r = \sqrt{(-5)^2 + (5)^2} = \sqrt{50} = 5\sqrt{2}$. For $x = -5$, $y = 5$, and $r = 5\sqrt{2}$, we obtain

$$\sin \theta = \frac{y}{r} = \frac{5}{5\sqrt{2}} \qquad \cos \theta = \frac{x}{r} = \frac{-5}{5\sqrt{2}} \qquad \tan \theta = \frac{y}{x} = \frac{5}{-5}$$

$$= \frac{\sqrt{2}}{2} \qquad\qquad = -\frac{\sqrt{2}}{2} \qquad\qquad = -1$$

The remaining functions can be evaluated using reciprocals.

$$\csc \theta = \frac{2}{\sqrt{2}} = \sqrt{2} \qquad \sec \theta = -\frac{2}{\sqrt{2}} = -\sqrt{2} \qquad \cot \theta = -1$$

**Now try Exercises 25 through 40** ▶

---

**EXAMPLE 4** ▶ **Evaluating Trig Functions Given the Terminal Side Is on $y = mx$**

Given that $P(x, y)$ is a point on the terminal side of angle $\theta$ in standard position, find the value of $\sin \theta$ and $\cos \theta$, if

**a.** The terminal side is in QII and coincident with the line $y = -\frac{12}{5}x$,
**b.** The terminal side is in QIV and coincident with the line $y = -\frac{12}{5}x$.

Solution ▶ **a.** Select any convenient point in QII that satisfies this equation. We select $x = -5$ since $x$ is negative in QII, which gives $y = 12$ and the point $(-5, 12)$.

Solving for $r$ gives $r = \sqrt{(-5)^2 + (12)^2} = 13$. The ratios are

$$\sin \theta = \frac{y}{r} = \frac{12}{13} \qquad \cos \theta = \frac{x}{r} = \frac{-5}{13}$$

**b.** In QIV we select $x = 10$ since $x$ is positive in QIV, giving $y = -24$ and the point $(10, -24)$. Solving for $r$ gives $r = \sqrt{(10)^2 + (-24)^2} = 26$. The ratios are

$$\sin \theta = \frac{y}{r} = \frac{-24}{26} \qquad \cos \theta = \frac{x}{r} = \frac{10}{26}$$

$$= -\frac{12}{13} \qquad\qquad = \frac{5}{13}$$

☑ **A.** You've just learned how to define the six trigonometric functions using the coordinates of a point on the terminal side of an angle

**Now try Exercises 41 through 44** ▶

In Example 2, note the ratios are the same in QII and QIV *except for their sign*. We will soon use this observation to great advantage.

## B. The Signs of the Trig Functions

Finding the value of each trig function for a given angle depends heavily on the quadrant of the terminal side, since this will dictate the signs for $x$ and $y$. Students are strongly encouraged to make quadrant and sign observations the *first step* in any solution process involving the trig functions.

**Figure 1.20**

The best way to remember the signs of the trig functions is to keep in mind that sine is associated with $y$, cosine with $x$, and tangent with both $x$ and $y$ ($r$ is always positive). In addition, there are several mnemonic devices (memory tools) to assist you. One is to use the first letter of the function that is positive in each quadrant and create a catchy acronym. For instance **ASTC** → **A**ll **S**tudents **T**ake **C**lasses (see Figure 1.20). Note that a trig function and its reciprocal function will always have the same sign.

| Quadrant II | Quadrant I |
|---|---|
| Sine is positive | All are positive |
| Tangent is positive | Cosine is positive |
| Quadrant III | Quadrant IV |

---

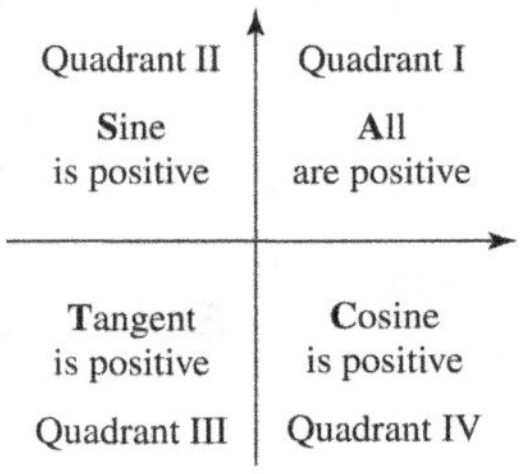

**EXAMPLE 5** ▶ **Determining the Quadrant of the Terminal Side of an Angle**

Determine the quadrant that contains the terminal side of an angle in standard position, given

  **a.** $\sin \alpha > 0$ and $\tan \alpha < 0$    **b.** $\cos \beta < 0$ and $\cot \beta > 0$

**Solution** ▶ To begin, we recall that sine is associated with $y$, cosine with $x$, and tangent with both $x$ and $y$ ($r$ is always positive).

  **a.** (1)  With $\sin \alpha > 0$, we know $y > 0$ and the terminal side of $\alpha$ must lie in QI or QII.
  
  (2)  Since $\tan \alpha < 0$, $x$ and $y$ must have opposite signs, indicating the terminal side must lie in QII or QIV.
  
  Since both (1) and (2) must be true, the terminal side of $\alpha$ is in QII.
  
  **b.** (1)  For $\cos \beta < 0$, the terminal side of $\beta$ must lie in QII or QIII.
  
  (2)  As reciprocal functions, tangent and cotangent will share the same sign. This means that for $\cot \beta > 0$, the terminal side lies in QI or QIII (as is true for $\tan \beta > 0$).
  
  As in part (a), both conditions (1) and (2) have to be met, so the terminal side of $\beta$ must be in QIII.

**Now try Exercises 45 through 54** ▶

---

**EXAMPLE 6** ▶ **Finding Function Values Using a Quadrant and Sign Analysis**

Given $\sin \theta = \dfrac{5}{13}$ and $\cos \theta < 0$, find the value of the other ratios.

**Solution** ▶ Always begin with a quadrant and sign analysis: $\sin \theta$ is positive in QI and QII, while $\cos \theta$ is negative in QII and QIII. Both conditions are satisfied in QII only. For $r = 13$ and $y = 5$, the Pythagorean theorem shows $x = \pm\sqrt{13^2 - 5^2} = \pm\sqrt{144} = \pm 12$.

☑ **B.** You've just learned how to analyze the signs of the trigonometric functions of an angle based on the quadrant of the terminal side

With $\theta$ in QII, $x = -12$ and this gives $\cos \theta = \dfrac{-12}{13}$ and $\tan \theta = \dfrac{5}{-12}$. The reciprocal values are $\csc \theta = \dfrac{13}{5}$, $\sec \theta = \dfrac{13}{-12}$, and $\cot \theta = \dfrac{-12}{5}$.

**Now try Exercises 55 through 62** ▶

**Figure 1.21**

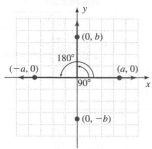

## C. Quadrantal Angles

Now that we've defined the trig functions in terms of ratios involving $x$, $y$, and $r$, the question arises as to their value when $x$ or $y$ equals 0. In standard position, the terminal sides of the 90°, 180°, 270°, and 360° angles coincide with one of the axes and are called **quadrantal angles.** For 90° and 270°, any point on the terminal side of the angle has an $x$-value of zero, meaning tan 90°, sec 90°, tan 270°, and sec 270° are all undefined since $x = 0$ is in the denominator. Similarly, at 180° and 360°, the $y$-value of any point on the terminal side is zero, so cot 180°, csc 180°, cot 360°, and csc 360° are likewise undefined (see Figure 1.21).

---

**EXAMPLE 7** ▶ **Evaluating the Trig Functions for $\theta = 90°k$, $k$ an Integer**

Evaluate the six trig functions for $\theta = 270°$.

**Solution** ▶ Here, $\theta$ is the quadrantal angle whose terminal side separates QIII and QIV. Since the evaluation is independent of the point chosen on this side, we choose $(0, -1)$ for convenience, giving $r = 1$. For $x = 0$, $y = -1$, and $r = 1$ we obtain

$$\sin \theta = \frac{-1}{1} = -1 \qquad \cos \theta = \frac{0}{-1} = 0 \qquad \tan \theta = \frac{-1}{0} \ (\textit{undefined})$$

The remaining ratios can be evaluated using reciprocals.

$$\csc \theta = -1 \qquad \sec \theta = \frac{-1}{0} \ (\textit{undefined}) \qquad \cot \theta = \frac{0}{-1} = 0$$

**Now try Exercises 63 through 72** ▶

---

Results for the quadrantal angles are summarized in Table 1.1.

**Table 1.1**

| $\theta$ | $\sin \theta = \dfrac{y}{r}$ | $\cos \theta = \dfrac{x}{r}$ | $\tan \theta = \dfrac{y}{x}$ | $\csc \theta = \dfrac{r}{y}$ | $\sec \theta = \dfrac{r}{x}$ | $\cot \theta = \dfrac{x}{y}$ |
|---|---|---|---|---|---|---|
| $0°/360° \rightarrow (1, 0)$ | 0 | 1 | 0 | undefined | 1 | undefined |
| $90° \rightarrow (0, 1)$ | 1 | 0 | undefined | 1 | undefined | 0 |
| $180° \rightarrow (-1, 0)$ | 0 | -1 | 0 | undefined | -1 | undefined |
| $270° \rightarrow (0, -1)$ | -1 | 0 | undefined | -1 | undefined | 0 |

☑ **C.** You've just learned how to evaluate the trigonometric functions of quadrantal angles

---

## TECHNOLOGY HIGHLIGHT

### $x$, $y$, $r$, and Functions of any Angle

Graphing calculators offer a number of features that can assist a study of the trig functions of any angle. On the TI-84 Plus, the keystrokes [2nd] [APPS] **(ANGLE)** will bring up the menu shown in Figure 1.22. Options 1 through 4 are basically used for angle conversions (DMS degrees to decimal degrees, degrees to radians, and so on). Of interest to us here are options 5 and 6, which can be used to determine the radius $r$ (option 5) or the angle $\theta$ (option 6) related to a given point $(x, y)$. For $(-12, 35)$, [CLEAR] the home screen and press [2nd] [APPS]

**Figure 1.22**

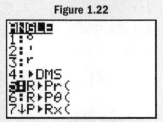

—continued

**(ANGLE) 5:R▶Pr(,** which will place the option on the home screen. This feature supplies the left parenthesis of the ordered pair, and you simply complete it: **5:R▶Pr(−12, 35).** As shown in Figure 1.23, the calculator returns 37, and $(−12)^2 + (35)^2 = (37)^2$✓. To find the related angle, it is assumed that $\theta$ is in standard position and $(x, y)$ is on the terminal side. Pressing  2nd   APPS   **(ANGLE) 6:R▶Pθ(** and completing the ordered pair as before, shows the corresponding angle is approximately 108.9° (Figure 1.23). Note this is a QII angle as expected, since $x < 0$ and $y > 0$. Use these features to complete the following exercises.

**Figure 1.23**

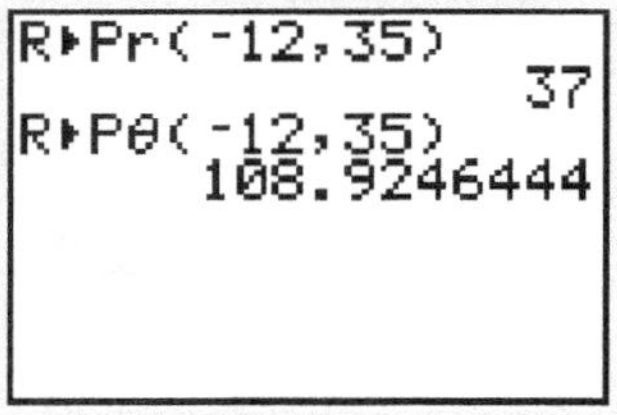

```
R▶Pr(-12,35)
                37
R▶Pθ(-12,35)
         108.9246444
```

**Exercise 1:** Find the radius corresponding to the point $(−5, 5\sqrt{3})$.

**Exercise 2:** Find the angle corresponding to $(−28, −45)$, then use a calculator to evaluate $\sin\theta$, $\cos\theta$, and $\tan\theta$ for this angle. Compare each result to the values given by $\sin\theta = \dfrac{y}{r}$, $\cos\theta = \dfrac{x}{r}$ and $\tan\theta = \dfrac{y}{x}$.

## 1.3 EXERCISES

### ▶ CONCEPTS AND VOCABULARY

**Fill in each blank with the appropriate word or phrase. Carefully reread the section if needed.**

1. An angle is in standard position if its vertex is at the _____ and the initial side is along the _____.

2. A(n) _____ angle is one where the _____ side is coincident with one of the coordinate axes.

3. Given angle $\theta$ is in standard position with point $P(x, y)$ on its terminal side, the six trig ratios are

   _____ $= \dfrac{x}{r}$,  _____ $= \dfrac{y}{r}$,  _____ $= \dfrac{y}{x}$,

   $\sec\theta = $ _____,  $\csc\theta = $ _____, and

   $\cot\theta = $ _____.

4. If the terminal side of an angle in standard position lies in the third quadrant, _____ and _____ are the only two trig functions that are positive. The other four are _____.

5. Discuss/Explain what is needed to establish the quadrant in which the terminal side of an angle lies. Why are the signs of any two of the three trig functions cosine, sine, and tangent sufficient?

6. Discuss/Explain why there are two possible angles $\theta$ in $[0, 360°)$ such that $\sin\theta = \dfrac{2}{5}$. Is this true for $\sin\theta = 1$? Explain why or why not.

### ▶ DEVELOPING YOUR SKILLS

**Write the equation of the line coincident with the terminal side of a nonquadrantal angle containing the point $P(x, y)$. Include the domain restriction and quadrant of the terminal side.**

7. $(12, 15)$

8. $(8, −20)$

9. $(−2, −2\sqrt{3})$

10. $(−3\sqrt{2}, 6)$

11. $(6.3, −10.5)$

12. $(−9.8, −4.2)$

13. $\left(-\dfrac{5}{8}, \dfrac{3}{4}\right)$

14. $\left(\dfrac{6}{21}, \dfrac{12}{7}\right)$

**Find any two points on the terminal side of the angle $\theta$ (indicated by the equation $y = mx$), then evaluate the ratios $\dfrac{y}{x}$ and $\dfrac{x}{y}$ at both points.**

15. $y = \dfrac{1}{2}x$; QIII

16. $y = −2x$; QII

17. $y = 3x$; $x \in [0, \infty)$

18. $y = −2x$; $x \in [0, \infty)$

19. $y = −1.5x$; $x \in (−\infty, 0]$

20. $y = 2.2x$; $x \in (−\infty, 0]$

**21.** $y = \dfrac{4}{3}x$; QIII          **22.** $y = -\dfrac{3}{5}x$; QIV

**23.** $2x + 7y = 0$; QIV          **24.** $4x - 5y = 0$; QIII

**Find the value of the six trigonometric functions given $P(x, y)$ is on the terminal side of angle $\theta$, with $\theta$ in standard position.**

**25.** $(8, 15)$          **26.** $(7, 24)$

**27.** $(-20, 21)$          **28.** $(-3, -1)$

**29.** $(7.5, -7.5)$          **30.** $(9, -9)$

**31.** $(4\sqrt{3}, 4)$          **32.** $(-6, 6\sqrt{3})$

**33.** $(2, 8)$          **34.** $(6, -15)$

**35.** $(-3.75, -2.5)$          **36.** $(6.75, 9)$

**37.** $\left(-\dfrac{5}{9}, \dfrac{2}{3}\right)$          **38.** $\left(\dfrac{3}{4}, -\dfrac{7}{16}\right)$

**39.** $\left(\dfrac{1}{4}, -\dfrac{\sqrt{5}}{2}\right)$          **40.** $\left(-\dfrac{\sqrt{3}}{5}, \dfrac{22}{25}\right)$

**Graph each linear equation and state the quadrants it traverses. Then pick one point on the line from each quadrant and evaluate the functions $\sin\theta$, $\cos\theta$, and $\tan\theta$ using these points.**

**41.** $y = \dfrac{3}{4}x$          **42.** $y = \dfrac{5}{12}x$

**43.** $y = -\dfrac{\sqrt{3}}{3}x$          **44.** $y = -\dfrac{\sqrt{3}}{2}x$

**State the quadrant of the terminal side of $\theta$, using the information given.**

**45.** $\sin\theta > 0$, $\cos\theta < 0$

**46.** $\cos\theta < 0$, $\tan\theta < 0$

**47.** $\tan\theta < 0$, $\sin\theta > 0$

**48.** $\sec\theta > 0$, $\tan\theta > 0$

**Find the sign of the following expressions, given the terminal side of $\theta$ lies in the quadrant indicated.**

**49.** $\sin\theta\cos\theta$; QIII          **50.** $\tan\theta\sec\theta$; QII

**51.** $\dfrac{\cot\theta}{\cos\theta}$; QIV          **52.** $\dfrac{\csc\theta}{\cot\theta}$; QI

**53.** $\cos\theta \cdot \dfrac{\tan\theta}{\sec\theta}$; QII          **54.** $\sin\theta \cdot \dfrac{\sec\theta}{\cot\theta}$; QIV

**For the information given, find the values of $x$, $y$, and $r$. Clearly indicate the quadrant of the terminal side of $\theta$, then state the values of the six trig functions of $\theta$.**

**55.** $\cos\theta = \dfrac{4}{5}$ and $\sin\theta < 0$

**56.** $\tan\theta = -\dfrac{12}{5}$ and $\cos\theta > 0$

**57.** $\csc\theta = -\dfrac{37}{35}$ and $\tan\theta > 0$

**58.** $\sin\theta = -\dfrac{20}{29}$ and $\cot\theta < 0$

**59.** $\csc\theta = 3$ and $\cos\theta > 0$

**60.** $\csc\theta = -2$ and $\cos\theta > 0$

**61.** $\sin\theta = -\dfrac{7}{8}$ and $\sec\theta < 0$

**62.** $\cos\theta = \dfrac{5}{12}$ and $\sin\theta < 0$

**63.** Evaluate the six trig functions in terms of $x$, $y$, and $r$ for $\theta = 90°$.

**64.** Evaluate the six trig functions in terms of $x$, $y$, and $r$ for $\theta = 180°$.

**Without using a calculator or referring to the table on p. 27, find the value of $\beta \in [0, 360°)$ using the information given.**

**65.** $\cos\beta = 0$, $\sin\beta = 1$

**66.** $\sin\beta = 0$, $\cos\beta = -1$

**67.** $\tan\beta$ is undefined, $\csc\beta = -1$

**68.** $\cot\beta = 0$, $\csc\beta = 1$

**69.** $\tan\beta = 0$, $\sec\beta = 1$

**70.** $\sec\beta$ is undefined, $\sin\beta = -1$

**71.** $\csc\beta$ is undefined, $\cos\beta = -1$

**72.** $\cot\beta$ is undefined, $\sec\beta = 1$

**For each exercise, state the quadrant of the terminal side and the sign of the function in that quadrant.**

**73.** $\sin 719°$          **74.** $\cos 528°$

**75.** $\tan -419°$          **76.** $\sec -621°$

**77.** $\csc 681°$          **78.** $\tan 995°$

**79.** $\cos 805°$          **80.** $\sin 772°$

## ► WORKING WITH FORMULAS

**81. Cosine $\theta$ in terms of $x$ and $y$:** $\cos \theta = \dfrac{x}{\sqrt{x^2 + y^2}}$

Using $r = \sqrt{x^2 + y^2}$, the cosine of $\theta$ can be written as shown. (a) Use the formula to find $\cos \theta$ given $(3, 4)$ is on the terminal side. (b) Use the formula to find $\cos \theta$ given $(3, 0)$ is on the terminal side. (c) Use this definition to explain why $\cos \theta$ can never be greater than 1.

**82. Cosine of an angle not in standard position:**

$$\cos \theta = \frac{x_1 x_2 + y_1 y_2}{\sqrt{(x_1^2 + y_1^2)(x_2^2 + y_2^2)}}$$

The cosine of an angle whose vertex is at the origin (but not necessarily in standard position) can be found using the formula shown, where $P(x_1, y_1)$ is any point on the initial side and $Q(x_2, y_2)$ is any point on the terminal side. (a) Find $\cos \theta$ given $(3, 4)$ is on the initial side and $(-12, 5)$ is on the terminal side. (b) Verify this formula also applies for an angle in standard position.

## ► APPLICATIONS

As our study of trigonometry progresses, we will learn to find the measure of an angle *based on its trig function values* (first studied in Section 2.2). Here we practice finding these trig function values.

**83. Billiards:** In Carolina's attempt to end a pool game by sinking the eight ball, she "scratches," accidentally sending the cue ball into the corner pocket located 60 in. to the west and 40 in. to the north of where it contacted the eight ball. Find $\tan \theta$, for the angle $\theta$ shown. For convenience, a coordinate system is shown with the point of contact at the origin.

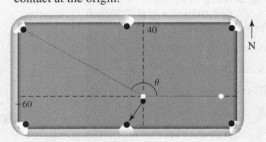

**84. Ice hockey:** Wydonyu Yustrig takes a low slap shot from the blue line, as shown in the figure.

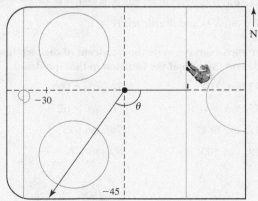

Unfortunately, the puck strikes the skate of a teammate and from there goes to the "boards," 45 ft south and 30 ft west. Find $\tan \theta$, where $\theta$ is the angle shown. For convenience, a coordinate system is shown with the point of deflection at the origin.

For Exercises 85 through 88, find the indicated value by drawing sketches similar to those used in Exercises 83 and 84. Carefully choose the location of the origin so the angle $\theta$ will be in standard position.

**85. Oil painting:** An aspiring artist begins her latest masterpiece by raising her 10″ Filbert paintbrush to horizontal. Keeping her hand steady, she then raises the the tip of the brush 3″. Find $\sin \theta$, where $\theta$ is the angle she inclined the brush.

**86. Violin:** When Lucy is practicing her violin, the bow makes contact with both the D and A strings when held horizontally (parallel to the ground). By raising the end of the bow in her hand 13 cm (with the far end resting on the strings), she prepares to make contact with the G string. Given that her bow is 65 cm long, find $\sin \theta$, where $\theta$ is the angle she inclined the bow.

**87. Baseball:** After a baseball is struck by a bat, it travels 70 ft through the air, at which time it is directly above the pitcher, 60 ft from the point of contact. Find $\cos \theta$, where $\theta$ is the acute angle formed by the path of the ball and a horizontal line.

**88. Golf:** The eighteenth hole at Pebble Beach is a 543-yd, par 5 beauty. A slow-motion review of Kevin's tee shot showed that the ball traveled 9.5 yd through the air as it moved 7.6 yd toward the pin. Find $\cos \theta$, where $\theta$ is the acute angle formed by the path of the ball and a horizontal line.

▶ **EXTENDING THE CONCEPT**

**89.** Find the values of the other five trig functions of $\alpha$ given $\cos \alpha = \dfrac{a}{b}$ and the terminal side of $\alpha$ lies in QI.

**90.** Find the values of the other five trig functions of $\beta$ given $\sin \beta = x$ and the terminal side of $\beta$ lies in QII.

**91.** The cosine of an angle $\theta$ whose vertex is at the origin, initial side passes through the point $P(x_1, y_1)$ in QI, and terminal side passes through the point, $Q(x_2, y_2)$ in QII is $\cos \theta = \dfrac{x_1 x_2 + y_1 y_2}{r_1 r_2}$ (see Exercise 82). Find an expression for $\sin \theta$, paying attention to signs.

▶ **MAINTAINING YOUR SKILLS**

**92. (1.1)** Convert from DMS to decimal degrees $-183°24'18''$.

**93. (1.1)** Find the supplement of the following angles.

    **a.** $117.26°$        **b.** $85°59'37''$

**94. (1.2)** A pane of glass must be ordered for a window. The window is an isosceles triangle whose base angles measure $48°$. What is the measure of the third angle?

**95. (1.2)** In $\triangle ABC$, $A = (3x - 8)°$, $B = 3x°$, and $C = (5x + 1)°$. Solve for $x$ and state the measures of $A$, $B$, and $C$.

**96. (1.2)** In Bemidji, Minnesota, there are two giant statues of Paul Bunyan and his blue ox, Babe. Babe casts a shadow that is 16 ft long while Paul's shadow is 24 ft long. If Babe is 24 ft tall, how tall is Paul?

**97. (1.1)** Find two positive and two negative angles that are coterminal with $-93°$. Answers may vary.

## 1.4 | Fundamental Identities and Families of Identities

### Learning Objectives

*In Section 1.4 you will learn how to:*

☐ **A.** Use fundamental identities to help understand and recognize identity "families"

☐ **B.** Verify other identities using the fundamental identities and basic algebra skills

☐ **C.** Use fundamental identities to express a given trig function in terms of the other five

In this section, we begin laying the foundation necessary to work with identities successfully. The cornerstone of this effort is a healthy respect for the fundamental identities and vital role they play. Students are strongly encouraged to do more than memorize them—they should be *internalized,* meaning they must become a natural and instinctive part of your core mathematical knowledge.

### A. Fundamental Identities and Identity Families

An **identity** is an equation that is true for all elements in the domain. In trigonometry, some identities result directly from the way the trig functions are defined. For instance, since $\sin \theta = \dfrac{y}{r}$ and $\csc \theta = \dfrac{r}{y}$, $\dfrac{1}{\csc \theta} = \dfrac{y}{r}$, and the identity $\sin \theta = \dfrac{1}{\csc \theta}$ immediately follows. We call identities of this type *fundamental identities.* Successfully working with *other* identities will depend a great deal on your mastery of these fundamental types. For convenience, the definition of the trig functions are reviewed here, followed by the fundamental identities that result.

Given point $P(x, y)$ is on the terminal side of angle $\theta$ in standard position, with $r = \sqrt{x^2 + y^2}$ the distance from the origin to $(x, y)$, we have

$$\cos \theta = \frac{x}{r} \qquad \sin \theta = \frac{y}{r} \qquad \tan \theta = \frac{y}{x}; x \neq 0$$

$$\sec \theta = \frac{r}{x}; x \neq 0 \qquad \csc \theta = \frac{r}{y}; y \neq 0 \qquad \cot \theta = \frac{x}{y}; y \neq 0$$

For use in the Pythagorean identities that follow and elsewhere in the text, note the expression $\sin^2\theta$ is simply a more convenient way of writing $(\sin \theta)^2$.

**WORTHY OF NOTE**

The word *fundamental* itself means, "a basis or foundation supporting an essential structure or function" (Merriam Webster).

## Fundamental Trigonometric Identities

| Reciprocal identities | Ratio identities | Pythagorean identities |
|---|---|---|
| $\sin\theta = \dfrac{1}{\csc\theta}$ | $\tan\theta = \dfrac{\sin\theta}{\cos\theta}$ | $\sin^2\theta + \cos^2\theta = 1$ |
| $\cos\theta = \dfrac{1}{\sec\theta}$ | $\tan\theta = \dfrac{\sec\theta}{\csc\theta}$ | $\tan^2\theta + 1 = \sec^2\theta$ |
| $\tan\theta = \dfrac{1}{\cot\theta}$ | $\cot\theta = \dfrac{\cos\theta}{\sin\theta}$ | $1 + \cot^2\theta = \csc^2\theta$ |

These identities seem to naturally separate themselves into the three groups or families listed, with each group having additional relationships that can be inferred from the definitions. For instance, since $\sin\theta$ is the reciprocal of $\csc\theta$, $\csc\theta$ must be the reciprocal of $\sin\theta$. Similar statements can be made regarding $\cos\theta$ and $\sec\theta$ as well as $\tan\theta$ and $\cot\theta$. Recognizing these additional "family members" enlarges the number of identities you can work with, and will help you use them more effectively. In particular, since they *are* reciprocals: $\sin\theta \csc\theta = 1$, $\cos\theta \sec\theta = 1$, and $\tan\theta \cot\theta = 1$. **See Exercises 7 and 8.**

**EXAMPLE 1** ▶ **Identifying Families of Identities**

Use algebra to write four additional identities that belong to the Pythagorean family.

Solution ▶   Starting with $\sin^2\theta + \cos^2\theta = 1$,

$$\sin^2\theta + \cos^2\theta = 1 \qquad \text{original identity}$$
$$\bullet \quad \sin^2\theta = 1 - \cos^2\theta \qquad \text{subtract } \cos^2\theta$$
$$\bullet \quad \sin\theta = \pm\sqrt{1 - \cos^2\theta} \qquad \text{take square root}$$
$$\sin^2\theta + \cos^2\theta = 1 \qquad \text{original identity}$$
$$\bullet \quad \cos^2\theta = 1 - \sin^2\theta \qquad \text{subtract } \sin^2\theta$$
$$\bullet \quad \cos\theta = \pm\sqrt{1 - \sin^2\theta} \qquad \text{take square root}$$

For the identities involving a radical, the choice of sign will depend on the quadrant of the terminal side.

**Now try Exercises 9 and 10 ▶**

The four additional Pythagorean identities are marked with a "•" in Example 1. The fact that each of them represents an equality gives us more options when attempting to verify or prove more complex identities. For instance, since $\cos^2\theta = 1 - \sin^2\theta$, we can replace $\cos^2\theta$ with $1 - \sin^2\theta$, or replace $1 - \sin^2\theta$ with $\cos^2\theta$, *any time they occur in an expression*. Note there are many other members of this family, since similar steps can be performed on the other Pythagorean identities. In fact, each of the fundamental identities can be similarly rewritten and there are a variety of exercises at the end of this section for practice.

☑ **A.** You've just learned how to use fundamental identities to help understand and recognize identity "families"

## B. Verifying an Identity Using Algebra

Note that we cannot *prove* an equation is an identity by repeatedly substituting input values and obtaining a true equation. This would be an infinite exercise and we might easily miss a value or even a range of values for which the equation is false. Instead we attempt to rewrite one side of the equation until we obtain a match with the other side, so there can be no doubt. As hinted at earlier, this is done using basic algebra skills combined with the fundamental identities and the substitution principle. For now we'll focus on verifying identities by using algebra. In Section 5.1 we'll introduce some guidelines and ideas that will help you verify a wider range of identities.

**EXAMPLE 2** ▶ **Using Algebra to Help Verify an Identity**

Use the distributive property to verify that $\sin \theta(\csc \theta - \sin \theta) = \cos^2\theta$ is an identity.

Solution ▶ Use the distributive property to simplify the left-hand side.

$$\sin \theta(\csc \theta - \sin \theta) = \sin \theta \csc \theta - \sin^2\theta \qquad \text{distribute}$$
$$= 1 - \sin^2\theta \qquad \text{substitute 1 for } \sin \theta \csc \theta$$
$$= \cos^2\theta \qquad 1 - \sin^2\theta = \cos^2\theta$$

Since we were able to transform the left-hand side into a duplicate of the right, there can be no doubt the original equation is an identity.

Now try Exercises 11 through 20 ▶

Often we must *factor* an expression, rather than multiply, to begin the verification process.

**EXAMPLE 3** ▶ **Using Algebra to Help Verify an Identity**

Verify that $1 = \cot^2\alpha \sec^2\alpha - \cot^2\alpha$ is an identity.

Solution ▶ The left side is as simple as it gets. The terms on the right side have a common factor and we begin there.

$$\cot^2\alpha \sec^2\alpha - \cot^2\alpha = \cot^2\alpha \,(\sec^2\alpha - 1) \qquad \text{factor out } \cot^2\alpha$$
$$= \cot^2\alpha \tan^2\alpha \qquad \text{substitute } \tan^2\alpha \text{ for } \sec^2\alpha - 1$$
$$= (\cot \alpha \tan \alpha)^2 \qquad \text{power property of exponents}$$
$$= 1^2 = 1 \qquad \cot \alpha \ \tan \alpha = 1$$

Now try Exercises 21 through 28 ▶

Examples 2 and 3 show you can begin the verification process on either the left or right side of the equation, whichever seems more convenient. Example 4 shows how the special products $(A + B)(A - B) = A^2 - B^2$ and/or $(A \pm B)^2 = A^2 \pm 2AB + B^2$ can be used in the verification process.

**EXAMPLE 4** ▶ **Using a Special Product to Help Verify an Identity**

Use a special product and fundamental identities to verify that $(\sin \beta - \cos \beta)^2 = 1 - 2 \sin \beta \cos \beta$ is an identity.

Solution ▶ Begin by squaring the left-hand side, in hopes of using a Pythagorean identity.

☑ **B. You've just learned how to verify other identities using the fundamental identities and basic algebra skills**

$$(\sin \beta - \cos \beta)^2 = \sin^2\beta - 2 \sin \beta \cos \beta + \cos^2\beta \qquad \text{binomial square}$$
$$= \sin^2\beta + \cos^2\beta - 2 \sin \beta \cos \beta \qquad \text{rewrite terms}$$
$$= 1 - 2 \sin \beta \cos \beta \qquad \text{substitute 1 for } \sin^2\beta + \cos^2\beta$$

Now try Exercises 29 through 34 ▶

Another common method used to verify identities is simplification by combining terms, using the model $\dfrac{A}{B} \pm \dfrac{C}{D} = \dfrac{AD \pm BC}{BD}$. For $\sec \theta = \dfrac{\sin^2\theta}{\cos \theta} + \cos \theta$, the right-hand side immediately becomes $\dfrac{\sin^2\theta + \cos^2\theta}{\cos \theta}$, which gives $\dfrac{1}{\cos \theta} = \sec \theta$. **See Exercises 35 through 40.**

## C. Writing One Function in Terms of Another

Any one of the six trigonometric functions can be written in terms of any of the other functions using fundamental identities. The process involved offers practice in working with identities, highlights how each function is related to the other, and has practical applications in verifying more complex identities.

---

**EXAMPLE 5** ▶ **Writing One Trig Function in Terms of Another**

Write the function $\cos \theta$ in terms of the tangent function.

**Solution** ▶ Begin by noting these functions share "common ground" via $\sec \theta$, since $\sec^2\theta = 1 + \tan^2\theta$ and $\cos \theta = \dfrac{1}{\sec \theta}$. Starting with $\sec^2\theta$,

$$\sec^2\theta = 1 + \tan^2\theta \qquad \text{Pythagorean identity}$$
$$\sec \theta = \pm\sqrt{1 + \tan^2\theta} \qquad \text{square roots}$$

We can now substitute $\pm\sqrt{1 + \tan^2\theta}$ for $\sec \theta$ in $\cos \theta = \dfrac{1}{\sec \theta}$.

$$\cos \theta = \dfrac{1}{\pm\sqrt{1 + \tan^2\theta}} \qquad \text{substitute } \pm\sqrt{1 + \tan^2\theta} \text{ for } \sec \theta$$

---

**WORTHY OF NOTE**

Although identities are valid where both expressions are defined, this does not preclude a difference in the domains of each function. For example, the result of Example 5 is indeed an identity, even though the left side is defined at $\dfrac{\pi}{2}$ while the right side is not.

---

**Now try Exercises 41 through 46** ▶

Example 5 also reminds us of a very important point—the sign we choose for the final answer is dependent on the terminal side of the angle. If the terminal side is in QI or QIV we chose the positive sign since $\cos \theta > 0$ in those quadrants. If the angle terminates in QII or QIII, the final answer is negative since $\cos \theta < 0$ in those quadrants.

Similar to our work in Section 1.3, given the value of $\cot \theta$ and the quadrant of $\theta$, the fundamental identities enable us to find the value of the other five functions at $\theta$. In fact, this is generally true for any given trig function and angle $\theta$.

---

**EXAMPLE 6** ▶ **Using a Known Value and Quadrant Analysis to Find Other Function Values**

Given $\cot \alpha = \dfrac{-9}{40}$ with the terminal side of $\alpha$ in QIV, find the value of the other five functions of $\alpha$.

**Solution** ▶ The function value $\tan \alpha = -\dfrac{40}{9}$ follows immediately, since cotangent and tangent are reciprocals. The value of $\sec \alpha$ can be found using $\sec^2\alpha = 1 + \tan^2\alpha$.

$$\sec^2\alpha = 1 + \tan^2\alpha \qquad \text{Pythagorean identity}$$
$$= 1 + \left(-\dfrac{40}{9}\right)^2 \qquad \text{substitute } -\dfrac{40}{9} \text{ for } \tan \alpha$$
$$= \dfrac{81}{81} + \dfrac{1600}{81} \qquad \text{square } -\dfrac{40}{9}, \text{ substitute } \dfrac{81}{81} \text{ for } 1$$
$$= \dfrac{1681}{81} \qquad \text{combine terms}$$
$$\sec \alpha = \pm\dfrac{41}{9} \qquad \text{take square roots}$$

**C.** You've just learned how to use fundamental identities to express a given trig function in terms of the other five

Since $\sec \alpha$ is positive when the terminal side is in QIV, we have $\sec \alpha = \dfrac{41}{9}$. This automatically gives $\cos \alpha = \dfrac{9}{41}$ (reciprocal identities), and we find $\sin \alpha = -\dfrac{40}{41}$ using $\sin^2\alpha = 1 - \cos^2\alpha$ or the ratio identity $\tan \alpha = \dfrac{\sin \alpha}{\cos \alpha}$ (verify).

Now try Exercises 47 through 56 ▶

# 1.4 EXERCISES

## ▶ CONCEPTS AND VOCABULARY

**Fill in each blank with the appropriate word or phrase. Carefully reread the section if needed.**

1. Three fundamental ratio identities are
$\tan \theta = \dfrac{?}{\cos \theta}$, $\tan \theta = \dfrac{?}{\csc \theta}$, and $\cot \theta = \dfrac{?}{\sin \theta}$.

2. The three fundamental reciprocal identities are $\sin \theta = 1/\underline{\hspace{1cm}}$, $\cos \theta = 1/\underline{\hspace{1cm}}$, and $\tan \theta = 1/\underline{\hspace{1cm}}$. From these, we can infer three additional reciprocal relationships: $\csc \theta = 1/\underline{\hspace{1cm}}$, $\sec \theta = 1/\underline{\hspace{1cm}}$, and $\cot \theta = 1/\underline{\hspace{1cm}}$.

3. Starting with the Pythagorean identity $\sin^2\theta + \cos^2\theta = 1$, the identity $\tan^2\theta + 1 = \sec^2\theta$ can be derived by dividing both sides by $\underline{\hspace{1cm}}$. Alternatively, dividing both sides of this equation by $\sin^2\theta$, we obtain the identity $\underline{\hspace{2cm}}$.

4. An $\underline{\hspace{1cm}}$ is an equation that is true for all elements in the $\underline{\hspace{1cm}}$. To show an equation is an identity, we employ basic algebra skills combined with the $\underline{\hspace{1cm}}$ identities and the substitution principle.

5. Use the pattern $\dfrac{A}{B} \pm \dfrac{C}{D} = \dfrac{AD \pm BC}{BD}$ to add the following terms, and comment on this process versus "finding a common denominator."
$\dfrac{\cos \theta}{\sin \theta} - \dfrac{\sin \theta}{\sec \theta}$

6. Name at least four algebraic skills that are used with the fundamental identities in order to rewrite a trigonometric expression. Use algebra to quickly rewrite $(\sin \theta + \cos \theta)^2$.

## ▶ DEVELOPING YOUR SKILLS

**Starting with the ratio identity given, use substitution and fundamental identities to write four new identities belonging to the ratio family. Answers may vary.**

7. $\tan \theta = \dfrac{\sin \theta}{\cos \theta}$       8. $\cot \theta = \dfrac{\cos \theta}{\sin \theta}$

**Starting with the Pythagorean identity given, use algebra to write four additional identities belonging to the Pythagorean family. Answers may vary.**

9. $1 + \tan^2\theta = \sec^2\theta$    10. $1 + \cot^2\theta = \csc^2\theta$

**Verify the equation is an identity using multiplication and fundamental identities.**

11. $\sin \theta \cot \theta = \cos \theta$    12. $\cos \theta \tan \theta = \sin \theta$

13. $\sec^2\theta \cot^2\theta = \csc^2\theta$    14. $\csc^2\theta \tan^2\theta = \sec^2\theta$

15. $\cos \theta (\sec \theta - \cos \theta) = \sin^2\theta$

16. $\tan \theta (\cot \theta + \tan \theta) = \sec^2\theta$

17. $\sin \theta (\csc \theta - \sin \theta) = \cos^2\theta$

18. $\cot \theta (\tan \theta + \cot \theta) = \csc^2\theta$

19. $\tan \theta (\csc \theta + \cot \theta) = \sec \theta + 1$

20. $\cot \theta (\sec \theta + \tan \theta) = \csc \theta + 1$

**Verify the equation is an identity using factoring and fundamental identities.**

21. $\tan^2\theta \csc^2\theta - \tan^2\theta = 1$

22. $\sin^2\theta \cot^2\theta + \sin^2\theta = 1$

23. $\dfrac{\sin \theta \cos \theta + \sin \theta}{\cos \theta + \cos^2\theta} = \tan \theta$

**24.** $\dfrac{\sin\theta\cos\theta + \cos\theta}{\sin\theta + \sin^2\theta} = \cot\theta$

**25.** $\dfrac{1 + \sin\theta}{\cos\theta + \cos\theta\sin\theta} = \sec\theta$

**26.** $\dfrac{1 + \cos\theta}{\sin\theta + \cos\theta\sin\theta} = \csc\theta$

**27.** $\dfrac{\sin\theta\tan\theta + \sin\theta}{\tan\theta + \tan^2\theta} = \cos\theta$

**28.** $\dfrac{\cos\theta\cot\theta + \cos\theta}{\cot\theta + \cot^2\theta} = \sin\theta$

**Verify the equation is an identity using special products and fundamental identities.**

**29.** $\dfrac{(\sin\theta + \cos\theta)^2}{\cos\theta} = \sec\theta + 2\sin\theta$

**30.** $\dfrac{(1 + \tan\theta)^2}{\sec\theta} = \sec\theta + 2\sin\theta$

**31.** $(1 + \sin\theta)(1 - \sin\theta) = \cos^2\theta$

**32.** $(\sec\theta + 1)(\sec\theta - 1) = \tan^2\theta$

**33.** $\dfrac{(\csc\theta - \cot\theta)(\csc\theta + \cot\theta)}{\tan\theta} = \cot\theta$

**34.** $\dfrac{(\sec\theta + \tan\theta)(\sec\theta - \tan\theta)}{\csc\theta} = \sin\theta$

**Verify the equation is an identity using fundamental identities and $\dfrac{A}{B} \pm \dfrac{C}{D} = \dfrac{AD \pm BC}{BD}$ to combine terms.**

**35.** $\dfrac{\cos^2\theta}{\sin\theta} + \dfrac{\sin\theta}{1} = \csc\theta$

**36.** $\dfrac{\sec\alpha}{1} - \dfrac{\tan^2\alpha}{\sec\alpha} = \cos\alpha$

**37.** $\dfrac{\tan\theta}{\csc\theta} - \dfrac{\sin\theta}{\cos\theta} = \dfrac{\sin\theta - 1}{\cot\theta}$

**38.** $\dfrac{\cot\theta}{\sec\theta} - \dfrac{\cos\theta}{\sin\theta} = \dfrac{\cos\theta - 1}{\tan\theta}$

**39.** $\dfrac{\sec\theta}{\sin\theta} - \dfrac{\csc\theta}{\sec\theta} = \tan\theta$   **40.** $\dfrac{\csc\theta}{\cos\theta} - \dfrac{\sec\theta}{\csc\theta} = \cot\theta$

**Write the given function entirely in terms of the second function indicated.**

**41.** $\tan\theta$ in terms of $\sin\theta$   **42.** $\tan\theta$ in terms of $\sec\theta$

**43.** $\sec\theta$ in terms of $\cot\theta$   **44.** $\sec\theta$ in terms of $\sin\theta$

**45.** $\cot\theta$ in terms of $\sin\theta$   **46.** $\cot\theta$ in terms of $\csc\theta$

**For the function $f(\theta)$ and the quadrant in which $\theta$ terminates, state the value of the other five trig functions.**

**47.** $\cos\theta = -\dfrac{20}{29}$ with $\theta$ in QII

**48.** $\sin\theta = \dfrac{12}{37}$ with $\theta$ in QII

**49.** $\tan\theta = \dfrac{15}{8}$ with $\theta$ in QIII

**50.** $\sec\theta = \dfrac{45}{27}$ with $\theta$ in QIV

**51.** $\cot\theta = \dfrac{x}{5}$ with $\theta$ in QI

**52.** $\csc\theta = \dfrac{7}{x}$ with $\theta$ in QII

**53.** $\sin\theta = -\dfrac{7}{13}$ with $\theta$ in QIII

**54.** $\cos\theta = \dfrac{23}{25}$ with $\theta$ in QIV

**55.** $\sec\theta = -\dfrac{9}{7}$ with $\theta$ in QII

**56.** $\cot\theta = -\dfrac{11}{2}$ with $\theta$ in QIV

▶ **WORKING WITH FORMULAS**

**57. The versine function:** $V = 2\sin^2\theta$

For centuries, the haversine formula has been used in navigation to calculate the nautical distance between any two points on the surface of the Earth. One part of the formula requires the calculation of $V$, where $\theta$ is *half the difference of latitudes* between the two points. Use a fundamental identity to express $V$ in terms of cosine.

**58. Area of a regular polygon:** $A = \left(\dfrac{nx^2}{4}\right)\dfrac{\cos\left(\frac{180°}{n}\right)}{\sin\left(\frac{180°}{n}\right)}$

The area of a regular polygon is given by the formula shown, where $n$ represents the number of sides and $x$ is the length of each side.

**a.** Rewrite the formula in terms of a single trig function.

**b.** Verify the formula for a square with sides of 8 m given the point (2, 2) is on the terminal side of a 45° angle in standard position.

▶ **APPLICATIONS**

Writing a given expression in an alternative form is an idea used at all levels of mathematics. In future classes, it is often helpful to decompose a power into smaller powers (as in writing $A^3$ as $A \cdot A^2$) or to rewrite an expression using known identities so that it can be factored.

**59.** Show that $\cos^3\theta$ can be written as $\cos\theta(1 - \sin^2\theta)$.

**60.** Show that $\tan^3\theta$ can be written as $\tan\theta(\sec^2\theta - 1)$.

**61.** Show that $\tan\theta + \tan^3\theta$ can be written as $\tan\theta(\sec^2\theta)$.

**62.** Show that $\cot^3\theta$ can be written as $\cot\theta(\csc^2\theta - 1)$.

**63.** Show $\tan^2\theta\sec\theta - 4\tan^2\theta$ can be factored into $(\sec\theta - 4)(\sec\theta - 1)(\sec\theta + 1)$.

**64.** Show $2\sin^2\theta\cos\theta - \sqrt{3}\sin^2\theta$ can be factored into $(1 - \cos\theta)(1 + \cos\theta)(2\cos\theta - \sqrt{3})$.

**65.** Show $\cos^2\theta\sin\theta - \cos^2\theta$ can be factored into $-1(1 + \sin\theta)(1 - \sin\theta)^2$.

**66.** Show $2\cot^2\theta\csc\theta + 2\sqrt{2}\cot^2\theta$ can be factored into $2(\csc\theta + \sqrt{2})(\csc\theta - 1)(\csc\theta + 1)$.

**67. Angle of intersection:** At their point of intersection, the angle $\theta$ between any two nonparallel lines satisfies the relationship $(m_2 - m_1)\cos\theta = \sin\theta + m_1 m_2 \sin\theta$, where $m_1$ and $m_2$ represent the slopes of the two lines. Rewrite the equation in terms of a single trig function.

**68. Angle of intersection:** Use the result of Exercise 67 to find the tangent of the angle between the lines
$$Y_1 = \frac{2}{5}x - 3 \text{ and } Y_2 = \frac{7}{3}x + 1.$$

**69. Angle of intersection:** Use the result of Exercise 67 to find the tangent of the angle between the lines $Y_1 = 3x - 1$ and $Y_2 = -2x + 7$.

▶ **EXTENDING THE CONCEPT**

**70.** The word *tangent* literally means "to touch," which in mathematics we take to mean *touches in only and exactly one point*. In the figure, the circle has a radius of 1 and the vertical line is "tangent" to the circle at the *x*-axis. The figure can be used to verify the Pythagorean identity for sine and cosine, as well as the ratio identity for tangent. Discuss/Explain how.

**71.** Simplify $-2\sin^4\theta + \sqrt{3}\sin^3\theta + 2\sin^2\theta - \sqrt{3}\sin\theta$ using factoring and fundamental identities.

**Exercise 70**

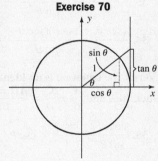

▶ **MAINTAINING YOUR SKILLS**

**72. (1.1)** Find the exact lengths of the unknown sides of a 30-60-90 triangle whose hypotenuse measures 7 in.

**73. (1.1)** Find the exact lengths of the unknown sides of a 45-45-90 triangle whose hypotenuse measures 7 in.

**74. (1.3)** Find $\tan -270°$.

**75. (1.2)** Is the triangle shown possible? Why/why not?

**Exercise 75**

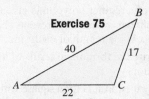

**76. (1.3)** Given $\cos\beta = -\dfrac{12}{13}$ and $\sin\beta < 0$, find the value of the other trig functions.

**77. (1.2)** Classify the triangle shown by angle and side measure.

**Exercise 77**

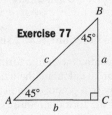

# SUMMARY AND CONCEPT REVIEW

## SECTION 1.1    Angle Measure and Special Triangles

### KEY CONCEPTS

- An angle can be defined as the joining of two rays at a common endpoint called the vertex.
- Angle measure can be viewed as the amount of rotation from a fixed (initial) side to a terminal side.
- A counterclockwise rotation gives a positive angle, a clockwise rotation gives a negative angle.
- One degree (1°) is defined to be $\frac{1}{360}$ of a full revolution.
- Straight angles measure 180°; right angles measure 90°.
- Degrees can be divided into smaller units called minutes: $1° = 60'$; minutes can be divided into smaller units called seconds: $1' = 60''$. This implies $1° = 3600''$.
- Two angles are complementary if they sum to 90° and supplementary if they sum to 180°.
- Angles that share the same initial and terminal sides are coterminal angles. Their measures will always differ by integer multiples of 360°.
- If $\triangle ABC$ is a right triangle with hypotenuse $c$, then $a^2 + b^2 = c^2$ (Pythagorean theorem). For $\triangle ABC$ with longest side $c$, if $a^2 + b^2 = c^2$, then $\triangle ABC$ is a right triangle (converse of Pythagorean theorem).
- In a 45-45-90 triangle, the sides are in the proportion $1x:1x:\sqrt{2}x$.
- In a 30-60-90 triangle, the sides are in the proportion $1x:\sqrt{3}x:2x$.

### EXERCISES

1. Find the complement of 47°03′49″.
2. Find the supplement of 59°0′17″.
3. Convert 147°36′48″ to decimal degrees.
4. Convert 32.87° to degrees, minutes, and seconds.
5. Find two positive angles and two negative angles that are coterminal with $\theta = 207°$.
6. Find three negative angles that are coterminal with 444°. Answers may vary.
7. Use special triangles to find the length of the bridge needed to cross the lake shown in the figure.
8. If the hypotenuse of a 45-45-90 triangle measures 14 cm, find the length of the legs.

**Exercise 7**

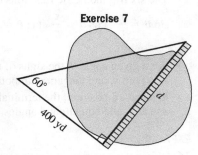

## SECTION 1.2    Properties of Triangles; Similar Triangles

### KEY CONCEPTS

- Triangles can be classified (a) by their angles as acute, right, or obtuse or (b) by their side lengths as scalene, isosceles, or equilateral.
- Properties of triangles: (I) the sum of the angles is 180°; (II) the combined length of any two sides must exceed that of the third side and; (III) larger angles are opposite larger sides.
- Given two triangles, if all three corresponding angles are equal, the triangles are said to be similar. If two triangles are similar, then corresponding sides are in proportion.

**Exercise 9**

### EXERCISES

9. Classify the triangle shown by angle and side measures.

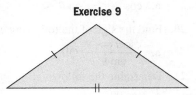

10. Which of the following types of triangles are not possible?

    **i.** Right and equilateral    **ii.** Obtuse and scalene

    **iii.** Isosceles and scalene   **iv.** Acute and equilateral

11. Determine the measure of angle $A$ in $\triangle ABC$ given $B = 32°$ and $C = 87°$.

12. Given $A = 2x°$, $B = (4x - 9)°$, and $C = (x^2 + 2x + 9)°$, find the measures of the angles in $\triangle ABC$.

13. All of the right triangles shown are similar. Find the dimensions of the largest triangle.

14. The original 42-ft tall rocket slide at Sutton Park is dwarfed by the new Titan slide. If the shadow of the original slide is 28 ft long when Titan's shadow is 38 ft long, how tall is the Titan slide?

15. Use properties of similar triangles to find the length of the side involving $x$ in both triangles. Note the figures are not to scale.

**Exercise 13**

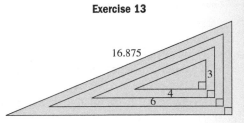

**Exercise 15**

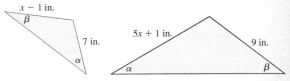

## SECTION 1.3   Trigonometry: A View from the Coordinate Plane

### KEY CONCEPTS

- An angle is in standard position when its vertex is at the origin and its initial side is along the positive $x$-axis.
- Two angles in standard position are coterminal if they have the same terminal side.
- The terminal side of any angle in standard position is coincident with a line $y = mx$ for some constant $m$.
- Given $P(x, y)$ is any point on the terminal side of an angle $\theta$ in standard position, $r = \sqrt{x^2 + y^2}$ is its distance from the origin $(0, 0)$.
- The six trigonometric functions of $\theta$ are defined as

$$\sin \theta = \frac{y}{r} \quad \cos \theta = \frac{x}{r} \quad \tan \theta = \frac{y}{x} \quad \csc \theta = \frac{r}{y} \quad \sec \theta = \frac{r}{x} \quad \cot \theta = \frac{x}{y}$$

$$x \neq 0 \qquad y \neq 0 \qquad x \neq 0 \qquad y \neq 0$$

- For a given angle $\theta$, the signs of the trig functions can be determined by noting that cosine is associated with $x$, sine with $y$, and tangent with both $x$ and $y$.
- In standard position, the terminal sides of the 0°, 90°, 180°, 270°, and 360° angles coincide with one of the axes and are called quadrantal angles.

### EXERCISES

16. Write the equation of the line coincident with the terminal side of an angle containing the point $(5, 3)$, and state its quadrant.

17. Given the terminal side of $\theta$ is in QIII and coincident with $y = 3x$, state the values of the six trig functions of $\theta$.

18. Find the value of the six trigonometric functions, given $P(x, y)$ is on the terminal side of angle $\theta$ in standard position.

    **a.** $(-12, 35)$             **b.** $(12, -18)$

19. Find the value of $x$, $y$, and $r$ using the information given, and state the quadrant of the terminal side of $\theta$. Then state the values of the six trig functions of $\theta$.

    **a.** $\cos \theta = \frac{4}{5}$, $\sin \theta < 0$        **b.** $\tan \theta = -\frac{12}{5}$, $\cos \theta > 0$

20. Find the sign of the following expressions, given the indicated quadrant of the terminal side of $\theta$.

    **a.** $\dfrac{\csc \theta \cos \theta}{\tan \theta}$; QII        **b.** $\dfrac{\cot \theta}{\sin \theta \sec \theta}$; QIII

21. Determine the following:

    **a.** $\sec 90°$                **b.** $\tan 180°$

    **c.** $\cot 270°$               **d.** $\csc 360°$

## SECTION 1.4   Fundamental Identities and Families of Identities

### KEY CONCEPTS

- The fundamental identities include the *reciprocal, ratio,* and *Pythagorean* identities.
- A given identity can algebraically be rewritten to obtain other identities in an identity "family."
- Standard algebraic skills like distribution, factoring, combining terms, and special products play an important role in working with identities.
- The pattern $\dfrac{A}{B} \pm \dfrac{C}{D} = \dfrac{AD \pm BC}{BD}$ gives an efficient method for combining rational terms.
- Using fundamental identities, a given trig function can be expressed in terms of any other trig function.
- Once the value of a given trig function is known, the value of the other five can be uniquely determined using fundamental identities, *if the quadrant of the terminal side is known.*

### EXERCISES

Verify using the method specified and fundamental identities.

**22.** multiplication

$$\sin \theta (\csc \theta - \sin \theta) = \cos^2\theta$$

**23.** factoring

$$\frac{\tan^2\theta \csc \theta + \csc \theta}{\sec^2\theta} = \csc \theta$$

**24.** special products

$$\frac{(\sec \theta - \tan \theta)(\sec \theta + \tan \theta)}{\csc \theta} = \sin \theta$$

**25.** combine terms using

$$\frac{A}{B} \pm \frac{C}{D} = \frac{AD \pm BC}{BD}$$

$$\frac{\sec^2\theta}{\csc \theta} - \sin \theta = \frac{\tan^2\theta}{\csc \theta}$$

Find the value of all six trigonometric functions using the information given.

**26.** $\cos \theta = -\dfrac{12}{37}$; $\theta$ in QIII

**27.** $\sec \theta = \dfrac{25}{23}$; $\theta$ in QIV

1. The shortest leg of a 30-60-90 triangle has a length of $5\sqrt{3}$ cm. (a) What is the length of the longer leg? (b) What is the length of the hypotenuse?

2. Classify $\triangle ABC$ by angle and side measures if $A = 27°$, $B = 126°$, $C = 27°$, $a = 7.8$ in., $b = 13.9$ in., and $c = 7.8$ in.

3. The terminal side of angle $\beta$ in standard position is coincident with $y = -\frac{7}{8}x$; $x \in (-\infty, 0]$. Identify two points on the terminal side. Answers may vary.

4. Given $\sin \theta = \frac{8}{\sqrt{185}}$ with $\theta$ in QII, state the value of the other five trig functions.

5. Convert to DMS form: $220.813\overline{8}°$.

6. Find two negative angles and two positive angles that are coterminal with (a) $57°$ and (b) $135°$.

7. To finish the top row of the tile pattern on our bathroom wall, $12''$ by $12''$ tiles must be cut diagonally. Use a standard triangle to find the length of each cut and the width of the wall covered by tiles.

**Exercise 7**

8. Given $\triangle ABC$, determine the measure of angles $A$ and $C$ given $A = 2x°$, $B = 73°$, and $C = (3x - 8)°$.

9. State the quadrant of the terminal side of $\theta$, using the information given.
   a. $\sin \theta > 0$, $\cos \theta > 0$
   b. $\tan \theta < 0$, $\sec \theta > 0$
   c. $\cot \theta > 0$, $\csc \theta < 0$
   d. $\sec \theta < 0$, $\csc \theta > 0$

10. The sign in front of the home offices of Schwa Inc. contains two similar right triangles. If the longer triangle is $30''$ tall by $56''$ long, how tall is the $21''$ long smaller triangle?

11. Convert from DMS to decimal degrees: $86°54'54''$.

12. Find the angle $\theta$, given $\csc \theta = -1$ and $\tan \theta$ is undefined.

13. Find the value of all six trig functions of $\theta$, given the point $(15, -8)$ is on the terminal side.

**Verify that each equation is an identity.**

14. $\sec \theta = \tan \theta \csc \theta$

15. $\csc \theta \tan \theta - \cos \theta = \dfrac{\sin^2\theta}{\cos \theta}$

16. $\dfrac{(\cos \theta + \sin \theta)^2}{\tan \theta} = \cot \theta + 2\cos^2\theta$

17. Find the value of all six trig functions given $\csc \theta = \dfrac{\sqrt{117}}{6}$; $\theta$ in QII.

18. In 2002, a retrapped Manx Shearwater was estimated to have flown *five million miles* during its 50+ years. A GPS tracking ring attached to one of these birds reports a feeding flight that went due north 12 mi, due east 16 mi, and then directly home for 34 mi. How does the ornithologist know the tracking ring is malfunctioning?

19. Write $\tan \theta$ entirely in terms of the cosine function.

20. On his honeymoon in Acapulco, Mexico, Fred observed the famous "La Quebrada" cliff cast a 60-ft-long shadow, just crossing the narrow inlet below. If a 6-ft-tall Fred casts a 2.4-ft-long shadow, how tall is the cliff?

## PRACTICE TEST

1. State the complement and supplement of 35°.

2. The hypotenuse of a 45-45-90 triangle measures 17 cm. What is the length of the legs?

3. Find two negative angles and two positive angles that are coterminal with $\theta = 30°$. Many solutions are possible.

4. Convert from DMS to decimal degrees or decimal degrees to DMS as indicated.

   **a.** $100°45'18''$ to decimal degrees

   **b.** $48.2125°$ to DMS

5. Four Corners USA is the point at which Utah, Colorado, Arizona, and New Mexico meet. The southern border of Colorado, the western border of Kansas, and the point $P$ where Colorado, Nebraska, and Kansas meet, very nearly approximates a 30-60-90 triangle. If the western border of Kansas is 215 mi

**Exercise 5**

long, (a) what is the distance from Four Corners USA to point $P$? (b) How long is Colorado's southern border?

6. Find the measure of angle $C$ and classify each triangle $ABC$ described.

   **a.** $A = 37°$, $B = 53°$

   **b.** $A = 19°$, $B = 69°$

7. The cross section of an ice cream cone is an isosceles triangle, as shown. If the cone manufacturer increases the size of the vertex angle by a factor of $\frac{3}{2}$, what will the measure of the upper angles be?

**Exercise 7**

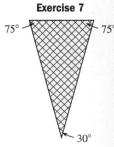

8. Given $a = 32$ mm and $b = 64$ mm in triangle $ABC$, (a) express the possible lengths of $c$ using interval notation. (b) To the nearest tenth, what length of $c$ will make $B = 90°$ and $A = 30°$?

9. In triangles $ABC$ and $DEF$, $\angle A = \angle D$ and $\angle B = \angle E$. If $a = 3x$, $c = 2x + 2$, $d = 2x$, and $f = 8$ yd, find the lengths of sides $a$, $c$, and $d$.

10. Steve is hiking in California's Redwood National Park, and sees the reflection of a Sequoia in a calm pond. Use similar triangles and the diagram shown to help Steve determine the height of this tree (to the nearest meter). Note figure is not to scale.

**Exercise 10**

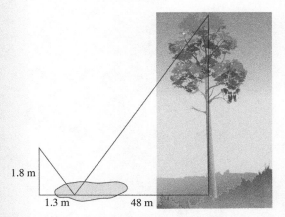

1.8 m

1.3 m          48 m

11. Given angle $\beta$ is in standard position, and its terminal side passes through the point $(-7, 9)$, (a) write the equation of the line coincident with the terminal side of $\beta$ and (b) find another point on the terminal side.

12. Find the value of the six trig functions of the angle $\beta$ from Exercise 11.

13. Given $\cos \theta = \dfrac{2}{5}$ and $\tan \theta < 0$, find the value of the other five trig functions of $\theta$.

14. Complete the following table. If a function is undefined, so state.

| $\theta$ | $\sin \theta$ | $\cos \theta$ | $\tan \theta$ | $\csc \theta$ | $\sec \theta$ | $\cot \theta$ |
|---|---|---|---|---|---|---|
| 0° | | | | | | |
| 90° | | | | | | |
| 180° | | | | | | |
| 270° | | | | | | |

15. Find the sign of the following expressions, given the indicated quadrant of the terminal side of $\theta$.

a. $\sin \theta \cos \theta \tan \theta$; QIV    b. $\csc \theta \cot^3 \theta$; QII

c. $\dfrac{\sin \theta \sec \theta}{\csc \theta}$; QI    d. $\dfrac{1}{\cot \theta \cos \theta}$; QIII

**Verify each identity using fundamental identities and the method specified.**

16. Multiplication: $\csc \theta (\tan \theta + \sin \theta) = \sec \theta + 1$

17. Special products:

$$\dfrac{(\csc \theta - \cot \theta)(\csc \theta + \cot \theta)}{\sec \theta} = \cos \theta$$

18. Factoring: $\dfrac{\sin^3 \theta - \cos^3 \theta}{1 + \cos \theta \sin \theta} = \sin \theta - \cos \theta$

19. Find the value of all six trigonometric functions given $\cos \theta = \dfrac{48}{73}$; $\theta$ in QIV.

20. Write $\cot \theta$ in terms of secant.

### The Range of Sine $\theta$ and Cosine $\theta$

In Section 1.3, we defined the trig functions in terms of the $(x, y)$ coordinates of a point on the terminal side of an angle $\theta$. In particular, $\sin \theta = \dfrac{y}{r}$ and $\cos \theta = \dfrac{x}{r}$, where $r = \sqrt{x^2 + y^2}$. We also found that $\sin \theta$ can be expressed in terms of $x$ and $y$ alone by substituting $\sqrt{x^2 + y^2}$ for $r$: $\sin \theta = \dfrac{y}{\sqrt{x^2 + y^2}}$. We also learned to express the terminal side of an angle using the line $y = mx$. For example, the terminal side of $\angle DAE$ shown in Figure 1.24 can be expressed as $y = 1x$ for $x \geq 0$. Investigating the effect of different values for $m$ on the trig functions seems a natural next step, and the graphing calculator lends itself quite well to such an exploration.

**Figure 1.24**

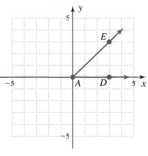

On the $\boxed{Y=}$ screen, enter the terminal sides of three angles $\theta_1$, $\theta_2$, and $\theta_3$ as $Y_1 = 1x$, $Y_2 = 2x$, and $Y_3 = 3x$, respectively (note that larger angles produce larger slope values). Pressing $\boxed{ZOOM}$ $\boxed{6}$ gives a standard viewing window of $[-10, 10]$ for $x$, and $[-10, 10]$ for $y$, where we focus our attention on the first quadrant. To find the coordinates of points on these lines, we can use the $\boxed{2nd}$ $\boxed{TRACE}$ (CALC) **1:value** feature of the calculator while choosing any convenient $x$-value ($x > 0$ for QI). Pressing $\boxed{3}$ $\boxed{ENTER}$ sets X = 3 and produces the screen shown in Figure 1.25. Substituting the coordinates shown (X = 3 and Y = 3) into the formula $\sin\theta = \dfrac{y}{\sqrt{x^2 + y^2}}$ gives us $\sin\theta_1 = \dfrac{3}{\sqrt{3^2 + 3^2}} \approx 0.707$. If we press the $\boxed{\blacktriangledown}$ key, the cursor jumps to the graph of $Y_2$ *while maintaining* X = 3, and gives us the coordinates of the new point (3, 6). Pressing the $\boxed{\blacktriangledown}$ key once more takes the cursor to the point (3, 9) on the graph of $Y_3$. Using the *x-y* formula for sine at these two points yields $\sin\theta_2 \approx 0.894$ and $\sin\theta_3 \approx 0.949$ (verify this), and we note $\sin\theta$ is becoming very close to 1.

**Figure 1.25**

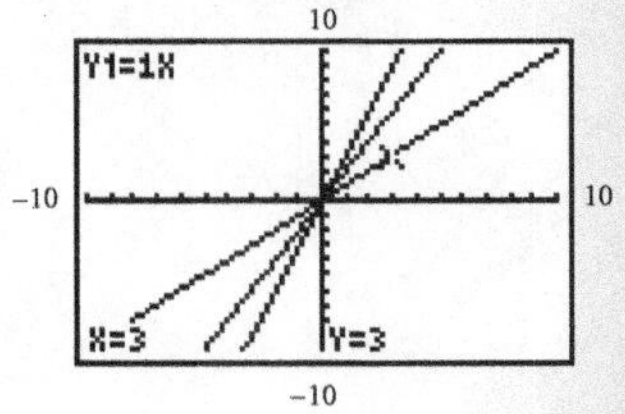

While this might be enough to convince us that $\sin\theta$ approaches 1 as $\theta$ approaches 90° (and *m* becomes infinitely large), we can use another feature of the calculator to provide more evidence. Using the keystrokes $\boxed{\text{STAT}}$ $\boxed{1}$, enter the List Editor of the calculator. If L1, L2, or L3 have any data in them, clear them out using the up arrow key to highlight the list name, and the keystrokes $\boxed{\text{CLEAR}}$ $\boxed{\text{ENTER}}$. Once the lists are empty, fill L1 with the integers 1 through 20. These will be the slopes of the terminal sides of 20 different QI angles. In L2, we will automatically calculate the *y*-value of a point on each of these terminal sides using our initial choice for *x* (*x* = 3). We first highlight the name L2, then define L2 = L1 × 3 by pressing $\boxed{\text{2nd}}$ $\boxed{1}$ $\boxed{\times}$ $\boxed{3}$. Since the slopes *m* are stored in L1, the equation is the equivalent of *y = mx* for *x* = 3. After pressing $\boxed{\text{ENTER}}$, the *y*-values are now stored in L2. We can likewise store the sine of each angle in L3. Highlight L3 and enter $L3 = \dfrac{L_2}{\sqrt{3^2 + L_2{}^2}}$ as the equivalent of $\sin\theta = \dfrac{y}{\sqrt{x^2 + y^2}}$ (Figure 1.26).

**Figure 1.26**

Pressing $\boxed{\text{ENTER}}$ yields the result shown in Figure 1.27, where we recognize the first three entries from before. Scrolling down through all 20 values of $\sin\theta$ strongly supports what we suspected earlier: namely, $\sin\theta$ approaches a maximum of 1 as $\theta$ approaches 90°.

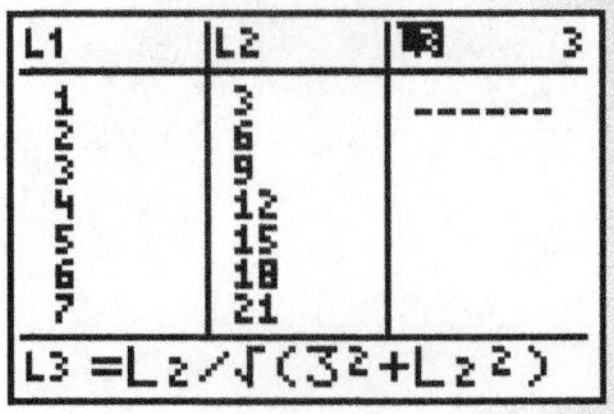

**Figure 1.27**

**Exercise 1:** Make any necessary adjustments and repeat this procedure to find the sine of angles approaching −90°. What do you notice? What appears to be the range of $y = \sin\theta$?

**Exercise 2:** Repeat the procedure to find the cosine of angles approaching 0° [the slopes need to approach 0 (i.e., 1, 0.95, 0.90, etc.)]. What do you notice?

**Exercise 3:** Adjust and repeat the procedure to find the cosine of angles approaching 180°. What do you notice? What appears to be the range of $y = \cos\theta$?

## Creating New Identities

In Example 2 of Section 1.4, we showed $\sin\theta\,(\csc\theta - \sin\theta) = \cos^2\theta$ was an identity by transforming the left-hand side into $\cos^2\theta$. There, the instructions were very specific: "Use the distributive property to . . . ." When verifying identities, one of the biggest issues students face is that the directions are deliberately vague—because there is no single, fail-proof approach for verifying an identity. This sometimes leaves students feeling they don't know where to start, or what to do first. To help overcome this discomfort, we'll first *create an identity* by substituting fundamental identities into a given expression, then reverse these steps to get back the original expression. This return to the original illustrates the essence of verifying identities, namely, if two things are equal, one can be substituted for the other at any time. The process may seem arbitrary (actually—it *is*), and the steps could vary. But try to keep the underlying message in mind, rather than any specific steps. When working with identities, there is actually *no right place* to start, and the process begins by using the substitution principle to create an equivalent expression as you work toward the expression you're trying to match.

**Illustration 1** ▷ Starting with the expression $\csc\theta + \cot\theta$, use fundamental identities to rewrite the expression and create a new identity. Then verify the identity by reversing the steps.

**Solution** ▷ $\csc\theta + \cot\theta$    original expression

$$= \frac{1}{\sin\theta} + \frac{\cos\theta}{\sin\theta}$$    substitute reciprocal and ratio identities

$$= \frac{1 + \cos\theta}{\sin\theta}$$    write as a single term

**Resulting Identity** ▷ $\csc\theta + \cot\theta = \dfrac{1 + \cos\theta}{\sin\theta}$

**Verify Identity** ▷ Working with the right-hand side, we reverse each step with a view toward the original expression.

$$\frac{1 + \cos\theta}{\sin\theta} = \frac{1}{\sin\theta} + \frac{\cos\theta}{\sin\theta}$$    rewrite as individual terms

$$= \csc\theta + \cot\theta$$    substitute reciprocal and ratio identities

In actual practice, all you'll see is this instruction, "Verify the following is an identity: $\csc\theta + \cot\theta = \dfrac{1 + \cos\theta}{\sin\theta}$," and it will be up to you to employ the algebra and fundamental identities needed.

**Illustration 2** ▷ Starting with the expression $2\tan\theta\sec\theta$, use fundamental identities to rewrite the expression and create a new identity. Then verify the identity by reversing the steps.

**Solution** ▷ $2\tan\theta\sec\theta$    original expression

$$= 2 \cdot \frac{\sin\theta}{\cos\theta} \cdot \frac{1}{\cos\theta}$$    substitute ratio and reciprocal identities

$$= \frac{2\sin\theta}{\cos^2\theta}$$    multiply

$$= \frac{2\sin\theta}{1 - \sin^2\theta}$$    substitute $1 - \sin^2\theta$ for $\cos^2\theta$

**Resulting Identity** ▷ $2\tan\theta\sec\theta = \dfrac{2\sin\theta}{1 - \sin^2\theta}$    identity

**Verify Identity** ▷ Working with the right-hand side, we reverse each step with a view toward the original expression.

$$\frac{2\sin\theta}{1 - \sin^2\theta} = \frac{2\sin\theta}{\cos^2\theta}$$    substitute $\cos^2\theta$ for $1 - \sin^2\theta$

$$= 2 \cdot \frac{\sin\theta}{\cos\theta} \cdot \frac{1}{\cos\theta}$$    substitute $\cos\theta \cdot \cos\theta$ for $\cos^2\theta$

$$= 2\tan\theta\sec\theta$$    substitute ratio and reciprocal identities

Using algebra and the fundamental identities, rewrite each given expression to create a new identity relationship. Then verify your identity by reversing the steps. Answers will vary.

**Exercise 1:** $\sec\theta + \tan\theta$                          **Exercise 2:** $(\cos\theta + \sin\theta)^2$

**Exercise 3:** $(1 - \sin^2\theta)\sec\theta$                    **Exercise 4:** $2\cot\theta\csc\theta$

**Exercise 5:** $\dfrac{\sin\theta - \sin\theta\cos\theta}{\sin^2\theta}$          **Exercise 6:** $(\cos\theta + \sin\theta)(\cos\theta - \sin\theta)$

# Right Triangles and Static Trigonometry

rain drop

42°

# Right Triangles and Static Trigonometry

## CHAPTER OUTLINE

## CHAPTER CONNECTIONS

While rainbows have been admired for centuries for their beauty and color, understanding the physics of rainbows is of fairly recent origin. Answers to questions regarding their seven-color constitution, the order the colors appear, the circular shape of the bow, and their relationship to moisture all have answers deeply rooted in mathematics. The relationship between light and color can be understood in terms of trigonometry, with questions regarding the apparent height of the rainbow, as well as the height of other natural and man-made phenomena, found using the trigonometry of right triangles.

▶ This application appears as
Exercise 55 in Section 2.2

## Learning Objectives

*In Section 2.1 you will learn how to:*

☐ **A.** Find values of the six trigonometric functions from their ratio definitions

☐ **B.** Bridge the two definitions of the trigonometric functions by positioning a right triangle in the coordinate plane

☐ **C.** Use cofunctions and complements to write equivalent expressions

Over a long period of time, what began as a study of chord lengths by Hipparchus, Ptolemy, Aryabhata, and others became a systematic application of the ratios of the sides of a right triangle. In this section, we develop the sine, cosine, and tangent functions from a right triangle perspective, and explore certain relationships that exist between them. This view of the trig functions also leads to a number of significant applications.

## A. Trigonometric Ratios and Their Values

In Section 1.1, we looked at applications involving 45-45-90 and 30-60-90 triangles, using the fixed ratios that exist between their sides. To apply this concept more generally using other right triangles, each side is given a specific name using its location relative to a specified angle. For the 30-60-90 triangle in Figure 2.1(a), the side **opposite (opp)** and the side **adjacent (adj)** are named with respect to the 30° angle, with the **hypotenuse (hyp)** always across from the right angle. Likewise for the 45-45-90 triangle in Figure 2.1(b).

**Figure 2.1**

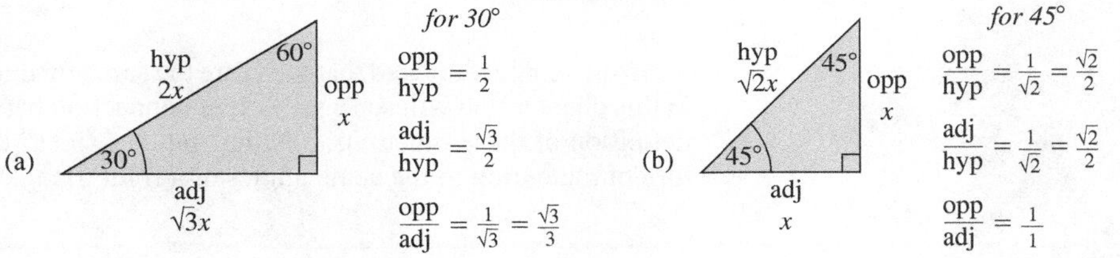

*for 30°*

$$\frac{\text{opp}}{\text{hyp}} = \frac{1}{2}$$

$$\frac{\text{adj}}{\text{hyp}} = \frac{\sqrt{3}}{2}$$

$$\frac{\text{opp}}{\text{adj}} = \frac{1}{\sqrt{3}} = \frac{\sqrt{3}}{3}$$

*for 45°*

$$\frac{\text{opp}}{\text{hyp}} = \frac{1}{\sqrt{2}} = \frac{\sqrt{2}}{2}$$

$$\frac{\text{adj}}{\text{hyp}} = \frac{1}{\sqrt{2}} = \frac{\sqrt{2}}{2}$$

$$\frac{\text{opp}}{\text{adj}} = \frac{1}{1}$$

Using these designations to define the various trig ratios, we can now develop a systematic method for applying them. Note that the $x$'s "cancel" in each ratio, reminding us the ratios are independent of the triangle's size (if two triangles are similar, the ratio of corresponding sides is constant).

Ancient mathematicians were able to find values for the ratios corresponding to *any acute angle* in a right triangle, and realized that *naming* each ratio would be helpful. These names are $\frac{\text{opp}}{\text{hyp}} \rightarrow$ **sine,** $\frac{\text{adj}}{\text{hyp}} \rightarrow$ **cosine,** and $\frac{\text{opp}}{\text{adj}} \rightarrow$ **tangent.** Since each ratio depends on the measure of an acute angle $\theta$, they are often referred to as **functions of an acute angle** and written in function form.

$$\text{sine } \theta = \frac{\text{opp}}{\text{hyp}} \qquad \text{cosine } \theta = \frac{\text{adj}}{\text{hyp}} \qquad \text{tangent } \theta = \frac{\text{opp}}{\text{adj}}$$

The reciprocal of these ratios, for example, $\frac{\text{hyp}}{\text{opp}}$ instead of $\frac{\text{opp}}{\text{hyp}}$, also play a significant role in this view of trigonometry, and are likewise given names:

$$\text{cosecant } \theta = \frac{\text{hyp}}{\text{opp}} \qquad \text{secant } \theta = \frac{\text{hyp}}{\text{adj}} \qquad \text{cotangent } \theta = \frac{\text{adj}}{\text{opp}}$$

The definitions hold regardless of the triangle's orientation or which of the acute angles is used.

In actual use, each function name is written in abbreviated form as sin $\theta$, cos $\theta$, tan $\theta$, csc $\theta$, sec $\theta$, and cot $\theta$ respectively. Note that based on these designations, we have the following reciprocal relationships:

$$\sin \theta = \frac{1}{\csc \theta} \qquad \cos \theta = \frac{1}{\sec \theta} \qquad \tan \theta = \frac{1}{\cot \theta}$$

$$\csc \theta = \frac{1}{\sin \theta} \qquad \sec \theta = \frac{1}{\cos \theta} \qquad \cot \theta = \frac{1}{\tan \theta}$$

In general:

### Trigonometric Functions of an Acute Angle

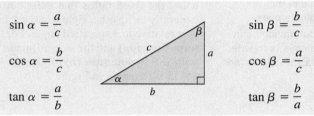

$$\sin \alpha = \frac{a}{c} \qquad\qquad\qquad\qquad\qquad\qquad \sin \beta = \frac{b}{c}$$

$$\cos \alpha = \frac{b}{c} \qquad\qquad\qquad\qquad\qquad\qquad \cos \beta = \frac{a}{c}$$

$$\tan \alpha = \frac{a}{b} \qquad\qquad\qquad\qquad\qquad\qquad \tan \beta = \frac{b}{a}$$

**WORTHY OF NOTE**

Over the years, a number of memory tools have been invented to help students recall these ratios correctly. One such tool is the acronym SOH CAH TOA, from the first letter of the function and the corresponding ratio. It is often recited as, "Sit On a Horse, Canter Away Hurriedly, To Other Adventures." Try making up a memory tool of your own.

You've likely noticed that these are the same functions we used in Chapter 1. Later in this chapter you will see a very close connection between the "ratio of coordinates" definition of these functions, and the "ratio of sides" definition. In any case, we now turn our attention to the acute angles of a right triangle.

**EXAMPLE 1** ▶ **Finding Function Values Using a Right Triangle**

Find the function values for the sine, cosine, and tangent of each angle, using the 30-60-90 triangle shown.

**a.** 30°                                    **b.** 60°

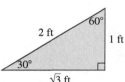

**Solution** ▶  **a.** From the 30° angle: the side *opposite* measures 1 ft, the side *adjacent* measures $\sqrt{3}$ ft, and the *hypotenuse* measures 2 ft. Using the ratios from page 46, we have:

$$\sin 30° = \frac{\text{opp}}{\text{hyp}} = \frac{1}{2} \qquad \cos 30° = \frac{\text{adj}}{\text{hyp}} = \frac{\sqrt{3}}{2} \qquad \tan 30° = \frac{\text{opp}}{\text{adj}} = \frac{1}{\sqrt{3}} = \frac{\sqrt{3}}{3}$$

**b.** From the 60° angle, the perspective changes: the *hypotenuse* still measures 2 ft, but now the *opposite* side measures $\sqrt{3}$ ft, and the *adjacent* side measures 1 ft.

$$\sin 60° = \frac{\text{opp}}{\text{hyp}} = \frac{\sqrt{3}}{2} \qquad \cos 60° = \frac{\text{adj}}{\text{hyp}} = \frac{1}{2} \qquad \tan 60° = \frac{\text{opp}}{\text{adj}} = \frac{\sqrt{3}}{1} = \sqrt{3}$$

**Now try Exercises 7 through 14** ▶

Example 1 gave values of the sine, cosine, and tangent functions for 30° and 60°. Using the special triangles, we can state the value of all six trig functions for 30°, 45°, and 60° based on the related ratio (see the figures given and Table 2.1). These values are used extensively in a study of trigonometry and must be committed to memory.

**Table 2.1**

| $\theta$ | $\sin\theta$ | $\cos\theta$ | $\tan\theta$ | $\csc\theta$ | $\sec\theta$ | $\cot\theta$ |
|---|---|---|---|---|---|---|
| 30° | $\dfrac{1}{2}$ | $\dfrac{\sqrt{3}}{2}$ | $\dfrac{1}{\sqrt{3}}=\dfrac{\sqrt{3}}{3}$ | 2 | $\dfrac{2}{\sqrt{3}}=\dfrac{2\sqrt{3}}{3}$ | $\sqrt{3}$ |
| 45° | $\dfrac{\sqrt{2}}{2}$ | $\dfrac{\sqrt{2}}{2}$ | 1 | $\sqrt{2}$ | $\sqrt{2}$ | 1 |
| 60° | $\dfrac{\sqrt{3}}{2}$ | $\dfrac{1}{2}$ | $\sqrt{3}$ | $\dfrac{2}{\sqrt{3}}=\dfrac{2\sqrt{3}}{3}$ | 2 | $\dfrac{1}{\sqrt{3}}=\dfrac{\sqrt{3}}{3}$ |

Expanding on this study of the special triangles, we can state values of all six functions given the ratio for *any one* of the functions.

---

**EXAMPLE 2** ▶ **Finding Function Values Using a Right Triangle**

Given $\sin\theta = \frac{4}{7}$, find the values of the remaining trig functions.

Solution ▶ For $\sin\theta = \dfrac{4}{7} = \dfrac{\text{opp}}{\text{hyp}}$, we draw a triangle with a side of 4 units opposite a designated angle $\theta$, and label a hypotenuse of 7 (see the figure). Using the Pythagorean theorem we find the length of the adjacent side: $\text{adj} = \sqrt{7^2 - 4^2} = \sqrt{33}$. The ratios are

$$\sin\theta = \frac{4}{7} \qquad \cos\theta = \frac{\sqrt{33}}{7} \qquad \tan\theta = \frac{4}{\sqrt{33}}$$

$$\csc\theta = \frac{7}{4} \qquad \sec\theta = \frac{7}{\sqrt{33}} \qquad \cot\theta = \frac{\sqrt{33}}{4}$$

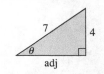

**Now try Exercises 15 through 24 ▶**

☑ **A.** You've just learned how to find values of the six trigonometric functions from their ratio definitions

Note that due to the properties of similar triangles, identical results would be obtained using any ratio of sides that is equal to $\frac{4}{7}$. In other words, $\frac{2}{3.5} = \frac{4}{7} = \frac{8}{14} = \frac{16}{28}$ and so on, will all give the same value for $\sin\theta$.

## B. Right Triangles and the Coordinate Plane

Regardless of where a right triangle is situated or how it is oriented, each trig function is defined as a given ratio of sides with respect to a given angle. In Section 1.3, we defined the trig functions in terms of the coordinates of a point on the terminal side of an angle in standard position. We can reconcile these two approaches by simply placing a right triangle in the coordinate plane. Consider a 30-60-90 triangle placed in the first quadrant with the 30° angle at the origin and the longer leg coincident with the x-axis. From our previous review of similar triangles, the trig ratios will have the same value regardless of the triangle's size so for convenience, we'll use a hypotenuse of 10 giving sides of 5, $5\sqrt{3}$ and 10. From the diagram in Figure 2.2 we note the 30° angle is in standard position and the point $(x, y)$ marking the vertex at the 60° angle has coordinates $(5\sqrt{3}, 5)$. Further, the diagram shows sin 30°, cos 30°, and tan 30° can all be expressed in terms of these coordinates *or*

**Figure 2.2**

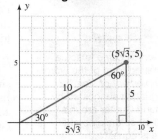

**WORTHY OF NOTE**

This same 30-60-90 triangle could be drawn with the 60° angle in standard position. In so doing, the point $(5, 5\sqrt{3})$ marks the vertex of the 30° angle.

*triangle side lengths* since $\frac{y}{r} = \frac{5}{10} = \frac{\text{opp}}{\text{hyp}}$ (sine), $\frac{x}{r} = \frac{5\sqrt{3}}{10} = \frac{\text{adj}}{\text{hyp}}$ (cosine), and

$\frac{y}{x} = \frac{5}{5\sqrt{3}} = \frac{\text{opp}}{\text{adj}}$ (tangent), where $r$ is the distance from $(x, y)$ to the origin. Each result

reduces to the more familiar values seen earlier: $\sin 30° = \frac{1}{2}$, $\cos 30° = \frac{\sqrt{3}}{2}$, and

$\tan 30° = \frac{1}{\sqrt{3}} = \frac{\sqrt{3}}{3}$.

**EXAMPLE 3** ▶ **Positioning a Right Triangle in the First Quadrant**

For the figure shown, evaluate $\sin B$ by

**a.** using a ratio of sides, and

**b.** placing the triangle on the coordinate plane with angle $B$ in standard position [vertex at (0,0)].

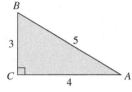

Solution ▶ **a.** From the ratios on page 46, we have

$$\sin B = \frac{\text{opp}}{\text{hyp}} = \frac{4}{5} \quad \text{ratio of sides definition}$$

**b.** Begin by placing vertex $B$ at the origin, with side $BC$ along the positive $x$-axis. This shows the point $(x, y)$ at vertex $A$ must be $(3, 4)$, and that $(3, 4)$ is *a point on the terminal side of angle B*. The distance formula verifies that $r = \sqrt{3^2 + 4^2} = \sqrt{25} = 5$, and from the "ratio of coordinates" definition,

$$\sin B = \frac{y}{r} = \frac{4}{5} \quad \text{as before.}$$

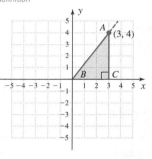

☑ **B. You've just learned how to bridge the two definitions of the trig functions by positioning a right triangle in the coordinate plane**

**Now try Exercises 25 through 34** ▶

In Section 2.4, we will extend the relationships explored here to *all nonquadrantal angles.*

## C. Using Cofunctions and Complements to Write Equivalent Expressions

For the right triangle in Figure 2.3, $\angle\alpha$ and $\angle\beta$ must be complements since the sum of the three angles must be 180°. The complementary angles in a right triangle have a unique relationship that is often used. Specifically, since $\alpha + \beta = 90°$,

$\beta = 90° - \alpha$. Note that $\sin \alpha = \frac{a}{c}$ and $\cos \beta = \frac{a}{c}$. This means

$\sin \alpha = \cos \beta$ or $\sin \alpha = \cos(90° - \alpha)$ by substitution. In words, "The sine of an angle is equal to the cosine of its complement." For this reason sine and cosine are called **cofunctions** (hence the name **co**sine), as are secant/cosecant, and tangent/cotangent. As a test, we check the statement $\sin 30° = \cos(90° - 30°)$

**Figure 2.3**

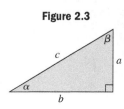

$$\sin 30° \overset{?}{=} \cos 60°$$
$$\frac{1}{2} = \frac{1}{2} \checkmark$$

**WORTHY OF NOTE**

The word *cosine* is actually a shortened form of the words *"complement of sine,"* a designation suggested by Edmund Gunter around 1620 since the sine of an angle is equal to the cosine of its complement [$\sin(\theta) = \cos(90° - \theta)$].

To verify the cofunction relationship for sec $\theta$ and csc $\theta$, recall their reciprocal relationship to cosine and sine, respectively.

$$\sec 30° \overset{?}{=} \csc 60°$$

$$\frac{1}{\cos 30°} \overset{?}{=} \frac{1}{\sin 60°}$$

$$\frac{1}{\dfrac{\sqrt{3}}{2}} \overset{?}{=} \frac{1}{\dfrac{\sqrt{3}}{2}}$$

$$\frac{2}{\sqrt{3}} = \frac{2}{\sqrt{3}} \checkmark$$

The cofunction relationship for tan $\theta$ and cot $\theta$ can similarly be verified.

**Summary of Cofunctions**

| sine and cosine | tangent and cotangent | secant and cosecant |
|---|---|---|
| $\sin \theta = \cos(90° - \theta)$ | $\tan \theta = \cot(90° - \theta)$ | $\sec \theta = \csc(90° - \theta)$ |
| $\cos \theta = \sin(90° - \theta)$ | $\cot \theta = \tan(90° - \theta)$ | $\csc \theta = \sec(90° - \theta)$ |

**EXAMPLE 4** ▶ **Applying the Cofunction Relationship**

Given $\cot 75° = 2 - \sqrt{3}$ in exact form, find the exact value of $\tan^2 15°$ using a cofunction.

**Solution** ▶ Using $\cot 75° = \tan(90° - 75°) = \tan 15°$ gives

$$\tan^2 15° = \cot^2 75° \quad \text{cofunctions}$$
$$= (2 - \sqrt{3})^2 \quad \text{substitute known value}$$
$$= 4 - 4\sqrt{3} + 3 \quad \text{square as indicated}$$
$$= 7 - 4\sqrt{3} \quad \text{result}$$

**Now try Exercises 35 through 48** ▶

**WORTHY OF NOTE**

In Chapter 5, we will find the cofunction relationships hold true for *any* angle.

Since these cofunction relationships are true for all acute angles, they are often referred to as the cofunction *identities* and can be used in conjunction with the fundamental identities to verify many other relationships involving complementary angles.

**EXAMPLE 5** ▶ **Using Cofunction Relationships to Help Verify an Identity**

Given $\alpha$ and $\beta$ are complementary angles, verify that $\cos^2\alpha = 1 - \cos^2\beta$ is an identity.

**Solution** ▶ Since $\alpha$ and $\beta$ are complementary, $\beta = 90° - \alpha$. Beginning with the right-hand side we have

$$1 - \cos^2\beta = \sin^2\beta \quad \text{from the Pythagorean identity}$$
$$= (\sin \beta)^2 \quad \text{rewrite expression}$$
$$= [\sin(90° - \alpha)]^2 \quad \text{substitute } 90° - \alpha \text{ for } \beta$$
$$= (\cos \alpha)^2 \quad \text{substitute cos } \alpha \text{ for sin}(90° - \alpha) \text{ (cofunctions)}$$
$$= \cos^2\alpha \quad \text{result—identity verified}$$

☑ **C.** You've just learned how to use cofunctions and complements to write equivalent expressions

**Now try Exercises 49 through 54** ▶

**2.1 EXERCISES**

### ▶ CONCEPTS AND VOCABULARY

**Fill in each blank with the appropriate word or phrase. Carefully reread the section if needed.**

**1.** Every right triangle contains two _____ angles. The word _____ is actually a shortened form of "complement of tangent."

**2.** Given $\sin \theta = \frac{7}{24}$, $\csc \theta = $ _____ because they are _____.

**3.** The sine of an angle is the ratio of the _____ side to the _____.

**4.** The cosine of an angle is the ratio of the _____ side to the _____.

**5.** Discuss/Explain how the definition of the trig functions using the ratio of sides in a right triangle, and the ratio of the coordinates of a point on the terminal side of an angle in standard position, can be reconciled.

**6.** Discuss/Explain how the ratio of sides in a right triangle shows the value of $\sin \theta$ and $\cos \theta$ can never be greater than 1.

### ▶ DEVELOPING YOUR SKILLS

**Given the following triangles, find the values of the indicated functions.**

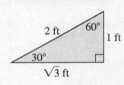

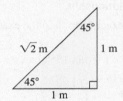

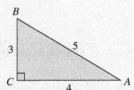

**7. a.** $\sec 30°$    **b.** $\csc 30°$    **c.** $\cot 30°$

**8. a.** $\sec 60°$    **b.** $\csc 60°$    **c.** $\cot 60°$

**9. a.** $\cos 45°$    **b.** $\sin 45°$    **c.** $\tan 45°$

**10. a.** $\sec 45°$    **b.** $\csc 45°$    **c.** $\cot 45°$

**11. a.** $\cos A$    **b.** $\sin A$    **c.** $\tan A$

**12. a.** $\cos B$    **b.** $\sin B$    **c.** $\tan B$

**13. a.** $\sec B$    **b.** $\csc B$    **c.** $\cot B$

**14. a.** $\sec A$    **b.** $\csc A$    **c.** $\cot A$

**Use the function value given to determine the value of the other five trig functions of the acute angle $\theta$. Answer in exact form (a diagram will help).**

**15.** $\cos \theta = \frac{5}{13}$      **16.** $\sin \theta = \frac{20}{29}$

**17.** $\tan \theta = \frac{84}{13}$      **18.** $\sec \theta = \frac{53}{45}$

**19.** $\cot \theta = \frac{2}{11}$      **20.** $\cos \theta = \frac{2}{3}$

**21.** $\tan \theta = 2$      **22.** $\csc \theta = 3$

**23.** $\cot \theta = t$      **24.** $\sin \theta = t$

**Use the given side lengths of the general triangle shown to identify the coordinates of a point on the terminal side of the indicated angle, when it is in standard position.**

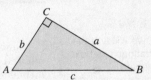

**25.** $a = 20, b = 21, c = 29$; angle $A$

**26.** $a = 20, b = 21, c = 29$; angle $B$

**27.** $a = 2, b = \sqrt{5}, c = 3$; angle $A$

**28.** $a = 2, b = \sqrt{5}, c = 3$; angle $B$

**29.** $a = 6.5, b = 7.2, c = 9.7$; angle $B$

**30.** $a = 6.5, b = 7.2, c = 9.7$; angle $A$

**31.** $a = a, b = b$; angle $B$

**32.** $a = a, b = b$; angle $A$

**33.** $a = 48, c = 73$; angle $A$

**34.** $a = 48, c = 73$; angle $B$

**Fill in the blank so that the functions given are equal.**

35. $\sin 47°$, $\cos$ \_\_\_

36. $\cos$ \_\_\_, $\sin 12°$

37. $\cot 69°$, $\tan$ \_\_\_

38. $\csc 17°$, $\sec$ \_\_\_

**Find the value of $x$ that makes the given functions equal.**

39. $\sin(4x)°$, $\cos(5x)°$

40. $\cos(2x)°$, $\sin(3x)°$

41. $\cot(6x - 1)°$, $\tan(5x + 3)°$

42. $\csc(6x - 3)°$, $\sec(2x + 5)°$

**Complete the following tables without referring to the text or using a calculator.**

43. $\theta = 30°$

| | $\sin \theta$ | $\cos \theta$ | $\tan \theta$ | $\sin(90° - \theta)$ |
|---|---|---|---|---|
| | | | | |
| $\cos(90° - \theta)$ | $\tan(90° - \theta)$ | $\csc \theta$ | $\sec \theta$ | $\cot \theta$ |
| | | | | |

44. $\theta = 45°$

| | $\sin \theta$ | $\cos \theta$ | $\tan \theta$ | $\sin(90° - \theta)$ |
|---|---|---|---|---|
| | | | | |
| $\cos(90° - \theta)$ | $\tan(90° - \theta)$ | $\csc \theta$ | $\sec \theta$ | $\cot \theta$ |
| | | | | |

**Evaluate the following expressions without a calculator, using the cofunction relationship and the following exact forms: $\sec 75° = \sqrt{6} + \sqrt{2}$; $\tan 75° = 2 + \sqrt{3}$.**

45. $\sqrt{6} \csc 15°$          46. $\csc^2 15°$

47. $\cot^2 15°$          48. $\sqrt{3} \cot 15°$

**Given $\alpha$ and $\beta$ are complementary angles, verify the following equations are identities.**

49. $\dfrac{\sin \alpha}{\sin \beta} = \tan \alpha$

50. $\dfrac{\cos \beta}{\cos \alpha} = \tan \alpha$

51. $\sec^2 \alpha = \cot^2 \beta + 1$

52. $\cot^2 \alpha = \sec^2 \beta - 1$

53. $\tan^2 \alpha \sec^2 \beta - \cot^2 \beta = 1$

54. $\sin^2 \alpha \tan^2 \beta - \cos^2 \beta = 1$

▶ **WORKING WITH FORMULAS**

55. **Velocity of a child on a slide:** $v = \dfrac{32\,kt}{\cos \theta}$

The velocity $v$ (in ft/sec) of a child on a slide is given by the formula shown, where $k$ is a value based on the friction between the child and the slide, $t$ is how long the child has been sliding (in seconds), and $\theta$ is the acute angle the slide makes with the horizontal ground. How fast will Camila be going after 0.8 sec if $k = 0.2$ and $\theta = 45°$ for a particular slide? Round to the nearest tenth.

56. **Average stress in a gypsum wall:** $\sigma = \dfrac{9.8\,m \sin \theta}{0.01\,\pi r \sec \theta}$

The average stress $\sigma$ [in kilopascals (kPa)] applied to the interior of a gypsum wall by hanging an object on a nail is given by the formula shown, where $m$ is the mass of the object (in kilograms), $r$ is the radius of the nail (in millimeters), and $\theta$ is the acute angle the nail makes with the wall (see illustration). If an average stress greater than 700 kPa will cause the nail to rip out, what is the heaviest painting that can be supported by a 1-mm-radius nail driven at a 30° angle? Round to the nearest tenth.

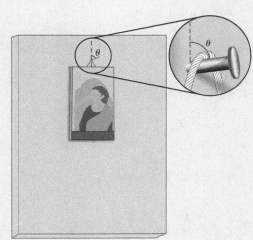

▶**APPLICATIONS**

**57. Volleyball:** Greg spikes the volleyball in such a way that it just clears the 8-ft-high net and strikes his opponents' baseline, 30 ft back. Find $\tan \theta$, where $\theta$ is the angle shown in the figure.

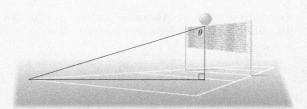

**58. Rock climbing:** Laura and Daryl are rock climbing at the *Garden of the Gods* in Southern Illinois. Daryl is standing 6 ft from Laura at the base of a cliff when he says "on belay." If the anchor point of the rope is 36 ft directly above Laura, find $\cot \theta$, where $\theta$ is the angle the rope makes at the anchor point (see figure).

**59. City planning:** To get to the heart of Miramar, a car must travel 8 blocks along the coastal avenue, and then head inland (see figure). For pedestrian safety, the city is constructing a 12-block-long diagonal street connecting the coastal avenue with the center of its downtown. Find $\sec \theta$, where $\theta$ is the angle shown in the figure.

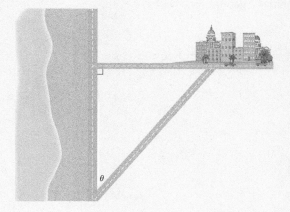

**60. Utility pole reinforcement:** A utility pole consists of a vertical post and two horizontal cable support beams. Each end of the longer, lower beam needs to be supported by two 8-ft-long reinforcing beams, as shown in the figure. If the reinforcing beam is attached to the vertical post 6 ft below the longer support beam, find $\csc \theta$, where $\theta$ is the angle shown in the figure.

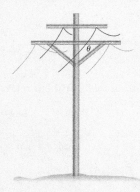

**61. Dodgeball:** At the end of a grueling dodgeball match, an unarmed Andy is pinned against a long wall by Mandy and Sandy, who each have a ball. Mandy is 12 ft directly in front of Andy, with Sandy 9 ft to her left, parallel to the wall. Assuming their aim is true, find the cosine of the angle at which their two balls will strike Andy.

**62. Piñatas:** A piñata is attached to one end of a string that passes through a ceiling hook 10 ft above the floor. The other end of the string is anchored to the floor, 7.5 ft from a point directly below the hook. Find the sine of the angle the string makes with the floor.

**63. Diagonal of a cube:** A cubical box has sides measuring 10 cm long. (a) Find the length of the diagonal that passes through the center of the box and (b) the sine of the angle $\theta$ it makes at the lower corner of the box.

**64. Diagonal of a rectangular parallelepiped:** A rectangular box has a width of 25 cm, a length of 45 cm, and a height of 10 cm. Find (a) the length of the diagonal that passes through the center of the box and (b) the cosine of the angle $\theta$ it makes at the lower corner of the box.

▶ **EXTENDING THE CONCEPT**

**65.** The formula $h = \dfrac{d}{\cot u - \cot v}$ can be used to calculate the height $h$ of a building when distance $x$ is unknown but distance $d$ is known (see the diagram). Use the ratios for $\cot u$ and $\cot v$ to derive the formula (note $x$ is "absent" from the formula).

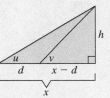

**66.** Use the diagram given and the ratios for sine and tangent to show that $\cos \alpha = \dfrac{a}{d}$. Then use this result and the cofunction relationships to show $\cos \beta = \dfrac{\sqrt{d^2 - a^2}}{d}$.

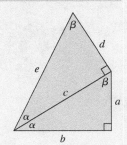

▶ **MAINTAINING YOUR SKILLS**

**67.** **(1.4)** Verify $\dfrac{\sin \theta}{\tan^2 \theta} = \cot \theta \cos \theta$ is an identity.

**68.** **(1.4)** Verify $\cos \alpha + \tan \alpha \sin \alpha = \sec \alpha$ is an identity.

**69.** **(1.2)** Using the diagram from Exercise 66, find $e$ if $a = 7$ m, $b = 9$ m, and $d = 8.75$ m.

**70.** **(1.3)** Find the values of the five remaining trig functions of an angle $\theta$ given $\sin \theta = -\dfrac{2}{3}$ and $\cos \theta > 0$.

**71.** **(1.3)** What is the value of the expression $\cos^2 \theta \tan^2 \theta$ given $(-2, -5)$ is on the terminal side of $\theta$?

**72.** **(1.3)** Find the value of $\cot \left[90(2k + 1)\right]^\circ$, where $k$ is any integer.

**Learning Objectives**

*In Section 2.2 you will learn how to:*

☐ **A.** Solve a right triangle given one angle and one side

☐ **B.** Solve a right triangle given two sides

In this section, we begin to understand some of the power and utility of right triangle trigonometry. By combining an understanding of similar triangles with the right triangle, "ratio of sides" definition, we find that *two triangles are no longer needed* to solve many applications. In fact, all six parts of a right triangle (three angles and three sides) can be found, given just the right angle, one side, and one other part.

## A. Solving Right Triangles Given One Angle and One Side

To **solve a right triangle** means to find the measure of all three angles and all three sides. This is accomplished using combinations of the Pythagorean theorem, the properties of triangles, and the trigonometric ratios. We will adopt the convention of naming each angle with a capital letter at the vertex or using a Greek letter on the interior. Each side is labeled using the related lowercase letter from the angle opposite. The complete solution should be organized in table form as in Example 1. Note the quantities shown in **bold** were given, and the remaining values were found using the techniques mentioned.

---

**EXAMPLE 1** ▶ **Solving a Right Triangle**

Solve the triangle given.

**Solution** ▶ Applying the sine ratio (since the side opposite 30° is given), we have: $\sin 30° = \dfrac{\text{opp}}{\text{hyp}}$.

For side $c$:  $\sin 30° = \dfrac{17.9}{c}$   $\sin 30° = \dfrac{\text{opposite}}{\text{hypotenuse}}$

$c \sin 30° = 17.9$   multiply by $c$

$c = \dfrac{17.9}{\sin 30°}$   divide by $\sin 30° = \dfrac{1}{2}$

$= 35.8$   result

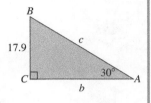

Using the Pythagorean theorem shows $b \approx 31$, and since $\angle A$ and $\angle B$ are complements, $B = 60°$. Note the results would have been identical if the special ratios from the 30-60-90 triangle were applied. The hypotenuse is twice the shorter side: $c = 2(17.9) = 35.8$, and the longer side is $\sqrt{3}$ times the shorter: $b = 17.9(\sqrt{3}) \approx 31$.

| Angles | Sides |
|--------|-------|
| A = 30° | a = 17.9 |
| B = 60° | b ≈ 31 |
| C = 90° | c = 35.8 |

**Now try Exercises 7 through 10** ▶

---

Prior to the widespread availability of handheld calculators, a table of values was used to find $\sin \theta$, $\cos \theta$, and $\tan \theta$ for nonstandard angles. Table 2.2 shows the sine of 49°30′ is approximately 0.7604.

**Table 2.2**
**sin θ**

| θ | 0′ | 10′ | 20′ | 30′ |
|-----|--------|--------|--------|--------|
| 45° | 0.7071 | 0.7092 | 0.7112 | 0.7133 |
| 46 | 0.7193 | 0.7214 | 0.7234 | 0.7254 |
| 47 | 0.7314 | 0.7333 | 0.7353 | 0.7373 |
| 48 | 0.7431 | 0.7451 | 0.7470 | 0.7490 |
| ⑷9 ← | 0.7547 | 0.7566 | 0.7585 | 0.7604 |

Today these trig values are programmed into your calculator and we can retrieve them with the push of a button (or two). To find the sine of 48°, make sure your calculator is in degree MODE, then press the SIN key, 48, and ENTER. The result should be very close to 0.7431 as the table indicates.

---

**EXAMPLE 2** ▶ **Solving a Right Triangle**

Solve the triangle shown in the figure.

**Solution** ▶ We know $\angle B = 58°$ since $A + B = 90°$. We can find length $b$ using the tangent function:

$\tan 32° = \dfrac{24}{b}$   $\tan 32° = \dfrac{\text{opp}}{\text{adj}}$

$b \tan 32° = 24$   multiply by $b$

$b = \dfrac{24}{\tan 32°}$   divide by $\tan 32°$

$\approx 38.41$ mm   result

We can find the length $c$ by simply applying the Pythagorean theorem, or by using another trig ratio and a known angle.

For side $c$:    $\sin 32° = \dfrac{24}{c}$          $\sin 32° = \dfrac{\text{opp}}{\text{hyp}}$

$\qquad\qquad c \sin 32° = 24$          multiply by $c$

$\qquad\qquad\qquad c = \dfrac{24}{\sin 32°}$          divide by $\sin 32°$

$\qquad\qquad\qquad\quad \approx 45.29$ mm    result

| Angles | Sides |
|--------|-------|
| $A = 32°$ | $a = 24$ |
| $B = 58°$ | $b \approx 38.41$ |
| $C = 90°$ | $c \approx 45.29$ |

The complete solution is shown in the table.

**Now try Exercises 11 through 16** ▶

When solving a right triangle, any of the triangle relationships can be employed: (1) angles must sum to 180°, (2) Pythagorean theorem, (3) special triangles, and (4) the trigonometric functions of an acute angle. However, the resulting equation must have only one unknown or it cannot be used. For the triangle shown in Figure 2.4, we cannot begin with the Pythagorean theorem since sides $a$ and $b$ are unknown, and tan 51° is unusable for the same reason. Since the hypotenuse is given, we could begin with $\cos 51° = \dfrac{b}{152}$ and solve for $b$, or with $\sin 51° = \dfrac{a}{152}$ and solve for $a$, then work out a complete solution. Verify that $a \approx 118.13$ ft and $b \approx 95.66$ ft.

**Figure 2.4**

☑ **A.** You've just learned how to solve a right triangle given one angle and one side

## B. Solving Right Triangles Given Two Sides

The partial table for sin $\theta$ given earlier was also used in times past to find an angle whose sine was known, meaning if sin $\theta \approx 0.7604$, then $\theta$ must be 49.5° (see the last line of Table 2.2). The modern notation for "an angle whose sine is known" is $\theta = \sin^{-1}x$ or $\theta = \arcsin x$, where $x$ is the known value for sin $\theta$. The values for the acute angles $\theta = \sin^{-1}x$, $\theta = \cos^{-1}x$, and $\theta = \tan^{-1}x$ are also programmed into your calculator and are generally accessed using the INV or 2nd keys with the related SIN, COS, or TAN key. With these we are completely equipped to find all six measures of a right triangle, given at least one side and any two other measures.

**EXAMPLE 3** ▶ **Solving a Right Triangle**

Solve the triangle given in the figure.

Solution ▶ Since the hypotenuse is unknown, we cannot begin with the sine or cosine ratios. The opposite and adjacent sides for $\alpha$ *are* known, so we use tan $\alpha$. For $\tan \alpha = \dfrac{17}{25}$

we find $\alpha = \tan^{-1}\left(\dfrac{17}{25}\right) \approx 34.2°$ [verify that $\tan(34.2°) \approx$

$0.6795992982 \approx \dfrac{17}{25}$]. Since $\alpha$ and $\beta$ are complements,

$\beta \approx 90° - 34.2° = 55.8°$. The Pythagorean theorem shows the hypotenuse is about 30.23 m.

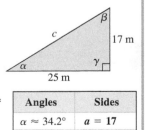

| Angles | Sides |
|--------|-------|
| $\alpha \approx 34.2°$ | $a = 17$ |
| $\beta \approx 55.8°$ | $b = 25$ |
| $\gamma = 90°$ | $c \approx 30.23$ |

☑ **B.** You've just learned how to solve a right triangle given two sides

**Now try Exercises 17 through 48** ▶

 **2.2 EXERCISES**

▶ **CONCEPTS AND VOCABULARY**

**Fill in each blank with the appropriate word or phrase. Carefully reread the section if needed.**

1. The phrase, "an angle whose tangent is known," is written notationally as _____.

2. To _____ a triangle means to find the measure of all _____ angles and all three _____.

3. Given the two legs of a right triangle, you can begin solving the triangle by using the _____ theorem to find the measure of the _____ *or* using the _____ calculator key to find the measure of a(n) _____.

4. Given an acute angle and the length of the hypotenuse of a right triangle, the only trig functions that cannot be used to determine the length of another side are _____ and _____ (drawing a diagram may help).

5. Discuss/Explain exactly what is meant when you are asked to "solve a triangle." Include an illustrative example.

6. Given an acute angle and the length of the adjacent leg, which four (of the six) trig functions could be used to begin solving the triangle?

▶ **DEVELOPING YOUR SKILLS**

**Solve each triangle using trig functions of an acute angle θ. Give a complete answer (in table form) using exact values.**

7.
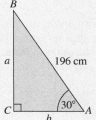

8.
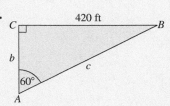

9.             10.
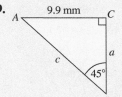 

**Solve the triangles shown and write answers in table form. Round sides to the nearest 100th of a unit. Verify that angles sum to 180° and that the three sides satisfy (approximately) the Pythagorean theorem.**

11.
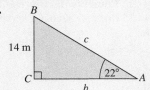

12.
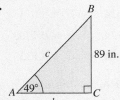

13.
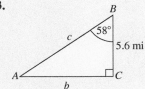

**14.**

**15.**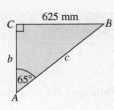

**16.**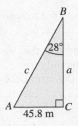

**Use a calculator to find the value of each expression, rounded to four decimal places.**

**17.** sin 27°

**18.** cos 72°

**19.** tan 40°

**20.** cot 57.3°

**21.** sec 40.9°

**22.** csc 39°

**23.** sin 65°

**24.** tan 84.1°

**Use a calculator to find the acute angle whose corresponding ratio is given. Round to the nearest 10th of a degree. For Exercises 25 through 32, use Exercises 17 through 24 as a check.**

**25.** sin $A$ = 0.4540

**26.** cos $B$ = 0.3090

**27.** tan $\theta$ = 0.8391

**28.** cot $A$ = 0.6420

**29.** sec $B$ = 1.3230

**30.** csc $\beta$ = 1.5890

**31.** sin $A$ = 0.9063

**32.** tan $B$ = 9.6768

**33.** tan $\alpha$ = 0.9896

**34.** cos $\alpha$ = 0.7408

**35.** sin $\alpha$ = 0.3453

**36.** tan $\alpha$ = 3.1336

**Select an appropriate function to find the angle indicated (round to 10ths of a degree).**

**37.**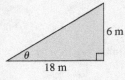

**38.**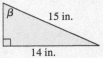

**39.**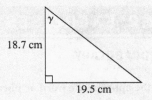

**40.**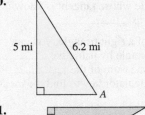

**41.**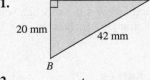

**42.**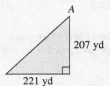

**Draw a right triangle $ABC$ as shown, using the information given. Then select an appropriate ratio to find the side indicated. Round to the nearest 100th.**

**Exercises 43 to 48**

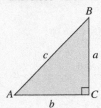

**43.** $\angle A$ = 25°
   $c$ = 52 mm
   find side $a$

**44.** $\angle B$ = 55°
   $b$ = 31 ft
   find side $c$

**45.** $\angle A$ = 32°
   $a$ = 1.9 mi
   find side $b$

**46.** $\angle B$ = 29.6°
   $c$ = 9.5 yd
   find side $a$

**47.** $\angle A$ = 62.3°
   $b$ = 82.5 furlongs
   find side $c$

**48.** $\angle B$ = 12.5°
   $a$ = 32.8 km
   find side $b$

## ▶ WORKING WITH FORMULAS

**49. The sine of an angle between two sides of a triangle:** $\sin \theta = \dfrac{2A}{ab}$

If the area $A$ and two sides $a$ and $b$ of a triangle are known, the sine of the angle between the two sides is given by the formula shown. Find the angle $\theta$ for the triangle shown given $A \approx 38.9$, and use it to solve the triangle. (*Hint:* Apply the same concept to angle $\gamma$ or $\beta$.)

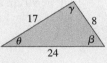

**50. Illumination of a surface:** $E = \dfrac{I \cos \theta}{d^2}$

The illumination $E$ of a surface by a light source is a measure of the luminous flux per unit area that reaches the surface. The value of $E$ [in lumens (lm) per square foot] is given by the formula shown, where $d$ is the distance from the light source (in feet), $I$ is the intensity of the light [in candelas (cd)], and $\theta$ is the angle the light source makes with the vertical. For reading a book, an illumination $E$ of at least 18 lm/ft² is recommended. Assuming the open book is lying on a horizontal surface, how far away should a light source be placed if it has an intensity of 90 cd (about 75 W) and the light flux makes an angle of 65° with the book's surface (i.e., $\theta = 25°$)?

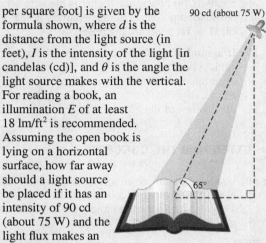

90 cd (about 75 W)

65°

## ▶ APPLICATIONS

**Alternating current:** In AC (alternating current) applications, the relationship between measures known as the impedance ($Z$), resistance ($R$), and the phase angle ($\theta$) can be demonstrated using a right triangle. Both the resistance and the impedance are measured in ohms ($\Omega$).

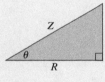

$Z$

$\theta$

$R$

**51.** Find the impedance $Z$ if the phase angle $\theta$ is 34°, and the resistance $R$ is 320 $\Omega$.

**52.** Find the phase angle $\theta$ if the impedance $Z$ is 420 $\Omega$, and the resistance $R$ is 290 $\Omega$.

**53. Contour maps:** In the figure shown, the *contour interval* is 175 m (each concentric line represents an increase of 175 m in elevation), and the scale of horizontal distances is 1 cm = 500 m. (a) Find the vertical change from $A$ to $B$ (the increase in elevation); (b) use a proportion to find the horizontal change between points $A$ and $B$ if the measured distance on the map is 2.4 cm; and (c) draw the corresponding right triangle and use it to estimate the length of the trail up the mountain side that connects $A$ and $B$, then use trig to compute the approximate angle of incline as the hiker climbs from point $A$ to point $B$.

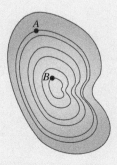

$A$

$B$

**54. Contour maps:** In the figure shown, the *contour interval* is 150 m (each concentric line represents an increase of 150 m in elevation), and the scale of horizontal distances is 1 cm = 250 m. (a) Find the vertical change from $A$ to $B$ (the increase in elevation); (b) use a proportion to find the horizontal change between points $A$ and $B$ if the measured distance on the map is 4.5 cm; and (c) draw the corresponding right triangle and use it to estimate the length of the trail up the mountain side that connects $A$ and $B$, then use trig to compute the approximate angle of incline as the hiker climbs from point $A$ to point $B$.

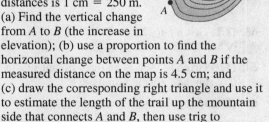

$B$

$A$

**55. Height of a rainbow:** While visiting the Lapahoehoe Memorial on the island of Hawaii, Bruce and Carma see a spectacularly vivid rainbow arching over the bay. Bruce speculates the rainbow is 500 ft away, while Carma estimates the angle of elevation to the highest point of the rainbow is about 42°. What was the approximate height of the rainbow?

**56. High-wire walking:** As part of a circus act, a high-wire walker not only "walks the wire," she walks a wire that is *set at an incline of* 10° to the horizontal! If the length of the (inclined) wire is 25.39 m, (a) how much higher is the wire set at the destination pole than at the departure pole? (b) How far apart are the poles?

**57. Diagonal of a cube:** A cubical box has a diagonal measure of 35 cm. (a) Find the dimensions of the box

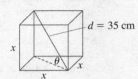

and (b) the angle $\theta$ that the diagonal makes at the lower corner of the box.

**58. Diagonal of a rectangular parallelepiped:** A rectangular box has a width of 50 cm and a length of 70 cm. (a) Find the height $h$ that ensures the diagonal across the middle of the box

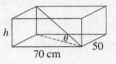

will be 90 cm and (b) the angle $\theta$ that the diagonal makes at the lower corner of the box.

► **EXTENDING THE CONCEPT**

**59.** Use the diagram given to derive a formula for the height $h$ of the taller building in terms of the height $x$ of the shorter building and the ratios for tan $u$ and tan $v$. Then use the formula to find $h$ given the shorter building is 75 m tall with $u = 40°$ and $v = 50°$.

**Exercises 59 and 60**

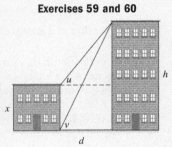

**60.** Use the diagram given to derive a formula for the distance $d$ between the two buildings in terms of the height $x$ of the shorter building and the ratios for tan $u$ and tan $v$. Then use the formula to find $d$ given the shorter building is 75 m tall with $u = 40°$ and $v = 50°$.

► **MAINTAINING YOUR SKILLS**

**61. (1.1)** Convert from DMS to decimal degrees. 132°42′54″

**62. (1.1)** Convert from decimal degrees to DMS. 36.4525°

**63. (2.1)** Given tan 22.5° = $\sqrt{2} - 1$, find $\sqrt{8}$ cot 22.5°.

**64. (1.3)** Given $(-2, 5)$ is on the terminal side of angle $\theta$ in standard position, find csc $\theta$.

**65. (2.1)** Using the figure given, find sin $\beta$.

**66. (1.4)** Verify sec $\theta$ = tan $\theta$ sin $\theta$ + cos $\theta$ is an identity.

**Exercise 64**

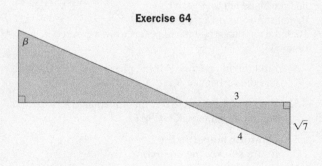

## MID-CHAPTER CHECK

**1.** Given $\cos\theta = \dfrac{12}{13}$, determine the exact value of the other five trig functions of the acute angle $\theta$.

**2.** Given the triangle shown in the diagram, find the exact values of the following trig functions.

**Exercise 2**

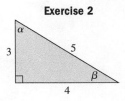

   **a.** $\tan\alpha$    **b.** $\sec\beta$

   **c.** $\csc\alpha$    **d.** $\cot\beta$

**3.** Given $\alpha$ and $\beta$ are complementary angles, verify $\tan\alpha = \dfrac{\cos\beta}{\cos\alpha}$ is an identity.

**4.** Evaluate using a calculator. Round to four decimal places.

   **a.** $\tan 53°$    **b.** $\sin 28.4°$

   **c.** $\cos 61.6°$    **d.** $\tan 45°$

5. Solve the triangle shown in the diagram.

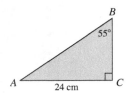

6. Given tan 75° = 2 + √3, what is the value of cot 15°? Why?

7. Solve the triangle shown in the diagram.

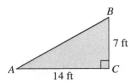

8. Complete the table from memory.

| $\theta$ | sin $\theta$ | cos $\theta$ | tan $\theta$ | csc $\theta$ | sec $\theta$ | cot $\theta$ |
|------|-------|-------|-------|-------|-------|-------|
| 30° | | | | | | |
| 45° | | | | | | |
| 60° | | | | | | |

9. The day before the Macy's Thanksgiving Day Parade, the 14-ft-wide planet Earth balloon is inflated and anchored on 77th Street. One end of a 20-ft anchor line is attached to a tether on the bottom of the balloon, 16 ft above the ground. To the nearest degree, find the acute angle the anchor line makes with the street.

10. The doors of a public library are 24 in. above the level front plaza. If a wheelchair access ramp must make an angle of 4° with the horizontal, how far from the door landing must it begin? Round to one decimal place.

## REINFORCING BASIC CONCEPTS

### The Area of a Triangle

While you're likely familiar with the most common formula for the area of a triangle, $\mathcal{A} = \frac{1}{2}bh$, you might be surprised to learn that over 20 different formulas exist for computing this area. Many of these involve very basic trigonometric ideas, and we'll use some of these ideas to develop two additional formula types here. For $\mathcal{A} = \frac{1}{2}bh$, recall that $b$ represents the length of a designated base of the triangle, and $h$ represents the length of the altitude drawn to that base (Figure 2.5). If the height $h$ of the triangle isn't given, but two sides $a$ and $b$ and the angle $C$ between them are known (Figure 2.6), $h$ canbe found using a sine ratio: $\sin C = \frac{h}{a}$, giving $a \sin C = h$. Substituting $a \sin C$ for $h$ in the formula $\mathcal{A} = \frac{1}{2}bh$ gives $\mathcal{A} = \frac{1}{2} ba \sin C = \frac{1}{2}ab \sin C$. By designating the other sides as "the base," and drawing altitudes from the opposite vertex (Figures 2.7 and 2.8), the formulas $\mathcal{A} = \frac{1}{2} bc \sin A$ and $\mathcal{A} = \frac{1}{2} ac \sin B$ are likewise obtained.

**Figure 2.5**

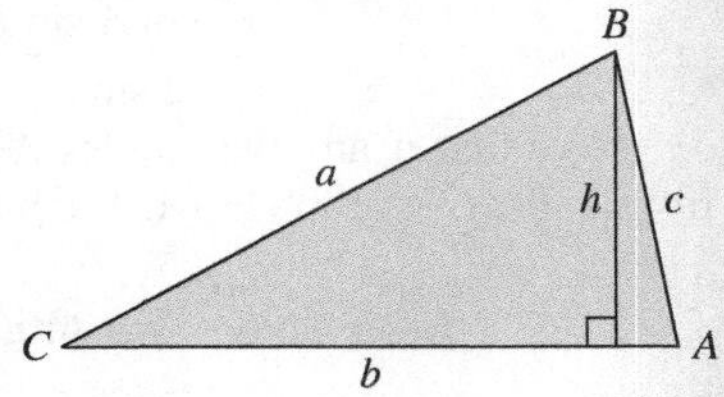

**Figure 2.6**

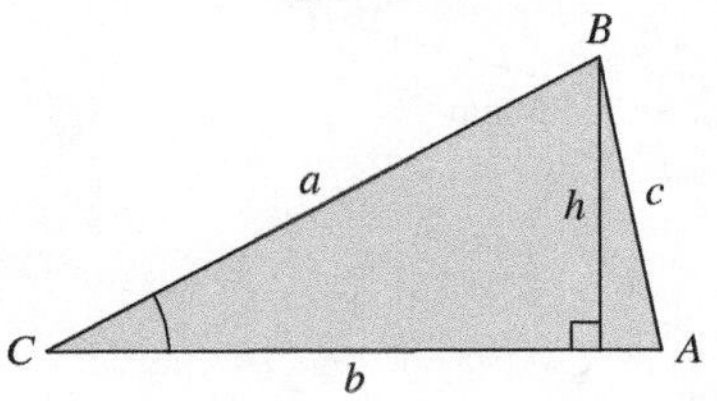

**Figure 2.7**

**Figure 2.8**

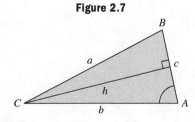

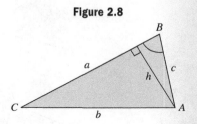

| Area Given Two Sides and an Included Angle (SAS) | | |
|---|---|---|
| 1. $\mathcal{A} = \frac{1}{2} ab \sin C$ | 2. $\mathcal{A} = \frac{1}{2} bc \sin A$ | 3. $\mathcal{A} = \frac{1}{2} ac \sin B$ |

In words, the formulas say the area of a triangle is equal to one-half the product of two sides times the sine of the angle between them.

---

**Illustration 1** ▶ Find the area of $\triangle ABC$ given $a = 16.2$ cm, $b = 25.6$ cm, and $C = 28.3°$.

**Solution** ▶ Since sides $a$, $b$, and angle $C$ are given, we apply the first formula.

$$\mathcal{A} = \frac{1}{2}\, ab \sin C \qquad \text{area formula}$$

$$= \frac{1}{2}(16.2)(25.6) \sin 28.3° \qquad \text{substitute 16.2 for } a, \text{ 25.6 for } b, \text{ and 28.3° for } C$$

$$\approx 98.3 \text{ cm}^2 \qquad \text{result}$$

The area of this triangle is approximately 98.3 cm².

---

Using the SAS formulas, a formula requiring two angles and one side can be developed. Observe that formula 1 can be written in terms of $b$: $b = \dfrac{2\mathcal{A}}{c \sin A}$; and formula 3 can be written in terms of $a$: $a = \dfrac{2\mathcal{A}}{c \sin B}$.

Substituting $\dfrac{2\mathcal{A}}{c \sin A}$ for $b$ and $\dfrac{2\mathcal{A}}{c \sin B}$ for $a$ in formula 2 gives the following:

$$\mathcal{A} = \frac{1}{2}\, ab \sin C \qquad \text{given formula}$$

$$2\mathcal{A} = \frac{2\mathcal{A}}{c \sin B}\, \frac{2\mathcal{A}}{c \sin A}\, \sin C \qquad \text{substitute } \tfrac{2\mathcal{A}}{c \sin B} \text{ for } a, \tfrac{2\mathcal{A}}{c \sin A} \text{ for } b$$

$$c^2 \sin A \sin B = 2\mathcal{A} \sin C \qquad \text{multiply by } c\sin A \text{ and } c\sin B, \text{ divide by 2 sin } C$$

$$\frac{c^2 \sin A \sin B}{2 \sin C} = \mathcal{A} \qquad \text{solve for } \mathcal{A}$$

Note that if any two angles $A$ and $B$ are given, the third can easily be found by subtracting the sum of these two from 180°: $C = 180° - (A + B)$. As with the previous formula, versions relying on side $b$ or side $a$ can also be found.

| **Area Given Two Angles and Any Side (AAS/ASA)** | | |
|---|---|---|
| 1. $\mathcal{A} = \dfrac{c^2 \sin A \sin B}{2 \sin C}$ | 2. $\mathcal{A} = \dfrac{a^2 \sin B \sin C}{2 \sin A}$ | 3. $\mathcal{A} = \dfrac{b^2 \sin A \sin C}{2 \sin B}$ |

In Chapter 7, yet another useful relationship for the area of a triangle will be developed, called Heron's formula. The formula requires only the length of the three sides, and can be developed both algebraically and using trigonometry. Use the appropriate formula to find the area of the following triangles. Round to the nearest tenth.

**1.**

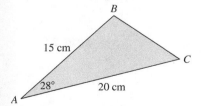

**2.**

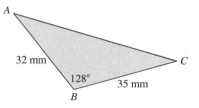

**3.**

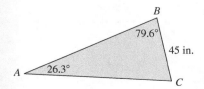

**4.**

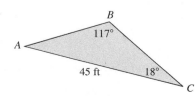

# 2.3 | Applications of Static Trigonometry

## Learning Objectives

*In Section 2.3 you will learn how to:*

☐ **A.** Solve applications involving angles of elevation and depression

☐ **B.** Solve applications involving angles of rotation

☐ **C.** Solve general applications of right triangles

In Section 2.2, we essentially developed the techniques and skills necessary to solve a right triangle apart from any real context. However, many real-world relationships can be modeled by superimposing a right triangle in their study and these same skills are indispensable to the solution process. Architects, surveyors, and scientists routinely use right triangle relationships in their work.

## A. Applications Using Angles of Elevation/Depression

While the name seems self-descriptive, in more formal terms an **angle of elevation** is defined to be the acute angle formed by a **horizontal line of orientation** (parallel to level ground) and the line of sight (see Figure 2.9). An **angle of depression** is likewise defined but involves a line of sight that is below the horizontal line of orientation (Figure 2.10).

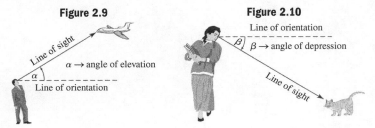

**Figure 2.9**

Line of sight
$\alpha \rightarrow$ angle of elevation
$\alpha$
Line of orientation

**Figure 2.10**

Line of orientation
$\beta$
$\beta \rightarrow$ angle of depression
Line of sight

Angles of elevation/depression make distance and length computations of all sizes a relatively easy matter and are extensively used by surveyors, engineers, astronomers, and even the casual observer who is familiar with the basics of trigonometry.

---

**EXAMPLE 1** ▶ **Applying Angles of Elevation**

A group of campers has pitched their tent 250 yd from the base of a tall cliff. The evening's conversation turns to a discussion of the cliff's height, and they all lodge an estimate. If the angle of elevation from the campsite to the top of the cliff is 40°, how tall is the cliff?

**Solution** ▶ As described we want to know the height of the opposite side, given the adjacent side, so we use the tangent function.

For height $h$:

$$\tan 40° = \frac{h}{250} \qquad \tan 40° = \frac{\text{opp}}{\text{adj}}$$

$$250 \tan 40° = h \qquad \text{multiply by 250}$$

$$209.8 \approx h \qquad \text{result } (\tan 40° \approx 0.8391)$$

The cliff is approximately 209.8 yd high (about 629 ft).

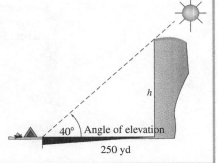

Angle of elevation
40°
250 yd
$h$

**Now try Exercises 7 through 12** ▶

**EXAMPLE 2** ▶ **Applying Angles of Depression**

From the edge of the Perito Moreno glaciar in Patagonia, Argentina, Gary notices a kayak on the lake 30 m below. If the angle of depression at that point is 35°, what is the distance $d$ from the kayak to the glacier?

Solution ▶ From the diagram, we note that $d$ is the side opposite a 55° angle (the complement of the 35° angle). Since the adjacent side is known, we use the tangent function to solve for $d$.

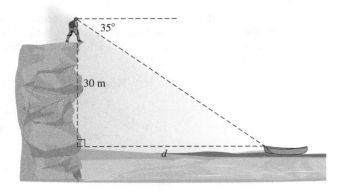

$$\tan 55° = \frac{d}{30} \quad \tan 55° = \frac{opp}{adj}$$

$$30 \tan 55° = d \quad \text{multiply by 30 (exact form)}$$

$$42.8 \approx d \quad \text{result (approximate form)}$$

☑ **A.** You've just learned how to solve applications involving angles of elevation and depression

The kayak is approximately 42.8 m (141 ft) from the glacier.

**Now try Exercises 13 through 18** ▶

## B. Applications of Angles of Rotation

Closely related to angles of depression/elevation are acute angles of *rotation* from a fixed orientation to a fixed line of sight. In this case, the movement is simply horizontal rather than vertical. Land surveyors use a special type of measure called **bearings**, where they indicate the acute angle the line of sight makes with a due north or due south line of reference. For instance, Figure 2.11(a) shows a bearing of N 60° E and Figure 2.11(b) shows a bearing of S 40° W.

**Figure 2.11**

(a)

(b)

**EXAMPLE 3** ▶ **Applying Angles of Rotation**

A city building code requires a new shopping complex to be built at least 150 ft from an avenue that runs due east and west. Using a modern theodolite set up on the avenue, a surveyor finds the tip of the shopping complex closest to the avenue lies 200 ft away on a bearing of N 41°17′15″ W. How far from the avenue is this tip of the building?

**Solution** ▶ To find the distance $d$, we first convert the given angle to decimal degrees, then find its complement. For 41°17′15″ we have $[41 + 17(1/60) + (15/3600)]° = 41.2875°$. The complement of this angle is $90° − 41.2875° = 48.7125°$. Since we need the side opposite this angle and the hypotenuse is known, we use a sine function to solve for $d$.

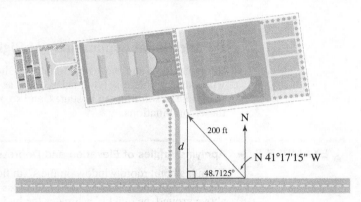

$$\sin 48.7125° = \frac{d}{200} \qquad \sin 48.7125° = \frac{\text{opp}}{\text{hyp}}$$

$$200 \sin 48.7125° = d \qquad \text{multiply by 200 (exact form)}$$

$$150.28 \approx d \qquad \text{result (approximate form)}$$

The shopping complex is approximately 150.28 ft from the avenue, just barely in compliance with the city code.

**Now try Exercises 19 through 26** ▶

Distance, velocity, and time are related by the standard formula for uniform motion, $D = rt$. Often we must use this relationship in applications requiring trigonometry, as follows in Example 4.

**EXAMPLE 4** ▶ **Applying Angles of Rotation**

To thwart drivers who have radar detection equipment, a state trooper takes up a hidden position 50 ft from the roadway. Using a sighting device she finds the angle between her position and a road sign in the distance is 79°. She then uses a stop watch to determine how long it takes a vehicle to pass her location and reach the road sign. In quick succession, an 18-wheeler, a truck, and a car pass her position, with the time each takes to travel this distance noted. Find the speed of each vehicle in miles per hour if

  **a.** The 18-wheeler takes 2.7 sec.
  **b.** The truck takes 2.3 sec.
  **c.** The car takes 1.9 sec.

Solution ▶  We begin by finding the distance traveled by each vehicle. Using $\tan 79° = \dfrac{d}{50}$ gives $d = 50 \tan 79° \approx 257$ ft. To convert a rate given in feet per second to miles per hour, recall there are 5280 ft in 1 mi and 3600 sec in 1 hr.

a.  18-wheeler: $\left(\dfrac{257 \text{ ft}}{2.7 \text{ sec}}\right)\left(\dfrac{1 \text{ mi}}{5280 \text{ ft}}\right)\left(\dfrac{3600 \text{ sec}}{1 \text{ hr}}\right) \approx \left(\dfrac{65 \text{ mi}}{1 \text{ hr}}\right)$

☑ **B.** You've just learned how to solve applications involving angles of rotation

The 18-wheeler is traveling approximately 65 mph.

b.  Using the same calculation with 2.3 sec shows the truck was going about 76 mph.

c.  At 1.9 sec, the car was traveling about 92 mph.

Now try Exercises 27 through 32 ▶

## C. Additional Applications of Right Triangles

In their widest and most beneficial use, the trig functions of acute angles are used with other problem-solving skills, such as drawing a diagram, labeling unknowns, working the solution out in stages, and so on. Example 5 serves to illustrate some of these combinations.

**EXAMPLE 5** ▶  **Applying Angles of Elevation and Depression**

From his hotel room window on the sixth floor, Singh notices some window washers high above him on the hotel across the street. Curious as to their height above ground, he quickly estimates the buildings are 50 ft apart, the angle of elevation to the workers is about 80°, and the angle of depression to the base of the hotel is about 50°.

a.  How high above ground is the window of Singh's hotel room?

b.  How high above ground are the workers?

Solution ▶  a.  Begin by drawing a diagram of the situation (see figure). To find the height of the window we'll use the tangent ratio, since the adjacent side of the angle is known, and the opposite side is the height we desire.

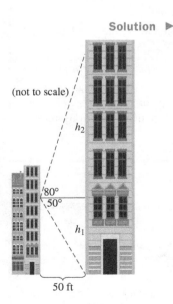

(not to scale)

For the height $h_1$:  $\qquad \tan 50° = \dfrac{h_1}{50} \quad$ $\tan 50° = \frac{\text{opp}}{\text{adj}}$

$\qquad\qquad\qquad\qquad 50 \tan 50° = h_1 \quad$ solve for $h_1$

$\qquad\qquad\qquad\qquad\quad 59.6 \approx h_1 \quad$ result ($\tan 50° \approx 1.1918$)

The window is approximately 59.6 ft above ground.

b.  For the height $h_2$:  $\qquad \tan 80° = \dfrac{h_2}{50} \quad$ $\tan 80° = \frac{\text{opp}}{\text{adj}}$

$\qquad\qquad\qquad\qquad 50 \tan 80° = h_2 \quad$ solve for $h_2$

$\qquad\qquad\qquad\qquad\quad 283.6 \approx h_2 \quad$ result ($\tan 80° \approx 5.6713$)

The workers are approximately $283.6 + 59.6 = 343.2$ ft above ground.

Now try Exercises 43 through 46 ▶

There are a number of additional, interesting applications in the exercise set.

☑ **C.** You've just learned how to solve general applications of right triangles

## TECHNOLOGY HIGHLIGHT

## Using the Storage and Recall Features of a Graphing Calculator

Computations involving the trig ratios often produce irrational numbers. Sometimes the number is used numerous times in an application, and it helps to store the value in a memory location so it can instantly be recalled without having to look it up, recompute its value, or enter it digit by digit. Storage locations are also used when writing programs for your graphing calculator. Suppose the value $\frac{1 + \sqrt{5}}{2} \approx 1.6180339887$ were to be used repeatedly. You could store this value in the *temporary memory location* X,T,θ,n using the keystrokes $\frac{1 + \sqrt{5}}{2}$ STO▸ X,T,θ,n , or in a permanent memory location using the ALPHA locations A through Z. In temporary storage, the value could potentially be overwritten once you leave the home screen. To use a stored value, we simply bring up the location name to the home screen.

**Example 1:** Save the value of $\frac{1 + \sqrt{5}}{2}$ in location X,T,θ,n , then investigate the relationship between (a) this number and its reciprocal and (b) this number and its square. What do you notice? Why does the value of $x^{-1}$ seem to be off by one decimal place?

**Solution:** After storing the number, as shown in Figure 2.12, we find its reciprocal is equal to the original number minus 1, while its square is equal to the original number plus 1. The value of $x^{-1}$ appears off due to rounding.

**Figure 2.12**

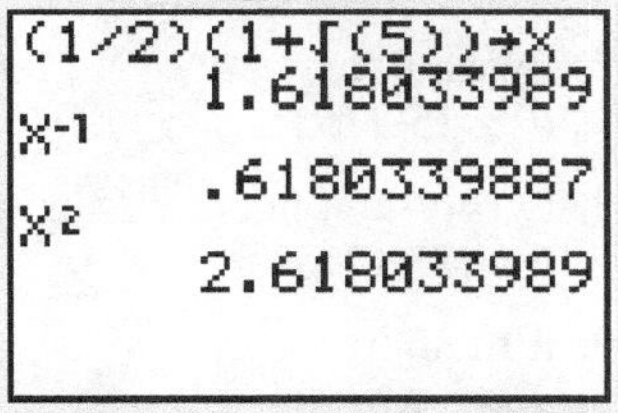

```
(1/2)(1+√(5))→X
              1.618033989
X-1
       .6180339887
X²
        2.618033989
```

Now suppose we wanted to investigate the trigonometric formula for a triangle's area: $A = \frac{1}{2}ab \sin \theta$, where $b$ is the base, $a$ is the length of one side, and $\theta$ is the angle between them. The formula has four unknowns, $A$, $a$, $b$, and $\theta$. The idea here is to let $\theta$ represent the independent variable $x$, and $A$ the dependent variable $y$, then evaluate the function for different values of $a$ and $b$. On the Y= screen, enter the formula as $Y_1 = 0.5 AB \sin X$. On the home screen, store a value of 2 in location A and 12 in location B using 2 STO▸ ALPHA MATH and 12 STO▸ ALPHA APPS , respectively, as shown in Figure 2.13. The final result can be computed on the home screen (or using the TABLE feature) by supplying a value to memory location X,T,θ,n , then calling up Y1( VARS ▶ **(Y-VARS)**

**Figure 2.13**

```
2→A
              2
12→B
             12
30→X
             30
Y₁(X)
```

1:Function ENTER ) and evaluating $Y_1(X)$. As Figure 2.13 shows, we used 30 STO▸ X,T,θ,n , and the area of a triangle with $a = 2$, $b = 12$, and $\theta = 30°$ is 6 units$^2$ (although the display couldn't hold all of the information without scrolling).

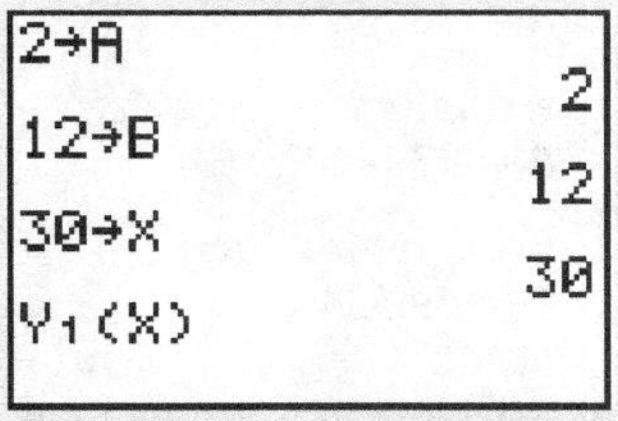

**Exercise 1:** Evaluate the area formula once again, using $a = 5$ and $b = 5\sqrt{3}$. What values of X will give an area greater than 10 units$^2$?

## 2.3 EXERCISES

▶ **CONCEPTS AND VOCABULARY**

**Fill in each blank with the appropriate word or phrase. Carefully reread the section if needed.**

1. A horizontal line of _____ is an imaginary line _____ to level ground.

2. The acute angle formed by a line of _____ that falls *below* a horizontal line of orientation is called an angle of _____.

3. Because most _____ are programmed with the trig functions _____, _____, and _____, we will often use these three when solving applications.

4. The bearing S 35° __ indicates a line of sight that forms an angle of __ to the east of a line heading due _____.

5. Compare/Contrast applications of angles of elevation/depression with those using angles of rotation.

6. Discuss/Explain how an angle of elevation/depression naturally yields two right triangles that can be used to solve an application. Include an illustrative sketch.

▶ **DEVELOPING YOUR SKILLS**

**Find the height of the indicated floor of a skyscraper, given the angle of elevation $\theta$ at a point 40 m from the base of the building.**

**Exercises 7 to 12**

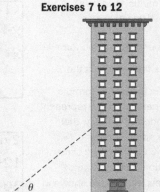

7. fourth floor; $\theta = 15.3763°$

8. twenty-first floor; $\theta = 57.1715°$

9. fifth floor; $\theta = 19.2900°$

10. twenty-second floor; $\theta = 58.3925°$

11. sixth floor; $\theta = 23.0255°$

12. twenty-third floor; $\theta = 59.5346°$

40 m

**Find the depth of a fishing hook given $\alpha$, the angle of depression that the 35 ft of fishing line makes with the surface of the water.**

13. $\alpha = 45.5847°$

**Exercises 13 to 18**

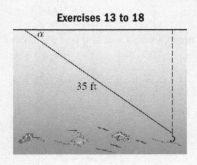

35 ft

14. $\alpha = 8.2132°$

15. $\alpha = 55.9523°$

16. $\alpha = 14.9006°$

17. $\alpha = 70.5370°$

18. $\alpha = 21.8037°$

**From a sketch of the following bearings, find the measure of the acute angles formed with (a) the north/south line and (b) the east/west line.**

19. N 63° W          20. N 81° E

21. S 49° E          22. S 39° W

23. N 23°31′ E       24. N 42°24′ W

25. S 15°32′49″ W    26. S 77°18′06″ E

**A jogger parks her car 80 m directly across from a trail that is parallel to the parking lot. Given the acute angle $\beta$ formed by the shortest distance to the trail and the path she took, find (a) the distance she jogged to the trail and (b) the amount of time it took her to reach the trail, jogging at a constant rate of 3 m/sec.**

**Exercises 27 to 32**

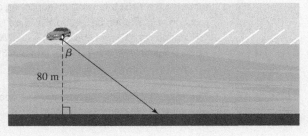

80 m

27. $\beta = 10°$          28. $\beta = 65°$

29. $\beta = 15°$          30. $\beta = 70°$

31. $\beta = 20°$          32. $\beta = 75°$

## ▶ WORKING WITH FORMULAS

**33. Height of a building:** $h = \dfrac{d}{\cot \alpha - \cot \beta}$

The given formula can be used to calculate the height $h$ of a building when the distance $d$ and angles of elevation $\alpha$ and $\beta$ are known (see the diagram). Use the formula to find the height of the building shown.

$\alpha = 45°$    $\beta = 60°$

$d = 50$ ft

**34. Distance between two planes departing from the same airport:** $d = \sqrt{r_1^2 t_1^2 + r_2^2 t_2^2 + 2r_1 t_1 r_2 t_2 \cos \theta}$

The formula shown gives the surface distance between two planes when the first plane flies due north at rate $r_1$ for time $t_1$ and the second plane flies at a bearing of S $\theta$ E at rate $r_2$ for time $t_2$. To the nearest mile, find the distance between two planes departing from Dallas Fort Worth given the first plane heads due north at 450 mph for 2.5 hr and the second plane heads S 15° E at 500 mph for 3 hr.

## ▶ APPLICATIONS

**35. Angle of elevation:** For a person standing 100 m from the center of the base of the Eiffel Tower, the angle of elevation to the top of the tower is 71.6°. How tall is the Eiffel Tower?

**36. Angle of elevation:** In 2001, the tallest building in the world was the Petronas Tower I in Kuala Lumpur, Malaysia. For a person standing 25.9 ft from the base of the tower, the angle of elevation to the top of the tower is 89°. How tall is the Petronas tower?

**37. Angle of depression:** A person standing near the top of the Eiffel Tower notices a car wreck some distance from the tower. If the angle of depression from the person's eyes to the wreck is 32°, how far away is the accident from the base of the tower? See Exercise 35.

**38. Angle of depression:** A person standing on the top of the Petronas Tower I looks out across the city and pinpoints her residence. If the angle of depression from the person's eyes to her home is 5°, how far away (in feet and in miles) is the residence from the base of the tower? See Exercise 36.

**39. Angles of rotation:** From a point 110 ft due south of the eastern end of a planned east/west bridge spanning the Illinois river, a surveyor notes the western end lies on a bearing of N 38°35′15″ W. To the nearest inch, how long will the bridge be?

N

110 ft

**40. Angles of rotation:** A large sign spans an east/west highway. From a point 35 m due west of the southern base of the sign, a surveyor finds the northern base lies on a bearing of N 67°11′42″ E. To the nearest centimeter, how wide is the sign?

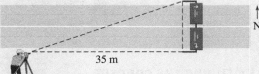

35 m    N

**41. Crop duster's speed:**
While standing near
the edge of a farmer's
field, Johnny watches a
crop duster dust the
farmer's field for insect
control. Curious as to
the plane's speed
during each drop,

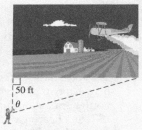

Johnny attempts an estimate using the angle of
rotation from one end of the field to the other,
while standing 50 ft from one corner. Using a
stopwatch he finds the plane makes each pass in
2.35 sec. If the angle of rotation was 83°, how fast
(in miles per hour) is the plane flying as it applies
the insecticide?

**42. Train speed:** While driving to their next gig,
Josh and the boys get stuck in a line of cars at a
railroad crossing as the gates go down. As the
sleek, speedy express train approaches, Josh
decides to pass the time estimating its speed. He
spots a large oak tree beside the track some
distance away, and figures the angle of rotation
from the crossing to the tree is about 80°. If their
car is 60 ft from the crossing and it takes the train
3 sec to reach the tree, how fast is the train moving
in miles per hour?

**43. Height of a climber:** A local Outdoors Club has
just hiked to the south rim of a large canyon, when
they spot a climber attempting to scale the taller
northern face. Knowing the distance between the
sheer walls of the northern and southern faces of the
canyon is
approximately
175 yd, they
attempt to
compute the
distance
remaining for
the climbers to
reach the top of
the northern

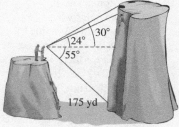

rim. Using a homemade transit, they sight an angle
of depression of 55° to the bottom of the north face,
and angles of elevation of 24° and 30° to the
climbers and top of the northern rim respectively.
(a) How high is the southern rim of the canyon?
(b) How high is the northern rim? (c) How much
farther until the climber reaches the top?

**44. Observing wildlife:** From her elevated observation
post 300 ft away, a naturalist spots a troop of
baboons high up in a tree. Using the small transit
attached to her telescope, she finds the angle of
depression to the bottom of this tree is 14°, while the
angle of elevation to the top of the tree is 25°. The
angle of elevation to the troop of baboons is 21°.
Use this information to find (a) the height of the
observation post, (b) the height of the baboons' tree,
and (c) the height of the baboons above ground.

**45. Angle of elevation:** The
tallest free-standing tower
in the world is the CNN
Tower in Toronto, Canada.
The tower includes a
rotating restaurant high
above the ground. From a
distance of 500 ft the angle
of elevation to the pinnacle
of the tower is 74.6°. The
angle of elevation to the
restaurant from the same

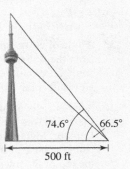

vantage point is 66.5°. How tall is the CNN Tower?
How far below the pinnacle of the tower is the
restaurant located?

**46. Angle of elevation:** In January 2009, Burj Dubai
unofficially captured the record as the world's tallest
building, according to the Council on Tall Buildings
and Urban Habitat (*Source:* www.ctbuh.org).
Measured at a point 159 m from its base, the angle
of elevation to the top of the spire is 79°. From a
distance of about 134 m, the angle of elevation to
the top of the roof is also 79°. How tall is Burj
Dubai from street level to the top of the spire? How
tall is the spire itself?

▶ **EXTENDING THE CONCEPT**

**47.** One of the challenges facing any terrestrial exploration of Mars is its weak and erratic magnetic field. An unmanned
rover begins a critical mission at landing site **A** where magnetic north lies on a bearing of N 30° W of true
(polar) north (see figure). The rover departs in the magnetic direction of S 20° E and travels straight for 1.4 km
to site **B**. At this point, magnetic north lies on a bearing of N 45° E of true north. The rover turns to magnetic
direction of N 5° W and travels 2 km straight to site **C**. At **C**, magnetic north lies on a bearing of N 10° W of true
north. In what magnetic direction should the rover head to return to site **A**?

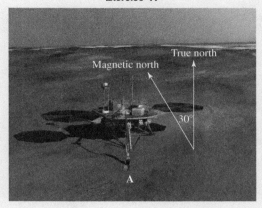

**Exercise 47**

**Exercise 48**

**48.** As of the year 2009, the Bailong elevator outside of Zhangjiajie, China, was the highest exterior glass elevator in the world. While Christine was descending in the red car, she noticed Simon ascending in the yellow car, below her at an angle of depression of 50°. Seven seconds later, Simon was above her at an angle of elevation of 50°. If the cars have the same velocity ascending and descending, and the horizontal distance between the two cars is 47 ft, how fast do the cars travel?

▶ **MAINTAINING YOUR SKILLS**

**49. (1.1)** The hypotenuse of a 30-60-90 triangle measures $14\sqrt{3}$ in. Find the lengths of the two legs.

**50. (2.1)** Given $\sec \theta = 5$, find the exact value of $\csc^2(90° - \theta)$

**51. (1.3)** Given the terminal side of $\theta$ is coincident with the ray $y = -3x$, $x > 0$, evaluate

    **a.** $\sin \theta$         **b.** $\cos \theta$

**52. (1.2)** Find the measure of angle $C$ in triangle $ABC$, given $A = 48°36'$ and $B = 91°44'21''$.

**53. (2.1)** Given $\sin \alpha = \dfrac{2}{5}$, find the value of the other five trig functions of the acute angle $\alpha$.

**54. (2.2)** Solve the triangle shown and write the answers in table form. Round sides to the nearest tenth.

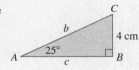

## 2.4 | Extending Beyond Acute Angles

In Section 2.1, we developed the "ratio of sides" definition of the six trig functions. While extremely useful, the ratio of two sides of a right triangle limits their application to acute angles. Using the concept of a reference angle, we can extend our understanding of right triangle trigonometry to cover *all* nonquadrantal angles as well, and consequently expand our ability to solve applications involving trigonometry.

### A. Reference Angles

For any nonquadrantal angle $\theta$ in standard position, the acute angle $\theta_r$ formed by the terminal side and the nearest $x$-axis is called the ***reference angle.*** Several examples of this definition are illustrated in Figures 2.14 through 2.17 for $\theta > 0°$ (note that if $0° < \theta < 90°$, then $\theta_r = \theta$).

**Figure 2.14**

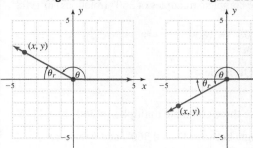

$90° < \theta < 180°$
$\theta_r = 180° - \theta$

**Figure 2.15**

$180° < \theta < 270°$
$\theta_r = \theta - 180°$

**Figure 2.16**

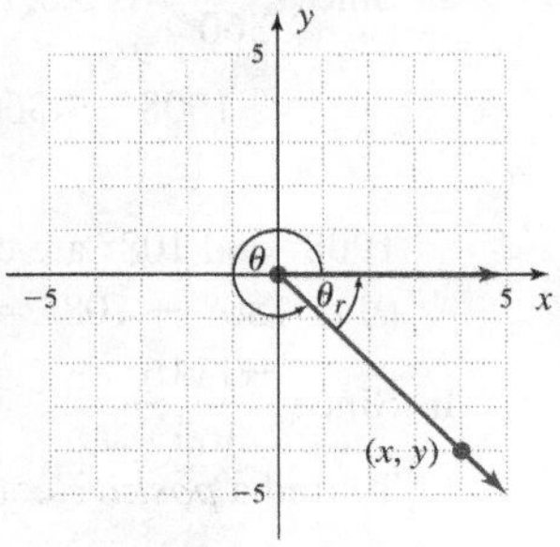

$270° < \theta < 360°$
$\theta_r = 360° - \theta$

**Figure 2.17**

$360° < \theta < 450°$
$\theta_r = \theta - 360°$

---

**EXAMPLE 1** ▶ **Finding Reference Angles**

Determine the reference angle for

  **a.** 315°      **b.** 150°      **c.** 239°      **d.** 425°

**Solution** ▶ Begin by mentally visualizing each angle and the quadrant where it terminates.

  **a.** 315° is a QIV angle:        **c.** 239° is a QIII angle:
  $\theta_r = 360° - 315° = 45°$        $\theta_r = 239° - 180° = 59°$

  **b.** 150° is a QII angle:        **d.** 425° is a QI angle:
  $\theta_r = 180° - 150° = 30°$        $\theta_r = 425° - 360° = 65°$

Now try Exercises 9 through 18 ▶

In our everyday experience, there are many actions and activities where angles greater than or equal to 360° are applied. Some common instances are a professional basketball player who "does a three-sixty" (360°) while going to the hoop, a diver who completes a "two-and-a-half" (900°) off the high board, and a skater who executes a perfect triple axel ($3\frac{1}{2}$ turns or 1260°). As these examples suggest, angles greater than 360° must still terminate on a quadrantal axis, or in one of the four quadrants, allowing a reference angle to be found and the functions to be evaluated for any angle *regardless of size*. Figure 2.18

**Figure 2.18**

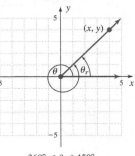

illustrates that $\alpha = 135°$, $\beta = -225°$, and $\theta = 495°$ are all coterminal, with *each having a reference angle of* 45°.

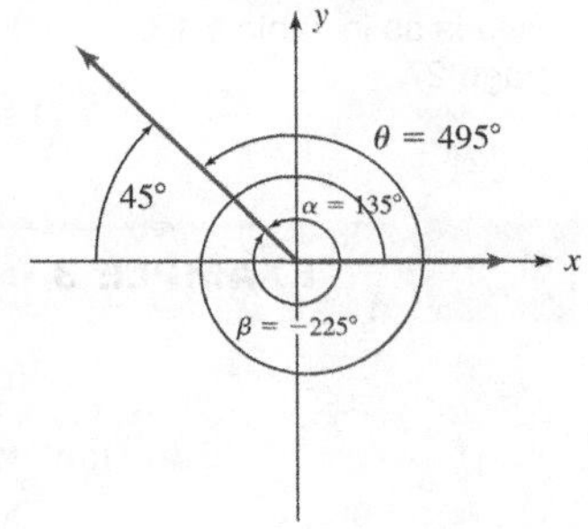

Since 360° is one full rotation, all angles $\theta + 360°k$ will be coterminal for any integer $k$. For angles with a very large magnitude, we can find the quadrant of the terminal side by adding or subtracting as many integer multiples of 360° as needed until $\theta < 360°$.

---

**EXAMPLE 2** ▶ **Finding Reference Angles**

Determine the reference angle for

  **a.** 1908°                    **b.** −1116°

**Solution** ▶ **a.** Since $\dfrac{1908°}{360°} = 5.3$, there are five complete multiples of 360° (rotations) in 1908°.

$$1908° - 360°(5) = 1908° - 1800° \quad \text{subtract five multiples of } 360°$$
$$= 108° \qquad\qquad \text{simplify}$$

1908° and 108° are coterminal QII angles:

$$\theta_r = 180° - 108° = 72°$$

**b.** Since $\dfrac{-1116°}{360°} = -3.1$, there are three complete multiples of 360° in $-1116°$.

To find a *positive* coterminal angle between 0° and 360°, add one more

multiple of 360° (in this case, $3 + 1 = 4$ multiples of 360°).

$$-1116° + 360°(4) = -1116° + 1440° \quad \text{add four multiples of } 360°$$
$$= 324° \qquad\qquad \text{simplify}$$

☑ **A.** You've just learned how to find the reference angle of any nonquadrantal angle

$-1116°$ and 324° are coterminal QIV angles:

$$\theta_r = 360° - 324° = 36°$$

**Now try Exercises 19 through 26** ▶

---

## B. The Trig Functions of Any Angle

**WORTHY OF NOTE**

We cannot use right triangles to find the trig functions of the quadrantal angles, so for consistency we define their values as in Table 1.1 on page 27.

In Section 2.1, we reconciled the two definitions of the trig functions of *acute angles* by placing a right triangle in the first quadrant. When an angle $\theta$ is *not acute,* we draw a vertical line segment from the terminal side of $\theta$ to the $x$-axis, forming a right triangle with the reference angle $\theta_r$. For any trig function $T$, we find the value of $T(\theta)$ by simply finding $T(\theta_r)$ and applying the correct sign based on the quadrant of the terminal side (see Figure 2.19).

**Figure 2.19**

| Quadrant II | Quadrant I |
|---|---|
| Sine is positive | All are positive |
| Tangent is positive | Cosine is positive |
| Quadrant III | Quadrant IV |

**EXAMPLE 3** ▶ **Evaluating Trig Functions Using $\theta_r$**

Use a reference angle to evaluate $\sin\theta$, $\cos\theta$, and $\tan\theta$ for $\theta = 315°$.

**Solution** ▶ The terminal side is in QIV where cosine is positive while sine and tangent are negative. With $\theta_r = 45°$, we consider a 45-45-90 triangle placed in the coordinate plane as shown in the margin and we have:

$$\sin 315° = -\sin\theta_r \quad \text{QIV: } \sin\theta < 0$$
$$= -\sin 45° \quad \text{replace } \theta_r \text{ with } 45°$$
$$= -\frac{\sqrt{2}}{2} \quad \sin 45° = \frac{\sqrt{2}}{2}$$

Similarly, the values for cosine and tangent are

$$\cos 315° = +\cos\theta_r \qquad\qquad \tan 315° = -\tan\theta_r$$
$$= \cos 45° \qquad\qquad\qquad = -\tan 45°$$
$$= \frac{\sqrt{2}}{2} \qquad\qquad\qquad = -1$$

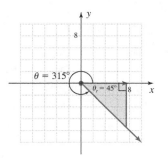

**Now try Exercises 27 through 42** ▶

**EXAMPLE 4** ▶ **Evaluating Trig Functions of Any Angle**
Evaluate sin 150°, cos (−210°), and tan 510°.

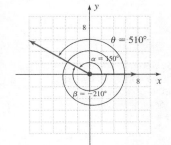

**Solution** ▶ The three angles are coterminal in QII where sine is positive while cosine and tangent are negative. With $\theta_r = 30°$, we visualize a 30-60-90 triangle in the coordinate plane, as shown.

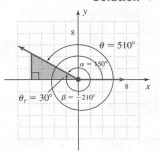

$$\begin{aligned}
\sin 150° &= +\sin \theta_r & \cos(-210°) &= -\cos \theta_r & \tan 510° &= -\tan \theta_r \\
&= \sin 30° & &= -\cos 30° & &= -\tan 30° \\
&= \frac{1}{2} & &= -\frac{\sqrt{3}}{2} & &= -\frac{\sqrt{3}}{3}
\end{aligned}$$

☑ **B.** You've just learned how to use reference angles to evaluate the trig functions for any nonquadrantal angle

**Now try Exercises 43 through 54** ▶

Note the reference angles in Examples 3 and 4 called for the use of special triangles, but the principles demonstrated apply for reference angles of any size. **See Exercises 55 through 62.**

**Figure 2.20**

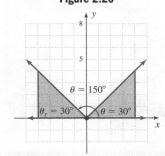

## C. Applications of the Trig Functions of Any Angle

One of the most basic uses of coterminal angles is determining *all* values of $\theta$ that satisfy a stated relationship. For example, by now you are aware that if $\sin \theta = \frac{1}{2}$ (positive one-half), then $\theta = 30°$ or $\theta = 150°$ (see Figure 2.20). But this is also true for all angles coterminal with these two, and we would write the solutions as $\theta = 30° + 360°k$ and $\theta = 150° + 360°k$ for all integers $k$.

**EXAMPLE 5** ▶ **Finding All Angles that Satisfy a Given Equation**
Find all angles satisfying the relationship given. Answer in degrees.

    **a.** $\cos \theta = -\dfrac{\sqrt{2}}{2}$          **b.** $\tan \theta = -1.3764$

**Figure 2.21**

**Solution** ▶ **a.** Cosine is negative in QII and QIII. Recognizing $\cos 45° = \dfrac{\sqrt{2}}{2}$, we reason $\theta_r = 45°$ and two solutions are $\theta = 135°$ from QII and $\theta = 225°$ from QIII. For all values of $\theta$ satisfying the relationship, we have $\theta = 135° + 360°k$ and $\theta = 225° + 360°k$. See Figure 2.21.

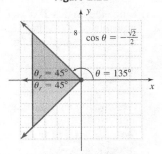

**b.** Tangent is negative in QII and QIV. For $-1.3764$ we find $\theta_r$ using a calculator: 2nd TAN (tan$^{-1}$) 1.3764 ENTER shows $\tan^{-1}(1.3764) \approx 54$, so $\theta_r = 54°$. Two solutions are $\theta = 180° - 54° = 126°$ from QII, and in QIV $\theta = 360° - 54° = 306°$. The result is $\theta = 126° + 360°k$ and $\theta = 306° + 360°k$. Note these can be combined into the single statement $\theta = 126° + 180°k$. See Figure 2.22.

**Figure 2.22**

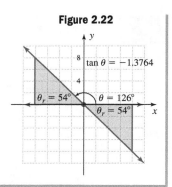

> **WORTHY OF NOTE**
>
> Since reference angles are acute, we find them by using the sin$^{-1}$, cos$^{-1}$, or tan$^{-1}$ keys for positive values.

**Now try Exercises 65 through 72 ▶**

We close this section with an additional application of the concepts related to trigonometric functions of any angle.

**EXAMPLE 6 ▶**  **Applications of Coterminal Angles: Location on Radar**

A radar operator calls the captain over to her screen saying, "Sir, we have an unidentified aircraft at bearing N 20° E (a standard 70° rotation). I think it's a UFO." The captain asks, "What makes you think so?" To which the sailor replies, "Because it's at 5000 ft and not moving!" Name all angles for which the UFO causes a "blip" to occur on the radar screen.

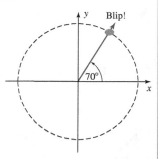

**Solution ▶**  Since radar typically sweeps out a 360° angle, a blip will occur on the screen for all angles $\theta = 70° + 360°k$, where $k$ is an integer.

☑ **C.** You've just learned how to solve applications using the trig functions of any angle

**Now try Exercises 73 through 78 ▶**

---

## 2.4 EXERCISES

▶ **CONCEPTS AND VOCABULARY**

**Fill in each blank with the appropriate word or phrase. Carefully reread the section if needed.**

**1.** Since the angles 280° and $-440°$ differ by a multiple of 360°, they are _____ and both have a _____ angle of 80°. While not coterminal with these two angles, 100° also has a reference angle of ___.

**2.** The trig function values of 150° can be found with the function values of the 30° _____ angle. The signs of the trig function values are determined by the _____ of the _____ side of the angle.

**3.** If $\theta$ satisfies a given trigonometric relationship, then for all _____ $k$, $\theta +$ _____ does as well.

**4.** For any angle $\theta$, its reference angle $\theta_r$ is the positive _____ angle formed by the _____ side and the nearest $x$-axis.

**5.** Discuss the similarities and differences between the trigonometry of right triangles and the trigonometry of *any* angle.

**6.** Let $T(x)$ represent any one of the six basic trig functions. Explain why the equation $T(x) = k$ will always have exactly two solutions in $[0, 360°)$ if $x$ is not a quadrantal angle.

▶ **DEVELOPING YOUR SKILLS**

**7.** Draw a 30-60-90 triangle with the 60° angle at the origin and the short side along the positive *x*-axis. Determine the slope and equation of the line coincident with the hypotenuse, then pick any point on this line and evaluate sin 60°, cos 60°, and tan 60°. Comment on what you notice.

**8.** Draw a 45-45-90 triangle with a 45° angle at the origin and one side along the positive *x*-axis. Determine the slope and equation of the line coincident with the hypotenuse, then pick any point on this line and evaluate sin 45°, cos 45°, and tan 45°. Comment on what you notice.

**Name the reference angle $\theta_r$ for the angle $\theta$ given.**

**9.** $\theta = 50°$     **10.** $\theta = 120°$

**11.** $\theta = 210°$     **12.** $\theta = 315°$

**13.** $\theta = -45°$     **14.** $\theta = -150°$

**15.** $\theta = 112°$     **16.** $\theta = 417°$

**17.** $\theta = 404.4°$     **18.** $\theta = 222.2°$

**19.** $\theta = 500°$     **20.** $\theta = 1125°$

**21.** $\theta = -168.4°$     **22.** $\theta = -328.2°$

**23.** $\theta = -382.1°$     **24.** $\theta = 1646.3°$

**25.** $\theta = 1361°30'$     **26.** $\theta = -969°45'$

**Find the exact value of sin $\theta$, cos $\theta$, and tan $\theta$ using reference angles.**

**27.** $\theta = 330°$     **28.** $\theta = 390°$

**29.** $\theta = -45°$     **30.** $\theta = -120°$

**31.** $\theta = 240°$     **32.** $\theta = 315°$

**33.** $\theta = -150°$     **34.** $\theta = -210°$

**35.** $\theta = 600°$     **36.** $\theta = 480°$

**37.** $\theta = -840°$     **38.** $\theta = -930°$

**39.** $\theta = 570°$     **40.** $\theta = 495°$

**41.** $\theta = -1230°$     **42.** $\theta = 3270°$

**Find two positive and two negative angles that are coterminal with the angle given. Answers will vary.**

**43.** 52°     **44.** 12°

**45.** 87.5°     **46.** 22.8°

**47.** 225°     **48.** 175°

**49.** −107°     **50.** −215°

**Evaluate in exact form as indicated.**

**51.** sin 120°, cos −240°, tan 480°

**52.** sin 225°, cos 585°, tan −495°

**53.** sin −30°, cos −390°, tan −690°

**54.** sin 210°, cos 570°, tan −150°

**For each exercise, state the quadrant of the terminal side of $\theta$ and the sign of the function in that quadrant. Then find the reference angle $\theta_r$ and evaluate the function at both $\theta$ and $\theta_r$ using a calculator. Round to four decimal places.**

**55.** $\theta = 719°$; sine     **56.** $\theta = 528°$; cosine

**57.** $\theta = -419°$; tangent     **58.** $\theta = -621°$; secant

**59.** $\theta = 681°$; cosecant     **60.** $\theta = 995°$; tangent

**61.** $\theta = 805°$; cosine     **62.** $\theta = 772°$; sine

▶ **WORKING WITH FORMULAS**

**63. The area of a parallelogram: $A = ab \sin \theta$**

The area of a parallelogram is given by the formula shown, where *a* and *b* are the lengths of the sides and $\theta$ is the angle between them. Use the formula to complete the following: (a) find the area of a parallelogram with sides $a = 9$ and $b = 21$ given $\theta = 50°$. (b) What is the smallest integer value of $\theta$ where the area is greater than 150 units²? (c) State what happens when $\theta = 90°$. (d) How can you find the area of a triangle using this formula?

**64. The angle between two intersecting lines:**

$$\tan \theta = \frac{m_2 - m_1}{1 + m_2 m_1}$$

Given line 1 and line 2 with slopes $m_1$ and $m_2$, respectively, the angle between the two lines is given by the formula shown. Find the angle $\theta$ if the equation of line 1 is $y_1 = \frac{3}{4}x + 2$ and line 2 has equation $y_2 = -\frac{2}{3}x + 5$.

► APPLICATIONS

Find all angles satisfying the stated relationship. For standard angles, express your answer in exact form. For nonstandard values, use a calculator and round function values to tenths.

**65.** $\cos\theta = \dfrac{1}{2}$       **66.** $\sin\theta = \dfrac{\sqrt{2}}{2}$

**67.** $\sin\theta = -\dfrac{\sqrt{3}}{2}$       **68.** $\tan\theta = -\dfrac{\sqrt{3}}{1}$

**69.** $\sin\theta = 0.8754$       **70.** $\cos\theta = 0.2378$

**71.** $\tan\theta = -2.3512$       **72.** $\cos\theta = -0.0562$

**73. Nonacute angles:** At a recent carnival, one of the games on the midway was played using a large spinner that turns clockwise. On Jorge's spin the number 25 began at the 12 o'clock (top/center) position, returned to this position five times during the spin and stopped at the 3 o'clock position. What angle $\theta$ did the spinner spin through? Name all angles that are coterminal with $\theta$.

Exercise 73

**74. Nonacute angles:** One of the four blades on a ceiling fan has a decal on it and begins at a designated "12 o'clock" position. Turning the switch on and then immediately off causes the blade to make over three complete, counterclockwise rotations, with the blade stopping at the 8 o'clock position. What angle $\theta$ did the blade turn through? Name all angles that are coterminal with $\theta$.

**75. High dives:** As part of a diving competition, David executes a perfect reverse two-and-a-half flip. Does he enter the water feet first or head first? Through what angle did he turn from takeoff until the moment he entered the water?

Exercise 75

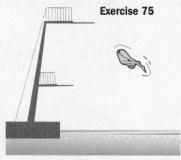

**76. Gymnastics:** While working out on a trampoline, Charlene does three complete, forward flips and then belly-flops on the trampoline before returning to the upright position. What angle did she turn through from the start of this maneuver to the moment she belly-flops?

**77. Spiral of Archimedes:** The graph shown is called the spiral of Archimedes. Through what angle $\theta$ has the spiral turned, given the spiral terminates at $(6, -2)$ as indicated?

Exercise 77

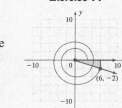

**78. Involute of a circle:** The graph shown is called the involute of a circle. Through what angle $\theta$ has the involute turned, given the graph terminates at $(-4, -3.5)$ as indicated?

Exercise 78

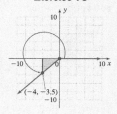

► EXTENDING THE CONCEPT

**79.** In an elementary study of trigonometry, the hands of a clock are often studied because of the angle relationship that exists between the hands. For example, at 3 o'clock, the angle between the two hands is a right angle and measures 90°.

  **a.** What is the angle between the two hands at 1 o'clock? 2 o'clock? Explain why.

  **b.** What is the angle between the two hands at 6:30? 7:00? 7:30? Explain why.

  **c.** Name four times at which the hands will form a 45° angle.

**80.** In the diagram shown, the indicated ray is of arbitrary length. (a) Through what additional angle $\alpha$ would the ray have to be rotated to create triangle $ABC$? (b) What will be the length of side $AC$ once the triangle is complete?

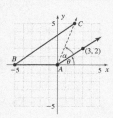

**81.** Referring to Exercise 74, suppose the fan blade had a radius of 20 in. and is turning at a rate of 12 revolutions per second. (a) Find the angle the blade turns through in 3 sec. (b) Find the circumference of the circle traced out by the tip of the blade. (c) Find the total distance traveled by the blade tip in 10 sec. (d) Find the speed, in miles per hour, that the tip of the blade is traveling.

▶ **MAINTAINING YOUR SKILLS**

**82. (2.3)** Jazon is standing 117 ft from the base of the Washington Monument in Washington, D.C. If his eyes are 5 ft above level ground and he must hold his head at a 78° angle from horizontal to see the top of the monument (the angle of elevation of 78°), estimate the height of the monument. Answer to the nearest tenth of a foot.

**83. (2.1)** Given tan 40° ≈ 0.8391, what is the value of cot 50°? Why?

**84. (2.2)** Solve the given triangle using a calculator. Express all angles and sides to the nearest tenth of a unit. Answer in table form.

**Exercise 84**

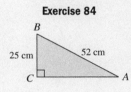

**85. (2.2)** Solve the given triangle using special angles. Express all angles and sides in exact form. Answer in table form.

**Exercise 85**

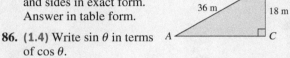

**86. (1.4)** Write sin θ in terms of cos θ.

**87. (1.1)** Find the complement and supplement of 12°34′56″.

# SUMMARY AND CONCEPT REVIEW

## SECTION 2.1   A Right Triangle View of Trigonometry

### KEY CONCEPTS

• The sides of a right triangle can be named relative to their location with respect to a given angle.

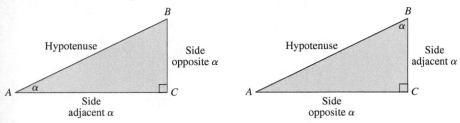

• The ratios of two sides with respect to a given angle are named as follows:

$$\sin \alpha = \frac{\text{opp}}{\text{hyp}} \qquad \cos \alpha = \frac{\text{adj}}{\text{hyp}} \qquad \tan \alpha = \frac{\text{opp}}{\text{adj}}$$

• The reciprocal of the ratios above play a vital role and are likewise given special names:

$$\csc \alpha = \frac{\text{hyp}}{\text{opp}} \qquad \sec \alpha = \frac{\text{hyp}}{\text{adj}} \qquad \cot \alpha = \frac{\text{adj}}{\text{opp}}$$

$$\csc \alpha = \frac{1}{\sin \alpha} \qquad \sec \alpha = \frac{1}{\cos \alpha} \qquad \cot \alpha = \frac{1}{\tan \alpha}$$

- In certain applications, using the coordinate plane to define the trig functions is advantageous, while at other times, the right triangle definitions are more useful. By positioning a right triangle in QI, we can reconcile the two definitions.
- Each trig function of $\alpha$ is equal to the cofunction of its complement. For instance, the complement of sine is *co*sine and $\sin \alpha = \cos(90° - \alpha)$.

## EXERCISES

Use the triangle shown to find the values of the indicated functions.

**Exercise 1 to 6**

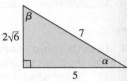

1. **a.** $\sin \alpha$      2. **a.** $\cos \alpha$      3. **a.** $\tan \alpha$
   **b.** $\sin \beta$         **b.** $\cos \beta$         **b.** $\tan \beta$

4. **a.** $\csc \alpha$      5. **a.** $\sec \alpha$      6. **a.** $\cot \alpha$
   **b.** $\csc \beta$         **b.** $\sec \beta$         **b.** $\cot \beta$

7. Given $\tan \theta = 3$, determine the exact values of the other five trig functions of the acute angle $\theta$.

8. Rewrite each expression in terms of a cofunction.

   **a.** $\tan 57.4°$
   **b.** $\sin(19°30'15'')$

## SECTION 2.2    Solving Right Triangles

### KEY CONCEPTS

- To solve a right triangle means to apply any combination of the trig functions, along with the triangle properties, until all sides and all angles are known.
- A right triangle can be solved if (a) two sides are given or (b) one side and one acute angle are given.
- The expression $\cos^{-1}x$ represents an angle $\theta$ whose cosine is $x$ ($\cos \theta = x$).

### EXERCISES

9. Use a calculator to solve for $A$:

   **a.** $\cos 37° = A$
   **b.** $\cos A = 0.4340$

Solve each triangle. Round angles to the nearest tenth and sides to the nearest hundredth.

10.

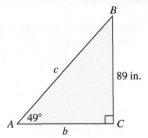

11.

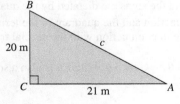

12. Josephine is to weld a vertical support to a 20-m ramp so that the incline is exactly 15°. What is the height $h$ of the support that must be used?

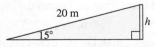

13. A slice of bread is roughly 14 cm by 10 cm. If the slice is cut diagonally in half, what acute angles are formed?

## SECTION 2.3    Applications of Static Trigonometry

### KEY CONCEPTS

- An angle of elevation is the angle formed by a horizontal line of orientation (parallel to level ground) and the line of sight. An angle of depression is likewise formed, but with the line of sight below the line of orientation.
- Bearings (e.g. N 26°W) are specified with three pieces of information: (1) the direction **North** or **South** of an east/west reference line, (2) the acute angle the bearing forms with a north/south reference line, and (3) the direction **East** or **West** of this north/south reference line.
- Accurate sketches are a key component to solving more complex applications.

### EXERCISES

**14.** Directly above center court, the Yakima SunDome in Yakima, Washington, rises to its maximum height of 92 ft. The angle of elevation from Justin's parking spot at a Yakama Sun Kings home game to the top of the dome is 11°. To the nearest foot, how far from center court is Justin parked?

**15.** What are the four bearings that make an angle of 31° with a north/south line and 59° with an east/west line?

**16.** Dr. Stampfli is waiting for a helicopter to land on the hospital helipad, 120 ft from where he is standing. The angle of elevation to the helicopter from the doctor's position is 14°. How fast is the helicopter descending if it takes 20 sec to land? Assume the descent is strictly vertical.

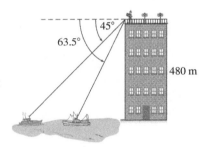

**17.** From the observation deck of a seaside building 480 m high, Armando sees two fishing boats in the distance. The angle of depression to the nearer boat is 63.5°, while for the boat farther away the angle is 45°.
(a) How far out to sea is the nearer boat? (b) How far apart are the two boats?

## SECTION 2.4    Extending Beyond Acute Angles

### KEY CONCEPTS

- A reference angle $\theta_r$ is defined to be the acute angle formed by the terminal side of a given angle $\theta$ and the x-axis.
- By placing a right triangle in the coordinate plane with one acute angle at the origin and a leg along the x-axis, we note the trig functions can be defined in terms of the ratio of sides of the right triangle, or the ratio of coordinates of a point $P(x, y)$ on the hypotenuse of this triangle.
- Reference angles can be used to evaluate the trig functions of any nonquadrantal angle, since the values are fixed by the ratio of sides and the signs are dictated by the quadrant of the terminal side.
- If the value of a trig function and the quadrant of the terminal side are known, the related angle $\theta$ can be found using a reference angle in conjunction with the special triangles or the $\sin^{-1}$, $\cos^{-1}$, or $\tan^{-1}$ features of a calculator.
- If $\theta$ is a solution to $\sin \theta = k$, then $\theta + 360°n$ is also a solution for any integer $n$.

### EXERCISES

**18.** Name the reference angle for the angles $\theta = -152°$, $\theta = 521°$, and $\theta = 210°$.

**19.** Find the exact value of $\sin \theta$, $\cos \theta$, and $\tan \theta$, given $\theta = -870°$.

**20.** Evaluate in exact form as indicated.

    **a.** $\sin 135°$         **b.** $\cos -225°$         **c.** $\tan 855°$

**21.** Find all angles satisfying the stated relationship. For standard angles, express your answer in exact form. For nonstandard angles, use a calculator and round to the nearest tenth.

    **a.** $\tan \theta = -1$         **b.** $\cos \theta = \dfrac{\sqrt{3}}{2}$         **c.** $\tan \theta = 4.0108$         **d.** $\sin \theta = -0.4540$

# MIXED REVIEW

1. Evaluate $\sin \alpha$ and $\tan \beta$ given $a = 6$, $b = 5$, and $c = \sqrt{61}$ for the triangle shown.

**Exercise 1**

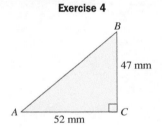

2. The front door of city hall is 225 ft directly north of a statue of Abraham Lincoln. The police station is due east of city hall and its front door lies on a bearing of N 36° E from the statue. How far is the police station door from the city hall door? Round to the nearest tenth.

3. Find the exact value of $\sin \theta$, $\cos \theta$, and $\tan \theta$ given $\theta = 1200°$.

4. Solve the triangle shown and write answers in table form. Round to the nearest tenth.

**Exercise 4**

*(triangle with B at top, 47 mm vertical side, A at bottom left, 52 mm base to C at right angle)*

5. Jonas, a tornado chaser, notes the angle of elevation to the top of an F2 tornado is 17.3° when it just touches down in Smallville, 3.2 km away. How tall is the tornado at that moment?

6. Find the value of $x$ that makes the statement an identity. $\csc(2x)° = \sec(3x - 5)°$

7. Given $\cos \theta = \dfrac{36}{85}$, determine the exact value of the other five trig functions of the acute angle $\theta$.

8. The service door into the foyer of a large office building is 36″ wide by 78″ tall. The building manager has ordered a large wall painting 85″ by 85″ to add some atmosphere to the foyer area. (a) Can the painting be brought in the service door? (b) If so, at what two integer-valued angles (with respect to level ground) could the painting be tilted?

9. Evaluate in exact form as indicated.

   **a.** $\sin -30°$      **b.** $\cos 330°$      **c.** $\tan -750°$

10. Given $\sin \theta = \dfrac{16}{63}$, what is the value of $\cos(90° - \theta)$? Why?

11. Pat watches Jeff try to start the lawn mower directly in front of his second-story window. Pat is 16 ft above the level lawn below, and the angle of depression to the lawn mower is $\theta = 38°39'$. How far is the mower from the house?

**Exercise 11**

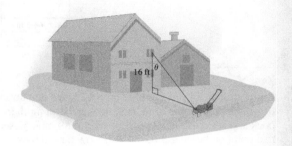

12. Name the reference angle $\theta_r$ for the angle $\theta$ given.

    **a.** 735°                **b.** −135°

13. From midnight through 9:00 P.M. the following day, what *signed* angle does a clock's hour hand rotate through?

14. Given $\alpha$ and $\beta$ are complementary angles, verify $\cos \alpha \cot \beta = \cos \beta$.

15. On your approach shot to the ninth green, the Global Positioning System (GPS) your cart is equipped with tells you the pin is 115.47 yd away. The distance plate states the straight line distance to the hole is 100 yd (see the diagram). Relative to a straight line between the plate and the hole, at what acute angle $\theta$ should you hit the shot?

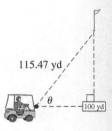

16. The electricity supply lines to the top of Lone Eagle Plateau must be replaced, and the new lines will be run in conduit buried slightly beneath the surface. The scale of elevation is 1:150 (each closed figure indicates an increase of 150 ft of elevation), and the scale of horizontal distance is 1 in. = 200 ft. (a) Find the increase in elevation from point $A$ to point $B$,

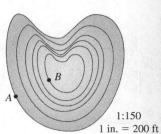

(b) use a proportion to find the horizontal distance from *A* to *B* if the measured distance on the map is $2\frac{1}{4}$ in., (c) draw the corresponding right triangle and use it to estimate the length of conduit needed from *A* to *B* and the angle of incline the installers will experience while installing the conduit.

**17.** Solve the triangle *ABC* shown by completing the table. Round to the nearest tenth.

**Exercise 17**

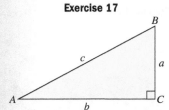

| Angles | Sides |
|--------|-------|
| A = 11.3° | |
| | b = 60.5 m |
| C = 90° | |

**18.** Ron set up his bird watching outpost 135 yd due north of a duck nest. Some time later, he watches a mother duck and her ducklings swim due west for 9 min, 52 sec to a point on bearing S 65°30′ W. How far did they swim? How fast were they swimming?

**19.** Use a reference angle to find the value of tan 780°.

**20.** Virtually everyone is familiar with the Statue of Liberty in New York Bay, but fewer know that America is home to a second "Statue of Liberty" standing proudly atop the iron dome of the Capitol Building. From a distance of 600 ft, the angle of elevation from ground level to the top of the statue (from the east side) is 25.60°. The angle of elevation to the base of the statue is 24.07°. How tall is the statue *Freedom* (the name sculptor Thomas Crawford gave this statue)?

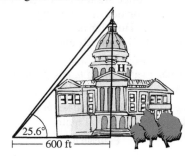

## PRACTICE TEST

1. In the right triangle shown, find $b$ given $\alpha = 41°$ and $c = 25$ cm. Round to the nearest hundredth.

**Exercise 1**

2. Name the reference angle of each angle given.

   **a.** $225°$      **b.** $-510°$

3. Given $\csc \theta = 4$, find the other five trig functions of the acute angle $\theta$.

Solve the triangles shown. Answer in table form.

4.

**Exercise 4**

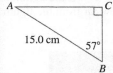

15.0 cm   57°

5. $a = 138$ ft, $b = 174$ ft

**Exercise 5**

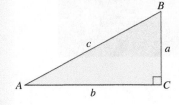

6. From her Brooklyn apartment, Catherine has a perfect view of a cell phone tower on the roof of a neighboring building, 73 ft away. From her window, the angle of elevation to the top of the tower is 32° and the angle of depression to the bottom of the tower is 17°. How tall is the tower?

**Exercise 6**

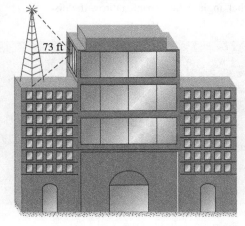

73 ft

**7.** Complete the table using reference angles and exact values.

| $\theta$ | $\sin \theta$ | $\cos \theta$ | $\tan \theta$ | $\csc \theta$ | $\sec \theta$ | $\cot \theta$ |
|---|---|---|---|---|---|---|
| 30° | | | | | | |
| 45° | | | | | | |
| 60° | | | | | | |
| 135° | | | | | | |
| 240° | | | | | | |
| 330° | | | | | | |

**8.** Given the figure shown, find the following:

**a.** $\sin(180° + B)$

**b.** $\cos(180° - B)$

**c.** $\tan(-B)$

**Exercise 8**

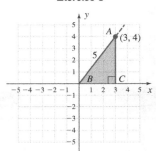

**9.** During halftime of a professional football game, Maya the disc dog and her handler Veronica put on an amazing performance. The show begins with Maya on one side line and Veronica 160 ft directly across from her on the opposite sideline. Maya streaks down her sideline for 5.5 sec at a speed of 32 ft/sec before she makes a spectacular behind-the-back catch. At what angle $\theta$ did Veronica throw the disc?

**Exercise 10**

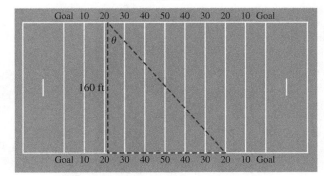

**10.** Given $\sin 15° = \dfrac{1}{2}\sqrt{2 - \sqrt{3}}$ in exact form, find the exact value of $4 \cos^2 75°$ using a cofunction.

**11.** The "plow" is a yoga position in which a person lying on their back brings their feet up, over, and behind their head and touches them to the floor. If distance from hip to shoulder (at the right angle) is 57 cm and from hip to toes is 88 cm, find the distance from shoulders to toes and the angle formed at the hips.

**Exercise 11**

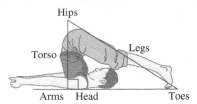

**12.** While doing some night fishing, you round a peninsula and a tall light house comes into view. Taking a sighting, you find the angle of elevation to the top of the lighthouse is 25°. If the lighthouse is known to be 27 m tall, how far from the lighthouse are you?

**Exercise 12**

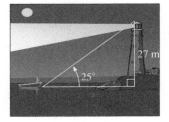

**13.** The control tower at Ocala International Airport is tracking two inbound flights. Flight 178 is 2.3 mi away at a bearing of N 22.1° E and Flight 259 is on a bearing of N 67.9° W. If the onboard radar of Flight 178 shows Flight 259 at a bearing of S 57.1° W, how far apart are the two planes?

**14.** Find all angles that satisfy $\cos \theta = -\dfrac{\sqrt{3}}{2}$.

**15.** Using the given figure, identify the following ratios as trig functions of the angle $\alpha$.

**a.** $\dfrac{b}{a}$     **b.** $\dfrac{c}{a}$

**c.** $\dfrac{b}{c}$     **d.** $\dfrac{a}{c}$

**e.** $\dfrac{c}{b}$     **f.** $\dfrac{a}{b}$

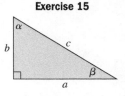

**Exercise 15**

**16.** Find the angle $\theta$ that the diagonal across the middle of the box makes at the upper corner.

**Exercise 16**

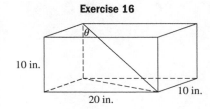

10 in.

20 in.    10 in.

**17.** Given $\alpha$ and $\beta$ are complementary angles, verify $\sin \alpha(\sec \beta - \sin \alpha) = \sin^2 \beta$ is an identity.

**18.** On a calm, clear day, a helium balloon is released and begins rising. (a) How high is the balloon if the angle of elevation is 38° from a distance of 50 ft? (b) If a second reading of 56° is taken five seconds later, how high is the balloon? (c) How fast is the balloon rising in miles per hour (round to tenths)?

**19.** Given $\sin 32° \approx 0.53$, find the value of $\sin 148°$, $\sin 212°$, and $\sin 328°$ without using a calculator.

**20.** The cities of Cairo, Alexandria, and Port Said, on the boundaries of the Nile River Delta, approximate the vertices of a right triangle, as shown. If the distance from Cairo to Port Said is 168 km, how far is Alexandria from Port Said?

**Exercise 20**

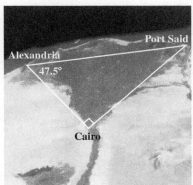

Port Said

Alexandria
47.5°

Cairo

### Finding the Distance from the Earth to the Sun

Aristarchus of Samos (~310–230 B.C.) was a Greek astronomer and mathematician. He appears to be among the first to realize that when the Moon is in its first quarter, the triangle formed by the Sun, the Earth, and the Moon ($\triangle EMS$ in the figure) must be a right triangle.

Although he did not have trigonometry or even degree measure at his disposal, in effect he estimated $\angle E$ to be 87° and used this right triangle to reckon how many times farther the Sun was from the Earth, than the Moon was from the Earth. Since $\overline{EM}$ is the side adjacent to $\angle E$ and $\overline{ES}$ is the hypotenuse of the right triangle, we can use either the cosine or secant functions to find this same information. Here we'll use the secant function.

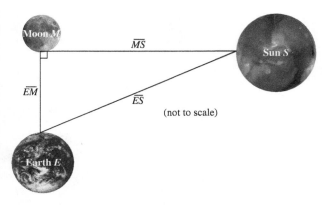

(not to scale)

$$\sec 87° = \frac{\overline{ES}}{\overline{EM}} \qquad \sec 87° = \frac{\text{hypotenuse}}{\text{adjacent}}$$

$$\overline{EM} \sec 87° = \overline{ES} \qquad \text{multiply by } \overline{EM}$$

$$19.1\,\overline{EM} \approx \overline{ES} \qquad \sec 87° \approx 19.1$$

Using Aristarchus' estimate of 87° for $\angle E$, the distance from the Earth to the Sun would be about 19 times the distance from the Earth to the Moon. While his reasoning was sound, the actual distance from the Earth to the Sun is about *387 times* the distance from the Earth to the Moon. This huge difference can partially be attributed to a lack of precise measurements, but the principal reason is the *behavior of the secant function* as its input values approach 90°. By entering the secant function as $Y_1 = 1/\cos(X)$ on the ｜Y=｜ screen and setting up a table using ｜2nd｜ ｜WINDOW｜ (**TBLEST**) as shown in Figure 2.23, we obtain the table shown in Figure 2.24. Knowing the value for $Y_1$ should be about 387 for this application, we infer that the measure of $\angle E$ must be somewhere between 89.5° and 90°. We improve this estimate by resetting the table to start at 89.5, with $\Delta$Tbl = 0.05. Scrolling downward, we identify 89.85° as a close estimate for $\angle E$, since $Y_1 \approx 382$ (see Figure 2.25). With accurate estimates of this angle, we can closely approximate the average distance from the Sun to the Earth, which is now known to be 92,960,000 mi (*Source:* www.nasa.gov/worldbook/sun_worldbook.html).

**Figure 2.23**

**Figure 2.24**

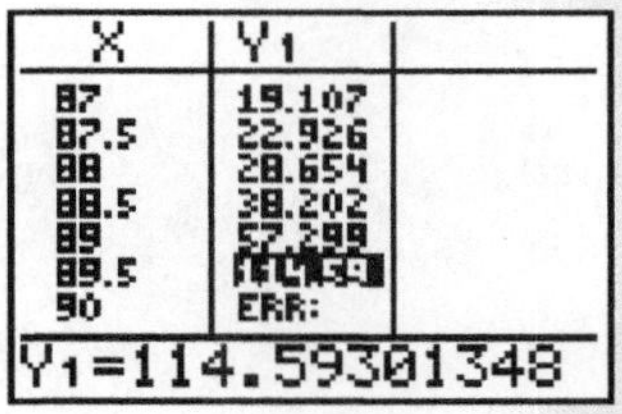

**Figure 2.25**

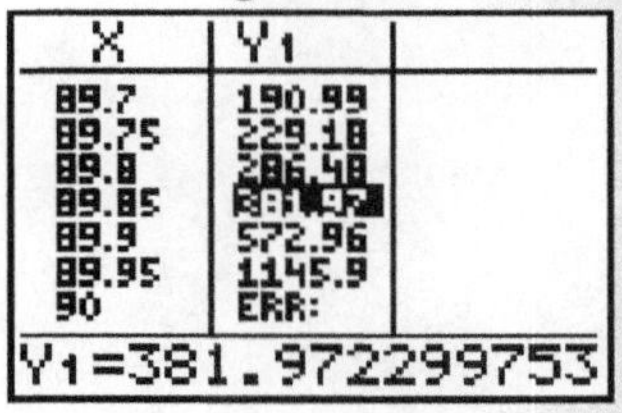

**Exercise 1:** Using 240,000 mi as the average distance from the Earth to the Moon, what would have been Aristarchus' original estimate of the Sun's distance from the Earth? Round your answer to the nearest thousand miles.

**Exercise 2:** Using 240,000 mi as the average distance from the Earth to the Moon and 89.85° as an improved estimate of $\angle E$, estimate the Sun's distance from the Earth. Round your answer to the nearest thousand miles.

**Exercise 3:** Use the table feature of your graphing calculator as shown earlier to find an estimate of $\angle E$, correct to the nearest thousandth.

**Exercise 4:** Using 240,000 mi as the average distance from the Earth to the Moon and your result from Exercise 3, estimate the Sun's distance from the Earth. Round your answer to the nearest thousand miles.

## Standard Angles, Reference Angles, and the Trig Functions

A review of the main ideas discussed in this chapter indicates there are four of what might be called "core skills." These are skills that (a) play a fundamental part in the acquisition of concepts, (b) hold the overall structure together as we move from concept to concept, and (c) are ones we return to again and again throughout our study. The first of these is *(1) knowing the standard angles and standard values.* These values are "standard" because no estimation, interpolation, or special methods are required to name their value, and each can be expressed as a single factor. This gives them a great advantage in that further conceptual development can take place without the main points being obscured by large expressions or decimal approximations. Knowing the value of the trig functions for each standard angle will serve you very well throughout this study. *Know* the chart on page 48 and the ideas that led to it.

**Figure 2.26**

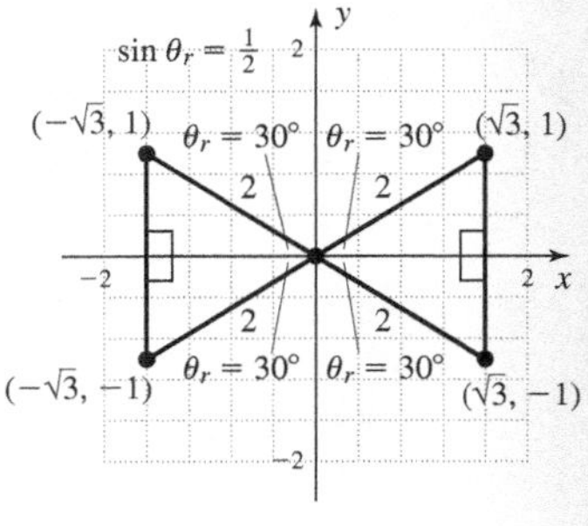

The standard angles/values brought us to the trigonometry of any angle, forming a strong bridge to the second core skill: *(2) using reference angles to determine the value of the trig functions in each quadrant.* For review, a 30-60-90 triangle will always have sides that are in the proportion $1x:\sqrt{3}x:2x$, regardless of its size. This means for any angle $\theta$, where $\theta_r = 30°$, $\sin\theta = \frac{1}{2}$ or $\sin\theta = -\frac{1}{2}$ since the *ratio is fixed* but the sign *depends on the quadrant of $\theta$*: $\sin 30° = \frac{1}{2}$ [QI], $\sin 150° = \frac{1}{2}$ [QII], $\sin 210° = -\frac{1}{2}$ [QIII], $\sin 330° = -\frac{1}{2}$ [QII], and so on (see Figure 2.26).

In turn, the reference angles led us to a third core skill, helping us realize that if $\theta$ was not a quadrantal angle, *(3) equations like* $\cos(\theta) = -\dfrac{\sqrt{3}}{2}$ *must have two solutions in* $[0, 360°)$. From the standard angles and standard values we learn to recognize that for $\cos \theta = -\dfrac{\sqrt{3}}{2}$, $\theta_r = 30°$, which will occur as a reference angle in the two quadrants where cosine is negative, QII and QIII. The solutions in $[0, 360°)$ are $\theta = 150°$ and $\theta = 210°$ (see Figure 2.27).

**Figure 2.27**

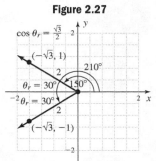

Of necessity, this brings us to the fourth core skill, *(4) effective use of a calculator.* The standard angles are a wonderful vehicle for introducing the basic ideas of trigonometry, and actually occur quite frequently in real-world applications. But by far, most of the values we encounter will be nonstandard values where $\theta_r$ must be found using a calculator. However, once $\theta_r$ is found, the reason and reckoning inherent in these ideas can be directly applied.

The *Summary and Concept Review Exercises*, as well as the *Practice Test* offer ample opportunities to refine these skills, so that they will serve you well in future chapters as we continue our attempts to explain and understand the world around us in mathematical terms.

**Exercise 1:** Fill in the table from memory.

| $\theta$ | 0 | 30° | 45° | 60° | 90° | 120° | 135° | 150° | 180° | 210° | 225° |
|---|---|---|---|---|---|---|---|---|---|---|---|
| $\sin \theta$ | | | | | | | | | | | |
| $\cos \theta$ | | | | | | | | | | | |
| $\tan \theta$ | | | | | | | | | | | |

**Exercise 2:** Solve each equation in $[0, 360°)$ without the use of a calculator.

**a.** $2 \sin \theta + \sqrt{3} = 0$          **b.** $-3\sqrt{2} \cos \theta + 4 = 1$

**c.** $-\sqrt{3} \tan \theta + 2 = 1$          **d.** $\sqrt{2} \sec \theta + 1 = 3$

**Exercise 3:** Solve each equation in $[0, 360°)$ using a calculator and rounding answers to one decimal place.

**a.** $\sqrt{6} \sin \theta - 2 = 1$          **b.** $-3\sqrt{2} \cos \theta + \sqrt{2} = 0$

**c.** $3 \tan \theta + \dfrac{1}{2} = -\dfrac{1}{4}$          **d.** $2 \sec \theta = -5$

**1.** Given that $\tan \theta = \dfrac{80}{39}$, draw a right triangle that corresponds to this ratio, then use the Pythagorean theorem to find the length of the missing side. Finally, find the two acute angles.

**2.** During a storm, a tall tree snapped, as shown in the diagram. Find the tree's original height. Round to tenths of a meter.

**Exercise 2**

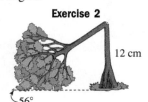

12 cm

56°

**3.** Find the measure of angle $\alpha$ for the triangle shown and convert it to decimal degrees.

**Exercise 3**

$\alpha$

29° 24' 54"

**4.** For $\theta = 729.5°$, find the value of $\sin \theta$, $\cos \theta$, and $\tan \theta$ using reference angles and a calculator. Round to four decimal places.

**5.** The world's tallest indoor waterfall is in Detroit, Michigan, in the lobby of the International Center Building. Standing 66 ft from the base of the falls, the angle of elevation is 60°. How tall is the waterfall?

6. It's a warm, lazy Saturday and Hank is watching a county maintenance crew mow the park across the street. He notices the mower takes 29 sec to pass through 77° of rotation from one end of the park to the other. If the corner of the park is 60 ft directly across the street from his house, (a) how wide is the park? (b) How fast (in mph) does the mower travel as it cuts the grass?

7. Find $f(\theta)$ for all six trig functions, given the point $P(-9, 40)$ is a point on the terminal side of the angle. Then find the angle $\theta$ in degrees, rounded to tenths.

8. State true or false and explain your response: $(\sin t)(\sec t) = 1$.

9. Complete the following statement: The cofunction of sine is cosine because . . . .

10. Find the value of all six trig functions given $\tan t = -\dfrac{68}{51}$ and $\sin t > 0$.

11. Find two positive and two negative angles that are coterminal with $-100°$.

12. Find the lengths of all unknown sides in the triangles shown.

**Exercise 12**

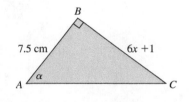 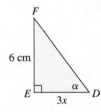

13. Without using a calculator, find the angle $\theta$ in $[0°, 360°)$ such that $\tan \theta$ is undefined and $\cos(\theta - 90°) = -1$.

14. Verify $\tan \theta(\cos \theta + \csc \theta) = \sin \theta + \sec \theta$.

15. Given $a = b = 12.1$ in., find $\sin \beta$.

**Exercise 15**

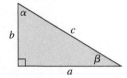

Solve the right triangles by completing each table. Round sides to the nearest hundredth of a unit and angles to the nearest tenth of a degree.

**Exercises 16 and 17**

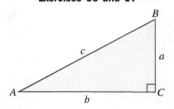

16.

| Angles | Sides |
|--------|-------|
|        |       |
| B = 23° | b = 3 ft |
| C = 90° |       |

17.

| Angles | Sides |
|--------|-------|
|        | a = 11 m |
|        | b = 10 m |
| C = 90° |       |

18. John and Georgeline are buying their first home and need a plot survey for the mortgage. The surveyor stakes out the rectangular property and notes the front border runs due east/west. From the western front corner, she finds the eastern back corner is on a bearing of N 11°18′36″ E. If the property measures 150 ft from the front to the back, how wide is it?

19. Find the exact values of $\sin(-390°)$, $\cos(-390°)$, and $\tan(-390°)$ using reference angles.

20. Convert 64.5575° to DMS notation.

21. Solve triangle $ABC$ given $a = 1.2$ mm, $b = 2.9$ mm, and $c = 1.5$ mm if possible. If not, explain why.

22. Write $\csc \theta$ entirely in terms of $\cos \theta$.

23. Using the right triangle shown, find the values of the six trig functions of $\beta$ given $a = 7$ m and $b = \sqrt{15}$ m.

**Exercise 23**

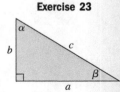

24. Find all angles that satisfy $\cos \theta = -0.29$. Use a calculator and round to tenths.

25. The longer leg of a 30-60-90 triangle measures 5 in. Find the lengths of the other two sides of the triangle.

# Radian Measure and Dynamic Trigonometry

# Radian Measure and Dynamic Trigonometry

## CHAPTER CONNECTIONS

The great green circles produced by the process of pivot irrigation often arouse the curiosity of airline passengers flying overhead. Here, the tools of trigonometry can be used to investigate the sprinkler's angular velocity (the number of revolutions per hour), its linear velocity (how fast each sprinkler along the radial arm is moving), as well as the size of the area being irrigated. In calculations like these, the measure of an angle is often given in a new unit called radians, as this contributes to the simplification of the formulas involved, and many other formulas and procedures. The use of radians also enables a clearer view of the trigonometric functions as functions of a real number (rather than merely functions of an angle), thus extending their influence on both pure and applied mathematics.

▶ This application appears as
  Exercise 60 in Section 3.2

# 3.1 | Angle Measure in Radians

## Learning Objectives

*In Section 3.1 you will learn how to:*

☐ **A.** Use radians for angle measure

☐ **B.** Find the radian measure of the standard angles

☐ **C.** Convert between degrees and radians for nonstandard angles

While angle measure based on a 360° circle has been accepted for centuries, its basic construct is no better than other measures proposed and used over time (stadia, gons, cirs, points, mils, gradients, and so on). In the 1870s, mathematicians Thomas Muir and James Thomson (the brother of Lord Kelvin) advocated the need for a new unit that stated the measure of an angle in terms of a circle's inherent characteristics, rather than arbitrarily declared numbers like 360 (degrees), 400 (gradients), or 1000 (mils).

## A. The Radian Measure of an Angle

To help develop this new unit of angle measure, we use a **central circle,** which is a circle in the *xy*-plane with its center at the origin. A **central angle** is an angle whose vertex is at the center of the circle. For central angle $\theta$ intersecting the circle at points *B* and *C*, we say circular arc *BC*, denoted $\overset{\frown}{BC}$, **subtends** $\angle BAC$, as shown in Figure 3.1. The letter *s* is commonly used to represent arc length, and if we define **1 radian** (abbreviated *rad*) to be the measure of an angle subtended by an arc equal in length to the radius, then $\theta = 1$ rad when $s = r$ (see Figure 3.2). We can then find the radian measure of any central angle by dividing the length of the subtended arc by *r:*

$$\frac{s}{r} = \theta \text{ radians.}$$

**Figure 3.1**

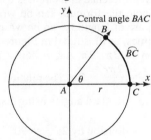

Central angle *BAC*

**Figure 3.2**

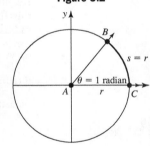

### Radians

If central angle $\theta$ is subtended by an arc that is equal in length to the radius, then
$$\theta = 1 \text{ } radian.$$

### Radian Measure of an Angle

If $\theta$ is a central angle in a circle of radius *r*, and is subtended by an arc of length *s*, then the measure of $\theta$ in radians is

$$\theta = \frac{s}{r}.$$

**EXAMPLE 1** ▶ **Finding the Radian Measure of an Angle**

If the circle shown in the figure has radius $r = 8$ cm, what is the radian measure of angle $\theta$?

Solution ▶ Using the formula $\theta = \dfrac{s}{r}$ with $s = 18$ and $r = 8$ gives

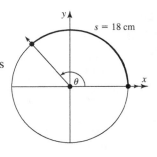

$$\theta = \frac{18}{8} \qquad \text{substitute 18 for } s \text{ and 8 for } r$$

$$= \frac{9}{4} \qquad \text{result}$$

The angle $\theta$ measures $\dfrac{9}{4}$, or 2.25 rad.

**Now try Exercises 7 through 18** ▶

☑ **A.** You've just learned how to find the radian measure of an angle

The angle in Example 1 was formed by a counter-clockwise rotation. Recall that angles formed by a clockwise rotation are considered negative angles. The formula for radian measure still applies, but with $\theta < 0$. **See Exercises 19 through 24.**

## B. Radian Measure of the Standard Angles

Recall the circumference of a circle is $C = 2\pi r$. While you may not have considered this before, note the formula can be written as $C = 2\pi \cdot r$, which implies that the radius, or an arc of length $r$, can be wrapped around the circumference of the circle $2\pi \approx 6.28$ times, as illustrated in Figure 3.3. This shows the radian measure of a full $360°$ rotation is $2\pi$: $2\pi\ rad = 360°$. This can be verified using the relation $\theta$ radians $= \dfrac{s}{r} = \dfrac{2\pi r}{r} = 2\pi$. The relation $2\pi$ rad $= 360°$ enables us to state the radian measures of the standard angles using a simple division. For $\pi$ rad $= 180°$ we have

division by 2: $\dfrac{\pi}{2} = 90°$         division by 3: $\dfrac{\pi}{3} = 60°$

division by 4: $\dfrac{\pi}{4} = 45°$         division by 6: $\dfrac{\pi}{6} = 30°$.

See Figure 3.4. The radian measures of these standard angles play a major role in this chapter, and you are encouraged to become very familiar with them. Additional conversions can quickly be found using multiples of these four.

**WORTHY OF NOTE**

We will often use the convention that unless degree measure is explicitly implied or noted with the ° symbol, radian measure is being used. In other words,

$\theta = \dfrac{\pi}{2}, \theta = 2$, and $\theta = 32.76$

all indicate angles measured in radians.

**Figure 3.3**

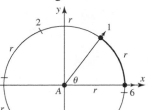

**Figure 3.4**

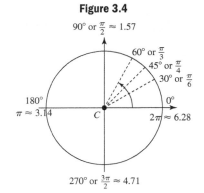

**EXAMPLE 2** ▶  **Finding the Radian Measure of Standard Angles**

Use multiples of a standard angle to find the exact radian measure of the angles given.

a. $120°$          b. $-225°$          c. $270°$

Solution ▶   a. Since $120°$ is a multiple of both $30°$ and $60°$, we can use either angle. If we use $30° = \dfrac{\pi}{6}$, we have

$$120° = 4(30°) \qquad \text{\footnotesize 120° is a multiple of 30°}$$
$$= 4\left(\frac{\pi}{6}\right) \qquad \text{\footnotesize substitute 30° with } \tfrac{\pi}{6} \text{ rad}$$
$$= \frac{2\pi}{3} \qquad \text{\footnotesize simplify}$$

b.  $-225° = -5(45°)$              c.  $270° = 3(90°)$
$$= -5\left(\frac{\pi}{4}\right) \qquad\qquad = 3\left(\frac{\pi}{2}\right)$$
$$= -\frac{5\pi}{4} \qquad\qquad\quad = \frac{3\pi}{2}$$

Now try Exercises 29 through 36 ▶

> **WORTHY OF NOTE**
>
> Since a full rotation is $2\pi$ radians, angles $\theta$ and $\theta + 2\pi k$ are coterminal for any integer $k$ when $\theta$ is measured in radians.
> **See Exercises 25 through 28.**

☑ **B.** You've just learned how to find the radian measure of the standard angles

Note in Example 2(c), we could have treated $270°$ as a multiple of $30°$ or $45°$, and obtained the same answer after simplification.

## C. Converting between Degrees and Radians

The relationship $\pi = 180°$ also gives the factors needed for converting from degrees to radians or from radians to degrees, even if $\theta$ is a nonstandard angle. Dividing by $\pi$ we have $1 = \dfrac{180°}{\pi}$, while division by $180°$ shows $1 = \dfrac{\pi}{180°}$. Multiplying a given angle by the appropriate conversion factor gives the equivalent measure.

| Degrees/Radians Conversion Factors | |
|---|---|
| To convert from radians to degrees: | To convert from degrees to radians: |
| multiply by $\dfrac{180°}{\pi}$. | multiply by $\dfrac{\pi}{180°}$. |

**EXAMPLE 3** ▶  **Converting from Degrees to Radians**

Convert each angle from degrees to radians. Write each result in exact form and in approximate form, rounded to thousandths.

a. $-75°$          b. $250°12'$

Solution ▶ **a.** For degrees to radians, use the conversion factor $\dfrac{\pi}{180°}$.

$$-75° = -75° \cdot \frac{\pi}{180°} \qquad \text{apply conversion factor}$$

$$= -\frac{75}{180}\pi \qquad \text{rewrite expression}$$

$$= -\frac{5\pi}{12} \qquad \text{exact form}$$

$$\approx -1.309 \qquad \text{approximate form (to thousandths)}$$

**b.** Begin by converting from DMS notation to decimal degrees, then use the conversion factor $\dfrac{\pi}{180°}$.

$$250°12' = 250.2° \qquad \left(250 + \frac{12}{60}\right)° = 250.2°$$

$$= 250.2°\left(\frac{\pi}{180°}\right) \qquad \text{apply conversion factor}$$

$$= \frac{250.2}{180}\pi \qquad \text{rewrite expression}$$

$$= 1.39\pi \qquad \text{exact form}$$

$$\approx 4.367 \qquad \text{approximate form (to thousandths)}$$

**Now try Exercises 37 through 48** ▶

**EXAMPLE 4** ▶ **Converting from Radians to Degrees**

Convert each angle from radians to degrees. Write each result in exact form and in approximate form, rounded to hundredths as needed.

**a.** $\dfrac{\pi}{24}$      **b.** $-5$

Solution ▶ **a.** For radians to degrees, use the conversion factor $\dfrac{180°}{\pi}$.

$$\frac{\pi}{24} = \frac{\pi}{24}\left(\frac{180°}{\pi}\right) \qquad \text{apply conversion factor}$$

$$= \frac{\pi}{\pi}\left(\frac{180°}{24}\right) \qquad \text{rewrite expression}$$

$$= 7.5° \qquad \text{exact form, } \frac{\pi}{\pi} = 1, \frac{180}{24} = 7.5$$

**b.**
$$-5 = -5\left(\frac{180°}{\pi}\right) \qquad \text{apply conversion factor}$$

$$= -\frac{5}{1}\left(\frac{180°}{\pi}\right) \qquad \text{rewrite expression}$$

$$= -\frac{900°}{\pi} \qquad \text{exact form}$$

$$\approx -286.48° \qquad \text{approximate form (to hundredths)}$$

☑ **C.** You've just learned how to convert between degrees and radians for nonstandard angles

**Now try Exercises 49 through 64** ▶

As in Example 3, approximating the radian measure of an angle lends insight to its size. Figure 3.3 on page 91 is a useful tool for determining the quadrant of the terminal side of an angle measured in radians and shows that the angle in Example 3(a) terminates in QIV, while the angle in 3(b) terminates in QIII. **See Exercises 65 through 72.**

## TECHNOLOGY HIGHLIGHT

### Decimal Degree and Radian Conversions

Most graphing calculators are programmed to compute conversions involving angle measure. On the TI-84 Plus, this is accomplished using the "°" feature for degree to radian conversions *while in radian* MODE, and the "r" feature for radian to degree conversions *while in degree* MODE. Both are found on the **ANGLE** submenu located at 2nd APPS, as is the **4:▶DMS** feature used for conversion to the degrees, minutes, seconds format (see Figure 3.5). We'll illustrate by converting both standard and nonstandard angles. To convert 180°, 72°, and −45° to radians, be sure you are in radian MODE then enter 180 2nd APPS ENTER (the **1:°** feature is the default), then ENTER once again to execute the operation. The screen shows a value of 3.141592654, which we expected since 180° = $\pi$. For 72° and −45°, we simply recall 180° ( 2nd ENTER ) and overwrite the desired value (see Figure 3.6). For radian-to-degree conversions, be sure you are in degree MODE and complete the conversions in a similar manner, using 2nd APPS **3:r** instead of **1:°**.

**Figure 3.5**

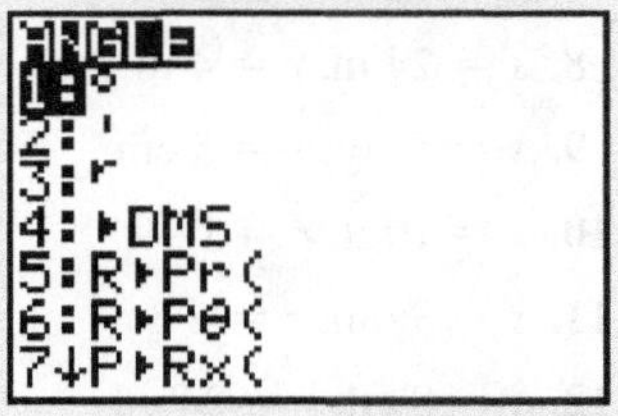

```
ANGLE
1:°
2:'
3:r
4:▶DMS
5:R▶Pr(
6:R▶Pθ(
7↓P▶Rx(
```

**Figure 3.6**

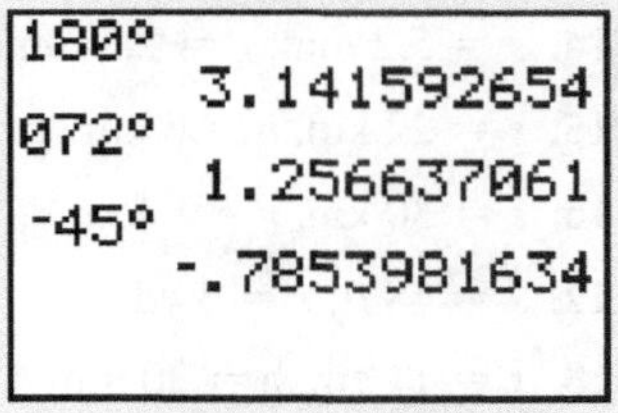

```
180°
        3.141592654
072°
        1.256637061
-45°
        -.7853981634
```

**Exercise 1:** Use your graphing calculator to convert the radian measures $\frac{\pi}{2}$, $\pi$, $\frac{25\pi}{12}$, and 2.37 to degrees, then verify each using standard angles or a conversion factor.

**Exercise 2:** Experiment with the 2nd APPS **3:▶DMS** feature, and use it to convert 108.716° to the DMS format. Verify the result manually.

## 3.1 EXERCISES

▶ CONCEPTS AND VOCABULARY

**Fill in each blank with the appropriate word or phrase. Carefully reread the section if needed.**

1. A _____ circle of radius _____ will have x-intercepts of (−5, 0) and (5, 0). On this circle, an arc of length $5\pi$ subtends an angle of __ radians.

2. The expression "theta equals two degrees" is written _____ using the "°" notation. The expression, "theta equals two radians" is simply written _____.

3. For the radian measure of a standard angle in simplified form, the numerator will always be a multiple of __. All such nonquadrantal angles will have a denominator of _____, _____, or _____, while the quadrantal angles will have a denominator of _____ or _____.

4. If $\theta$ is not a special angle, multiply by _____ to convert radians to degrees. To convert degrees to radians, multiply by _____.

5. Discuss/Explain how the radian measure of the standard angles (30°, 45°, and 60°) and their multiples can be found without using a conversion factor.

6. Discuss/Explain the difference between 1° and 1 radian. Exactly what is a radian? Without any conversions, explain why an angle of 4 rad terminates in QIII.

▶ **DEVELOPING YOUR SKILLS**

**Use the diagram shown and information given to find the radian measure of each angle $\alpha$.**

7. $s = 12$ in., $r = 3$ in.

8. $s = 24$ m, $r = 4$ m

9. $s = 5$ cm, $r = 5$ cm

10. $s = 10$ ft, $r = 10$ ft

11. $s = 3$ dm, $r = 6$ dm

12. $s = 8$ yd, $r = 24$ yd

13. $s = 4.2$ mi, $r = 1.4$ mi

14. $s = 5.2$ mm, $r = 2.6$ mm

15. $s = 22$ km, $r = 6$ km

16. $s = 30$ km, $r = 8$ km

17. $s = 48$ ft, $r = 3$ yd

18. $s = 11$ cm, $r = 20$ mm

**Use the diagram shown and information given to find the radian measure of each angle $\beta$.**

19. $s = 21$ cm, $r = 7$ cm

20. $s = 25$ ft, $r = 5$ ft

21. $s = 6$ in., $r = 2.5$ in.

22. $s = 12.6$ m, $r = 7$ m

23. $s = 3\frac{2}{5}$ yd, $r = \frac{4}{5}$ yd

24. $s = 3\frac{2}{7}$ mm, $r = \frac{6}{7}$ mm

**Find two positive angles and two negative angles that are coterminal with the angle given. Answers may vary.**

25. $\theta = \dfrac{\pi}{6}$       26. $\theta = \dfrac{\pi}{4}$

27. $\theta = \dfrac{\pi}{3}$       28. $\theta = \dfrac{\pi}{2}$

**Convert the following degree measures to radians in exact form, without the use of a calculator.**

29. $\theta = 360°$       30. $\theta = 180°$

31. $\theta = 45°$        32. $\theta = 30°$

33. $\theta = 210°$       34. $\theta = 330°$

35. $\theta = -120°$      36. $\theta = -225°$

**Convert each degree measure to radians. Leave in exact form.**

37. $\theta = 40°$         38. $\theta = 230°$

39. $\theta = -305°$       40. $\theta = -35°$

41. $\theta = 100°24'$     42. $\theta = 200°48'$

**Convert each degree measure to radians. Round to the nearest ten-thousandth.**

43. $\theta = 27°$          44. $\theta = 52°$

45. $\theta = 227.9°$       46. $\theta = 154.4°$

47. $\theta = -52°35'$      48. $\theta = -191°23'$

**Convert each radian measure to degrees, without the use of a calculator.**

49. $\theta = \dfrac{\pi}{3}$        50. $\theta = \dfrac{\pi}{4}$

51. $\theta = \dfrac{\pi}{6}$        52. $\theta = \dfrac{\pi}{2}$

53. $\theta = \dfrac{2\pi}{3}$       54. $\theta = \dfrac{5\pi}{6}$

55. $\theta = 4\pi$                  56. $\theta = 6\pi$

**Convert each radian measure to degrees. Round to the nearest tenth.**

57. $\theta = \dfrac{11\pi}{12}$     58. $\theta = \dfrac{17\pi}{36}$

59. $\theta = 3.2541$                60. $\theta = 1.0257$

61. $\theta = 3$                     62. $\theta = 5$

63. $\theta = -2.5$                  64. $\theta = -3.7$

**If the following angles are drawn in standard position on the central circle shown, identify the point $a$–$f$ through which the terminal side passes.**

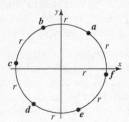

65. a. $\theta = 2$        66. a. $\theta = 4$

   b. $\theta = 5$            b. $\theta = 1$

   c. $\theta = 3$            c. $\theta = 6$

**Without using a calculator, identify the terminal side quadrant of the given angles in standard position.**

**67.** $\theta = 2.5$                    **68.** $\theta = 5.4$                    **69.** $\theta = 1.2$

**70.** $\theta = 3.9$                    **71.** $\theta = -1.9$                    **72.** $\theta = -4.3$

## ▶ WORKING WITH FORMULAS

**73. Torque applied by a wrench:** $\tau = rF \sin \theta$

A wrench used to free a stuck nut applies a torque $\tau$ (measured in foot-pounds) when a force $F$ (in pounds) is applied $r$ feet from the nut at an angle $\theta$ to the wrench. Find how much torque is being applied to a particularly stubborn nut if 54 lb of force is being applied 8 in. from the nut, at an angle of $\dfrac{\pi}{3}$ to the wrench. How much force should be applied at this angle and point if the nut will only release when the applied torque reaches 50 ft-lb?

**74. Horsepower for an electric winch:** $H = \dfrac{\pi\, rw\omega}{198{,}000}$

Ignoring the fact that the cable may wind over itself, an electric winch with drum of radius $r$ (in inches) turning at $\omega$ rpm is applying $H$ units of horsepower when it lifts a weight of $w$ pounds. How much horsepower is required of a winch to lift 100 lb if the drum has radius 8 in. and is turning at 90 rpm? If the maximum horsepower of the motor is 5 hp, what is the greatest weight this winch can lift?

## ▶ APPLICATIONS

**75. Automobile racing:** While preparing the annual Bonneville Speedway, the Utah State Highway Department marks out a 1.75-mi-radius circular track in the Bonneville Salt Flats. If a mechanical failure ends Andy's race after only 7 mi, through what central angle (in radians) did he travel?

**76. Planetary orbits:** The moon Triton orbits the planet Neptune in a near perfect circular path of radius 354,759 km. When the moon has traveled 3,192,831 km, what central angle does its path subtend?

**77. Automobile racing:** An endurance race on the circular track at the Bonneville Speedway (see Exercise 75) consists of 45.5 laps. What is the radian measure of the central angle swept out by a car that completes the race?

**78. Planetary orbits:** Triton completes one full orbit of Neptune every 6 days (see Exercise 76). What is the radian measure of the central angle Triton makes in 15 days?

**79. Automobile testing:** A 300-ft-diameter circle painted on a smooth, flat piece of pavement is known as a skid pad. A small car gradually accelerates over 2000 ft before it begins to slip off the pad. To the nearest whole degree, what is the measure of the central angle swept out by the car?

**80. Amusement park rides:** The Tumble Bug travels on a 100-ft-diameter circular track. What central angle is subtended by the 70-ft-long train of six cars? Round to the nearest whole degree.

**81. The Pantheon:** The tomb of the artist Raphael is in one of the eight niches of the circular rotunda of this ancient building. Express in radians the central angle of 112.5° formed by the main entrance and the commemorative bust of this great painter.

**82. Submarine design:** The top-hatch of a research submarine is opened by rotating the hatch wheel 123.75° counterclockwise. Express this angle in radians.

Section 3.2 Arc Length, Velocity, and the Area of a Circular Sector

▶ EXTENDING THE CONCEPT

83. Determine the radian measure of both 1 minute and 1 second. Use your results to determine the radian measure of 67°33′18″. Check your results by first converting the angle to decimal form.

84. Triton completes one orbit of Neptune every six Earth days (see Exercise 78) in the opposite direction of the planet's 16-hr-long rotation. From the point of view of an astronaut on the surface of Neptune, find the central angle (in radians) Triton *appears* to sweep out in 24 hr.

▶ MAINTAINING YOUR SKILLS

85. (2.4) Find the exact value of sin 210°, cos 210°, and tan 210° using reference angles.

86. (1.4) Write sec $\theta$ in terms of csc $\theta$.

87. (2.2) Find the acute angle $A$ such that cos $A = 0.2525$. Round to the nearest tenth of a degree.

88. (1.3) Find cot $\theta$ given the terminal side of $\theta$ in standard position is coincident with $y = 2.1x, x < 0$.

89. (2.4) Find the reference angle of the following:
    a. 512°          b. −762°

90. (1.2) For triangle $ABC$, find the measures of all three angles if $A = (x + 2)°$, $B = (7x)°$, and $C = (4x − 2)°$.

## 3.2 | Arc Length, Velocity, and the Area of a Circular Sector

**Learning Objectives**

*In Section 3.2 you will learn how to:*

☐ **A.** Use radians to compute the length of a subtended arc

☐ **B.** Solve applications involving angular velocity and linear velocity

☐ **C.** Calculate the area of a circular sector

Prior to the widespread use of radians, the length of an arc was found using a proportional part of 360°: $\dfrac{\text{amount of rotation}}{360°} = \dfrac{\text{length of arc}}{2\pi r}$, or $\dfrac{\theta}{360°} = \dfrac{s}{2\pi r}$. Solving for $s$ yields $s = \left(\dfrac{\theta}{360°}\right)2\pi r$, or $s = \left(\dfrac{2\pi}{360°}\right)r\theta$ after regrouping. While this formula is certainly usable, it's very unwieldy and has limited value in many practical applications. With $\theta$ in radians we know $2\pi = 360°$, giving $\dfrac{2\pi}{360°} = 1$ by division. After substituting 1 for $\dfrac{2\pi}{360°}$, the formula quickly simplifies to $s = r\theta$, a much more elegant result but once again, *θ must be expressed in radians.*

### A. The Length of a Subtended Arc

Recall that in a circle of radius $r$, the radian measure of a central angle $\theta$ is $\dfrac{s}{r}$, where $s$ is the length of the subtended arc (see Figure 3.7). In practice, measuring the length of an arc is often a more difficult task than measuring the angle $\theta$. Note that by multiplying both sides of $\theta = \dfrac{s}{r}$ by $r$, we obtain a formula for the length of an arc: $s = r\theta$ provided $\theta$ is in radians.

**Figure 3.7**

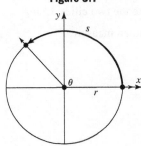

> **Arc Length**
>
> If $\theta$ is a central angle in a circle of radius $r$, then the length of the subtended arc $s$ is
> $$s = r\theta,$$
> *provided θ is expressed in radians.*

**EXAMPLE 1** ▶ **Using the Formula for Arc Length**

If the circle in Figure 3.7 has radius $r = 10$ cm, what is the length of the arc subtended by an angle of 3.5 rad?

Solution ▶ Using the formula $s = r\theta$ with $r = 10$ and $\theta = 3.5$ gives

$$s = 10(3.5) \quad \text{substitute 10 for } r \text{ and 3.5 for } \theta$$
$$= 35 \quad \text{result}$$

The subtended arc has a length of 35 cm.

**Now try Exercises 7 through 18** ▶

Note that if the angle is expressed in degrees, we first convert it to radians before applying the formula. One area where these conversions are necessary is applications involving longitude and latitude (see Figure 3.8). The **latitude** of a fixed point on the Earth's surface tells how many degrees north or south of the equator the point is, as measured from the center of the Earth. The **longitude** of a fixed point on the Earth's surface tells how many degrees east or west of the Prime Meridian (through Greenwich, England) the point is, as measured along the equator to the longitude line going through the point. For example, the city of New Orleans, Louisiana, is located at 30°N latitude, 90°W longitude (see Figure 3.8).

**Figure 3.8**

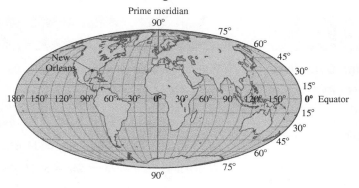

**EXAMPLE 2** ▶ **Applying the Arc Length Formula: Distances Between Cities**

The cities of Quito, Ecuador, and Macapá, Brazil, both lie very near the equator, at a latitude of 0°. However, Quito is at approximately 78° west longitude, while Macapá is at 51° west longitude (see Figure 3.8). Assuming the Earth has a radius of 3960 mi, how far apart are these cities?

Solution ▶ First we note that $(78 - 51)° = 27°$ of longitude separate the two cities. Using the conversion factor $1 = \dfrac{\pi}{180°}$ we find the equivalent radian measure

is $27°\left(\dfrac{\pi}{180°}\right) = \dfrac{3\pi}{20}$. The arc length formula gives

$$s = r\theta \quad \text{arc length formula; } \theta \text{ in radians}$$
$$= 3960\left(\frac{3\pi}{20}\right) \quad \text{substitute 3960 for } r \text{ and } \frac{3\pi}{20} \text{ for } \theta$$
$$= 594\pi \quad \text{result}$$

Quito and Macapá are approximately 1866 mi apart (see *Worthy of Note* in the margin).

**WORTHY OF NOTE**

Note that $r = 3960$ mi was used because Quito and Macapá *are both on the equator.* For other cities sharing the same longitude but not on the equator, the radius of the Earth *at that longitude* must be used. **See Exercise 61.**

**Now try Exercises 49 and 50** ▶

☑ **A.** You've just learned how to use radians to compute the length of a subtended arc

## B. Angular and Linear Velocity

The **angular velocity** of an object is defined as the *amount of rotation* per unit time. Here, we often use the symbol $\omega$ (omega) to represent the angular velocity, and $\theta$ to represent the angle through which the terminal side has rotated, measured in radians: $\omega = \dfrac{\theta}{t}$. For instance, a Ferris wheel turning at 10 revolutions per minute has an angular velocity of

$$\omega = \frac{10 \text{ revolutions}}{1 \text{ min}} \qquad \omega = \frac{\theta}{t}$$

$$= \frac{10(2\pi)}{1 \text{ min}} \qquad \text{substitute } 2\pi \text{ for 1 revolution}$$

$$= \frac{20\pi \text{ rad}}{1 \text{ min}} \qquad 10(2) = 20$$

> **WORTHY OF NOTE**
>
> Generally speaking, the *velocity* of an object is its change in position per unit time, and can be either positive or negative. The *rate* or *speed* of an object is the magnitude of the velocity, regardless of direction.

The **linear velocity** of an object is defined as a *change of position* or *distance traveled* per unit time. In the context of angular motion, we consider the distance traveled by a point on the circumference of the Ferris wheel, *which is equivalent to the length of the resulting arc s*. This relationship is expressed as $V = \dfrac{s}{t}$, a formula that can be written directly in terms of the angular velocity since $s = r\theta$: $V = \dfrac{r\theta}{t} = r\left(\dfrac{\theta}{t}\right) = r\omega$.

---

### Angular and Linear Velocity

Given a circle of radius $r$ with point $P$ on the circumference, and central angle $\theta$ in radians with $P$ on the terminal side. If $P$ moves along the circumference at a uniform rate:

**1.** The rate at which $\theta$ changes is called the *angular velocity* $\omega$,

$$\omega = \frac{\theta}{t}.$$

**2.** The rate at which the position of $P$ changes is called the *linear velocity V,*

$$V = \frac{r\theta}{t} \quad \Rightarrow \quad V = r\omega.$$

---

**EXAMPLE 3** ▶ **Using the Velocity Formulas**

A point $P$ is rotating around the circumference of a circle with radius $r = 2$ ft at a constant rate. If it takes 5 sec for the point to rotate through an angle of $510°$,

**a.** What is the angular velocity of $P$?

**b.** What is the linear velocity of $P$?

Solution ▶ **a.** Since our formulas require $\theta$ to be in radians, we first convert from degrees to radians.

$$510° = 510°\left(\frac{\pi}{180°}\right) \qquad \text{apply conversion factor}$$

$$= \frac{510°}{180°}\pi \qquad \text{rewrite expression}$$

$$= \frac{17\pi}{6} \qquad \text{result}$$

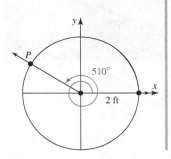

Applying the formula for angular velocity gives:

$$\omega = \frac{\theta}{t} \qquad \text{angular velocity formula}$$

$$= \frac{\left(\dfrac{17\pi}{6}\right)}{5} \qquad \text{substitute } \frac{17\pi}{6} \text{ for } \theta \text{ and 5 for } t$$

$$= \left(\frac{17\pi}{6}\right)\frac{1}{5} \qquad \text{invert and multiply}$$

$$= \frac{17}{30}\pi \qquad \text{result (exact form)}$$

$P$ is moving at an angular velocity of $\dfrac{17}{30}\pi \approx 1.78$ radians per second.

**b.** Using the exact result from part (a) and the formula for linear velocity, we have

$$V = r\omega \qquad \text{linear velocity formula}$$

$$= (2)\frac{17}{30}\pi \qquad \text{substitute 2 for } r \text{ and } \frac{17}{30}\pi \text{ for } \omega$$

$$= \frac{17}{15}\pi \qquad \text{result (exact form)}$$

$P$ is moving at a linear velocity of $\dfrac{17}{15}\pi \approx 3.56$ feet per second.

**Now try Exercises 19 through 34** ▶

Revolutions per unit time is a common unit of measure for angular velocity, as in revolutions per second (rps) for modern dental drills and revolutions per minute (rpm) for automotive engines. For this reason, many applications are stated using this unit. But in computations involving the formulas for angular and linear velocity, the units must be expressed in *radians* per unit time.

---

**EXAMPLE 4** ▶  **Using Angular Velocity to Determine Linear Velocity**

The wheels on a racing bicycle have a radius of 13 in. How fast is the cyclist traveling in miles per hour, if the wheels are turning at 300 rpm?

**Solution** ▶  Note that $\omega = \dfrac{300 \text{ rev}}{1 \text{ min}} = \dfrac{300(2\pi)}{1 \text{ min}} = \dfrac{600\pi}{1 \text{ min}}$.

Using the formula $V = r\omega$ gives a linear velocity of

$$V = (13 \text{ in.})\frac{600\pi}{1 \text{ min}} \approx \frac{24{,}504.4 \text{ in.}}{1 \text{ min}}.$$

To convert this to miles per hour we convert minutes to hours (1 hr = 60 min) and inches to miles (1 mi = 5280 × 12 in.):

$$\left(\frac{24{,}504.4 \text{ in.}}{1 \text{ min}}\right)\left(\frac{60 \text{ min}}{1 \text{ hr}}\right)\left(\frac{1 \text{ mi}}{63{,}360 \text{ in.}}\right) \approx 23.2 \text{ mph.}$$

The bicycle is traveling about 23.2 mph.

**Now try Exercises 51 through 54** ▶

To help understand the relationship between angular velocity and linear velocity, consider two large rollers with a radius of 1.6 ft, used to move an industrial conveyor belt. The rollers have a circumference of $C = 2\pi(1.6 \text{ ft}) \approx 10.05 \text{ ft}$, meaning that for each revolution of the rollers, an object on the belt will move 10.05 ft (from $P_1$ to $P_2$).

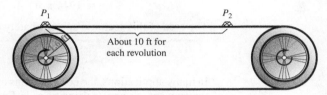

If the rollers are rotating at 20 rpm, an object on the belt (or a point on the circumference of a roller), will be moving at a rate of $20 \cdot 10.05 = 201$ ft/min (about 2.3 miles per hour). In other words,

$$\omega = \frac{20 \text{ revolutions}}{1 \text{ min}} \qquad \omega = \frac{\theta}{t}$$

$$= \frac{20 \cdot 2\pi}{1 \text{ min}} = \frac{40\pi}{1 \text{ min}} \qquad \text{substitute } 2\pi \text{ for 1 revolution}$$

$$V = r\omega \qquad \text{formula for velocity}$$

$$= (1.6 \text{ ft}) \frac{40\pi}{1 \text{ min}} \qquad \text{substitute 1.6 ft for } r, 40\pi \text{ for } \omega$$

$$\approx 201 \text{ ft per min} \qquad \text{result}$$

☑ **B.** You've just learned how to solve applications involving angular velocity and linear velocity

## C. The Area of a Circular Sector

Using a central angle $\theta$ measured in radians, we can also develop a formula for the **area of a circular sector** (a pie slice) using a proportion. Recall the total area of a circle is $\pi r^2$ and the radian measure of a 360° rotation is $2\pi$. The ratio of the area of a sector to the total area will be identical to the ratio of the subtended angle to one full rotation. See Figure 3.9. Using $\mathcal{A}$ to represent the area of the sector, we have $\dfrac{\mathcal{A}}{\pi r^2} = \dfrac{\theta}{2\pi}$ and solving for $\mathcal{A}$ gives $\mathcal{A} = \dfrac{1}{2}r^2\theta$.

**Figure 3.9**

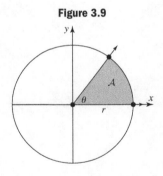

| Area of a Sector |
|---|
| If $\theta$ is a central angle in a circle of radius $r$, the area of the sector formed is $$\mathcal{A} = \frac{1}{2}r^2\theta,$$ *provided $\theta$ is expressed in radians.* |

**EXAMPLE 5** ▶ **Using the Formula for the Area of a Sector**

What is the area of the circular sector formed by a central angle of $\dfrac{3\pi}{4}$, if the radius of the circle is 72 ft? Round to tenths.

Solution ▶ Using the formula $\mathcal{A} = \dfrac{1}{2}r^2\theta$ we have

$$\mathcal{A} = \left(\dfrac{1}{2}\right)(72)^2\left(\dfrac{3\pi}{4}\right) \qquad \text{substitute 72 for } r, \dfrac{3\pi}{4} \text{ for } \theta$$

$$= 1944\pi \ \text{ft}^2 \qquad \text{result}$$

The area of this sector is approximately 6107.3 ft².

**Now try Exercises 35 through 46 ▶**

In many applications, the computations of circular areas and sectors are combined with the concept of angular velocity, as in Example 6.

**EXAMPLE 6 ▶ Finding the Area of a Circular Sector**

The second hand of a wristwatch measures 12 mm from the central axis to its tip. Find the area of the watch face the second hand passes over in a 20-sec time period.

Solution ▶ To begin, we find the angle the second hand passes through in 20 sec. Since the second hand moves one full revolution ($2\pi$) in 60 sec, its angular velocity is

$$\omega = \dfrac{\theta}{t} \qquad \text{angular velocity formula}$$

$$= \dfrac{2\pi}{60} \qquad \text{substitute } 2\pi \text{ for } \theta \text{ and 60 for } t$$

$$= \dfrac{\pi}{30} \qquad \text{simplify}$$

Multiplying both sides of the angular velocity formula $\omega = \dfrac{\theta}{t}$ by $t$ yields a formula for the angle: $\theta = \omega t$. Using this formula and the value of $\omega$, we can find the angle the second hand passes through in 20 sec.

$$\theta = \omega t \qquad \text{angle formula}$$

$$= \dfrac{\pi}{30}(20) \qquad \text{substitute } \dfrac{\pi}{30} \text{ for } \omega \text{ and 20 for } t$$

$$= \dfrac{20}{30}\pi \qquad \text{rewrite expression}$$

$$= \dfrac{2}{3}\pi \qquad \text{result}$$

With $\theta = \dfrac{2}{3}\pi$ radians, we now compute the area as before.

$$\mathcal{A} = \dfrac{1}{2}r^2\theta \qquad \text{area of a sector formula}$$

$$= \dfrac{1}{2}(12)^2\left(\dfrac{2}{3}\pi\right) \qquad \text{substitute 12 for } r \text{ and } \dfrac{2}{3}\pi \text{ for } \theta$$

$$= \dfrac{288}{6}\pi \qquad \text{multiply}$$

$$= 48\pi \ \text{mm}^2 \qquad \text{result (exact form)}$$

☑ **C. You've just learned how to calculate the area of a circular sector**

The second hand of the watch passes over an area of $48\pi \approx 150.8$ mm² in 20 sec.

**Now try Exercises 55 and 56 ▶**

## 3.2 EXERCISES

### ▶ CONCEPTS AND VOCABULARY

**Fill in each blank with the appropriate word or phrase. Carefully reread the section if needed.**

1. For any fixed point on the Earth's surface, _____ gives its location as the number of degrees north or south of the _____, while _____ gives the number of degrees east or west of the _____.

2. The formula for arc length is _____. The formula for the area of a sector is $\mathcal{A} =$ _____. For both formulas, $\theta$ must be in _____.

3. The formula for angular velocity is _____. The formula for the linear velocity of a point $P$ on the circumference of a circle moving with an angular velocity $\omega$ is _____, as long as $\omega$ is in _____ per unit time.

4. The angle $\theta$ can be found by _____ both sides of the formula for _____ velocity by __. If the formula for _____ velocity is multiplied by __, the arc length is the result.

5. Discuss/Explain the difference between angular velocity and linear velocity. In particular, why does one depend on the radius while the other does not? Include an example from your own experience.

6. Develop a formula for the area of a sector, if the angle is in degrees. Discuss what you discover.

### ▶ DEVELOPING YOUR SKILLS

**Use the formula for arc length to find the value of the unknown quantity: $s = r\theta$.**

7. $\theta = 3.5; r = 280$ m

8. $\theta = 2.3; r = 129$ cm

9. $s = 2007$ mi; $r = 2676$ mi

10. $s = 4435.2$ km; $r = 12{,}320$ km

11. $\theta = \dfrac{3\pi}{4}; s = 4146.9$ yd

12. $\theta = \dfrac{11\pi}{6}; s = 28.8$ nautical miles

13. $\theta = \dfrac{4\pi}{3}; r = 2$ mi

14. $\theta = \dfrac{3\pi}{2}; r = 424$ in.

15. $s = 252.35$ ft; $r = 980$ ft

16. $s = 942.3$ mm; $r = 1800$ mm

17. $\theta = 320°; s = 52.5$ km

18. $\theta = 220.5°; s = 7627$ m

**Point $P$ passes through a central angle $\theta$ in time $t$ as it travels around a circle. Find its exact angular velocity in radians per unit time.**

19. $\theta = 360°; t = 8$ sec    20. $\theta = 540°; t = 9$ yr

21. $\theta = 450°; t = 10$ hr    22. $\theta = 270°; t = 12$ min

23. $\theta = 210°; t = 7$ days    **24.** $\theta = 690°; t = 5$ sec

25. $\theta = 420°; t = 4$ min    **26.** $\theta = 300°; t = 5$ hr

**Point $P$ travels around a circle of radius $r$ as described. Find its linear velocity, rounded to the nearest hundredth as necessary.**

27. $\omega = 5$ rad/sec; $r = 8$ in.

28. $\omega = 12$ rad/min; $r = 15$ ft

29. $\omega = 14\pi$ rad/hr; $r = 3.2$ mi

30. $\omega = 2312\pi$ rad/hr; $r = 0.01$ km

31. $\theta = 168°; t = 0.28$ sec; $r = 3$ mm

32. $\theta = 282°; t = 4.1$ min; $r = 1.2$ yd

33. $\theta = 30; t = 6$ hr; $r = 1.2$ km

34. $\theta = 45; t = 3$ hr; $r = 2$ mi

**Use the formula for area of a circular sector to find the value of the unknown quantity: $\mathcal{A} = \frac{1}{2}r^2\theta$.**

35. $\theta = 5; r = 6.8$ km

36. $\theta = 3; r = 45$ mi

37. $\mathcal{A} = 1080$ mi$^2$; $r = 60$ mi

38. $\mathcal{A} = 437.5$ cm$^2$; $r = 12.5$ cm

39. $\theta = \dfrac{7\pi}{6}; \mathcal{A} = 16.5$ m$^2$

40. $\theta = \dfrac{19\pi}{12}; \mathcal{A} = 753$ cm$^2$

**Find the angle, radius, arc length, and/or area as needed, until all values are known.**

**41.**
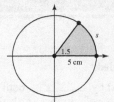

**42.**
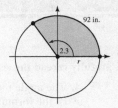

**43.**
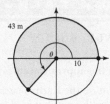

**44.**
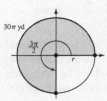

**45.**
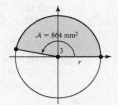

**46.**
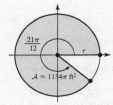

▶ **WORKING WITH FORMULAS**

**47. Haversine formula, first part:**

$$h = \sin^2\left(\frac{\alpha_2 - \alpha_1}{2}\right) + \cos \alpha_2 \cos \alpha_1 \sin^2\left(\frac{\beta_2 - \beta_1}{2}\right)$$

The great circles of a sphere have the same center and radius as the sphere itself. As a result, the shortest path between two points on a sphere will always be an arc of a great circle. In navigation, the haversine formula is often used to determine the shortest distance between two points on the surface of the Earth, and uses the value of $h$ determined by the formula shown. Here, the respective latitudes of each point are given by $\alpha_1$ and $\alpha_2$, and their longitudes by $\beta_1$ and $\beta_2$, with all angles in *radians*. Find the value of $h$ for the cities of Houston, Texas (30°N, 95°W), and San Francisco, California (38°N, 122°W).

**48. Haversine formula, second part:**
$$d = 2R \sin^{-1}(\sqrt{h})$$

The distance $d$ between two points on a great circle of radius $R$ is found using the formula shown, where $h$ is the value determined by the haversine formula in Exercise 47. Given the radius of the Earth is 3960 mi, use your calculator in radian mode and the result from Exercise 47 to find the distance between Houston and San Francisco. Check your result using any Internet distance calculator or GPS device (which will most likely be using this formula anyway).

▶ **APPLICATIONS**

**49. Arc length:** The city of Pittsburgh, Pennsylvania, is directly north of West Palm Beach, Florida. Pittsburg is at 40.3° north latitude, while West Palm Beach is at 26.4° north latitude. Assuming the Earth has a radius of 3960 mi, how far apart are these cities?

**50. Arc length:** Both Libreville, Gabon, and Jamame, Somalia, lie near the equator, but on opposite ends of the African continent. If Libreville is at 9.3° east longitude and Jamame is at 42.5° east longitude, how wide is the continent of Africa at the equator?

**51. Riding a round-a-bout:** At the park two blocks from our home, the kids' round-a-bout has a radius of 56 in. About the time the kids stop screaming, "Faster, Daddy, faster!" I estimate the round-a-bout is turning at $\frac{3}{4}$  revolutions per second. (a) What is the related angular velocity? (b) What is the linear velocity (in miles per hour) of Eli and Reno, who are "hanging on for dear life" at the rim of the round-a-bout?

**52. Carnival rides:** At carnivals and fairs, the *Gravity Drum* is a popular ride. People stand along the wall of a circular drum with radius 12 ft, which begins spinning very fast, pinning them against the wall. The drum is then turned on its side by an armature, with the riders screaming and squealing with delight. As the drum is raised to a near-vertical position, it is spinning at a rate of 35 rpm. (a) What is the angular velocity in radians? (b) What is the linear velocity (in miles per hour) of a person on this ride?

**53. Speed of a winch:** A winch is being used to lift a turbine off the ground so that a tractor-

trailer can back under it and load it up for transport. The winch drum has a radius of 3 in. and is turning at 20 rpm. Find (a) the angular velocity of the drum in radians, (b) the linear velocity of the turbine in feet per second as it is being raised, and (c) how long it will take to get the load to the desired height of 6 ft (ignore the fact that the cable may wind over itself on the drum).

**54. Speed of a current:** An instrument called a flowmeter is used to measure the speed of flowing water, like that in a river or stream. A cruder method involves placing a paddle wheel in the current, and using the wheel's radius and angular velocity to calculate the speed of water flow. If the paddle wheel has a radius of 5.6 ft and is turning at 30 rpm, find (a) the angular velocity of the wheel in radians and (b) the linear velocity of the water current in miles per hour.

**55. Area of a sector:** A water sprinkler is set to shoot a stream of water a distance of 12 m and rotate through an angle of 40°. (a) What is the area of the lawn it waters? (b) For $r = 12$ m, what angle is required to water twice as much area? (c) For

$\theta = 40°$, what range for the water stream is required to water twice as much area?

**56. Area of a sector:** A motion detector can detect movement up to 25 m away through an angle of 75°. (a) What area can the motion detector monitor? (b) For $r = 25$ m, what angle is required to monitor 50% more area? (c) For $\theta = 75°$, what range is required for the detector to monitor 50% more area?

**57. Angular and linear velocity:** The planet Jupiter's largest moon, Ganymede, rotates around the planet at a distance of about 656,000 mi, in an orbit that is perfectly circular. If the moon completes one rotation about Jupiter in 7.15 days, (a) find the angle $\theta$ that the moon moves through in 1 day, in both degrees and radians, (b) find the angular velocity of the moon in radians per hour, and (c) find the moon's linear velocity in miles per second as it orbits Jupiter.

**58. Angular and linear velocity:** The planet Neptune has an orbit that is nearly circular. It orbits the Sun at a distance of 4497 million km and completes one revolution every 165 yr. (a) Find the angle $\theta$ that the planet moves through in 1 yr in both degrees and radians and (b) find the linear velocity (km/hr) as it orbits the Sun.

**59. Center-pivot irrigation:** A standard ¼-mi irrigation system has a radius of 400 m and rotates once every 3 days. Find the linear velocity of the outside set of wheels to the nearest tenth of a meter per hour.

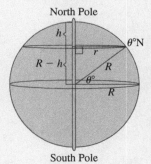

**60. Area of crop field:** If a center-pivot irrigation system with radius of 500 m rotates once every 100 hr, find the area of a crop field irrigated in 1 day. Round to the nearest square meter.

▶ **EXTENDING THE CONCEPT**

**61.** The radius of the Earth at the equator (0°N latitude) is approximately 3960 mi. Beijing, China, is located at 39.5°N latitude, 116°E longitude. Philadelphia, Pennsylvania, is located at the same latitude, but at 75°W longitude. (a) Use the diagram given and a cofunction relationship to find the radius $r$ of the Earth (parallel to the equator) at this latitude; (b) use the arc length formula to compute the *shortest distance* between these two cities along this latitude; and (c) if the supersonic Concorde flew a direct flight between Beijing and Philadelphia along this latitude, approximate the flight time assuming a cruising speed of 1250 mph. Note: The shortest distance is actually traversed by heading northward, using the arc of a "great circle" that goes through these two cities.

**62.** The Duvall family is out on a family bicycle ride around Creve Couer Lake. The adult bikes have a pedal sprocket with a 4-in. radius, wheel sprocket with 2-in. radius, and tires with a 13-in. radius. The kids' bikes have pedal sprockets with a 2.5-in. radius, wheel sprockets with 1.5-in. radius, and tires with a 9-in. radius. (a) If adults and kids both pedal at 50 rpm, how far ahead (in yards) are the adults after 2 min? (b) If adults pedal at 50 rpm, how fast do the kids have to pedal to keep up?

▶ **MAINTAINING YOUR SKILLS**

**63. (3.1)** Convert $\theta$ to degrees.

$$\theta = \frac{4\pi}{3}$$

**64. (3.1)** Convert to radians. Leave the result in terms of $\pi$.

$$\theta = 150°$$

**65. (1.1)** Find the exact length of the legs of a 45-45-90 triangle whose hypotenuse measures 10 in.

**66. (2.3)** A small boat is 1403 ft away from the base of one of the towers of the Golden Gate Bridge. The angle of elevation from its position to the top of the tower is 28°. To the nearest foot, how tall is the tower?

Given $a = \sqrt{30}$, $b = \sqrt{19}$, and $c = 7$ use the triangle shown to find the following.

**Exercises 67 and 68**

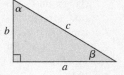

**67. (2.1)** $\csc \alpha$

**68. (2.1)** $\cot \beta$

1. The city of Las Vegas, Nevada, is located at 36°06′36″ north latitude, 115°04′48″ west longitude. (a) Convert both measures to decimal degrees. (b) If the radius of the Earth is 3960 mi, how far north of the equator is Las Vegas?

**Exercise 2**

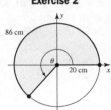

2. Find the angle subtended by the arc shown in the figure, then determine the area of the sector.

3. Find the exact radian measure of the following angles.
   **a.** 210°          **b.** −135°          **c.** 480°

4. Convert the following angles to degree measure. Round to the nearest hundredth if necessary.
   **a.** 4          **b.** −2.34          **c.** $\dfrac{3\pi}{2}$

5. Name one positive and one negative angle that are coterminal with $\dfrac{5\pi}{6}$. Answers may vary.

6. At a kid's carnival, the merry-go-round makes 10 revolutions per minute, with the outermost riders a distance of 15 ft from the center. (a) What is the angular velocity of these riders? (b) What is the linear velocity of these riders in miles per hour?

7. A windshield wiper has a radius of 15 in. and sweeps through an angle of 105° as it wipes the windshield. (a) To the nearest whole, what is the area of the windshield it wipes? (b) To the nearest whole, what angle (in degrees) would be needed for the wiper to wipe an area of $\mathcal{A} = 226$ in²?

8. Identify the quadrant of the terminal side of the given angles when in standard position.
   **a.** 2.9          **b.** −2
   **c.** −5.1          **d.** 6.2

9. In a 1941 naval battle, a faulty torpedo launched by the *HMS Trinidad* followed a circular path and struck its own ship. Given the velocity of the torpedo was 35 m/s during its 81-sec trip, find the radius of the circular path it took.

10. Before it closed in 1971, the Langhorne Speedway was better known as "The Big Left Turn" because of its 1-mi-long circular track. On April 24, 1960, a young A. J. Foyt captured the checkered flag in a 50-lap championship race at this speedway. Through what central angle had he driven during the first 19.1 mi of the 50-mi race?

# REINFORCING BASIC CONCEPTS

## More on Radians

To increase your understanding and appreciation of radian measure, consider the protractor shown in Figure 3.10, which is marked in both degrees and radians. Besides the obvious conversions it illustrates, $15° = \dfrac{\pi}{12}$, $30° = \dfrac{\pi}{6}$, and so on, we note that either system is adequate for measuring the amount of rotation for an angle in standard position. As drawn, this would be particularly true for multiples of $15° = \dfrac{\pi}{12}$. However, angles measured in radians have a twofold advantage over those measured in degrees.

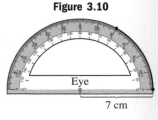

**Figure 3.10**

7 cm

First, the formula $s = r\theta$ ($\theta$ in radians) enables us to find the length of the related circular arc directly, without having to determine a proportional part of the $360°$ in a full circle. For the protractor shown, $r = 7$ cm and using an angle of $60° = \dfrac{\pi}{3}$, we have $s = 7\left(\dfrac{\pi}{3}\right) \approx 7.33$ cm. To verify calculations of this kind, take any semicircular protractor you have available and determine its radius $r$. On a sheet of paper, stand the protractor on the $0°$ end, mark where the $0°$ meets the paper and roll the protractor along a straight line to $60° = \dfrac{\pi}{3}$ and make another mark. Then draw a line segment between these two marks and measure its length—the result will be very close to $s = r\left(\dfrac{\pi}{3}\right)$. Repeat this process for other angles measured in radians.

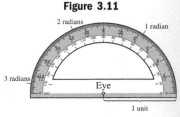

**Figure 3.11**

Second, if we also mark the protractor in *unit radians*, as shown in Figure 3.11 $\left(\text{note } \dfrac{\pi}{3} = 1.047 \text{ or just more than } 1 \text{ rad}\right)$, the measure of the arc will be numerically equal to the measure of the angle. If you repeat the previous experiment and "roll the protractor" to $t = 2$ rad, the resulting line segment will be exactly twice as long as the radius. Try it! This again shows that we can view $t$ as either an angle in radians *or* as the length of the related arc. More importantly, when this "unit protractor" is seen as the upper half of a unit circle (see Figure 3.12), we are also reminded of why we can view the trig functions as functions of a real number. Specifically, this is because the arc length $t$, $t \in \mathbb{R}$, acts as a "circular number line" that associates any real number $t$ with a unique point $(x, y)$ on the unit circle.

For $\cos t = x$ and $\sin t = y$, the trig functions are now indeed functions of any real number, since the real number line, circular or otherwise, is infinite in length and extends in both a positive and negative direction (note that this view of trigonometry *is independent of the right triangle view*). Using the grid provided in Figure 3.12, we estimate that an arc length of $t = 1.25$ units corresponds to the point $(0.32, 0.95)$ on the unit circle. After verifying $(0.32)^2 + (0.95)^2 \approx 1$, we use a calculator to support our findings and sure enough, $\cos 1.25 = 0.3153223624$ and $\sin 1.25 = 0.9489846194$. Use this information to complete the following exercises.

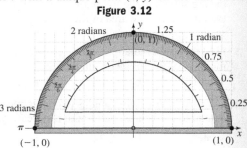

**Figure 3.12**

**Exercise 1:** Estimate the point $(x, y)$ on the unit circle associated with the values of $t$ indicated, then verify that $x^2 + y^2 \approx 1$. Finally, use a calculator to show $x \approx \cos t$ and $y \approx \sin t$ for (a) $t = 0.25$, (b) $t = 0.5$, (c) $t = 0.75$, and (d) $t = 1$.

**Exercise 2:** Estimate the point $(x, y)$ on the unit circle associated with the values of $t$ indicated, then verify that $x^2 + y^2 \approx 1$.

Finally, use standard values to show $x \approx \cos t$ and $y \approx \sin t$ for (a) $t = \dfrac{2\pi}{3}$, (b) $t = \dfrac{3\pi}{4}$, (c) $t = \dfrac{5\pi}{6}$, and (d) $t = \pi$.

## 3.3 | The Unit Circle

### Learning Objectives

*In Section 3.3 you will learn how to:*

☐ **A.** Locate points on a unit circle and use symmetry to locate other points

☐ **B.** Use special triangles to find points on a unit circle and locate other points using symmetry

☐ **C.** Define the six trig functions in terms of a point on the unit circle

In Section 3.2, we noted that using radians as a unit of angle measure simplified calculations involving arc length, angular and linear velocity, and the area of a circular sector. In much the same way, the definitions of the trig functions seen in Chapter 1 can be simplified by considering points *on the circumference of a unit circle* ($r = 1$).

For example, recall that $\cos \theta = \dfrac{x}{r}$. If $r = 1$, we have $\cos \theta = x$, with each of the other trig functions likewise more simple. In practice, the importance of using a unit circle goes far beyond these algebraic simplifications and is truly the beginning of a more modern (and more useful) view of trigonometry.

### A. The Unit Circle

A circle is defined as the set of all points in a plane that are a *fixed distance* called the **radius,** from a *fixed point* called the **center.** Since the definition involves distance, we can construct the general equation of a circle using the distance formula. Assume the center has coordinates $(h, k)$ and let $(x, y)$ represent any point on the graph. Since the distance between these points is the radius $r$, the distance formula yields $\sqrt{(x - h)^2 + (y - k)^2} = r$. Squaring both sides gives $(x - h)^2 + (y - k)^2 = r^2$. For central circles both $h$ and $k$ are zero, and the result is the equation for a **central circle** of radius $r$: $x^2 + y^2 = r^2 (r > 0)$. The **unit circle** is defined as a central circle with radius 1 unit: $x^2 + y^2 = 1$. As such, the figure can easily be graphed by drawing a circle through the four **quadrantal points** $(1, 0)$, $(-1, 0)$, $(0, 1)$, and $(0, -1)$ as in Figure 3.13. To find other points on the circle, we simply select any value of $x$, where $|x| < 1$, then substitute and solve for $y$; or any value of $y$, where $|y| < 1$, then solve for $x$.

**Figure 3.13**

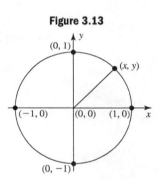

---

EXAMPLE 1 ▶ **Finding Points on a Unit Circle**

Find a point on the unit circle given $y = \frac{1}{2}$ with $(x, y)$ in QII.

Solution ▶ Using the equation of a unit circle, we have

$$x^2 + y^2 = 1 \qquad \text{unit circle equation}$$

$$x^2 + \left(\frac{1}{2}\right)^2 = 1 \qquad \text{substitute } \tfrac{1}{2} \text{ for } y$$

$$x^2 + \frac{1}{4} = 1 \qquad \left(\tfrac{1}{2}\right)^2 = \tfrac{1}{4}$$

$$x^2 = \frac{3}{4} \qquad \text{subtract } \tfrac{1}{4}$$

$$x = \pm\frac{\sqrt{3}}{2} \qquad \text{result}$$

With $(x, y)$ in QII, we choose $x = -\dfrac{\sqrt{3}}{2}$. The point is $\left(-\dfrac{\sqrt{3}}{2}, \dfrac{1}{2}\right)$.

**Now try Exercises 7 through 18 ▶**

---

Additional points on the unit circle can be found using symmetry. The simplest examples come from the quadrantal points, where $(1, 0)$ and $(-1, 0)$ are on opposite sides of the $y$-axis, and $(0, 1)$ and $(0, -1)$ are on opposite sides of the $x$-axis. In general, if $a$ and $b$ are positive real numbers and $(a, b)$ is on the unit circle, then $(-a, b)$, $(a, -b)$, and $(-a, -b)$ are also on the circle *because a circle is symmetric to both axes and the origin*! For the point $\left(-\dfrac{\sqrt{3}}{2}, \dfrac{1}{2}\right)$ from Example 1, three other points are $\left(-\dfrac{\sqrt{3}}{2}, -\dfrac{1}{2}\right)$ in QIII, $\left(\dfrac{\sqrt{3}}{2}, -\dfrac{1}{2}\right)$ in QIV, and $\left(\dfrac{\sqrt{3}}{2}, \dfrac{1}{2}\right)$ in QI. See Figure 3.14.

**Figure 3.14**

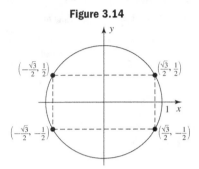

---

**EXAMPLE 2** ▶  **Using Symmetry to Locate Points on a Unit Circle**

Name the quadrant containing $\left(-\dfrac{3}{5}, -\dfrac{4}{5}\right)$ and verify it's on a unit circle. Then use symmetry to find three other points on the circle.

**Solution** ▶  Since both coordinates are negative, $\left(-\dfrac{3}{5}, -\dfrac{4}{5}\right)$ is in QIII. Substituting into the equation for a unit circle yields

$$x^2 + y^2 = 1 \qquad \text{unit circle equation}$$

$$\left(\dfrac{-3}{5}\right)^2 + \left(\dfrac{-4}{5}\right)^2 \stackrel{?}{=} 1 \qquad \text{substitute } \tfrac{-3}{5} \text{ for } x \text{ and } \tfrac{-4}{5} \text{ for } y$$

$$\dfrac{9}{25} + \dfrac{16}{25} \stackrel{?}{=} 1 \qquad \text{simplify}$$

$$\dfrac{25}{25} = 1 \qquad \text{result checks}$$

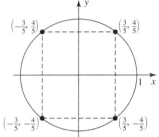

Since $\left(\dfrac{-3}{5}, \dfrac{-4}{5}\right)$ is on the unit circle, $\left(\dfrac{3}{5}, \dfrac{-4}{5}\right)$, $\left(\dfrac{-3}{5}, \dfrac{4}{5}\right)$, and $\left(\dfrac{3}{5}, \dfrac{4}{5}\right)$ are also on the circle due to symmetry (see figure).

**Now try Exercises 19 through 26** ▶

---

☑ **A. You've just learned how to locate points on a unit circle and use symmetry to locate other points**

## B. Special Triangles and the Unit Circle

The special triangles from Section 1.1 can also be used to find points on a unit circle. As usually written, the triangles state a proportional relationship between their sides after assigning a value of 1 to the shortest side. However, precisely due to this proportional relationship, *we can divide all sides by the length of the hypotenuse,* giving *it* a length of 1 unit (see Figures 3.15 and 3.16).

**Figure 3.15**                                   **Figure 3.16**

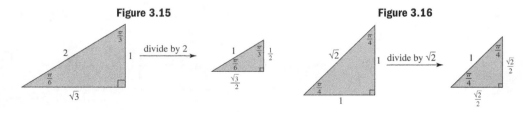

We then place the triangle within the unit circle, and reflect it from quadrant to quadrant to find additional points. We use *the sides* of the triangle to determine the absolute value of each coordinate, and *the quadrant* to give each coordinate the appropriate sign. Note the angles in these special triangles are now expressed in radians.

---

**EXAMPLE 3** ▶ **Using a Special Triangle and Symmetry to Locate Points on a Unit Circle**

Use the $\frac{\pi}{4}$: $\frac{\pi}{4}$: $\frac{\pi}{2}$ triangle from Figure 3.16 to find four points on the unit circle.

**Solution** ▶ Begin by superimposing the triangle in QI, noting it gives the point $\left(\frac{\sqrt{2}}{2}, \frac{\sqrt{2}}{2}\right)$ shown in Figure 3.17. By reflecting the triangle into QII, we find the additional point $\left(-\frac{\sqrt{2}}{2}, \frac{\sqrt{2}}{2}\right)$ on this circle. Realizing we can simply apply the circle's remaining symmetries, we obtain the two additional points $\left(-\frac{\sqrt{2}}{2}, -\frac{\sqrt{2}}{2}\right)$ and $\left(\frac{\sqrt{2}}{2}, -\frac{\sqrt{2}}{2}\right)$ shown in Figure 3.18.

**Figure 3.17**     **Figure 3.18**

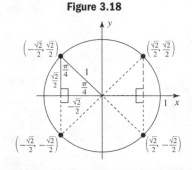

Now try Exercises 27 and 28 ▶

---

Applying the same idea to a $\frac{\pi}{6}$: $\frac{\pi}{3}$: $\frac{\pi}{2}$ triangle would give the points $\left(\frac{\sqrt{3}}{2}, \frac{1}{2}\right)$, $\left(-\frac{\sqrt{3}}{2}, \frac{1}{2}\right)$, $\left(-\frac{\sqrt{3}}{2}, -\frac{1}{2}\right)$ and $\left(\frac{\sqrt{3}}{2}, -\frac{1}{2}\right)$, *which includes the same point we found in Example 1.*

When a central angle $\theta$ is viewed as a rotation, each rotation can be associated with a unique point $(x, y)$ on the terminal side, where it intersects the unit circle (see Figure 3.19). For the quadrantal angles $\frac{\pi}{2}, \pi, \frac{3\pi}{2}$, and $2\pi$, we associate the points $(0, 1)$, $(-1, 0)$, $(0, -1)$, and $(1, 0)$, respectively. When this rotation results in a special angle $\theta$, the association can be found using a special triangle in a manner

**Figure 3.19**

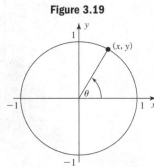

similar to Example 3. Figure 3.20 shows we associate the point $\left(\dfrac{\sqrt{3}}{2}, \dfrac{1}{2}\right)$ with $\theta = \dfrac{\pi}{6}$, $\left(\dfrac{\sqrt{2}}{2}, \dfrac{\sqrt{2}}{2}\right)$ with $\theta = \dfrac{\pi}{4}$, and by reorienting the $\dfrac{\pi}{6}$: $\dfrac{\pi}{3}$: $\dfrac{\pi}{2}$ triangle, $\left(\dfrac{1}{2}, \dfrac{\sqrt{3}}{2}\right)$ is associated with a rotation of $\theta = \dfrac{\pi}{3}$.

**Figure 3.20**

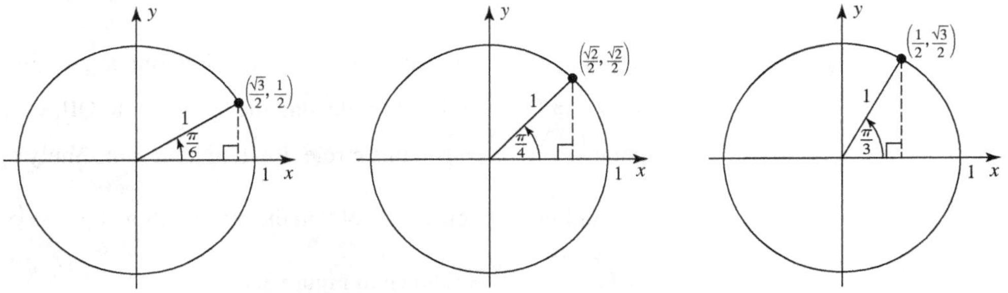

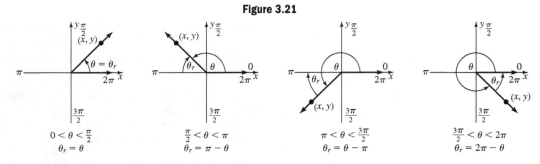

For standard rotations from $\theta = 0$ to $\theta = \dfrac{\pi}{2}$ we have the following:

| Rotation $\theta$ | $0$ | $\dfrac{\pi}{6}$ | $\dfrac{\pi}{4}$ | $\dfrac{\pi}{3}$ | $\dfrac{\pi}{2}$ |
|---|---|---|---|---|---|
| Associated point $(x, y)$ | $(0, 0)$ | $\left(\dfrac{\sqrt{3}}{2}, \dfrac{1}{2}\right)$ | $\left(\dfrac{\sqrt{2}}{2}, \dfrac{\sqrt{2}}{2}\right)$ | $\left(\dfrac{1}{2}, \dfrac{\sqrt{3}}{2}\right)$ | $(0, 1)$ |

Each of these points give rise to three others using the symmetry of the circle. With this symmetry and a reference angle $\theta_r$, we can associate additional points on a unit circle for $\theta > \dfrac{\pi}{2}$. Several examples of the reference angle concept are shown in Figure 3.21 for $\theta > 0$ in radians.

**Figure 3.21**

$0 < \theta < \dfrac{\pi}{2}$
$\theta_r = \theta$

$\dfrac{\pi}{2} < \theta < \pi$
$\theta_r = \pi - \theta$

$\pi < \theta < \dfrac{3\pi}{2}$
$\theta_r = \theta - \pi$

$\dfrac{3\pi}{2} < \theta < 2\pi$
$\theta_r = 2\pi - \theta$

Due to the symmetries of the circle, reference angles of $\dfrac{\pi}{6}$, $\dfrac{\pi}{4}$, and $\dfrac{\pi}{3}$ serve to fix the absolute value of the coordinates for $x$ and $y$, and we simply *use the appropriate sign for each coordinate* ($r$ is always positive). As before, this depends solely on the quadrant of the terminal side.

**EXAMPLE 4** ▶ **Finding Points on a Unit Circle Associated with a Rotation $\theta$**

Determine the reference angle for each rotation given, then find the associated point $(x, y)$ on the unit circle.

a. $\theta = \dfrac{5\pi}{6}$     b. $\theta = \dfrac{4\pi}{3}$     c. $\theta = \dfrac{7\pi}{4}$

**Figure 3.22**

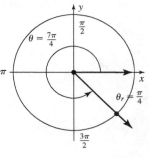

Solution ▶ a. A rotation of $\dfrac{5\pi}{6}$ terminates in QII:

$\theta_r = \pi - \dfrac{5\pi}{6} = \dfrac{\pi}{6}$. The associated point is

$\left(-\dfrac{\sqrt{3}}{2}, \dfrac{1}{2}\right)$ since $x < 0$ in QII. See Figure 3.22.

b. A rotation of $\dfrac{4\pi}{3}$ terminates in QIII:

$\theta_r = \dfrac{4\pi}{3} - \pi = \dfrac{\pi}{3}$. The associated point is

$\left(-\dfrac{1}{2}, -\dfrac{\sqrt{3}}{2}\right)$ since $x < 0$ and $y < 0$ in QIII.

**Figure 3.23**

c. A rotation of $\dfrac{7\pi}{4}$ terminates in QIV:

$\theta_r = 2\pi - \dfrac{7\pi}{4} = \dfrac{\pi}{4}$. The associated point is

$\left(\dfrac{\sqrt{2}}{2}, -\dfrac{\sqrt{2}}{2}\right)$ since $y < 0$ in QIV. See Figure 3.23.

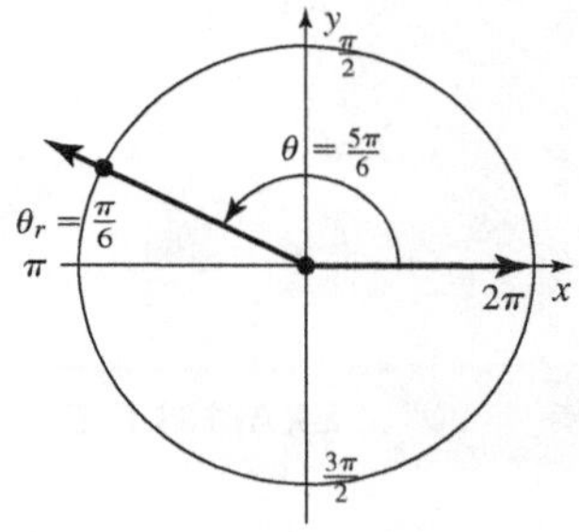

☑ **B. You've just learned how to use special triangles to find points on a unit circle and locate other points using symmetry**

Now try Exercises 29 through 36 ▶

## C. Trigonometric Functions and Points on the Unit Circle

We can now define the six trigonometric functions in terms of a point $(x, y)$ on the unit circle, with the use of right triangles fading from view. For this reason they are sometimes called the **circular functions.**

### The Circular Functions

For any rotation $\theta$ and point $P(x, y)$ on the unit circle associated with $\theta$,

$$\cos \theta = x \qquad \sin \theta = y \qquad \tan \theta = \dfrac{y}{x}; x \neq 0$$

$$\sec \theta = \dfrac{1}{x}; x \neq 0 \qquad \csc \theta = \dfrac{1}{y}; y \neq 0 \qquad \cot \theta = \dfrac{x}{y}; y \neq 0$$

**Figure 3.24**

Note that once $\sin\theta$, $\cos\theta$, and $\tan\theta$ are known, the values of $\csc\theta$, $\sec\theta$, and $\cot\theta$ follow automatically since a number and its reciprocal always have the same sign. See Figure 3.24.

| QII | QI |
|---|---|
| $x < 0, y > 0$ | $x > 0, y > 0$ |
| (only $y$ is positive) | (both $x$ and $y$ are positive) |
| $\sin\theta$ is positive | All functions are positive |
| $\tan\theta$ is positive | $\cos\theta$ is positive    $x$ |
| QIII | QIV |
| $x < 0, y < 0$ | $x > 0, y < 0$ |
| (both $x$ and $y$ are negative) | (only $x$ is positive) |

---

**EXAMPLE 5** ▶ **Evaluating Trig Functions for a Rotation $\theta$**

Evaluate the six trig functions for $\theta = \dfrac{5\pi}{4}$.

**Solution** ▶ A rotation of $\dfrac{5\pi}{4}$ terminates in QIII, so

$\theta_r = \dfrac{5\pi}{4} - \pi = \dfrac{\pi}{4}$. The associated point is

$\left(-\dfrac{\sqrt{2}}{2}, -\dfrac{\sqrt{2}}{2}\right)$ since $x < 0$ and $y < 0$ in QIII.

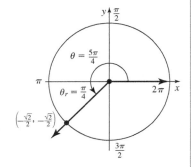

This yields

$$\cos\left(\frac{5\pi}{4}\right) = -\frac{\sqrt{2}}{2} \qquad \sin\left(\frac{5\pi}{4}\right) = -\frac{\sqrt{2}}{2} \qquad \tan\left(\frac{5\pi}{4}\right) = 1$$

Noting the reciprocal of $-\dfrac{\sqrt{2}}{2}$ is $-\sqrt{2}$ after rationalizing, we have

$$\sec\left(\frac{5\pi}{4}\right) = -\sqrt{2} \qquad \csc\left(\frac{5\pi}{4}\right) = -\sqrt{2} \qquad \cot\left(\frac{5\pi}{4}\right) = 1$$

☑ **C.** You've just learned how to define the six trig functions in terms of a point on the unit circle

**Now try Exercises 37 through 40** ▶

---

## TECHNOLOGY HIGHLIGHT

### Graphing the Unit Circle

When using a graphing calculator to study the unit circle, it's important to keep two things in mind. First, most graphing calculators are only capable of graphing *functions,* which means we must modify the equation of the circle (and relations like ellipses, hyperbolas, horizontal parabolas, and so on) before it can be graphed. Second, most standard viewing windows have the $x$- and $y$-values preset at $[-10, 10]$ even though the calculator screen is 94 pixels wide and 64 pixels high. This tends to compress the $y$-values and give a skewed image of the graph. Consider the equation $x^2 + y^2 = 1$. From our work in this section, we know this is the equation of a circle centered at (0, 0) with radius $r = 1$. For the calculator to graph this relation, we must define it in two pieces, each of which is a function, by solving for $y$:

$$x^2 + y^2 = 1 \qquad \text{original equation}$$
$$y^2 = 1 - x^2 \qquad \text{isolate } y^2$$
$$y = \pm\sqrt{1 - x^2} \qquad \text{solve for } y$$

*—continued*

Note that we can separate this result into two parts, each of which is a function. The graph of $Y_1 = \sqrt{1 - x^2}$ gives the "upper half" of the circle, while $Y_2 = -\sqrt{1 - x^2}$ gives the "lower half." We can enter these on the [ Y= ] screen as shown, using the expression $-Y_1$ instead of reentering the entire expression. The function variables $Y_1$, $Y_2$, $Y_3$, and so on, can be accessed using [ VARS ] [ ▶ ] (Y-VARS) [ ENTER ] (1:Function). Graphing $Y_1$ and $Y_2$ on the standard screen, the result appears very small and more elliptical than circular (Figure 3.25). One way to fix this (there are many others), is to use the [ ZOOM ] 4:ZDecimal option, which places the tic marks equally spaced on both axes, instead of trying to force both to display points from $-10$ to $10$. Using this option gives the screen shown in Figure 3.26. An even better graph can be obtained using the [ ZOOM ] 2:Zoom In option (or by manually resetting the window size). Using the [ TRACE ] feature enables us to view points on the unit circle, but recall that this image is actually the union of two graphs and we may need to jump between the upper and lower halves using the up [ ▲ ] or down [ ▼ ] arrows.

**Figure 3.25**

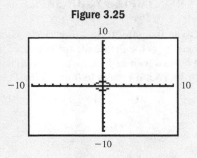

**Figure 3.26**

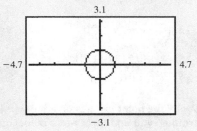

**Exercise 1:** Use the [ TRACE ] feature to verify the point (0.6, 0.8) is on the unit circle, as well as the other three related points given by symmetry (as shown in Example 2).

**Exercise 2:** Use the [ 2nd ] [ TRACE ] (CALC) feature to evaluate the function at $\frac{\sqrt{2}}{2}$. What do you notice about the output? For $\cos \theta$ or $\sin \theta$, what value of $\theta$ can we associate with this point?

**Exercise 3:** What other standard values can you identify as you [ TRACE ] around the circle?

## 3.3 EXERCISES

### ▶ CONCEPTS AND VOCABULARY

**Fill in each blank with the appropriate word or phrase. Carefully reread the section if needed.**

1. A central circle is symmetric to the _____ axis, the _____ axis and to the _____.

2. Since $(\frac{5}{13}, -\frac{12}{13})$ is on the unit circle, the point _____ in QII is also on the circle.

3. On a unit circle, $\cos \theta =$ _____, $\sin \theta =$ _____, and $\tan \theta =$ _____; while $\frac{1}{x} =$ _____, $\frac{1}{y} =$ _____, and $\frac{x}{y} =$ _____.

4. Reference angles are the _____ angles formed by the terminal side of angles in standard position and the _____. They must measure between ___ and ___ radians.

5. Discuss/Explain how knowing only one point on the unit circle, actually gives the location of four points. Why is this helpful to a study of the circular functions?

6. Discuss/Explain how the unit circle simplifies the definitions of the trig functions and why the points on this circle are sufficient to describe any rotation.

▶ **DEVELOPING YOUR SKILLS**

Given the point is on a unit circle, complete the ordered pair $(x, y)$ for the quadrant indicated. For Exercises 7 to 14, answer in radical form as needed. For Exercises 15 to 18, round results to four decimal places.

7. $(x, -0.8)$; QIII

8. $(-0.6, y)$; QII

9. $\left(\dfrac{5}{13}, y\right)$; QIV

10. $\left(x, -\dfrac{8}{17}\right)$; QIV

11. $\left(\dfrac{\sqrt{11}}{6}, y\right)$; QI

12. $\left(x, -\dfrac{\sqrt{13}}{7}\right)$; QIII

13. $\left(-\dfrac{\sqrt{11}}{4}, y\right)$; QII

14. $\left(x, \dfrac{\sqrt{6}}{5}\right)$; QI

15. $(x, -0.2137)$; QIII

16. $(0.9909, y)$; QIV

17. $(x, 0.1198)$; QII

18. $(0.5449, y)$; QI

Verify the point given is on a unit circle, then use symmetry to find three more points on the circle. Results for Exercises 19 to 22 are exact, results for Exercises 23 to 26 are approximate.

19. $\left(-\dfrac{\sqrt{3}}{2}, \dfrac{1}{2}\right)$

20. $\left(\dfrac{\sqrt{7}}{4}, -\dfrac{3}{4}\right)$

21. $\left(\dfrac{\sqrt{11}}{6}, -\dfrac{5}{6}\right)$

22. $\left(-\dfrac{\sqrt{6}}{3}, -\dfrac{\sqrt{3}}{3}\right)$

23. $(0.3325, 0.9431)$

24. $(0.7707, -0.6372)$

25. $(0.9937, -0.1121)$

26. $(-0.2029, 0.9792)$

27. Use a $\dfrac{\pi}{6} : \dfrac{\pi}{3} : \dfrac{\pi}{2}$ triangle with a hypotenuse of length 1 to verify that $\left(\dfrac{1}{2}, \dfrac{\sqrt{3}}{2}\right)$ is a point on the unit circle.

28. Use the results from Exercise 27 to find three additional points on the circle and name the quadrant of each point.

Find the reference angle associated with each rotation, then find the associated point $(x, y)$ on the unit circle.

29. $\theta = \dfrac{5\pi}{4}$

30. $\theta = \dfrac{5\pi}{3}$

31. $\theta = -\dfrac{5\pi}{6}$

32. $\theta = -\dfrac{7\pi}{4}$

33. $\theta = \dfrac{11\pi}{4}$

34. $\theta = \dfrac{11\pi}{3}$

35. $\theta = \dfrac{25\pi}{6}$

36. $\theta = \dfrac{39\pi}{4}$

Without the use of a calculator, state the exact value of the trig functions for the given angle. A diagram may help.

37.
a. $\sin\left(\dfrac{\pi}{4}\right)$
b. $\sin\left(\dfrac{3\pi}{4}\right)$
c. $\sin\left(\dfrac{5\pi}{4}\right)$
d. $\sin\left(\dfrac{7\pi}{4}\right)$
e. $\sin\left(\dfrac{9\pi}{4}\right)$
f. $\sin\left(-\dfrac{\pi}{4}\right)$
g. $\sin\left(-\dfrac{5\pi}{4}\right)$
h. $\sin\left(-\dfrac{11\pi}{4}\right)$

38.
a. $\tan\left(\dfrac{\pi}{3}\right)$
b. $\tan\left(\dfrac{2\pi}{3}\right)$
c. $\tan\left(\dfrac{4\pi}{3}\right)$
d. $\tan\left(\dfrac{5\pi}{3}\right)$
e. $\tan\left(\dfrac{7\pi}{3}\right)$
f. $\tan\left(-\dfrac{\pi}{3}\right)$
g. $\tan\left(-\dfrac{4\pi}{3}\right)$
h. $\tan\left(-\dfrac{10\pi}{3}\right)$

39.
a. $\cos \pi$
b. $\cos 0$
c. $\cos\left(\dfrac{\pi}{2}\right)$
d. $\cos\left(\dfrac{3\pi}{2}\right)$

40.
a. $\sin \pi$
b. $\sin 0$
c. $\sin\left(\dfrac{\pi}{2}\right)$
d. $\sin\left(\dfrac{3\pi}{2}\right)$

▶ **WORKING WITH FORMULAS**

41. **Unit sphere:** $x^2 + y^2 + z^2 = 1$

The unit circle is actually the intersection of the unit sphere with the $xy$-plane $(z = 0)$. Any ordered triple $(x, y, z)$ in three dimensional space that satisfies this equation is on the surface of the unit sphere. Find two possible values of each missing variable for the following points on the unit sphere.

a. $\left(x, -\dfrac{4}{9}, \dfrac{1}{9}\right)$

b. $\left(\dfrac{2}{11}, y, -\dfrac{9}{11}\right)$

c. $\left(\dfrac{2}{7}, \dfrac{3}{7}, z\right)$

**42. From Pythagorean triples to points on the unit circle:** $(x, y, r) \rightarrow \left( \dfrac{x}{r}, \dfrac{y}{r}, 1 \right)$

While not strictly a "formula," dividing a Pythagorean triple by $r$ is a simple algorithm for rewriting any Pythagorean triple as a triple with hypotenuse 1. This enables us to identify certain points on a unit circle, and to evaluate the six trig functions of the related acute angle. Rewrite each triple as a triple with hypotenuse 1, verify $\left( \dfrac{x}{r}, \dfrac{y}{r} \right)$ is a point on the unit circle, and evaluate the six trig functions using this point.

   **a.** $(5, 12, 13)$        **b.** $(7, 24, 25)$        **c.** $(12, 35, 37)$        **d.** $(9, 40, 41)$

▶ **APPLICATIONS**

**Unit circle points:** In Exercises 23 through 26, four decimal approximations of unit circle points were given. Find such unit circle points that are on the terminal side of the following angles in standard position. (*Hint:* Use the definitions of the circular functions.)

**43.** $\theta = 40°$          **44.** $\theta = 140°$          **45.** $\theta = 201°$          **46.** $\theta = 339°$

**47.** $\theta = 2$            **48.** $\theta = 1$             **49.** $\theta = 5$             **50.** $\theta = 4$

**Mosaic design:** The floor of a local museum contains a mosaic zodiac circle as shown. The circle is 1 m (= 100 cm) in radius, with all 12 zodiac signs represented by small, evenly spaced bronze disks on the circumference.

**51.** If the disk representing Libra is 96.6 cm to the right of and 25.9 cm above the center of the zodiac, what is the distance $d$ (see illustration) from Libra's disk to Pisces' disk? What is the distance from Libra's disk to Virgo's disk?

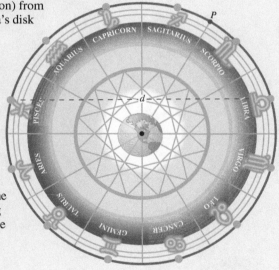

**Exercises 51 to 54**

**52.** If the disk representing Taurus is 70.7 cm to the left of and 70.7 cm below the center of the zodiac, what is the distance from Taurus' disk to Leo's disk? What is the distance from Taurus' disk to Scorpio's disk?

**53.** Using a special triangle, identify (in relation to the center of the zodiac) the location of the point $P$ (see illustration) where the steel rod separating Scorpio and Sagittarius intersects the circumference. Round to the nearest tenth of a centimeter.

**54.** Using a special triangle, identify (in relation to the center of the zodiac) the location of the point where the steel rod separating Aquarius and Pisces intersects the circumference. Round to the nearest tenth of a centimeter.

▶ **EXTENDING THE CONCEPT**

**55.** Use the figure shown to verify the ratio identity for tangent and the reciprocal identity for secant.

**Exercise 55**

**56.** In addition to the symmetry across the $x$- and $y$-axes, the unit circle has a "rotational" symmetry that we can also use to find additional points. Consider the unit circle point $\left( \dfrac{\sqrt{3}}{2}, \dfrac{1}{2} \right)$ and its associated angle $\dfrac{\pi}{6}$. (a) Rotate this point an additional $\dfrac{\pi}{2}$ radians around the unit circle and identify the new associated angle and coordinates.
(b) Repeat this rotation three more times and comment on what you notice. (c) Given $(0.8, 0.6)$ is on the unit circle, use rotational symmetry to find three additional points on the circle.

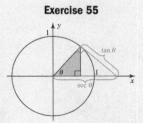

▶ **MAINTAINING YOUR SKILLS**

**57.** **(3.2)** For emissions testing, automobiles are held stationary while a heavy roller installed in the floor allows the wheels to turn freely. If the large wheels of a customized pickup have a radius of 18 in. and are turning at 300 rpm, what speed is the speedometer of the truck reading in miles per hour?

**58.** **(3.1)** Complete the table from memory or mental calculation only.

| Degrees | 30° | 45° | 60° | 90° | 180° | 270° | 360° |
|---------|-----|-----|-----|-----|------|------|------|
| Radians |     |     |     |     |      |      |      |

**59.** **(3.2)** Find (a) the radian measure of $\theta$, and (b) the area of the circular sector.

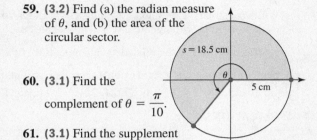

**60.** **(3.1)** Find the complement of $\theta = \dfrac{\pi}{10}$.

**61.** **(3.1)** Find the supplement of $\theta = 3$.

**62.** **(1.3)** Find the values of the remaining trig functions of $\theta$ given $\tan \theta = \dfrac{5}{7}$ and $\cos \theta < 0$.

# 3.4 | The Trigonometry of Real Numbers

## Learning Objectives

*In Section 3.4 you will learn how to:*

☐ **A.** Define the six trig functions in terms of a real number $t$

☐ **B.** Find the real number $t$ corresponding to special values of $\sin t$, $\cos t$, and $\tan t$

☐ **C.** Find the real number $t$ corresponding to any trig function value

In this section, we introduce the **trigonometry of real numbers,** a view of trigonometry that can exist free of its historical roots in a study of right triangles. In fact, the ultimate value of these functions is not in their classical study, but in the implications and applications that follow from understanding them as functions of a real number, rather than simply as functions of a given angle.

## A. The Trigonometry of Real Numbers

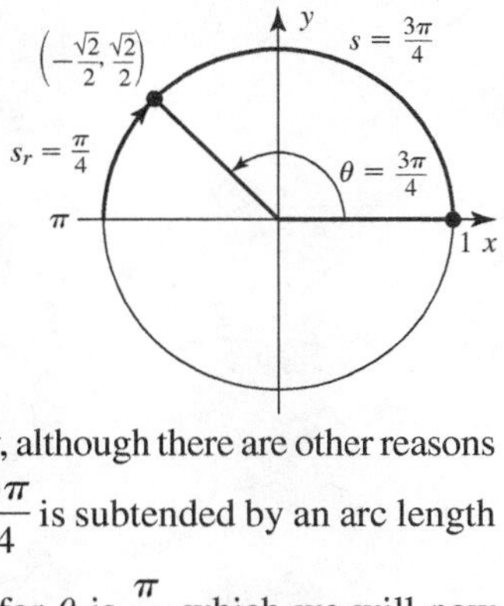

Defining the trig functions in terms of a point on the unit circle is precisely what we needed to work with them as functions of real numbers. This is because when $r = 1$ and $\theta$ is in radians, *the length of the subtended arc is numerically the same as the measure of the angle:* $s = (1)\theta \Rightarrow s = \theta$! This means we can view any function of $\theta$ as a like function of arc length $s$, where $s \in \mathbb{R}$ (see the *Strengthening Core Skills* feature at the end of this chapter). As a compromise the variable $t$ is commonly used, with $t$ representing *either* the amount of rotation *or* the length of the arc. As such we will assume $t$ is a unitless quantity, although there are other reasons

**Figure 3.27**

for this assumption. In Figure 3.27, a rotation of $\theta = \dfrac{3\pi}{4}$ is subtended by an arc length

of $s = \dfrac{3\pi}{4}$ (about 2.356 units). The reference angle for $\theta$ is $\dfrac{\pi}{4}$, which we will now

refer to as a **reference arc.** As you work through the remaining examples and the exercises that follow, it will often help to draw a quick sketch similar to that in Figure 3.27 to determine the quadrant of the terminal side, the reference arc, and the sign of each function.

**EXAMPLE 1** ▶ **Evaluating Trig Functions for a Real Number *t***

Evaluate the six trig functions for the given value of *t*.

**a.** $t = \dfrac{11\pi}{6}$   **b.** $t = \dfrac{3\pi}{2}$

Solution ▶ **a.** For $t = \dfrac{11\pi}{6}$, the arc terminates in QIV where $x > 0$ and $y < 0$. The

reference arc is $\dfrac{\pi}{6}$ and from our previous work we know the corresponding

point $(x, y)$ is $\left(\dfrac{\sqrt{3}}{2}, -\dfrac{1}{2}\right)$. This gives

$$\cos\left(\frac{11\pi}{6}\right) = \frac{\sqrt{3}}{2} \qquad \sin\left(\frac{11\pi}{6}\right) = -\frac{1}{2} \qquad \tan\left(\frac{11\pi}{6}\right) = -\frac{\sqrt{3}}{3}$$

$$\sec\left(\frac{11\pi}{6}\right) = \frac{2\sqrt{3}}{3} \qquad \csc\left(\frac{11\pi}{6}\right) = -2 \qquad \cot\left(\frac{11\pi}{6}\right) = -\sqrt{3}$$

**b.** $t = \dfrac{3\pi}{2}$ is a quadrantal angle and the associated point is $(0, -1)$.

This yields

$$\cos\left(\frac{3\pi}{2}\right) = 0 \qquad \sin\left(\frac{3\pi}{2}\right) = -1 \qquad \tan\left(\frac{3\pi}{2}\right) = \text{undefined}$$

$$\sec\left(\frac{3\pi}{2}\right) = \text{undefined} \qquad \csc\left(\frac{3\pi}{2}\right) = -1 \qquad \cot\left(\frac{3\pi}{2}\right) = 0$$

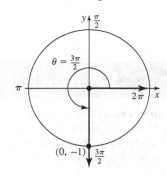

**Now try Exercises 7 through 10** ▶

As Example 1(b) indicates, as functions of a real number the concept of domain comes into play. From their definition it is apparent there are no restrictions on the domain of cosine and sine, but the domains of the other functions must be restricted to exclude division by zero. For functions with $x$ in the denominator, we cast out the odd multiples of $\dfrac{\pi}{2}$, since the $x$-coordinate of the related quadrantal points is zero: $\dfrac{\pi}{2} \to (0, 1), \dfrac{3\pi}{2} \to (0, -1)$, and so on. The excluded values can be stated as $t \neq \dfrac{\pi}{2} + \pi k$ for all integers $k$. For functions with $y$ in the denominator, we cast out all multiples of $\pi$ ($t \neq \pi k$ for all integers $k$) since the $y$-coordinate of these points is zero: $0 \to (1, 0), \pi \to (-1, 0), 2\pi \to (1, 0)$, and so on.

**The Domains of the Trig Functions as Functions of a Real Number**

For $t \in \mathbb{R}$ and $k \in \mathbb{Z}$, the domains of the trig functions are:

| $\cos t = x$ | $\sin t = y$ | $\tan t = \dfrac{y}{x}; x \neq 0$ |
|---|---|---|
| $t \in \mathbb{R}$ | $t \in \mathbb{R}$ | $t \neq \dfrac{\pi}{2} + \pi k$ |
| $\sec t = \dfrac{1}{x}; x \neq 0$ | $\csc t = \dfrac{1}{y}; y \neq 0$ | $\cot t = \dfrac{x}{y}; y \neq 0$ |
| $t \neq \dfrac{\pi}{2} + \pi k$ | $t \neq \pi k$ | $t \neq \pi k$ |

For a given point $(x, y)$ on the unit circle associated with the real number $t$, the value of each function at $t$ can still be determined even if $t$ is unknown.

---

**EXAMPLE 2** ▶ **Finding Function Values Given a Point on the Unit Circle**

Given $\left(\frac{-7}{25}, \frac{24}{25}\right)$ is a point on the unit circle corresponding to a real number $t$, find the value of all six trig functions of $t$.

**Solution** ▶ Using the definitions from the previous box we have $\cos t = \frac{-7}{25}$, $\sin t = \frac{24}{25}$, and $\tan t = \frac{\sin t}{\cos t} = \frac{24}{-7}$. The values of the reciprocal functions are then $\sec t = \frac{25}{-7}$, $\csc t = \frac{25}{24}$, and $\cot t = \frac{-7}{24}$.

✓ **A.** You've just learned how to define the six trig functions in terms of a real number $t$

**Now try Exercises 11 through 36** ▶

---

## B. Finding a Real Number $t$ Whose Function Value Is Special

In Example 2, we were able to determine the values of the trig functions even though $t$ was unknown. In many cases, however, we need to *find* the value of $t$. For instance, what is the value of $t$ given $\cos t = -\frac{\sqrt{3}}{2}$ with $t$ in QII? Exercises of this type fall into two broad categories: (1) you recognize the given number as one of the special values: $\pm\left\{0, \frac{1}{2}, \frac{\sqrt{2}}{2}, \frac{\sqrt{3}}{2}, \frac{\sqrt{3}}{3}, \sqrt{3}, 1\right\}$; or (2) you don't. If you recognize a special value, you can often name the real number $t$ after a careful consideration of the related quadrant and required sign.

**Figure 3.28**

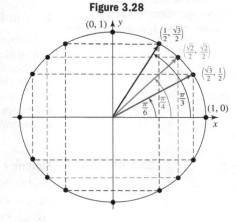

The diagram in Figure 3.28 reviews these special values for $0 \le t \le \frac{\pi}{2}$ but remember—all other special values can be found using reference arcs and the symmetry of the circle.

---

**EXAMPLE 3** ▶ **Finding $t$ for Given Special Values and Conditions**

Find the value of $t$ that corresponds to the given function values.

**a.** $\cos t = -\frac{\sqrt{2}}{2}$; $t$ in QII    **b.** $\tan t = \sqrt{3}$; $t$ in QIII

**Solution** ▶ **a.** The cosine function is negative in QII and QIII, where $x < 0$. We recognize $-\frac{\sqrt{2}}{2}$ as a standard value for sine and cosine, related to certain multiples of $t = \frac{\pi}{4}$. In QII, we have $t = \frac{3\pi}{4}$.

**b.** The tangent function is positive in QI and QIII, where $x$ and $y$ have like signs. We recognize $\sqrt{3}$ as a standard value for tangent and cotangent, related to certain multiples of $t = \frac{\pi}{3}$. For tangent in QIII, we have $t = \frac{4\pi}{3}$.

**Now try Exercises 37 through 52** ▶

The following table summarizes the relationship between a special arc $t$ ($t$ in QI) and the value of each trig function at $t$. Due to the frequent use of these relationships, students are encouraged to commit them to memory.

| $t$ | $\sin t$ | $\cos t$ | $\tan t$ | $\csc t$ | $\sec t$ | $\cot t$ |
|---|---|---|---|---|---|---|
| 0 | 0 | 1 | 0 | undefined | 1 | undefined |
| $\dfrac{\pi}{6}$ | $\dfrac{1}{2}$ | $\dfrac{\sqrt{3}}{2}$ | $\dfrac{1}{\sqrt{3}}=\dfrac{\sqrt{3}}{3}$ | 2 | $\dfrac{2}{\sqrt{3}}=\dfrac{2\sqrt{3}}{3}$ | $\sqrt{3}$ |
| $\dfrac{\pi}{4}$ | $\dfrac{\sqrt{2}}{2}$ | $\dfrac{\sqrt{2}}{2}$ | 1 | $\sqrt{2}$ | $\sqrt{2}$ | 1 |
| $\dfrac{\pi}{3}$ | $\dfrac{\sqrt{3}}{2}$ | $\dfrac{1}{2}$ | $\sqrt{3}$ | $\dfrac{2}{\sqrt{3}}=\dfrac{2\sqrt{3}}{3}$ | 2 | $\dfrac{1}{\sqrt{3}}=\dfrac{\sqrt{3}}{3}$ |
| $\dfrac{\pi}{2}$ | 1 | 0 | undefined | 1 | undefined | 0 |

☑ **B.** You've just learned how to find the real number $t$ corresponding to special values of $\sin t$, $\cos t$, and $\tan t$

## C. Finding a Real Number $t$ for Any Function Value

In Example 3, we recognized the values given as those of a special arc, and we were able to identify $t$ using a reference arc and quadrant analysis. If the given function value is not one of the "special values," we use the $\sin^{-1}$, $\cos^{-1}$, and $\tan^{-1}$ keys of our calculator (in radian $\boxed{\text{MODE}}$), as in Section 2.2. By applying the correct inverse function to the *absolute value* of the given trig function value of $t$, we find the associated **reference arc $t_r$**. Now as in Example 3, we can find the real number $t$ with a careful consideration of the related quadrant.

---

**EXAMPLE 4** ▶ **Finding $t$ for Given Values and Conditions**

Find the value of $t \in [0, 2\pi)$ that corresponds to the given function values.

**a.** $\cos t = 0.1217$; $\sin t < 0$

**b.** $\cot t = -0.7259$; $\cos t < 0$

Solution ▶ **a.** The cosine function is positive in QI and QIV, while the sine function is negative in QIII and QIV. Since both must be true, the arc terminates in QIV. To find the reference arc

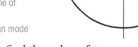

$$t_r = \cos^{-1}|0.1217| \qquad \text{take inverse cosine of absolute value}$$

$$\approx 1.4488 \qquad \text{calculator in radian mode}$$

Using the sketch shown, we can quickly find the value of $t$.

$$t = 2\pi - t_r \qquad \text{arc terminates in QIV}$$

$$\approx 2\pi - 1.4488 \qquad \text{replace } t_r \text{ with 1.4488}$$

$$\approx 4.8344 \qquad \text{result}$$

A quick check on your calculator shows $\cos 4.8344 \approx 0.1217$ and $\sin 4.8344 \approx -0.9926 < 0$.

  **C.** You've just learned how to find the real number $t$ corresponding to any trig function value

**b.** The arc terminates in QII where cotangent and cosine are both negative (see figure). Since we don't have a $\cot^{-1}$ key on our calculator, we use the ratio identity $\tan t = \dfrac{1}{\cot t} = \dfrac{1}{-0.7259} \approx -1.3776$ to use the $\tan^{-1}$ key. For the reference arc $t_r$ we then have

$$t_r \approx \tan^{-1}|-1.3776| \qquad t = \pi - t_r$$
$$= \tan^{-1} 1.3776 \qquad\qquad \approx \pi - 0.9429$$
$$\approx 0.9429 \qquad\qquad\qquad \approx 2.1987$$

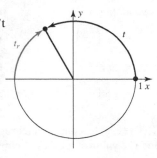

**Now try Exercises 53 through 68** ▶

Whether the unit is 1 cm, 1 m, 1 km, or even 1 light-year, using 1 unit designations serves to simplify a great many practical applications, including those involving the arc length formula, $s = r\theta$. **See Exercises 71 through 78.** With the trigonometry of real numbers, we'll see radian measure and the unit circle are much more than simple conveniences.

# 3.4 EXERCISES

▶ **CONCEPTS AND VOCABULARY**

**Fill in each blank with the appropriate word or phrase. Carefully reread the section if needed.**

1. On a unit circle, the _____ of the arc subtended is numerically _____ to the _____ measure of the central angle. The variable _ is used as a compromise between the variables $s$ and _.

2. A _____ arc is the shortest path from a point on the unit circle to the _____. Its measure is always between 0 and _.

3. On a unit circle, $\cos t =$ _____, $\sin t =$ _____, and $\tan t =$ _____; while $\dfrac{1}{x} =$ _____, $\dfrac{1}{y} =$ _____, and $\dfrac{x}{y} =$ _____.

4. On a unit circle with $\theta$ in radians, the length of a(n) _____ is numerically the same as the measure of the _____, since for $s = r\theta$, $s = \theta$ when $r = 1$.

5. Complete the unit circle shown in Figure 3.28 by identifying all special points. Be sure to include the quadrantal points.

6. A student is asked to find $t$ using a calculator, given $\sin t \approx 0.5592$ with $t$ in QII. The answer submitted is $t = \sin^{-1} 0.5592 \approx 34°$. Discuss/Explain why this answer is not correct. What is the correct response?

▶ **DEVELOPING YOUR SKILLS**

**Use the symmetry of the circle and reference arcs as needed to state the exact value of the trig functions for the given real number, without the use of a calculator. A diagram may help.**

7. **a.** $\cos\left(\dfrac{\pi}{6}\right)$    **b.** $\cos\left(\dfrac{5\pi}{6}\right)$

   **c.** $\cos\left(\dfrac{7\pi}{6}\right)$    **d.** $\cos\left(\dfrac{11\pi}{6}\right)$

   **e.** $\cos\left(\dfrac{13\pi}{6}\right)$    **f.** $\cos\left(-\dfrac{\pi}{6}\right)$

   **g.** $\cos\left(-\dfrac{5\pi}{6}\right)$    **h.** $\cos\left(-\dfrac{23\pi}{6}\right)$

8. **a.** $\csc\left(\dfrac{\pi}{6}\right)$    **b.** $\csc\left(\dfrac{5\pi}{6}\right)$

   **c.** $\csc\left(\dfrac{7\pi}{6}\right)$    **d.** $\csc\left(\dfrac{11\pi}{6}\right)$

   **e.** $\csc\left(\dfrac{13\pi}{6}\right)$    **f.** $\csc\left(-\dfrac{\pi}{6}\right)$

   **g.** $\csc\left(-\dfrac{11\pi}{6}\right)$    **h.** $\csc\left(-\dfrac{17\pi}{6}\right)$

9. **a.** $\tan \pi$                   **b.** $\tan 0$

   **c.** $\tan\left(\dfrac{\pi}{2}\right)$    **d.** $\tan\left(\dfrac{3\pi}{2}\right)$

10. **a.** $\cot \pi$                  **b.** $\cot 0$

   **c.** $\cot\left(\dfrac{\pi}{2}\right)$    **d.** $\cot\left(\dfrac{3\pi}{2}\right)$

**Given $(x, y)$ is a point on a unit circle corresponding to $t$, find the value of all six circular functions of $t$.**

11.                          12.

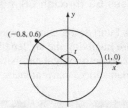    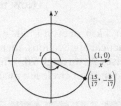

13.                          14.

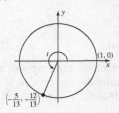    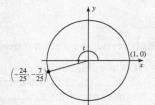

15.                          16.

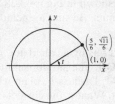    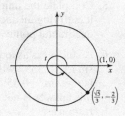

17. $\left(-\dfrac{2}{5}, \dfrac{\sqrt{21}}{5}\right)$    18. $\left(\dfrac{\sqrt{7}}{4}, -\dfrac{3}{4}\right)$

19. $\left(-\dfrac{1}{3}, -\dfrac{2\sqrt{2}}{3}\right)$    20. $\left(-\dfrac{2\sqrt{6}}{5}, -\dfrac{1}{5}\right)$

21. $\left(\dfrac{1}{2}, \dfrac{\sqrt{3}}{2}\right)$    22. $\left(\dfrac{\sqrt{3}}{2}, \dfrac{1}{2}\right)$

23. $\left(-\dfrac{\sqrt{2}}{2}, \dfrac{\sqrt{2}}{2}\right)$    24. $\left(\dfrac{\sqrt{2}}{3}, -\dfrac{\sqrt{7}}{3}\right)$

On a unit circle, the real number $t$ can represent either the amount of rotation or the *length of the arc* when we associate $t$ with a point $(x, y)$ on the circle. In the circle diagram shown, the real number $t$ in radians is marked off along the circumference. For Exercises 25 through 36, name the quadrant in which $t$ terminates and use the figure to estimate function values to one decimal place (use a straightedge). Check results using a calculator.

**Exercises 25 to 36**

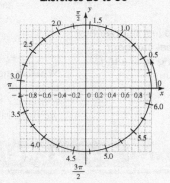

25. $\sin 0.75$              26. $\cos 2.75$

27. $\cos 5.5$              28. $\sin 4.0$

29. $\tan 0.8$              30. $\sec 3.75$

31. $\csc 2.0$              32. $\cot 0.5$

33. $\cos\left(\dfrac{5\pi}{8}\right)$    34. $\sin\left(\dfrac{5\pi}{8}\right)$

35. $\tan\left(\dfrac{8\pi}{5}\right)$    36. $\sec\left(\dfrac{8\pi}{5}\right)$

**Without using a calculator, find the value of $t$ in $[0, 2\pi)$ that corresponds to the following functions.**

37. $\sin t = \dfrac{\sqrt{3}}{2}$; $t$ in QII   38. $\cos t = \dfrac{1}{2}$; $t$ in QIV

39. $\cos t = -\dfrac{\sqrt{3}}{2}$ ; $t$ in QIII

40. $\sin t = -\dfrac{1}{2}$; $t$ in QIV

41. $\tan t = -\sqrt{3}$; $t$ in QII

42. $\sec t = -2$; $t$ in QIII

43. $\sin t = 1$; $t$ is quadrantal

44. $\cos t = -1$; $t$ is quadrantal

Without using a calculator, find the two values of $t$ (where possible) in $[0, 2\pi)$ that make each equation true.

**45.** $\sec t = -\sqrt{2}$

**46.** $\csc t = -\dfrac{2}{\sqrt{3}}$

**47.** $\tan t$ undefined

**48.** $\csc t$ undefined

**49.** $\cos t = -\dfrac{\sqrt{2}}{2}$

**50.** $\sin t = \dfrac{\sqrt{2}}{2}$

**51.** $\sin t = 0$

**52.** $\cos t = -1$

Using a calculator, find the value of $t$ in $[0, 2\pi)$ that corresponds to the following functions. Round to four decimal places.

**53.** $\sin t = 0.3215$, $\cos t > 0$

**54.** $\cos t = 0.7402$, $\sin t > 0$

**55.** $\cos t = -0.1424$, $\tan t > 0$

**56.** $\sin t = -0.5252$, $\cot t < 0$

**57.** $\cot t = -1.2345$, $\sec t < 0$

**58.** $\sec t = -2.0025$, $\tan t < 0$

**59.** $\csc t = -1.9709$, $\cot t < 0$

**60.** $\cot t = 0.6352$, $\csc t < 0$

Find an additional value of $t$ in $[0, 2\pi)$ that makes the equation true.

**61.** $\sin 0.8 \approx 0.7174$

**62.** $\cos 2.12 \approx -0.5220$

**63.** $\cos 4.5 \approx -0.2108$

**64.** $\sin 5.23 \approx -0.8690$

**65.** $\tan 0.4 \approx 0.4228$

**66.** $\sec 5.7 \approx 1.1980$

**67.** Given $\left(\frac{3}{4}, -\frac{4}{5}\right)$ is a point on the unit circle that corresponds to $t$. Find the coordinates of the point corresponding to (a) $-t$ and (b) $t + \pi$.

**68.** Given $\left(-\frac{7}{25}, \frac{24}{25}\right)$ is a point on the unit circle that corresponds to $t$. Find the coordinates of the point corresponding to (a) $-t + \pi$ and (b) $t - \pi$.

▶ **WORKING WITH FORMULAS**

**69.** The sine and cosine of $(2k + 1)\dfrac{\pi}{4}$; $k \in \mathbb{Z}$

In the solution to Example 3(a), we mentioned $\pm\dfrac{\sqrt{2}}{2}$ were standard values for sine and cosine, "related to certain multiples of $\dfrac{\pi}{4}$." Actually, we meant "odd multiples of $\dfrac{\pi}{4}$." The odd multiples of $\dfrac{\pi}{4}$ are given by the "formula" shown, where $k$ is any integer. (a) What multiples of $\dfrac{\pi}{4}$ are generated by $k = -3, -2, -1, 0, 1, 2, 3$? (b) Find similar formulas for Example 3(b), where $\sqrt{3}$ is a standard value for tangent and cotangent, "related to certain multiples of $\dfrac{\pi}{6}$."

**70.** Polynomial approximation of inverse sine: $\sin^{-1}x \approx x + \dfrac{1}{6}x^3 + \dfrac{3}{40}x^5$

Approximations such as the one shown are one of many useful results from calculus. (a) Use the polynomial given to verify your results of Exercise 53 by approximating $\sin^{-1} 0.3215$. (b) Compare the approximations of $\sin^{-1}0.99$ and $\sin^{-1}0.01$ with your calculator results. What do you notice?

▶ **APPLICATIONS**

**71. Laying new sod:** When new sod is laid, a heavy roller is used to press the sod down to ensure good contact with the ground beneath. The radius of the roller is 1 ft. (a) Through what angle (in radians) has the roller turned after being pulled across 5 ft of yard? (b) What angle must the roller turn through to press a length of 30 ft?

**72. Cable winch:** A large winch with a radius of 1 ft winds in 3 ft of cable. (a) Through what angle (in radians) has it turned? (b) What angle must it turn through in order to winch in 12.5 ft of cable?

**73. Wiring an apartment:** In the wiring of an apartment complex, electrical wire is being pulled from a spool with radius 1 decimeter (1 dm = 10 cm). (a) What length (in decimeters) is removed as the spool turns through 5 rad? (b) How many decimeters are removed in one complete turn ($t = 2\pi$) of the spool?

**74. Barrel races:** In the barrel races popular at some family reunions, contestants stand on a hard rubber barrel with a radius of 1 cubit (1 cubit = 18 in.), and try to "walk the barrel" from the start line to the finish line without falling. (a) What distance (in cubits) is traveled as the barrel is walked through an angle of 4.5 rad? (b) If the race is 25 cubits long, through what angle will the winning barrel walker walk the barrel?

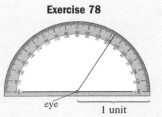

**Interplanetary measurement:** In the year 1905, astronomers began using astronomical units or AU to study the distances between the celestial bodies of our solar system. One AU represents the average distance between the Earth and the Sun, which is about 93 million miles. Pluto is roughly 39.24 AU from the Sun.

**75.** If the Earth travels through an angle of 2.5 rad about the Sun, (a) what distance in astronomical units (AU) has it traveled? (b) How many AU does it take for one complete orbit around the Sun?

**76.** If you include the dwarf planet Pluto, Jupiter is the middle (fifth of nine) planet from the Sun. Suppose astronomers had decided to use *its* average distance from the Sun as 1 AU. In this case, 1 AU would be 480 million miles. If Jupiter travels through an angle of 4 rad about the Sun, (a) what distance in the "new" astronomical units (AU) has it traveled? (b) How many of the new AU does it take to complete one-half an orbit about the Sun? (c) What distance in the new AU is the dwarf planet Pluto from the Sun?

**77. Compact disk circumference:** A standard compact disk has a radius of 6 cm. Call this length "1 unit." Mark a starting point on any large surface, then carefully roll the compact disk along this line without slippage, through one full revolution ($2\pi$ rad) and mark this spot. Take an accurate measurement of the resulting line segment. Is the result close to $2\pi$ "units" ($2\pi \times 6$ cm)?

**78. Verifying $s = r\theta$:**
On a protractor, carefully measure the distance from the middle of the protractor's eye to the edge of the protractor along the 0° mark, to the nearest half-millimeter. Call this length "1 unit." Then use a ruler to draw a straight line on a blank sheet of paper, and with the protractor on edge, start the zero degree mark at one end of the line, carefully roll the protractor until it reaches 1 radian (57.3°), and mark this spot. Now measure the length of the line segment created. Is it very close to 1 "unit" long?

**Exercise 78**

eye    1 unit

▶ **EXTENDING THE CONCEPT**

**79.** In this section, we discussed the *domain* of the circular functions, but said very little about their *range*. Review the concepts presented here and determine the range of $y = \cos t$ and $y = \sin t$. In other words, what are the smallest and largest output values we can expect?

**80.** Since $\tan t = \dfrac{\sin t}{\cos t}$, what can you say about the range of the tangent function?

**Use the radian grid given with Exercises 25–36 to answer Exercises 81 and 82.**

**81.** Given $\cos(2t) = -0.6$ with the terminal side of the arc in QII, (a) what is the value of $2t$? (b) What quadrant is $t$ in? (c) What is the value of $\cos t$? (d) Does $\cos(2t) = 2\cos t$?

**82.** Given $\sin(2t) = -0.8$ with the terminal side of the arc in QIII, (a) what is the value of $2t$? (b) What quadrant is $t$ in? (c) What is the value of $\sin t$? (d) Does $\sin(2t) = 2\sin t$?

▶ **MAINTAINING YOUR SKILLS**

**83. (3.2)** The armature for the rear windshield wiper has a length of 24 in., with a rubber wiper blade that is 20 in. long. What area of my rear windshield is cleaned as the armature swings back-and-forth through an angle of 110°?

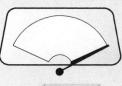

**84. (1.1)** The boxes used to ship some washing machines are perfect cubes with edges measuring 38 in. Use a special triangle to find the length of the diagonal $d$ of one side, and the length of the interior diagonal $D$ (through the middle of the box).

**85. (1.3)** Given $\sin \theta = \frac{21}{29}$ and $\cos \theta < 0$, find the value of the other five trig functions of $\theta$.

**86. (2.3)** From the far end of a 50 ft pool, the angle of elevation to the highest diving board is 19.8°. To the nearest foot, how high is the board?

**87. (3.3)** For $\theta = \dfrac{11\pi}{6}$, use a reference angle $\theta_r$ to evaluate the six trig functions of $\theta$.

**88. (2.2)** Triangle $ABC$ has sides of $a = 12$ m, $b = 35$ m, and $c = 37$ m. Verify that this is a right triangle and find the measure of angles $A$, $B$, and $C$, rounded to the nearest tenth.

# SUMMARY AND CONCEPT REVIEW

## SECTION 3.1    Angle Measure in Radians

### KEY CONCEPTS
- One (1) radian is the measure of a central angle subtended by an arc equal in length to the radius.
- Since $C = 2\pi r$, there are $2\pi$ radians in a complete revolution.
- The radian measure of an angle is $\theta = \dfrac{s}{r}$, where $r$ is the radius of the circle and $s$ is the length of the arc subtended by $\theta$.
- With $\theta$ measured in radians, $\theta$ and $\theta + 2\pi k$ are coterminal for any integer $k$.
- To convert degree measure to radians, multiply by $\dfrac{\pi}{180°}$; for radians to degrees, multiply by $\dfrac{180°}{\pi}$.
- Special angle conversions: $30° = \dfrac{\pi}{6}$, $45° = \dfrac{\pi}{4}$, $60° = \dfrac{\pi}{3}$, $90° = \dfrac{\pi}{2}$.

### EXERCISES
1. A central angle of a circle of radius 5 in. subtends a 15 in. long arc. Find the radian measure of this angle.
2. Convert to degrees and round to the nearest tenth: 2 rad.
3. Convert to radians and round to the nearest hundredth: $-101°$.
4. Convert to degrees: $\dfrac{2\pi}{3}$
5. Convert to radians: $210°$.
6. Find two positive and two negative angles that are coterminal with $\theta = \dfrac{\pi}{5}$. Answers may vary.

## SECTION 3.2    Arc Length, Velocity, and the Area of a Circular Sector

### KEY CONCEPTS
- The formula for arc length: $s = r\theta$, $\theta$ in radians.
- The formula for the area of a circular sector: $\mathcal{A} = \dfrac{1}{2}r^2\theta$, $\theta$ in radians.

- A location north or south of the equator is given in degrees latitude; a location east or west of the Greenwich Meridian is given in degrees longitude.

- Angular velocity is a rate of rotation per unit time: $\omega = \dfrac{\theta}{t}$.

- Linear velocity is a change in position per unit time: $V = \dfrac{r\theta}{t}$ or $V = r\omega$, $\theta$ in radians.

## EXERCISES

**7.** Find the arc length if $r = 5$ and $\theta = 57°$.

Find the angle, radius, arc length, and/or area as needed, until all values are known.

**8.**
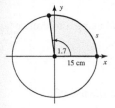

**9.**
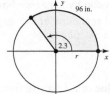

**10.**
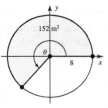

**11.** With great effort, 5-yr-old Mackenzie has just rolled her bowling ball down the lane, and it is traveling painfully slow. So slow, in fact, that you can count the number of revolutions the ball makes using the finger holes as a reference. (a) If the ball is rolling at 1.5 revolutions per second, what is the angular velocity? (b) If the ball's radius is 5 in., what is its linear velocity in feet per second? (c) If the distance to the first pin is 60 ft and the ball is true, how many seconds until it hits?

## SECTION 3.3  The Unit Circle

### KEY CONCEPTS

- A central unit circle is a circle with radius 1 unit having its center at the origin.
- A central circle is symmetric to both axes and the origin. This means that if $(a, b)$ is a point on the circle, then $(-a, b)$, $(-a, -b)$, and $(a, -b)$ are also on the circle and satisfy the equation of the circle.
- The points on the unit circle that correspond to the special angles are:

$$\frac{\pi}{6} \rightarrow \left(\frac{\sqrt{3}}{2}, \frac{1}{2}\right), \frac{\pi}{4} \rightarrow \left(\frac{\sqrt{2}}{2}, \frac{\sqrt{2}}{2}\right), \frac{\pi}{3} \rightarrow \left(\frac{1}{2}, \frac{\sqrt{3}}{2}\right).$$

- A reference angle is defined to be the acute angle formed by the terminal side of a given angle and the x-axis.
- For any rotation $\theta$ and a point on the unit circle associated with $\theta$, we have:

$$\cos \theta = x \qquad \sin \theta = y \qquad \tan \theta = \frac{y}{x} \qquad \sec \theta = \frac{1}{x} \qquad \csc \theta = \frac{1}{y} \qquad \cot \theta = \frac{x}{y}$$
$$x \neq 0 \qquad\quad x \neq 0 \qquad\quad y \neq 0 \qquad\quad y \neq 0$$

### EXERCISES

**12.** Given $\left(\dfrac{\sqrt{13}}{7}, y\right)$ is on a unit circle, find $y$ if the point is in QIV, then use the symmetry of the circle to locate three other points.

**13.** Find the reference angle associated with $\theta = \dfrac{16\pi}{6}$ and the associated point.

**14.** Evaluate without using a calculator: $\sin\left(\dfrac{7\pi}{6}\right)$

**15.** Verify the approximate point $(-0.7431, -0.6691)$ is on the unit circle and find the tangent of the associated angle.

**16.** Find the point on the unit circle that corresponds to $\theta = 6$. Round to four decimal places.

## SECTION 3.4   The Trigonometry of Real Numbers

### KEY CONCEPTS

- On a unit circle with $\theta$ in radians, the length of a subtended arc is numerically the same as the subtended angle, making the arc a "circular number line" and associating any given rotation with a unique real number.
- For functions of a real number we refer to a reference arc rather than a reference angle.
- For any real number $t$ and a point on the unit circle associated with $t$, we have:

$$\cos t = x \qquad \sin t = y \qquad \tan t = \frac{y}{x} \qquad \sec t = \frac{1}{x} \qquad \csc t = \frac{1}{y} \qquad \cot t = \frac{x}{y}$$
$$\qquad\qquad\qquad\qquad\qquad\qquad x \neq 0 \qquad\quad x \neq 0 \qquad\quad y \neq 0 \qquad\quad y \neq 0$$

- The domain of each trig function must exclude division by zero (see box on page 118).
- Given the specific value of any function, the related real number $t$ or angle $\theta$ can be found using a reference arc/angle, or the $\sin^{-1}$, $\cos^{-1}$, or $\tan^{-1}$ features of a calculator.

### EXERCISES

17. Given $\left( \dfrac{3}{4}, -\dfrac{\sqrt{7}}{4} \right)$ is on the unit circle, find the value of all six trig functions of $t$ without the use of a calculator.

18. Without using a calculator, find two values in $[0, 2\pi)$ that make the equation true: $\csc t = \dfrac{2}{\sqrt{3}}$.

19. Use a calculator to find the value of $t$ that corresponds to the situation described: $\cos t = -0.7641$ with $t$ in QII.

20. A crane used for lifting heavy equipment has a winch-drum with a 1-yd radius. (a) If 59 ft of cable has been wound in while lifting some equipment to the roof-top of a building, what radian angle has the drum turned through? (b) What angle must the drum turn through to wind in 75 ft of cable?

**1.** Name two values in $[0, 2\pi]$ where $\tan t = 1$.

**2.** Name two values in $[0, 2\pi]$ where $\cos t = -\dfrac{1}{2}$.

**3.** Find the arc length and area of the shaded sector.

**4.** Name the reference angle $\theta_r$ for the angle $\theta$ given.

**Exercise 3**

    **a.** $\dfrac{5\pi}{6}$     **b.** $-\dfrac{5\pi}{3}$

**5.** Verify that $\left(-\dfrac{\sqrt{2}}{2}, \dfrac{\sqrt{2}}{2}\right)$ is a point on the unit circle and find the value of all six trig functions at this point.

$(-4\sqrt{3}, -4)$

**6.** A salad spinner consists of a colander basket inside a large bowl, and is used to wash and dry lettuce and other salad ingredients. In vigorous use, the spinner is turned at about 3 revolutions per second. (a) Find the angular velocity and (b) find the linear velocity of a point of the circumference if the basket has a 20-cm radius.

**7.** Use a reference angle to find the value of $\cos\left(\dfrac{37\pi}{4}\right)$.

**8.** Solve each equation in $[0, 2\pi)$ without the use of a calculator. If the expression is undefined, so state.

    **a.** $x = \sin\left(-\dfrac{\pi}{4}\right)$     **b.** $\sec x = \sqrt{2}$

    **c.** $\cot\left(\dfrac{\pi}{2}\right) = x$     **d.** $\cos \pi = x$

    **e.** $\csc x = \dfrac{2\sqrt{3}}{3}$     **f.** $\tan\left(\dfrac{\pi}{2}\right) = x$

**9.** Convert the following to radian measure. Round to the nearest ten-thousandth when necessary.

    **a.** $-135°$     **b.** $258.1°$

**10.** Find the radius of a circle if an angle of $114.6°$ subtends an arc of length 3.2 m.

**11.** Convert the following to degree measure. Round to the nearest tenth when necessary.

    **a.** $\dfrac{7\pi}{3}$     **b.** $-\dfrac{1}{2}$

12. Given $\left(x, \dfrac{3}{4}\right)$ is on a unit circle, find $x$ if the point is in QII, then use the symmetry of the circle to locate three other points.

13. Find two positive and two negative angles that are coterminal with $\dfrac{3\pi}{7}$. Answers may vary.

14. Use a calculator to find two values in $[0, 2\pi)$ that make the equation true: $\cot t = -2.8127$.

15. The minute hand on Big Ben in London, England, measures 3.5 m from the center of the clock to its tip. To the nearest hundredth, find the area of the circular sector it passes over in 35 min.

16. Identify the terminal side quadrant of the following angles.
    a. $\theta = 4$        b. $\theta = -5$

17. As of 2009, the maximum speed of a standard 12-cm-wide Blu-ray disk is 10,000 rpm. In kilometers per hour, how fast is a point on the circumference of a standard disk moving?

18. What values of $t$ must be excluded from the domain of $f(t) = \tan t$?

19. Find the point on the unit circle that corresponds to $\theta = 8.25$. Round to the nearest ten-thousandth.

20. Find the radian measure of $\beta$ given $r = 4.4$ in. and $s = 7.7$ in.

**Exercise 20**

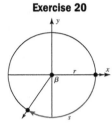

1. Name the reference angle of each angle $\theta$ given.

   **a.** $\dfrac{7\pi}{6}$      **b.** $\dfrac{25\pi}{3}$

2. Complete the table using reference angles and exact values. If a function is undefined, so state.

| $t$ | $\sin t$ | $\cos t$ | $\tan t$ | $\csc t$ | $\sec t$ | $\cot t$ |
|---|---|---|---|---|---|---|
| $0$ | | | | | | |
| $\dfrac{2\pi}{3}$ | | | | | | |
| $\dfrac{7\pi}{6}$ | | | | | | |
| $\dfrac{5\pi}{4}$ | | | | | | |
| $\dfrac{5\pi}{3}$ | | | | | | |
| $\dfrac{7\pi}{4}$ | | | | | | |
| $\dfrac{13\pi}{6}$ | | | | | | |

3. Verify that $\left(\dfrac{1}{3}, -\dfrac{2\sqrt{2}}{3}\right)$ is a point on the unit circle, then find the value of all six trig functions associated with this point.

4. In order to take pictures of a dance troupe as it performs, a camera crew rides in a cart on tracks that trace a circular arc. The radius of the arc is 75 ft, and from end to end the cart sweeps out an angle of 172.5° in 20 seconds. Use this information to find (a) the length of the track in feet and inches, (b) the angular velocity of the cart, and (c) the linear velocity of the cart in both ft/sec and mph.

5. Find the value of $t \in [0, 2\pi)$ satisfying the conditions given.

   **a.** $\sin t = -\dfrac{1}{2}$, $t$ in QIII

   **b.** $\sec t = \dfrac{2\sqrt{3}}{3}$, $t$ in QIV

   **c.** $\tan t = -1$, $t$ in QII

6. Memphis, Tennessee, is directly north of New Orleans, Louisiana, at 90°W longitude. Find the approximate distance between the cities in kilometers, given the Earth has a radius of 6373 km and Memphis is at 35°N latitude, while New Orleans is at 29.6°N latitude.

7. Given that $\left(\dfrac{20}{29}, \dfrac{21}{29}\right)$ is a point on the central unit circle, use the symmetry of the circle to name three other points on the circle.

**Exercise 8**

8. Show that the length of chord $\mathcal{L}$ in the diagram is given by $\mathcal{L} = 2r$, where $R$ is the radius of the circle and $r = R \cos \theta$. If the radius $R$ is 15.7 cm and $\theta = 33°$, how long is the chord?

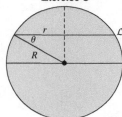

9. Find the value of $t$ satisfying the given conditions.
   a. $\sin t = -0.7568$; $t$ in QIII
   b. $\sec t = -1.5$; $t$ in QII

10. Convert the following to radian measure. Round all nonstandard angles to the nearest ten-thousandth.
    a. $300°$       b. $-72°39'$       c. $\pi°$

11. Convert the following to degree measure. Round all nonstandard angles to the nearest tenth.

    a. $9.29$       b. $-\dfrac{3\pi}{2}$       c. $45$

12. While Malena is jumping rope, her hands move in a circular path of radius 3 in. at a rate of 50 rpm. A point $P$ on the middle of the rope also moves in a circular path at the same rate, but of radius 3 ft. To the nearest tenth of a mile per hour, find the linear velocity of (a) her hands and (b) the point $P$.

    **Exercise 12**

13. Find the measure of the angle $\theta$ shown. Round to the nearest tenth of a degree.

14. Find the area $\mathcal{A}$ of the circular sector shown. Round to the nearest tenth.

    **Exercises 13 and 14**

    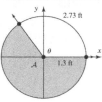

15. What values of $t$ must be excluded from the domain of $f(t) = \csc t$?

16. Identify the terminal side quadrant of the following angles.
    a. $\theta = 1$       b. $\theta = 5$
    c. $\theta = -3.14$       d. $\theta = -4$

17. Walking to her car one frigid Minnesota morning, Sheena noticed a tire was low. On the way to work, she adds air to the tire, returning it to its original circular shape of radius 12.9 in. What central angle subtends the portion of the tire that was flattened against Sheena's driveway (see figure)? Round to the nearest tenth of a degree.

    **Exercise 17**

    2.3 in.

18. Dragon the hamster runs on his stationary wheel at a speed of 200 rpm. If the wheel has a radius of 1 dm, how long would it take him to run 1 km at this rate?

19. Find the point on the unit circle that corresponds to $\theta = -2.22$. Round to the nearest ten-thousandth.

20. Find two positive and two negative angles that are coterminal with $-\dfrac{5\pi}{9}$. Answers may vary.

### Signs, Quadrants, and Reference Arcs

Graphing calculators can help us visualize the concept of reference arcs and angles, and better understand their connection to the circular functions. Just prior to Example 3 from Section 2.1, we placed a 30-60-90 triangle in QI, with the 30° angle at the origin and the longer leg along the $x$-axis. We later noted that the slope of the line coincident with the hypotenuse must be $m = \dfrac{1}{\sqrt{3}} = \dfrac{\sqrt{3}}{3}$, since the $\dfrac{\text{rise}}{\text{run}}$ ratio was identical to the ratio of the shorter leg to the longer leg of the triangle.

**Figure 3.29**

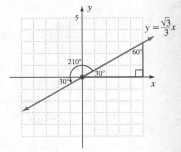

The equation of this line is then $y = \dfrac{\sqrt{3}}{3}x$. From elementary geometry, we know that vertical angles are equal, and so the acute angle in QIII formed by this line and the negative $x$-axis must also measure 30°, and is the reference angle for 210° (see Figure 3.29). By reorienting the same triangle in QII, two additional 30° angles can be formed, where the line coincident with this hypotenuse has an equation of $y = -\dfrac{\sqrt{3}}{3}x$. These are the 30° reference angles for 150° and 330°. From our work in Section 3.3, the equation of a unit circle is given by $x^2 + y^2 = 1$, which is $y = \pm\sqrt{1 - x^2}$ in function form. By graphing these functions on a graphing calculator, we can verify two important concepts: (1) that the point on a unit circle associated with $30° = \dfrac{\pi}{6}$ is $\left(\dfrac{\sqrt{3}}{2}, \dfrac{1}{2}\right)$ and (2) that the coordinates of the points associated with reference angles/arcs of similar measure are identical except for their sign. Using a graphing calculator, enter $Y_1 = \sqrt{1 - x^2}$ (the upper half of a unit circle), $Y_2 = \dfrac{\sqrt{3}}{3}x$, $Y_3 = -\sqrt{1 - x^2}$ (the lower half of a unit circle), and $Y_4 = -\dfrac{\sqrt{3}}{3}x$ (see Figure 3.30). Graphing the functions using the $\boxed{\text{ZOOM}}$ **4:ZDecimal** feature will produce a "friendly" and square viewing window, but with a relatively small unit circle. Using the $\boxed{\text{ZOOM}}$ **2:Zoom In** feature will give a better view, with the final window size depending on the settings of your zoom factors. Our settings were at XFactor = 2 and YFactor = 2, which produced the screen shown in Figure 3.31 (to access the zoom factors, press $\boxed{\text{ZOOM}}$ $\boxed{\blacktriangleright}$ **4:SetFactors**). Now comes the fun part. To find the point on the unit circle corresponding to $30° = \dfrac{\pi}{6}$, we need only find where the line intersects the unit circle in QI. This is accomplished using the keystrokes $\boxed{\text{2nd}}$ $\boxed{\text{TRACE}}$ (CALC) **5:Intersect,** and identifying the graphs we're interested in. After doing so, the calculator returns the values shown in Figure 3.32, which are indeed the equivalent of $\left(\dfrac{\sqrt{3}}{2}, \dfrac{1}{2}\right)$. Using the down arrow $\boxed{\blacktriangledown}$ at this point will "jump the cursor" to the point where $Y_3 = -\sqrt{1 - x^2}$ and $Y_4 = -\dfrac{\sqrt{3}}{3}x$ intersect, where we note *the output values remain the same* except that in QIV, the $y$-coordinate is negative (see Figure 3.33). In addition, since the calculator stores the last used $x$-value in the temporary location $\boxed{\text{X, T, θ, n}}$ we can find the point of intersection in QIII $\left(Y_3 = -\sqrt{1 - x^2} \text{ with } Y_2 = \dfrac{\sqrt{3}}{3}x\right)$ by simply using the keystrokes $\boxed{(-)}$ $\boxed{\text{X, T, θ, n}}$ $\boxed{\text{ENTER}}$, and the point of intersection in QII $\left(Y_1 = \sqrt{1 - x^2} \text{ with } Y_4 = -\dfrac{\sqrt{3}}{3}x\right)$ using the up arrow $\boxed{\blacktriangle}$ (press the up and down arrows repeatedly for effect). Exercises of this type help to reinforce the value of reference angles and arcs, and give visual support for the unit circle definition of the trig functions, as we can more clearly see, for example, that for $\cos t = x$: $\cos 30°$ in QI and $\cos 330°$ in QIV are both equal to $\dfrac{\sqrt{3}}{2}$, while $\cos 150°$ in QII and $\cos 210°$ in QIII are both equal to $-\dfrac{\sqrt{3}}{2}$.

**Figure 3.30**

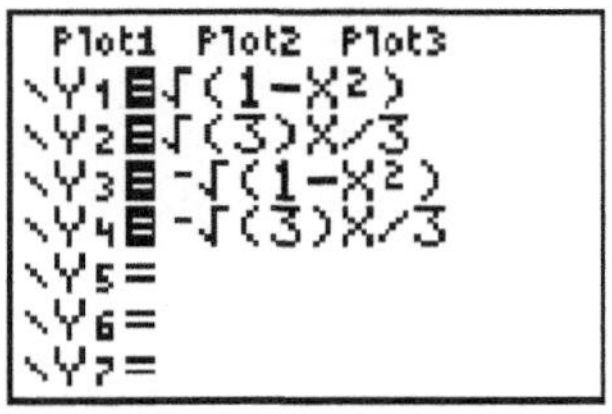

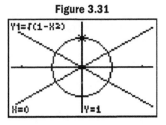

**Figure 3.31**

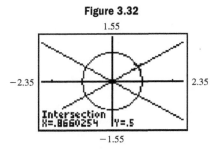

**Figure 3.32**

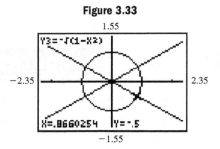

**Figure 3.33**

**Exercise 1:** Place a 45-45-90 triangle in QI, with a 45° angle at the origin and one side along the positive $x$-axis, then answer the following questions.

　**a.** What is the equation of the line coincident with the hypotenuse?

　**b.** What acute angle is formed in QIII by the line from (a) and the negative $x$-axis? Why?

　**c.** The acute angle from (b) is the reference angle for what positive angle $\theta$ $(0 < \theta < 360°)$?

　**d.** If the 45-45-90 triangle were reoriented in QII, what would be the equation of the line coincident with the hypotenuse?

　**e.** Using the triangle and line from (d), reference angles of $\theta_r = 45°$ in QII and QIV are created. Find $\theta$ for each of these angles $(0 < \theta < 360°)$.

　**f.** Use a graphing calculator to determine where the lines from (a) and (d) intersect with the unit circle, and use the results to find/verify the value of sin 45°, sin 135°, sin 225° and sin 315°.

**Exercise 2:** Repeat Exercise 1 using a 30-60-90 triangle with the *shorter side* along the $x$-axis. Use the results to find the value of tan 60°, tan 120°, tan 240° and tan 300°.

 **STRENGTHENING CORE SKILLS**

## Trigonometry of the Real Numbers and the Wrapping Function

The circular functions are sometimes discussed in terms of what is called a *wrapping function,* in which the real number line is literally wrapped around the unit circle. This approach can help illustrate how the trig functions can be seen as functions of the real numbers, and apart from any reference to a right triangle. Figure 3.34 shows (1) a unit circle with the location of certain points on the circumference clearly marked and (2) a number line that has been marked in multiples of $\frac{\pi}{12}$ to coincide with the length of the special arcs (integers are shown in the background). Figure 3.35 shows this same number line wrapped counterclockwise around the unit circle in the positive direction. Note how the resulting diagram confirms that an arc of length $t = \frac{\pi}{4}$ is associated with the point $\left(\frac{\sqrt{2}}{2}, \frac{\sqrt{2}}{2}\right)$ on the unit circle: $\cos\frac{\pi}{4} = \frac{\sqrt{2}}{2}$ and $\sin\frac{\pi}{4} = \frac{\sqrt{2}}{2}$; while an arc of length of $t = \frac{5\pi}{6}$ is associated with the point $\left(-\frac{\sqrt{3}}{2}, \frac{1}{2}\right)$: $\cos\frac{5\pi}{6} = -\frac{\sqrt{3}}{2}$ and $\sin\frac{5\pi}{6} = \frac{1}{2}$. Use this information to complete the exercises given.

**Figure 3.34**

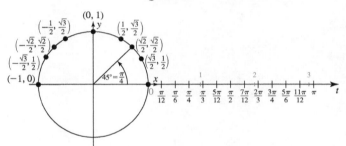

**Figure 3.35**

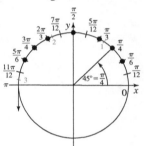

1. What is the ordered pair associated with an arc length of $t = \frac{2\pi}{3}$? What is the value of $\cos t$? $\sin t$?

2. What arc length $t$ is associated with the ordered pair $\left(-\frac{\sqrt{3}}{2}, \frac{1}{2}\right)$? Is $\cos t$ positive or negative? Why?

3. If we continued to wrap this number line all the way around the circle, in what quadrant would an arc length of $t = \frac{11\pi}{6}$ terminate? Would $\sin t$ be positive or negative?

4. Suppose we wrapped a number line with negative values clockwise around the unit circle. In what quadrant would an arc length of $t = -\frac{5\pi}{3}$ terminate? What is $\cos t$? $\sin t$? What positive rotation terminates at the same point?

**1.** Without a calculator, what values in $[0, 2\pi)$ make the equation true: $\sin t = -\dfrac{\sqrt{3}}{2}$?

**2.** Given $\left(\dfrac{3}{4}, -\dfrac{\sqrt{7}}{4}\right)$ is a point on the unit circle corresponding to $t$, find all six trig functions of $t$.

**3.** Find the complement of $67°22'39''$.

**4.** Given $\cot \dfrac{\pi}{8} = \sqrt{2} + 1$, find $\tan^2 \dfrac{3\pi}{8}$ without a calculator.

**5.** Given $A = 9x°$, $B = (6x + 4)°$, and $C = 7x°$, find the measures of the angles of $\triangle ABC$.

6. As of 2009, the Key Tower in Cleveland was the fifty-fifth tallest building in the world. If Lewis is standing 457 m from the base of the tower, the angle of elevation to the top of the tower is 32.31°. To the nearest meter, how tall is the Key Tower?

7. Find the measure of angle α for the triangle shown and convert it to radians. Round to four decimal places.

**Exercise 7**

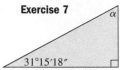

31°15′18″

8. Verify the point $\left(\dfrac{8}{17}, \dfrac{15}{17}\right)$ is on a unit circle, and use the circle's symmetry to find three other points on the circle.

9. Find the value of the six trigonometric functions, given $(-5, -8)$ is on the terminal side of angle θ in standard position.

10. Given $t = \dfrac{11\pi}{6}$, use reference arcs to state the value of all six trig functions of $t$ without using a calculator.

Solve each triangle by completing the table. Round angles to the nearest tenth and sides to the nearest hundredth.

11.

| Angles | Sides |
|---|---|
| | a = 7 ft |
| C = 90° | c = 14 ft |

**Exercises 11 and 12**

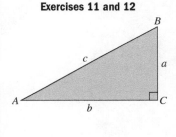

12.

| Angles | Sides |
|---|---|
| A = 38° | |
| C = 90° | c = 11 cm |

13. The conveyor belt used in many grocery check-out lines is on rollers that have a 2-in. radius and turn at 252 rpm. (a) What is the angular velocity of the rollers? (b) How fast are your groceries moving (in mph) when the belt is moving?

14. The planet Mars has a near-circular orbit (its eccentricity is 0.093—the closer to zero, the more circular the orbit). It orbits the Sun at an average distance of 142,000,000 mi and takes 687 days to complete one circuit. (a) Find the angular velocity of its orbit in radians per year, and (b) find the planet's linear velocity as it orbits the Sun, in miles per second.

15. Verify the equation is an identity using factoring and fundamental identities. $\dfrac{\sin x \cos x + \cos x}{\sin x + \sin^2 x} = \cot x$

16. Given $t = 5.37$, (a) in what quadrant does the arc terminate? (b) What is the reference arc? (c) Find the value of sin $t$ rounded to four decimal places.

17. A jet-stream water sprinkler shoots water a distance of 15 m and turns back and forth through an angle of $t = 1.2$ rad. (a) What is the length of the arc that the sprinkler reaches? (b) What is the area in $m^2$ of the yard that is watered?

18. Find the exact value of sin θ, cos θ, and tan θ given $\theta = 225°$.

19. Find two negative angles that are coterminal with 1000°. Answers may vary.

20. Use the triangle shown to find the values of the indicated functions, given $a = 4$, $b = 2\sqrt{5}$, and $c = 6$.

**Exercise 20**

a. sin β

b. cot α

c. sec β

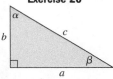

21. The Earth has a radius of 3960 mi. Mexico City, Mexico, is located at approximately 19°N latitude, and is almost exactly due south of Hutchinson, Kansas, located at about 38°N latitude. How many miles separate the two cities?

22. Ryan is playing catch with himself, throwing a baseball high into the air and catching it. At the ball's maximum height, the *shadow* of the ball is 35 ft away from him. If Ryan is 4.2 ft tall and casts a 2.8-ft shadow, how high is he throwing the baseball?

23. Given $(\sin \theta)(\tan \theta) > 0$ and $(\cos^2\theta)(\sin \theta) < 0$, determine the terminal side quadrant of θ.

24. Given $\theta = 321°54'$, find the reference angle $\theta_r$.

25. Find the value of the indicated function. If it is undefined, so state.

a. sec 360°          b. tan 270°

c. csc π             d. $\cot \dfrac{\pi}{2}$

# Trigonometric Graphs and Models

# Trigonometric Graphs and Models

4

## CHAPTER CONNECTIONS

While written records of trigonometry are much more recent than those of geometry and algebra, the *roots* of trigonometry are likely just as ancient. Peering into the nighttime heavens, ancient scholars noticed patterns among the celestial bodies, giving rise to the desire to model their regular recurrence. But even at the beginning of the modern age, with the tools of geometry at hand and the study of algebra maturing, astronomers were unable to come up with accurate models. This had to wait for the study of periodic functions to mature. These functions also enable us to model and predict many other types of cyclic phenomena, including critical ocean and wave behavior. To accomplish this, the National Oceanic and Atmospheric Administration (NOAA) uses a network of buoys such as the DART® II shown to ensure the early detection and warning of tsunamis.

▶ This application appears as Exercise 55 in Section 4.1

**Graphs of the Sine and Cosine Functions**

## Learning Objectives

*In Section 4.1 you will learn how to:*

☐ **A.** Graph $f(t) = \sin t$ using special values and symmetry

☐ **B.** Graph $f(t) = \cos t$ using special values and symmetry

☐ **C.** Graph sine and cosine functions with various amplitudes and periods

☐ **D.** Write the equation for a given graph

As with the graphs of other functions, trigonometric graphs contribute a great deal toward the understanding of each function and its applications. For now, our primary interest is the general shape of each basic graph and some of the transformations that can be applied. We will also learn to analyze each graph, and to capitalize on the features that enable us to apply the functions as real-world models.

## A. Graphing $f(t) = \sin t$

Consider the following table of values (Table 4.1) for $\sin t$ and the special angles in QI.

**Table 4.1**

| $t$ | 0 | $\dfrac{\pi}{6}$ | $\dfrac{\pi}{4}$ | $\dfrac{\pi}{3}$ | $\dfrac{\pi}{2}$ |
|---|---|---|---|---|---|
| $\sin t$ | 0 | $\dfrac{1}{2}$ | $\dfrac{\sqrt{2}}{2}$ | $\dfrac{\sqrt{3}}{2}$ | 1 |

Observe that in this interval, sine values are increasing from 0 to 1. From $\dfrac{\pi}{2}$ to $\pi$ (QII), special values taken from the unit circle show sine values are decreasing from 1 to 0, *but through the same output values as in* QI. See Figures 4.1 through 4.3.

**Figure 4.1**

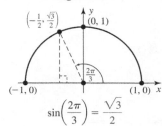

$$\sin\left(\frac{2\pi}{3}\right) = \frac{\sqrt{3}}{2}$$

**Figure 4.2**

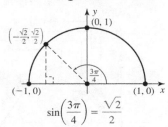

$$\sin\left(\frac{3\pi}{4}\right) = \frac{\sqrt{2}}{2}$$

**Figure 4.3**

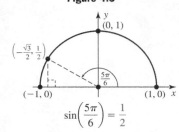

$$\sin\left(\frac{5\pi}{6}\right) = \frac{1}{2}$$

With this information we can extend our table of values through $\pi$, noting that $\sin \pi = 0$ (see Table 4.2).

**Table 4.2**

| $t$ | 0 | $\dfrac{\pi}{6}$ | $\dfrac{\pi}{4}$ | $\dfrac{\pi}{3}$ | $\dfrac{\pi}{2}$ | $\dfrac{2\pi}{3}$ | $\dfrac{3\pi}{4}$ | $\dfrac{5\pi}{6}$ | $\pi$ |
|---|---|---|---|---|---|---|---|---|---|
| $\sin t$ | 0 | $\dfrac{1}{2}$ | $\dfrac{\sqrt{2}}{2}$ | $\dfrac{\sqrt{3}}{2}$ | 1 | $\dfrac{\sqrt{3}}{2}$ | $\dfrac{\sqrt{2}}{2}$ | $\dfrac{1}{2}$ | 0 |

Using the symmetry of the circle and the fact that $y$ is negative in QIII and QIV, we can complete the table for values between $\pi$ and $2\pi$.

**EXAMPLE 1** ▶ **Finding Function Values Using Symmetry**

Use the symmetry of the unit circle and reference arcs of special values to complete Table 4.3. Recall that $y$ is negative in QIII and QIV.

**Table 4.3**

| $t$ | $\pi$ | $\dfrac{7\pi}{6}$ | $\dfrac{5\pi}{4}$ | $\dfrac{4\pi}{3}$ | $\dfrac{3\pi}{2}$ | $\dfrac{5\pi}{3}$ | $\dfrac{7\pi}{4}$ | $\dfrac{11\pi}{6}$ | $2\pi$ |
|---|---|---|---|---|---|---|---|---|---|
| $\sin t$ | | | | | | | | | |

**Solution** ▶ Symmetry shows that for any odd multiple of $t = \dfrac{\pi}{4}$, $\sin t = \pm\dfrac{\sqrt{2}}{2}$ depending on the quadrant of the terminal side. Similarly, for any reference arc of $\dfrac{\pi}{6}$, $\sin t = \pm\dfrac{1}{2}$, while any reference arc of $\dfrac{\pi}{3}$ will give $\sin t = \pm\dfrac{\sqrt{3}}{2}$. The completed table is shown in Table 4.4.

**Table 4.4**

| $t$ | $\pi$ | $\dfrac{7\pi}{6}$ | $\dfrac{5\pi}{4}$ | $\dfrac{4\pi}{3}$ | $\dfrac{3\pi}{2}$ | $\dfrac{5\pi}{3}$ | $\dfrac{7\pi}{4}$ | $\dfrac{11\pi}{6}$ | $2\pi$ |
|---|---|---|---|---|---|---|---|---|---|
| $\sin t$ | $0$ | $-\dfrac{1}{2}$ | $-\dfrac{\sqrt{2}}{2}$ | $-\dfrac{\sqrt{3}}{2}$ | $-1$ | $-\dfrac{\sqrt{3}}{2}$ | $-\dfrac{\sqrt{2}}{2}$ | $-\dfrac{1}{2}$ | $0$ |

**Now try Exercises 7 and 8** ▶

Noting that $\dfrac{1}{2} = 0.5$, $\dfrac{\sqrt{2}}{2} \approx 0.71$, and $\dfrac{\sqrt{3}}{2} \approx 0.87$, we plot these points and connect them with a smooth curve to graph $y = \sin t$ in the interval $[0, 2\pi]$. The first five plotted points are labeled in Figure 4.4.

**Figure 4.4**

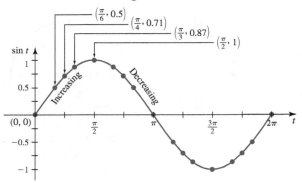

Expanding the table from $2\pi$ to $4\pi$ using reference arcs and the unit circle shows that function values begin to repeat. For example, $\sin\left(\dfrac{13\pi}{6}\right) = \sin\left(\dfrac{\pi}{6}\right)$ since $\theta_r = \dfrac{\pi}{6}$, $\sin\left(\dfrac{9\pi}{4}\right) = \sin\left(\dfrac{\pi}{4}\right)$ since $\theta_r = \dfrac{\pi}{4}$, and so on. Functions that cycle through a set pattern of values are said to be **periodic functions.**

**Periodic Functions**

A function $f$ is said to be periodic if there is a positive number $P$ such that
$$f(t + P) = f(t)$$
for all $t$ in the domain. The smallest number $P$ for which this occurs is called the **period** of $f$.

For the sine function we have $\sin t = \sin(t + 2\pi)$, as in $\sin\left(\dfrac{13\pi}{6}\right) = \sin\left(\dfrac{\pi}{6} + 2\pi\right)$ and $\sin\left(\dfrac{9\pi}{4}\right) = \sin\left(\dfrac{\pi}{4} + 2\pi\right)$, with the idea extending to all other real numbers $t$: $\sin t = \sin(t + 2\pi k)$ for all integers $k$. The sine function is periodic with period $P = 2\pi$.

Although we initially focused on positive values of $t$ in $[0, 2\pi]$, $t < 0$ and $k < 0$ are certainly possibilities and we note the graph of $f(t) = \sin t$ extends infinitely in both directions (see Figure 4.5).

**Figure 4.5**

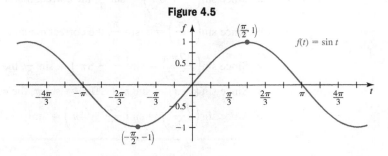

Finally, both the graph and the unit circle confirm that the range of $f(t) = \sin t$ is $[-1, 1]$, and that $f(t) = \sin t$ is an odd function. In particular, the graph shows $\sin\left(-\dfrac{\pi}{2}\right) = -\sin\left(\dfrac{\pi}{2}\right)$, and the unit circle shows $\sin t = y$, and $\sin(-t) = -y$ (see Figure 4.6), from which we obtain $\sin(-t) = -\sin t$ by substitution. As a handy reference, the following box summarizes the main characteristics of $f(t) = \sin t$.

**Figure 4.6**

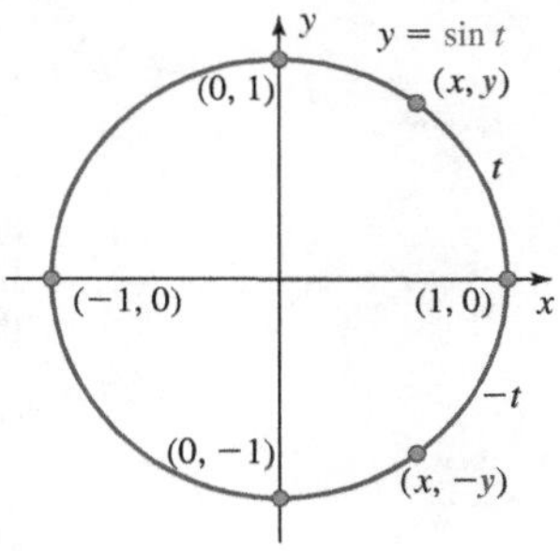

### Characteristics of $f(t) = \sin t$

For all real numbers $t$ and integers $k$,

| Domain | Range | Period |
|--------|-------|--------|
| $(-\infty, \infty)$ | $[-1, 1]$ | $2\pi$ |
| **Symmetry** | **Maximum value** | **Minimum value** |
| odd | $\sin t = 1$ | $\sin t = -1$ |
| $\sin(-t) = -\sin t$ | at $t = \dfrac{\pi}{2} + 2\pi k$ | at $t = \dfrac{3\pi}{2} + 2\pi k$ |
| **Increasing** | **Decreasing** | **Zeroes** |
| $\left(0, \dfrac{\pi}{2}\right) \cup \left(\dfrac{3\pi}{2}, 2\pi\right)$ | $\left(\dfrac{\pi}{2}, \dfrac{3\pi}{2}\right)$ | $t = k\pi$ |

**EXAMPLE 2** ▶ **Using the Period of sin t to Find Function Values**

Use the characteristics of $f(t) = \sin t$ to match the given value of $t$ to the correct value of $\sin t$.

a. $t = \left(\dfrac{\pi}{4} + 8\pi\right)$     b. $t = -\dfrac{\pi}{6}$     c. $t = \dfrac{17\pi}{2}$     d. $t = 21\pi$     e. $t = \dfrac{11\pi}{2}$

I. $\sin t = 1$    II. $\sin t = -\dfrac{1}{2}$    III. $\sin t = -1$    IV. $\sin t = \dfrac{\sqrt{2}}{2}$    V. $\sin t = 0$

Solution ▶   **a.** Since $\sin\left(\dfrac{\pi}{4} + 8\pi\right) = \sin\dfrac{\pi}{4}$, the correct match is (IV).

**b.** Since $\sin\left(-\dfrac{\pi}{6}\right) = -\sin\dfrac{\pi}{6}$, the correct match is (II).

**c.** Since $\sin\left(\dfrac{17\pi}{2}\right) = \sin\left(\dfrac{\pi}{2} + 8\pi\right) = \sin\dfrac{\pi}{2}$, the correct match is (I).

**d.** Since $\sin(21\pi) = \sin(\pi + 20\pi) = \sin\pi$, the correct match is (V).

**e.** Since $\sin\left(\dfrac{11\pi}{2}\right) = \sin\left(\dfrac{3\pi}{2} + 4\pi\right) = \sin\left(\dfrac{3\pi}{2}\right)$, the correct match is (III).

**Now try Exercises 9 and 10 ▶**

Many of the transformations applied to algebraic graphs can also be applied to trigonometric graphs. These transformations may stretch, reflect, or translate the graph, but it will still retain its basic shape. In numerous applications, it will help if you're able to draw a quick, accurate sketch of the transformations involving $f(t) = \sin t$. To assist this effort, we'll begin with the interval $[0, 2\pi]$, combine the characteristics just listed with some simple geometry, and offer the following four-step process. Steps I through IV are illustrated in Figures 4.7 through 4.10.

**Figure 4.7**

**Figure 4.8**

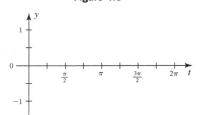

**Figure 4.9**

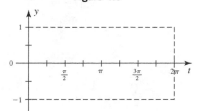

**Figure 4.10**

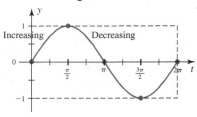

**Step I:**    Draw the $y$-axis, mark zero halfway up, with $-1$ and $1$ an equal distance from this zero. Then draw an extended $t$-axis and tick mark $2\pi$ to the extreme right (Figure 4.7).

**Step II:**   On the $t$-axis, mark halfway between 0 and $2\pi$ and label it "$\pi$," mark halfway between $\pi$ on either side and label the marks $\dfrac{\pi}{2}$ and $\dfrac{3\pi}{2}$. Halfway between these you can draw additional tick marks to represent the remaining multiples of $\dfrac{\pi}{4}$ (Figure 4.8).

**Step III:**  Next, lightly draw a rectangular frame, which we'll call the **reference rectangle,** $P = 2\pi$ units wide and 2 units tall, centered on the $t$-axis and with the $y$-axis along the left side (Figure 4.9).

**Step IV:** Knowing $y = \sin t$ is positive and increasing in QI, that the range is $[-1, 1]$, that the zeroes are $0$, $\pi$, and $2\pi$, and that maximum and minimum values *occur halfway between the zeroes* (since there is no horizontal shift), we can draw a reliable graph of $y = \sin t$ by partitioning the rectangle into four equal parts to locate these values (note **bold** tick-marks). We will call this partitioning of the reference rectangle the **rule of fourths,** since we are then scaling the $t$-axis in increments of $\frac{P}{4}$ (Figure 4.10).

**EXAMPLE 3 ▶ Graphing $y = \sin t$ Using a Reference Rectangle**

Use steps I through IV to draw a sketch of $y = \sin t$ for the interval $\left[-\frac{\pi}{2}, \frac{3\pi}{2}\right]$.

**Solution ▶** Start by completing steps I and II, then extend the $t$-axis to include $-2\pi$. Beginning at $t = 0$, draw a reference rectangle $2\pi$ units wide and 2 units tall, centered on the $t$-axis. After applying the rule of fourths, we note the zeroes occur at $t = 0$, $t = \pi$, and $t = 2\pi$, while the max/min values fall halfway between them at $t = \frac{\pi}{2}$ and $t = \frac{3\pi}{2}$ (see Figure 4.11). Plot these points and connect them with a smooth, dashed curve. This is the primary period of the sine curve.

**Figure 4.11**

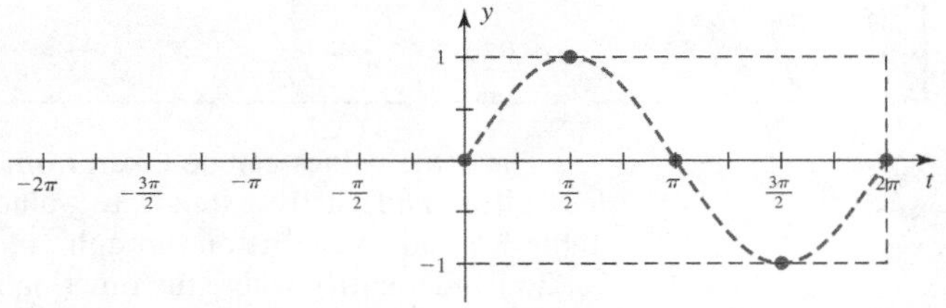

Using the periodic nature of the sine function, we can also graph the sine curve on the interval $[-2\pi, 0]$, as shown in Figure 4.12. The rule of fourths again helps to locate the zeroes and max/min values (note the bold tick-marks) over this interval.

**Figure 4.12**

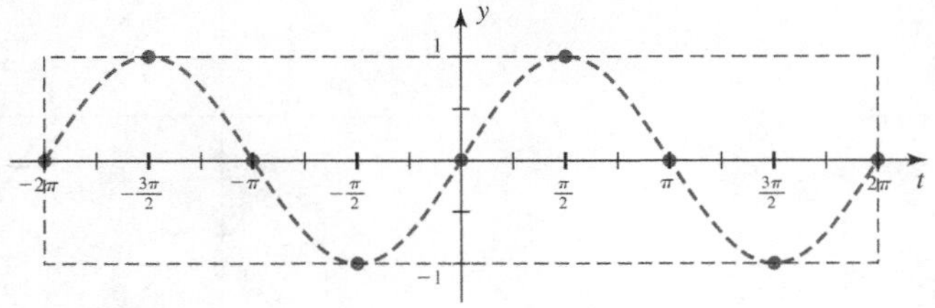

For the graph of $y = \sin t$ in $\left[-\frac{\pi}{2}, \frac{3\pi}{2}\right]$, we simply highlight the graph in this interval using a solid curve, as shown in Figure 4.13.

**Figure 4.13**

**WORTHY OF NOTE**

Since the interval $\left[-\frac{\pi}{2}, \frac{3\pi}{2}\right]$ is $P = 2\pi$ units wide, this section of the graph can generate the entire graph of $y = \sin t$.

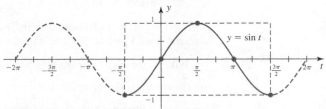

**A. You've just learned how to graph $f(t) = \sin t$ using special values and symmetry**

Now try Exercises 11 and 12 ▶

## B. Graphing $f(t) = \cos t$

With the graph of $f(t) = \sin t$ established, sketching the graph of $f(t) = \cos t$ is a very natural next step. First, note that when $t = 0$, $\cos t = 1$ so the graph of $y = \cos t$ will begin at $(0, 1)$ in the interval $[0, 2\pi]$. Second, we've seen $\left(\pm\frac{1}{2}, \pm\frac{\sqrt{3}}{2}\right)$, $\left(\pm\frac{\sqrt{3}}{2}, \pm\frac{1}{2}\right)$ and $\left(\pm\frac{\sqrt{2}}{2}, \pm\frac{\sqrt{2}}{2}\right)$ are all points on the unit circle since they satisfy $x^2 + y^2 = 1$. Since $\cos t = x$ and $\sin t = y$, the Pythagorean identity $\cos^2 t + \sin^2 t = 1$ can be obtained by direct substitution. This means if $\sin t = \pm\frac{1}{2}$, then $\cos t = \pm\frac{\sqrt{3}}{2}$ and vice versa, with the signs taken from the appropriate quadrant.

Similarly, if $\sin t = 0$, then $\cos t = \pm 1$ and vice versa. The table of values for cosine then becomes a simple variation of the table for sine, as shown in Table 4.5 for $t \in [0, \pi]$.

### Table 4.5

| $t$ | 0 | $\frac{\pi}{6}$ | $\frac{\pi}{4}$ | $\frac{\pi}{3}$ | $\frac{\pi}{2}$ | $\frac{2\pi}{3}$ | $\frac{3\pi}{4}$ | $\frac{5\pi}{6}$ | $\pi$ |
|---|---|---|---|---|---|---|---|---|---|
| $\sin t$ | 0 | $\frac{1}{2} = 0.5$ | $\frac{\sqrt{2}}{2} \approx 0.71$ | $\frac{\sqrt{3}}{2} \approx 0.87$ | 1 | $\frac{\sqrt{3}}{2} \approx 0.87$ | $\frac{\sqrt{2}}{2} \approx 0.71$ | $\frac{1}{2} = 0.5$ | 0 |
| $\cos t$ | 1 | $\frac{\sqrt{3}}{2} \approx 0.87$ | $\frac{\sqrt{2}}{2} \approx 0.71$ | $\frac{1}{2} = 0.5$ | 0 | $-\frac{1}{2} = -0.5$ | $-\frac{\sqrt{2}}{2} \approx -0.71$ | $-\frac{\sqrt{3}}{2} \approx -0.87$ | $-1$ |

The same values can be taken from the unit circle, but this view requires much less effort and easily extends to values of $t$ in $[\pi, 2\pi]$. Using the points from Table 4.5 and its extension through $[\pi, 2\pi]$, we can draw the graph of $y = \cos t$ in $[0, 2\pi]$ and identify where the function is increasing and decreasing in this interval. See Figure 4.14.

### Figure 4.14

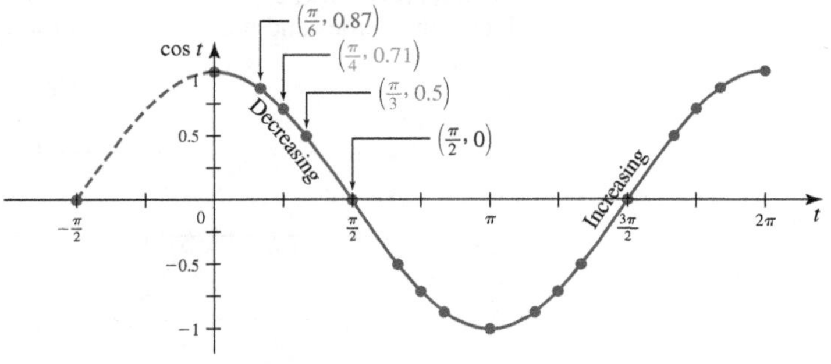

The function is decreasing for $t$ in $(0, \pi)$, and increasing for $t$ in $(\pi, 2\pi)$. The end result appears to be the graph of $y = \sin t$ shifted to the left $\frac{\pi}{2}$ units, a fact more easily seen if we extend the graph to $-\frac{\pi}{2}$ as shown. This is in fact the case, and is a relationship we will later prove in Chapter 5. Like $y = \sin t$, the function $y = \cos t$ is periodic with period $P = 2\pi$, with the graph extending infinitely in both directions.

Finally, we note that cosine is an **even function**, meaning $\cos(-t) = \cos t$ for all $t$ in the domain. For instance, $\cos\left(-\frac{\pi}{2}\right) = \cos\left(\frac{\pi}{2}\right) = 0$ (see Figure 4.14). Here is a summary of important characteristics of the cosine function.

| Characteristics of $f(t) = \cos t$ | | |
|---|---|---|
| For all real numbers $t$ and integers $k$, | | |
| **Domain** | **Range** | **Period** |
| $(-\infty, \infty)$ | $[-1, 1]$ | $2\pi$ |
| **Symmetry** | **Maximum value** | **Minimum value** |
| even | $\cos t = 1$ | $\cos t = -1$ |
| $\cos(-t) = \cos t$ | at $t = 2\pi k$ | at $t = \pi + 2\pi k$ |
| **Increasing** | **Decreasing** | **Zeroes** |
| $(\pi, 2\pi)$ | $(0, \pi)$ | $t = \dfrac{\pi}{2} + \pi k$ |

**EXAMPLE 4** ▶ **Graphing $y = \cos t$ Using a Reference Rectangle**

Draw a sketch of $y = \cos t$ for $t$ in $\left[-\dfrac{\pi}{2}, \dfrac{3\pi}{2}\right]$.

Solution ▶ As with the graph of $y = \sin t$, begin by completing steps I and II, then extend the $t$-axis to include $-2\pi$. Beginning at $t = 0$, draw a reference rectangle $2\pi$ units wide and 2 units tall, centered on the $t$-axis. After applying the rule of fourths, we note the zeroes occur at $t = \dfrac{\pi}{2}$ and $t = \dfrac{3\pi}{2}$ with the max/min values at $t = 0$, $t = \pi$, and $t = 2\pi$. Plot these points and connect them with a smooth, dashed curve (see Figure 4.15). This is the primary period of the cosine curve.

**Figure 4.15**

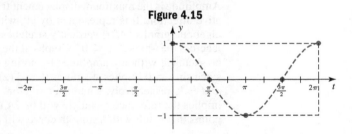

### WORTHY OF NOTE

We also could have graphed the cosine curve in this interval using the table

| $t$ | $\cos t$ |
|---|---|
| $-\dfrac{\pi}{2}$ | 0 |
| 0 | 1 |
| $\dfrac{\pi}{2}$ | 0 |
| $\pi$ | $-1$ |
| $\dfrac{3\pi}{2}$ | 0 |

and connecting these points with a smooth curve.

Using the periodic nature of the cosine function, we can also graph the cosine curve on the interval $[-2\pi, 0]$, as shown in Figure 4.16. The rule of fourths again helps to locate the zeroes and max/min values (note the bold tick-marks) over this interval.

**Figure 4.16**

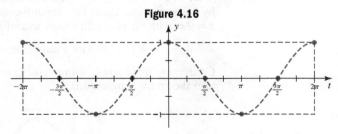

For the graph of $y = \cos t$ in $\left[-\dfrac{\pi}{2}, \dfrac{3\pi}{2}\right]$, we simply highlight the graph in this interval using a solid curve, as shown in Figure 4.17

**Figure 4.17**

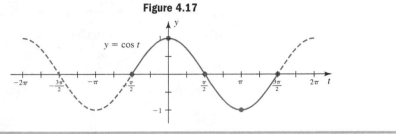

☑ **B. You've just learned how to graph** $f(t) = \cos t$ **using special values and symmetry**

Now try Exercises 13 and 14 ▶

## C.  Graphing $y = A\sin(Bt)$ and $y = A\cos(Bt)$

In many applications, trig functions have maximum and minimum values other than 1 and $-1$, and periods other than $2\pi$. For instance, in tropical regions the daily maximum and minimum temperatures may vary by no more than 20°, while for desert regions this difference may be 40° or more. This variation is modeled by the *amplitude* of the sine and cosine functions.

### Amplitude and the Coefficient $A$ (assume $B = 1$)

For functions of the form $y = A\sin t$ and $y = A\cos t$, let $M$ represent the *Maximum* value and $m$ the *minimum* value of the functions. Then the quantity $\dfrac{M+m}{2}$ gives the **average value** of the function, while $\dfrac{M-m}{2}$ gives the **amplitude** of the function.

Amplitude is the maximum displacement from the average value in the positive or negative direction. It is represented by $|A|$, with $A$ playing a role similar to that seen for algebraic graphs $[Af(t)$ vertically stretches or compresses the graph of $f$, and reflects it across the $t$-axis if $A < 0]$. Graphs of the form $y = \sin t$ (and $y = \cos t$) can quickly be sketched with any amplitude by noting (1) the *zeroes of the function remain fixed* since $\sin t = 0$ implies $A\sin t = 0$, and (2) the *maximum and minimum values are A and $-A$*, respectively, since $\sin t = 1$ or $-1$ implies $A\sin t = A$ or $-A$. Note this implies the reference rectangle will be $2A$ units tall and $P$ units wide. Connecting the points that result with a smooth curve will complete the graph.

> #### WORTHY OF NOTE
> Note that the equations $y = A\sin t$ and $y = A\cos t$ both indicate $y$ is a function of $t$, with no reference to the unit circle definitions $\cos t = x$ and $\sin t = y$.

**EXAMPLE 5** ▶ **Graphing $y = A\sin t$ Where $A \neq 1$**

Draw a sketch of $y = 4\sin t$ in the interval $[0, 2\pi]$.

**Solution** ▶ With an amplitude of $|A| = 4$, the reference rectangle will be $2(4) = 8$ units tall, by $2\pi$ units wide. Using the rule of fourths, the zeroes are still $t = 0$, $t = \pi$, and $t = 2\pi$, with the max/min values spaced equally between. The maximum value is $4\sin\left(\dfrac{\pi}{2}\right) = 4(1) = 4$, with a minimum value of $4\sin\left(\dfrac{3\pi}{2}\right) = 4(-1) = -4$.

Connecting these points with a "sine curve" gives the graph shown ($y = \sin t$ is also shown for comparison).

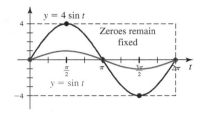

Now try Exercises 15 through 20 ▶

## Period and the Coefficient *B*

While basic sine and cosine functions have a period of $2\pi$, in many applications the period may be very long (tsunamis) or very short (electromagnetic waves). For the equations $y = A\sin(Bt)$ and $y = A\cos(Bt)$, the period depends on the value of $B$. To see why, consider the function $y = \cos(2t)$ and Table 4.6. Multiplying input values by 2 means each cycle will be completed twice as fast. The table shows that $y = \cos(2t)$ completes a full cycle in $[0, \pi]$, giving a period of $P = \pi$ (Figure 4.18, red graph).

**Table 4.6**

| $t$ | 0 | $\dfrac{\pi}{4}$ | $\dfrac{\pi}{2}$ | $\dfrac{3\pi}{4}$ | $\pi$ |
|---|---|---|---|---|---|
| $2t$ | 0 | $\dfrac{\pi}{2}$ | $\pi$ | $\dfrac{3\pi}{2}$ | $2\pi$ |
| $\cos(2t)$ | 1 | 0 | $-1$ | 0 | 1 |

Dividing input values by 2 (or multiplying by $\frac{1}{2}$) will cause the function to complete a cycle only half as fast, doubling the time required to complete a full cycle. Table 4.7 shows $y = \cos\left(\frac{1}{2}t\right)$ completes only one-half cycle in $2\pi$ (Figure 4.18, blue graph).

**Table 4.7**

(values in blue are approximate)

| $t$ | 0 | $\dfrac{\pi}{4}$ | $\dfrac{\pi}{2}$ | $\dfrac{3\pi}{4}$ | $\pi$ | $\dfrac{5\pi}{4}$ | $\dfrac{3\pi}{2}$ | $\dfrac{7\pi}{4}$ | $2\pi$ |
|---|---|---|---|---|---|---|---|---|---|
| $\dfrac{1}{2}t$ | 0 | $\dfrac{\pi}{8}$ | $\dfrac{\pi}{4}$ | $\dfrac{3\pi}{8}$ | $\dfrac{\pi}{2}$ | $\dfrac{5\pi}{8}$ | $\dfrac{3\pi}{4}$ | $\dfrac{7\pi}{8}$ | $\pi$ |
| $\cos\left(\dfrac{1}{2}t\right)$ | 1 | 0.92 | $\dfrac{\sqrt{2}}{2}$ | 0.38 | 0 | $-0.38$ | $-\dfrac{\sqrt{2}}{2}$ | $-0.92$ | $-1$ |

The graphs of $y = \cos t$, $y = \cos(2t)$, and $y = \cos\left(\frac{1}{2}t\right)$ shown in Figure 4.18 clearly illustrate this relationship and how the value of $B$ affects the period of a graph.

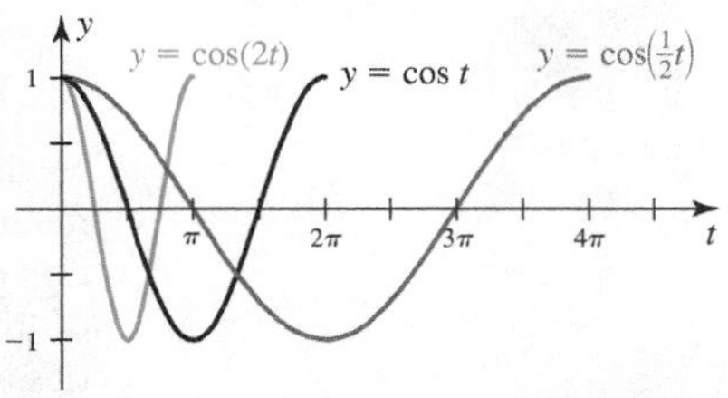

To find the period for arbitrary values of $B$, the formula $P = \dfrac{2\pi}{|B|}$ is used. Note for $y = \cos(2t)$, $B = 2$ and $P = \dfrac{2\pi}{2} = \pi$, as shown. For $y = \cos\left(\dfrac{1}{2}t\right)$, $|B| = \dfrac{1}{2}$ and $P = \dfrac{2\pi}{1/2} = 4\pi$.

**Figure 4.18**

### Period Formula for Sine and Cosine

For $B$ a real number and functions $y = A\sin(Bt)$ and $y = A\cos(Bt)$,
$$P = \frac{2\pi}{|B|}.$$

To sketch these functions for periods other than $2\pi$, we still use a reference rectangle of height $2A$ and length $P$, then break the enclosed $t$-axis in four equal parts to help draw the graph. In general, if the period is "very large" one full cycle is appropriate for the graph. If the period is "very small," graph at least two cycles.

Note the value of $B$ in Example 6 includes a factor of $\pi$. This actually happens quite frequently in applications of the trig functions.

---

**EXAMPLE 6** ▶ **Graphing $y = A \cos(Bt)$, Where $A, B \neq 1$**

Draw a sketch of $y = -2 \cos(0.4\pi t)$ for $t$ in $[-\pi, 2\pi]$.

**Solution** ▶ The amplitude is $|A| = 2$, so the reference rectangle will be $2(2) = 4$ units high. Since $A < 0$, the *graph will be vertically reflected across the t-axis.* The period is

$$P = \frac{2\pi}{0.4\pi} = 5 \text{ (note the factors of } \pi \text{ reduce to 1), so the reference rectangle will}$$

be 5 units in length. Breaking the $t$-axis into four parts within the frame (rule of fourths) gives $\left(\frac{1}{4}\right)5 = \frac{5}{4}$ units, indicating that we should scale the $t$-axis in multiples of $\frac{1}{4}$. Note the zeroes occur at $\frac{5}{4}$ and $\frac{15}{4}$, with a maximum value at $\frac{10}{4}$. In cases where the $\pi$ factor reduces, we scale the $t$-axis as a "standard" number line, and *estimate the location of multiples of $\pi$.* For practical reasons, we first draw the unreflected graph (shown in blue) for guidance in drawing the reflected graph, which is then extended to fit the given interval.

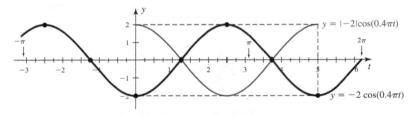

**☑ C.** You've just learned how to graph sine and cosine functions with various amplitudes and periods

*Now try Exercises 21 through 32* ▶

---

## D. Writing Equations from Graphs

Mathematical concepts are best reinforced by working with them in both "forward and reverse." Where graphs are concerned, this means we should attempt to find the equation of a given graph, rather than only using an equation to sketch the graph. Exercises of this type require that you become very familiar with the graph's basic characteristics and how each is expressed as part of the equation.

---

**EXAMPLE 7** ▶ **Determining the Equation of a Given Graph**

The graph shown here is of the form $y = A \sin(Bt)$. Find the value of $A$ and $B$.

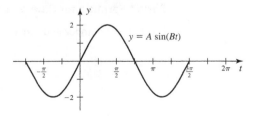

**Solution** ▶ By inspection, the graph has an amplitude of $A = 2$ and a period of $P = \frac{3\pi}{2}$.

To find $B$ we used the period formula $P = \frac{2\pi}{|B|}$, substituting $\frac{3\pi}{2}$ for $P$ and solving.

$$P = \frac{2\pi}{|B|} \quad \text{period formula}$$

$$\frac{3\pi}{2} = \frac{2\pi}{B} \quad \text{substitute } \frac{3\pi}{2} \text{ for } P;\ B > 0$$

$$3\pi B = 4\pi \quad \text{multiply by } 2B$$

$$B = \frac{4}{3} \quad \text{solve for } B$$

**D. You've just learned how to write the equation for a given graph**

The result is $B = \frac{4}{3}$, which gives us the equation $y = 2\sin\left(\frac{4}{3}t\right)$.

**Now try Exercises 33 through 52** ▶

There are a number of interesting applications of this "graph to equation" process in the exercise set. **See Exercises 55 to 66.**

## TECHNOLOGY HIGHLIGHT

### Exploring Amplitudes and Periods

In practice, trig applications offer an immense range of coefficients, creating amplitudes that are sometimes very large and sometimes extremely small, as well as periods ranging from nanoseconds, to many years. This *Technology Highlight* is designed to help you use the calculator more effectively in the study of these functions. To begin, we note that many calculators offer a preset ZOOM option that automatically sets a window size convenient to many trig graphs. The resulting WINDOW after pressing ZOOM **7:ZTrig** on a TI-84 Plus is shown in Figure 4.19 for a calculator set in **Radian** MODE.

In Section 4.1 we noted that a change in amplitude will not change the location of the zeroes or max/min values. On the Y= screen, enter $Y_1 = \frac{1}{2}\sin x$, $Y_2 = \sin x$, $Y_3 = 2\sin x$, and $Y_4 = 4\sin x$, then use ZOOM **7:ZTrig** to graph the functions. As you see in Figure 4.20, each graph rises to the expected amplitude at the expected location, while "holding on" to the zeroes.

To explore concepts related to the coefficient $B$ and the period of a trig function, enter $Y_1 = \sin\left(\frac{1}{2}x\right)$ and $Y_2 = \sin(2x)$ on the Y= screen and graph using ZOOM **7:ZTrig.** While the result is "acceptable," the graphs are difficult to read and compare, so we manually change the window size to obtain a better view (Figure 4.21).

**Figure 4.19**

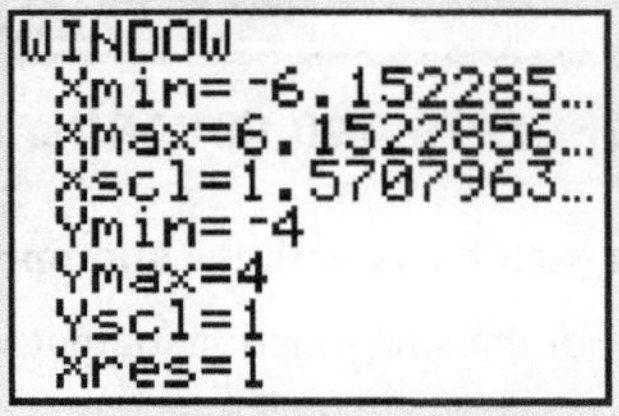

WINDOW
Xmin=-6.152285...
Xmax=6.1522856...
Xscl=1.5707963...
Ymin=-4
Ymax=4
Yscl=1
Xres=1

**Figure 4.20**

4
Y1=(1/2)sin(X)
-6.2
6.2
X=0
Y=0
-4

**Figure 4.21**

1.4
Y1=sin((1/2)X)
0
2π
X=3.1415927 Y=1
-1.4

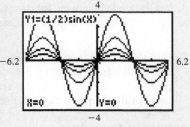

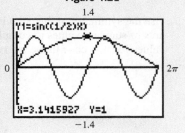

*—continued*

A true test of effective calculator use comes when the amplitude or period is a very large or very small number. For instance, the tone you hear while pressing "5" on your telephone is actually a combination of the tones modeled by $Y_1 = \sin[2\pi(770)t]$ and $Y_2 = \sin[2\pi(1336)t]$. Graphing these functions requires a careful analysis of the period, otherwise the graph can appear garbled, misleading, or difficult to read—try graphing $Y_1$ on the ⎡ZOOM⎤ **7:ZTrig** or ⎡ZOOM⎤ **6:ZStandard** screens. First note $A = 1$, and $P = \dfrac{2\pi}{2\pi 770}$ or $\dfrac{1}{770}$. With a period this short, even graphing the function from Xmin = −1 to Xmax = 1 gives a distorted graph (see Figure 4.22). Setting Xmin to −1/770, Xmax to 1/770, and Xscl to (1/770)/10 gives the graph in Figure 4.23, which can be used to investigate characteristics of the function.

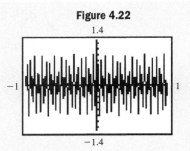

Figure 4.22

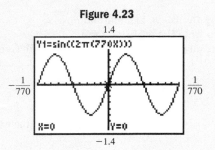

Figure 4.23

**Exercise 1:** Graph the second tone $Y_2 = \sin[2\pi(1336)t]$ and find its value at $t = 0.00025$ sec.

**Exercise 2:** Graph the function $Y_1 = 950 \sin(0.005t)$ on a "friendly" window and find the value at $t = 550$.

## 4.1 EXERCISES

### ▶ CONCEPTS AND VOCABULARY

**Fill in each blank with the appropriate word or phrase. Carefully reread the section if needed.**

1. For the sine function, output values are _____ in the interval $\left[0, \dfrac{\pi}{2}\right]$.

2. For the cosine function, output values are _____ in the interval $\left[0, \dfrac{\pi}{2}\right]$.

3. For the sine and cosine functions, the domain is _____ and the range is _____.

4. The amplitude of sine and cosine is defined to be the maximum _____ from the _____ value in the positive and negative directions.

5. Discuss/Explain how the values generated by the unit circle can be used to graph the function $f(t) = \sin t$. Be sure to include the domain and range of this function in your discussion.

6. Discuss/Describe the four-step process outlined in this section for the graphing of basic trig functions. Include a worked-out example and a detailed explanation.

### ▶ DEVELOPING YOUR SKILLS

7. Use the symmetry of the unit circle and reference arcs of standard values to complete a table of values for $y = \cos t$ in the interval $t \in [\pi, 2\pi]$.

8. Use the standard values for $y = \cos t$ for $t \in [\pi, 2\pi]$ to create a table of values for $y = \sin t$ on the same interval.

**Use the characteristics of $f(t) = \sin t$ to match the given value of $t$ to the correct value of $\sin t$.**

9.  a. $t = \left(\dfrac{\pi}{6} + 10\pi\right)$     b. $t = -\dfrac{\pi}{4}$     c. $t = \dfrac{-15\pi}{4}$     d. $t = 13\pi$     e. $t = \dfrac{21\pi}{2}$

   I. $\sin t = 0$     II. $\sin t = \dfrac{1}{2}$     III. $\sin t = 1$     IV. $\sin t = \dfrac{\sqrt{2}}{2}$     V. $\sin t = -\dfrac{\sqrt{2}}{2}$

10. a. $t = \left(\dfrac{\pi}{4} - 12\pi\right)$     b. $t = \dfrac{11\pi}{6}$     c. $t = \dfrac{23\pi}{2}$     d. $t = -19\pi$     e. $t = -\dfrac{25\pi}{4}$

   I. $\sin t = -\dfrac{1}{2}$     II. $\sin t = -\dfrac{\sqrt{2}}{2}$     III. $\sin t = 0$     IV. $\sin t = \dfrac{\sqrt{2}}{2}$     V. $\sin t = -1$

**Use steps I through IV given in this section to draw a sketch of each graph.**

11. $y = \sin t$ for $t \in \left[-\dfrac{3\pi}{2}, \dfrac{\pi}{2}\right]$

12. $y = \sin t$ for $t \in [-\pi, \pi]$

13. $y = \cos t$ for $t \in \left[-\dfrac{\pi}{2}, 2\pi\right]$

14. $y = \cos t$ for $t \in \left[-\dfrac{\pi}{2}, \dfrac{5\pi}{2}\right]$

**Use a reference rectangle and the *rule of fourths* to draw an accurate sketch of the following functions through two complete cycles—one where $t > 0$, and one where $t < 0$. Clearly state the amplitude and period as you begin.**

15. $y = 3 \sin t$     16. $y = 4 \sin t$

17. $y = -2 \cos t$     18. $y = -3 \cos t$

19. $y = \dfrac{1}{2} \sin t$     20. $y = \dfrac{3}{4} \sin t$

21. $y = -\sin(2t)$     22. $y = -\cos(2t)$

23. $y = 0.8 \cos(2t)$     24. $y = 1.7 \sin(4t)$

25. $f(t) = 4 \cos\left(\dfrac{1}{2}t\right)$     26. $y = -3 \cos\left(\dfrac{3}{4}t\right)$

27. $f(t) = 3 \sin(4\pi t)$     28. $g(t) = 5 \cos(8\pi t)$

29. $y = 4 \sin\left(\dfrac{5\pi}{3}t\right)$     30. $y = 2.5 \cos\left(\dfrac{2\pi}{5}t\right)$

31. $f(t) = 2 \sin(256\pi t)$     32. $g(t) = 3 \cos(184\pi t)$

**Clearly state the amplitude and period of each function, then match it with the corresponding graph.**

33. $y = -2 \cos(4t)$     34. $y = 2 \sin(4t)$

35. $y = 3 \sin(2t)$     36. $y = -3 \cos(2t)$

37. $f(t) = \dfrac{3}{4} \cos(0.4t)$     38. $g(t) = \dfrac{7}{4} \cos(0.8t)$

39. $y = 4 \sin(144\pi t)$     40. $y = 4 \cos(72\pi t)$

a. 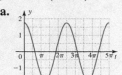     b.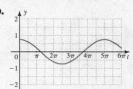

c. 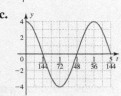     d.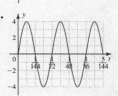

e. 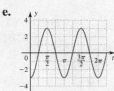     f.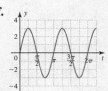

g. 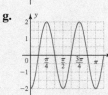     h.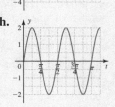

**The graphs shown are of the form $y = A \cos(Bt)$. Use the characteristics illustrated for each graph to determine its equation.**

41. 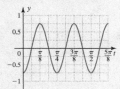     42.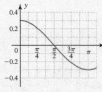

43. 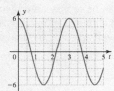     44.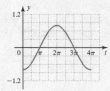

The graphs shown are of the form $y = A \sin(Bt)$. Use the characteristics illustrated for each graph to determine its equation.

Match each graph to its equation, then graphically estimate the points of intersection. Confirm or contradict your estimate(s) by substituting the values into the given equations using a calculator.

**45.**

**46.**
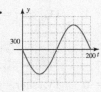

**49.** $y = -\cos x$;
    $y = \sin x$
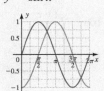

**50.** $y = -\cos x$;
    $y = \sin(2x)$
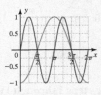

**47.**
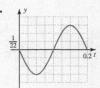

**48.**
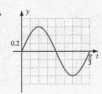

**51.** $y = -2 \cos x$;
    $y = 2 \sin(3x)$

**52.** $y = 2 \cos(2\pi x)$;
    $y = -2 \sin(\pi x)$
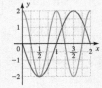

▶ **WORKING WITH FORMULAS**

**53. Area of a regular polygon inscribed in a circle:**

$$A = \frac{nr^2}{2} \sin\left(\frac{2\pi}{n}\right)$$

**Exercise 53**

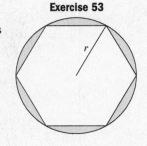

The formula shown gives the area of a regular polygon inscribed in a circle, where $n$ is the number of sides ($n \geq 3$) and $r$ is the radius of the circle. Given $r = 10$ cm,

  **a.** What is the area of the circle?

  **b.** What is the area of the polygon when $n = 4$? Find the length of the sides of the polygon using two different methods.

  **c.** Calculate the area of the polygon for $n = 10, 20, 30$, and $100$. What do you notice?

**54. Hydrostatics, surface tension, and contact**

angles: $y = \dfrac{2\gamma \cos \theta}{kr}$

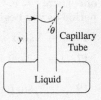

Capillary Tube

Liquid

The height that a liquid will rise in a capillary tube is given by the formula shown, where $r$ is the radius of the tube, $\theta$ is the contact angle of the liquid (the meniscus), $\gamma$ is the surface tension of the liquid-vapor film, and $k$ is a constant that depends on the weight-density of the liquid. How high will the liquid rise given that the surface tension $\gamma = 0.2706$, the tube has radius $r = 0.2$ cm, the contact angle $\theta = 22.5°$, and $k = 1.25$?

▶ **APPLICATIONS**

**Tidal waves:** Tsunamis, also known as tidal waves, are ocean waves produced by earthquakes or other upheavals in the Earth's crust and can move through the water undetected for hundreds of miles at great speed. While traveling in the open ocean, these waves can be represented by a sine graph with a very long wavelength (period) and a very small amplitude. Tsunami waves only attain a monstrous size as they approach the shore, and represent a very different phenomenon than the ocean swells created by heavy winds over an extended period of time.

**55.** A graph modeling a tsunami wave is given in the figure. (a) What is the height of the tsunami wave (from crest to trough)? Note that $h = 0$ is considered the level of a calm ocean. (b) What is the tsunami's wavelength? (c) Find an equation for this wave.

**56.** A heavy wind is kicking up ocean swells approximately 10 ft high (from crest to trough), with wavelengths of 250 ft. (a) Find an equation that models these swells. (b) Graph the equation. (c) Determine the height of a wave measured 200 ft from the trough of the previous wave.

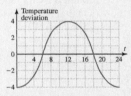

**Sinusoidal models:** The sine and cosine functions are of great importance to meteorological studies, as when modeling the temperature based on the time of day, the illumination of the Moon as it goes through its phases, or even the prediction of tidal motion.

**57.** The graph given shows the deviation from the average daily temperature for the hours of a given day, with $t = 0$ corresponding to 6 A.M. (a) Use the graph to determine the related equation. (b) Use the equation to find the deviation at $t = 11$ (5 P.M.) and confirm that this point is on the graph. (c) If the average temperature for this day was 72°, what was the temperature at midnight?

**58.** The equation $y = 7 \sin\left(\dfrac{\pi}{6}t\right)$ models the height of the tide along a certain coastal area, as compared to average sea level. Assuming $t = 0$ is midnight, (a) graph this function over a 12-hr period. (b) What will the height of the tide be at 5 A.M.? (c) Is the tide rising or falling at this time?

**Sinusoidal movements:** Many animals exhibit a wavelike motion in their movements, as in the tail of a shark as it swims in a straight line or the wingtips of a large bird in flight. Such movements can be modeled by a sine or cosine function and will vary depending on the animal's size, speed, and other factors.

**59.** The graph shown models the position of a shark's tail at time $t$, as measured to the left (negative) and

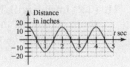

right (positive) of a straight line along its length. (a) Use the graph to determine the related equation. (b) Is the tail to the right, left, or at center when $t = 6.5$ sec? How far? (c) Would you say the shark is "swimming leisurely," or "chasing its prey"? Justify your answer.

**60.** The State Fish of Hawaii is the *humuhumunukunukuapua'a*, a small colorful fish found abundantly in coastal waters. Suppose the tail motion of an adult fish is modeled by the equation $d(t) = \sin(15\pi t)$ with $d(t)$ representing the position of the fish's tail at time $t$, as measured in inches to the left (negative) or right (positive) of a straight line along its length. (a) Graph the equation over two periods. (b) Is the tail to the left or right of center at $t = 2.7$ sec? How far? (c) Would you say this fish is "swimming leisurely," or "running for cover"? Justify your answer.

**Kinetic energy:** The kinetic energy a planet possesses as it orbits the Sun can be modeled by a cosine function. When the planet is at its apogee (greatest distance from the Sun), its kinetic energy is at its lowest point as it slows down and "turns around" to head back toward the Sun. The kinetic energy is at its highest when the planet "whips around the Sun" to begin a new orbit.

**61.** Two graphs are given here. (a) Which of the graphs could represent the kinetic energy of a planet orbiting the Sun if the planet is at its perigee (closest distance to the Sun) when $t = 0$? (b) For what value(s) of $t$ does this planet possess 62.5% of its maximum kinetic energy with the kinetic energy increasing? (c) What is the orbital period of this planet?

**a.** 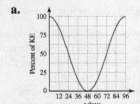     **b.**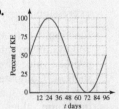

**62.** The *potential energy* of the planet is the antipode of its kinetic energy, meaning when kinetic energy is at 100%, the potential energy is 0%, and when kinetic energy is at 0% the potential energy is at 100%. (a) How is the graph of the kinetic energy related to the graph of the potential energy? In other words, what transformation could be applied to the kinetic energy graph to obtain the potential energy graph? (b) If the kinetic energy is at 62.5% and increasing, what can be said about the potential energy in the planet's orbit at this time?

**Visible light:** One of the narrowest bands in the electromagnetic spectrum is the region involving visible light. The wavelengths (periods) of visible light vary from 400 nanometers (purple/violet colors) to 700 nanometers (bright red). The approximate wavelengths of the other colors are shown in the diagram.

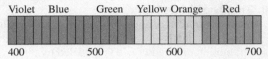

63. The equations for the colors in this spectrum have the form $y = \sin(\gamma t)$, where $\dfrac{2\pi}{\gamma}$ gives the length of the sine wave. (a) What color is represented by the equation $y = \sin\left(\dfrac{\pi}{240}t\right)$? (b) What color is represented by the equation $y = \sin\left(\dfrac{\pi}{310}t\right)$?

64. Name the color represented by each of the graphs (a) and (b) and write the related equation.

**a.**

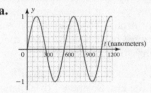

**b.**

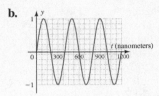

**Alternating current:** Surprisingly, even characteristics of the electric current supplied to your home can be modeled by sine or cosine functions. For alternating current (AC), the amount of current $I$ (in amps) at time $t$ can be modeled by $I = A \sin(\omega t)$, where $A$ represents the maximum current that is produced, and $\omega$ is related to the frequency at which the generators turn to produce the current.

65. Find the equation of the household current modeled by the graph, then use the equation to determine $I$ when $t = 0.045$ sec. Verify that the resulting ordered pair is on the graph.

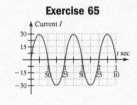

**Exercise 65**

66. If the *voltage* produced by an AC circuit is modeled by the equation $E = 155 \sin(120\pi t)$, (a) what is the period and amplitude of the related graph? (b) What voltage is produced when $t = 0.2$?

▶ **EXTENDING THE CONCEPT**

67. For $y = A \sin(Bx)$ and $y = A \cos(Bx)$, the expression $\dfrac{M + m}{2}$ gives the average value of the function, where $M$ and $m$ represent the maximum and minimum values, respectively. What was the average value of every function graphed in this section? Compute a table of values for $y = 2 \sin t + 3$, and note its maximum and minimum values. What is the average value of this function? What transformation has been applied to change the average value of the function? Can you name the average value of $y = -2 \cos t + 1$ by inspection?

68. To understand where the period formula $P = \dfrac{2\pi}{B}$ came from, consider that if $B = 1$, the graph of $y = \sin(Bt) = \sin(1t)$ completes one cycle from $1t = 0$ to $1t = 2\pi$. If $B \neq 1$, $y = \sin(Bt)$ completes one cycle from $Bt = 0$ to $Bt = 2\pi$. Discuss how this observation validates the period formula.

69. The tone you hear when pressing the digit "9" on your telephone is actually a combination of two separate tones, which can be modeled by the functions $f(t) = \sin[2\pi(852)t]$ and $g(t) = \sin[2\pi(1477)t]$. Which of the two functions has the shortest period? By carefully scaling the axes, graph the function having the shorter period using the steps I through IV discussed in this section.

▶ **MAINTAINING YOUR SKILLS**

70. **(3.4)** Given $\sin 1.12 \approx 0.9$, find an additional value of $t$ in $[0, 2\pi)$ that makes the equation $\sin t \approx 0.9$ true.

71. **(3.2)** Invercargill, New Zealand, is at $46°14'24''$ south latitude. If the Earth has a radius of 3960 mi, how far is Invercargill from the equator?

**72. (1.3)** Given $\cos t = \dfrac{28}{53}$ with $\tan t < 0$: (a) find the related values of $x$, $y$, and $r$; (b) state the quadrant of the terminal side; and (c) give the value of the other five trig functions of $t$.

**73. (1.1)** Use a standard triangle to calculate the distance from the ball to the pin on the seventh hole, given the ball is in a straight line with the 100-yd plate, as shown in the figure.

**Exercise 73**

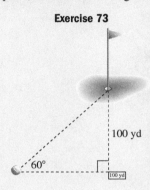

100 yd

60°

100 yd

**74. (3.2)** The Ferris wheel shown has a radius of 25 ft and is turning at a rate of 14 rpm. (a) What is the angular velocity in radians? (b) What distance does a seat on the rim travel as the Ferris wheel turns through an angle of 225°? (c) What is the linear velocity (in miles per hour) of a person sitting in a seat at the rim of the Ferris wheel?

**Exercise 74**

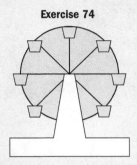

**75. (2.3)** The world's tallest unsupported flagpole was erected in 1985 in Vancouver, British Columbia. Standing 60 ft from the base of the pole, the angle of elevation is 78°. How tall is the pole?

Unlike sine and cosine, the cosecant, secant, tangent, and cotangent functions have no maximum or minimum values over their domains. However, it is precisely this unique feature that adds to their value as mathematical models. Collectively, these six trig functions give scientists the tools they need to study, explore, and investigate a wide range of phenomena, extending our understanding of the world around us.

## A. Graphs of $y = A\csc(Bt)$ and $y = A\sec(Bt)$

From our earlier work, recall that $y = \sin t$ and $y = \csc t$ are reciprocal functions: $\csc t = \dfrac{1}{\sin t}$. Likewise, we have $\sec t = \dfrac{1}{\cos t}$. The graphs of these reciprocal functions follow quite naturally from the graphs of $y = A\sin(Bt)$ and $y = A\cos(Bt)$ by using these observations:

1. You cannot divide by zero.
2. The reciprocal of a very small number ($<1$) is a very large number (and vice versa).
3. The reciprocal of $\pm 1$ is $\pm 1$.

Just as with rational functions, division by zero creates a vertical asymptote, so the graph of $y = \csc t = \dfrac{1}{\sin t}$ will have a vertical asymptote at every point where $\sin t = 0$. This occurs at $t = \pi k$, where $k$ is an integer $(\ldots -2\pi,\ -\pi,\ 0,\ \pi,\ 2\pi, \ldots)$. Further, when $\sin(Bt) = \pm 1$, $\csc(Bt) = \pm 1$ since the reciprocal of 1 and $-1$ are still 1 and $-1$, respectively. Finally, due to observation 2, the graph of the cosecant function will be increasing when the sine function is decreasing, and decreasing when the sine function is increasing.

Considering the case where $A = 1$, we can graph $y = \csc(Bt)$ by first drawing a sketch of $y = \sin(Bt)$. Then using the previous observations and a few well-known values, we can accurately complete the graph of $y = \csc(Bt)$. See Example 1. From the graph, we discover that the period of the cosecant function is also $\dfrac{2\pi}{B}$ and that $y = \csc(Bt)$ is an *odd* function.

---

**EXAMPLE 1** ▶ **Graphing $y = A \csc(Bt)$ for $A = 1$**

Graph the function $y = \csc t$ over the interval $[0, 4\pi]$.

Solution ▶ Begin by sketching the function $y = \sin t$, using a standard reference rectangle $2A = 2(1) = 2$ units high by $\dfrac{2\pi}{B} = \dfrac{2\pi}{1} = 2\pi$ units in length.

Since $\csc t = \dfrac{1}{\sin t}$, the graph of $y = \csc t$ will be asymptotic at the zeroes of $y = \sin t \, (t = 0, \pi, \text{and } 2\pi)$. As in Section 4.1, we can then extend the graph into the interval $[2\pi, 4\pi]$ by reproducing the graph from $[0, 2\pi]$. A partial table and the resulting graph are shown.

| $t$ | $\sin t$ | $\csc t$ |
|:---:|:---:|:---:|
| $0$ | $0$ | $\dfrac{1}{0} \to$ undefined |
| $\dfrac{\pi}{6}$ | $\dfrac{1}{2} = 0.5$ | $\dfrac{2}{1} = 2$ |
| $\dfrac{\pi}{4}$ | $\dfrac{\sqrt{2}}{2} \approx 0.71$ | $\dfrac{2}{\sqrt{2}} \approx 1.41$ |
| $\dfrac{\pi}{3}$ | $\dfrac{\sqrt{3}}{2} \approx 0.87$ | $\dfrac{2}{\sqrt{3}} \approx 1.15$ |
| $\dfrac{\pi}{2}$ | $1$ | $1$ |

• Vertical asymptotes where sine is zero

• When $\sin(Bt) = \pm 1$, $\csc(Bt) = \pm 1$

• Output values are reciprocated

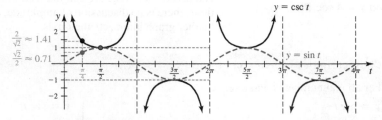

**Now try Exercises 7 through 10** ▶

---

Similar to Example 1, the graph of $y = \sec t = \dfrac{1}{\cos t}$ will have vertical asymptotes where $\cos t = 0 \left( t = \dfrac{\pi}{2} \text{ and } \dfrac{3\pi}{2} \right)$. Note that if $A \neq 1$, we would then use the graph of $y = A \cos(Bt)$ to graph $y = A \sec(Bt)$, as in Example 2.

**EXAMPLE 2**  ▶  Graphing $y = A \sec(Bt)$ for $A, B \neq 1$

Graph the function $y = 3 \sec\left(\dfrac{\pi}{2}t\right)$ over the interval $[-2, 6]$.

Solution  ▶  Begin by sketching the function $y = 3 \cos\left(\dfrac{\pi}{2}t\right)$ using a reference rectangle

6 units high by $\dfrac{2\pi}{B} = \dfrac{2\pi}{\pi/2} = 4$ units long
as a guide. Within the rectangle, each tick
mark will be 1 unit apart, with the
asymptotes occurring at the zeroes of
$y = 3 \cos\left(\dfrac{\pi}{2}t\right)$ ($t = 1$ and $t = 3$).
We then extend the graph to cover the
interval $[-2, 6]$ by reproducing the
appropriate sections of the graph. A partial
table and the resulting graph are shown.

| $t$ | $3 \cos\left(\dfrac{\pi}{2}t\right)$ | $3 \sec\left(\dfrac{\pi}{2}t\right)$ |
|---|---|---|
| $0$ | $3$ | $3$ |
| $\dfrac{1}{3}$ | $3 \cdot \dfrac{\sqrt{3}}{2} \approx 2.60$ | $3 \cdot \dfrac{2}{\sqrt{3}} \approx 3.46$ |
| $\dfrac{1}{2}$ | $3 \cdot \dfrac{\sqrt{2}}{2} \approx 2.12$ | $3 \cdot \dfrac{2}{\sqrt{2}} \approx 4.24$ |
| $\dfrac{2}{3}$ | $3 \cdot \dfrac{1}{2} = 1.5$ | $3 \cdot \dfrac{2}{1} = 6$ |
| $1$ | $0$ | $\dfrac{1}{0} \rightarrow$ undefined |

- Vertical asymptotes
  where cosine is zero
- When $A \cos(Bt) = \pm A$,
  $A \sec(Bt) = \pm A$

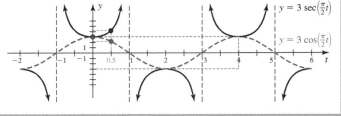

$y = 3 \sec\left(\frac{\pi}{2}t\right)$

$y = 3 \cos\left(\frac{\pi}{2}t\right)$

Now try Exercises 11 through 14  ▶

☑ **A. You've just learned
how to graph $y = A \csc(Bt)$
and $y = A \sec(Bt)$**

From the graph, we discover that the period of the secant function is also $\dfrac{2\pi}{B}$, and that
$y = A \sec(Bt)$ is an *even* function. The most important characteristics of the cosecant
and secant functions are summarized in the following box. Note that for these functions, there is no discussion of amplitude, and no mention is made of their zeroes since
neither graph intersects the $t$-axis.

## Characteristics of $f(t) = \csc t$ and $f(t) = \sec t$

For all real numbers $t$ and integers $k$,

| $y = \csc t$ | | | $y = \sec t$ | | |
|---|---|---|---|---|---|
| **Domain** | **Range** | **Asymptotes** | **Domain** | **Range** | **Asymptotes** |
| $t \neq k\pi$ | $(-\infty, -1] \cup [1, \infty)$ | $t = k\pi$ | $t \neq \dfrac{\pi}{2} + \pi k$ | $(-\infty, -1] \cup [1, \infty)$ | $t = \dfrac{\pi}{2} + \pi k$ |
| | **Period** | **Symmetry** | | **Period** | **Symmetry** |
| | $2\pi$ | odd | | $2\pi$ | even |
| | | $\csc(-t) = -\csc t$ | | | $\sec(-t) = \sec t$ |

**Figure 4.24**

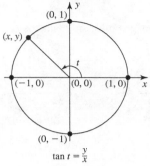

$$\tan t = \frac{y}{x}$$

## B. The Graph of $y = \tan t$

Like the secant and cosecant functions, tangent is defined in terms of a ratio, creating asymptotic behavior at the zeroes of the denominator. In terms of the unit circle, $\tan t = \frac{y}{x}$, which means in $[-\pi, 2\pi]$, vertical asymptotes occur at $t = -\frac{\pi}{2}$, $t = \frac{\pi}{2}$, and $\frac{3\pi}{2}$, since the $x$-coordinate on the unit circle is zero (see Figure 4.24). We further note $\tan t = 0$ when the $y$-coordinate is zero, so the function will have $t$-intercepts at $t = -\pi, 0, \pi$, and $2\pi$ in the same interval. This produces the framework for graphing the tangent function shown in Figure 4.25.

**Figure 4.25**

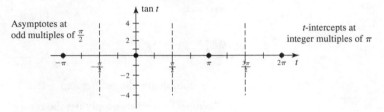

Knowing the graph must go through these zeroes and approach the asymptotes, we are left with determining the *direction of the approach*. This can be discovered by noting that in QI, the $y$-coordinates of points on the unit circle start at 0 and increase, while the $x$-values start at 1 and decrease. This means the ratio $\frac{y}{x}$ defining $\tan t$ is increasing, and in fact becomes infinitely large as $t$ gets very close to $\frac{\pi}{2}$. A similar observation can be made for a negative rotation of $t$ in QIV. Using the additional points provided by $\tan\left(-\frac{\pi}{4}\right) = -1$ and $\tan\left(\frac{\pi}{4}\right) = 1$, we find the graph of $\tan t$ is increasing throughout the interval $\left(-\frac{\pi}{2}, \frac{\pi}{2}\right)$ and that the function has a period of $\pi$. We also note $y = \tan t$ is an odd function (symmetric about the origin), since $\tan(-t) = -\tan t$ as evidenced by the two points just computed. The completed graph is shown in Figure 4.26 with the primary interval in red.

**Figure 4.26**

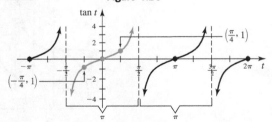

The graph can also be developed by noting $\sin t = y$, $\cos t = x$, and $\tan t = \frac{y}{x}$. This gives $\tan t = \frac{\sin t}{\cos t}$ by direct substitution and we can quickly complete a table of values for $\tan t$, as shown in Example 3.

**EXAMPLE 3** ▶ **Constructing a Table of Values for $f(t) = \tan t$**

Complete Table 4.8 shown for $\tan t = \dfrac{y}{x}$ using the values given for $\sin t$ and $\cos t$, then graph the function by plotting points.

**Table 4.8**

| $t$ | 0 | $\dfrac{\pi}{6}$ | $\dfrac{\pi}{4}$ | $\dfrac{\pi}{3}$ | $\dfrac{\pi}{2}$ | $\dfrac{2\pi}{3}$ | $\dfrac{3\pi}{4}$ | $\dfrac{5\pi}{6}$ | $\pi$ |
|---|---|---|---|---|---|---|---|---|---|
| $\sin t = y$ | 0 | $\dfrac{1}{2}$ | $\dfrac{\sqrt{2}}{2}$ | $\dfrac{\sqrt{3}}{2}$ | 1 | $\dfrac{\sqrt{3}}{2}$ | $\dfrac{\sqrt{2}}{2}$ | $\dfrac{1}{2}$ | 0 |
| $\cos t = x$ | 1 | $\dfrac{\sqrt{3}}{2}$ | $\dfrac{\sqrt{2}}{2}$ | $\dfrac{1}{2}$ | 0 | $-\dfrac{1}{2}$ | $-\dfrac{\sqrt{2}}{2}$ | $-\dfrac{\sqrt{3}}{2}$ | $-1$ |
| $\tan t = \dfrac{y}{x}$ | | | | | | | | | |

**Solution** ▶ For the noninteger values of $x$ and $y$, the "twos will cancel" each time we compute $\dfrac{y}{x}$. This means we can simply list the ratio of numerators. The resulting points are shown in Table 4.9, along with the plotted points. The graph shown in Figure 4.27 was completed using symmetry and the previous observations.

**Table 4.9**

| $t$ | 0 | $\dfrac{\pi}{6}$ | $\dfrac{\pi}{4}$ | $\dfrac{\pi}{3}$ | $\dfrac{\pi}{2}$ | $\dfrac{2\pi}{3}$ | $\dfrac{3\pi}{4}$ | $\dfrac{5\pi}{6}$ | $\pi$ |
|---|---|---|---|---|---|---|---|---|---|
| $\sin t = y$ | 0 | $\dfrac{1}{2}$ | $\dfrac{\sqrt{2}}{2}$ | $\dfrac{\sqrt{3}}{2}$ | 1 | $\dfrac{\sqrt{3}}{2}$ | $\dfrac{\sqrt{2}}{2}$ | $\dfrac{1}{2}$ | 0 |
| $\cos t = x$ | 1 | $\dfrac{\sqrt{3}}{2}$ | $\dfrac{\sqrt{2}}{2}$ | $\dfrac{1}{2}$ | 0 | $-\dfrac{1}{2}$ | $-\dfrac{\sqrt{2}}{2}$ | $-\dfrac{\sqrt{3}}{2}$ | $-1$ |
| $\tan t = \dfrac{y}{x}$ | 0 | $\dfrac{1}{\sqrt{3}} \approx 0.58$ | 1 | $\sqrt{3} \approx 1.7$ | undefined | $-\sqrt{3}$ | $-1$ | $-\dfrac{1}{\sqrt{3}}$ | 0 |

**Figure 4.27**

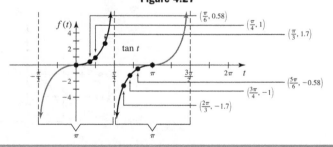

Now try Exercises 15 and 16 ▶

☑ **B.** You've just learned how to graph $y = \tan t$ using asymptotes, zeroes, and the ratio $\dfrac{\sin t}{\cos t}$

Additional values can be found using a calculator as needed. For future use and reference, it will help to recognize the approximate decimal equivalent of all special values and radian angles. In particular, note that $\sqrt{3} \approx 1.73$ and $\dfrac{1}{\sqrt{3}} \approx 0.58$. **See Exercises 17 through 22.**

## C. The Graph of $y = \cot t$

Since the cotangent function is also defined in terms of a ratio, it too displays asymptotic behavior at the zeroes of the denominator, with $t$-intercepts at the zeroes of the numerator. Like the tangent function, $\cot t = \dfrac{x}{y}$ can be written in terms of $\cos t = x$ and $\sin t = y$: $\cot t = \dfrac{\cos t}{\sin t}$, and the graph obtained by plotting points.

---

**EXAMPLE 4** ▶ **Constructing a Table of Values for $f(t) = \cot t$**

Complete a table of values for $\cot t = \dfrac{x}{y}$ for $t$ in $[0, \pi]$ using its ratio relationship with $\cos t$ and $\sin t$. Use the results to graph the function for $t$ in $(-\pi, 2\pi)$.

**Solution** ▶ The completed table is shown here. In this interval, the cotangent function has asymptotes at 0 and $\pi$ since $y = 0$ at these points, and has a $t$-intercept at $\dfrac{\pi}{2}$ since $x = 0$. The graph shown in Figure 4.28 was completed using the period $P = \pi$.

| $t$ | 0 | $\dfrac{\pi}{6}$ | $\dfrac{\pi}{4}$ | $\dfrac{\pi}{3}$ | $\dfrac{\pi}{2}$ | $\dfrac{2\pi}{3}$ | $\dfrac{3\pi}{4}$ | $\dfrac{5\pi}{6}$ | $\pi$ |
|---|---|---|---|---|---|---|---|---|---|
| $\sin t = y$ | 0 | $\dfrac{1}{2}$ | $\dfrac{\sqrt{2}}{2}$ | $\dfrac{\sqrt{3}}{2}$ | 1 | $\dfrac{\sqrt{3}}{2}$ | $\dfrac{\sqrt{2}}{2}$ | $\dfrac{1}{2}$ | 0 |
| $\cos t = x$ | 1 | $\dfrac{\sqrt{3}}{2}$ | $\dfrac{\sqrt{2}}{2}$ | $\dfrac{1}{2}$ | 0 | $-\dfrac{1}{2}$ | $-\dfrac{\sqrt{2}}{2}$ | $-\dfrac{\sqrt{3}}{2}$ | $-1$ |
| $\cot t = \dfrac{x}{y}$ | undefined | $\sqrt{3}$ | 1 | $\dfrac{1}{\sqrt{3}}$ | 0 | $-\dfrac{1}{\sqrt{3}}$ | $-1$ | $-\sqrt{3}$ | undefined |

**Figure 4.28**

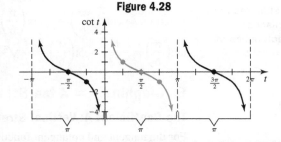

☑ **C. You've just learned how to graph $y = \cot t$ using asymptotes, zeroes, and the ratio $\dfrac{\cos t}{\sin t}$**

**Now try Exercises 23 and 24** ▶

---

## D. Characteristics of $y = \tan t$ and $y = \cot t$

The most important characteristics of the tangent and cotangent functions are summarized in the following box. There is no discussion of amplitude, maximum, or minimum values, since maximum or minimum values do not exist. For future use and reference, perhaps the most significant characteristic distinguishing $\tan t$ from $\cot t$ is that *$\tan t$ increases,* while *$\cot t$ decreases* over their respective domains. Also note that due to symmetry, the zeroes of each function are always located halfway between the asymptotes.

---

**Characteristics of $f(t) = \tan t$ and $f(t) = \cot t$**

For all real numbers $t$ and integers $k$,

| $y = \tan t$ | | | $y = \cot t$ | | |
|---|---|---|---|---|---|
| **Domain** | **Range** | **Asymptotes** | **Domain** | **Range** | **Asymptotes** |
| $t \neq \dfrac{\pi}{2} + \pi k$ | $(-\infty, \infty)$ | $t = \dfrac{\pi}{2} + \pi k$ | $t \neq k\pi$ | $(-\infty, \infty)$ | $t = k\pi$ |
| **Period** | **Behavior** | **Symmetry** | **Period** | **Behavior** | **Symmetry** |
| $\pi$ | increasing | odd | $\pi$ | decreasing | odd |
| | | $\tan(-t) = -\tan t$ | | | $\cot(-t) = -\cot t$ |

---

**EXAMPLE 5** ▶ **Using the Period of $f(t) = \tan t$ to Find Additional Points**

Given $\tan\left(\dfrac{\pi}{6}\right) = \dfrac{1}{\sqrt{3}}$, what can you say about $\tan\left(\dfrac{7\pi}{6}\right)$, $\tan\left(\dfrac{13\pi}{6}\right)$, and $\tan\left(-\dfrac{5\pi}{6}\right)$?

**Solution** ▶ Each value of $t$ differs from $\dfrac{\pi}{6}$ by a multiple of $\pi$: $\tan\left(\dfrac{7\pi}{6}\right) = \tan\left(\dfrac{\pi}{6} + \pi\right)$,

$\tan\left(\dfrac{13\pi}{6}\right) = \tan\left(\dfrac{\pi}{6} + 2\pi\right)$, and $\tan\left(-\dfrac{5\pi}{6}\right) = \tan\left(\dfrac{\pi}{6} - \pi\right)$. Since the period of

the tangent function is $P = \pi$, all of these expressions have a value of $\dfrac{1}{\sqrt{3}}$.

**Now try Exercises 25 through 30** ▶

Since the tangent function is more common than the cotangent, many needed calculations will first be done using the tangent function and its properties, then reciprocated. For instance, to evaluate $\cot\left(-\dfrac{\pi}{6}\right)$ we reason that $\cot t$ is an odd

☑ **D.** You've just learned how to identify and discuss important characteristics of $y = \tan t$ and $y = \cot t$

function, so $\cot\left(-\dfrac{\pi}{6}\right) = -\cot\left(\dfrac{\pi}{6}\right)$. Since cotangent is the reciprocal of tangent and

$\tan\left(\dfrac{\pi}{6}\right) = \dfrac{1}{\sqrt{3}}$, $-\cot\left(\dfrac{\pi}{6}\right) = -\sqrt{3}$. **See Exercises 31 and 32.**

## E. Graphing $y = A \tan(Bt)$ and $y = A \cot(Bt)$

### The Coefficient $A$: Vertical Stretches and Compressions

For the tangent and cotangent functions, the role of coefficient $A$ is best seen through an analogy from basic algebra (the concept of amplitude is foreign to these functions). Consider the graph of $y = x^3$ (Figure 4.29). Comparing the parent function $y = x^3$ with functions $y = Ax^3$, the graph is stretched vertically if $|A| > 1$ (see Figure 4.30) and compressed if $0 < |A| < 1$. In the latter case the graph becomes very "flat" near the zeroes, as shown in Figure 4.31.

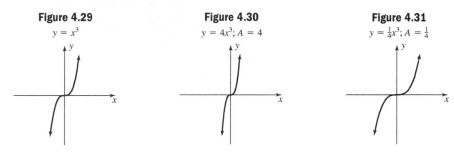

**Figure 4.29**
$y = x^3$

**Figure 4.30**
$y = 4x^3; A = 4$

**Figure 4.31**
$y = \frac{1}{4}x^3; A = \frac{1}{4}$

While ***cubic functions are not asymptotic,*** they are a good illustration of $A$'s effect on the tangent and cotangent functions. Fractional values of $A$ ($|A| < 1$) compress the graph, flattening it out near its zeroes. Numerically, this is because a fractional part of a small quantity is an even smaller quantity. For instance, compare $\tan\left(\dfrac{\pi}{6}\right)$ with $\dfrac{1}{4}\tan\left(\dfrac{\pi}{6}\right)$. To two decimal places, $\tan\left(\dfrac{\pi}{6}\right) = 0.57$, while $\dfrac{1}{4}\tan\left(\dfrac{\pi}{6}\right) = 0.14$, so the graph must be "nearer the $t$-axis" at this value.

---

**EXAMPLE 6** ▶ **Comparing the Graph of $f(t) = \tan t$ and $g(t) = A \tan t$**

Draw a "comparative sketch" of $y = \tan t$ and $y = \frac{1}{4}\tan t$ on the same axis and discuss similarities and differences. Use the interval $[-\pi, 2\pi]$.

Solution ▶ Both graphs will maintain their essential features (zeroes, asymptotes, period, increasing, and so on). However, the graph of $y = \frac{1}{4}\tan t$ is vertically compressed, causing it to flatten out near its zeroes and changing how the graph approaches its asymptotes in each interval.

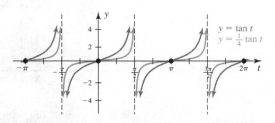

Now try Exercises 33 through 36 ▶

---

## The Coefficient $B$: The Period of Tangent and Cotangent

Like the other trig functions, the value of $B$ has a material impact on the period of the function, and with the same effect. The graph of $y = \cot(2t)$ completes a cycle twice as fast as $y = \cot t$ $\left(P = \dfrac{\pi}{2} \text{ versus } P = \pi\right)$, while $y = \cot\left(\dfrac{1}{2}t\right)$ completes a cycle one-half as fast ($P = 2\pi$ versus $P = \pi$).

This reasoning leads us to a **period formula** for tangent and cotangent, namely, $P = \dfrac{\pi}{|B|}$, where $B$ is the coefficient of the input variable.

Similar to the four-step process used to graph sine and cosine functions, we can graph tangent and cotangent functions using a rectangle $P = \dfrac{\pi}{B}$ units in length and $2A$ units high, centered on the primary interval. After dividing the length of the rectangle into fourths, the $t$-intercept will always be the halfway point, with $y$-values of $|A|$ occurring at the $\frac{1}{4}$ and $\frac{3}{4}$ marks. See Example 7.

**EXAMPLE 7** ▶ **Graphing $y = A \cot(Bt)$ for $A, B \neq 1$**

Sketch the graph of $y = 3 \cot(2t)$ over the interval $[-\pi, \pi]$.

**Solution** ▶ For $y = 3 \cot(2t)$, $|A| = 3$, which results in a vertical stretch, and $|B| = 2$, which gives a period of $\frac{\pi}{2}$. The function is still undefined (asymptotic) at $t = 0$ and then at all integer multiples of $P = \frac{\pi}{2}$. We also know the graph is decreasing, with zeroes of the function halfway between the asymptotes. The inputs $t = \frac{\pi}{8}$ and $t = \frac{3\pi}{8}$ (the $\frac{1}{4}$ and $\frac{3}{4}$ marks between 0 and $\frac{\pi}{2}$) yield the points $\left(\frac{\pi}{8}, 3\right)$ and $\left(\frac{3\pi}{8}, -3\right)$, which we'll use along with the period and symmetry of the function to complete the graph:

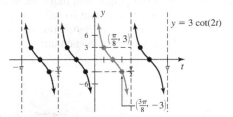

**Now try Exercises 37 through 48** ▶

As with the trig functions from Section 4.1, it is possible to determine the equation of a tangent or cotangent function from a given graph. Where previously we used the amplitude, period, and max/min values to obtain our equation, here we first determine the period of the function by calculating the "distance" between asymptotes, then choose any convenient point on the graph (other than a $t$-intercept) and substitute in the equation to solve for $A$.

**EXAMPLE 8** ▶ **Constructing the Equation for a Given Graph**

Find the equation of the graph, given it's of the form $y = A \tan(Bt)$.

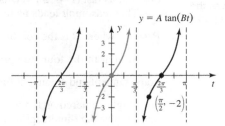

**Solution** ▶ Using the primary interval and the asymptotes at $t = -\frac{\pi}{3}$ and $t = \frac{\pi}{3}$, we find the period is $P = \frac{\pi}{3} - \left(-\frac{\pi}{3}\right) = \frac{2\pi}{3}$. To find the value of $B$ we substitute $\frac{2\pi}{3}$ for $P$ in $P = \frac{\pi}{B}$ and find $B = \frac{3}{2}$ (verify). This gives the equation $y = A \tan\left(\frac{3}{2}t\right)$.

To find $A$, we take the point $\left(\dfrac{\pi}{2}, -2\right)$ shown, and use $t = \dfrac{\pi}{2}$ with $y = -2$ to solve for $A$:

$$y = A \tan\left(\frac{3}{2}t\right) \qquad \text{substitute } \frac{3}{2} \text{ for } B$$

$$-2 = A \tan\left[\left(\frac{3}{2}\right)\left(\frac{\pi}{2}\right)\right] \qquad \text{substitute } -2 \text{ for } y \text{ and } \frac{\pi}{2} \text{ for } t$$

$$-2 = A \tan\left(\frac{3\pi}{4}\right) \qquad \text{multiply}$$

$$A = \frac{-2}{\tan\left(\dfrac{3\pi}{4}\right)} \qquad \text{solve for } A$$

☑ **E.** You've just learned how to graph $y = A\tan(Bt)$ and $y = A\cot(Bt)$ with various values of $A$ and $B$

$$= 2 \qquad \text{result; } \tan\left(\frac{3\pi}{4}\right) = -1$$

The equation of the graph is $y = 2\tan(\frac{3}{2}t)$.

**Now try Exercises 49 through 58 ▶**

## TECHNOLOGY HIGHLIGHT

### Zeroes, Asymptotes, and the Tangent/Cotangent Functions

In this *Technology Highlight*, we'll explore the tangent and cotangent functions from the perspective of their ratio definition. While we could easily use $Y_1 = \tan x$ to generate and explore the graph, we would miss an opportunity to note the many important connections that emerge from a ratio definition perspective. To begin, enter

$Y_1 = \sin x$, $Y_2 = \cos x$, and $Y_3 = \dfrac{Y_1}{Y_2}$, as shown in Figure 4.32 [recall

that function variables are accessed using $\boxed{\text{VARS}}$ $\boxed{\blacktriangleright}$

**(Y-VARS)** $\boxed{\text{ENTER}}$ **(1:Function)].** Note that $Y_2$ has been disabled by overlaying the cursor on the equal sign and pressing $\boxed{\text{ENTER}}$. In addition, note the slash next to $Y_1$ is more **bold** than the other slashes. The TI-84 Plus offers options that help distinguish between graphs when more than one is being displayed, and we selected a **bold** line for $Y_1$ by moving the cursor to the far left position and repeatedly pressing $\boxed{\text{ENTER}}$ until the desired option appeared. Pressing $\boxed{\text{ZOOM}}$ **7:ZTrig** at this point produces the screen shown in Figure 4.33, where we note that tan $x$ is zero everywhere that sin $x$ is zero. This is hardly surprising since $\tan x = \dfrac{\sin x}{\cos x}$, but is a point that is often overlooked. Going back to the $\boxed{\text{Y=}}$ screen and disabling $Y_1$ while enabling $Y_2$ will produce the graph shown in Figure 4.34.

**Figure 4.32**

**Figure 4.33**

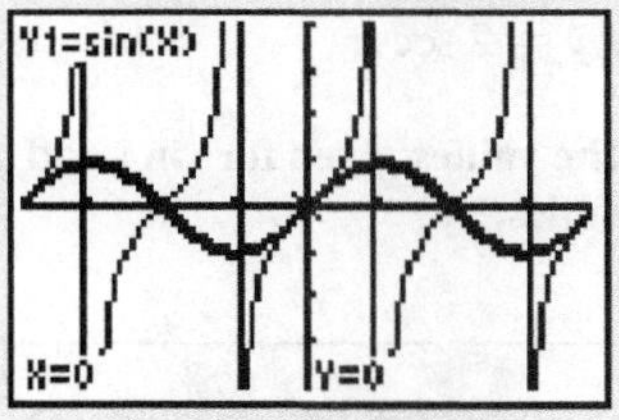

**Figure 4.34**

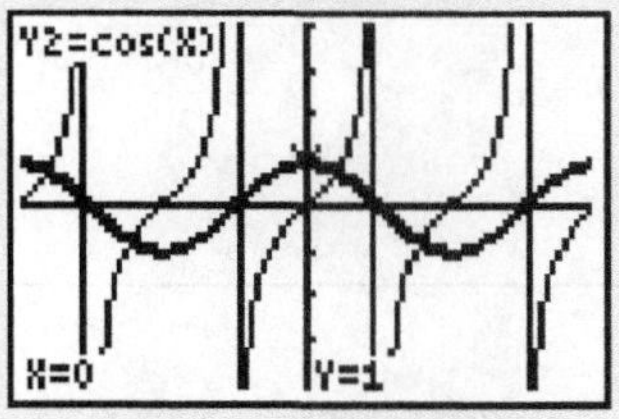

**Exercise 1:**  What do you notice about the zeroes of cos $x$ as they relate to the graph of $Y_3 = \tan x$?

**Exercise 2:**  Go to the $\boxed{\text{Y=}}$ screen and change $Y_3$ from $\dfrac{Y_1}{Y_2}$ (tangent) to $\dfrac{Y_2}{Y_1}$ (cotangent), then repeat the previous investigation regarding $y = \sin x$ and $y = \cos x$.

## 4.2 EXERCISES

▶ **CONCEPTS AND VOCABULARY**

**Fill in each blank with the appropriate word or phrase. Carefully reread the section if needed.**

1. The period of $y = \tan t$ and $y = \cot t$ is _____.
   To find the period of $y = \tan(Bt)$ and $y = \cot(Bt)$,
   the formula _____ is used.

2. The function $y = \tan t$ is _____ everywhere
   it is defined. The function $y = \cot t$ is
   _____ everywhere it is defined.

3. Tan $t$ and cot $t$ are _____ functions, so
   $f(-t) =$ _____. If $\tan\left(-\dfrac{11\pi}{12}\right) \approx 0.268$,
   then $\tan\left(\dfrac{11\pi}{12}\right) \approx$ _____.

4. The asymptotes of $y =$ _____ are located
   at odd multiples of $\dfrac{\pi}{2}$. The asymptotes of
   $y =$ _____ are located at integer multiples of $\pi$.

5. Discuss/Explain (a) how you could obtain a table
   of values for $y = \sec t$ in $[0, 2\pi]$, with the values
   for $y = \cos t$, and (b) how you could obtain a table
   of values for $y = \csc\left(\dfrac{3}{2}t\right)t$ in $[0, 2\pi]$, given the
   values for $y = \sin\left(\dfrac{3}{2}t\right)$.

6. Explain/Discuss how the zeroes of $y = \sin t$ and
   $y = \cos t$ are related to the graphs of $y = \tan t$ and
   $y = \cot t$. How can these relationships help graph
   functions of the form $y = A \tan(Bt)$ and
   $y = A \cot(Bt)$?

▶ **DEVELOPING YOUR SKILLS**

**Draw the graph of each function by first sketching the related sine and cosine graphs, and applying the observations from this section.**

7. $y = \csc(2t)$

8. $y = \csc(\pi t)$

9. $y = \sec\left(\dfrac{1}{2}t\right)$

10. $y = \sec(2\pi t)$

11. $y = 3 \csc t$

12. $g(t) = 2 \csc(4t)$

13. $y = 2 \sec t$

14. $f(t) = 3 \sec(2t)$

**Use the values given for sin $t$ and cos $t$ to complete the tables.**

15.

| $t$ | $\pi$ | $\dfrac{7\pi}{6}$ | $\dfrac{5\pi}{4}$ | $\dfrac{4\pi}{3}$ | $\dfrac{3\pi}{2}$ |
|---|---|---|---|---|---|
| $\sin t = y$ | 0 | $-\dfrac{1}{2}$ | $-\dfrac{\sqrt{2}}{2}$ | $-\dfrac{\sqrt{3}}{2}$ | $-1$ |
| $\cos t = x$ | $-1$ | $-\dfrac{\sqrt{3}}{2}$ | $-\dfrac{\sqrt{2}}{2}$ | $-\dfrac{1}{2}$ | 0 |
| $\tan t = \dfrac{y}{x}$ | | | | | |

16.

| | $\dfrac{3\pi}{2}$ | $\dfrac{5\pi}{3}$ | $\dfrac{7\pi}{4}$ | $\dfrac{11\pi}{6}$ | $2\pi$ |
|---|---|---|---|---|---|
| $\sin t = y$ | $-1$ | $-\dfrac{\sqrt{3}}{2}$ | $-\dfrac{\sqrt{2}}{2}$ | $-\dfrac{1}{2}$ | 0 |
| $\cos t = x$ | 0 | $\dfrac{1}{2}$ | $\dfrac{\sqrt{2}}{2}$ | $\dfrac{\sqrt{3}}{2}$ | 1 |
| $\tan t = \dfrac{y}{x}$ | | | | | |

17. Without reference to a text or calculator, attempt to name the decimal equivalent of the following values to one decimal place.

$$\dfrac{\pi}{2} \quad \dfrac{\pi}{4} \quad \dfrac{\pi}{6} \quad \sqrt{2} \quad \dfrac{\sqrt{2}}{2} \quad \dfrac{2}{\sqrt{3}}$$

18. Without reference to a text or calculator, attempt to name the decimal equivalent of the following values to one decimal place.

$$\dfrac{\pi}{3} \quad \pi \quad \dfrac{3\pi}{2} \quad \sqrt{3} \quad \dfrac{\sqrt{3}}{2} \quad \dfrac{1}{\sqrt{3}}$$

**19.** State the value of each expression without the use of a calculator.

    **a.** $\tan\left(-\dfrac{\pi}{4}\right)$      **b.** $\cot\left(\dfrac{\pi}{6}\right)$

    **c.** $\cot\left(\dfrac{3\pi}{4}\right)$      **d.** $\tan\left(\dfrac{\pi}{3}\right)$

**20.** State the value of $t$ without the use of a calculator.

    **a.** $\cot\left(\dfrac{\pi}{2}\right)$      **b.** $\tan\pi$

    **c.** $\tan\left(-\dfrac{5\pi}{4}\right)$      **d.** $\cot\left(-\dfrac{5\pi}{6}\right)$

**21.** State the value of $t$ without the use of a calculator, given $t \in [0, 2\pi)$ terminates in the quadrant indicated.

    **a.** $\tan t = -1$, $t$ in QIV

    **b.** $\cot t = \sqrt{3}$, $t$ in QIII

    **c.** $\cot t = -\dfrac{1}{\sqrt{3}}$, $t$ in QIV

    **d.** $\tan t = -1$, $t$ in QII

**22.** State the value of each expression without the use of a calculator, given $t \in [0, 2\pi)$ terminates in the quadrant indicated.

    **a.** $\cot t = 1$, $t$ in QI

    **b.** $\tan t = -\sqrt{3}$, $t$ in QII

    **c.** $\tan t = \dfrac{1}{\sqrt{3}}$, $t$ in QI

    **d.** $\cot t = 1$, $t$ in QIII

**Use the values given for $\sin t$ and $\cos t$ to complete the tables.**

**23.**

| $t$ | $\pi$ | $\dfrac{7\pi}{6}$ | $\dfrac{5\pi}{4}$ | $\dfrac{4\pi}{3}$ | $\dfrac{3\pi}{2}$ |
|---|---|---|---|---|---|
| $\sin t = y$ | 0 | $-\dfrac{1}{2}$ | $-\dfrac{\sqrt{2}}{2}$ | $-\dfrac{\sqrt{3}}{2}$ | $-1$ |
| $\cos t = x$ | $-1$ | $-\dfrac{\sqrt{3}}{2}$ | $-\dfrac{\sqrt{2}}{2}$ | $-\dfrac{1}{2}$ | 0 |
| $\cot t = \dfrac{x}{y}$ | | | | | |

**24.**

| | $\dfrac{3\pi}{2}$ | $\dfrac{5\pi}{3}$ | $\dfrac{7\pi}{4}$ | $\dfrac{11\pi}{6}$ | $2\pi$ |
|---|---|---|---|---|---|
| $\sin t = y$ | $-1$ | $-\dfrac{\sqrt{3}}{2}$ | $-\dfrac{\sqrt{2}}{2}$ | $-\dfrac{1}{2}$ | 0 |
| $\cos t = x$ | 0 | $\dfrac{1}{2}$ | $\dfrac{\sqrt{2}}{2}$ | $\dfrac{\sqrt{3}}{2}$ | 1 |
| $\cot t = \dfrac{x}{y}$ | | | | | |

**25.** Given $t = \dfrac{11\pi}{24}$ is a solution to $\tan t \approx 7.6$, use the period of the function to name three additional solutions. Check your answer using a calculator.

**26.** Given $t = \dfrac{7\pi}{24}$ is a solution to $\cot t \approx 0.77$, use the period of the function to name three additional solutions. Check your answer using a calculator.

**27.** Given $t \approx 1.5$ is a solution to $\cot t = 0.07$, use the period of the function to name three additional solutions. Check your answers using a calculator.

**28.** Given $t \approx 1.25$ is a solution to $\tan t = 3$, use the period of the function to name three additional solutions. Check your answers using a calculator.

**Verify the value shown for $t$ is a solution to the equation given, then use the period of the function to name all real roots. Check two of these roots on a calculator.**

**29.** $t = \dfrac{\pi}{10}$; $\tan t \approx 0.3249$

**30.** $t = -\dfrac{\pi}{16}$; $\tan t \approx -0.1989$

**31.** $t = \dfrac{\pi}{12}$; $\cot t = 2 + \sqrt{3}$

**32.** $t = \dfrac{5\pi}{12}$; $\cot t = 2 - \sqrt{3}$

**Graph each function over the interval indicated, noting the period, asymptotes, zeroes, and value of $A$. Include a comparative sketch of $y = \tan t$ or $y = \cot t$ as indicated.**

**33.** $f(t) = 2\tan t$; $[-2\pi, 2\pi]$

**34.** $g(t) = \dfrac{1}{2}\tan t$; $[-2\pi, 2\pi]$

**35.** $h(t) = 3\cot t$; $[-2\pi, 2\pi]$

**36.** $r(t) = \dfrac{1}{4}\cot t$; $[-2\pi, 2\pi]$

**Graph each function over the interval indicated, noting the period, asymptotes, zeroes, and value of A and B.**

**37.** $y = \tan(2t)$; $\left[-\dfrac{\pi}{2}, \dfrac{\pi}{2}\right]$

**38.** $y = \tan\left(\dfrac{1}{4}t\right)$; $[-4\pi, 4\pi]$

**39.** $y = \cot(4t)$; $\left[-\dfrac{\pi}{4}, \dfrac{\pi}{4}\right]$

**40.** $y = \cot\left(\dfrac{1}{2}t\right)$; $[-2\pi, 2\pi]$

**41.** $y = 2\tan(4t)$; $\left[-\dfrac{\pi}{4}, \dfrac{\pi}{4}\right]$

**42.** $y = 4\tan\left(\dfrac{1}{2}t\right)$; $[-2\pi, 2\pi]$

**43.** $y = 5\cot\left(\dfrac{1}{3}t\right)$; $[-3\pi, 3\pi]$

**44.** $y = \dfrac{1}{2}\cot(2t)$; $\left[-\dfrac{\pi}{2}, \dfrac{\pi}{2}\right]$

**45.** $y = 3\tan(2\pi t)$; $\left[-\dfrac{1}{2}, \dfrac{1}{2}\right]$

**46.** $y = 4\tan\left(\dfrac{\pi}{2}t\right)$; $[-2, 2]$

**47.** $f(t) = 2\cot(\pi t)$; $[-1, 1]$

**48.** $p(t) = \dfrac{1}{2}\cot\left(\dfrac{\pi}{4}t\right)$; $[-4, 4]$

**Clearly state the period of each function, then match it with the corresponding graph.**

**49.** $y = 2\csc\left(\dfrac{1}{2}t\right)$

**50.** $y = 2\sec\left(\dfrac{1}{4}t\right)$

**51.** $y = \sec(8\pi t)$

**52.** $y = \csc(12\pi t)$

**a.**
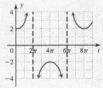

**b.**
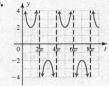

**c.**
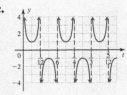

**d.**
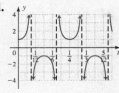

**Find the equation of each graph, given it is of the form $y = A\csc(Bt)$.**

**53.**
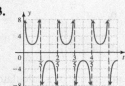

**54.**
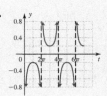

**Find the equation of each graph, given it is of the form $y = A\tan(Bt)$.**

**55.**
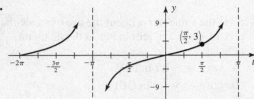

**56.**
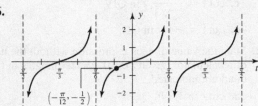

**Find the equation of each graph, given it is of the form $y = A\cot(Bt)$.**

**57.**
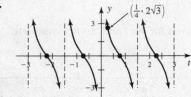

**58.**
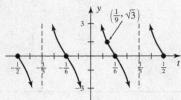

**59.** Given that $t = -\dfrac{\pi}{8}$ and $t = -\dfrac{3\pi}{8}$ are solutions to $\cot(3t) = \tan t$, use a graphing calculator to find two additional solutions in $[0, 2\pi]$.

**60.** Given $t = \dfrac{1}{6}$ is a solution to $\tan(2\pi t) = \cot(\pi t)$, use a graphing calculator to find two additional solutions in $[-1, 1]$.

▶ **WORKING WITH FORMULAS**

**61. The height of an object calculated from a distance:** $h = \dfrac{d}{\cot u - \cot v}$

The height $h$ of a tall structure can be computed using two angles of elevation measured some distance apart along a straight line with the object. This height is given by the formula shown, where $d$ is the distance between the two points from which angles $u$ and $v$ were measured. Find the height $h$ of a building if $u = 40°$, $v = 65°$, and $d = 100$ ft.

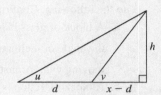

**62. Position of an image reflected from a spherical lens:** $\tan \theta = \dfrac{h}{s - k}$

The equation shown is used to help locate the position of an image reflected by a spherical mirror, where $s$ is the distance of the object from the lens along a horizontal axis, $\theta$ is the angle of elevation from this axis, $h$ is the altitude of the right triangle indicated, and $k$ is distance from the lens to the foot of altitude $h$. Find the distance $k$ given $h = 3$ mm, $\theta = \dfrac{\pi}{24}$, and that the object is 24 mm from the lens.

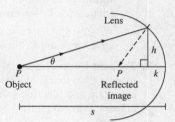

▶ **APPLICATIONS**

**63. Circumscribed polygons:** The *perimeter* of a regular polygon circumscribed about a circle of radius $r$ is given by $P = 2nr \tan\left(\dfrac{\pi}{n}\right)$, where $n$ is the number of sides ($n \geq 3$) and $r$ is the radius of the circle. Given $r = 10$ cm, (a) What is the circumference of the circle? (b) What is the perimeter of the polygon when $n = 4$? Why? (c) Calculate the perimeter of the polygon for $n = 10, 20, 30$, and $100$. What do you notice? See Exercise 53 from Section 4.1.

**Exercise 63**

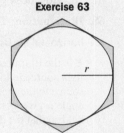

**64. Circumscribed polygons:** The *area* of a regular polygon circumscribed about a circle of radius $r$ is given by $A = nr^2\tan\left(\dfrac{\pi}{n}\right)$, where $n$ is the number of sides ($n \geq 3$) and $r$ is the radius of the circle. Given $r = 10$ cm,

   **a.** What is the area of the circle?

   **b.** What is the area of the polygon when $n = 4$? Why?

   **c.** Calculate the area of the polygon for $n = 10, 20, 30$, and $100$. What do you notice?

**Coefficients of friction:** Pulling someone on a sled is much easier during the winter than in the summer, due to a phenomenon known as the *coefficient of friction*. The friction between the sled's skids and the snow is much lower than the friction between the skids and the dry ground or pavement. Basically, the coefficient of friction is defined by the relationship $\mu = \tan \theta$, where $\theta$ is the angle at which a block composed of one material will slide down an inclined plane made of another material, with a constant velocity. Coefficients of friction have been established experimentally for many materials and a short list is shown here.

| Material | Coefficient |
| --- | --- |
| steel on steel | 0.74 |
| copper on glass | 0.53 |
| glass on glass | 0.94 |
| copper on steel | 0.68 |
| wood on wood | 0.5 |

**65.** Graph the function $\mu = \tan \theta$, with $\theta$ in degrees over the interval $[0°, 60°]$ and use the graph to estimate solutions to the following. Confirm or contradict your estimates using a calculator.

   **a.** A block of copper is placed on a sheet of steel, which is slowly inclined. Is the block of copper moving when the angle of inclination is 30°? At what angle of inclination will the copper block be moving with a constant velocity down the incline?

   **b.** A block of copper is placed on a sheet of cast-iron. As the cast-iron sheet is slowly inclined, the copper block begins sliding at a constant velocity when the angle of inclination is approximately 46.5°. What is the coefficient of friction for copper on cast-iron?

   **c.** Why do you suppose coefficients of friction greater than $\mu = 2.5$ are extremely rare? Give an example of two materials that likely have a high $\mu$-value.

**66.** Graph the function $\mu = \tan \theta$ with $\theta$ in radians over the interval $\left[ 0, \dfrac{5\pi}{12} \right]$ and use the graph to estimate solutions

to the following. Confirm or contradict your estimates using a calculator.

   **a.** A block of glass is placed on a sheet of glass, which is slowly inclined. Is the block of glass moving when

       the angle of inclination is $\dfrac{\pi}{4}$? What is the smallest angle of inclination for which the glass block will be

       moving with a constant velocity down the incline (rounded to four decimal places)?

   **b.** A block of Teflon is placed on a sheet of steel. As the steel sheet is slowly inclined, the Teflon block begins
sliding at a constant velocity when the angle of inclination is approximately 0.04. What is the coefficient of
friction for Teflon on steel?

   **c.** Why do you suppose coefficients of friction less than $\mu = 0.04$ are extremely rare for two solid materials?
Give an example of two materials that likely have a very low $\mu$ value.

**67. Tangent lines:** The actual definition of the word *tangent* comes from the Latin *tangere*,
meaning "to touch." In mathematics, a tangent line touches the graph of a circle at only
one point and function values for tan $\theta$ are obtained from the length of the line segment
tangent to a unit circle.

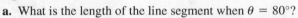

   **a.** What is the length of the line segment when $\theta = 80°$?

   **b.** If the line segment is 16.35 units long, what is the value of $\theta$?

   **c.** Can the line segment ever be greater than 100 units long? Why or why not?

   **d.** How does your answer to (c) relate to the asymptotic behavior of the graph?

**68. Illumination:** The angle $\alpha$ made by a light source and a point on a

horizontal surface can be found using the formula $\csc \alpha = \dfrac{I}{r^2 E}$, where

$E$ is the illuminance (in lumens/m$^2$) at the point, $I$ is the intensity of the
light source in lumens, and $r$ is the distance in meters from the light
source to the point. Use the graph from Example 1 to help determine the
angle $\alpha$ given $I = 700$ lumens, $E = 55$ lumens/m$^2$, and the flashlight is
held so that the distance $r$ is 3 m.

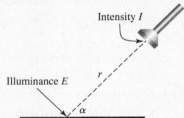

**69. Area of a polygon:** The area of a regular polygon that has been circumscribed about

a circle of radius $r$ (see figure) is given by the formula $A = nr^2 \sin\left(\dfrac{\pi}{n}\right)\sec\left(\dfrac{\pi}{n}\right)$, where

$n$ represents the number of sides. (a) Verify the formula for a square circumscribed
about a circle with radius 4 m. (b) Find the area of a dodecagon (12 sides) circumscribed
about the same circle.

**70. Perimeter of a polygon:** The perimeter of a regular polygon circumscribed about a

circle of radius $r$ is given by the formula $P = 2nr \sin\left(\dfrac{\pi}{n}\right) \sec\left(\dfrac{\pi}{n}\right)$, where $n$ represents the number of sides.

(a) Verify the formula for a square circumscribed about a circle with radius 4 m. (b) Find the perimeter of a
dodecagon (12 sides) circumscribed about the same circle.

▶ **EXTENDING THE CONCEPT**

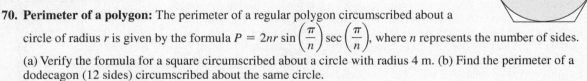

**71.** The golden ratio $\dfrac{-1 + \sqrt{5}}{2}$ has long been thought to be the most pleasing ratio in art and architecture. It is

commonly believed that many forms of ancient architecture were constructed using this ratio as a guide. The
ratio actually turns up in some surprising places, far removed from its original inception as a line segment cut in
"mean and extreme" ratio. Given $x = 0.6662394325$, try to find a connection between $y = \cos x$, $y = \tan x$,
$y = \sin x$, and the golden ratio.

**72.** Determine the slope of the line drawn *through* the parabola (called a **secant** line) in Figure I. Use the same method (any two points on the line) to calculate the slope of the line drawn **tangent** to the parabola in Figure II. Compare your calculations to the tangent of the angles $\alpha$ and $\beta$ that each line makes with the *x*-axis. What can you conclude? Write a formula for the point/slope equation of a line using $\tan \theta$ instead of *m*.

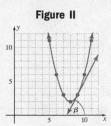

**Figure I**                                    **Figure II**

▶ **MAINTAINING YOUR SKILLS**

**73. (2.3)** A tent rope is 4 ft long and attached to the tent wall 2 ft above the ground. How far from the tent is the stake holding the rope?

**Exercise 73**                                              **Exercise 74**

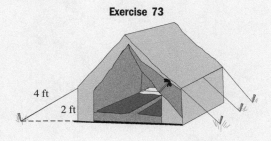

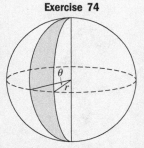

**74. (3.2)** A lune is a section of surface area on a sphere, which is subtended by an angle $\theta$ at the circumference. For $\theta$ *in radians,* the surface area of a lune is $A = 2r^2\theta$, where *r* is the radius of the sphere. Find the area of a lune on the surface of the Earth which is subtended by an angle of 15°. Assume the radius of the Earth is 6373 km.

**75. (3.3)** Use a reference arc to determine the value of $\cos\left(\dfrac{29\pi}{6}\right)$.

**76. (3.4)** State the points on the unit circle that correspond to $t = 0$, $\dfrac{\pi}{4}$, $\dfrac{\pi}{2}$, $\pi$, $\dfrac{3\pi}{4}$, $\dfrac{3\pi}{2}$, and $2\pi$. What is the value of $\tan\left(\dfrac{\pi}{2}\right)$? Why?

**77. (2.4)** Given $\sin 212° \approx -0.53$, find another angle $\theta$ in $[0°, 360°)$ that satisfies $\sin \theta \approx -0.53$ without using a calculator.

**78. (4.1)** At what value(s) of *t* does the horizontal line $y = 3$ intersect the graph of $y = -3 \sin t$?

## MID-CHAPTER CHECK

**1.** Which function, $y = \tan t$ or $y = \cot t$, is decreasing on its domain? Which function, $y = \cos t$ or $y = \sin t$, begins at (0, 1) in the interval $t \in [0, 2\pi)$?

**2.** State the period of $y = \sin\left(\dfrac{\pi}{2}t\right)$. Where will the max/min values occur in the primary interval?

**3.** Evaluate without using a calculator: (a) $\cot 60°$ and (b) $\sin\left(\dfrac{7\pi}{4}\right)$.

**4.** Evaluate using a calculator: (a) $\sec\left(\dfrac{\pi}{12}\right)$ and (b) $\tan 4.3$.

5. Which of the six trig functions are even functions?

6. State the domain of $y = \sin t$ and $y = \tan t$.

7. Name the location of the asymptotes and graph

$y = 3 \tan\left(\dfrac{\pi}{2}t\right)$ for $t \in [-2\pi, 2\pi]$.

8. Clearly state the amplitude and period, then sketch

the graph: $y = -3 \cos\left(\dfrac{\pi}{2}t\right)$.

9. On a unit circle, if arc $t$ has length 5.94, (a) in what quadrant does it terminate? (b) What is its reference arc? (c) Of $\sin t$, $\cos t$, and $\tan t$, which are negative for this value of $t$?

10. For the graph given here, (a) clearly state the amplitude and period; (b) find the equation of the graph; (c) graphically find $f(\pi)$ and then confirm/contradict your estimation using a calculator.

**Exercise 10**

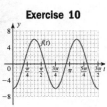

## REINFORCING BASIC CONCEPTS

### Trigonometric Potpourri

This *Reinforcing Basic Concepts* is simply a collection of patterns, observations, hints, and reminders connected with an introduction to trigonometry. Individually the points may seem trivial, but taken together they tend to reinforce the core fundamentals of trig, enabling you to sequence and store the ideas in your own way. Having these basic elements available for instant retrieval builds a stronger bridge to future concepts, assists in the discovery of additional connections, and enables a closer tie between these concepts and the real-world situations to which they will be applied. Just a little work now pays big dividends later. As Louis Pasteur once said, "Fortune favors a prepared mind."

1. The collection begins with an all-encompassing view of the trig functions, as seen by the imposition of a right triangle in a unit circle, on the coordinate grid. This allows all three approaches to trigonometry to be seen at one time:

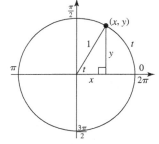

$$\text{right triangle: } \cos t = \frac{\text{adj}}{\text{hyp}} \quad \text{any angle: } \cos t = \frac{x}{r}$$

$$\text{real number: } \cos t = x$$

Should you ever forget the association of *x with cosine and y with sine,* just remember that *c* comes before *s* in the alphabet in the same way the *x* comes before *y*: $\cos t \rightarrow x$ and $\sin t \rightarrow y$.

2. *Know the standard angles and the standard values.* As mentioned earlier, they are used repeatedly throughout higher mathematics to introduce new concepts and skills without the clutter and distraction of large decimal values. It is interesting to note the standard values (from QI) can always be recreated using the *pattern of fourths.* Simply write the fractions with integer numerators from $\frac{0}{4}$ through $\frac{4}{4}$, and take their square root:

$$\sqrt{\frac{0}{4}} = 0 \qquad \sqrt{\frac{1}{4}} = \frac{1}{2} \qquad \sqrt{\frac{2}{4}} = \frac{\sqrt{2}}{2} \qquad \sqrt{\frac{3}{4}} = \frac{\sqrt{3}}{2} \qquad \sqrt{\frac{4}{4}} = 1$$

3. There are many *decimal equivalents* in elementary mathematics that contribute to concept building. In the same way you recognize the decimal values of $\frac{1}{4}$, $\frac{1}{2}$, $\frac{3}{4}$, and others, it helps *tremendously* to recognize or "know" decimal equivalents for values that are commonly used in a study of trig. They help to identify the quadrant of an arc/angle's terminal side when *t* is expressed in radians, they assist in graphing and estimation skills, and are used extensively throughout this text and in other areas of mathematics. In terms of $\pi$ these are $\frac{\pi}{2}$, $\pi$, $\frac{3\pi}{2}$, and $2\pi$. In

terms of radicals they are $\sqrt{2}, \dfrac{\sqrt{2}}{2}, \sqrt{3},$ and $\dfrac{\sqrt{3}}{2}$. Knowing $\pi \approx 3.14$ leads directly to $\dfrac{\pi}{2} \approx 1.57$ and

$2\pi \approx 6.28$, while adding the decimal values for $\pi$ and $\dfrac{\pi}{2}$ gives $\dfrac{3\pi}{2} \approx 4.71$. Further, since $\sqrt{2} \approx 1.41, \dfrac{\sqrt{2}}{2} \approx 0.7$,

and since $\sqrt{3} \approx 1.73, \dfrac{\sqrt{3}}{2} \approx 0.87$.

**4.** To specifically remember what standard value is associated with a standard angle or arc, recall that

   **a.** If $t$ is a quadrantal arc/angle, it's easiest to use the coordinates $(x, y)$ of a point on a unit circle.

   **b.** If $t$ is any odd multiple of $\dfrac{\pi}{4}$, sin $t$ and cos $t$ must be $-\dfrac{\sqrt{2}}{2}$ or $\dfrac{\sqrt{2}}{2}$, with the choice depending on the quadrant

      of the terminal side. The values of the other functions can be found using these.

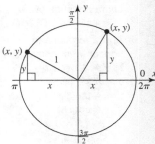

   **c.** If $t$ is a multiple of $\dfrac{\pi}{6}$ (excluding the quadrantal angles), the value for sine and

      cosine must be either $\pm\dfrac{1}{2}$ or $\pm\dfrac{\sqrt{3}}{2}$, depending on the quadrant of the terminal

      side. If there's any hesitation about which value applies to sine and

      which to cosine, mental imagery can once again help. Since

      $\dfrac{\sqrt{3}}{2} \approx 0.87 > \dfrac{1}{2} = 0.5$, we simply apply the larger value

      to the larger arc/angle. Note that for the triangle drawn in

      QI $\left(\dfrac{\pi}{3} = 60° \text{ angle at vertex}\right)$, $y$ is obviously longer than $x$, meaning the

      association must be sin $t = \dfrac{\sqrt{3}}{2}$ and cos $t = \dfrac{1}{2}$. For the triangle in QII $\left(\dfrac{5\pi}{6} = 150° \text{ whose reference angle}\right.$

      is $30°\Big)$, $x$ is longer than $y$, meaning the association must be cos $t = -\dfrac{\sqrt{3}}{2}$ and sin $t = \dfrac{1}{2}$.

**5.** Although they are often neglected or treated lightly in a study of trig, the secant, cosecant, and cotangent functions play an integral role in more advanced mathematics classes. Be sure you're familiar with their reciprocal relationship to the more common cosine, sine, and tangent functions:

$$\sec t = \frac{1}{\cos t}, \quad \cos t = \frac{1}{\sec t}, \quad \sec t \cos t = 1; \quad \cos\left(\frac{2\pi}{3}\right) = -\frac{1}{2} \rightarrow \sec\left(\frac{2\pi}{3}\right) = -2$$

$$\csc t = \frac{1}{\sin t}, \quad \sin t = \frac{1}{\csc t}, \quad \csc t \sin t = 1; \quad \sin\left(\frac{2\pi}{3}\right) = \frac{\sqrt{3}}{2} \rightarrow \csc\left(\frac{2\pi}{3}\right) = \frac{2}{\sqrt{3}}$$

$$\cot t = \frac{1}{\tan t}, \quad \tan t = \frac{1}{\cot t}, \quad \cot t \tan t = 1; \quad \tan 60° = \sqrt{3} \rightarrow \cot 60° = \frac{1}{\sqrt{3}}$$

**6.** Finally, the need to be very familiar with the basic graphs of the trig functions would be hard to overstate. As with transformations of the toolbox functions (from algebra), transformations of the basic trig graphs are a huge help to the understanding and solution of trig equations and inequalities, as well as to their application in the context of real-world phenomena.

From your algebra experience, you may remember a study of the toolbox functions (sometimes called the *Library of Functions*), and how these basic graphs were transformed (shifted, reflected, stretched, and so on). These transformations helped us investigate and understand some powerful applications in a study of variations. A study of trigonometry follows a similar pattern, in that once the basic trigonometric graphs have been introduced, transforming these graphs will enable us to look at some significant and powerful *trigonometric* applications in Section 4.4.

## A. Vertical Translations: $y = A \sin(Bt) + D$ and $y = A \cos(Bt) + D$

On any given day, outdoor temperatures tend to follow a **sinusoidal pattern,** or a pattern that can be modeled by a sine function. As the Sun rises, the morning temperature begins to warm and rise until reaching its high in the late afternoon, then begins to cool during the early evening and nighttime hours until falling to its nighttime low just prior to sunrise. Next morning, the cycle begins again. In the northern latitudes where the winters are very cold, it's not unreasonable to assume an average daily temperature of 0°C (32°F), and a temperature graph in degrees Celsius that looks like the one in Figure 4.35. For the moment, we'll assume that $t = 0$ corresponds to 12:00 noon. Note that $|A| = 15$ and $P = 24$, yielding $24 = \dfrac{2\pi}{B}$ or $B = \dfrac{\pi}{12}$.

**Figure 4.35**

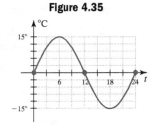

If you live in a more temperate area, the daily temperatures still follow a sinusoidal pattern, but the average temperature could be much higher. This is an example of a **vertical shift,** and is the role $D$ plays in the equation $y = A \sin(Bt) + D$. All other aspects of a graph remain the same; it is simply shifted $D$ units up if $D > 0$ and $D$ units down if $D < 0$. As in Section 4.1, for maximum value $M$ and minimum value $m$, $\dfrac{M - m}{2}$ gives the amplitude $A$ of a sine curve, while $\dfrac{M + m}{2}$ gives the **average value** $D$. In a more tropical climate, the average temperature may be 20°C, and for this graph we need only shift the graph 20 units upward, centering it at $y = 20$ (see Figure 4.36). This is simply another example of the following general concept:

**Figure 4.36**

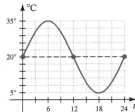

### Vertical Translations of a Basic Graph

Given any function whose graph is determined by $y = f(x)$ and a constant $k > 0$,

1. The graph of $y = f(x) + k$ is the graph of $f(x)$ shifted *upward* $k$ units.
2. The graph of $y = f(x) - k$ is the graph of $f(x)$ shifted *downward* $k$ units.

Note that the graphs of $f(t) = A \sin(Bt) + D$ and $g(t) = A \cos(Bt) + D$ are similarly obtained from the graphs of $y = A \sin(Bt)$ and $y = A \cos(Bt)$. As discussed, the only adjustment required in our graphing procedure is centering the graph on the new average value, the horizontal line $y = D$.

**EXAMPLE 1** ▶  Graphing $y = A \sin(Bt) + D$

Draw a sketch of $y = 3 \sin\left(\dfrac{1}{2}t\right) + 4$ for $t$ in $\left[-2\pi, 6\pi\right]$.

Solution ▶  The amplitude is $|A| = 3$, so the reference rectangle will be $2(3) = 6$ units high.

The period is $P = \dfrac{2\pi}{1/2} = 4\pi$, so the rectangle will be $4\pi$ units in length. Since $D = 4$, the graph will be centered on the line $y = 4$. Using the rule of fourths continues to reveal the location of the zeroes and maximum/minimum values, which will be $(\tfrac{1}{4})4\pi = \pi$ units apart. As in Section 4.1, after completing the graph within the reference rectangle, we carefully extend the graph over the desired interval.

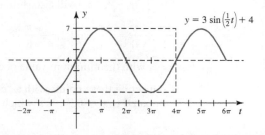

☑ **A. You've just learned how to graph vertical translations of sine and cosine**

Now try Exercises 7 through 12 ▶

## B.  Horizontal Translations: $y = A \sin(Bt + C) + D$ and $y = A \cos(Bt + C) + D$

In Example 1, $t = 0$ yields the average value of the function. In some cases, scientists would rather "benchmark" their study of periodic phenomena by placing the maximum or minimum value at $t = 0$ instead of the average value. Rather than make additional studies or recompute using available data, *we can simply shift these graphs using a horizontal translation*. To help understand how, consider the graph of $y = x^2$. The graph is a parabola, concave up, with a vertex at the origin. Comparing this function with $y_1 = (x - 3)^2$ and $y_2 = (x + 3)^2$, we note $y_1$ is simply the parent graph shifted 3 units right, and $y_2$ is the parent graph shifted 3 units left ("opposite the sign"). See Figures 4.37 through 4.39.

While *quadratic functions have no maximum value if $A > 0$,* these graphs are a good reminder of how a basic graph can be horizontally shifted. We simply *replace the independent variable x with $(x \pm h)$ or t with $(t \pm h)$,* where $h$ is the desired shift and the sign is chosen depending on the direction of the shift.

**Figure 4.37**
$y = x^2$

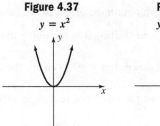

**Figure 4.38**
$y_1 = (x - 3)^2$

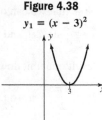

**Figure 4.39**
$y_2 = (x + 3)^2$

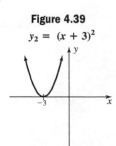

**EXAMPLE 2** ▶ Graphing $y = A \cos(Bt + C)$, $B = 1$

Draw a sketch of $y = 0.7 \cos\left(t - \dfrac{\pi}{6}\right)$ over one period.

Solution ▶ With an amplitude of $|A| = 0.7$ and a period of $P = \dfrac{2\pi}{1} = 2\pi$, the reference
rectangle will be $2(0.7) = 1.4$ units high and $2\pi$ units long. With $C = -\dfrac{\pi}{6}$, the
graph is shifted $\dfrac{\pi}{6}$ units right ("opposite the sign"). Because of this horizontal shift,
the zeroes and maximum/minimum values given by the rule of fourths
$\left(0, \dfrac{\pi}{2}, \pi, \dfrac{3\pi}{2}, 2\pi\right)$ will also shift, giving $0 + \dfrac{\pi}{6} = \dfrac{\pi}{6}$, $\dfrac{\pi}{2} + \dfrac{\pi}{6} = \dfrac{2\pi}{3}$, $\pi + \dfrac{\pi}{6} = \dfrac{7\pi}{6}$,
$\dfrac{3\pi}{2} + \dfrac{\pi}{6} = \dfrac{5\pi}{3}$, and $2\pi + \dfrac{\pi}{6} = \dfrac{13\pi}{6}$. The maximum values will occur at $\dfrac{\pi}{6}$ and
$\dfrac{13\pi}{6}$, with the minimum value occuring at $\dfrac{7\pi}{6}$. The zeroes occur at $\dfrac{2\pi}{3}$ and $\dfrac{5\pi}{3}$.
Connecting these points with a "cosine curve" gives the translated graph shown, as
compared to $y = 0.7 \cos t$, which is shown in the background for reference.

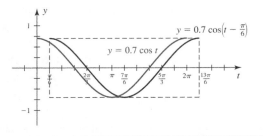

Now try Exercises 13 through 18 ▶

Using special values, transformations, and the rule of fourths, we can easily graph
any horizontally and/or vertically shifted function.

**EXAMPLE 3** ▶ Graphing $f(t) = A \sin(Bt + C) + D$, $B \neq 1$

Draw a sketch of $f(t) = \dfrac{5}{4} \sin\left[2\left(t + \dfrac{\pi}{4}\right)\right] - 1$ for $t$ in $\left[-\dfrac{\pi}{2}, \pi\right]$.

Solution ▶ Note that we can obtain the graph of the function given, by first considering
$y = \dfrac{5}{4} \sin(2t)$, and shifting it to the left $\dfrac{\pi}{4}$ units (opposite the sign), then shifting this
result one unit down. For $y = \dfrac{5}{4} \sin(2t)$, the amplitude is $|A| = \dfrac{5}{4}$ and the period is
$P = \dfrac{2\pi}{2} = \pi$, so the reference rectangle will be $\dfrac{5}{2}$ units high and $\pi$ units wide.

With a period of $\pi$, applying the rule of fourths and a horizontal shift of $\dfrac{\pi}{4}$ units gives, $0 - \dfrac{\pi}{4} = -\dfrac{\pi}{4}$, $\dfrac{\pi}{4} - \dfrac{\pi}{4} = 0$, $\dfrac{\pi}{2} - \dfrac{\pi}{4} = \dfrac{\pi}{4}$, $\dfrac{3\pi}{4} - \dfrac{\pi}{4} = \dfrac{\pi}{2}$, and $\pi - \dfrac{\pi}{4} = \dfrac{3\pi}{4}$.

The zeroes of the graph of $y = \dfrac{5}{4}\sin\left[2\left(t + \dfrac{\pi}{4}\right)\right]$ occur at $-\dfrac{\pi}{4}$, $\dfrac{\pi}{4}$ and $\dfrac{3\pi}{4}$,

with the max/min values spaced equally in between $\left(\text{at } 0 \text{ and } \dfrac{\pi}{2}\right)$. Connecting

these points with a "sine curve" gives the graph shown here, which we then extend
across the indicated interval.

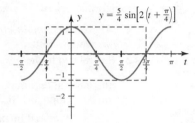

Shifting the graph down 1 unit gives the graph of $f(t) = \dfrac{5}{4}\sin\left[2\left(t + \dfrac{\pi}{4}\right)\right] - 1$

shown.

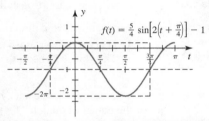

☑ **B.** You've just learned
how to graph horizontal
translations of sine and
cosine

**Now try Exercises 19 through 22** ▶

In Section 4.1, we saw that the graph of $y = \cos t$ could be viewed as the graph of
$y = \sin t$ shifted to the left $\dfrac{\pi}{2}$ units. We also see this concept demonstrated in Example 3, where the sine graph shown can be viewed as that of the *cosine* function:
$g(t) = \dfrac{5}{4}\cos(2t) - 1$.

## C. Important Characteristics of $y = A\sin(Bt \pm C) + D$

Equations like $f(t) = \dfrac{5}{4}\sin\left[2\left(t + \dfrac{\pi}{4}\right) - 1\right]$ from Example 3 are said to be written
in **shifted form,** since changes to the input variable are seen directly and we can easily
tell the magnitude and direction of the shift. To obtain the **standard form** *we distribute
the value of B:* $f(t) = \dfrac{5}{4}\sin\left(2t + \dfrac{\pi}{2}\right) - 1$. As the comments following Example 3
indicate, any cosine function can be written as a shifted sine function (also see the
Worthy of Note). Because of this, the *standard form* combines sine and cosine functions into a single family called the sinusoids, which are generally written as
$y = A\sin(Bt \pm C) + D$. The result is called a **sinusoidal equation** in standard form,
with the *shifted form* found by factoring out $B$ from $Bt \pm C$:

$$y = A\sin(Bt \pm C) + D \rightarrow y = A\sin\left[B\left(t \pm \dfrac{C}{B}\right)\right] + D$$

In either case, $C$ gives what is known as the **phase angle** of the function, and is used in a study of AC circuits and other areas, to discuss how far a given function is "out of phase" with a reference function. In the latter case, $\dfrac{C}{B}$ is simply the horizontal shift (or phase shift) of the function and gives the magnitude and direction of this shift (opposite the sign).

---

### Characteristics of Sinusoidal Equations

Transformations of the graph of $y = \sin t$ are written as $y = A \sin(Bt)$, where

1. $|A|$ gives the *amplitude* of the graph, or the maximum displacement from the average value.
2. $B$ is related to the *period P* of the graph according to the ratio $P = \dfrac{2\pi}{B}$

   (the interval required for one complete cycle). Translations of $y = A \sin(Bt)$ can be written as follows:

   | **Standard form** | **Shifted form** |
   |---|---|
   | $y = A \sin(Bt \pm C) + D$ | $y = A \sin\left[ B\left( t \pm \dfrac{C}{B} \right) \right] + D$ |

3. In either case, $C$ is called the *phase angle* of the graph, while $\pm \dfrac{C}{B}$ gives the magnitude and direction of the *horizontal shift* (opposite the given sign).
4. $D$ gives the *vertical shift* of the graph, and the location of the average value. The shift will be in the same direction as the given sign.

Knowing where each cycle begins and ends is a helpful part of sketching a graph of the equation model. The **primary interval** for a sinusoidal graph can be found by solving the inequality $0 \le Bt \pm C < 2\pi$, with the reference rectangle and *rule of fourths* giving the zeroes, max/min values, and a sketch of the graph in this interval. The graph can then be extended in either direction, and shifted vertically as needed.

---

**EXAMPLE 4** ▶ **Analyzing the Transformation of a Trig Function**

Identify the amplitude, period, horizontal shift, vertical shift (average value), and endpoints of the primary interval.

$$y = 2.5 \sin\left( \frac{\pi}{4}t + \frac{3\pi}{4} \right) + 6$$

Solution ▶ The equation gives an amplitude of $|A| = 2.5$, with an average value of $D = 6$. The maximum value will be $y = 2.5(1) + 6 = 8.5$, with a minimum of $y = 2.5(-1) + 6 = 3.5$. With $B = \dfrac{\pi}{4}$, the period is $P = \dfrac{2\pi}{\pi/4} = 8$. To find the horizontal shift, we factor out $\dfrac{\pi}{4}$ to write the equation in shifted form: $\left( \dfrac{\pi}{4}t + \dfrac{3\pi}{4} \right) = \dfrac{\pi}{4}(t + 3)$. The horizontal shift is 3 units left. For the endpoints of the primary interval we solve $0 \le \dfrac{\pi}{4}(t + 3) < 2\pi$, which gives $-3 \le t < 5$.

**Now try Exercises 23 through 34** ▶

**GRAPHICAL SUPPORT**

The analysis of $y = 2.5 \sin\left[\dfrac{\pi}{4}(t + 3)\right] + 6$ from

Example 4 can be verified on a graphing calculator. Enter the function as $Y_1$ on the [ Y = ] screen and set an appropriate window size using the information gathered. Press the [ TRACE ] key and $-3$ [ ENTER ] and the calculator gives the average value $y = 6$ as output. Repeating this for $x = 5$ shows one complete cycle has been completed.

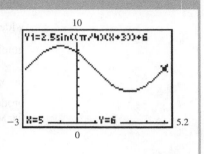

To help gain a better understanding of sinusoidal functions, their graphs, and the role the coefficients $A$, $B$, $C$, and $D$ play, it's often helpful to reconstruct the equation of a given graph.

**EXAMPLE 5** ▶  **Determining the Equation of a Trig Function from Its Graph**

Determine the equation of the given graph using a sine function.

Solution ▶  From the graph it is apparent the maximum value is 300, with a minimum of 50. This gives a value

of $\dfrac{300 + 50}{2} = 175$ for $D$ and $\dfrac{300 - 50}{2} = 125$

for $A$. The graph completes one cycle from $t = 2$

to $t = 18$, showing $P = 18 - 2 = 16$ and $B = \dfrac{\pi}{8}$.

The average value first occurs at $t = 2$, so the basic graph has been shifted to the right 2 units.

The equation is $y = 125 \sin\left[\dfrac{\pi}{8}(t - 2)\right] + 175$.

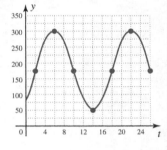

☑ **C.** You've just learned how to identify and apply important characteristics of $y = A \sin(Bt \pm C) + D$

**Now try Exercises 35 through 40** ▶

## D. Vertical and Horizontal Translations of Other Trig Functions

In Section 4.2, we used the graphs of $y = A \sin(Bt)$ and $y = A \cos(Bt)$ to help graph $y = A \csc(Bt)$ and $y = A \sec(Bt)$, respectively. If a vertical or horizontal translation is being applied to a cosecant/secant function, we simply apply the same translations to the underlying sine/cosine function as an aid to graphing the function at hand.

**EXAMPLE 6** ▶  **Graphing $y = A \sec(Bt + C) + D$**

Draw a sketch of $y = 2 \sec\left(\dfrac{\pi}{3}t - \dfrac{\pi}{2}\right) - 3$ for $t$ in $[0, 9]$.

Solution ▶  To graph this secant function, consider the function $y = 2 \cos\left(\dfrac{\pi}{3}t - \dfrac{\pi}{2}\right) - 3$. In

shifted form, we have $y = 2 \cos\left[\dfrac{\pi}{3}\left(t - \dfrac{3}{2}\right)\right] - 3$. With an amplitude of $|A| = 2$

and period of $P = \dfrac{2\pi}{\pi/3} = 6$, the reference rectangle will be 4 units high and 6 units wide. The rule of fourths shows the zeroes and max/min values of the unshifted graph will occur at $0, \dfrac{3}{2}, 3, \dfrac{9}{2}$, and 6. Applying a horizontal shift of $+\dfrac{3}{2}$ units gives the values $\dfrac{3}{2}, 3, \dfrac{9}{2}, 6$, and $\dfrac{15}{2}$, which we combine with the reference rectangle to produce the cosine and secant graphs shown next. Note the vertical asymptotes of the secant function occur at the zeroes of the cosine function.

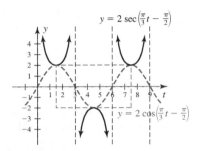

By shifting these results 3 units downward (centered on the line $y = -3$), we obtain the graph of $y = 2\sec\left(\dfrac{\pi}{3}t - \dfrac{\pi}{2}\right) - 3$.

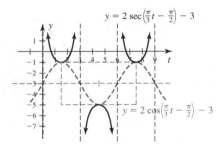

**Now try Exercises 41 through 44** ▶

To horizontally and/or vertically translate the graphs of $y = A\tan(Bt)$ and $y = A\cot(Bt)$, we once again apply the translations to the basic graph. Recall for these two functions:

**1.** The primary interval of $y = \tan t$ is $\left[-\dfrac{\pi}{2}, \dfrac{\pi}{2}\right]$, while that of $y = \cot t$ is $[0, \pi]$.

**2.** $y = \tan t$ increases while $y = \cot t$ decreases on their respective domains.

**EXAMPLE 7** ▶ Graphing $y = A \tan(Bt + C)$

Draw a sketch of $y = 2.5 \tan(0.5t + 1.5)$ over two periods.

Solution ▶ In shifted form, this equation is $y = 2.5 \tan[0.5(t + 3)]$. With $A = 2.5$ and $B = 0.5$, the graph is vertically stretched with a period of $2\pi$. Note that $t = -\pi$ and $\pi$ gives the location of the asymptotes for the unshifted graph, while $t = -\dfrac{\pi}{2}$ and $\dfrac{\pi}{2}$ gives $-2.5$ and $2.5$, respectively.

Shifting the graph 3 units left produces the one shown ($-\pi - 3 \approx -6.14$, $-\dfrac{\pi}{2} - 3 \approx -4.57$, $0 - 3 = -3$, $\dfrac{\pi}{2} - 3 \approx -1.43$, and $\pi - 3 \approx 0.14$).

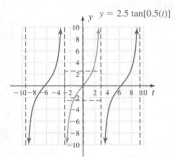

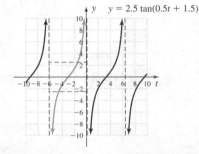

**WORTHY OF NOTE**

The reference rectangle shown is 5 units high by $2\pi$ units wide.

☑ **D.** You've just learned how to apply vertical and horizontal translations to cosecant, secant, tangent, and cotangent

**Now try Exercises 45 through 48** ▶

---

**TECHNOLOGY HIGHLIGHT**

## Locating Zeroes, Roots, and x-Intercepts

As you know, the zeroes of a function are *input* values that cause an *output* of zero. Graphically, these show up as x-intercepts and once a function is graphed they can be located (if they exist) using the [2nd] [CALC] **2:zero** feature. This feature is similar to the **3:minimum** and **4:maximum** features, in that we have the calculator search a specified interval by giving a **left bound** and a **right bound.** To illustrate, enter $Y_1 = 3 \sin\left(\dfrac{\pi}{2}x\right) - 1$ on the [Y=] screen and graph it

**Figure 4.40**

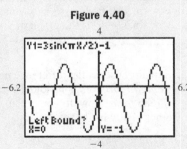

using the [ZOOM] **7:ZTrig** option. The resulting graph shows there are six zeroes in this interval and we'll locate the first negative root. Knowing the **7:Trig** option uses tick marks that are spaced every $\dfrac{\pi}{2}$ units, this root is in the interval $\left(-\pi, -\dfrac{\pi}{2}\right)$. After pressing [2nd] [CALC] **2:zero** the calculator returns you to the graph, and requests a "Left Bound" (see Figure 4.40). We enter $-\pi$ (press [ENTER]) and the calculator marks this choice with a "▶" marker (pointing to the right), then asks for a "Right Bound." After entering $-\dfrac{\pi}{2}$, the calculator marks this with a "◀" marker and asks

*—continued*

for a "Guess." Bypass this option by pressing ENTER once again (see Figure 4.41). The calculator searches the interval until it locates a zero (Figure 4.42) or displays an error message indicating it was unable to comply (no zeroes in the interval). Use these ideas to locate the zeroes of the following functions in $[0, \pi]$.

**Figure 4.41**

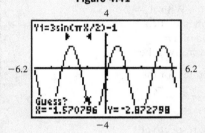

**Figure 4.42**

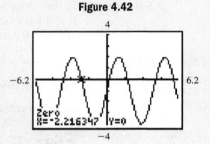

**Exercise 1:**　$y = -2\cos(\pi t) + 1$

**Exercise 3:**　$y = \dfrac{3}{2}\tan(2x) - 1$

**Exercise 2:**　$y = 0.5\sin[\pi(t - 2)]$

**Exercise 4:**　$y = x^3 - \cos x$

## 4.3 EXERCISES

### ▶ CONCEPTS AND VOCABULARY

**Fill in each blank with the appropriate word or phrase. Carefully reread the section if needed.**

1. A sinusoidal wave is one that can be modeled by functions of the form _____ or _____.

2. To find the primary interval of a sinusoidal graph, solve the inequality _____.

3. The graph of $y = \sin x + k$ is the graph of $y = \sin x$ shifted _____ $k$ units. The graph of $y = \sin(x - h)$ is the graph of $y = \sin x$ shifted _____ $h$ units.

4. To graph $y = A\csc(Bt + C) + D$, first sketch a graph of _____. The vertical asymptotes of $y = A\csc(Bt)$ will occur at the _____ of this sine function. Then shift the graph horizontally _____ units, and vertically ____ units.

5. Explain/Discuss the difference between the *standard form* of a sinusoidal equation, and the *shifted form*. How do you obtain one from the other? For what benefit?

6. Write out a step-by-step procedure for sketching the graph of $y = 30\sin\left(\dfrac{\pi}{2}t - \dfrac{1}{2}\right) + 10$. Include use of the reference rectangle, primary interval, zeroes, max/mins, and so on. Be complete and thorough.

### ▶ DEVELOPING YOUR SKILLS

**Sketch the following functions over the indicated interval.**

7. $y = 2\sin(4t) + 3; [0, \pi]$

8. $y = 3\cos(2t) + 5; [0, 2\pi]$

9. $y = 10\cos\left(\dfrac{\pi}{6}t\right) - 5; [-6, 18]$

10. $y = 5\sin\left(\dfrac{\pi}{8}t\right) - 3; [-8, 24]$

**11.** $y = -4\sin\left(\dfrac{\pi}{2}t\right) + 4; [-4, 4]$

**12.** $y = -6\cos\left(\dfrac{\pi}{3}t\right) + 6; [-6, 6]$

**13.** $y = \dfrac{1}{2}\cos\left(t - \dfrac{\pi}{2}\right); [0, 3\pi]$

**14.** $y = \dfrac{1}{3}\sin(t - \pi); [0, 3\pi]$

**15.** $y = 3\sin\left(t + \dfrac{\pi}{3}\right); [-\pi, 2\pi]$

**16.** $y = 2\cos\left(t + \dfrac{\pi}{4}\right); [-\pi, 2\pi]$

**17.** $y = 3\sin(4t - \pi); [0, \pi]$

**18.** $y = -2\cos\left(3t - \dfrac{\pi}{2}\right); \left[0, \dfrac{4\pi}{3}\right]$

**Sketch one complete period of each function.**

**19.** $f(t) = 25\sin\left[\dfrac{\pi}{4}(t - 2)\right] + 55$

**20.** $g(t) = 24.5\sin\left[\dfrac{\pi}{10}(t - 2.5)\right] + 15.5$

**21.** $h(t) = 1500\sin\left(\dfrac{\pi}{8}t + \dfrac{\pi}{4}\right) + 7000$

**22.** $p(t) = 350\sin\left(\dfrac{\pi}{6}t + \dfrac{\pi}{3}\right) + 420$

**Identify the amplitude (A), period (P), horizontal shift (HS), vertical shift (VS), and endpoints of the primary interval (PI) for each function given.**

**23.** $y = 120\sin\left[\dfrac{\pi}{12}(t - 6)\right]$

**24.** $y = 560\sin\left[\dfrac{\pi}{4}(t + 4)\right]$

**25.** $h(t) = \sin\left(\dfrac{\pi}{6}t - \dfrac{\pi}{3}\right)$ **26.** $r(t) = \sin\left(\dfrac{\pi}{10}t - \dfrac{2\pi}{5}\right)$

**27.** $y = \sin\left(\dfrac{\pi}{4}t - \dfrac{\pi}{6}\right)$ **28.** $y = \sin\left(\dfrac{\pi}{3}t + \dfrac{5\pi}{12}\right)$

**29.** $f(t) = 24.5\sin\left[\dfrac{\pi}{10}(t - 2.5)\right] + 15.5$

**30.** $g(t) = 40.6\sin\left[\dfrac{\pi}{6}(t - 4)\right] + 13.4$

**31.** $g(t) = 28\sin\left(\dfrac{\pi}{6}t - \dfrac{5\pi}{12}\right) + 92$

**32.** $f(t) = 90\sin\left(\dfrac{\pi}{10}t - \dfrac{\pi}{5}\right) + 120$

**33.** $y = 2500\sin\left(\dfrac{\pi}{4}t + \dfrac{\pi}{12}\right) + 3150$

**34.** $y = 1450\sin\left(\dfrac{3\pi}{4}t + \dfrac{\pi}{8}\right) + 2050$

**Find the equation of the graph given. Write answers in the form $y = A\sin(Bt + C) + D$.**

**35.** 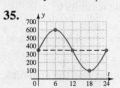 **36.**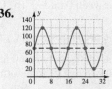

**37.** 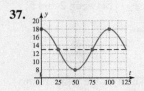 **38.**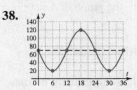

**39.** 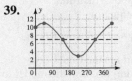 **40.**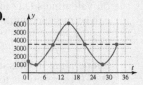

**Sketch the following functions over the indicated interval.**

**41.** $y = 5\sec\left[\dfrac{1}{3}\left(t + \dfrac{3\pi}{2}\right)\right] + 2; [-3\pi, 6\pi]$

**42.** $y = 3\csc\left[\dfrac{1}{2}(t + \pi)\right] + 1; [-2\pi, 4\pi]$

**43.** $y = 0.7\csc\left(\pi t - \dfrac{\pi}{4}\right) - 1.2; [-1.25, 1.75]$

**44.** $y = 1.3\sec\left(\dfrac{\pi}{3}t - \dfrac{\pi}{6}\right) - 1.6; [-2, 6]$

**Sketch two complete periods of each function.**

**45.** $y = 0.5\tan\left[\dfrac{\pi}{4}(t + 2)\right]$

**46.** $y = 1.5\cot\left[\dfrac{\pi}{2}(t + 1)\right]$

**47.** $y = 10\cot(2t - 1)$

**48.** $y = 8\tan(3t - 2)$

## ▶ WORKING WITH FORMULAS

**49. The area between $y = A\sin(Bt)$ and the $t$-axis, for $t \in \left[0, \dfrac{\pi}{B}\right]$: $\mathcal{A} = \dfrac{2A}{B}$**

The formula shown gives the exact area between the indicated graph and the $t$-axis, for the interval indicated. (a) Use the formula to calculate the area between the graph of $y = 5\sin(4t)$ and the $t$-axis, between 0 and $\dfrac{\pi}{4}$. (b) Use the formula to calculate the area between the graph of $y = 4\sin\left(\dfrac{\pi}{3}t\right)$ and the $t$-axis, between 0 and 3. (c) Use your knowledge of transformations to find the area under the graph of $4\sin\left(\dfrac{\pi}{3}t - \dfrac{2\pi}{3}\right)$ between 2 and 5.

**50. Number of daylight hours:**
$$D(t) = \frac{K}{2}\sin\left[\frac{2\pi}{365}(t - 79)\right] + 12$$

The number of daylight hours for a particular day of the year is modeled by the formula given, where $D(t)$ is the number of daylight hours on day $t$ of the year and $K$ is a constant related to the total variation of daylight hours, latitude of the location, and other factors. For the city of Reykjavik, Iceland, $K \approx 17$, while for Detroit, Michigan, $K \approx 6$. How many hours of daylight will each city receive on June 30 (the 182nd day of the year)?

## ▶ APPLICATIONS

**51. Temperature models:** The average temperature on Valentine's Day in Sydney, Australia, can be modeled with the equation $T(t) = 4\cos\left(\dfrac{\pi}{12}t + \dfrac{9\pi}{12}\right) + 22$, where $T$ is the temperature in Celsius and $t$ is the time of day ($t = 0$ corresponds to midnight). Use the model to (a) find the period of the model; (b) find the average minimum and maximum temperature; and (c) when these "extreme" temperatures occur.

**52. Temperature models:** The average temperature on Valentine's Day in Sydney, North Dakota, can be modeled with the equation $T(t) = 5\cos\left(\dfrac{\pi}{12}t + \dfrac{9\pi}{12}\right) - 8$, where $T$ is the temperature in Celsius and $t$ is the time of day ($t = 0$ corresponds to midnight). Use the model to (a) find the period of the model; (b) find the average minimum and maximum temperature; and (c) when these *extreme* temperatures occur.

**53. Wave height:** A data buoy placed off the coast of Santa Cruz, California, measures wave height and transmits the information to a monitoring station. For the minute 12:28 PDT (low tide), the wave height can be modeled with the equation $y = 2.6\sin\left(\dfrac{2\pi}{6}t\right) - 0.6$, where $t$ is measured in seconds and $y$ is in feet ($y = 0$ corresponds to the height of calm sea between high and low tide). Use the model to find (a) the time between each wave and (b) wave height from peak to trough.

**54. Wave height:** The same buoy from Exercise 53 transmits data that is used to model wave height during high tide. For the minute 20:12 PDT, wave height can be modeled with the equation $y = 3.1\sin\left(\dfrac{2\pi}{10}t\right) + 3.8$, where $t$ is measured in seconds and $y$ is in feet. Use the model to find (a) the maximum height of a wave (above calm sea) and (b) how many waves break during this minute.

**55. Height of the Orion crew vehicle:** A new Ares I-X rocket carrying an Orion crew vehicle is set for liftoff. As it accelerates vertically for the first 20 sec (before pitch over), the crew vehicle's height in miles, $t$ sec after liftoff can be modeled by the function $h(t) = 3\tan\left(\dfrac{\pi}{80}t\right)$. Use the model to (a) find the period of the function; (b) estimate when the height is 2 mi; and (c) find the height when pitch over begins.

**56. Construction height:** During the 54 months the skyscraper Burj Dubai was being built (see Section 2.3, Exercise 46), its ever-changing height in meters could be modeled by the function $h(t) = 472\tan\left(\dfrac{\pi}{162}t\right)$, where $t$ is the number of months after construction began. Use the model to (a) find the period of the function; (b) estimate when the height is 409 m; and (c) find the topped-out height.

**Daylight hours model:** Solve using a graphing calculator and the formula given in Exercise 50.

57. For the city of Caracas, Venezuela, $K \approx 1.3$, while for Tokyo, Japan, $K \approx 4.8$.

   a. How many hours of daylight will each city receive on January 15th (the 15th day of the year)?

   b. Graph the equations modeling the hours of daylight on the same screen. Then determine (i) what days of the year these two cities will have the same number of hours of daylight, and (ii) the number of days each year that each city receives 11.5 hr or less of daylight.

58. For the city of Houston, Texas, $K \approx 3.8$, while for Pocatello, Idaho, $K \approx 6.2$.

   a. How many hours of daylight will each city receive on December 15 (the 349th day of the year)?

   b. Graph the equations modeling the hours of daylight on the same screen. Then determine (i) how many days each year Pocatello receives more daylight than Houston, and (ii) the number of days each year that each city receives 13.5 hr or more of daylight.

### ▶ EXTENDING THE CONCEPT

59. The formulas we use in mathematics can sometimes seem very mysterious. We know they "work," and we can graph and evaluate them—but where did they come from? Consider the formula for the number of daylight hours from Exercise 50:

$$D(t) = \frac{K}{2} \sin\left[ \frac{2\pi}{365}(t - 79) \right] + 12.$$

   a. We know that the addition of 12 represents a vertical shift, but what does a vertical shift of 12 mean *in this context*?

   b. We also know the factor $(t - 79)$ represents a phase shift of 79 to the right. But what does a horizontal (phase) shift of 79 mean *in this context*?

   c. Finally, the coefficient $\frac{K}{2}$ represents a change in amplitude, but what does a change of amplitude mean *in this context*? Why is the coefficient bigger for the northern latitudes?

 60. Use a graphing calculator to graph the equation $f(x) = \frac{3x}{2} - 2 \sin(2x) - 1.5$.

   a. Determine the interval between each peak of the graph. What do you notice?

   b. Graph $g(x) = \frac{3x}{2} - 1.5$ on the same screen and comment on what you observe.

   c. What would the graph of

   $$f(x) = -\frac{3x}{2} + 2 \sin(2x) + 1.5 \text{ look like?}$$

   What is the $x$-intercept?

61. Use the formula from Exercise 49 and basic geometry to find the exact area of a "valley" in the graph of $y = 2 \sin\left( \frac{\pi}{3}t - \frac{2\pi}{3} \right)$. These "valleys" go from one "peak" (maximum point) to the next.

### ▶ MAINTAINING YOUR SKILLS

62. (3.4) In what quadrant does the angle $t = 3.7$ terminate? What is the reference arc?

63. (3.1) The planet Venus orbits the Sun in a path that is nearly circular, with a radius of 67.2 million miles. Through what angle of its orbit has the planet moved after traveling 168 million miles?

64. (1.3) Given $\sin \theta = -\frac{5}{12}$ with $\tan \theta < 0$, find the value of all six trig functions of $\theta$.

65. (2.3) While waiting for John in the parking lot of the hotel, Rick passes the time by estimating the angle of elevation of the hotel's exterior elevator. By careful observation, he notes that from an angle of elevation of 20°, it takes the elevator 5 sec until

the angle grows to 52° and reaches the penthouse floor. If his car is parked 150 ft from the hotel, (a) how far does the elevator move during this time? (b) What is the average speed (in miles per hour) of the elevator?

66. (2.2) The vertices of a triangle have coordinates $(-2, 6)$, $(1, 10)$, and $(2, 3)$. Verify that a right triangle is formed and find the measures of the two acute angles.

67. (4.1/4.2) Draw a quick sketch of $y = 2 \sin x$, $y = 2 \cos x$, and $y = 2 \tan x$ for $x \in \left[ -\frac{\pi}{2}, 2\pi \right]$.

## 4.4 | Trigonometric Applications and Models

### Learning Objectives

*In Section 4.4 you will learn how to:*

☐ **A.** Model simple harmonic motion

☐ **B.** Solve applications using sinusoidal models

☐ **C.** Solve applications involving the tangent, cotangent, secant, and cosecant functions

While sinusoidal applications are very common, the tangent, cotangent, secant, and cosecant functions have their own claim to significance in the applications they model. For instance, tangent functions are used to model the movement of a rotating light, while secant functions can be used to model shadow lengths.

### A. Simple Harmonic Motion: $y = A \sin(Bt)$ or $y = A \cos(Bt)$

The periodic motion of springs, tides, sound, and other phenomena all exhibit what is known as **harmonic motion**, which can be modeled using sinusoidal functions.

### Harmonic Models—Springs

Consider a spring hanging from a beam with a weight attached to one end. When the weight is at rest, we say it is in **equilibrium**, or has zero displacement from center. Stretching the spring and then releasing it causes the weight to "bounce up and down," with its displacement from center neatly modeled over time by a sine wave (see Figure 4.43).

**Figure 4.43**

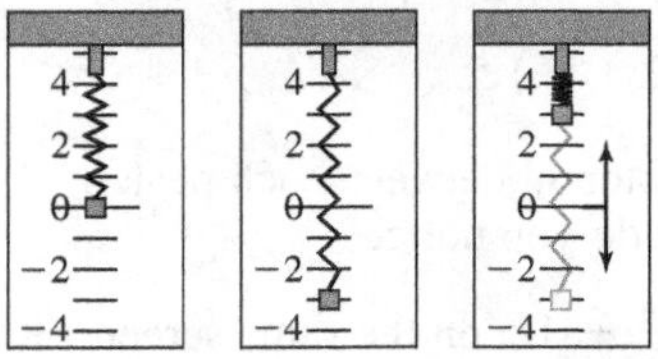

At rest    Stretched    Released

For objects in harmonic *motion* (there are other harmonic models), the input variable $t$ is always a time unit (seconds, minutes, days, etc.), so in addition to the period of the sinusoid, we are very interested in its **frequency**—the number of cycles it completes per unit time (see Figure 4.44). Since the period gives the time required to complete one cycle, the frequency $f$ is given by $f = \dfrac{1}{P} = \dfrac{B}{2\pi}$.

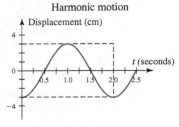

**Figure 4.44**

Harmonic motion

---

**EXAMPLE 1** ▶ **Applications of Sine and Cosine: Harmonic Motion**

For the harmonic motion modeled by the sinusoid in Figure 4.44,

   **a.** Find an equation of the form $y = A \cos(Bt)$.

   **b.** Determine the frequency.

   **c.** Use the equation to find the position of the weight at $t = 1.8$ sec.

**Solution** ▶    **a.** By inspection the graph has an amplitude $|A| = 3$ and a period $P = 2$. After substitution into $P = \dfrac{2\pi}{B}$, we obtain $B = \pi$ and the equation $y = -3 \cos(\pi t)$.

   **b.** Frequency is the reciprocal of the period so $f = \dfrac{1}{2}$, showing one-half a cycle is completed each second (as the graph indicates).

   **c.** Evaluating the model at $t = 1.8$ gives $y = -3 \cos[\pi(1.8)] \approx -2.43$, meaning the weight is 2.43 cm below the equilibrium point at this time.

**Now try Exercises 23 through 26** ▶

---

### Harmonic Models—Sound Waves

A second example of harmonic motion is the production of sound. For the purposes of this study, we'll look at musical notes. The vibration of matter produces a **pressure wave** or **sound energy**, which in turn vibrates the eardrum. Through the intricate structure of the middle ear, this sound energy is converted into mechanical energy and sent to the inner ear where it is converted to nerve impulses and transmitted to the brain. If the sound wave has a high frequency, the eardrum vibrates with greater frequency, which the brain interprets as a "high-pitched" sound. The *intensity* of the sound wave can also be transmitted to the brain via these mechanisms, and if the arriving sound wave has a high amplitude, the eardrum vibrates more forcefully and the sound is interpreted as "loud" by the brain. These characteristics are neatly modeled using $y = A \sin(Bt)$. For the moment we will focus on the frequency, keeping the amplitude constant at $A = 1$.

The musical note known as $A_4$ or "the A above middle C" is produced with a frequency of 440 vibrations per second, or 440 hertz (Hz) (this is the note most often used in the tuning of pianos and other musical instruments). For any given note, the same note one octave higher will have double the frequency, and the same note one octave lower will have one-half the frequency. In addition, with $f = \dfrac{1}{P}$ the value of

$B = 2\pi\left(\dfrac{1}{P}\right)$ can always be expressed as $B = 2\pi f$, so $A_4$ has the equation

$y = \sin[440(2\pi t)]$ (after rearranging the factors). The same note one octave lower is $A_3$ and has the equation $y = \sin[220(2\pi t)]$, with one-half the frequency. To draw the representative graphs, we must scale the *t*-axis in very small increments (seconds $\times 10^{-3}$) since $P = \dfrac{1}{440} \approx 0.0023$ for $A_4$, and

$P = \dfrac{1}{220} \approx 0.0045$ for $A_3$. Both are graphed in Figure 4.45, where we see that the higher note completes two cycles in the same interval that the lower note completes one.

**Figure 4.45**

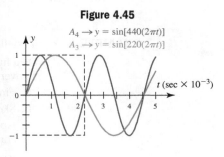

$A_4 \rightarrow y = \sin[440(2\pi t)]$
$A_3 \rightarrow y = \sin[220(2\pi t)]$

---

**EXAMPLE 2** ▶ **Applications of Sine and Cosine: Sound Frequencies**

The table here gives the frequencies for three octaves of the 12 "chromatic" notes with frequencies between 110 Hz and 840 Hz. Two of the 36 notes are graphed in the figure. Which two?

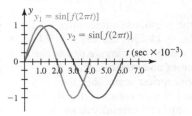

$y_1 = \sin[f(2\pi t)]$
$y_2 = \sin[f(2\pi t)]$

| Note | Frequency by Octave | | |
|------|---------|---------|---------|
|      | Octave 2 | Octave 3 | Octave 4 |
| A    | 110.00  | 220.00  | 440.00  |
| A#   | 116.54  | 233.08  | 466.16  |
| B    | 123.48  | **246.96**  | 493.92  |
| C    | 130.82  | 261.64  | 523.28  |
| C#   | 138.60  | 277.20  | 554.40  |
| D    | 146.84  | 293.68  | 587.36  |
| D#   | 155.56  | 311.12  | 622.24  |
| E    | **164.82**  | 329.24  | 659.28  |
| F    | 174.62  | 349.24  | 698.48  |
| F#   | 185.00  | 370.00  | 740.00  |
| G    | 196.00  | 392.00  | 784.00  |
| G#   | 207.66  | 415.32  | 830.64  |

Solution ▶ Since amplitudes are equal, the only difference is the frequency and period of the notes. It appears that $y_1$ has a period of about 0.004 sec, giving a frequency of

☑ **A. You've just learned how to model simple harmonic motion**

$\dfrac{1}{0.004}$ = 250 Hz—very likely a $B_3$ (in bold). The graph of $y_2$ has a period of about

$0.006$, for a frequency of $\dfrac{1}{0.006} \approx 167$ Hz—probably an $E_2$ (also in bold).

**Now try Exercises 27 through 30** ▶

## B. Sinusoidal Models in Applications

Recall that in Section 4.3, we considered the sinusoidal pattern outdoor temperatures tend to follow. The necessity of vertical translations was made clear by comparing the cold temperatures of northern latitudes with those of more tropical climates. In Example 3 of this section, we apply what we learned there to actually *construct and use* a sinusoidal model for temperature. As a reminder, for a sinusoidal function with maximum value $M$ and minimum value $m$, the amplitude $A = \dfrac{M - m}{2}$ and the average value $D = \dfrac{M + m}{2}$.

**EXAMPLE 3** ▶ **Modeling Temperature Using a Sine Function**

On a fine day in Galveston, Texas, the high temperature might be about 85°F with an overnight low of 61°F.
   **a.** Find a sinusoidal equation model for the daily temperature.
   **b.** Sketch the graph.
   **c.** Approximate what time(s) of day the temperature is 65°F. Assume $t = 0$ corresponds to 12:00 noon.

Solution ▶ **a.** We first note the period is still $P = 24$, so $B = \dfrac{\pi}{12}$, and the equation model will have the form $y = A \sin\left(\dfrac{\pi}{12}t\right) + D$. Using $\dfrac{M + m}{2} = \dfrac{85 + 61}{2}$, we find

the *average value* $D = 73$, with amplitude $A = \dfrac{85 - 61}{2} = 12$. The resulting

equation is $y = 12 \sin\left(\dfrac{\pi}{12}t\right) + 73$.

**b.** To sketch the graph, use a reference rectangle $2A = 24$ units tall and $P = 24$ units wide, along with the *rule of fourths* to locate zeroes and max/min values. Using an appropriate scale, shift the rectangle and plotted points vertically upward 73 units and carefully draw the finished graph through the points and within the rectangle (see Figure 4.46).

**Figure 4.46**

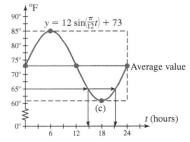

This gives the graph of $y = 12 \sin\left(\dfrac{\pi}{12}t\right) + 73$. Note the broken-line notation

"$\gtrless$" in Figure 4.46 indicates that certain values along an axis are unused (in this case, we skipped 0° to 60°), and we began scaling the axis with the values needed.
   **c.** As indicated in Figure 4.46, the temperature hits 65° twice, at about 15 and 21 hr after 12:00 noon, or at 3:00 A.M. and 9:00 A.M. Verify by computing $f(15)$ and $f(21)$.

**WORTHY OF NOTE**

Recall from Section 4.3 that transformations of any function $y = f(x)$ remain consistent regardless of the function $f$ used. For the sine function, the transformation $y = af(x \pm h) \pm k$ is more commonly written $y = A \sin(t \pm C) \pm D$, and $|A|$ gives a vertical stretch or compression, $C$ is a horizontal shift opposite the sign, and $D$ is a vertical shift, as seen in Example 3.

**Now try Exercises 31 through 34** ▶

Sinusoidal graphs actually include both sine and cosine graphs, the difference being that sine graphs begin at the average value, while cosine graphs begin at the maximum value. Sometimes it's more advantageous to use one over the other, but equivalent forms can easily be found. In Example 4, a cosine function is used to model an animal population that fluctuates sinusoidally due to changes in food supplies.

**EXAMPLE 4 ▶ Modeling Population Fluctuations Using a Cosine Function**

The population of a certain animal species can be modeled by the function

$P(t) = 1200\cos\left(\frac{\pi}{5}t\right) + 9000$, where $P(t)$ represents the population in year $t$.

Use the model to
**a.** Find the period of the function.
**b.** Graph the function over one period.
**c.** Find the maximum and minimum values.
**d.** Estimate the number of years the population is less than 8000.

**Solution ▶**
**a.** Since $B = \frac{\pi}{5}$, the period is $P = \frac{2\pi}{\pi/5} = 10$, meaning the population of this species fluctuates over a 10-yr cycle.

**b.** Use a reference rectangle ($2A = 2400$ by $P = 10$ units) and the *rule of fourths* to locate zeroes and max/min values, which occur at $t = 0, 2.5, 5, 7.5,$ and $10$. Shift this graph upward 9000 units (using an appropriate scale) to obtain the graph of $P(t)$ shown.

$P(t) = 1200\cos(\frac{\pi}{5}t) + 9000$

**c.** The maximum value is $9000 + 1200 = 10{,}200$ and the minimum value is $9000 - 1200 = 7800$.

**d.** As determined from the graph, the population drops below 8000 animals for approximately 2 yr. Verify by computing $P(4)$ and $P(6)$.

☑ **B.** You've just learned how to solve applications using sinusoidal models

**Now try Exercises 35 through 38 ▶**

## C. Applications of the Remaining Trig Functions

We end this section with two examples of how tangent, cotangent, secant, and cosecant functions can be applied. Numerous others can be found in the exercise set.

**EXAMPLE 5 ▶ Applications of $y = A\tan(Bt)$: Modeling the Movement of a Light Beam**

One evening, in port during a *Semester at Sea,* Richard is debating a project choice for his Precalculus class. Looking out his porthole, he notices a revolving light turning at a constant speed near the corner of a long warehouse. The light throws its beam along the length of the warehouse, then disappears into the air, and then returns time and time again. Suddenly—Richard has his project. He notes the time it takes the beam to traverse the warehouse wall is very close to 4 sec, and in the morning he measures the wall's length at 127.26 m. His project? Modeling the distance of the beam from the corner of the warehouse as a function of time using a tangent function. Can you help?

Solution ▶ The equation model will have the form $D(t) = A\tan(Bt)$, where $D(t)$ is the distance (in meters) of the beam from the corner after $t$ sec. The distance along the wall is measured in positive values so we're using only $\frac{1}{2}$ the period of the function, giving $\frac{1}{2}P = 4$ (the beam "disappears" at $t = 4$) so $P = 8$. Substitution in the period formula gives $B = \dfrac{\pi}{8}$ and the equation $D = A\tan\left(\dfrac{\pi}{8}t\right)$.

Knowing the beam travels 127.26 m in about 4 sec (when it disappears into infinity), we'll use $t = 3.9$ and $D = 127.26$ in order to solve for $A$ and complete our equation model (see note following this example).

$$A\tan\left(\frac{\pi}{8}t\right) = D \qquad \text{equation model}$$

$$A\tan\left[\frac{\pi}{8}(3.9)\right] = 127.26 \qquad \text{substitute 127.26 for } D \text{ and 3.9 for } t$$

$$A = \frac{127.26}{\tan\left[\dfrac{\pi}{8}(3.9)\right]} \qquad \text{solve for } A$$

$$\approx 5 \qquad \text{result}$$

One equation approximating the distance of the beam from the corner of the warehouse is $D(t) = 5\tan\left(\dfrac{\pi}{8}t\right)$.

**Now try Exercises 39 through 42 ▶**

For Example 5, we should note the choice of 3.9 for $t$ was arbitrary, and while we obtained an "acceptable" model, different values of $A$ would be generated for other choices. For instance, $t = 3.95$ gives $A \approx 2.5$, while $t = 3.99$ gives $A \approx 0.5$. The true value of $A$ depends on the distance of the light from the corner of the warehouse wall. In any case, it's interesting to note that at $t = 2$ sec (one-half the time it takes the beam to disappear), the beam has traveled only 5 m from the corner of the building: $D(2) = 5\tan\left(\dfrac{\pi}{4}\right) = 5$ m. Although the light is rotating at a constant angular speed, the speed of the beam along the wall increases *dramatically* as $t$ gets close to 4 sec.

EXAMPLE 6 ▶ **Applications of $y = A\csc(Bt)$: Modeling the Length of a Shadow**

During the long winter months in southern Michigan, Daniel begins planning for his new solar-powered water heater. He needs to choose a panel location on his roof, and is primarily concerned with the moving shadows of the trees throughout the day. To this end, he begins studying the changing shadow length of a tree in front of his house. At sunrise, the shadow is too long to measure. As the  morning progresses, the shadow decreases in length, until at high noon it measures its shortest length of 7 ft. As the day moves on, the shadow increases in length, until at sunset it is again too long to measure. Given sunrise occurs at 6:00 A.M. and sunset at 6:00 P.M.:

a. Use the cosecant function to model the tree's shadow length.

b. Approximate the shadow length at 10:00 A.M.

**Solution** ▶    **a.** It appears the function $L(t) = A \csc(Bt)$ will model the shadow length, since the shadow decreases from an "infinitely large" height to a minimum height, then returns to an infinite height. Let $t = 0$ correspond to 6:00 A.M. and note Daniel's observations over the 12 hr of daylight. Since the length of the shadow is measured in positive values, we need only $\frac{1}{2}$ the period of the function, giving $\frac{1}{2}P = 12$ (so $P = 24$). The period formula gives $B = \dfrac{\pi}{12}$ and the equation model is $L(t) = A \csc\left(\dfrac{\pi}{12}t\right)$. We solve for $A$ to complete the model, using $L = 7$ when $t = 6$ (noon).

$$L(t) = A \csc\left(\frac{\pi}{12}t\right) \qquad \text{equation model}$$

$$7 = A \csc\left[\frac{\pi}{12}(6)\right] \qquad \text{substitute 7 for } L \text{ and 6 for } t$$

$$A = \frac{7}{\csc\left(\dfrac{\pi}{2}\right)} \qquad \text{solve for } A; \ \frac{6\pi}{12} = \frac{\pi}{2}$$

$$= \frac{7}{1} \qquad\qquad \csc\left(\frac{\pi}{2}\right) = 1$$

$$= 7 \qquad\qquad \text{result}$$

The equation modeling the shadow length of the tree is $L(t) = 7 \csc\left(\dfrac{\pi}{12}t\right)$.

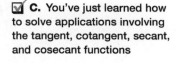 **C.** You've just learned how to solve applications involving the tangent, cotangent, secant, and cosecant functions

   **b.** Evaluating the model at $t = 4$ (10 A.M.) gives $L = 7 \csc\left(\dfrac{\pi}{3}\right) = 7\left(\dfrac{2\sqrt{3}}{3}\right) \approx 8.08$, meaning the shadow is approximately 8 ft, 1 in. long at 10 A.M.

**Now try Exercises 43 and 44** ▶

---

 **4.4 EXERCISES**

▶ **CONCEPTS AND VOCABULARY**

**Fill in each blank with the appropriate word or phrase. Carefully reread the section if needed.**

**1.** For $y = A \sin(Bx + C) + D$, the maximum value occurs when _____ $= 1$, leaving $y = $ ___.

**2.** For $y = A \sin(Bx + C) + D$, the minimum value occurs when _____ $= -1$, leaving $y = $ ___.

**3.** Any phenomenon with sinusoidal behavior regularly fluctuates between a _____ and _____ value.

**4.** Given the period $P$, the frequency is ___. Given the frequency $f$, the value of $B$ is ___.

**5.** Explain/Discuss how to find an equation model of the form $y = A \cos(Bt)$ given the graph of a function that models simple harmonic motion.

**6.** Sketch a right triangle that illustrates the situation presented in Example 5, and use it to explain why the model has the form $D(t) = A \tan(Bt)$. Be sure to explain what physical dimension the constant $A$ represents.

## ▶ DEVELOPING YOUR SKILLS

Use the graphs given to (a) state the amplitude $A$ and period $P$ of the function; (b) estimate the value at $x = 14$; and (c) estimate the interval in $[0, P]$ where $f(x) \geq 20$.

**7.**

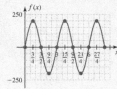

**8.**

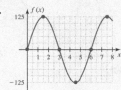

Use the graphs given to (a) state the amplitude $A$ and period $P$ of the function; (b) estimate the value at $x = 2$; and (c) estimate the interval in $[0, P]$, where $f(x) \leq -100$.

**9.**

**10.**

Use the information given to write a sinusoidal equation and sketch its graph. Recall $B = \dfrac{2\pi}{P}$.

**11.** Max: 100, min: 20, $P = 30$

**12.** Max: 95, min: 40, $P = 24$

**13.** Max: 20, min: 4, $P = 360$

**14.** Max: 12,000, min: 6500, $P = 10$

Find the frequency of the following harmonic motion models.

**15.** $y = 4 \cos\left(\dfrac{\pi}{2}t\right)$      **16.** $y = 3 \sin\left(\dfrac{\pi}{3}t\right)$

**17.** $y = 3.14 \sin(2t)$      **18.** $y = 0.07 \cos(4t)$

**19.** $y = \dfrac{3}{4}\cos\left(\dfrac{4}{3}t\right)$      **20.** $y = \dfrac{5}{3}\sin\left(\dfrac{6}{5}t\right)$

## ▶ WORKING WITH FORMULAS

**21. The relationship between the coefficient $B$, the frequency $f$, and the period $P$**

In many applications of trigonometric functions, the equation $y = A \sin(Bt)$ is written as $y = A \sin[(2\pi f)t]$, where $B = 2\pi f$. Justify the new equation using $f = \dfrac{1}{P}$ and $P = \dfrac{2\pi}{B}$. In other words, explain how $A \sin(Bt)$ becomes $A \sin[(2\pi f)t]$, as though you were trying to help another student with the ideas involved.

**22. Orbiting distance north or south of the equator: $D(t) = A \cos(Bt)$**

Unless a satellite is placed in a strict equatorial orbit, its distance north or south of the equator will vary according to the sinusoidal model shown, where $D(t)$ is the distance $t$ min after entering orbit. Negative values indicate it is south of the equator, and the distance $D$ is actually a two-dimensional distance, as seen from a vantage point in outer space. The value of $B$ depends on the speed of the satellite and the time it takes to complete one orbit, while $|A|$ represents the maximum distance from the equator. (a) Find the equation model for a satellite whose maximum distance north of the equator is 2000 miles and that completes one orbit every 2 hr ($P = 120$). (b) How many minutes after entering orbit is the satellite directly above the equator $[D(t) = 0]$? (c) Is the satellite north or south of the equator 257 min after entering orbit? How far north or south?

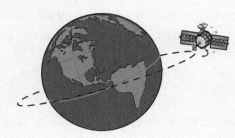

▶ **APPLICATIONS**

23. **Harmonic motion:** A weight on the end of a spring is oscillating in harmonic motion. The equation model for the oscillations is

    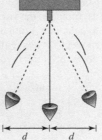

    $d(t) = 6 \sin\left(\dfrac{\pi}{2}t\right)$, where $d$ is the

    distance (in centimeters) from the equilibrium point in $t$ sec.

    a. What is the period of the motion? What is the frequency of the motion?

    b. What is the displacement from equilibrium at $t = 2.5$? Is the weight moving toward the equilibrium point or away from equilibrium at this time?

    c. What is the displacement from equilibrium at $t = 3.5$? Is the weight moving toward the equilibrium point or away from equilibrium at this time?

    d. How far does the weight move between $t = 1$ and $t = 1.5$ sec? What is the average velocity for this interval? Do you expect a greater or lesser velocity for $t = 1.75$ to $t = 2$? Explain why.

24. **Harmonic motion:** The bob on the end of a 24-in. pendulum is oscillating in harmonic motion. The equation model for the oscillations is $d(t) = 20 \cos(4t)$, where $d$ is the distance (in inches) from the equilibrium point, $t$ sec after being released from one side.

    a. What is the period of the motion? What is the frequency of the motion?

    b. What is the displacement from equilibrium at $t = 0.25$ sec? Is the weight moving toward the equilibrium point or away from equilibrium at this time?

    c. What is the displacement from equilibrium at $t = 1.3$ sec? Is the weight moving toward the equilibrium point or away from equilibrium at this time?

    d. How far does the bob move between $t = 0.25$ and $t = 0.35$ sec? What is its average velocity for this interval? Do you expect a greater velocity for the interval $t = 0.55$ to $t = 0.6$? Explain why.

25. **Harmonic motion:** A simple pendulum 36 in. in length is oscillating in harmonic motion. The bob at the end of the pendulum swings through an arc of 30 in. (from the far left to the far right, or one-half

cycle) in about 0.8 sec. What is the equation model for this harmonic motion?

26. **Harmonic motion:** As part of a study of wave motion, the motion of a floater is observed as a series of uniform ripples of water move beneath it. By careful observation, it is noted that the floater bobs up and down through a distance of 2.5 cm every 0.2 sec. What is the equation model for this harmonic motion?

27. **Sound waves:** Two of the musical notes from the chart on page 181 are graphed in the figure. Use the graphs given to determine which two.

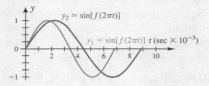

28. **Sound waves:** Two chromatic notes *not on the chart from page* 181 are graphed in the figure. Use the graphs and the discussion regarding octaves to determine which two. Note the scale of the $t$-axis *has been changed* to hundredths of a second.

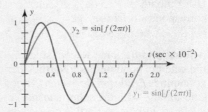

**Sound waves: Use the chart on page 181 to write the equation for each note in the form $y = \sin[f(2\pi t)]$ and clearly state the period of each note.**

29. notes $D_2$ and $G_3$     30. notes $A_4$ and $C\#_2$

**Use the information given to write a sinusoidal equation, sketch its graph, and answer the question posed.**

31. **Temperature models:** In Geneva, Switzerland, the daily temperature in January ranges from an average high of 39°F to an average low of 29°F. (a) Find a sinusoidal equation model for the daily temperature; (b) sketch the graph; and (c) approximate the time(s) each January day the temperature reaches the freezing point (32°F). Assume $t = 0$ corresponds to noon.

    *Source: 2004 Statistical Abstract of the United States,* Table 1331.

32. **Temperature models:** In Nairobi, Kenya, the daily temperature in January ranges from an average high of 77°F to an average low of 58°F. (a) Find a sinusoidal equation model for the daily temperature; (b) sketch the graph; and (c) approximate the time(s) each January day the temperature reaches a comfortable 72°F. Assume $t = 0$ corresponds to noon.

    *Source: 2004 Statistical Abstract of the United States, Table 1331.*

33. **Daylight hours:** In Oslo, Norway, the number of hours of daylight reaches a low of 6 hr in January, and a high of nearly 18.8 hr in July. (a) Find a sinusoidal equation model for the number of daylight hours each month; (b) sketch the graph; and (c) approximate the number of *days* each year there are more than 15 hr of daylight. Use 1 month $\approx$ 30.5 days. Assume $t = 0$ corresponds to January 1.

    *Source: www.visitnorway.com/templates.*

34. **Daylight hours:** In Vancouver, British Columbia, the number of hours of daylight reaches a low of 8.3 hr in January, and a high of nearly 16.2 hr in July. (a) Find a sinusoidal equation model for the number of daylight hours each month; (b) sketch the graph; and (c) approximate the number of *days* each year there are more than 15 hr of daylight. Use 1 month $\approx$ 30.5 days. Assume $t = 0$ corresponds to January 1.

    *Source: www.bcpassport.com/vital/temp.*

35. **Animal populations:** Recent studies seem to indicate the population of North American porcupine (*Erethizon dorsatum*) varies sinusoidally with the solar (sunspot) cycle due to its effects on Earth's ecosystems. Suppose the population of this species in a certain locality is modeled by the function $P(t) = 250 \cos\left(\dfrac{2\pi}{11}t\right) + 950$, where $P(t)$ represents the population of porcupines in year $t$. Use the model to (a) find the period of the function; (b) graph the function over one period; (c) find the maximum and minimum values; and (d) estimate the number of years the population is less than 740 animals.

    *Source: Ilya Klvana, McGill University (Montreal), Master of Science thesis paper, November 2002.*

36. **Animal populations:** The population of mosquitoes in a given area is primarily influenced by precipitation, humidity, and temperature. In tropical regions, these tend to fluctuate sinusoidally in the course of a year. Using trap counts and statistical projections, fairly accurate estimates of a mosquito

population can be obtained. Suppose the population in a certain region was modeled by the function $P(t) = 50 \cos\left(\dfrac{\pi}{26}t\right) + 950$, where $P(t)$ was the mosquito population (in thousands) in week $t$ of the year. Use the model to (a) find the period of the function; (b) graph the function over one period; (c) find the maximum and minimum population values; and (d) estimate the number of weeks the population is less than 915,000.

37. **Animal populations:** Use a horizontal translation to shift the graph from Exercise 35 so that the average population of the North American porcupine begins at $t = 0$. Verify results on a graphing calculator, then find a sine function that gives the same graph as the shifted cosine function.

38. **Animal populations:** Use a horizontal translation to shift the graph from Exercise 36 so that the average population of mosquitoes begins at $t = 0$. Verify results on a graphing calculator, then find a sine function that gives the same graph as the shifted cosine function.

**Tangent function data models:** Model the data in Exercises 39 and 40 using the function $y = A \tan(Bx)$. State the period of the function, the location of the asymptotes, the value of $A$, and name the point $(x, y)$ used to calculate $A$ (answers may vary). Use your equation model to evaluate the function at $x = -2$ and $x = 2$. What observations can you make? Also see Exercise 45.

39.

| Input | Output | Input | Output |
|-------|--------|-------|--------|
| −6 | −∞ | 1 | 1.4 |
| −5 | −20 | 2 | 3 |
| −4 | −9.7 | 3 | 5.2 |
| −3 | −5.2 | 4 | 9.7 |
| −2 | −3 | 5 | 20 |
| −1 | −1.4 | 6 | ∞ |
| 0 | 0 | | |

40.

| Input | Output | Input | Output |
|-------|--------|-------|--------|
| −3 | −∞ | 0.5 | 6.4 |
| −2.5 | −91.3 | 1 | 13.7 |
| −2 | −44.3 | 1.5 | 23.7 |
| −1.5 | −23.7 | 2 | 44.3 |
| −1 | −13.7 | 2.5 | 91.3 |
| −0.5 | −6.4 | 3 | ∞ |
| 0 | 0 | | |

**41.** As part of a lab setup, a laser pen is made to swivel on a large protractor as illustrated in the figure. For their lab project, students are asked to take the instrument to one end of a long hallway and measure the distance of the projected beam relative to the angle the pen is being held, and collect the data in a table. Use the data to find a function of the form $y = A \tan(B\theta)$. State the period of the function, the location of the asymptotes, the value of $A$, and name the point $(\theta, y)$ you used to calculate $A$ (answers may vary).

**Exercise 41**

| $\theta$ (degrees) | Distance (cm) |
|---|---|
| 0 | 0 |
| 10 | 2.1 |
| 20 | 4.4 |
| 30 | 6.9 |
| 40 | 10.1 |
| 50 | 14.3 |
| 60 | 20.8 |
| 70 | 33.0 |
| 80 | 68.1 |
| 89 | 687.5 |

Based on the result, can you approximate the length of the laser pen? Note that in degrees, the period formula for tangent is $P = \dfrac{180°}{B}$.

**42.** Use the equation model obtained in Exercise 41 to compare the values given by the equation with the actual data. As a percentage, what was the largest deviation between the two?

**43. Shadow length:** At high noon, a flagpole in Oslo, Norway, casts a 10-m-long shadow during the month of January. Using information from Exercise 33, (a) find a cosecant function that models the shadow length, and (b) use the model to find the length of the shadow at 2:00 P.M.

**44. Shadow length:** At high noon, the "Living Shangri-La" skyscraper in Vancouver, British Columbia, casts a 15-m-long shadow during the month of June. Given there are 16 hr of daylight that month, (a) find a cosecant function that models the shadow length, and (b) use the model to find the length of the shadow at 7:30 A.M.

▶ **EXTENDING THE CONCEPT**

 **45.** Rework Exercises 39 and 40, obtaining a new equation for the data using a different ordered pair to compute the value of $A$. What do you notice? Try yet another ordered pair and calculate $A$ once again for another equation $Y_2$. Complete a table of values using the given inputs, with the outputs of the three equations generated (original, $Y_1$, and $Y_2$). Does any one equation seem to model the data better than the others? Are all of the equation models "acceptable"? Please comment.

 **46.** Regarding Example 5, we can use the standard distance/rate/time formula $D = RT$ to compute the average velocity of the beam of light along the wall in any interval of time: $R = \dfrac{D}{T}$. For example, using $D(t) = 5 \tan\left(\dfrac{\pi}{8}t\right)$, the average velocity in the interval $[0, 2]$ is $\dfrac{D(2) - D(0)}{2 - 0} = 2.5$ m/sec. Calculate the average velocity of the beam in the time intervals $[2, 3]$, $[3, 3.5]$, and $[3.5, 3.8]$ sec. What do you notice? How would the average velocity of the beam in the interval $[3.9, 3.99]$ sec compare?

**47.** A *dampening factor* is any function whose product with a sinusoidal function causes a systematic change in amplitude. In the graph shown, $y = \sin(3x)$ is dampened by the function $y = -\dfrac{1}{4}x + 2$. Notice the peaks and valleys of the sine graph are points on the graph of this line. The table given shows points of intersection for $y = \sin(3x)$ and another dampening factor. Use the regression capabilities of a graphing calculator to find its equation and graph both functions on the same screen.

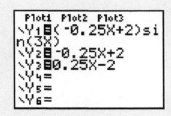

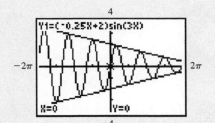

| $x$ | $y$ | $x$ | $y$ |
|---|---|---|---|
| $-\dfrac{7\pi}{4}$ | 4.64 | $\dfrac{5\pi}{4}$ | 1.33 |
| $-\dfrac{3\pi}{4}$ | 3.14 | $\dfrac{9\pi}{4}$ | 1.02 |
| $\dfrac{\pi}{4}$ | 2.04 | $\dfrac{13\pi}{4}$ | 1.09 |

▶ **MAINTAINING YOUR SKILLS**

**48.** **(4.2)** Draw a quick sketch
of $y = -\tan x$ for
$x \in \left[ -\dfrac{3\pi}{2}, 2\pi \right]$.

**Exercise 48**

**49.** **(3.4)** What four values of $t$
satisfy the equation
$|\cos t| = \dfrac{1}{2}$?

**50.** **(4.3)** Determine the equation of the graph shown,
given it's of the form $y = A\cos(Bt \pm C) + D$.

**51.** **(4.3)** The graph of $y = \sec x$ is shifted to the right
$\dfrac{\pi}{3}$ units. What is the equation of the shifted graph?

**52.** **(2.3)** Clarke is standing between two tall buildings.
The angle of elevation to the top of the building to
her north is 60°, while the angle of elevation to the
top of the building to her south is 70°. If she is
400 m from the northern building and 200 m from
the southern building, which one is taller?

**53.** **(3.2)** Lying on his back in three inches of newly
fallen snow, Mitchell stretches out his arms and
moves them back and forth (like a car's wiper
blades) to form a snow angel. If his arms are 24 in.
long and move through an angle of 35° at the
shoulders, what is the area of the angel's wings that
are formed?

# SUMMARY AND CONCEPT REVIEW

## SECTION 4.1  Graphs of the Sine and Cosine Functions

### KEY CONCEPTS

- Graphing sine and cosine functions using the special values from the unit circle results in a periodic, wavelike graph with domain $(-\infty, \infty)$.

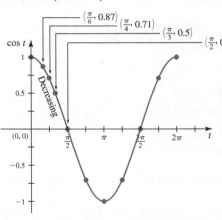

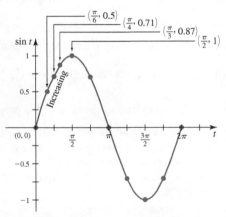

- The characteristics of each graph play a vital role in their contextual application, and these are summarized on pages 136 and 140.
- The amplitude of a sine or cosine graph is the maximum displacement from the average value.
  For $y = A \sin(Bt)$ and $y = A \cos(Bt)$, the amplitude is $|A|$.
- The period of a periodic function is the smallest interval required to complete one cycle.
  For $y = A \sin(Bt)$ and $y = A \cos(Bt)$, $P = \dfrac{2\pi}{B}$ gives the period.
- If $|A| > 1$, the graph is vertically stretched, if $0 < |A| < 1$ the graph is vertically compressed, and if $A < 0$ the graph is reflected across the $x$-axis.
- If $B > 1$, the graph is horizontally compressed (the period is smaller/shorter);
  if $B < 1$ the graph is horizontally stretched (the period is larger/longer).

- To graph $y = A \sin(Bt)$ or $A \cos(Bt)$, draw a reference rectangle $2A$ units high and $P = \dfrac{2\pi}{B}$ units wide, centered on the $x$-axis, then use the *rule of fourths* to locate zeroes and max/min values. Connect these points with a smooth curve.

### EXERCISES

Use a reference rectangle and the *rule of fourths* to draw an accurate sketch of the following functions through at least one full period. Clearly state the amplitude and period as you begin.

**1.** $y = 3 \sin t$            **2.** $y = -\cos(2t)$            **3.** $y = 1.7 \sin(4t)$

**4.** $f(t) = 2 \cos(4\pi t)$         **5.** $g(t) = 3 \sin(398\pi t)$

**6.** The given graph is of the form $y = A \sin(Bt)$. Determine the equation of the graph.

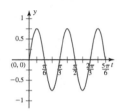

**7.** Referring to the chart of colors visible in the electromagnetic spectrum (page 149), what color is represented by the equation $y = \sin\left(\dfrac{\pi}{270}t\right)$? By $y = \sin\left(\dfrac{\pi}{320}t\right)$?

## SECTION 4.2   Graphs of the Cosecant, Secant, Tangent, and Cotangent Functions

### KEY CONCEPTS

- The graph of $y = \sec t = \dfrac{1}{\cos t}$ will be asymptotic everywhere $\cos t = 0$, increasing where $\cos t$ is decreasing, and decreasing where $\cos t$ is increasing.

- The graph of $y = \csc t = \dfrac{1}{\sin t}$ will be asymptotic everywhere $\sin t = 0$, increasing where $\sin t$ is decreasing, and decreasing where $\sin t$ is increasing.

- Since $\tan t$ is defined in terms of the ratio $\dfrac{y}{x}$, the graph will be asymptotic everywhere $x = 0$ on the unit circle, meaning all odd multiples of $\dfrac{\pi}{2}$.

- Since $\cot t$ is defined in terms of the ratio $\dfrac{x}{y}$, the graph will be asymptotic everywhere $y = 0$ on the unit circle, meaning all integer multiples of $\pi$.

- The graph of $y = \tan t$ is increasing everywhere it is defined; the graph of $y = \cot t$ is decreasing everywhere it is defined.

- The characteristics of each graph play a vital role in their contextual application, and these are summarized on pages 152 and 156.

- For the more general tangent and cotangent graphs $y = A \tan(Bt)$ and $y = A \cot(Bt)$, if $|A| > 1$, the graph is vertically stretched, if $0 < |A| < 1$ the graph is vertically compressed, and if $A < 0$ the graph is reflected across the $x$-axis.

- If $B > 1$, the graph is horizontally compressed (the period is smaller/shorter); if $B < 1$ the graph is horizontally stretched (the period is larger/longer).

- To graph $y = A \tan(Bt)$, note $A \tan(Bt)$ is zero at $t = 0$. Compute the period $P = \dfrac{\pi}{B}$ and draw asymptotes a distance of $\dfrac{P}{2}$ on either side of the $y$-axis. Plot zeroes halfway between the asymptotes and use symmetry to complete the graph.

- To graph $y = A \cot(Bt)$, note it is asymptotic at $t = 0$. Compute the period $P = \dfrac{\pi}{B}$ and draw asymptotes a distance $P$ on either side of the $y$-axis. Plot zeroes halfway between the asymptotes and use symmetry to complete the graph.

## EXERCISES

**8.** Use a reference rectangle and the *rule of fourths* to draw an accurate sketch of $y = 3 \sec t$ through at least one full period. Clearly state the period as you begin.

**9.** The given graph is of the form $y = A \csc(Bt)$. Determine the equation of the graph.

**Exercise 9**

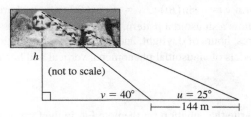

**10.** State the value of each expression without the aid of a calculator:

    **a.** $\tan\left(\dfrac{7\pi}{4}\right)$      **b.** $\cot\left(\dfrac{\pi}{3}\right)$

**11.** State the value of each expression without the aid of a calculator, given that $t$ terminates in QII.

    **a.** $\tan^{-1}(-\sqrt{3})$      **b.** $\cot^{-1}\left(-\dfrac{1}{\sqrt{3}}\right)$

**12.** Graph $y = 6 \tan\left(\dfrac{1}{2}t\right)$ in the interval $[-2\pi, 2\pi]$.      **13.** Graph $y = \dfrac{1}{2}\cot(2\pi t)$ in the interval $[-1, 1]$.

**14.** Use the period of $y = \cot t$ to name three additional solutions to $\cot t = 0.0208$, given $t = 1.55$ is a solution. Many solutions are possible.

**15.** Given $t = 0.4444$ is a solution to $\cot^{-1}(t) = 2.1$, use an analysis of signs and quadrants to name an additional solution in $[0, 2\pi)$.

**16.** Find the approximate height of Mount Rushmore, using $h = \dfrac{d}{\cot u - \cot v}$ and the values shown.

$h$

(not to scale)

$v = 40°$      $u = 25°$

$\longmapsto$ 144 m $\longmapsto$

## SECTION 4.3  Transformations of Trigonometric Graphs

### KEY CONCEPTS

- The equation $y = A \sin(Bt \pm C) + D$ is called the *standard form* of a general sinusoid. The equation $y = A \sin\left[B\left(t \pm \dfrac{C}{B}\right)\right] + D$ is called the *shifted form* of a general sinusoid.

- In either form, $D$ represents the average value of the function and a vertical shift $D$ units upward if $D > 0$, $D$ units downward if $D < 0$. For a maximum value $M$ and minimum value $m$, $\dfrac{M + m}{2} = D$, $\dfrac{M - m}{2} = A$.

- The shifted form $y = A \sin\left[B\left(t \pm \dfrac{C}{B}\right)\right] + D$ enables us to quickly identify the horizontal shift of the function: $\dfrac{C}{B}$ units in a direction opposite the given sign.

- To graph a shifted sinusoid, locate the primary interval by solving $0 \le Bt + C < 2\pi$, then use a reference rectangle along with the *rule of fourths* to sketch the graph in this interval. The graph can then be extended as needed, then shifted vertically $D$ units.

EXERCISES

For each equation given, (a) identify/clearly state the amplitude, period, horizontal shift, and vertical shift; then (b) graph the equation using the primary interval, a reference rectangle, and *rule of fourths*.

**17.** $y = 240 \sin\left[\dfrac{\pi}{6}(t - 3)\right] + 520$

**18.** $y = 3.2 \cos\left(\dfrac{\pi}{4}t + \dfrac{3\pi}{2}\right) + 6.4$

For each graph given, identify the amplitude, period, horizontal shift, and vertical shift, and give the equation of the graph.

**19.**

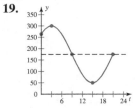

**20.**

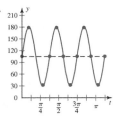

## SECTION 4.4   Trigonometric Applications and Models

KEY CONCEPTS

- One basic application of sinusoidal graphs involves phenomena in harmonic motion, or motion that can be modeled by functions of the form $y = A \sin(Bt)$ or $y = A \cos(Bt)$ (with no horizontal or vertical shift).
- Many everyday phenomena follow a sinusoidal pattern, or a pattern that can be modeled by a sine or cosine function (e.g., daily temperatures, hours of daylight, and some animal populations).
- To obtain accurate equation models of sinusoidal phenomena, vertical and horizontal shifts of a basic function are used.

EXERCISES

**21.** Use the chart on page 181 to write the equation for the note F#$_3$ in the form $y = \sin[f(2\pi t)]$ and state its period.

**22.** Monthly precipitation in Cheyenne, Wyoming, can be modeled by a sine function, by using the average precipitation for July (2.26 in.) as a maximum (actually slightly higher in May), and the average precipitation for February (0.44 in.) as a minimum. Assume $t = 0$ corresponds to March. (a) Use the information to construct a sinusoidal model. (b) Use the model to estimate the inches of precipitation Cheyenne receives in August ($t = 5$) and December ($t = 9$).

*Source: 2004 Statistical Abstract of the United States,* Table 380.

**23.** Model the data in the table using a tangent function. Clearly state the period, the value of $A$, and the location of the asymptotes.

| Input | Output | Input | Output |
|-------|--------|-------|--------|
| −6 | −∞ | 1 | 1.4 |
| −5 | −19.4 | 2 | 3 |
| −4 | −9 | 3 | 5.2 |
| −3 | −5.2 | 4 | 9 |
| −2 | −3 | 5 | 19.4 |
| 1 | −1.4 | 6 | ∞ |
| 0 | 0 | | |

# MIXED REVIEW

State the equation of the function $f(t)$ shown using a

**1.** sine function           **2.** cosine function

**Exercises 1 and 2**

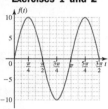

**3.** For the graph of periodic function $f$ given, state the (a) amplitude, (b) average value, (c) period, and (d) value of $f(4)$.

**Exercise 3**

State the equation of the function $g(t)$ shown using a

**4.** tangent function        **5.** cotangent function

**Exercises 4 and 5**

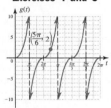

**6.** The data given in the table tracks the length of the shadow cast by an obelisk for the 12 daylight hours at a certain location (positive and negative values indicate lengths before noon and afternoon, respectively). Assume $t = 0$ corresponds to 6:00 A.M. (a) Use the data to construct an equation modeling the length $L$ of the shadow and graph the function. (b) Use the function to find the shadow's length at 1:30 P.M. (c) If the shadow is "$-52$ m" long, what time is it?

| Hour of Day | Length (m) | Hour of Day | Length (m) |
|---|---|---|---|
| 0 | $\infty$ | 7 | $-10.7$ |
| 1 | 149.3 | 8 | $-23.1$ |
| 2 | 69.3 | 9 | $-40$ |
| 3 | 40.0 | 10 | $-69.3$ |
| 4 | 23.1 | 11 | $-149.3$ |
| 5 | 10.7 | 12 | $-\infty$ |
| 6 | 0 | | |

Use a reference rectangle and the *rule of fourths* to graph the following functions in $[0, 2\pi)$.

**7.** $y = -2 \csc t$              **8.** $y = 3 \sec t$

**9.** $f(t) = \cos(2t) - 1$        **10.** $g(t) = -\sin(3t) + 1$

**11.** $h(t) = \dfrac{3}{2} \sin\!\left(\dfrac{\pi}{2} t\right)$       **12.** $p(t) = 6 \cos(\pi t)$

**13.** Monthly precipitation in Minneapolis, Minnesota, can be modeled by a sine function, by using the average precipitation for August (4.05 in.) as a maximum (actually slightly higher in June), and the average precipitation for February (0.79 in.) as a minimum. Assume $t = 0$ corresponds to April. (a) Use the information to construct a sinusoidal model, and (b) use the model to approximate the inches of precipitation Minneapolis receives in July ($t = 3$) and December ($t = 8$).

*Source: 2004 Statistical Abstract of the United States,* Table 380.

**14.** Which of the following functions indicates that the graph of $y = \sin(2t)$ has been shifted horizontally $\dfrac{\pi}{4}$ units left?

  **a.** $y = \sin\!\left[2\!\left(t + \dfrac{\pi}{4}\right)\right]$    **b.** $y = \sin\!\left(2t + \dfrac{\pi}{4}\right)$

  **c.** $y = \sin\!\left[2\!\left(t - \dfrac{\pi}{4}\right)\right]$    **d.** $y = \sin(2t) - \dfrac{\pi}{4}$

**15.** Find the frequency of the following harmonic motion models.

  **a.** $y = 5.2 \sin\!\left(\dfrac{\pi}{6} t\right)$    **b.** $y = \dfrac{\pi}{3} \cos\!\left(\dfrac{8}{3} t\right)$

**16.** Given $t = \dfrac{5\pi}{12}$ is a solution to $\tan t \approx 3.732$, use the period of the function to name three additional solutions. Answers may vary.

State the amplitude, period, horizontal shift, vertical shift, and endpoints of the primary interval, then sketch the graph using a reference rectangle and the *rule of fourths.*

**17.** $y = 5 \cos(2t) - 8$       **18.** $y = \dfrac{7}{2} \sin\!\left[\dfrac{\pi}{2}(x - 1)\right]$

State the period and phase shift, then sketch the graph of each function.

**19.** $y = 2 \tan\!\left(\dfrac{1}{4} t\right)$       **20.** $y = 3 \sec\!\left(x - \dfrac{\pi}{2}\right)$

## PRACTICE TEST

1. Complete the table using exact values, including the point on the unit circle associated with $t$.

| $t$ | 0 | $\dfrac{\pi}{6}$ | $\dfrac{\pi}{4}$ | $\dfrac{\pi}{2}$ | $\dfrac{2\pi}{3}$ | $\dfrac{5\pi}{6}$ | $\dfrac{5\pi}{4}$ | $\dfrac{4\pi}{3}$ | $\dfrac{3\pi}{2}$ |
|---|---|---|---|---|---|---|---|---|---|
| $\sin t$ | | | | | | | | | |
| $\cos t$ | | | | | | | | | |
| $\tan t$ | | | | | | | | | |
| $\csc t$ | | | | | | | | | |
| $\sec t$ | | | | | | | | | |
| $\cot t$ | | | | | | | | | |
| $P(x, y)$ | | | | | | | | | |

2. State the value of each expression without the use of a calculator:

   a. $\cos\left(\dfrac{3\pi}{2}\right)$ 

   b. $\sin \pi$

   c. $\tan\left(\dfrac{5\pi}{4}\right)$ 

   d. $\sec\left(\dfrac{\pi}{6}\right)$

3. State the value of each expression without the use of a calculator:

   a. $\tan^{-1}(\sqrt{3})$; QI 

   b. $\cos^{-1}\left(-\dfrac{1}{2}\right)$; QII

   c. $\sin^{-1}\left(-\dfrac{\sqrt{3}}{2}\right)$; QIII 

   d. $\sec^{-1}(\sqrt{2})$; QIV

State the amplitude (if it exists) and period of each function, then sketch the graph in the interval indicated using a reference rectangle and the *rule of fourths*.

4. $y = 3\sin\left(\dfrac{\pi}{5}t\right)$, $t \in [0, 10]$

5. $y = 2\sec(2t)$, $t \in [0, 2\pi]$

6. $y = 4\tan(3t)$, $t \in [0, \pi]$

State the amplitude (if it exists), period, horizontal shift, and vertical shift of each function, then sketch the graph in the interval indicated using a reference rectangle and the *rule of fourths*.

7. $y = 12\sin\left[3\left(t - \dfrac{\pi}{6}\right)\right] + 19$, $t \in [0, 2\pi]$

8. $y = \dfrac{3}{4}\cos\left(\dfrac{1}{2}\pi t\right) - \dfrac{1}{2}$, $t \in [-2, 6)$

9. $y = 2\cot\left[\dfrac{1}{3}\pi\left(t - \dfrac{3}{2}\right)\right]$, $t \in [0, 6)$

10. The revenue for Otake's Mower Repair is very seasonal, with business in the summer months far exceeding business in the winter months. Monthly revenue for the company can be modeled by the function $R(x) = 7.5\cos\left(\dfrac{\pi}{6}x + \dfrac{4\pi}{3}\right) + 12.5$, where $R(x)$ is the average revenue (in thousands of dollars) for month $x$ ($x = 1 \rightarrow$ Jan). (a) What is the average revenue for September? (b) For what months of the year is revenue at least \$12,500?

11. Given $t = 4.25$ is a solution to $\tan t \approx 2$, use the period $P = \pi$ to find two other solutions.

12. Given $t \approx 1.4602$ is a solution to $\tan^{-1}(9) = t$, find another solution using a reference angle/arc.

13. Although Reno, Nevada is a very arid city, the amount of monthly precipitation tends to follow a sinusoidal pattern. (a) Find an equation model for the precipitation in Reno, given the annual high is 1.06 in., while annual low is 0.24 in. and occurs in the month of July. (b) In what month does the annual high occur?

14. A weight on the end of a spring is oscillating in harmonic motion with a frequency of $f = 3$ cycles per second and a displacement of 5 cm. Find an equation of the form $y = A\cos(Bt)$ that models the motion.

**15.** Due to tidal motions, the depth of water in Brentwood Bay varies sinusoidally as shown in the diagram, where time is in hours and depth is in feet. Find an equation that models the depth of water at time $t$.

**Exercise 15**

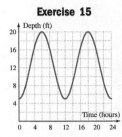

**16.** Determine the equation of the graph shown, given it is of the form $y = A \csc(Bt) + D$.

**Exercise 16**

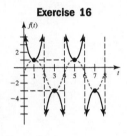

Match each equation with its corresponding graph.

**17.** $y = 3 \sin\left[2\left(t - \dfrac{\pi}{6}\right)\right]$   **18.** $y = 3 \sin(\pi t) - 1$

**19.** $y = -3 \sin(\pi t) + 1$   **20.** $y = 3 \sin\left(2t - \dfrac{\pi}{6}\right)$

**a.**

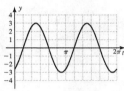

**b.**

**c.**

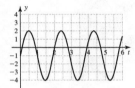

**d.**

## CALCULATOR EXPLORATION AND DISCOVERY

### Variable Amplitudes and Modeling the Tides

Tidal motion is often too complex to be modeled by a single sine function. In this *Exploration and Discovery*, we'll look at a method that combines two sine functions to help model a tidal motion with variable amplitude. In the process, we'll use much of what we know about the amplitude, horizontal shifts and vertical shifts of a sine function, helping to reinforce these important concepts and broaden our understanding about how they can be applied. The graph in Figure 4.47 shows three days of tidal motion for Davis Inlet, Canada.

**Figure 4.47**

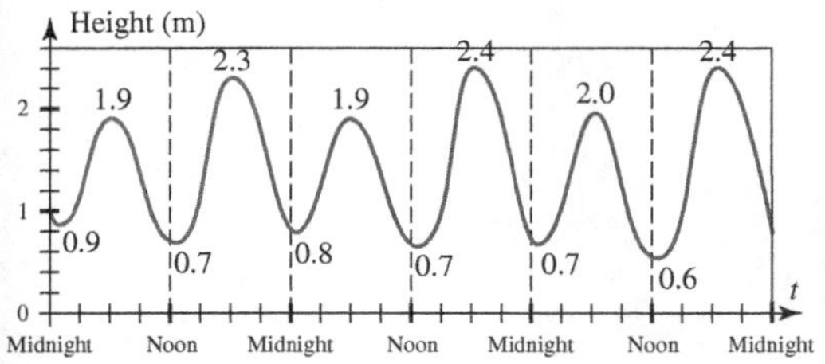

Height (m)

**Figure 4.48**

Height (m)

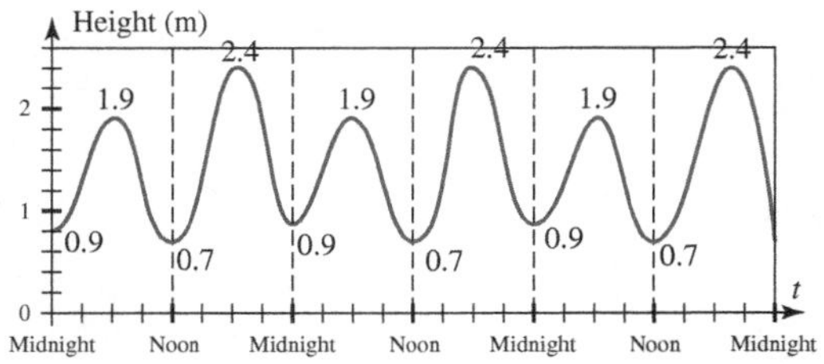

As you can see, the amplitude of the graph varies, and there is no *single* sine function that can serve as a model. However, notice that the amplitude *varies predictably*, and that the high tides and low tides can independently be modeled by a sine function. To simplify our exploration, we will use the assumption that tides have an exact 24-hr period (close, but no), that variations between high and low tides takes place every 12 hr (again close but not exactly true), and the variation between the "low-high" (1.9 m) and the "high-high" (2.4 m) is uniform. A similar assumption is made for the low tides. The result is the graph in Figure 4.48.

First consider the high tides, which vary from a maximum of 2.4 to a minimum of 1.9. Using the ideas from Section 4.4 to construct an equation model gives $A = \dfrac{2.4 - 1.9}{2} = 0.25$ and $D = \dfrac{2.4 + 1.9}{2} = 2.15$. With a period of $P = 24$ hr

we obtain the equation $Y_1 = 0.25 \sin\left(\dfrac{\pi}{12}x\right) + 2.15$. Using 0.9 and 0.7 as the maximum and minimum low tides, similar calculations yield the equation $Y_2 = 0.1\sin\left(\dfrac{\pi}{12}x\right) + 0.8$ (verify this).

Graphing these two functions over a 24-hr period yields the graph in Figure 4.49, where we note the high and low values are correct, but the two functions are in phase with each other. As can be determined from Figure 4.48, we want the high tide model to start at the average value and decrease, and the low tide equation model to start at high-low and decrease. Replacing $x$ with $x - 12$ in $Y_1$ and $x$ with $x + 6$ in $Y_2$ accomplishes this result (see Figure 4.50). Now comes the fun part! Since $Y_1$ represents the low/high maximum values for high tide, and $Y_2$ represents the low/high minimum values for low tide, *the amplitude and average value for the tidal motion at Davis Inlet are $A = \dfrac{Y_1 - Y_2}{2}$*

and $D = \dfrac{Y_1 + Y_2}{2}$! By entering $Y_3 = \dfrac{Y_1 - Y_2}{2}$ and $Y_4 = \dfrac{Y_1 + Y_2}{2}$, the equation for the tidal motion (with its variable amplitude) will have the form $Y_5 = Y_3\sin(Bx \pm C) + Y_4$, where the value of $B$ and $C$ must be determined. The key here is to note there is only a 12-hr difference between the changes in amplitude, so $P = 12$ (instead of 24) and $B = \dfrac{\pi}{6}$ for this function. Also, from the graph (Figure 4.48) we note the tidal motion begins at a minimum and increases, indicating a shift of 3 units to the right is required. Replacing $x$ with $x - 3$ gives the equation modeling these tides, and the final equation is $Y_5 = Y_3\sin\left[\dfrac{\pi}{6}(x - 3)\right] + Y_4$. Figure 4.51 gives a screen shot of $Y_1$, $Y_2$, and $Y_5$ in the interval [0, 24]. The tidal graph from Figure 4.48 is shown in Figure 4.52 with $Y_3$ and $Y_4$ superimposed on it.

**Figure 4.49**

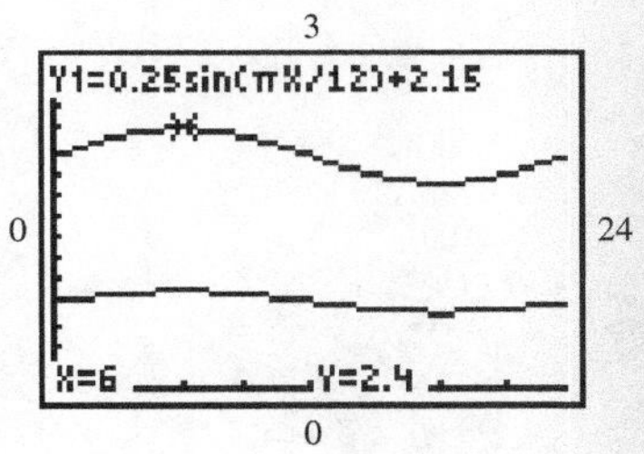

**Figure 4.50**

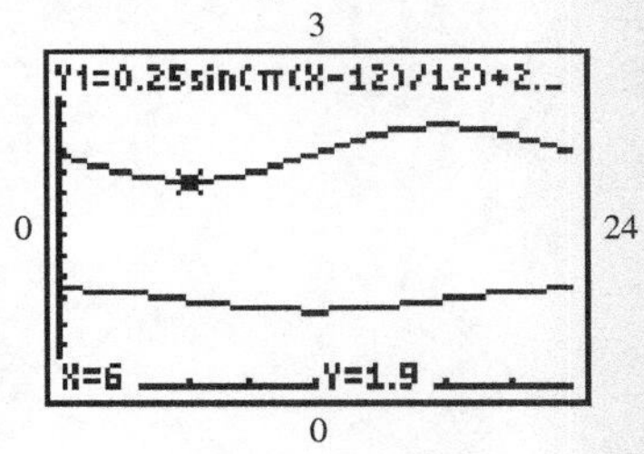

**Figure 4.51**

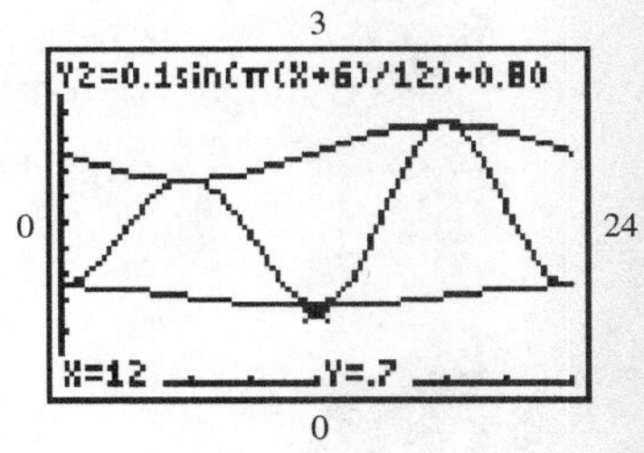

**Figure 4.52**

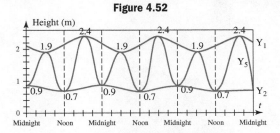

**Exercise 1:** The website www.tides.com/tcpred.htm offers both *t*ide and *c*urrent *pred*ictions for various locations around the world, in both numeric and graphical form. In addition, data for the "two" high tides and "two" low tides are clearly highlighted. Select a coastal area where tidal motion is similar to that of Davis Inlet, and repeat this exercise. Compare your model to the actual data given on the website. How good was the fit?

## Transformations via Composition

Historically, many of the transformations studied in this chapter played a fundamental role in the development of modern trigonometry. To make the connection, we note that many transformations can be viewed as a composition of functions.

For instance, for $f(t) = \cos t + 1$ (the cosine function shifted one unit up) and $g(t) = t - \dfrac{\pi}{3}$, the composition

$h(t) = f[g(t)]$ yields $h(t) = \cos\left(t - \dfrac{\pi}{3}\right) + 1$, a cosine curve shifted 1 unit up *and* $\dfrac{\pi}{3}$ units right. Enter $f(t)$ as $Y_1$ and $h(t)$ as $Y_2$ on your graphing calculator, then graph and inspect the results.

As you see, we do obtain the same curve shifted $\dfrac{\pi}{3}$ units to the right (see Figure

4.53). But now, notice what happens when we compose $h(t)$ with $j(t) = t - \dfrac{\pi}{6}$ (shifting

another $\dfrac{\pi}{6}$ units right). After simplification, $h[j(t)] = \cos\left(t - \dfrac{\pi}{2}\right) + 1$ and by obser-

vation of Figure 4.54, its graph is the same as $y = \sin t + 1$ (consider the cofunction properties). In Chapter 6, we'll look at solving trigonometric equations in
depth, but from algebra, a zero of a (trig) function is where its graph touches the
$t$-axis. With this in mind, the vertically shifted sine function is *a function whose*

*zeroes can easily be found*, using the rule of fourths. The zeroes of $h[j(t)]$ are

$t = \dfrac{3\pi}{2} + 2\pi k$, which means the zeroes of $h(t)$ (the original function) can be found by

shifting these zeroes $\dfrac{\pi}{6}$ units *left*, returning them to their original position. The zeroes of

$h(t)$ are $t = \left(\dfrac{3\pi}{2} - \dfrac{\pi}{6}\right) + 2\pi k = \dfrac{8\pi}{6} + 2\pi k = \dfrac{4\pi}{3} + 2\pi k$ (verify by substitution).

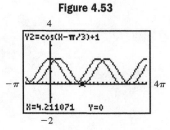

**Figure 4.53**

**Figure 4.54**

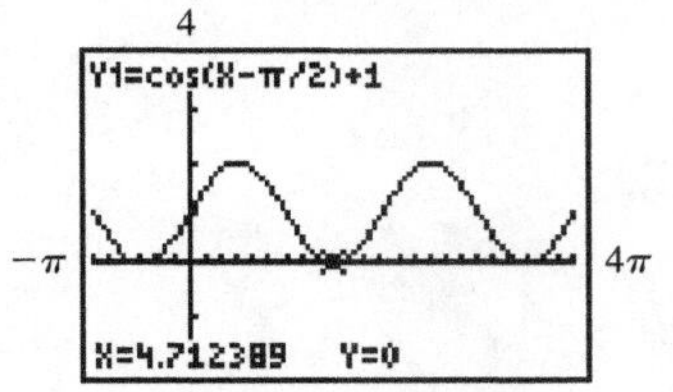

The key is to shift cosine functions to the right a total of $\dfrac{\pi}{2}$ units, and sine functions to the left a total of $\dfrac{\pi}{2}$ units, allowing

the use of the cofunction properties. A similar method can be employed with the secant and cosecant functions, while a
reflection and translation are necessary for the tangent and cotangent functions. For Exercises 1–3, use this method to
(a) compose $f(t)$ with a horizontal translation $g(t)$ to find such functions $h(t)$, and (b) use the zeroes of $h$ to find the zeroes
of $f$. Verify each solution by direct substitution.

**Exercise 1:**  $f(t) = \sin\left(t + \dfrac{\pi}{4}\right) - 1$      **Exercise 2:**  $f(t) = \cos\left(t + \dfrac{\pi}{6}\right) - 1$      **Exercise 3:**  $f(t) = 3\sin(t - 0.7) + 3$

1. Use a reference rectangle and the *rule of fourths* to graph $y = 2.5 \sin\left(\frac{\pi}{2}t\right)$ in $[-2, 6)$.

2. State the period, horizontal shift, and $x$-intercepts of the function $y = -\tan\left(2x + \frac{\pi}{2}\right)$ in $\left[-\frac{\pi}{2}, \pi\right)$. Then state whether the function is increasing or decreasing and sketch its graph.

3. Given that $\cot\theta = \frac{55}{48}$, use a right triangle that corresponds to this ratio to find the length of the missing side. Then find the two acute angles.

4. Without a calculator, what values in $[0, 2\pi)$ make the equation true? $\cos t = \frac{\sqrt{3}}{2}$?

5. Given $\left(-\frac{1}{3}, \frac{2\sqrt{2}}{3}\right)$ is a point on the unit circle corresponding to $t$, find all six trig functions of $t$.

6. A 12-ft-long ladder is leaning against a wall at an angle of 68°. To the nearest half-inch, how high up the wall does it reach?

7. Given $\alpha = 54°13'03''$, find the measure of angle $\beta$ for the triangle shown and convert it to

   **Exercises 7 and 8**

   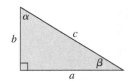

   a. decimal degrees
   b. radians

8. Given $b = 13.2$ cm, use Exercise 7 and the triangle shown to find the measure of the remaining two sides.

9. Verify the point $\left(\frac{13}{85}, \frac{84}{85}\right)$ is on a unit circle, and use the circle's symmetry to find three other points on the circle.

10. For $\theta = 701.2°$, find the reference angle and use it to find the value of $\sin\theta$, $\cos\theta$, and $\tan\theta$ with a calculator. Round to four decimal places.

11. Hunter and his dad are kiteboarding at the beach. Hunter is 10 m away from his dad, and the kite is directly above his dad's head. The angle of elevation from Hunter to the kite is 69°. To the nearest meter, how high is the kite?

**12.** Danielle scored her first soccer goal by firing a straight on blast from her left foot. From the point of view of the referee standing on the goal line, the ball passed through $52°$ of rotation in 2 sec. If the referee

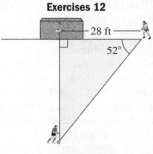

**Exercises 12**

was 28 ft from the point where the ball crossed the goal line, (a) how far was Danielle from the goal line? (b) What was the average velocity of the ball in ft/sec?

**13.** Given $t = \dfrac{4\pi}{3}$, use reference arcs to state the value of all six trig functions of $t$ without using a calculator.

**14.** A skateboard has wheels with a 1-in. radius. If Xihuan is cruising at 11 mph, find how fast the wheels are spinning (in rpm).

**15.** One lazy summer day, a butterfly is circling a purple geranium. The butterfly takes 4 sec to fly a circular path of radius 14 in. (a) Find the butterfly's angular velocity in radians per second. (b) Find the butterfly's linear velocity in inches per second.

**16.** Find $T(\theta)$ for all six trig functions $T$, given the point $P(8, -15)$ is a point on the terminal side of the angle. Then find the angle $\theta$ in degrees, rounded to tenths.

**17.** Given $t = 4.22$, (a) in what quadrant does the arc terminate? (b) What is the reference arc? (c) Find the value of tan $t$ rounded to four decimal places.

**18.** Determine the equation of the graph shown given it is of the form $y = A \tan(Bt)$.

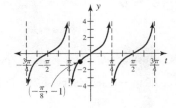

**19.** Determine the equation of the graph shown given it is of the form $y = A \sin(Bt \pm C) + D$.

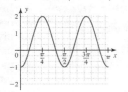

**20.** In London, the average temperature on a summer day ranges from a high of $72°F$ to a low of $56°F$. Use this information to write a sinusoidal equation model, assuming the low temperature occurs at 6:00 A.M. Clearly state the amplitude, average value, period, and horizontal shift.

*Source: 2004 Statistical Abstract of the United States,* Table 1331.

**21.** State true or false and explain your response: $(\cos t)(\csc t) = 1$.

**22.** Complete the following statement: The cofunction of tangent is cotangent because . . .

**23.** Find the value of all six trig functions given $\csc t = -\dfrac{13}{5}$ and $\cos t > 0$.

**24.** The Earth has a radius of 3960 mi. Tokyo, Japan, is located at approximately $36°$ N latitude, and is almost exactly due north of Lake Julius, Australia, located at $20°$ S latitude. How many miles separate these two locations?

**25.** The profits of Red-Bud Nursery can be modeled by a sinusoid, with profit peaking twice each year. Given profits reach a yearly low of $4000 in mid-January (month 1.5), and a yearly high of $14,000 in mid-April (month 4.5), (a) construct an equation for their yearly profits. (b) Use the model to find their profits for August. (c) Name the other month at which profit peaks.

# Modeling With Technology:    Trigonometric Equation Models

## Learning Objectives

*In MWT you will learn how to:*

- [ ] **A.** Create a trigonometric model from critical points or data
- [ ] **B.** Create a sinusoidal model from data using regression

In the most common use of the word, a cycle is any series of events or operations that occur in a predictable pattern and return to a starting point. This includes things as diverse as the wash cycle on a washing machine and the powers of *i*. There are a number of common events that occur in *sinusoidal* cycles, or events that can be modeled by a sine wave. As in Section 4.4, these include monthly average temperatures, monthly average daylight hours, and harmonic motion, among many others. Less well-known applications include alternating current, biorhythm theory, and animal populations that fluctuate over a known period of years. In this section, we develop two methods for creating a sinusoidal model. The first uses information about the critical points (where the cycle reaches its maximum or minimum values); the second involves computing the equation of best fit (a regression equation) for a set of data.

## A. Critical Points and Sinusoidal Models

Although future courses will define them more precisely, we will consider **critical points** to be *inputs* where a function attains a minimum or maximum value. If an event or phenomenon is known to behave sinusoidally (regularly fluctuating between a maximum and minimum), we can create an acceptable model of the form $y = A \sin(Bx + C) + D$ given these **critical points** $(x, y)$ and the period. For instance, many weather patterns have a period of 12 months. Using the formula $P = \dfrac{2\pi}{B}$, we find

$B = \dfrac{2\pi}{P}$ and substituting 12 for $P$ gives $B = \dfrac{\pi}{6}$ (always the case for phenomena with a 12-month cycle). The maximum value of $A \sin(Bx + C) + D$ will always occur when $\sin(Bx + C) = 1$, and the minimum at $\sin(Bx + C) = -1$, giving this system of equations: max value $M = A(1) + D$ and min value $m = A(-1) + D$. Solving the system for $A$ and $D$ gives $A = \dfrac{M - m}{2}$ and $D = \dfrac{M + m}{2}$ as before. To find $C$, assume the maximum and minimum values occur at $(x_2, M)$ and $(x_1, m)$, respectively. We can substitute the values computed for $A$, $B$, and $D$ in $y = A \sin(Bx + C) + D$, along with either $(x_2, M)$ or $(x_1, m)$, and solve for $C$. Using the minimum value $(x_1, m)$, where $x = x_1$ and $y = m$, we have

$$y = A \sin(Bx + C) + D \qquad \text{sinusoidal equation model}$$
$$m = A \sin(Bx_1 + C) + D \qquad \text{substitute } m \text{ for } y \text{ and } x_1 \text{ for } x$$
$$\frac{m - D}{A} = \sin(Bx_1 + C) \qquad \text{isolate sine function}$$

Fortunately, for sine models constructed from critical points we have $\dfrac{y - D}{A} \rightarrow \dfrac{m - D}{A}$, which is always equal to $-1$ **(see Exercise 26)**. This gives a simple result for $C$, since $-1 = \sin(Bx_1 + C)$ leads to $\dfrac{3\pi}{2} = Bx_1 + C$ or $C = \dfrac{3\pi}{2} - Bx_1$.

**See Exercises 1 through 6** for practice with these ideas.

**EXAMPLE 1** ▶ **Developing a Model for Polar Ice Cap Extent from Critical Points**

When the Spirit and Odyssey Rovers landed on Mars (January 2004), there was a renewed public interest in studying the planet. Of particular interest were the polar ice caps, which are now thought to hold frozen water, especially the northern cap. The Martian ice caps expand and contract with the seasons, just as they do here on Earth but there are about 687 days in a Martian year, making each Martian "month" just over 57 days long (1 Martian day ≈ 1 Earth day). At its smallest size, the northern ice cap covers an area of roughly 0.17 million square miles. At the height of winter, the cap covers about 3.7 million square miles (an area about the size of the 50 United States). Suppose these occur at the beginning of month 4 ($x = 4$) and month 10 ($x = 10$) respectively.

**a.** Use this information to create a sinusoidal model of the form
$f(x) = A \sin(Bx + C) + D$.

**b.** Use the model to predict the area of the ice cap in the eighth Martian month.

**c.** Use a graphing calculator to determine the number of months the cap covers less than 1 million mi².

**Solution** ▶ **a.** Assuming a "12-month" weather pattern, $P = 12$ and $B = \dfrac{\pi}{6}$. The maximum and minimum points are (10, 3.7) and (4, 0.17). Using this information, $D = \dfrac{3.7 + 0.17}{2} = 1.935$ and $A = \dfrac{3.7 - 0.17}{2} = 1.765$. Using $C = \dfrac{3\pi}{2} - Bx_1$ gives $C = \dfrac{3\pi}{2} - \dfrac{\pi}{6}(4) = \dfrac{5\pi}{6}$. The equation model is

$$f(x) = 1.765 \sin\left(\dfrac{\pi}{6}x + \dfrac{5\pi}{6}\right) + 1.935,$$ where $f(x)$ represents millions of square miles in month $x$.

**b.** For the size of the cap in month 8 we evaluate the function at $x = 8$.

$$f(8) = 1.765 \sin\left[\dfrac{\pi}{6}(8) + \dfrac{5\pi}{6}\right] + 1.935 \qquad \text{substitute 8 for } x$$

$$= 2.8175 \qquad\qquad\qquad\qquad\qquad \text{result}$$

In month 8, the polar ice cap will cover about 2,817,500 mi².

**c.** Of the many options available, we opt to solve by locating the points where $Y_1 = 1.765 \sin\left(\dfrac{\pi}{6}x + \dfrac{5\pi}{6}\right) + 1.935$ and $Y_2 = 1$ intersect. After entering the functions on the [Y=] screen, we set $x \in [0, 12]$ and $y \in [-1, 5]$ for a window with a frame around the output values. Press [2nd] [TRACE] (**CALC**) **5:intersect** to find the intersection points. To four decimal places they occur at $x = 2.0663$ and $x = 5.9337$. The ice cap at the northern pole of Mars has an area of less than 1 million mi² from early in the second month to late in the fifth month. The second intersection is shown in the figure.

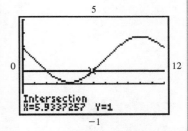

Now try Exercises 7 and 8 ▶

While this form of "equation building" can't match the accuracy of a regression model (computed from a larger set of data), it does lend insight as to how sinusoidal functions work. The equation will always contain the maximum and minimum values, and using the period of the phenomena, we can create a smooth sine wave that "fills in the blanks" between these critical points.

**EXAMPLE 2** ▶ **Developing a Model of Wildlife Population from Critical Points**

Naturalists have found that many animal populations, such as the arctic lynx, some species of fox, and certain rabbit breeds, tend to fluctuate sinusoidally over 10-year periods. Suppose that an extended study of a lynx population began in 2000, and in the third year of the study, the population had fallen to a minimum of 2500. In the eighth year the population hit a maximum of 9500.

**a.** Use this information to create a sinusoidal model of the form $P(x) = A \sin(Bx + C) + D$.

**b.** Use the model to predict the lynx population in the year 2006.

**c.** Use a graphing calculator to determine the number of years the lynx population is above 8000 in a 10-year period.

**Solution** ▶ **a.** Since $P = 10$, we have $B = \dfrac{2\pi}{10} = \dfrac{\pi}{5}$. Using 2000 as year zero, the minimum and maximum populations occur at (3, 2500) and (8, 9500). From the information given, $D = \dfrac{9500 + 2500}{2} = 6000$, and $A = \dfrac{9500 - 2500}{2} = 3500$. Using the minimum value we have $C = \dfrac{3\pi}{2} - \dfrac{\pi}{5}(3) = \dfrac{9\pi}{10}$, giving an equation model of $P(x) = 3500 \sin\left(\dfrac{\pi}{5}x + \dfrac{9\pi}{10}\right) + 6000$, where $P(x)$ represents the lynx population in year $x$.

 **b.** For the population in 2006 we evaluate the function at $x = 6$.

$$P(x) = 3500 \sin\left(\frac{\pi}{5}x + \frac{9\pi}{10}\right) + 6000 \qquad \text{sinusoidal function model}$$

$$P(6) = 3500 \sin\left[\frac{\pi}{5}(6) + \frac{9\pi}{10}\right] + 6000 \qquad \text{substitute 6 for } x$$

$$\approx 7082 \qquad \text{result}$$

In 2006, the lynx population was about 7082.

**c.** Using a graphing calculator and the functions

$Y_1 = 3500 \sin\left(\dfrac{\pi}{5}x + \dfrac{9\pi}{10}\right) + 6000$ and

$Y_2 = 8000$, we attempt to find points of intersection. Enter the functions (press Y= ) and set a viewing window (we used $x \in [0, 12]$ and $y \in [0, 10{,}000]$). Press 2nd TRACE (**CALC**) **5:intersect** to find where $Y_1$ and $Y_2$ intersect. To four decimal places this occurs at $x = 6.4681$ and $x = 9.5319$. The lynx population exceeded 8000 for roughly 3 years. The first intersection is shown.

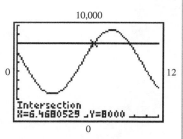

Now try Exercises 9 and 10 ▶

This type of equation building isn't limited to the sine function. In fact, there are many situations where a sine model cannot be applied. Consider the length of the shadows cast by a flagpole or radio tower as the Sun makes its way across the sky. The shadow's length follows a regular pattern (shortening then lengthening) and "always returns to a starting point," yet when the Sun is low in the sky the shadow becomes (theoretically) infinitely long, unlike the output values from a sine function. If we consider *signed* shadow lengths at a latitude where the Sun passes directly overhead (in contrast with Example 6 in Section 4.4), an equation involving tan $x$ might provide a good model. We'll attempt to model the data using $y = A \tan(Bx \pm C)$, with the $D$-term absent since a vertical shift in this context has no meaning. Recall that the period of the tangent function is $P = \dfrac{\pi}{|B|}$ and that $\pm\dfrac{C}{B}$ gives the magnitude and direction of the horizontal shift, in a direction opposite the sign.

---

**EXAMPLE 3** ▶ **Using Data to Develop a Function Model for Shadow Length**

The data given tracks the length of a gnomon's shadow for the 12 daylight hours at a certain location near the equator (positive and negative values indicate lengths before noon and after noon respectively). Assume $t = 0$ represents 6:00 A.M.

| Hour of the Day | Length (cm) | Hour of the Day | Length (cm) |
|---|---|---|---|
| 0 | ∞ | 7 | −2.1 |
| 1 | 29.9 | 8 | −4.6 |
| 2 | 13.9 | 9 | −8.0 |
| 3 | 8.0 | 10 | −13.9 |
| 4 | 4.6 | 11 | −29.9 |
| 5 | 2.1 | 12 | −∞ |
| 6 | 0 | | |

   **a.** Use the data to find an equation model of the form
$L(t) = A \tan(Bt \pm C)$.

   **b.** Graph the function and scatter plot.

   **c.** Find the shadow's length at 4:30 P.M.

   **d.** If the shadow is 6.1 cm long, what time in the morning is it?

**Solution** ▶ **a.** We begin by noting this phenomenon has a period of $P = 12$. Using the period formula for tangent we solve for $B$: $P = \dfrac{\pi}{B}$ gives $12 = \dfrac{\pi}{B}$, so $B = \dfrac{\pi}{12}$. Since we want $(6, 0)$ to be the "center" of the function [instead of $(0, 0)$], we desire a horizontal shift 6 units to the right. Using the ratio $\dfrac{C}{B}$ $\left(\text{with } B = \dfrac{\pi}{12}\right)$ gives

$-6 = \dfrac{12C}{\pi}$ so $C = -\dfrac{\pi}{2}$. To find $A$ we use the equation built so far:

$L(t) = A \tan\left(\dfrac{\pi}{12}t - \dfrac{\pi}{2}\right)$, and *any data point* to solve for $A$. Using $(3, 8)$

we obtain $8 = A \tan\left(\dfrac{\pi}{12}(3) - \dfrac{\pi}{2}\right)$:

$8 = A \tan\left(-\dfrac{\pi}{4}\right)$    simplify

$-8 = A$    solve for $A$: $\tan\left(-\dfrac{\pi}{4}\right) = -1$

The equation model is

$L(t) = -8 \tan\left(\dfrac{\pi}{12}t - \dfrac{\pi}{2}\right).$

**b.** The scatter plot and graph are shown in the figure.

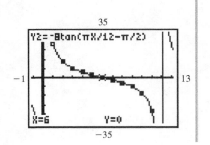

**WORTHY OF NOTE**

A gnomon is the protruding feature of a sundial, casting the shadow used to estimate the time of day (see photo).

**c.** 4:30 P.M. indicates $t = 10.5$. Evaluating $L(10.5)$ gives

$$L(t) = -8\tan\left(\frac{\pi}{12}t - \frac{\pi}{2}\right) \qquad \text{function model}$$

$$L(10.5) = -8\tan\left[\frac{\pi}{12}(10.5) - \frac{\pi}{2}\right] \qquad \text{substitute 10.5 for } t$$

$$= -8\tan\left(\frac{3\pi}{8}\right) \qquad \text{simplify}$$

$$\approx -19.31 \qquad \text{result}$$

At 4:30 P.M., the shadow has a length of $|-19.31| = 19.31$ cm.

**d.** Substituting 6.1 for $L(t)$ and solving for $t$ graphically gives the graph shown, where we note the day is about 3.5 hr old—it is about 9:30 A.M.

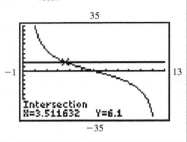

☑ **A.** You've just learned how to create a trigonometric model from critical points or data

Now try Exercises 11 through 14 ▶

## B. Data and Sinusoidal Regression

Most graphing calculators are programmed to handle numerous forms of polynomial and nonpolynomial regression, including **sinusoidal regression.** The sequence of steps used is the same regardless of the form chosen. **Exercises 15 through 18** offer further practice with regression fundamentals. Example 4 illustrates their use in context.

**EXAMPLE 4** ▶ **Calculating a Regression Equation for Seasonal Temperatures**

The data shown give the record high temperature for selected months in Bismarck, North Dakota.

| Month (Jan → 1) | Temp. (°F) | Month (Jan → 1) | Temp. (°F) |
|---|---|---|---|
| 1 | 63 | 9 | 105 |
| 3 | 81 | 11 | 79 |
| 5 | 98 | 12 | 65 |
| 7 | 109 | | |

**a.** Use the data to draw a scatter plot, then find a sinusoidal regression model and graph both on the same screen.

**b.** Use the equation model to estimate the record high temperatures for months 2, 6, and 8.

**c.** Determine what month gives the largest difference between the actual data and the computed results.

*Source: NOAA Comparative Climate Data 2004.*

**Solution** ▶ **a.** Entering the data and running the regression (in radian mode) results in the coefficients shown in Figure MWT 1. After entering the equation in $Y_1$ and pressing ZOOM **9:Zoom Stat** we obtain the graph shown in Figure MWT 2 (indicated window settings have been rounded).

**Figure MWT 1**          **Figure MWT 2**

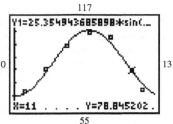

**b.** Using $x = 2$, $x = 6$, and $x = 8$ as inputs, the equation model projects record high temperatures of 68.5°, 108.0°, and 108.1°, respectively.

**c.** In the header of L3, use $Y_1(L1)$ [ENTER] to evaluate the regression model using the inputs from L1, and place the results in L3. Entering L2 − L3 in the header of L4 gives the results shown in Figure MWT 3 and we note the largest difference occurs in September—about 4°.

**Figure MWT 3**

| L2 | L3 | L4 | 4 |
|---|---|---|---|
| 63 | 61.805 | 1.195 | |
| 81 | 78.575 | 2.4248 | |
| 98 | 100.61 | -2.611 | |
| 109 | 110.65 | -1.652 | |
| 105 | 100.83 | 4.167 | |
| 79 | 78.845 | .1548 | |
| 65 | 68.661 | -3.661 | |

L4(1)=1.195267717...

Now try Exercises 19 through 22 ▶

Weather patterns differ a great deal depending on the locality. For example, the annual rainfall received by Seattle, Washington, far exceeds that received by Cheyenne, Wyoming. Our final example compares the two amounts and notes an interesting fact about the relationship.

**EXAMPLE 5** ▶ **Calculating a Regression Model for Seasonal Rainfall**

The average monthly rainfall (in inches) for Cheyenne, Wyoming, and Seattle, Washington, is shown in the table.

**a.** Use the data to find a sinusoidal regression model for the average monthly rainfall in each city. Enter or paste the equation for Cheyenne in $Y_1$ and the equation for Seattle in $Y_2$.

**b.** Graph both equations on the same screen (without the scatter plots) and use [TRACE] or [2nd] [TRACE] **(CALC) 5:intersect** to help estimate the number of months Cheyenne receives more rainfall than Seattle.

*Source:* NOAA Comparative Climate Data 2004.

| Month (Jan. → 1) | WY Rain | WA Rain |
|---|---|---|
| 1 | 0.45 | 5.13 |
| 2 | 0.44 | 4.18 |
| 3 | 1.05 | 3.75 |
| 4 | 1.55 | 2.59 |
| 5 | 2.48 | 1.77 |
| 6 | 2.12 | 1.49 |
| 7 | 2.26 | 0.79 |
| 8 | 1.82 | 1.02 |
| 9 | 1.43 | 1.63 |
| 10 | 0.75 | 3.19 |
| 11 | 0.64 | 5.90 |
| 12 | 0.46 | 5.62 |

Solution ▶ **a.** Setting the calculator in **Float 0 1 2 3 4 5 6 7 8 9** [MODE] and running sinusoidal regressions gives the equations shown in Figure MWT 4.

**b.** Both graphs are shown in Figure MWT 5. Using the [TRACE] feature, we find the graphs intersect at approximately (4.7, 2.0) and (8.4, 1.7). Cheyenne receives more rain than Seattle for about $8.4 - 4.7 = 3.7$ months of the year.

**Figure MWT 4**    **Figure MWT 5**

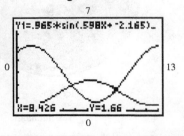

✔ **B.** You've just learned how to create a sinusoidal model from data using regression

Now try Exercises 23 and 24 ▶

# MODELING WITH TECHNOLOGY EXERCISES

**Find the sinusoidal equation for the information as given.**

1. minimum value at (9, 25); maximum value at (3, 75); period: 12 min

2. minimum value at (4.5, 35); maximum value at (1.5, 121); period: 6 yr

3. minimum value at (15, 3); maximum value at (3, 7.5); period: 24 hr

4. minimum value at (3, 3.6); maximum value at (7, 12); period: 8 hr

5. minimum value at (5, 279); maximum value at (11, 1285); period: 12 yr

6. minimum value at (6, 8280); maximum value at (22, 23,126); period: 32 yr

7. **Record monthly temperatures:** The U.S. National Oceanic and Atmospheric Administration (NOAA) keeps temperature records for most major U.S. cities. For Phoenix, Arizona, they list an average high temperature of 65.0°F for the month of January (month 1) and an average high temperature of 104.2°F for July (month 7). Assuming January and July are the coolest and warmest months of the year, (a) build a sinusoidal function model for temperatures in Phoenix, and (b) use the model to find the average high temperature in September. (c) If a person has a tremendous aversion to temperatures over 95°, during what months should they plan to vacation elsewhere?

8. **Seasonal size of polar ice caps:** Much like the polar ice cap on Mars, the sea ice that surrounds the continent of Antarctica (the Earth's southern

Ice caps

      mininum

      maximum

polar cap) varies seasonally, from about 8 million mi$^2$ in September to about 1 million mi$^2$ in March. Use this information to (a) build a sinusoidal equation that models the advance and retreat of the sea ice, and (b) determine the size of the ice sheet in May. (c) Find the months of the year that the sea ice covers more than 6.75 million mi$^2$.

9. **Body temperature cycles:** A phenomenon is said to be *circadian* if it occurs in 24-hr cycles. A person's body temperature is circadian, since there are normally small, sinusoidal variations in body temperature from a low of 98.2°F to a high of 99°F throughout a 24-hr day. Use this information to (a) build the circadian equation for a person's body temperature, given $t = 0$ corresponds to midnight and that a person usually reaches their minimum temperature at 5 A.M.; (b) find the time(s) during a day when a person reaches "normal" body temperature (98.6°); and (c) find the number of hours each day that body temperature is 98.4°F or less.

10. **Position of engine piston:** For an internal combustion engine, the position of a piston in the cylinder can be modeled by a sinusoidal function. For a particular engine size and idle speed, the piston head is 0 in. from the top of the cylinder (the minimum value) when $t = 0$ at the beginning of the intake stroke, and reaches a maximum distance of 4 in. from the top of the cylinder (the maximum value) when $t = \frac{1}{48}$ sec at the beginning of the compression stroke. Following the compression stroke is the power stroke ($t = \frac{2}{48}$), the exhaust stroke ($t = \frac{3}{48}$), and the intake stroke ($t = \frac{4}{48}$), after which it all begins again. Given the period of a four-stroke engine under these conditions is $P = \frac{1}{24}$ second, (a) find the sinusoidal equation modeling the position of the piston, and (b) find the distance of the piston from the top of the cylinder at $t = \frac{1}{9}$ sec. Which stroke is the engine in at this moment?

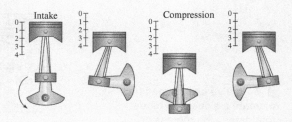

**Data and tangent functions:** Use the data given to find an equation model of the form $f(x) = A \tan(Bx + C)$. Then graph the function and scatter plot to help find (a) the output for $x = 2.5$, and (b) the value of $x$ where $f(x) = 16$.

**11.**

| x | y | x | y |
|---|---|---|---|
| 0 | ∞ | 7 | −1.4 |
| 1 | 20 | 8 | −3 |
| 2 | 9.7 | 9 | −5.2 |
| 3 | 5.2 | 10 | −9.7 |
| 4 | 3 | 11 | −20 |
| 5 | 1.4 | 12 | −∞ |
| 6 | 0 | | |

**12.**

| x | y | x | y |
|---|---|---|---|
| 0 | ∞ | 7 | 6.4 |
| 1 | −91.3 | 8 | 13.7 |
| 2 | −44.3 | 9 | 23.7 |
| 3 | −23.7 | 10 | 44.3 |
| 4 | −13.7 | 11 | 91.3 |
| 5 | −6.4 | 12 | ∞ |
| 6 | 0 | | |

**13. Distance and apparent height:**

| Distance Traveled (mi) | Height (cm) |
|---|---|
| 0 | 0 |
| 3 | 1 |
| 6 | 1.8 |
| 9 | 2.8 |
| 12 | 4.2 |
| 15 | 6.3 |
| 18 | 10 |
| 21 | 21 |
| 24 | ∞ |

While driving toward a Midwestern town on a long, flat stretch of highway, I decide to pass the time by measuring the apparent height of the tallest building in the downtown area as I approach. At the time the idea occurred to me, the buildings were barely visible. Three miles later I hold a 30-cm ruler up to my eyes at arm's length, and the apparent height of the tallest building is 1 cm. After three more miles the apparent height is 1.8 cm. Measurements are taken every 3 mi until I reach town and are shown in the table (assume I was 24 mi from the parking garage when I began this activity). (a) Use the data to come up with a tangent function model of the building's apparent height after traveling a distance of $x$ mi closer. (b) What was the apparent height of the building after I had driven 19 mi? (c) How many miles had I driven when the apparent height of the building took up all 30 cm of my ruler?

**14. Earthquakes and elastic rebound:** The **theory of elastic rebound** has been used by seismologists to study the cause of earthquakes. As seen in the figure, the Earth's crust is stretched to a breaking point by the slow movement of one tectonic plate in a direction opposite the other along a fault line, and when the rock snaps—each half violently rebounds to its original alignment causing the Earth to quake.

| x | y | x | y |
|---|---|---|---|
| −4.5 | −61 | 1 | 2.1 |
| −4 | −26 | 2 | 6.8 |
| −3 | −14.8 | 3 | 15.3 |
| −2 | −7.2 | 4 | 25.4 |
| −1 | −1.9 | 4.5 | 59 |
| 0 | 0 | | |

Suppose the *misalignment* of these plates through the stress and twist of crustal movement can be modeled by a tangent graph, where $x$ represents the horizontal distance from the original stress line, and $y$ represents the vertical distance from the fault line. Assume a "period" of 10.2 m. (a) Use the data from the table to come up with a trigonometric model of the deformed stress line. (b) At a point 4.8 m along the fault line, what is the distance to the deformed stress line (moving parallel to the original stress line)? (c) At what point along the fault line is the vertical distance to the deformed stress line 50 m?

**Data and sinusoidal regression models:** For the following sets of data (a) find a sinusoidal regression equation using your calculator; (b) construct an equation manually using the period and maximum/minimum values; and (c) graph both on the same screen, then use a TABLE to find the largest difference between output values.

**15.**

| Day of Month | Output |
|---|---|
| 1 | 15 |
| 4 | 41 |
| 7 | 69 |
| 10 | 91 |
| 13 | 100 |
| 16 | 90 |
| 19 | 63 |
| 22 | 29 |
| 25 | 5 |
| 28 | 2 |
| 31 | 18 |

**16.**

| Day of Month | Output |
|---|---|
| 1 | 179 |
| 4 | 201 |
| 7 | 195 |
| 10 | 172 |
| 13 | 145 |
| 16 | 120 |
| 19 | 100 |
| 22 | 103 |
| 25 | 124 |
| 28 | 160 |
| 31 | 188 |

**17.**

| Month (Jan. = 1) | Output |
|---|---|
| 1 | 16 |
| 2 | 19 |
| 3 | 21 |
| 4 | 22 |
| 5 | 21 |
| 6 | 19 |
| 7 | 16 |
| 8 | 13 |
| 9 | 11 |
| 10 | 10 |
| 11 | 11 |
| 12 | 13 |

**18.**

| Month (Jan. = 1) | Output |
|---|---|
| 1 | 86 |
| 2 | 96 |
| 3 | 99 |
| 4 | 95 |
| 5 | 83 |
| 6 | 72 |
| 7 | 56 |
| 8 | 48 |
| 9 | 43 |
| 10 | 49 |
| 11 | 58 |
| 12 | 73 |

**19. Record monthly temperatures:** The highest temperature of record for the even months of the year are given in the table for the city of Pittsburgh, Pennsylvania. (a) Use the data to draw a scatter plot, then find a sinusoidal regression model and graph both on the same screen. (b) Use the equation to estimate the record high temperature for the odd-numbered months. (c) What month shows the largest difference between the actual data and the computed results?

Source: 2004 Statistical Abstract of the United States, Table 378.

| Month (Jan. → 1) | High Temp. (°F) |
|---|---|
| 2 | 76 |
| 4 | 89 |
| 6 | 98 |
| 8 | 100 |
| 10 | 87 |
| 12 | 74 |

**20. River discharge rate:** The average discharge rate of the Alabama River is given in the table for the odd-numbered months of the year. (a) Use the data to draw a scatter plot, then find a sinusoidal regression model and graph both on the same screen. (b) Use the equation to estimate the flow rate for the even-

| Month (Jan. → 1) | Rate (m³/sec) |
|---|---|
| 1 | 1569 |
| 3 | 1781 |
| 5 | 1333 |
| 7 | 401 |
| 9 | 261 |
| 11 | 678 |

numbered months. (c) Use the graph and equation to estimate the number of days per year the flow rate is below 500 m³/sec.

Source: Global River Discharge Database Project; www.rivdis.sr.unh.edu.

**21. Illumination of the moon's surface:** The table given indicates the percent of the Moon that is illuminated for the days of a particular month, at a given latitude. (a) Use a graphing calculator to find a sinusoidal regression model. (b) Use the model to determine what percent of the Moon is illuminated on day 20. (c) Use the maximum and minimum values with the period and an appropriate horizontal shift to create your own model of the data. How do the values for $A$, $B$, $C$, and $D$ compare?

| Day | % Illum. | Day | % Illum. |
|---|---|---|---|
| 1 | 28 | 19 | 34 |
| 4 | 55 | 22 | 9 |
| 7 | 82 | 25 | 0 |
| 10 | 99 | 28 | 9 |
| 13 | 94 | 31 | 30 |
| 16 | 68 | | |

**22. Connections between weather and mood:** The mood of persons with SAD syndrome (seasonal affective disorder) often depends on the weather. Victims of SAD are typically more despondent in rainy weather than when the Sun is out, and more comfortable in the daylight hours than at night. The table shows the average number of daylight hours for Vancouver, British Columbia, for 12 months of a year. (a) Use a calculator to find a sinusoidal regression model. (b) Use the model to estimate the *number of days* per year (use 1 month ≈ 30.5 days) with more than 14 hr of daylight. (c) Use the maximum and minimum values with the period and an appropriate horizontal shift to *create* a model of the data. How do the values for $A$, $B$, $C$, and $D$ compare?

*Source:* Vancouver Climate at www.bcpassport.com/vital.

| Month | Hours | Month | Hours |
|-------|-------|-------|-------|
| 1 | 8.3 | 7 | 16.2 |
| 2 | 9.4 | 8 | 15.1 |
| 3 | 11.0 | 9 | 13.5 |
| 4 | 12.9 | 10 | 11.7 |
| 5 | 14.6 | 11 | 9.9 |
| 6 | 15.9 | 12 | 8.5 |

**23. Average monthly rainfall:** The average monthly rainfall (in inches) for Reno, Nevada, is shown in the table. (a) Use the data to find a sinusoidal regression model for the monthly rainfall. (b) Graph this equation model and the rainfall equation model for Cheyenne, Wyoming (from Example 5), on the same screen, and estimate the number of months that Reno gets more rainfall than Cheyenne.

*Source:* NOAA Comparative Climate Data 2004.

| Month (Jan → 1) | Reno Rainfall | Month (Jan → 1) | Reno Rainfall |
|-----------------|---------------|-----------------|---------------|
| 1 | 1.06 | 7 | 0.24 |
| 2 | 1.06 | 8 | 0.27 |
| 3 | 0.86 | 9 | 0.45 |
| 4 | 0.35 | 10 | 0.42 |
| 5 | 0.62 | 11 | 0.80 |
| 6 | 0.47 | 12 | 0.88 |

**24. Hours of daylight by month:** The number of daylight hours per month (as measured on the 15th of each month) is shown in the table for the cities of Beaumont, Texas, and Minneapolis, Minnesota. (a) Use the data to find a sinusoidal regression model of the daylight hours for each city. (b) Graph both equations on the same screen and use the graphs to estimate the *number of days* each year that Beaumont receives more daylight than Minneapolis (use 1 month = 30.5 days).

*Source:* www.encarta.msn.com/media_701500905/Hours_of_Daylight_by_Latitude.html.

| Month (Jan → 1) | TX Sunlight | MN Sunlight |
|-----------------|-------------|-------------|
| 1 | 10.4 | 9.1 |
| 2 | 11.2 | 10.4 |
| 3 | 12.0 | 11.8 |
| 4 | 12.9 | 13.5 |
| 5 | 14.4 | 16.2 |
| 6 | 14.1 | 15.7 |
| 7 | 13.9 | 15.2 |
| 8 | 13.3 | 14.2 |
| 9 | 12.4 | 12.6 |
| 10 | 11.5 | 11.0 |
| 11 | 10.7 | 9.6 |
| 12 | 10.2 | 8.7 |

**25. Biorhythm theory:** $P(d) = 50 \sin(Bd) + 50$ Advocates of biorhythm theory believe that human beings are influenced by certain biological cycles that begin at birth, have different periods, and continue throughout life. The classical cycles and their periods are physical potential (23 days), emotional potential (28 days), and intellectual potential (33 days). On any given day of life, the percent of potential in these three areas is purported to be modeled by the function shown, where $P(d)$ is the percent of available potential on day $d$ of life. Find the value of $B$ for each of the physical, emotional, and intellectual potentials and use it to see what the theory has to say about your potential today. Use day $d = 365.25(\text{age}) + \text{days}$ since last birthday.

**26. Verifying the amplitude formula:** For the equations from Examples 1 and 2, use the minimum value $(x, m)$ to show that $\dfrac{y - D}{A} \rightarrow \dfrac{m - D}{A}$ is equal to $-1$. Then verify this relationship in general by substituting $\dfrac{M - m}{2}$ for $A$, $\dfrac{M + m}{2}$ for $D$.

# Trigonometric Identities

# 5

# Trigonometric Identities

## CHAPTER CONNECTIONS

Have you ever noticed that people who arrive early at a movie tend to choose seats about halfway up the theater's incline and in the middle of a row? More than likely, this is due to a phenomenon called the *optimal viewing angle,* or the angle formed by the viewer's eyes and the top and bottom of the screen. Seats located in this area maximize the viewing angle, with the measure of the angle depending on factors such as the distance from the floor to the bottom of the screen, the height of the screen, the location of a seat, and the incline of the auditorium. Here, trigonometric functions and identities play an important role.

▶ This application appears as Exercise 65 of Section 5.1.

## 5.1 | More on Verifying Identities

### Learning Objectives

*In Section 5.1 you will learn how to:*

☐ **A.** Identify and use identities due to symmetry

☐ **B.** Verify general identities

☐ **C.** Use counterexamples and contradictions to show an equation is not an identity

---

**WORTHY OF NOTE**

The identities due to symmetry are sometimes referred to as the even/odd properties. These properties can help express the cofunction identities in shifted form. For example,

$$\sin t = \cos\left(\frac{\pi}{2} - t\right)$$
$$= \cos\left[-\left(t - \frac{\pi}{2}\right)\right]$$
$$= \cos\left(t - \frac{\pi}{2}\right).$$

---

In Section 1.4, our primary goal was to illustrate how basic algebra skills can be used to rewrite trigonometric expressions and verify simple identities. In this section, we'll sharpen and refine these skills so they can be applied more generally, as we develop the ability to verify a much wider range of identities.

### A. Identities Due to Symmetry

The symmetry of the unit circle and the wrapping function presented in Chapter 3's *Strengthening Core Skills* feature, lead us directly to the final group of fundamental identities. Given $t > 0$, consider the points on the unit circle associated with $t$ and $-t$, as shown in Figure 5.1. From our definitions of the trig functions, $\sin t = y$ and $\sin(-t) = -y$, and we recognize sine is an odd function: $\sin(-t) = -\sin t$. The remaining identities due to symmetry can similarly be developed, and are shown here with the complete family of fundamental identities.

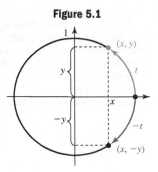

**Figure 5.1**

**Fundamental Trigonometric Identities**

| Reciprocal identities | Ratio identities | Pythagorean identities | Identities due to symmetry |
|---|---|---|---|
| $\sin t = \dfrac{1}{\csc t}$ | $\tan t = \dfrac{\sin t}{\cos t}$ | $\sin^2 t + \cos^2 t = 1$ | $\sin(-t) = -\sin t$ |
| $\cos t = \dfrac{1}{\sec t}$ | $\tan t = \dfrac{\sec t}{\csc t}$ | $\tan^2 t + 1 = \sec^2 t$ | $\cos(-t) = \cos t$ |
| $\tan t = \dfrac{1}{\cot t}$ | $\cot t = \dfrac{\cos t}{\sin t}$ | $1 + \cot^2 t = \csc^2 t$ | $\tan(-t) = -\tan t$ |

---

**EXAMPLE 1** ▶ **Using an Identity Due to Symmetry to Verify an Identity**

Verify the identity: $(1 - \tan t)^2 = \sec^2 t + 2\tan(-t)$

**Solution** ▶ Begin by squaring the left-hand side, in hopes of using a Pythagorean identity.

$$(1 - \tan t)^2 = 1 - 2\tan t + \tan^2 t \quad \text{binomial square}$$
$$= 1 + \tan^2 t - 2\tan t \quad \text{rewrite terms}$$
$$= \sec^2 t - 2\tan t \quad \text{substitute } \sec^2 t \text{ for } 1 + \tan^2 t$$

At this point, we appear to be off by two signs, but quickly recall that tangent is an odd function and $-\tan t = \tan(-t)$. By writing $\sec^2 t - 2\tan t$ as $\sec^2 t + 2(-\tan t)$, we can complete the verification.

$$= \sec^2 t + 2(-\tan t) \quad \text{rewrite expression to obtain } -\tan t$$
$$= \sec^2 t + 2\tan(-t) \quad \text{substitute } \tan(-t) \text{ for } -\tan t$$

☑ **A.** You've just learned how to identify and use identities due to symmetry

**Now try Exercises 7 through 12** ▶

### B. Verifying Identities

We're now ready to put these ideas, and the ideas from Section 1.4, to work for us. When verifying identities we attempt to mold, change, or rewrite one side of the equality until we obtain a match with the other side. What follows is a collection of the ideas and methods we've observed so far, which we'll call the *Guidelines for Verifying Identities*. But remember, there really is no *right* place to start. Think things over for a moment, then attempt a substitution, simplification, or operation and see where it leads. If you hit a dead end, that's okay! Just back up and try something else.

**Guidelines for Verifying Identities**

1. As a general rule, work on only one side of the identity.
   - We cannot assume the equation is true, so properties of equality cannot be applied.
   - We verify the identity by changing the form of one side until we get a match with the other.
2. Work with the more complex side, as it is easier to reduce/simplify than to "build."
3. If an expression contains more than one term, it is often helpful to combine terms using $\dfrac{A}{B} \pm \dfrac{C}{D} = \dfrac{AD \pm BC}{BD}$.
4. Converting all functions to sines and cosines can be helpful.
5. Apply other algebra skills as appropriate: distribute, factor, multiply by a conjugate, and so on.
6. *Know the fundamental identities inside out, upside down, and backward—they are the key!*

Note how these ideas are employed in Examples 2 through 4, particularly the frequent use of fundamental identities.

**EXAMPLE 2** ▶ **Verifying an Identity**

Verify the identity: $\sin^2\theta \tan^2\theta = \tan^2\theta - \sin^2\theta$.

**Solution** ▶ As a general rule, the side with the greater number of terms or the side with rational terms is considered "more complex," so we begin with the right-hand side.

$$\tan^2\theta - \sin^2\theta = \frac{\sin^2\theta}{\cos^2\theta} - \sin^2\theta \qquad \text{substitute } \tfrac{\sin^2\theta}{\cos^2\theta} \text{ for } \tan^2\theta$$

$$= \frac{\sin^2\theta}{1} \cdot \frac{1}{\cos^2\theta} - \sin^2\theta \qquad \text{decompose rational term}$$

$$= \sin^2\theta \sec^2\theta - \sin^2\theta \qquad \text{substitute } \sec^2\theta \text{ for } \tfrac{1}{\cos^2\theta}$$

$$= \sin^2\theta (\sec^2\theta - 1) \qquad \text{factor out } \sin^2\theta$$

$$= \mathbf{\sin^2\theta \tan^2\theta} \qquad \text{substitute } \tan^2\theta \text{ for } \sec^2\theta - 1$$

**Now try Exercises 13 through 18** ▶

Example 2 involved *factoring* out a common expression. Just as often, we'll need to *multiply* numerators and denominators by a common expression, as in Example 3.

**EXAMPLE 3** ▶ **Verifying an Identity by Multiplying Conjugates**

Verify the identity: $\dfrac{\cos t}{1 + \sec t} = \dfrac{1 - \cos t}{\tan^2 t}$.

**Solution** ▶ Both sides of the identity have a single term and one is really no more complex than the other. As a matter of choice we begin with the left side. Noting the denominator on the left has the term sec $t$, with a corresponding term of $\tan^2 t$ to the right, we reason that multiplication by a conjugate might be productive.

$$\frac{\cos t}{1 + \sec t} = \left(\frac{\cos t}{1 + \sec t}\right)\left(\frac{1 - \sec t}{1 - \sec t}\right)$$    multiply above and below by the conjugate

$$= \frac{\cos t - 1}{1 - \sec^2 t}$$    distribute: $\cos t \sec t = 1$, $(A + B)(A - B) = A^2 - B^2$

$$= \frac{\cos t - 1}{-\tan^2 t}$$    substitute $-\tan^2 t$ for $1 - \sec^2 t$
$(1 + \tan^2 t = \sec^2 t \Rightarrow 1 - \sec^2 t = -\tan^2 t)$

$$= \frac{1 - \cos t}{\tan^2 t}$$    multiply above and below by $-1$

**Now try Exercises 19 through 22** ▶

Example 3 highlights the need to be very familiar with families of identities. To replace $1 - \sec^2 t$, we had to use $-\tan^2 t$, not simply $\tan^2 t$, since the related Pythagorean identity is $1 + \tan^2 t = \sec^2 t$.

As noted in the *Guidelines,* combining rational terms is often helpful. At this point, students are encouraged to work with the pattern $\dfrac{A}{B} \pm \dfrac{C}{D} = \dfrac{AD \pm BC}{BD}$ as a means of combing rational terms quickly and efficiently.

**EXAMPLE 4** ▶ **Verifying an Identity by Combining Terms**

Verify the identity: $\dfrac{\sec x}{\sin x} - \dfrac{\sin x}{\sec x} = \dfrac{\tan^2 x + \cos^2 x}{\tan x}$.

**Solution** ▶ We begin with the left-hand side.

$$\frac{\sec x}{\sin x} - \frac{\sin x}{\sec x} = \frac{\sec^2 x - \sin^2 x}{\sin x \sec x}$$    combine terms: $\dfrac{A}{B} - \dfrac{C}{D} = \dfrac{AD - BC}{BD}$

$$= \frac{(1 + \tan^2 x) - (1 - \cos^2 x)}{\left(\dfrac{\sin x}{1}\right)\left(\dfrac{1}{\cos x}\right)}$$    substitute $1 + \tan^2 x$ for $\sec^2 x$, $1 - \cos^2 x$ for $\sin^2 x$, $\dfrac{1}{\cos x}$ for sec $x$

☑ **B. You've just learned how to verify general identities**

$$= \frac{\tan^2 x + \cos^2 x}{\tan x}$$    simplify numerator, substitute tan $x$ for $\dfrac{\sin x}{\cos x}$

**Now try Exercises 23 through 28** ▶

Identities come in an infinite variety and it would be impossible to illustrate all variations. Using the general ideas and skills presented should prepare you to verify any of those given in the exercise set, as well as those you encounter in your future studies. See **Exercises 29 through 58.**

## C. Showing an Equation Is Not an Identity

To show an equation is *not* an identity, we need only find a single value for which the functions involved are defined but the equation is *false*. This can often be done by trial and error, or even by inspection. To illustrate the process, we'll use two common misconceptions that arise in working with identities.

**EXAMPLE 5** ▶ **Showing an Equation Is Not an Identity**

Show the equations given are *not* identities.

**a.** $\sin(2x) = 2 \sin x$      **b.** $\cos(\alpha + \beta) = \cos \alpha + \cos \beta$

Solution ▶ **a.** The assumption here seems to be that we can factor out the coefficient from the argument. By inspection we note the amplitude of $\sin(2x)$ is $A = 1$, while the amplitude of $2 \sin x$ is $A = 2$. This means they cannot possibly be equal for all values of $x$, although they are equal for integer multiples of $\pi$. Verify they are not equivalent using $x = \dfrac{\pi}{6}$ or other standard values.

**GRAPHICAL SUPPORT**

While not a definitive method of proof, a graphing calculator can be used to investigate whether an equation is an identity. Since the left and right members of the equation must be equal for all values (where they are defined), their graphs must be identical. Graphing the left and right sides of the equation from Example 5(a) as $Y_1$ and $Y_2$ shows the equation $sin(2x) = 2 sin x$ is definitely *not* an identity.

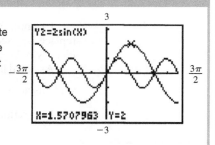

**b.** The assumption here is that we can distribute function values. This is similar to saying $\sqrt{x + 4} = \sqrt{x} + 2$, a statement obviously false for all values except $x = 0$. Here we'll substitute convenient values to prove the equation false, namely, $\alpha = \dfrac{3\pi}{4}$ and $\beta = \dfrac{\pi}{4}$.

$$\cos\left(\frac{3\pi}{4} + \frac{\pi}{4}\right) = \cos\left(\frac{3\pi}{4}\right) + \cos\left(\frac{\pi}{4}\right) \qquad \text{substitute } \tfrac{3\pi}{4} \text{ for } \alpha \text{ and } \tfrac{\pi}{4} \text{ for } \beta$$

$$\cos \pi = -\frac{\sqrt{2}}{2} + \frac{\sqrt{2}}{2} \qquad \text{simplify}$$

$$-1 \neq 0 \qquad \text{result is false}$$

☑ **C.** You've just learned how to use counterexamples and contradictions to show an equation is not an identity

**Now try Exercises 59 through 64** ▶

**TECHNOLOGY HIGHLIGHT**

**Identities and Graphical Tests**

Unless you are told to verify a known identity, how would you know ahead of time that it was possible? What if there was a misprint on a test, quiz, or homework assignment and what you were trying to prove wasn't possible? In cases like these, a *graphical test* can be used. While not fool-proof, seeing if the graphs appear identical can either *suggest* the identity is true, or definitely show it is not. When testing identities, it helps to [ENTER] the left-hand side of the equation as $Y_1$ on the [Y=] screen, and the right-hand side as $Y_2$. We can then test whether an identity relationship might exist by activating the two relations in question, graphing both relations, and noting whether two graphs or a single graph appears on the [GRAPH] screen. After entering the six functions shown in Figure 5.2, leave $Y_1$ and $Y_2$ active, then deactivate $Y_3$ through $Y_6$ by

**Figure 5.2**

```
Plot1  Plot2  Plot3
\Y1■1-cos(X)²
\Y2■sin(X)²
\Y3=cos(X)tan(X)
\Y4=sin(X)
\Y5=sin(2X)
\Y6=2sin(X)
```

*—continued*

overlaying the equal sign with the cursor and pressing ENTER . In this way, we'll test each pair to see if their graphs appear identical. Of course, the calculator's TABLE feature could also be used. Using the calculator's ZOOM **7:ZTrig** feature, we obtain the graph shown in Figure 5.3, which indicates that an identity relationship likely exists between $Y_1$ and $Y_2$. After deactivating $Y_1$ and $Y_2$ we activate $Y_3$ and $Y_4$ and again note the likelihood of an identity relationship, since only one graph can be seen. However, when testing $Y_5$ and $Y_6$, we note the existence of two distinct graphs (see Figure 5.4), and conclude as in Example 5(a) that $\sin(2x) \neq 2 \sin x$—even though $\sin(2x) = 2 \sin x$ for integer multiples of $\pi$ (the points of intersection). Use this technique to help determine which of the following equations are not identities.

**Figure 5.3**

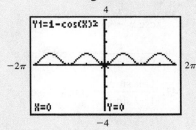

**Figure 5.4**

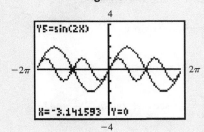

**Exercise 1:**  $\dfrac{1 - \sin^2\theta}{\cos \theta} = \cos \theta$      **Exercise 2:**  $\cos(2x) = 1 - 2\sin^2 x$

**Exercise 3:**  $\dfrac{\cos x}{1 + \sin x} = \dfrac{1 - \sin x}{\cos x}$      **Exercise 4:**  $\dfrac{\cos x}{1 - \sin x} = \sec x - \tan x$

# 5.1 EXERCISES

► **CONCEPTS AND VOCABULARY**

**Fill in each blank with the appropriate word or phrase. Carefully reread the section if needed.**

1. The identities $-\sin x \tan x = \sin(-x) \tan x$ and $\cos(-x) \cot x = \cos x \cot x$ are examples of _____ due to _____.

2. To show an equation is *not an identity,* we must find at least _____ input value where both sides of the equation are defined, but results in a _____ equation.

3. To verify an identity, always begin with the more _____ expression, since it is easier to _____ than to _____.

4. Converting all terms to functions of _____ and _____ may help verify an identity.

5. Discuss/Explain why you must not add, subtract, multiply, or divide both sides of the equation when verifying identities.

6. Discuss/Explain the difference between operating on both sides of an equation (see Exercise 5) and working on each side independently.

► **DEVELOPING YOUR SKILLS**

**Verify that the following equations are identities.**

7. $(1 + \sin x)[1 + \sin(-x)] = \cos^2 x$

8. $(\sec x + 1)[\sec(-x) - 1] = \tan^2 x$

9. $\sin^2(-x) + \cos^2 x = 1$

10. $1 + \cot^2(-x) = \csc^2 x$

11. $\dfrac{1 - \sin(-x)}{\cos x + \cos(-x)\sin x} = \sec x$

12. $\dfrac{1 + \cos(-x)}{\sin x - \cos x \sin(-x)} = \csc x$

13. $\cos^2 x \tan^2 x = 1 - \cos^2 x$

14. $\sin^2 x \cot^2 x = 1 - \sin^2 x$

15. $\tan x + \cot x = \sec x \csc x$

16. $\cot x \cos x = \csc x - \sin x$

17. $\dfrac{\cos x}{\tan x} = \csc x - \sin x$

18. $\dfrac{\sin x}{\cot x} = \sec x - \cos x$

19. $\dfrac{\cos \theta}{1 - \sin \theta} = \sec \theta + \tan \theta$

20. $\dfrac{\sin \theta}{1 - \cos \theta} = \csc \theta + \cot \theta$

21. $\dfrac{1 - \sin x}{\cos x} = \dfrac{\cos x}{1 + \sin x}$

22. $\dfrac{1 - \cos x}{\sin x} = \dfrac{\sin x}{1 + \cos x}$

23. $\dfrac{\csc x}{\cos x} - \dfrac{\cos x}{\csc x} = \dfrac{\cot^2 x + \sin^2 x}{\cot x}$

24. $\dfrac{1}{\cos^2 x} + \dfrac{1}{\sin^2 x} = \csc^2 x \sec^2 x$

25. $\dfrac{\sin x}{1 + \sin x} - \dfrac{\sin x}{1 - \sin x} = -2\tan^2 x$

26. $\dfrac{\cos x}{1 + \cos x} - \dfrac{\cos x}{1 - \cos x} = -2\cot^2 x$

27. $\dfrac{\cot x}{1 + \csc x} - \dfrac{\cot x}{1 - \csc x} = 2\sec x$

28. $\dfrac{\tan x}{1 + \sec x} - \dfrac{\tan x}{1 - \sec x} = 2\csc x$

29. $\dfrac{\sec^2 x}{1 + \cot^2 x} = \tan^2 x$

30. $\dfrac{\csc^2 x}{1 + \tan^2 x} = \cot^2 x$

31. $\sin^2 x \,(\cot^2 x - \csc^2 x) = -\sin^2 x$

32. $\cos^2 x \,(\tan^2 x - \sec^2 x) = -\cos^2 x$

33. $\cos x \cot x + \sin x = \csc x$

34. $\sin x \tan x + \cos x = \sec x$

35. $\dfrac{\sec x}{\cot x + \tan x} = \sin x$

36. $\dfrac{\csc x}{\cot x + \tan x} = \cos x$

37. $\dfrac{\sin x - \csc x}{\csc x} = -\cos^2 x$

38. $\dfrac{\cos x - \sec x}{\sec x} = -\sin^2 x$

39. $\dfrac{1}{\csc x - \sin x} = \tan x \sec x$

40. $\dfrac{1}{\sec x - \cos x} = \cot x \csc x$

41. $\dfrac{1 + \sin x}{1 - \sin x} = (\tan x + \sec x)^2$

42. $\dfrac{1 - \cos x}{1 + \cos x} = (\csc x - \cot x)^2$

43. $\dfrac{\cos x - \sin x}{1 - \tan x} = \dfrac{\cos x + \sin x}{1 + \tan x}$

44. $\dfrac{1 - \cot x}{1 + \cot x} = \dfrac{\sin x - \cos x}{\sin x + \cos x}$

45. $\dfrac{\tan^2 x - \cot^2 x}{\tan x - \cot x} = \csc x \sec x$

46. $\dfrac{\cot x - \tan x}{\cot^2 x - \tan^2 x} = \sin x \cos x$

47. $\dfrac{\cot x}{\cot x + \tan x} = 1 - \sin^2 x$

48. $\dfrac{\tan x}{\cot x + \tan x} = 1 - \cos^2 x$

49. $\dfrac{\sec^4 x - \tan^4 x}{\sec^2 x + \tan^2 x} = 1$

50. $\dfrac{\csc^4 x - \cot^4 x}{\csc^2 x + \cot^2 x} = 1$

51. $\dfrac{\cos^4 x - \sin^4 x}{\cos^2 x} = 2 - \sec^2 x$

52. $\dfrac{\sin^4 x - \cos^4 x}{\sin^2 x} = 2 - \csc^2 x$

53. $(\sec x + \tan x)^2 = \dfrac{(\sin x + 1)^2}{\cos^2 x}$

54. $(\csc x + \cot x)^2 = \dfrac{(\cos x + 1)^2}{\sin^2 x}$

**55.** $\dfrac{\cos x}{\sin x} + \dfrac{\sin x}{\cos x} + \dfrac{\csc x}{\sec x} = \dfrac{\sec x + \cos x}{\sin x}$

**56.** $\dfrac{\cos x}{\sin x} + \dfrac{\sin x}{\cos x} + \dfrac{\sec x}{\csc x} = \dfrac{\csc x + \sin x}{\cos x}$

**57.** $\dfrac{\sin^4 x - \cos^4 x}{\sin^3 x + \cos^3 x} = \dfrac{\sin x - \cos x}{1 - \sin x \cos x}$

**58.** $\dfrac{\sin^4 x - \cos^4 x}{\sin^3 x - \cos^3 x} = \dfrac{\sin x + \cos x}{1 + \sin x \cos x}$

**Show that the following equations *are not identities.***

**59.** $\sin\left(\theta + \dfrac{\pi}{3}\right) = \sin\theta + \sin\left(\dfrac{\pi}{3}\right)$

**60.** $\cos\left(\dfrac{\pi}{4}\right) + \cos\theta = \cos\left(\dfrac{\pi}{4} + \theta\right)$

**61.** $\cos(2\theta) = 2\cos\theta$

**62.** $\tan(2\theta) = 2\tan\theta$

**63.** $\tan\left(\dfrac{\theta}{4}\right) = \dfrac{\tan\theta}{\tan 4}$

**64.** $\cos^2\theta - \sin^2\theta = -1$

## ▶ WORKING WITH FORMULAS

**65. Distance to top of movie screen:**
$$d^2 = (20 + x\cos\theta)^2 + (20 - x\sin\theta)^2$$

At a theater, the optimum viewing angle depends on a number of factors, like the height of the screen, the incline of the auditorium, the location of a seat, the height of your eyes while seated, and so on. One of the measures needed to find the "best" seat is the distance from your eyes to the top of the screen. For a theater with the dimensions shown, this distance is given by the formula here ($x$ is the diagonal distance from the horizontal floor to your seat).
(a) Show the formula is equivalent to $800 + 40x(\cos\theta - \sin\theta) + x^2$.
(b) Find the distance $d$ if $\theta = 18°$ and you are sitting in the eighth row with the rows spaced 3 ft apart.

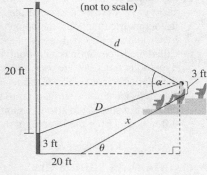
(not to scale)

**66. The area of triangle** $ABC$: $A = \dfrac{c^2 \sin A \sin B}{2 \sin C}$

If one side and three angles of a triangle are known, its area can be computed using this formula, where side $c$ is opposite angle $C$. Find the area of the triangle shown in the diagram.

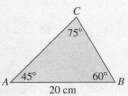

## ▶ APPLICATIONS

**67. Pythagorean theorem:** For the triangle shown,
(a) find an expression for the length of the hypotenuse in terms of $\tan x$ and $\cot x$, then determine the length of the hypotenuse when $x = 1.5$ rad; (b) show the expression you found in part (a) is equivalent to $h = \sqrt{\csc x \sec x}$ and recompute the length of the hypotenuse using this expression. Did the answers match?

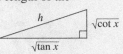

**68. Pythagorean theorem:** For the triangle shown,
(a) find an expression for the area of the triangle in terms of $\cot x$ and $\cos x$, then determine its area given $x = \dfrac{\pi}{6}$; (b) show the expression you found in part (a) is equivalent to $A = \dfrac{1}{2}(\csc x - \sin x)$ and recompute the area using this expression. Did the answers match?

**Exercise 68**

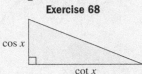

**69. Viewing distance:** Referring to Exercise 65, find a formula for $D$—the distance from this patron's eyes to the *bottom* of the movie screen. Simplify the result using a Pythagorean identity, then find the value of $D$.

**70. Viewing angle:** Referring to Exercises 65 and 69, once $d$ and $D$ are known, the viewing angle $\alpha$ (the angle subtended by the movie screen and the viewer's eyes) can be found using the formula $\cos \alpha = \dfrac{d^2 + D^2 - 20^2}{2dD}$. Find the value of $\cos \alpha$ for this particular theater, person, and seat.

**71. Intensity of light:** In a study of the luminous intensity of light, the expression

$$\sin \alpha = \frac{I_1 \cos \theta}{\sqrt{(I_1 \cos \theta)^2 + (I_2 \sin \theta)^2}} \text{ can occur.}$$

Simplify the equation for the moment $I_1 = I_2$.

**72. Intensity of light:** Referring to Exercise 71, find the angle $\theta$ given $I_1 = I_2$ and $\alpha = 60°$.

▶ **EXTENDING THE CONCEPT**

**73.** Just as the points $P(x, y)$ on the unit circle $x^2 + y^2 = 1$ are used to name the circular trigonometric functions, the points $P(x, y)$ on the unit hyperbola $x^2 - y^2 = 1$ are used to name what are called the **hyperbolic trigonometric functions.** The hyperbolic functions are used extensively in many of the applied sciences. The identities for these functions have many similarities to those for the circular functions, but also have some significant differences. Using the Internet or the resources of a

library, do some research on the functions sinh $t$, cosh $t$, and tanh $t$, where $t$ is any real number. In particular, see how the Pythagorean identities compare/contrast between the two forms of trigonometry.

**74.** Verify the identity $\dfrac{\sin^6 x - \cos^6 x}{\sin^4 x - \cos^4 x} = 1 - \sin^2 x \cos^2 x$.

**75.** Use factoring to show the equation is an identity: $\sin^4 x + 2 \sin^2 x \cos^2 x + \cos^4 x = 1$.

▶ **MAINTAINING YOUR SKILLS**

**76.** (3.3) Verify the point $\left( -\dfrac{3}{4}, \dfrac{\sqrt{7}}{4} \right)$ is on the unit circle and use it to give the value of the six trig functions of $\theta$.

**77.** (2.3) Standing 265 ft from the base of the Strastosphere Tower in Las Vegas, Nevada, the angle of elevation to the top of the tower is about 77°. Approximate the height of the tower to the nearest foot.

**78.** (4.2) The equation of the function graphed in the figure is of the form $y = \cot(Bx)$. What is the value of $B$?

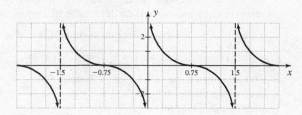

**79.** (1.3) Find $f(\theta)$ for all six trig functions, given $P(-16, -63)$ is on the terminal side of $\theta$.

**80.** (3.2) The Earth has a radius of 3960 mi. Charlotte, North Carolina, is located at 35°N latitude, 80.5°W longitude. Amarillo, Texas, is located at 35°N latitude, 101.5°W longitude. How many miles separate the two cities?

**81.** (4.1) Use a reference rectangle and the *rule of fourths* to sketch the graph of $y = 2 \sin(2t)$ for $t \in [0, 2\pi)$.

## Learning Objectives

*In Section 5.2 you will learn how to:*

☐ **A.** Develop and use sum and difference identities for cosine

☐ **B.** Use the cofunction identities to develop the sum and difference identities for sine and tangent

☐ **C.** Use the sum and difference identities to verify other identities

The sum and difference formulas for sine and cosine have a long and ancient history. Originally developed to help study the motion of celestial bodies, they were used centuries later to develop more complex concepts, such as the derivatives of the trig functions, complex number theory, and the study of wave motion in different mediums. These identities are also used to find exact results (in radical form) for many nonstandard angles, a result of great importance to the ancient astronomers and still of notable mathematical significance today.

### A. The Sum and Difference Identities for Cosine

On a unit circle with center $C$, consider the point $A$ on the terminal side of angle $\alpha$, and point $B$ on the terminal side of angle $\beta$, as shown in Figure 5.5. Since $r = 1$, the coordinates of $A$ and $B$ are $(\cos \alpha, \sin \alpha)$ and $(\cos \beta, \sin \beta)$, respectively. Using the distance formula, we find that $\overline{AB}$ is equal to

$$
\begin{aligned}
\overline{AB} &= \sqrt{(\cos \alpha - \cos \beta)^2 + (\sin \alpha - \sin \beta)^2} && \text{binomial} \\
&= \sqrt{\cos^2\alpha - 2\cos\alpha\cos\beta + \cos^2\beta + \sin^2\alpha - 2\sin\alpha\sin\beta + \sin^2\beta} && \text{squares} \\
&= \sqrt{(\cos^2\alpha + \sin^2\alpha) + (\cos^2\beta + \sin^2\beta) - 2\cos\alpha\cos\beta - 2\sin\alpha\sin\beta} && \text{regroup} \\
&= \sqrt{2 - 2\cos\alpha\cos\beta - 2\sin\alpha\sin\beta} && \cos^2 u + \sin^2 u = 1
\end{aligned}
$$

**Figure 5.5**

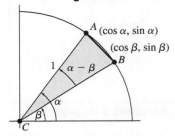

With no loss of generality, we can rotate sector $ACB$ clockwise, until side $\overline{CB}$ coincides with the $x$-axis. This creates new coordinates of $(1, 0)$ for $B$, and new coordinates of $(\cos(\alpha - \beta), \sin(\alpha - \beta))$ for $A$, *but the distance $\overline{AB}$ remains unchanged!* (see Figure 5.6). Recomputing the distance gives

$$
\begin{aligned}
\overline{AB} &= \sqrt{[\cos(\alpha - \beta) - 1]^2 + [\sin(\alpha - \beta) - 0]^2} \\
&= \sqrt{\cos^2(\alpha - \beta) - 2\cos(\alpha - \beta) + 1 + \sin^2(\alpha - \beta)} \\
&= \sqrt{[\cos^2(\alpha - \beta) + \sin^2(\alpha - \beta)] - 2\cos(\alpha - \beta) + 1} \\
&= \sqrt{2 - 2\cos(\alpha - \beta)}
\end{aligned}
$$

**Figure 5.6**

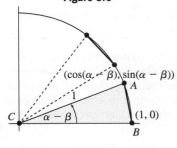

Since both expressions represent the same distance, we can set them equal to each other and solve for $\cos(\alpha - \beta)$.

$$
\begin{aligned}
\sqrt{2 - 2\cos(\alpha - \beta)} &= \sqrt{2 - 2\cos\alpha\cos\beta - 2\sin\alpha\sin\beta} && \overline{AB} = \overline{AB} \\
2 - 2\cos(\alpha - \beta) &= 2 - 2\cos\alpha\cos\beta - 2\sin\alpha\sin\beta && \text{property of radicals} \\
-2\cos(\alpha - \beta) &= -2\cos\alpha\cos\beta - 2\sin\alpha\sin\beta && \text{subtract 2} \\
\cos(\alpha - \beta) &= \cos\alpha\cos\beta + \sin\alpha\sin\beta && \text{divide both sides by } -2
\end{aligned}
$$

The result is called the **difference identity for cosine.** The **sum identity for cosine** follows immediately, by substituting $-\beta$ for $\beta$.

$$
\begin{aligned}
\cos(\alpha - \beta) &= \cos\alpha\cos\beta + \sin\alpha\sin\beta && \text{difference identity} \\
\cos(\alpha - [-\beta]) &= \cos\alpha\cos(-\beta) + \sin\alpha\sin(-\beta) && \text{substitute } -\beta \text{ for } \beta \\
\cos(\alpha + \beta) &= \cos\alpha\cos\beta - \sin\alpha\sin\beta && \cos(-\beta) = \cos\beta; \sin(-\beta) = -\sin\beta
\end{aligned}
$$

The sum and difference identities can be used to find exact values for the trig functions of certain angles (values written in nondecimal form using radicals), simplify expressions, and to establish additional identities.

**EXAMPLE 1** ▶ **Finding Exact Values for Non-Standard Angles**

Use the sum and difference identities for cosine to find exact values for

**a.** $\cos 15° = \cos(45° - 30°)$　　　　　**b.** $\cos 75° = \cos(45° + 30°)$

Check results on a calculator.

Solution ▶ Each involves a direct application of the related identity, and uses special values.

**a.**　　$\cos(\alpha - \beta) = \cos \alpha \cos \beta + \sin \alpha \sin \beta$　　difference identity

$\cos(45° - 30°) = \cos 45° \cos 30° + \sin 45° \sin 30°$　　$\alpha = 45°, \beta = 30°$

$$= \left(\frac{\sqrt{2}}{2}\right)\left(\frac{\sqrt{3}}{2}\right) + \left(\frac{\sqrt{2}}{2}\right)\left(\frac{1}{2}\right)$$　　standard values

$$\cos 15° = \frac{\sqrt{6} + \sqrt{2}}{4}$$　　combine terms

To 10 decimal places, $\cos 15° = 0.9659258263$.

**b.**　　$\cos(\alpha + \beta) = \cos \alpha \cos \beta - \sin \alpha \sin \beta$　　sum identity

$\cos(45° + 30°) = \cos 45° \cos 30° - \sin 45° \sin 30°$　　$\alpha = 45°, \beta = 30°$

$$= \left(\frac{\sqrt{2}}{2}\right)\left(\frac{\sqrt{3}}{2}\right) - \left(\frac{\sqrt{2}}{2}\right)\left(\frac{1}{2}\right)$$　　standard values

$$\cos 75° = \frac{\sqrt{6} - \sqrt{2}}{4}$$　　combine terms

To 10 decimal places, $\cos 75° = 0.2588190451$.

**Now try Exercises 7 through 12** ▶

⚠ **CAUTION** ▶ Be sure you clearly understand how these identities work. In particular, note that $\cos(60° + 30°) \neq \cos 60° + \cos 30° \left(0 \neq \frac{1}{2} + \frac{\sqrt{3}}{2}\right)$ and in general $f(a+b) \neq f(a) + f(b)$.

These identities are listed here using the "$\pm$" and "$\mp$" notation to avoid needless repetition. In their application, use both upper symbols or both lower symbols depending on whether you're evaluating the cosine of a sum (upper symbols) or difference (lower symbols). As with the other identities, these can be rewritten to form other members of the identity family, as when they are used to consolidate a larger expression. This is shown in Example 2.

**The Sum and Difference Identities for Cosine**

**cosine family:** $\cos(\alpha \pm \beta) = \cos \alpha \cos \beta \mp \sin \alpha \sin \beta$　　functions repeat, signs alternate

$\cos \alpha \cos \beta \mp \sin \alpha \sin \beta = \cos(\alpha \pm \beta)$　　can be used to *expand* or *contract*

**EXAMPLE 2** ▶ **Using a Sum/Difference Identity to Simplify an Expression**

Write as a single expression in cosine and evaluate: $\cos 57° \cos 78° - \sin 57° \sin 78°$

Solution ▶ Since the functions repeat and are expressed as a difference, we use the sum identity for cosine to rewrite the difference as a single expression.

$\cos \alpha \cos \beta - \sin \alpha \sin \beta = \cos(\alpha + \beta)$　　sum identity for cosine

$\cos 57° \cos 78° - \sin 57° \sin 78° = \cos(57° + 78°)$　　$\alpha = 57°, \beta = 78°$

The expression is equal to $\cos 135° = -\dfrac{\sqrt{2}}{2}$.

**Now try Exercises 13 through 16** ▶

The sum and difference identities can be used to evaluate the cosine of the sum of two angles, even when they are not adjacent, or even expressed in terms of cosine.

**EXAMPLE 3** ▶ **Computing the Cosine of a Sum**

Given $\sin\alpha = \frac{5}{13}$ with the terminal side in QI, and $\tan\beta = -\frac{24}{7}$ with the terminal side in QII. Compute the value of $\cos(\alpha + \beta)$.

**Solution** ▶ To use the sum formula we need the value of $\cos\alpha$, $\sin\alpha$, $\cos\beta$, and $\sin\beta$. Using the given information about the quadrants along with the Pythagorean theorem, we draw the triangles shown in Figures 5.7 and 5.8, yielding the values that follow.

**Figure 5.7**

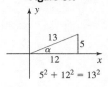

y
13
5
α
12
x
$5^2 + 12^2 = 13^2$

**Figure 5.8**

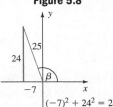

y
25
24
β
−7
x
$(-7)^2 + 24^2 = 25^2$

$$\cos\alpha = \frac{12}{13}\text{ (QI)}, \sin\alpha = \frac{5}{13}\text{ (QI)}, \cos\beta = -\frac{7}{25}\text{ (QII)}, \text{ and } \sin\beta = \frac{24}{25}\text{ (QII)}$$

Using $\cos(\alpha + \beta) = \cos\alpha\cos\beta - \sin\alpha\sin\beta$ gives this result:

$$\begin{aligned}\cos(\alpha + \beta) &= \left(\frac{12}{13}\right)\left(-\frac{7}{25}\right) - \left(\frac{5}{13}\right)\left(\frac{24}{25}\right)\\ &= -\frac{84}{325} - \frac{120}{325}\\ &= -\frac{204}{325}\end{aligned}$$

Now try Exercises 17 and 18 ▶

**A. You've just learned how to develop and use sum and difference identities for cosine**

## B. The Sum and Difference Identities for Sine and Tangent

The cofunction identities were actually introduced in Section 2.1, using the complementary angles in a right triangle. In this section we'll *verify* that $\cos\left(\frac{\pi}{2} - \theta\right) = \sin\theta$ and $\sin\left(\frac{\pi}{2} - \theta\right) = \cos\theta$. For the first, we use the difference identity for cosine to obtain

$$\begin{aligned}\cos\left(\frac{\pi}{2} - \theta\right) &= \cos\frac{\pi}{2}\cos\theta + \sin\frac{\pi}{2}\sin\theta\\ &= (0)\cos\theta + (1)\sin\theta\\ &= \sin\theta\end{aligned}$$

**WORTHY OF NOTE**

It is worth pointing out that in Example 3, if we approximate the values of $\alpha$ and $\beta$ using tables or a calculator, we find $\alpha \approx 22.62°$ and $\beta \approx 106.26°$. Sure enough, $\cos(22.62° + 106.26°) \approx -\frac{204}{325}$!

For the second, we use $\cos\left(\frac{\pi}{2} - \theta\right) = \sin\theta$, and replace $\theta$ with the real number $\frac{\pi}{2} - t$. This gives

$$\cos\left(\frac{\pi}{2} - \theta\right) = \sin\theta \quad \text{cofunction identity for cosine}$$

$$\cos\left(\frac{\pi}{2} - \left[\frac{\pi}{2} - t\right]\right) = \sin\left(\frac{\pi}{2} - t\right) \quad \text{replace } \theta \text{ with } \frac{\pi}{2} - t$$

$$\cos t = \sin\left(\frac{\pi}{2} - t\right) \quad \text{result, note } \left[\frac{\pi}{2} - \left(\frac{\pi}{2} - t\right)\right] = t$$

This establishes the cofunction relationship for sine: $\sin\left(\frac{\pi}{2} - t\right) = \cos t$ for any real number $t$. Both identities can be written in terms of the real number $t$. **See Exercises 19 through 24.**

### The Cofunction Identities

$$\cos\left(\frac{\pi}{2} - t\right) = \sin t \qquad \sin\left(\frac{\pi}{2} - t\right) = \cos t$$

The sum and difference identities for sine can easily be developed using cofunction identities. Since $\sin t = \cos\left(\frac{\pi}{2} - t\right)$, we need only rename $t$ as the sum $(\alpha + \beta)$ or the difference $(\alpha - \beta)$ and work from there.

$$\sin t = \cos\left(\frac{\pi}{2} - t\right) \qquad\qquad \text{cofunction identity}$$

$$\sin(\alpha + \beta) = \cos\left[\frac{\pi}{2} - (\alpha + \beta)\right] \qquad\qquad \text{substitute } (\alpha + \beta) \text{ for } t$$

$$= \cos\left[\left(\frac{\pi}{2} - \alpha\right) - \beta\right] \qquad\qquad \text{regroup argument}$$

$$= \cos\left(\frac{\pi}{2} - \alpha\right)\cos\beta + \sin\left(\frac{\pi}{2} - \alpha\right)\sin\beta \qquad \begin{array}{l}\text{apply difference identity}\\\text{for cosine}\end{array}$$

$$\sin(\alpha + \beta) = \sin\alpha\cos\beta + \cos\alpha\sin\beta \qquad\qquad \text{result}$$

The difference identity for sine is likewise developed. The sum and difference identities for tangent can be derived using ratio identities and their derivation is left as an exercise **(see Exercise 78).**

### The Sum and Difference Identities for Sine and Tangent

**sine family:** $\sin(\alpha \pm \beta) = \sin\alpha\cos\beta \pm \cos\alpha\sin\beta$    functions alternate, signs repeat

$\sin\alpha\cos\beta \pm \cos\alpha\sin\beta = \sin(\alpha \pm \beta)$    can be used to *expand* or *contract*

**tangent family:** $\tan(\alpha \pm \beta) = \dfrac{\tan\alpha \pm \tan\beta}{1 \mp \tan\alpha\tan\beta}$    signs match original in numerator, signs alternate in denominator

$\dfrac{\tan\alpha \pm \tan\beta}{1 \mp \tan\alpha\tan\beta} = \tan(\alpha \pm \beta)$    can be used to *expand* or *contract*

**EXAMPLE 4A** ▶ **Simplifying Expressions Using Sum/Difference Identities**

Write as a single expression in sine: $\sin(2t)\cos t + \cos(2t)\sin t$.

**Solution** ▶ Since the functions in each term alternate and the expression is written as a sum, we use the sum identity for sine:

$$\sin\alpha\cos\beta + \cos\alpha\sin\beta = \sin(\alpha + \beta) \qquad \text{sum identity for sine}$$

$$\sin(2t)\cos t + \cos(2t)\sin t = \sin(2t + t) \qquad \text{substitute } 2t \text{ for } \alpha \text{ and } t \text{ for } \beta$$

The expression is equal to $\sin(3t)$.

**EXAMPLE 4B** ▶ **Simplifying Expressions Using Sum/Difference Identities**

Use the sum or difference identity for tangent to find the exact value of $\tan\dfrac{11\pi}{12}$.

**Solution** ▶ Since an exact value is requested, $\dfrac{11\pi}{12}$ must be the sum or difference of two

standard angles. A casual inspection reveals $\dfrac{11\pi}{12} = \dfrac{2\pi}{3} + \dfrac{\pi}{4}$. This gives

$$\tan(\alpha + \beta) = \frac{\tan\alpha + \tan\beta}{1 - \tan\alpha\tan\beta} \qquad \text{sum identity for tangent}$$

$$\tan\left(\frac{2\pi}{3} + \frac{\pi}{4}\right) = \frac{\tan\left(\frac{2\pi}{3}\right) + \tan\left(\frac{\pi}{4}\right)}{1 - \tan\left(\frac{2\pi}{3}\right)\tan\left(\frac{\pi}{4}\right)} \qquad \alpha = \frac{2\pi}{3}, \beta = \frac{\pi}{4}$$

$$= \frac{-\sqrt{3} + 1}{1 - (-\sqrt{3})(1)} \qquad \tan\left(\frac{2\pi}{3}\right) = -\sqrt{3}, \tan\left(\frac{\pi}{4}\right) = 1$$

$$= \frac{1 - \sqrt{3}}{1 + \sqrt{3}} \qquad \text{simplify expression}$$

☑ **B.** You've just learned how to use the cofunction identities to develop the sum and difference identities for sine and tangent

Now try Exercises 25 through 54 ▶

## C. Verifying Other Identities

Once the sum and difference identities are established, we can simply add these to the tools we use to verify other identities.

**EXAMPLE 5** ▶ **Verifying an Identity**

Verify that $\tan\left(\theta - \dfrac{\pi}{4}\right) = \dfrac{\tan\theta - 1}{\tan\theta + 1}$ is an identity.

**Solution** ▶ Using a direct application of the difference formula for tangent we obtain

$$\tan\left(\theta - \frac{\pi}{4}\right) = \frac{\tan\theta - \tan\frac{\pi}{4}}{1 + \tan\theta\tan\frac{\pi}{4}} \qquad \alpha = \theta, \beta = \frac{\pi}{4}$$

$$= \frac{\tan\theta - 1}{1 + \tan\theta} = \frac{\tan\theta - 1}{\tan\theta + 1} \qquad \tan\left(\frac{\pi}{4}\right) = 1$$

Now try Exercises 55 through 60 ▶

**EXAMPLE 6** ▶ **Verifying an Identity**

Verify that $\sin(\alpha + \beta)\sin(\alpha - \beta) = \sin^2\alpha - \sin^2\beta$ is an identity.

**Solution** ▶ Using the sum and difference formulas for sine we obtain

$$\sin(\alpha + \beta)\sin(\alpha - \beta) = (\sin\alpha\cos\beta + \cos\alpha\sin\beta)(\sin\alpha\cos\beta - \cos\alpha\sin\beta)$$

$$= \sin^2\alpha\cos^2\beta - \cos^2\alpha\sin^2\beta \qquad (A+B)(A-B) = A^2 - B^2$$

$$= \sin^2\alpha(1 - \sin^2\beta) - (1 - \sin^2\alpha)\sin^2\beta \qquad \text{use } \cos^2x = 1 - \sin^2x \text{ to write the expression solely in terms of sine}$$

☑ **C.** You've just learned how to use the sum and difference identities to verify other identities

$$= \sin^2\alpha - \sin^2\alpha\sin^2\beta - \sin^2\beta + \sin^2\alpha\sin^2\beta \qquad \text{distribute}$$

$$= \sin^2\alpha - \sin^2\beta \qquad \text{simplify}$$

Now try Exercises 61 through 68 ▶

## TECHNOLOGY HIGHLIGHT

### Relationships Between the Sum/Difference Formulas

In Example 3, we found that for $\sin \alpha = \frac{5}{13}$ in QI and $\tan \beta = -\frac{24}{7}$ in QII, $\cos(\alpha + \beta) = -\frac{204}{325}$. Once this value has been found, the values of $\sin(\alpha + \beta)$ and $\tan(\alpha + \beta)$ can easily be found without having to apply the respective sum identity. Using the Pythagorean identity $1 - \cos^2\theta = \sin^2\theta$ (where $\alpha + \beta = \theta$) we have $\sin^2\theta = 1 - (-\frac{204}{325})^2$ yielding $\sin^2\theta = 0.6060023669$ (see Figure 5.9). To compute $\sqrt{0.6060023669}$, we use $\sqrt{\text{Ans}}$ where "Ans" is the result of the most recent calculation and can be accessed using ⟨2nd⟩ ⟨(−)⟩. Knowing the answer must be rational (discuss why), we convert this value to fraction form using ⟨MATH⟩ ⟨ENTER⟩ (1:▶Frac) ⟨ENTER⟩ giving $\sin \theta = \sin(\alpha + \beta) = \frac{253}{325}$ ($\alpha + \beta$ is in QII where $\sin \theta > 0$). At this point the value of $\tan(\alpha + \beta)$ is even easier to calculate, since $\dfrac{\sin \theta}{\cos \theta} = \tan \theta$ for all $\theta$ (including $\theta = \alpha + \beta$). Since the denominators from $\sin(\alpha + \beta)$ and $\cos(\alpha + \beta)$ are identical, they reduce to 1 leaving the ratio of numerators, giving $\tan \theta = \tan(\alpha + \beta) = -\frac{253}{204}$. Use these ideas to complete the following exercises.

**Figure 5.9**

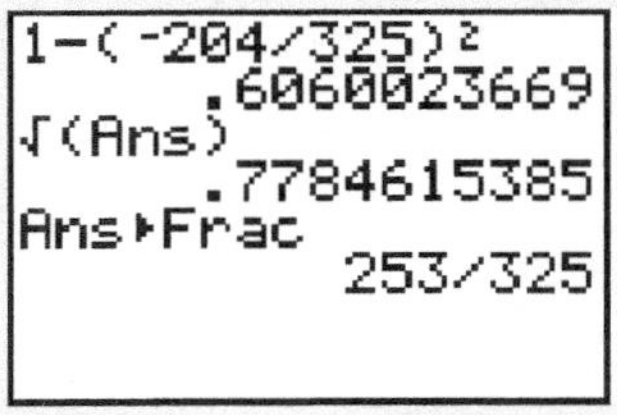

```
1-(-204/325)²
          .6060023669
√(Ans)
          .7784615385
Ans▶Frac
              253/325
```

**Exercise 1:**   For $\tan \alpha = \frac{40}{9}$ in QIII and $\cos \beta = \frac{12}{37}$ in QIV, find $\cos(\alpha - \beta)$, $\sin(\alpha - \beta)$, and $\tan(\alpha - \beta)$.

**Exercise 2:**   For $\cos \alpha = -\frac{8}{17}$ in QIII and $\sin \beta = \frac{20}{29}$ in QII, find $\sin(\alpha + \beta)$, $\cos(\alpha + \beta)$, and $\tan(\alpha + \beta)$.

## 5.2 EXERCISES

### ▶ CONCEPTS AND VOCABULARY

**Fill in each blank with the appropriate word or phrase. Carefully reread the section if needed.**

1. Since $\tan 45° + \tan 60° > 1$, we know $\tan 45° + \tan 60° = \tan 105°$ is _____ since $\tan \theta < 0$ in _____.

2. To find an exact value for $\tan 105°$, use the sum identity for tangent with $\alpha =$ _____ and $\beta =$ _____.

3. For the cosine sum/difference identities, the functions _____ in each term, with the _____ sign between them.

4. For the sine sum/difference identities, the functions _____ in each term, with the _____ sign between them.

5. Discuss/Explain how we know the exact value for $\cos \dfrac{11\pi}{12} = \cos\left(\dfrac{2\pi}{3} + \dfrac{\pi}{4}\right)$ will be negative, prior to applying any identity.

6. Discuss/Explain why $\tan(\alpha - \beta) = \dfrac{\sin(\alpha - \beta)}{\cos(\beta - \alpha)}$ is an identity, even though the arguments of cosine have been reversed. Then verify the identity.

## ▶ DEVELOPING YOUR SKILLS

**Find the exact value of the expression given using a sum or difference identity. Some simplifications may involve using symmetry and the formulas for negatives.**

**7.** $\cos 105°$

**8.** $\cos 135°$

**9.** $\cos\left(\dfrac{7\pi}{12}\right)$

**10.** $\cos\left(-\dfrac{5\pi}{12}\right)$

**Use sum/difference identities to verify that both expressions give the same result.**

**11. a.** $\cos(45° + 30°)$　　**b.** $\cos(120° - 45°)$

**12. a.** $\cos\left(\dfrac{\pi}{6} - \dfrac{\pi}{4}\right)$　　**b.** $\cos\left(\dfrac{\pi}{4} - \dfrac{\pi}{3}\right)$

**Rewrite as a single expression in cosine.**

**13.** $\cos(7\theta)\cos(2\theta) + \sin(7\theta)\sin(2\theta)$

**14.** $\cos\left(\dfrac{\theta}{3}\right)\cos\left(\dfrac{\theta}{6}\right) - \sin\left(\dfrac{\theta}{3}\right)\sin\left(\dfrac{\theta}{6}\right)$

**Find the exact value of the given expressions.**

**15.** $\cos 183° \cos 153° + \sin 183° \sin 153°$

**16.** $\cos\left(\dfrac{7\pi}{36}\right)\cos\left(\dfrac{5\pi}{36}\right) - \sin\left(\dfrac{7\pi}{36}\right)\sin\left(\dfrac{5\pi}{36}\right)$

**17.** For $\sin \alpha = -\dfrac{4}{5}$ with terminal side in QIV and $\tan \beta = -\dfrac{5}{12}$ with terminal side in QII, find $\cos(\alpha + \beta)$.

**18.** For $\sin \alpha = \dfrac{112}{113}$ with terminal side in QII and $\sec \beta = -\dfrac{89}{39}$ with terminal side in QII, find $\cos(\alpha - \beta)$.

**Use a cofunction identity to write an equivalent expression.**

**19.** $\cos 57°$　　**20.** $\sin 18°$　　**21.** $\tan\left(\dfrac{5\pi}{12}\right)$

**22.** $\sec\left(\dfrac{\pi}{10}\right)$　　**23.** $\sin\left(\dfrac{\pi}{6} - \theta\right)$　　**24.** $\cos\left(\dfrac{\pi}{3} + \theta\right)$

**Rewrite as a single expression.**

**25.** $\sin(3x)\cos(5x) + \cos(3x)\sin(5x)$

**26.** $\sin\left(\dfrac{x}{2}\right)\cos\left(\dfrac{x}{3}\right) - \cos\left(\dfrac{x}{2}\right)\sin\left(\dfrac{x}{3}\right)$

**27.** $\dfrac{\tan(5\theta) - \tan(2\theta)}{1 + \tan(5\theta)\tan(2\theta)}$

**28.** $\dfrac{\tan\left(\dfrac{x}{2}\right) + \tan\left(\dfrac{x}{8}\right)}{1 - \tan\left(\dfrac{x}{2}\right)\tan\left(\dfrac{x}{8}\right)}$

**Find the exact value of the given expressions.**

**29.** $\sin 137° \cos 47° - \cos 137° \sin 47°$

**30.** $\sin\left(\dfrac{11\pi}{24}\right)\cos\left(\dfrac{5\pi}{24}\right) + \cos\left(\dfrac{11\pi}{24}\right)\sin\left(\dfrac{5\pi}{24}\right)$

**31.** $\dfrac{\tan\left(\dfrac{11\pi}{21}\right) - \tan\left(\dfrac{4\pi}{21}\right)}{1 + \tan\left(\dfrac{11\pi}{21}\right)\tan\left(\dfrac{4\pi}{21}\right)}$

**32.** $\dfrac{\tan\left(\dfrac{3\pi}{20}\right) + \tan\left(\dfrac{\pi}{10}\right)}{1 - \tan\left(\dfrac{3\pi}{20}\right)\tan\left(\dfrac{\pi}{10}\right)}$

**33.** For $\cos \alpha = -\dfrac{7}{25}$ with terminal side in QII and $\cot \beta = \dfrac{15}{8}$ with terminal side in QIII, find

　**a.** $\sin(\alpha + \beta)$　　**b.** $\tan(\alpha + \beta)$

**34.** For $\csc \alpha = \dfrac{29}{20}$ with terminal side in QI and $\cos \beta = -\dfrac{12}{37}$ with terminal side in QII, find

　**a.** $\sin(\alpha - \beta)$　　**b.** $\tan(\alpha - \beta)$

**Find the exact value of the expression given using a sum or difference identity. Some simplifications may involve using symmetry and the formulas for negatives.**

**35.** $\sin 105°$　　　　**36.** $\sin(-75°)$

**37.** $\sin\left(\dfrac{5\pi}{12}\right)$　　**38.** $\sin\left(\dfrac{11\pi}{12}\right)$

**39.** $\tan 150°$　　　　**40.** $\tan 75°$

**41.** $\tan\left(\dfrac{2\pi}{3}\right)$　　**42.** $\tan\left(-\dfrac{\pi}{12}\right)$

**Use sum/difference identities to verify that both expressions give the same result.**

**43. a.** $\sin(45° - 30°)$     **44. a.** $\sin\left(\dfrac{\pi}{3} - \dfrac{\pi}{4}\right)$

   **b.** $\sin(135° - 120°)$     **b.** $\sin\left(\dfrac{\pi}{4} - \dfrac{\pi}{6}\right)$

**45.** Find $\sin 255°$ given $150° + 105° = 255°$. See Exercises 7 and 35.

**46.** Find $\cos\left(\dfrac{19\pi}{12}\right)$ given $2\pi - \dfrac{5\pi}{12} = \dfrac{19\pi}{12}$. See Exercises 10 and 37.

**47.** Given $\alpha$ and $\beta$ are acute angles with $\sin\alpha = \dfrac{12}{13}$ and $\tan\beta = \dfrac{35}{12}$, find

   **a.** $\sin(\alpha + \beta)$   **b.** $\cos(\alpha - \beta)$   **c.** $\tan(\alpha + \beta)$

**48.** Given $\alpha$ and $\beta$ are acute angles with $\cos\alpha = \dfrac{8}{17}$ and $\sec\beta = \dfrac{25}{7}$, find

   **a.** $\sin(\alpha + \beta)$   **b.** $\cos(\alpha - \beta)$   **c.** $\tan(\alpha + \beta)$

**49.** Given $\alpha$ and $\beta$ are obtuse angles with $\sin\alpha = \dfrac{28}{53}$ and $\cos\beta = -\dfrac{13}{85}$, find

   **a.** $\sin(\alpha - \beta)$   **b.** $\cos(\alpha + \beta)$   **c.** $\tan(\alpha - \beta)$

**50.** Given $\alpha$ and $\beta$ are obtuse angles with $\tan\alpha = -\dfrac{60}{11}$ and $\sin\beta = \dfrac{35}{37}$, find

   **a.** $\sin(\alpha - \beta)$   **b.** $\cos(\alpha + \beta)$   **c.** $\tan(\alpha - \beta)$

**51.** Use the diagram indicated to compute the following:

   **a.** $\sin A$       **b.** $\cos A$       **c.** $\tan A$

**Exercise 51**       **Exercise 52**

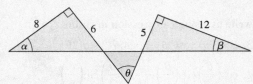

**52.** Use the diagram indicated to compute the following:

   **a.** $\sin\beta$       **b.** $\cos\beta$       **c.** $\tan\beta$

**53.** For the figure indicated, show that $\theta = \alpha + \beta$ and compute the following:

   **a.** $\sin\theta$       **b.** $\cos\theta$       **c.** $\tan\theta$

**Exercise 53**

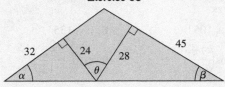

**54.** For the figure indicated, show that $\theta = \alpha + \beta$ and compute the following:

   **a.** $\sin\theta$       **b.** $\cos\theta$       **c.** $\tan\theta$

**Exercise 54**

**Verify each identity.**

**55.** $\sin(\pi - \alpha) = \sin\alpha$

**56.** $\cos(\pi - \alpha) = -\cos\alpha$

**57.** $\cos\left(x + \dfrac{\pi}{4}\right) = \dfrac{\sqrt{2}}{2}(\cos x - \sin x)$

**58.** $\sin\left(x + \dfrac{\pi}{4}\right) = \dfrac{\sqrt{2}}{2}(\sin x + \cos x)$

**59.** $\tan\left(x + \dfrac{\pi}{4}\right) = \dfrac{1 + \tan x}{1 - \tan x}$

**60.** $\tan\left(x - \dfrac{\pi}{4}\right) = \dfrac{\tan x - 1}{\tan x + 1}$

**61.** $\cos(\alpha + \beta) + \cos(\alpha - \beta) = 2\cos\alpha\cos\beta$

**62.** $\sin(\alpha + \beta) + \sin(\alpha - \beta) = 2\sin\alpha\sin\beta$

**63.** $\cos(2t) = \cos^2 t - \sin^2 t$

**64.** $\sin(2t) = 2\sin t\cos t$

**65.** $\sin(3t) = -4\sin^3 t + 3\sin t$

**66.** $\cos(3t) = 4\cos^3 t - 3\cos t$

**67.** Use a difference identity to show
$$\cos\left(x - \dfrac{\pi}{4}\right) = \dfrac{\sqrt{2}}{2}(\cos x + \sin x).$$

**68.** Use sum/difference identities to show
$$\sin\left(x + \dfrac{\pi}{4}\right) + \sin\left(x - \dfrac{\pi}{4}\right) = \sqrt{2}\sin x.$$

► **WORKING WITH FORMULAS**

**69. Force and equilibrium:** $F = \dfrac{Wk}{c} \tan(p - \theta)$

The force required to maintain equilibrium when a screw jack is used can be modeled by the formula shown, where $p$ is the pitch angle of the screw, $W$ is the weight of the load, $\theta$ is the angle of friction, with $k$ and $c$ being constants related to a particular jack. Simplify the formula using the difference formula for tangent given $p = \dfrac{\pi}{6}$ and $\theta = \dfrac{\pi}{4}$.

**70. Brewster's law of reflection:** $\tan \theta_p = \dfrac{n_2}{n_1}$

Brewster's law of optics states that when unpolarized light strikes a dielectric surface, the transmitted light rays and the reflected light rays are perpendicular to each other. The proof of Brewster's law involves the expression

$n_1 \sin \theta_p = n_2 \sin\left(\dfrac{\pi}{2} - \theta_p\right)$. Use the

difference identity for sine to verify that this expression leads to Brewster's law.

► **APPLICATIONS**

**71. AC circuits:** In a study of AC circuits, the equation

$R = \dfrac{\cos s \cos t}{\omega C \sin(s + t)}$ sometimes arises. Use a sum

identity and algebra to show this equation is equivalent to $R = \dfrac{1}{\omega C(\tan s + \tan t)}$.

**72. Fluid mechanics:** In studies of fluid mechanics, the equation $\gamma_1 V_1 \sin \alpha = \gamma_2 V_2 \sin(\alpha - \beta)$ sometimes arises. Use a difference identity to show that if $\gamma_1 V_1 = \gamma_2 V_2$, the equation is equivalent to $\cos \beta - \cot \alpha \sin \beta = 1$.

**73. Art and mathematics:** When working in two-point geometric perspective, artists must scale their work to fit on the paper or canvas they are using. In doing so, the equation $\dfrac{A}{B} = \dfrac{\tan \theta}{\tan(90° - \theta)}$ arises. Rewrite the expression on the right in terms of sine and cosine, then use the difference identities to show the equation can be rewritten as $\dfrac{A}{B} = \tan^2\theta$.

**74. Traveling waves:** If two waves of the same frequency, velocity, and amplitude are traveling along a string in opposite directions, they can be represented by the equations $Y_1 = A \sin(kx - \omega t)$ and $Y_2 = A \sin(kx + \omega t)$. Use the sum and difference formulas for sine to show the result $Y_R = Y_1 + Y_2$ of these waves can be expressed as $Y_R = 2A \sin(kx)\cos(\omega t)$.

**75. Pressure on the eardrum:** If a frequency generator is placed a certain distance from the ear, the pressure on the eardrum can be modeled by the function $P_1(t) = A \sin(2\pi ft)$, where $f$ is the frequency and $t$ is the time in seconds. If a second frequency generator with identical settings is placed slightly closer to the ear, its pressure on the eardrum could be represented by $P_2(t) = A \sin(2\pi ft + C)$, where

$C$ is a constant. Show that if $C = \dfrac{\pi}{2}$, the total

pressure on the eardrum $[P_1(t) + P_2(t)]$ is $P(t) = A[\sin(2\pi ft) + \cos(2\pi ft)]$.

**76. Angle between two cables:** Two cables used to steady a radio tower are attached to the tower at heights of 5 ft and 35 ft, with both secured to a stake 12 ft from the tower (see figure). Find the value of $\cos \theta$, where $\theta$ is the angle between the upper and lower cables.

**Exercise 76**

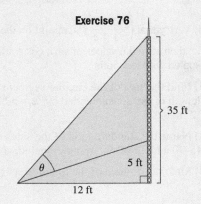

35 ft

5 ft

$\theta$

12 ft

**77. Difference quotient:** Given $f(x) = \sin x$, show that the difference quotient $\dfrac{f(x+h) - f(x)}{h}$ results in the expression $\sin x\left(\dfrac{\cos h - 1}{h}\right) + \cos x\left(\dfrac{\sin h}{h}\right)$.

**78. Difference identity:** Derive the difference identity for tangent using $\tan(\alpha - \beta) = \dfrac{\sin(\alpha - \beta)}{\cos(\alpha - \beta)}$.

(*Hint:* After applying the difference identities, divide the numerator and denominator by $\cos \alpha \cos \beta$.)

▶ **EXTENDING THE CONCEPT**

A family of identities called the *angle reduction formulas* will be of use in our study of complex numbers and other areas. These formulas use the period of a function to reduce large angles to an angle in $[0, 360°)$ or $[0, 2\pi)$ having an equivalent function value: (1) $\cos(t + 2\pi k) = \cos t$; (2) $\sin(t + 2\pi k) = \sin t$. Use the reduction formulas to find values for the following functions (note the formulas can also be expressed in degrees).

**79.** $\cos 1665°$

**80.** $\cos\left(\dfrac{91\pi}{6}\right)$

**81.** $\sin\left(\dfrac{41\pi}{6}\right)$

**82.** $\sin 2385°$

**83.** An alternative method of proving the difference formula for cosine uses a unit circle and the fact that equal arcs are subtended by equal chords ($D = d$ in the diagram). Using a combination of algebra, the distance formula, and a Pythagorean identity, show that $\cos(\alpha - \beta) = \cos \alpha \cos \beta + \sin \alpha \sin \beta$ (start by computing $D^2$ and $d^2$). Then discuss/explain how the sum identity can be found using the fact that $\beta = -(-\beta)$.

**84. A proof without words:** Verify the Pythagorean theorem for each right triangle in the diagram, then discuss/explain how the diagram offers a proof of the sum identities for sine and cosine. Be detailed and thorough.

**Exercise 83**

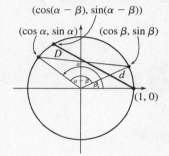

**Exercise 84**

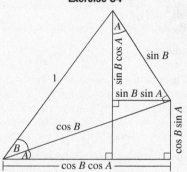

▶ **MAINTAINING YOUR SKILLS**

**85. (3.4)** Verify that $\left(\dfrac{\sqrt{7}}{4}, \dfrac{3}{4}\right)$ is a point on the unit circle, then state the values of $\sin t$, $\cos t$, and $\tan t$ associated with this point.

**86. (3.2)** Find the area of the circular segment and the length of the arc subtended by $\theta = 57°$ for $r = 2$ ft.

**87. (1.1)** Name the standard ratio of the sides for a 45-45-90 and 30-60-90 triangle. Include a diagram.

**88. (3.4)** State the domain of the function: $y = \tan t$.

**89. (4.3)** Graph using transformations of a basic function: $y = -2\cos\left(t + \dfrac{\pi}{4}\right)$; $t \in [0, 2\pi)$.

**90. (2.3)** Use an appropriate trig ratio to find the length of the bridge needed to cross the lake shown in the figure.

**Exercise 90**

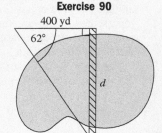

Verify that the following equations are identities.

**1.** $\cos^2 x - \cot^2 x = -\cos^2 x \cot^2 x$

**2.** $1 - \sin^4 t = (1 + \sin^2 t)\cos^2 t$

**3.** $\dfrac{2\sin x}{\sec x} - \dfrac{\cos x}{\csc x} = \cos x \sin x$

**4.** $\dfrac{1 - \cos t}{\cos t} + \dfrac{\sec t - 1}{\sec t} = \sec t - \cos t$

Show the equations given are not identities.

**5.** $1 + \sec^2 x = \tan^2 x$    **6.** $\cos^2 t = \sin^2 t - 1$

Rewrite as a single expression.

**7.** $\cos(6\alpha)\cos(2\alpha) + \sin(6\alpha)\sin(2\alpha)$

**8.** $\sin\left(\dfrac{\pi}{4}t\right)\cos\left(\dfrac{\pi}{3}t\right) + \cos\left(\dfrac{\pi}{4}t\right)\sin\left(\dfrac{\pi}{3}t\right)$

**9.** Given $\alpha$ and $\beta$ are acute angles with $\cos\alpha = \dfrac{3}{5}$ and $\cot\beta = \dfrac{5}{12}$, find

**a.** $\sin(\alpha + \beta)$    **b.** $\cos(\alpha - \beta)$

**c.** $\tan(\alpha + \beta)$

**10.** Given $\alpha$ and $\beta$ are obtuse angles with $\sin\alpha = \dfrac{56}{65}$ and $\tan\beta = -\dfrac{80}{39}$, find

**a.** $\sin(\alpha - \beta)$  **b.** $\cos(\alpha + \beta)$  **c.** $\tan(\alpha - \beta)$

## Understanding Identities

Sometimes a tactile verification of identities can help us understand and appreciate them. For the following exercises you will need a cm/mm ruler and a protractor.

**Exercise 1:** As carefully as you can (very carefully), measure the opposite and adjacent sides of each triangle below to the nearest half-millimeter (mm) with respect to the angle $\alpha$ or $\beta$ given. Then use the Pythagorean theorem to *compute* the length of the hypotenuse. Then *measure* the hypotenuse and compare your measured result with your computed result. What was the percent difference between the two measurements?

**Exercise 2:** Using the measured lengths, write the values for $\sin \alpha$, $\cos \alpha$, $\tan \alpha$, $\sin \beta$, $\cos \beta$, and $\tan \beta$ for each triangle. Compute $\sin^2\alpha + \cos^2\alpha$ and $\sin^2\beta + \cos^2\beta$. What do you notice?

**Exercise 3:** Is it true that $\tan \alpha = \dfrac{\sin \alpha}{\cos \alpha}$? $\tan \beta = \dfrac{\sin \beta}{\cos \beta}$?

As an additional tool to help *verify* identities, we can write each function in terms of its unit circle definition, enabling us to work through a proof in more algebraic terms. This sometimes makes the process less cumbersome. Recall that for $P(x, y)$ on the unit circle, $x^2 + y^2 = 1$.

Verify the identity: $\cos^2\theta - \sin^2\theta = \dfrac{1 - \tan^2\theta}{1 + \tan^2\theta}$. We begin with the rational term on the right.

$$\frac{1 - \tan^2\theta}{1 + \tan^2\theta} = \frac{1 - \dfrac{y^2}{x^2}}{1 + \dfrac{y^2}{x^2}} \qquad \tan\theta = \frac{y}{x}$$

$$= \frac{\dfrac{x^2 - y^2}{x^2}}{\dfrac{x^2 + y^2}{x^2}} \qquad \text{combine terms: } \frac{A}{B} \pm \frac{C}{D} = \frac{AD \pm BC}{BD}$$

$$= \frac{x^2 - y^2}{x^2 + y^2} \qquad \text{simplify}$$

$$= \frac{\cos^2\theta - \sin^2\theta}{1} \qquad \cos\theta = x; \ \sin\theta = y; \ x^2 + y^2 = 1$$

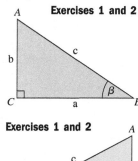

**Exercises 1 and 2**

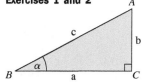

**Exercises 1 and 2**

**Exercise 4:** Use this method to verify the identity $\dfrac{\csc^2x - \cot^2x}{\cot^2x} = \sec^2x - 1$.

**The Double-Angle and Half-Angle Identities**

## Learning Objectives

*In Section 5.3 you will learn how to:*

☐ **A.** Derive and use the double-angle identities for cosine, tangent, and sine

☐ **B.** Develop and use the power reduction and half-angle identities

The derivation of the sum and difference identities in Section 5.2 was a "watershed event" in the study of identities. By making various substitutions, they lead us very naturally to many new identity families, giving us a heightened ability to simplify expressions, solve equations, find exact values, and model real-world phenomena. In fact, many of the identities are applied in very practical ways, as in a study of projectile motion and the conic sections.

## A. The Double-Angle Identities

The double-angle identities for sine, cosine, and tangent can all be derived using the related sum identities with two equal angles ($\alpha = \beta$). We'll illustrate the process here for the cosine of twice an angle.

$$\cos(\alpha + \beta) = \cos\alpha\cos\beta - \sin\alpha\sin\beta \qquad \text{sum identity for cosine}$$
$$\cos(\alpha + \alpha) = \cos\alpha\cos\alpha - \sin\alpha\sin\alpha \qquad \text{assume } \alpha = \beta \text{ and substitute } \alpha \text{ for } \beta$$
$$\cos(2\alpha) = \cos^2\alpha - \sin^2\alpha \qquad \text{simplify—double-angle identity for cosine}$$

Using the Pythagorean identity $\cos^2\alpha + \sin^2\alpha = 1$, we can easily find two additional members of this family, which are often quite useful. For $\cos^2\alpha = 1 - \sin^2\alpha$ we have

$$\cos(2\alpha) = \cos^2\alpha - \sin^2\alpha \qquad \text{double-angle identity for cosine}$$
$$= (1 - \sin^2\alpha) - \sin^2\alpha \qquad \text{substitute } 1 - \sin^2\alpha \text{ for } \cos^2\alpha$$
$$\cos(2\alpha) = 1 - 2\sin^2\alpha \qquad \text{double-angle in terms of sine}$$

Using $\sin^2\alpha = 1 - \cos^2\alpha$ we obtain an additional form:

$$\cos(2\alpha) = \cos^2\alpha - \sin^2\alpha \qquad \text{double-angle identity for cosine}$$
$$= \cos^2\alpha - (1 - \cos^2\alpha) \qquad \text{substitute } 1 - \cos^2\alpha \text{ for } \sin^2\alpha$$
$$\cos(2\alpha) = 2\cos^2\alpha - 1 \qquad \text{double-angle in terms of cosine}$$

The derivations of $\sin(2\alpha)$ and $\tan(2\alpha)$ are likewise developed and are asked for in **Exercise 83.** The double-angle identities are collected here for your convenience.

---

**The Double-Angle Identities**

**cosine:** $\cos(2\alpha) = \cos^2\alpha - \sin^2\alpha$ **sine:** $\sin(2\alpha) = 2\sin\alpha\cos\alpha$
$$= 1 - 2\sin^2\alpha$$
$$= 2\cos^2\alpha - 1$$

**tangent:** $\tan(2\alpha) = \dfrac{2\tan\alpha}{1 - \tan^2\alpha}$

---

**EXAMPLE 1** ▶ **Using a Double-Angle Identity to Find Function Values**

Given $\sin\alpha = \dfrac{5}{8}$, find the value of $\cos(2\alpha)$.

**Solution** ▶ Using the double-angle identity for cosine in terms of sine, we find

$$\cos(2\alpha) = 1 - 2\sin^2\alpha \quad \text{double-angle in terms of sine}$$
$$= 1 - 2\left(\frac{5}{8}\right)^2 \quad \text{substitute } \frac{5}{8} \text{ for } \sin\alpha$$
$$= 1 - \frac{25}{32} \quad 2\left(\frac{5}{8}\right)^2 = \frac{25}{32}$$
$$= \frac{7}{32} \quad \text{result}$$

If $\sin\alpha = \frac{5}{8}$, then $\cos(2\alpha) = \frac{7}{32}$.

**Now try Exercises 7 through 20 ▶**

Like the fundamental identities, the double-angle identities can be used to verify or develop others. In Example 2, we explore one of many **multiple-angle identities,** verifying that $\cos(3\theta)$ can be rewritten as $4\cos^3\theta - 3\cos\theta$ (in terms of powers of $\cos\theta$).

**EXAMPLE 2 ▶ Verifying a Multiple-Angle Identity**

Verify that $\cos(3\theta) = 4\cos^3\theta - 3\cos\theta$ is an identity.

**Solution** ▶ Use the sum identity for cosine, with $\alpha = 2\theta$ and $\beta = \theta$. Note that our goal is an expression using cosines only, with no multiple angles.

$$\cos(\alpha + \beta) = \cos\alpha\cos\beta - \sin\alpha\sin\beta \quad \text{sum identity for cosine}$$
$$\cos(2\theta + \theta) = \cos(2\theta)\cos\theta - \sin(2\theta)\sin\theta \quad \text{substitute } 2\theta \text{ for } \alpha \text{ and } \theta \text{ for } \beta$$
$$\cos(3\theta) = (2\cos^2\theta - 1)\cos\theta - (2\sin\theta\cos\theta)\sin\theta \quad \text{substitute for } \cos(2\theta) \text{ and } \sin(2\theta)$$
$$= 2\cos^3\theta - \cos\theta - 2\cos\theta\sin^2\theta \quad \text{multiply}$$
$$= 2\cos^3\theta - \cos\theta - 2\cos\theta(1 - \cos^2\theta) \quad \text{substitute } 1 - \cos^2\theta \text{ for } \sin^2\theta$$
$$= 2\cos^3\theta - \cos\theta - 2\cos\theta + 2\cos^3\theta \quad \text{multiply}$$
$$= 4\cos^3\theta - 3\cos\theta \quad \text{combine terms}$$

**Now try Exercises 21 and 22 ▶**

**EXAMPLE 3 ▶ Using a Double-Angle Formula to Find Exact Values**

Find the exact value of $\sin 22.5° \cos 22.5°$.

**Solution** ▶ A product of sines and cosines having the same argument hints at the double-angle identity for sine. Using $\sin(2\alpha) = 2\sin\alpha\cos\alpha$ and dividing by 2 gives

$$\sin\alpha\cos\alpha = \frac{\sin(2\alpha)}{2} \quad \text{double-angle identity for sine}$$
$$\sin 22.5°\cos 22.5° = \frac{\sin[2(22.5°)]}{2} \quad \text{replace } \alpha \text{ with } 22.5°$$
$$= \frac{\sin 45°}{2} \quad \text{multiply}$$

☑ **A.** You've just learned how to derive and use the double-angle identities for cosine, tangent, and sine

$$= \frac{\frac{\sqrt{2}}{2}}{2} = \frac{\sqrt{2}}{4} \quad \sin 45° = \frac{\sqrt{2}}{2}$$

**Now try Exercises 23 through 30 ▶**

## B. The Power Reduction and Half-Angle Identities

Expressions having a trigonometric function raised to a power occur quite frequently in various applications. We can rewrite even powers of these trig functions in terms of an expression containing only cosine to the power 1, using what are called the **power reduction identities.** This makes the expression easier to use and evaluate. It can legitimately be argued that the power reduction identities are actually members of the double-angle family, as all three are a direct consequence. To find identities for $\cos^2 x$ and $\sin^2 x$, we solve the related double-angle identity involving $\cos(2x)$.

$$1 - 2\sin^2\alpha = \cos(2\alpha) \qquad \text{cos}(2\alpha) \text{ in terms of sine}$$

$$-2\sin^2\alpha = \cos(2\alpha) - 1 \qquad \text{subtract 1, then divide by } -2$$

$$\sin^2\alpha = \frac{1 - \cos(2\alpha)}{2} \qquad \text{power reduction identity for sine}$$

Using the same approach for $\cos^2\alpha$ gives $\cos^2\alpha = \dfrac{1 + \cos(2\alpha)}{2}$. The identity for $\tan^2\alpha$ can be derived from $\tan(2\alpha) = \dfrac{2\tan\alpha}{1 - \tan^2\alpha}$ **(see Exercise 84),** but in this case, it's easier to use the identity $\tan^2 u = \dfrac{\sin^2 u}{\cos^2 u}$. The result is $\dfrac{1 - \cos(2\alpha)}{1 + \cos(2\alpha)}$.

### The Power Reduction Identities

$$\cos^2\alpha = \frac{1 + \cos(2\alpha)}{2} \qquad \sin^2\alpha = \frac{1 - \cos(2\alpha)}{2} \qquad \tan^2\alpha = \frac{1 - \cos(2\alpha)}{1 + \cos(2\alpha)}$$

**EXAMPLE 4** ▶ **Using a Power Reduction Formula**

Write $8\sin^4 x$ in terms of an expression containing only cosines to the power 1.

**Solution** ▶

$$8\sin^4 x = 8(\sin^2 x)^2 \qquad \text{original expression}$$

$$= 8\left[\frac{1 - \cos(2x)}{2}\right]^2 \qquad \text{substitute } \frac{1 - \cos(2x)}{2} \text{ for } \sin^2 x$$

$$= 2[1 - 2\cos(2x) + \cos^2(2x)] \qquad \text{multiply}$$

$$= 2\left[1 - 2\cos(2x) + \frac{1 + \cos(4x)}{2}\right] \qquad \text{substitute } \frac{1 + \cos(4x)}{2} \text{ for } \cos^2(2x)$$

$$= 2 - 4\cos(2x) + 1 + \cos(4x) \qquad \text{multiply}$$

$$= 3 - 4\cos(2x) + \cos(4x) \qquad \text{result}$$

**Now try Exercises 31 through 36** ▶

The half-angle identities follow directly from the power reduction identities, using algebra and a simple change of variable. For $\cos^2\alpha = \dfrac{1 + \cos(2\alpha)}{2}$, we first take square roots and obtain $\cos\alpha = \pm\sqrt{\dfrac{1 + \cos(2\alpha)}{2}}$. Using the substitution $u = 2\alpha$ gives $\alpha = \dfrac{u}{2}$, and making these substitutions results in the half-angle identity for cosine: $\cos\left(\dfrac{u}{2}\right) = \pm\sqrt{\dfrac{1 + \cos u}{2}}$, where the radical's sign depends on the quadrant in which $\dfrac{u}{2}$ terminates. Using the same substitution for sine gives $\sin\left(\dfrac{u}{2}\right) = \pm\sqrt{\dfrac{1 - \cos u}{2}}$, and for the tangent identity, $\tan\left(\dfrac{u}{2}\right) = \pm\sqrt{\dfrac{1 - \cos u}{1 + \cos u}}$. In the case of $\tan\left(\dfrac{u}{2}\right)$, we can actually develop identities that are free of radicals by rationalizing the denominator or numerator. We'll illustrate the former, leaving the latter as an exercise (**see Exercise 82**).

$$\tan\left(\frac{u}{2}\right) = \pm\sqrt{\frac{(1 - \cos u)(1 - \cos u)}{(1 + \cos u)(1 - \cos u)}} \qquad \text{multiply by the conjugate}$$

$$= \pm\sqrt{\frac{(1 - \cos u)^2}{1 - \cos^2 u}} \qquad \text{rewrite}$$

$$= \pm\sqrt{\frac{(1 - \cos u)^2}{\sin^2 u}} \qquad \text{Pythagorean identity}$$

$$= \pm\left|\frac{1 - \cos u}{\sin u}\right| \qquad \sqrt{x^2} = |x|$$

Since $1 - \cos u > 0$ and $\sin u$ has the same sign as $\tan\left(\dfrac{u}{2}\right)$ for all $u$ in its domain, the relationship can simply be written $\tan\left(\dfrac{u}{2}\right) = \dfrac{1 - \cos u}{\sin u}$.

---

**The Half-Angle Identities**

$$\cos\left(\frac{u}{2}\right) = \pm\sqrt{\frac{1 + \cos u}{2}} \qquad \sin\left(\frac{u}{2}\right) = \pm\sqrt{\frac{1 - \cos u}{2}} \qquad \tan\left(\frac{u}{2}\right) = \pm\sqrt{\frac{1 - \cos u}{1 + \cos u}}$$

$$\tan\left(\frac{u}{2}\right) = \frac{1 - \cos u}{\sin u} \qquad \tan\left(\frac{u}{2}\right) = \frac{\sin u}{1 + \cos u}$$

---

**EXAMPLE 5** ▶  **Using Half-Angle Formulas to Find Exact Values**

Use the half-angle identities to find exact values for (a) $\sin 15°$ and (b) $\tan 15°$.

**Solution** ▶  Noting that $15°$ is one-half the standard angle $30°$, we can find each value by applying the respective half-angle identity with $u = 30°$ in Quadrant I.

**a.** $\sin\left(\dfrac{30°}{2}\right) = \sqrt{\dfrac{1 - \cos 30°}{2}}$

$\qquad = \sqrt{\dfrac{1 - \dfrac{\sqrt{3}}{2}}{2}}$

$\qquad \sin 15° = \dfrac{\sqrt{2 - \sqrt{3}}}{2}$

**b.** $\tan\left(\dfrac{30°}{2}\right) = \dfrac{1 - \cos 30°}{\sin 30°}$

$\qquad \tan 15° = \dfrac{1 - \dfrac{\sqrt{3}}{2}}{\dfrac{1}{2}} = 2 - \sqrt{3}$

**Now try Exercises 37 through 48** ▶

---

**EXAMPLE 6** ▶  **Using Half-Angle Formulas to Find Exact Values**

For $\cos\theta = -\dfrac{7}{25}$ and $\theta$ in QIII, find exact values of $\sin\left(\dfrac{\theta}{2}\right)$ and $\cos\left(\dfrac{\theta}{2}\right)$.

Solution ▶  With $\theta$ in QIII $\rightarrow \pi < \theta < \dfrac{3\pi}{2}$, we know $\dfrac{\theta}{2}$ must be in QII $\rightarrow \dfrac{\pi}{2} < \dfrac{\theta}{2} < \dfrac{3\pi}{4}$ and

we choose our signs accordingly: $\sin\left(\dfrac{\theta}{2}\right) > 0$ and $\cos\left(\dfrac{\theta}{2}\right) < 0$.

$$\sin\left(\frac{\theta}{2}\right) = \sqrt{\frac{1 - \cos\theta}{2}} \qquad \cos\left(\frac{\theta}{2}\right) = -\sqrt{\frac{1 + \cos\theta}{2}}$$

$$= \sqrt{\frac{1 - \left(-\dfrac{7}{25}\right)}{2}} \qquad\qquad = -\sqrt{\frac{1 + \left(-\dfrac{7}{25}\right)}{2}}$$

**B.** You've just learned how to develop and use the power reduction and half-angle identities

$$= \sqrt{\frac{16}{25}} = \frac{4}{5} \qquad\qquad = -\sqrt{\frac{9}{25}} = -\frac{3}{5}$$

**Now try Exercises 49 through 64** ▶

For a mixed variety of identities, **see Exercises 65–80.**

## 5.3 EXERCISES

▶ **CONCEPTS AND VOCABULARY**

Fill in each blank with the appropriate word or phrase. Carefully reread the section if needed.

**1.** The double-angle identities can be derived using the _____ identities with $\alpha = \beta$. For $\cos(2\theta)$ we expand $\cos(\alpha + \beta)$ using _____.

**2.** If $\theta$ is in QIII then $180° < \theta < 270°$ and $\dfrac{\theta}{2}$ must be in _____ since _____ $< \dfrac{\theta}{2} <$ _____.

**3.** Multiple-angle identities can be derived using the sum and difference identities. For $\sin(3x)$ use $\sin$ ( _____ + _____ ).

**4.** For the half-angle identities the sign preceding the radical depends on the _____ in which $\dfrac{u}{2}$ _____.

**5.** Explain/Discuss how the three different identities for $\tan\left(\dfrac{u}{2}\right)$ are related. Verify that
$$\frac{1 - \cos x}{\sin x} = \frac{\sin x}{1 + \cos x}.$$

**6.** In Example 6, we were given $\cos\theta = -\dfrac{7}{25}$ and $\theta$ in QIII. Discuss how the result would differ if we stipulate that $\theta$ is in QII instead.

▶ **DEVELOPING YOUR SKILLS**

Find exact values for $\sin(2\theta)$, $\cos(2\theta)$, and $\tan(2\theta)$ using the information given.

**7.** $\sin\theta = \dfrac{5}{13}$; $\theta$ in QII

**8.** $\cos\theta = -\dfrac{21}{29}$; $\theta$ in QII

**9.** $\cos\theta = -\dfrac{9}{41}$; $\theta$ in QII

**10.** $\sin\theta = -\dfrac{63}{65}$; $\theta$ in QIII

**11.** $\tan\theta = \dfrac{13}{84}$; $\theta$ in QIII

**12.** $\sec\theta = \dfrac{53}{28}$; $\theta$ in QI

**13.** $\sin\theta = \dfrac{48}{73}$; $\cos\theta < 0$

**14.** $\cos\theta = -\dfrac{8}{17}$; $\tan\theta > 0$

**15.** $\csc\theta = \dfrac{5}{3}$; $\sec\theta < 0$

**16.** $\cot\theta = -\dfrac{80}{39}$; $\cos\theta > 0$

**Find exact values for sin $\theta$, cos $\theta$, and tan $\theta$ using the information given.**

**17.** $\sin(2\theta) = \dfrac{24}{25}$; $2\theta$ in QII

**18.** $\sin(2\theta) = -\dfrac{240}{289}$; $2\theta$ in QIII

**19.** $\cos(2\theta) = -\dfrac{41}{841}$; $2\theta$ in QII

**20.** $\cos(2\theta) = \dfrac{120}{169}$; $2\theta$ in QIV

**21.** Verify the following identity:
$\sin(3\theta) = 3\sin\theta - 4\sin^3\theta$

**22.** Verify the following identity:
$\cos(4\theta) = 8\cos^4\theta - 8\cos^2\theta + 1$

**Use a double-angle identity to find exact values for the following expressions.**

**23.** $\cos 75° \sin 75°$

**24.** $\cos^2 15° - \sin^2 15°$

**25.** $1 - 2\sin^2\left(\dfrac{\pi}{8}\right)$

**26.** $2\cos^2\left(\dfrac{\pi}{12}\right) - 1$

**27.** $\dfrac{2\tan 22.5°}{1 - \tan^2 22.5°}$

**28.** $\dfrac{2\tan\left(\frac{\pi}{12}\right)}{1 - \tan^2\left(\frac{\pi}{12}\right)}$

**29.** Use a double-angle identity to rewrite $9\sin(3x)\cos(3x)$ as a single function.
[*Hint:* $9 = \frac{9}{2}(2)$.]

**30.** Use a double-angle identity to rewrite $2.5 - 5\sin^2 x$ as a single term.
[*Hint:* Factor out a constant.]

**Rewrite in terms of an expression containing only cosines to the power 1.**

**31.** $\sin^2 x\cos^2 x$

**32.** $\sin^4 x\cos^2 x$

**33.** $3\cos^4 x$

**34.** $\cos^4 x\sin^4 x$

**35.** $2\sin^6 x$

**36.** $4\cos^6 x$

**Use a half-angle identity to find exact values for sin $\theta$, cos $\theta$, and tan $\theta$ for the given value of $\theta$.**

**37.** $\theta = 22.5°$

**38.** $\theta = 75°$

**39.** $\theta = \dfrac{\pi}{12}$

**40.** $\theta = \dfrac{5\pi}{12}$

**41.** $\theta = 67.5°$

**42.** $\theta = 112.5°$

**43.** $\theta = \dfrac{3\pi}{8}$

**44.** $\theta = \dfrac{11\pi}{12}$

**Use the results of Exercises 37–40 and a half-angle identity to find the exact value.**

**45.** $\sin 11.25°$

**46.** $\tan 37.5°$

**47.** $\sin\left(\dfrac{\pi}{24}\right)$

**48.** $\cos\left(\dfrac{5\pi}{24}\right)$

**Use a half-angle identity to rewrite each expression as a single, nonradical function.**

**49.** $\sqrt{\dfrac{1 + \cos 30°}{2}}$

**50.** $\sqrt{\dfrac{1 - \cos 45°}{2}}$

**51.** $\sqrt{\dfrac{1 - \cos(4\theta)}{1 + \cos(4\theta)}}$

**52.** $\dfrac{1 - \cos(6x)}{\sin(6x)}$

**53.** $\dfrac{\sin(2x)}{1 + \cos(2x)}$

**54.** $\dfrac{\sqrt{2(1 + \cos x)}}{1 + \cos x}$

**Find exact values for $\sin\left(\dfrac{\theta}{2}\right)$, $\cos\left(\dfrac{\theta}{2}\right)$, and $\tan\left(\dfrac{\theta}{2}\right)$ using the information given.**

**55.** $\sin\theta = \dfrac{12}{13}$; $\theta$ is obtuse

**56.** $\cos\theta = -\dfrac{8}{17}$; $\theta$ is obtuse

**57.** $\cos\theta = -\dfrac{4}{5}$; $\theta$ in QII

**58.** $\sin\theta = -\dfrac{7}{25}$; $\theta$ in QIII

**59.** $\tan\theta = -\dfrac{35}{12}$; $\theta$ in QII

**60.** $\sec\theta = -\dfrac{65}{33}$; $\theta$ in QIII

**61.** $\sin\theta = \dfrac{15}{113}$; $\theta$ is acute

**62.** $\cos\theta = \dfrac{48}{73}$; $\theta$ is acute

**63.** $\cot\theta = \dfrac{21}{20}$; $\pi < \theta < \dfrac{3\pi}{2}$

**64.** $\csc\theta = \dfrac{41}{9}$; $\dfrac{\pi}{2} < \theta < \pi$

**Verify the following identities.**

**65.** $\dfrac{2 \sin x \cos x}{\cos^2 x - \sin^2 x} = \tan(2x)$

**66.** $\dfrac{1 - 2 \sin^2 x}{2 \sin x \cos x} = \cot(2x)$

**67.** $(\sin x + \cos x)^2 = 1 + \sin(2x)$

**68.** $(\sin^2 x - 1)^2 = \sin^4 x + \cos(2x)$

**69.** $\cos(8\theta) = \cos^2(4\theta) - \sin^2(4\theta)$

**70.** $\sin(4x) = 4 \sin x \cos x (1 - 2 \sin^2 x)$

**71.** $\dfrac{\cos(2\theta)}{\sin^2 \theta} = \cot^2 \theta - 1$

**72.** $\csc^2 \theta - 2 = \dfrac{\cos(2\theta)}{\sin^2 \theta}$

**73.** $\tan(2\theta) = \dfrac{2}{\cot \theta - \tan \theta}$

**74.** $\cot \theta - \tan \theta = \dfrac{2 \cos(2\theta)}{\sin(2\theta)}$

**75.** $\tan x + \cot x = 2 \csc(2x)$

**76.** $\csc(2x) = \dfrac{1}{2} \csc x \sec x$

**77.** $\cos^2\left(\dfrac{x}{2}\right) - \sin^2\left(\dfrac{x}{2}\right) = \cos x$

**78.** $1 - 2 \sin^2\left(\dfrac{x}{4}\right) = \cos\left(\dfrac{x}{2}\right)$

**79.** $1 - \sin^2(2\theta) = 1 - 4 \sin^2 \theta + 4 \sin^4 \theta$

**80.** $2 \cos^2\left(\dfrac{x}{2}\right) - 1 = \cos x$

**81.** Show $\sin^2 \alpha + (1 - \cos \alpha)^2 = \left[2 \sin\left(\dfrac{\alpha}{2}\right)\right]^2$.

**82.** Show that $\tan\left(\dfrac{u}{2}\right) = \pm\sqrt{\dfrac{1 - \cos u}{1 + \cos u}}$ is equivalent to $\dfrac{\sin u}{1 + \cos u}$ by rationalizing the numerator.

**83.** Derive the identity for $\sin(2\alpha)$ and $\tan(2\alpha)$ using $\sin(\alpha + \beta)$ and $\tan(\alpha + \beta)$, where $\alpha = \beta$.

**84.** Derive the identity for $\tan^2(\alpha)$ using $\tan(2\alpha) = \dfrac{2 \tan(\alpha)}{1 - \tan^2(\alpha)}$. [*Hint:* Solve for $\tan^2 \alpha$ and work in terms of sines and cosines.]

---

▶ **WORKING WITH FORMULAS**

**85. Supersonic speeds, the sound barrier, and Mach numbers:** $\mathcal{M} = \csc\left(\dfrac{\theta}{2}\right)$

The speed of sound varies with temperature and altitude. At 32°F, sound travels about 742 mi/hr at sea level. A jet-plane flying faster than the speed of sound (called supersonic speed) has "broken the sound barrier." The plane projects three-dimensional sound waves about the nose of the craft that form the shape of a cone. The cone intersects the Earth along a hyperbolic path, with a sonic boom being heard by anyone along this path. The ratio of the plane's speed to the speed of sound is

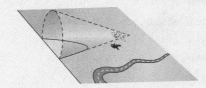

called its Mach number $\mathcal{M}$, meaning a plane flying at $\mathcal{M} = 3.2$ is traveling 3.2 times the speed of sound. This Mach number can be determined using the formula given here, where $\theta$ is the vertex angle of the cone described. For the following exercises, use the formula to find $\mathcal{M}$ or $\theta$ as required. For parts (a) and (b), answer in exact form (using a half-angle identity) and approximate form.

    **a.** $\theta = 30°$    **b.** $\theta = 45°$    **c.** $\mathcal{M} = 2$

**86. Malus's law:** $I = I_0 \cos^2 \theta$

When a beam of plane-polarized light with intensity $I_0$ hits an analyzer, the intensity $I$ of the transmitted beam of light can be found using the formula shown, where $\theta$ is the angle formed between the transmission axes of the polarizer and the analyzer. Find the intensity of the beam when $\theta = 15°$ and $I_0 = 300$ candelas (cd). Answer in exact form (using a power reduction identity) and approximate form.

▶ **APPLICATIONS**

**87. Clock angles:** Kirkland City has a large clock atop city hall, with a minute hand that is 3 ft long. Claire and Monica independently attempt to devise a function that will track the distance between the tip of the minute hand at $t$ minutes between the hours, and the tip of the minute hand when it is in the vertical position as shown. Claire finds the function $d(t) = \left| 6 \sin\left(\dfrac{\pi t}{60}\right) \right|$, while Monica devises $d(t) = \sqrt{18\left[1 - \cos\left(\dfrac{\pi t}{30}\right)\right]}$. Use the identities from this section to show the functions are equivalent.

**88. Origami:** The Japanese art of origami involves the repeated folding of a single piece of paper to create various art forms. When the upper right corner of a rectangular 21.6-cm by 28-cm piece of paper is folded down until the corner is flush with the other side, the length $L$ of the fold is related to the angle $\theta$ by $L = \dfrac{10.8}{\sin\theta\cos^2\theta}$. (a) Show this is equivalent to $L = \dfrac{21.6\sec\theta}{\sin(2\theta)}$, (b) find the length of the fold if $\theta = 30°$, and (c) find the angle $\theta$ if $L = 28.8$ cm.

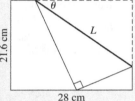

21.6 cm

$\theta$

$L$

28 cm

**89. Machine gears:** A machine part involves two gears. The first has a radius of 2 cm and the second a radius of 1 cm, so the smaller gear turns twice as fast as the larger gear. Let $\theta$ represent the angle of rotation in the larger gear, measured from a vertical and downward starting position. Let $P$ be a point on the circumference of the smaller gear, starting at the vertical and downward position. Four engineers working on an improved design for this component devise functions that track the height of point $P$ above the horizontal plane shown, for a rotation of $\theta°$ by the larger gear. The functions they develop are: Engineer A: $f(\theta) = \sin(2\theta - 90°) + 1$; Engineer B: $g(\theta) = 2\sin^2\theta$; Engineer C: $k(\theta) = 1 + \sin^2\theta - \cos^2\theta$; and Engineer D: $h(\theta) = 1 - \cos(2\theta)$. Use any of the identities you've learned so far to show these four functions are equivalent.

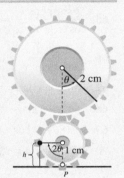

$\theta$ 2 cm

$h$   $2\theta$ 1 cm

$P$

**90. Working with identities:** Compute the value of $\sin 15°$ two ways, first using the half-angle identity for sine, and second using the difference identity for sine. (a) Find a decimal approximation for each to show the results are equivalent and (b) verify algebraically that they are equivalent. (*Hint:* Square both sides.)

**91. Working with identities:** Compute the value of $\cos 15°$ two ways, first using the half-angle identity for cosine, and second using the difference identity for cosine. (a) Find a decimal approximation for each to show the results are equivalent and (b) verify algebraically that they are equivalent. (*Hint:* Square both sides.)

▶ **EXTENDING THE CONCEPT**

**92. A proof without words:** From elementary geometry we have the following: (a) an angle inscribed in a semicircle is a right angle; and (b) the measure of an inscribed angle (vertex on the circumference) is one-half the measure of its

**Exercise 92**

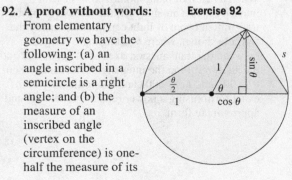

$\dfrac{\theta}{2}$

$1$

$\theta$

$1$   $\cos\theta$

$\sin\theta$

$s$

intercepted arc. Discuss/explain how the unit-circle diagram offers a proof that $\tan\left(\dfrac{x}{2}\right) = \dfrac{\sin x}{1 + \cos x}$. Be detailed and thorough.

**93.** Using $\theta = 30°$ and repeatedly applying the half-angle identity for cosine, show that $\cos 3.75°$ is equal to $\dfrac{\sqrt{2 + \sqrt{2 + \sqrt{2 + \sqrt{3}}}}}{2}$. Verify the result using a calculator, then use the patterns noted to write the value of $\cos 1.875°$ in closed form (also verify this result). As $\theta$ becomes very small, what appears to be happening to the value of $\cos\theta$?

## ▶ MAINTAINING YOUR SKILLS

**94. (4.3)** State the period of the functions given:

**a.** $y = 3 \sin\left(\dfrac{\pi}{8}x - \dfrac{\pi}{3}\right)$

**b.** $y = 4 \tan\left(2x + \dfrac{\pi}{4}\right)$

**95. (1.4)** State the three Pythagorean identities.

**96. (1.1)** Solve the triangles given using only special ratio/special triangle values.

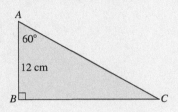 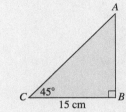

**97. (2.1)** Clarence the Clown is about to be shot from a circus cannon to a safety net on the other side of the main tent. If the cannon is 30 ft long and must be aimed at 40° for Clarence to hit the net, the end of the cannon must be how high from ground level?

**98. (3.2)** The area of a circular sector is $A = \dfrac{125\pi}{3} r^2$. If $r = 25$ m, what angle is subtended?

**99. (4.4)** Temperatures in Baghdad, Iraq, range from an average low of 58°F in January (month 1) to an average high of 110°F in July (month 7). Use this information to construct a sinusoidal model that approximates the average temperatures in Baghdad for the other 10 months.

## Learning Objectives

*In Section 5.4 you will learn how to:*

☐ **A.** Derive and use the product-to-sum and sum-to-product identities

☐ **B.** Solve applications using these and other identities

As you may have noticed, the identities we're studying are much more than an exercise in rewriting trigonometric expressions. In fact, most identities are the result of challenges that ancient astronomers and scientists faced in their attempt to understand the world around them, and even today these identities are applied in very practical ways. For instance, one of the most profound discoveries of the eighteenth century was that the behavior of electricity, light, and sound could all be modeled using sinusoidal waves. The product-to-sum and sum-to-product identities play a fundamental role in the investigation and study of these phenomena.

## A. The Product-to-Sum Identities

As mentioned in the introduction, the product-to-sum and sum-to-product identities are of immense importance to the study of any phenomenon that travels in waves, like light and sound. In fact, the tones you hear as you dial a telephone are actually the sum of two sound waves interacting with each other. Each derivation of a product-to-sum identity is very similar **(see Exercise 39),** and we illustrate by deriving the identity for $\cos \alpha \cos \beta$. Beginning with the sum and difference identities for cosine, we have

$$\cos \alpha \cos \beta + \sin \alpha \sin \beta = \cos(\alpha - \beta) \qquad \text{cosine of a difference}$$

$$+\ \underline{\cos \alpha \cos \beta - \sin \alpha \sin \beta = \cos(\alpha + \beta)} \qquad \text{cosine of a sum}$$

$$2 \cos \alpha \cos \beta = \cos(\alpha - \beta) + \cos(\alpha + \beta) \qquad \text{combine equations}$$

$$\cos \alpha \cos \beta = \frac{1}{2}[\cos(\alpha - \beta) + \cos(\alpha + \beta)] \qquad \text{divide by 2}$$

The identities from this family are listed here.

## The Product-to-Sum Identities

$$\cos \alpha \cos \beta = \frac{1}{2}[\cos(\alpha - \beta) + \cos(\alpha + \beta)] \qquad \sin \alpha \sin \beta = \frac{1}{2}[\cos(\alpha - \beta) - \cos(\alpha + \beta)]$$

$$\sin \alpha \cos \beta = \frac{1}{2}[\sin(\alpha + \beta) + \sin(\alpha - \beta)] \qquad \cos \alpha \sin \beta = \frac{1}{2}[\sin(\alpha + \beta) - \sin(\alpha - \beta)]$$

**EXAMPLE 1** ▶ **Rewriting a Product as an Equivalent Sum Using Identities**

Write the product $2 \cos(27t) \cos(15t)$ as the sum of two cosine functions.

Solution ▶ This is a direct application of the product-to-sum identity, with $\alpha = 27t$ and $\beta = 15t$.

$$\cos \alpha \cos \beta = \frac{1}{2}[\cos(\alpha - \beta) + \cos(\alpha + \beta)] \qquad \text{product-to-sum identity}$$

$$2 \cos(27t)\cos(15t) = 2\left(\frac{1}{2}\right)[\cos(27t - 15t) + \cos(27t + 15t)] \qquad \text{substitute}$$

$$= \cos(12t) + \cos(42t) \qquad \text{result}$$

**Now try Exercises 7 through 18** ▶

There are times we find it necessary to "work in the other direction," writing a sum of two trig functions as a product. This family of identities can be derived from the product-to-sum identities using a change of variable. We'll illustrate the process for $\sin u + \sin v$. You are asked for the derivation of $\cos u + \cos v$ in **Exercise 40.** To begin, we use $2\alpha = u + v$ and $2\beta = u - v$. This creates the sum $2\alpha + 2\beta = 2u$ and the difference $2\alpha - 2\beta = 2v$, yielding $\alpha + \beta = u$ and $\alpha - \beta = v$, respectively. Dividing the original expressions by 2 gives $\alpha = \dfrac{u + v}{2}$ and $\beta = \dfrac{u - v}{2}$, which all together make the derivation a matter of direct substitution. Using these values in any product-to-sum identity gives the related sum-to-product, as shown here.

$$\sin \alpha \cos \beta = \frac{1}{2}[\sin(\alpha + \beta) + \sin(\alpha - \beta)] \qquad \text{product-to-sum identity (sum of sines)}$$

$$\sin\left(\frac{u + v}{2}\right)\cos\left(\frac{u - v}{2}\right) = \frac{1}{2}(\sin u + \sin v) \qquad \text{substitute } \frac{u + v}{2} \text{ for } \alpha, \frac{u - v}{2} \text{ for } \beta,$$
$$\text{substitute } u \text{ for } \alpha + \beta \text{ and } v \text{ for } \alpha - \beta$$

$$2 \sin\left(\frac{u + v}{2}\right)\cos\left(\frac{u - v}{2}\right) = \sin u + \sin v \qquad \text{multiply by 2}$$

The sum-to-product identities follow.

## The Sum-to-Product Identities

$$\cos u + \cos v = 2 \cos\left(\frac{u + v}{2}\right)\cos\left(\frac{u - v}{2}\right) \qquad \sin u + \sin v = 2 \sin\left(\frac{u + v}{2}\right)\cos\left(\frac{u - v}{2}\right)$$

$$\sin u - \sin v = 2 \cos\left(\frac{u + v}{2}\right)\sin\left(\frac{u - v}{2}\right) \qquad \cos u - \cos v = -2 \sin\left(\frac{u + v}{2}\right)\sin\left(\frac{u - v}{2}\right)$$

**EXAMPLE 2** ▶ **Rewriting a Sum as an Equivalent Product Using Identities**

Given $y_1 = \sin(12\pi t)$ and $y_2 = \sin(10\pi t)$, express $y_1 + y_2$ as a product of trigonometric functions.

**Solution** ▶ This is a direct application of the sum-to-product identity $\sin u + \sin v$, with $u = 12\pi t$ and $v = 10\pi t$.

$$\sin u + \sin v = 2\sin\left(\frac{u+v}{2}\right)\cos\left(\frac{u-v}{2}\right) \qquad \text{sum-to-product identity}$$

☑ **A. You've just learned how to derive and use the product-to-sum and sum-to-product identities**

$$\sin(12\pi t) + \sin(10\pi t) = 2\sin\left(\frac{12\pi t + 10\pi t}{2}\right)\cos\left(\frac{12\pi t - 10\pi t}{2}\right) \qquad \substack{\text{substitute } 12\pi t \text{ for} \\ u \text{ and } 10\pi t \text{ for } v}$$

$$= 2\sin(11\pi t)\cos(\pi t) \qquad \text{substitute}$$

**Now try Exercises 19 through 30** ▶

For a mixed variety of identities, **see Exercises 31–38.**

## B. Applications of Identities

In more advanced mathematics courses, rewriting an expression using identities enables the extension or completion of a task that would otherwise be very difficult (or even impossible). In addition, there are a number of practical applications in the physical sciences.

### Sound Waves

Each tone you hear on a touch-tone phone is actually the combination of precisely two sound waves with different frequencies (frequency $f$ is defined as $f = \dfrac{B}{2\pi}$). This is why the tones you hear sound identical, regardless of what phone you use. The sum-to-product and product-to-sum formulas help us to understand, study, and use sound in very powerful and practical ways, like sending faxes and using other electronic media.

**EXAMPLE 3** ▶ **Using an Identity to Solve an Application**

On a touch-tone phone, the sound created by pressing 5 is produced by combining a sound wave with frequency 1336 cycles/sec, with another wave having frequency 770 cycles/sec. Their respective equations are $y_1 = \cos(2\pi\,1336t)$ and $y_2 = \cos(2\pi\,770t)$, with the resultant wave being $y = y_1 + y_2$ or $y = \cos(2672\pi t) + \cos(1540\pi t)$. Rewrite this sum as a product.

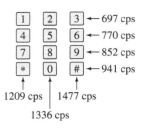

**Solution** ▶ This is a direct application of the sum-to-product identity, with $u = 2672\pi t$ and $v = 1540\pi t$. Computing one-half the sum/difference of $u$ and $v$ gives

$$\frac{2672\pi t + 1540\pi t}{2} = 2106\pi t \text{ and } \frac{2672\pi t - 1540\pi t}{2} = 566\pi t.$$

$$\cos u + \cos v = 2\cos\left(\frac{u+v}{2}\right)\cos\left(\frac{u-v}{2}\right) \qquad \text{sum-to-product identity}$$

$$\cos(2672\pi t) + \cos(1540\pi t) = 2\cos(2106\pi t)\cos(566\pi t) \qquad \substack{\text{substitute } 2672\pi t \text{ for } u \\ \text{and } 1540\pi t \text{ for } v}$$

**Now try Exercises 43 and 46** ▶

Note we can identify the button pressed when the wave is written as a sum. If we have only the resulting wave (written as a product), the product-to-sum formula must be used to identify which button was pressed.

### Projectile Motion

A projectile is any object that is thrown, shot, kicked, dropped, or otherwise given an initial velocity, but lacking a continuing source of propulsion. If air resistance is ignored, the range of the projectile depends only on its initial velocity $v$ and the angle $\theta$ at which it is propelled. This phenomenon is modeled by the function

$$r(\theta) = \frac{1}{16} v^2 \sin\theta \cos\theta.$$

---

**EXAMPLE 4** ▶ **Using Identities to Solve an Application**

a. Use an identity to show $r(\theta) = \dfrac{1}{16} v^2 \sin\theta \cos\theta$ is equivalent to

$$r(\theta) = \frac{1}{32} v^2 \sin(2\theta).$$

b. If the projectile is thrown with an initial velocity of $v = 96$ ft/sec, how far will it travel if $\theta = 15°$?

c. From the result of part (a), determine what angle $\theta$ will give the maximum range for the projectile.

Solution ▶ a. Note that we can use a double-angle identity if we rewrite the coefficient. Writing $\dfrac{1}{16}$ as $2\left(\dfrac{1}{32}\right)$ and commuting the factors gives

$$r(\theta) = \left(\frac{1}{32}\right) v^2 (2\sin\theta\cos\theta) = \left(\frac{1}{32}\right) v^2 \sin(2\theta).$$

b. With $v = 96$ ft/sec and $\theta = 15°$, the formula gives $r(15°) = \left(\dfrac{1}{32}\right)(96)^2 \sin 30°$.

Evaluating the result shows the projectile travels a horizontal distance of 144 ft.

c. For any initial velocity $v$, $r(\theta)$ will be maximized when $\sin(2\theta)$ is a maximum. This occurs when $\sin(2\theta) = 1$, meaning $2\theta = 90°$ and $\theta = 45°$. The maximum range is achieved when the projectile is released at an angle of 45°.

**Now try Exercises 47 and 48** ▶

---

**GRAPHICAL SUPPORT**

The result in Example 4(c) can be verified graphically by assuming an initial velocity of 96 ft/sec and entering the function

$$r(\theta) = \frac{1}{32}(96)^2 \sin(2\theta) = 288\sin(2\theta) \text{ as Y}_1 \text{ on a}$$

graphing calculator. With an amplitude of 288 and results confined to the first quadrant, we set an appropriate window, graph the function, and use the [2nd] [TRACE] (CALC 4:maximum) feature. As shown in the figure, the max occurs at $\theta = 45°$.

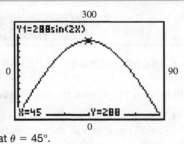

☑ **B. You've just learned how to solve applications using these and other identities**

**TECHNOLOGY HIGHLIGHT**

## Trigonometric Graphs and ZoomSto/ZoomRcl

In Chapter 4, we saw how the ZOOM **7:ZTrig** screen could be used to study trigonometric graphs. The calculator automatically creates a friendly window using the available pixels, setting Xmin $\approx -360°$ or $-2\pi$ and Xmax $\approx 360°$ or $2\pi$. In addition, it sets Ymin $= -4$ and Ymax $= 4$ since a large number of trig graphs fall within this amplitude range. However, a great deal of study, investigation, and comparison is done in the interval $[0, 2\pi]$ and with sine and cosine graphs having a much smaller amplitude. In these cases, it helps to use the ZOOM ► (MEMORY) feature of the TI-84 Plus. To use this feature, you set the window to the desired settings and press ZOOM ► (MEMORY) **2:ZoomSto,** which will store these settings for future use. The window size will be changed each time ZOOM **7:ZTrig,** ZOOM **4:ZDecimal,** or ZOOM **7:ZStandard** is used, but you can always return to the stored settings using ZOOM ► (MEMORY) **3:ZoomRcl.** Suppose we wanted to investigate the graph of $Y_1 = \cos(2x)$, along with the three related identities developed in the previous section. Using ZOOM **7:ZTrig** in degree mode gives the window shown in Figure 5.10. If our particular interest was $[0, 360]$ we could reset Xmin $= 0$, Xmax $= 360$, and Xscl $= 45$. Using the preset Ymin and Ymax values leaves too much "wasted space," so we reset these to Ymin $= -2$ and Ymax $= 2$ or some other desired setting. Press GRAPH to see $Y_1 = \cos(2x)$ with these settings (Figure 5.11), then (MEMORY) **2:ZoomSto** to store the settings for future use.

**Figure 5.10**

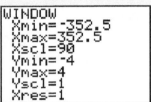

**Figure 5.11**

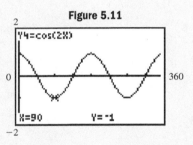

**Exercise 1:** Enter $Y_2 = \cos^2 x - \sin^2 x$ and $Y_3 = 1 - 2\sin^2 x$, then graph $Y_1$, $Y_2$, and $Y_3$ on the ZOOM **7:ZTrig** screen. What do you notice? Now use the keystrokes ZOOM ► (MEMORY) **3:ZoomRcl** to graph these functions using the stored settings. Can you distinguish between the graphs?

**Exercise 2:** Enter $Y_1 = \tan^2 x$ and $Y_2 = \dfrac{1 - \cos(2x)}{1 + \cos(2x)}$. Use the ZOOM **7:ZTrig** screen to graphically verify that $Y_1 = Y_2$ is an identity, then take a closer look at the graphs using ZOOM ► (MEMORY) **3:ZoomRcl.** Use this screen to approximate the values of x for which $\tan^2 x = 1$.

---

 **5.4 EXERCISES**

---

▶ **CONCEPTS AND VOCABULARY**

**Fill in each blank with the appropriate word or phrase. Carefully reread the section if needed.**

1. The _____-to-_____ identities can be derived using the addition and subtraction of the _____ and _____ identities.

2. Light and _____ can both be modeled using _____ waves. When modeling these phenomena, we define frequency as _____.

3. The function $r(\theta) =$ _____ models the _____ of a projectile when _____ is not taken into account.

4. By substituting $-v$ for $v$ and applying an identity due to symmetry, the sum-to-product identity
$$\sin u + \sin v = 2 \sin\left(\frac{u+v}{2}\right)\cos\left(\frac{u-v}{2}\right) \text{ can be}$$
used to develop sum-to-product identity: _____.

5. Explain/Discuss why many consider the sum and difference formulas the only non-fundamental formulas that must be memorized. Be sure to include the cofunction, double-angle, half-angle, and power reduction identities in your discussion.

6. In Example 4(a), a double-angle identity was used. Explain how a product-to-sum identity could have been used instead, with the same results.

▶ **DEVELOPING YOUR SKILLS**

**Write each product as a sum using the product-to-sum identities.**

7. $\sin(-4\theta)\sin(8\theta)$       8. $\cos(15\alpha)\sin(-3\alpha)$

9. $2\cos\left(\frac{7t}{2}\right)\sin\left(\frac{3t}{2}\right)$   10. $2\sin\left(\frac{5t}{2}\right)\sin\left(\frac{9t}{2}\right)$

11. $2\cos(1979\pi t)\cos(439\pi t)$

12. $2\cos(2150\pi t)\cos(268\pi t)$

13. $2\sin(x+2y)\cos(x-2y)$

14. $2\sin(3x+y)\cos(3x-y)$

**Find the exact value using product-to-sum identities.**

15. $2\cos 15°\sin 135°$       16. $2\cos 105°\cos 165°$

17. $\sin\left(\frac{7\pi}{8}\right)\cos\left(\frac{\pi}{8}\right)$   18. $\sin\left(\frac{7\pi}{12}\right)\sin\left(-\frac{\pi}{12}\right)$

**Write each sum as a product using the sum-to-product identities.**

19. $\cos(9h)+\cos(4h)$       20. $\sin(14k)+\sin(41k)$

21. $\sin\left(\frac{11x}{8}\right)-\sin\left(\frac{5x}{8}\right)$   22. $\cos\left(\frac{7x}{6}\right)-\cos\left(\frac{5x}{6}\right)$

23. $\cos(697\pi t)-\cos(1447\pi t)$

24. $\cos(852\pi t)+\cos(1209\pi t)$

25. $\sin(3x+y)+\sin(3x+5y)$

26. $\sin(2x-y)-\sin(4x+y)$

**Find the exact value using sum-to-product identities.**

27. $\cos 75° + \cos 15°$       28. $\cos 285° - \cos 195°$

29. $\sin\left(\frac{17\pi}{12}\right) - \sin\left(\frac{13\pi}{12}\right)$

30. $\sin\left(\frac{11\pi}{12}\right) + \sin\left(\frac{7\pi}{12}\right)$

**Verify the following identities.**

31. $\dfrac{\sin m + \sin n}{\cos m + \cos n} = \tan\left(\dfrac{m+n}{2}\right)$

32. $\dfrac{\sin m - \sin n}{\cos m - \cos n} = -\cot\left(\dfrac{m+n}{2}\right)$

33. $\dfrac{2\sin 2t \cos t - \sin 3t}{\cos t} = \tan t$

34. $\dfrac{2\cos 3t \cos 2t - \cos 5t}{\sin t} = \cot t$

35. $\dfrac{2\cos 2t}{\sin 3t - \sin t} = \csc t$   36. $\dfrac{2\sin 2t}{\cos t - \cos 3t} = \csc t$

37. $\dfrac{\sin(120\pi t) + \sin(80\pi t)}{\cos(120\pi t) - \cos(80\pi t)} = -\cot(20\pi t)$

38. $\dfrac{\cos(14\pi t) + \cos(6\pi t)}{\sin(14\pi t) - \sin(6\pi t)} = \cot(4\pi t)$

39. Derive the product-to-sum identity for $\sin\alpha\sin\beta$.

40. Derive the sum-to product identity for $\cos u + \cos v$.

▶ **WORKING WITH FORMULAS**

41. **A product-to-sum identity:** $\sin\alpha\cos\beta = \dfrac{1}{2}[\sin(\alpha+\beta)+\sin(\alpha-\beta)]$

   Using exact values, verify the identity shown is true when $\alpha = \dfrac{5\pi}{6}$ and $\beta = \dfrac{2\pi}{3}$.

42. **A product-to-sum identity:**
   $$\sin a \sin b \sin c = \frac{1}{4}[\sin(a+b-c)+\sin(b+c-a)+\sin(c+a-b)-\sin(a+b+c)]$$
   Using exact values, verify the identity shown is true when $a = 30°$, $b = 120°$, and $c = 240°$.

▶ **APPLICATIONS**

**Touch-tone phones:** The diagram given in Example 3 shows the various frequencies used to create the tones for a touch-tone phone. Use a sum-to-product identity to write the resultant wave when the following numbers are pressed.

**43.** ③

**44.** ⑧

One button is randomly pressed and the resultant wave is modeled by $y(t)$ shown. Use a product-to-sum identity to write the expression as a sum and determine the button pressed.

**45.** $y(t) = 2 \cos(2150\pi t)\cos(268\pi t)$

**46.** $y(t) = 2 \cos(1906\pi t)\cos(512\pi t)$

**Range of a projectile:** Exercises 47 and 48 refer to Example 4. In Example 4, we noted that the range of a projectile was maximized at $\theta = 45°$. If $\theta > 45°$ or $\theta < 45°$, the projectile falls short of its maximum potential distance. In Exercises 47 and 48 assume that the projectile has an initial velocity of 96 ft/sec.

**47.** Compute how many feet short of maximum the projectile falls if (a) $\theta = 22.5°$ and (b) $\theta = 67.5°$. Answer in both exact and approximate form.

**48.** Use a calculator to compute how many feet short of maximum the projectile falls if (a) $\theta = 40°$ and $\theta = 50°$ and (b) $\theta = 37.5°$ and $\theta = 52.5°$. Do you see a pattern? Discuss/explain what you notice and experiment with other values to confirm your observations.

**49.** A clapotic (or standing) wave is formed when a wave strikes and reflects off a seawall or other immovable object. Against one particular seawall, the standing wave that forms can be modeled by summing the incoming wave represented by the equation $y_i = 2 \sin(1.1x - 0.6t)$ with the outgoing wave represented by the equation $y_o = 2 \sin(1.1x + 0.6t)$. Use a sum-to-product identity to express the resulting wave $y = y_i + y_o$ as a product.

▶ **EXTENDING THE CONCEPT**

**50.** Can you find three distinct, real numbers whose sum is equal to their product? A little known fact from trigonometry stipulates that for any triangle, the sum of the tangents of the angles is equal to the products of their tangents. Use a calculator to test this statement, recalling the three angles must sum to 180°. Our website at www.mhhe.com/coburn shows a method that enables you to verify the statement using tangents that are all rational values.

**51.** Verify the product-to-sum identity given in Exercise 42:
$$\sin a \sin b \sin c = \frac{1}{4}\left[\sin(a + b - c) + \sin(b + c - a) + \sin(c + a - b) - \sin(a + b + c)\right]$$

▶ **MAINTAINING YOUR SKILLS**

**52.** (3.4) Use a calculator to find two values of $t$ that satisfy $\sin t \approx 0.9889$. Round to four decimal places.

**53.** (4.2) Given $Y_1 = \tan \alpha$ and $Y_2 = \cot \alpha$, which function is increasing? Which is defined for $\alpha \in (0, \pi)$?

**54.** (1.1) The hypotenuse of a certain right triangle is twice the shortest side. Solve the triangle.

**55.** (3.3) Verify that $\left(\frac{16}{65}, \frac{63}{65}\right)$ is on the unit circle, then find $\tan \theta$ and $\sec \theta$ to verify $1 + \tan^2\theta = \sec^2\theta$.

**56.** (4.3) Write the equation of the function graphed in terms of a sine function of the form $y = A \sin(Bx + C) + D$.

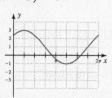

**57.** (5.2) Use the sum identity for cosine to find the exact value of $\cos(105°)$.

# SUMMARY AND CONCEPT REVIEW

## SECTION 5.1   More on Verifying Identities

### KEY CONCEPTS
- The sine and tangent functions are odd functions, while cosine is even.
- The steps used to verify an identity must be reversible.
- If two expressions are equal, one may be substituted for the other and the result will be equivalent.
- To verify an identity we mold, change, substitute, and rewrite one side until we "match" the other side.
- Verifying identities often involves a combination of algebraic skills with the fundamental trig identities. A collection and summary of the *Guidelines for Verifying Identities* can be found on page 213.
- To show an equation is not an identity, find any one value where the expressions are defined but the equation is false, or graph both functions on a calculator to see if the graphs are identical.

### EXERCISES
Verify that each equation is an identity.

**1.** $\dfrac{\csc^2 x(1 - \cos^2 x)}{\tan^2 x} = \cot^2 x$

**2.** $\dfrac{\cot x}{\sec x} - \dfrac{\csc x}{\tan x} = \cot x(\cos x - \csc x)$

**3.** $\dfrac{\sin^4 x - \cos^4 x}{\sin x \cos x} = \tan x - \cot x$

**4.** $\dfrac{(\sin x + \cos x)^2}{\sin x \cos x} = \csc x \sec x + 2$

## SECTION 5.2   The Sum and Difference Identities

### KEY CONCEPTS
The sum and difference identities can be used to
- Find exact values for nonstandard angles that are a sum or difference of two standard angles.
- Verify the cofunction identities and to rewrite a given function in terms of its cofunction.
- Find coterminal angles in $[0, 360°)$ for very large angles (the angle reduction formulas).
- Evaluate the difference quotient for $\sin x$, $\cos x$, and $\tan x$.
- Rewrite a sum as a single expression: $\cos \alpha \cos \beta + \sin \alpha \sin \beta = \cos(\alpha - \beta)$.

The sum and difference identities for sine and cosine can be remembered by noting
- For $\cos(\alpha \pm \beta)$, the function repeats and the signs alternate: $\cos(\alpha \pm \beta) = \cos \alpha \cos \beta \mp \sin \alpha \sin \beta$
- For $\sin(\alpha \pm \beta)$ the signs repeat and the functions alternate: $\sin(\alpha \pm \beta) = \sin \alpha \cos \beta \pm \cos \alpha \sin \beta$

### EXERCISES
Find exact values for the following expressions using sum and difference formulas.

**5. a.** $\cos 75°$     **b.** $\tan\left(\dfrac{\pi}{12}\right)$

**6. a.** $\tan 15°$     **b.** $\sin\left(-\dfrac{\pi}{12}\right)$

Evaluate exactly using sum and difference formulas.

**7. a.** $\cos 109° \cos 71° - \sin 109° \sin 71°$     **b.** $\sin 139° \cos 19° - \cos 139° \sin 19°$

Rewrite as a single expression using sum and difference formulas.

**8. a.** $\cos(3x)\cos(-2x) - \sin(3x)\sin(-2x)$     **b.** $\sin\left(\dfrac{x}{4}\right)\cos\left(\dfrac{3x}{8}\right) + \cos\left(\dfrac{x}{4}\right)\sin\left(\dfrac{3x}{8}\right)$

Evaluate exactly using sum and difference formulas, by reducing the angle to an angle in $[0, 360°)$ or $[0, 2\pi)$.

**9. a.** $\cos 1170°$     **b.** $\sin\left(\dfrac{57\pi}{4}\right)$

Use a cofunction identity to write an equivalent expression for the one given.

**10. a.** $\cos\left(\dfrac{x}{8}\right)$                                              **b.** $\sin\left(x - \dfrac{\pi}{12}\right)$

**11.** Verify that both expressions yield the same result using sum and difference formulas. $\tan 15° = \tan(45° - 30°)$ and $\tan 15° = \tan(135° - 120°)$.

**12.** Use sum and difference formulas to verify the following identity.

$$\cos\left(x + \dfrac{\pi}{6}\right) + \cos\left(x - \dfrac{\pi}{6}\right) = \sqrt{3}\cos x$$

## SECTION 5.3    The Double-Angle and Half-Angle Identities

### KEY CONCEPTS

- When multiple angle identities (identities involving $n\theta$) are used to find exact values, the terminal side of $\theta$ must be determined so the appropriate sign can be used.
- The power reduction identities for $\cos^2 x$ and $\sin^2 x$ are closely related to the double-angle identities, and can be derived directly from $\cos(2x) = 2\cos^2 x - 1$ and $\cos(2x) = 1 - 2\sin^2 x$.
- The half-angle identities can be developed from the power reduction identities by using a change of variable and taking square roots. The sign is then chosen based on the quadrant of the half angle.

### EXERCISES

Find exact values for $\sin(2\theta)$, $\cos(2\theta)$, and $\tan(2\theta)$ using the information given.

**13. a.** $\cos\theta = \dfrac{13}{85}$; $\theta$ in QIV                **b.** $\csc\theta = -\dfrac{29}{20}$; $\theta$ in QIII

Find exact values for $\sin\theta$, $\cos\theta$, and $\tan\theta$ using the information given.

**14. a.** $\cos(2\theta) = -\dfrac{41}{841}$; $\theta$ in QII        **b.** $\sin(2\theta) = -\dfrac{336}{625}$; $\theta$ in QII

Find exact values using the appropriate double-angle identity.

**15. a.** $\cos^2 22.5° - \sin^2 22.5°$                        **b.** $1 - 2\sin^2\left(\dfrac{\pi}{12}\right)$

Find exact values for $\sin\theta$ and $\cos\theta$ using the appropriate half-angle identity.

**16. a.** $\theta = 67.5°$                                    **b.** $\theta = \dfrac{5\pi}{8}$

Find exact values for $\sin\left(\dfrac{\theta}{2}\right)$ and $\cos\left(\dfrac{\theta}{2}\right)$ using the given information.

**17. a.** $\cos\theta = \dfrac{24}{25}$; $0° < \theta < 360°$; $\theta$ in QIV        **b.** $\csc\theta = -\dfrac{65}{33}$; $-90° < \theta < 0$; $\theta$ in QIV

**18.** The area of an isosceles triangle (two equal sides) is given by the formula $A = x^2\sin\left(\dfrac{\theta}{2}\right)\cos\left(\dfrac{\theta}{2}\right)$, where the equal sides have length $x$ and the vertex angle measures $\theta°$. (a) Use this formula and the half-angle identities to find the area of an isosceles triangle with vertex angle $\theta = 30°$ and equal sides of 12 cm. (b) Use substitution and a double-angle identity to verify that $x^2\sin\left(\dfrac{\theta}{2}\right)\cos\left(\dfrac{\theta}{2}\right) = \dfrac{1}{2}x^2\sin\theta$, then recompute the triangle's area. Do the results match?

## SECTION 5.4   The Product-to-Sum and Sum-to-Product Identities

### KEY CONCEPTS

- The product-to-sum and sum-to-product identities can be derived using the sum and difference formulas, and have important applications in many areas of science.
- The product-to-sum formula for $\sin \alpha \cos \beta$ can be used to find the product-to-sum formula for $\cos \alpha \sin \beta$ by carefully applying the commutative property of multiplication.
- If we set $\alpha = \beta = \theta$ in the product-to-sum formulas, we can quickly derive some of the double-angle and power reduction identities.

### EXERCISES

Write each product as a sum.

**19.** $\cos(3t)\sin(-9t)$

**20.** $\sin\left(\dfrac{2\pi}{3}t\right)\sin\left(\dfrac{4\pi}{3}t\right)$

Write each sum as a product.

**21.** $\cos t + \cos(3t)$

**22.** $\sin\left(-\dfrac{t}{4}\right) - \sin\left(\dfrac{3t}{8}\right)$

Find the exact values using identities.

**23.** $2\cos\left(\dfrac{11\pi}{12}\right)\cos\left(\dfrac{\pi}{12}\right)$

**24.** $\cos 75° - \cos 15°$

**25.** Verify the equation is an identity. $\dfrac{\cos(3\alpha) - \cos \alpha}{\cos(3\alpha) + \cos \alpha} = \dfrac{2\tan^2\alpha}{\sec^2\alpha - 2}$

1. Verify the equation is an identity:

$$\sin(-\theta)\tan(-\theta) + \cos\theta = \sec(-\theta)$$

2. Show that the following equation is not an identity:

$$\sqrt{\sin^2\theta} = \sin\theta$$

Find the exact value of each expression using a sum or difference identity.

3. $\tan 255°$

4. $\cos\left(\dfrac{19\pi}{12}\right)$

5. Find the exact value of $2\cos^2\left(\dfrac{\pi}{12}\right) - 1$ using an appropriate identity.

6. Find the exact value of $2\sin\left(\dfrac{\pi}{8}\right)\cos\left(\dfrac{\pi}{8}\right)$ using an appropriate identity.

Verify that each equation is an identity.

7. $\dfrac{1 - \cos^2\theta + \sin^2\theta}{\tan^2\theta} = 1 + \cos(2\theta)$

8. $\dfrac{(\cos t + \sin t)^2}{\tan t} = \cot t + 2\cos^2 t$

Find exact values for $\sin\left(\dfrac{x}{2}\right)$ and $\cos\left(\dfrac{x}{2}\right)$ using the information given.

9. $\sin x = \dfrac{-6}{7.5}$; $540° < x < 630°$

10. $\sec x = \dfrac{11.7}{4.5}$; $0 < x < \dfrac{\pi}{2}$

Verify the following identities *using a sum formula.*

11. $\sin(2\alpha) = 2\sin\alpha\cos\alpha$

12. $\cos(2\alpha) = \cos^2\alpha - \sin^2\alpha$

Find the value of each expression using sum-to-product and half-angle identities (without using a calculator).

13. $\sin 172.5° - \sin 52.5°$  14. $\cos 172.5° + \cos 52.5°$

Use the product-to-sum formulas to find the exact value of

15. $\sin\left(\dfrac{13\pi}{24}\right)\cos\left(\dfrac{7\pi}{24}\right)$  16. $\sin\left(\dfrac{13\pi}{24}\right)\sin\left(\dfrac{7\pi}{24}\right)$

17. Verify the identity:

$$\sin(\alpha + \beta)\sin(\alpha - \beta) = \sin^2\alpha - \sin^2\beta$$

18. Verify the identity:

$$\left[\cos\left(\dfrac{\theta}{2}\right) - \sin\left(\dfrac{\theta}{2}\right)\right]^2 = 1 - \sin\theta$$

The horizontal distance an object will travel when it is projected at angle $\theta$ with initial velocity $v$ is given by the equation $R = \frac{1}{16} v^2 \sin \theta \cos \theta$.

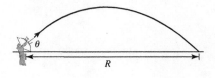

19. Use an identity to show this equation can be written as $R = \frac{1}{32} v^2 \sin(2\theta)$.

20. Use this equation to show why the horizontal distance traveled by the object is the same for any two complementary angles.

Verify each identity using fundamental identities.

**1.** $\dfrac{(\csc x - \cot x)(\csc x + \cot x)}{\sec x} = \cos x$

**2.** $\dfrac{\sin^3 x - \cos^3 x}{1 + \cos x \sin x} = \sin x - \cos x$

**3.** Find the value of all six trigonometric functions given $\cos \theta = \dfrac{48}{73}$; $\theta$ in QIV.

**4.** Find the exact value of $\tan 15°$ using a sum or difference formula.

**5.** Rewrite as a single expression and evaluate: $\cos 81° \cos 36° + \sin 81° \sin 36°$.

**6.** Evaluate $\cos 1935°$ exactly using an angle reduction formula.

**7.** Use sum and difference formulas to verify $\sin\left(x + \dfrac{\pi}{4}\right) - \sin\left(x - \dfrac{\pi}{4}\right) = \sqrt{2} \cos x$.

**8.** Find exact values for $\sin \theta$, $\cos \theta$, and $\tan \theta$ given $\cos(2\theta) = -\dfrac{161}{289}$; $\theta$ in QI.

**9.** Use a double-angle identity to evaluate $2 \cos^2 75° - 1$.

**10.** Find exact values for $\sin\left(\dfrac{\theta}{2}\right)$ and $\cos\left(\dfrac{\theta}{2}\right)$ given $\tan \theta = \dfrac{12}{35}$; $\theta$ in QI.

**11.** The area of a triangle is given geometrically as $A = \dfrac{1}{2}$ base $\cdot$ height.

The trigonometric formula for the triangle's area is $A = \dfrac{1}{2} bc \sin \alpha$, where $\alpha$ is the angle formed by the sides $b$ and $c$. In a certain triangle, $b = 8$, $c = 10$, and $\alpha = 22.5°$. Use the formula for $A$ given here and a half-angle identity to find the area of the triangle in exact form.

**12.** The equation $Ax^2 + Bxy + Cy^2 = 0$ can be written in an alternative form that makes it easier to graph. This is done by eliminating the mixed $xy$-term using the relation $\tan(2\theta) = \dfrac{B}{A - C}$ to find $\theta$. We can then find values for $\sin \theta$ and $\cos \theta$, which are used in a conversion formula. Find $\sin \theta$ and $\cos \theta$ for $17x^2 + 5\sqrt{3}xy + 2y^2 = 0$, assuming $2\theta$ in QI.

Verify that each equation is an identity.

**13.** $\dfrac{\tan \theta + \cot \theta}{\sin \theta \cos \theta} = \csc^2\theta \sec^2\theta$

**14.** $-2 \cos^4\theta + 3 \cos^2\theta - 1 = \sin^2\theta \cos(2\theta)$

Find exact values for the following expressions using sum and difference formulas.

**15.** $\tan(15°)$  **16.** $\cos(15°) - \sin(15°)$

**17.** Find exact values for $\sin(2\theta)$, $\cos(2\theta)$, and $\tan(2\theta)$ using the information given.

$\sin \theta = -\dfrac{12}{37}$; $\theta$ in QIII

**18.** Verify that the following equation is an identity: $\dfrac{\csc^2 x - 2}{2 \cot^2 x - \csc^2 x} = 1$

**19.** One of the buttons on a telephone is pressed, and the equation of the resultant wave is modeled by $y(t) = \cos(2\pi 1336 t) + \cos(2\pi 941 t)$. (a) Use the diagram on page 241 to determine which button on the touch-tone phone was pressed. (b) Use a sum-to-product identity to write this sum as a product.

**20.** Noise-canceling headphones rely on a microphone and sophisticated circuitry to generate sound waves that "cancel" unwanted waves before they reach the ear. If airplane wind noise modeled as $y_a = \sin 800\pi t$ is picked up by the mic, the headphones will generate a sound wave modeled by $y_h = \sin(800\pi t - \pi)$. Use a sum-to-product identity to rewrite $y_a + y_h$ as a product. What do you notice?

## CALCULATOR EXPLORATION AND DISCOVERY

### Seeing the Beats as the Beats Go On

When two sound waves of slightly different frequencies are combined, the resultant wave varies periodically in amplitude over time. These amplitude pulsations are called **beats.** In this *Exploration and Discovery,* we'll look at ways to "see" the beats more clearly on a graphing calculator, by representing sound waves very simplistically as $Y_1 = \cos(mt)$ and $Y_2 = \cos(nt)$ and noting a relationship between $m$, $n$, and the number of beats in $[0, 2\pi]$. Using a sum-to-product formula, we can represent the resultant wave as a single term. For $Y_1 = \cos(12t)$ and $Y_2 = \cos(8t)$ the result is

$$\cos(12t) + \cos(8t) = 2 \cos\left(\frac{12t + 8t}{2}\right) \cos\left(\frac{12t - 8t}{2}\right)$$

$$= 2 \cos(10t)\cos(2t)$$

The window used and resulting graph are shown in Figures 5.12 and 5.13, and it appears that "silence" occurs four times in this interval—where the graph of the combined waves is tangent to (bounces off of) the $x$-axis. This indicates a total of four beats. Note the number of beats is equal to the difference $m - n$: $12 - 8 = 4$. Further experimentation will show this is not a coincidence, and this enables us to construct two additional functions that will *frame these pul-sations* and make them easier to see. Since the maximum amplitude of the resulting wave is 2, we use functions of the form $\pm 2 \cos\left(\frac{k}{2}x\right)$ to construct the frame, where $k$ is the number of beats in the interval $(m - n = k)$. For $Y_1 = \cos(12t)$ and $Y_2 = \cos(8t)$, we have $k = \dfrac{12 - 8}{2} = 2$ and the functions we use will be $Y_2 = 2 \cos(2x)$ and $Y_3 = -2 \cos(2x)$ as shown in Figure 5.14. The result is shown in Figure 5.15, where the frame clearly shows the four beats or more precisely, the four moments of silence.

For each exercise, (a) express the sum $Y_1 + Y_2$ as a product, (b) graph $Y_R$ on a graphing calculator for $x \in [0, 2\pi]$ and identify the number of beats in this interval, and (c) determine what value of $k$ in $\pm 2 \cos\left(\frac{k}{2}x\right)$ would be used to frame the resultant $Y_R$, then enter these as $Y_2$ and $Y_3$ to check the result.

**Figure 5.12**

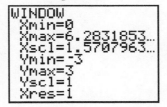

**Figure 5.13**

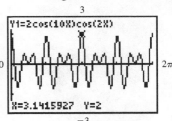

**Figure 5.14**

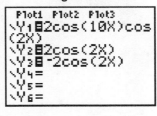

**Figure 5.15**

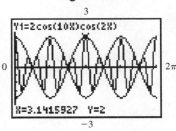

**Exercise 1:** $Y_1 = \cos(14t)$;     $Y_2 = \cos(8t)$

**Exercise 3:** $Y_1 = \cos(14t)$;     $Y_2 = \cos(6t)$

**Exercise 2:** $Y_1 = \cos(12t)$;     $Y_2 = \cos(9t)$

**Exercise 4:** $Y_1 = \cos(11t)$;     $Y_2 = \cos(10t)$

## Identities—Connections and Relationships

It is a well-known fact that information is retained longer and used more effectively when it is organized, sequential, and connected. In this *Strengthening Core Skills (SCS),* we attempt to do just that with our study of identities. In flowchart form we'll show that the entire range of identities has only two tiers, and that the fundamental identities and the sum and difference identities are really the keys to the entire range of identities. Beginning with the right triangle definition of sine, cosine, and tangent, the **reciprocal identities** and **ratio identities** are more semantic (word related) than mathematical, and the **Pythagorean identities** follow naturally from the properties of right triangles. These form the first tier.

**Basic Definitions**

$$\sin \theta = \frac{\text{opp}}{\text{hyp}} \qquad \cos \theta = \frac{\text{adj}}{\text{hyp}} \qquad \tan \theta = \frac{\text{opp}}{\text{adj}}$$

**Fundamental Identities**

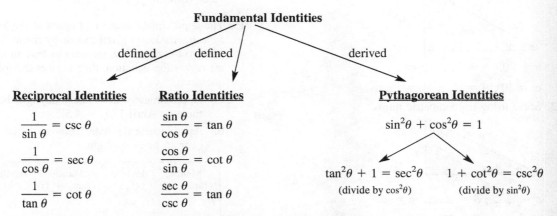

defined      defined          derived

**Reciprocal Identities**      **Ratio Identities**          **Pythagorean Identities**

$$\frac{1}{\sin \theta} = \csc \theta \qquad \frac{\sin \theta}{\cos \theta} = \tan \theta \qquad \sin^2\theta + \cos^2\theta = 1$$

$$\frac{1}{\cos \theta} = \sec \theta \qquad \frac{\cos \theta}{\sin \theta} = \cot \theta$$

$$\frac{1}{\tan \theta} = \cot \theta \qquad \frac{\sec \theta}{\csc \theta} = \tan \theta \qquad \tan^2\theta + 1 = \sec^2\theta \quad 1 + \cot^2\theta = \csc^2\theta$$

(divide by $\cos^2\theta$)   (divide by $\sin^2\theta$)

The reciprocal and ratio identities are actually *defined,* while the Pythagorean identities are *derived* from these two families. In addition, the identity $\sin^2\theta + \cos^2\theta = 1$ is the only Pythagorean identity we actually need to memorize; the other two follow by division of $\cos^2\theta$ and $\sin^2\theta$ as indicated.

In virtually the same way, the sum and difference identities for sine and cosine are the only identities that need to be memorized, as all other identities in the second tier flow from these.

**Sum/Difference Identities**

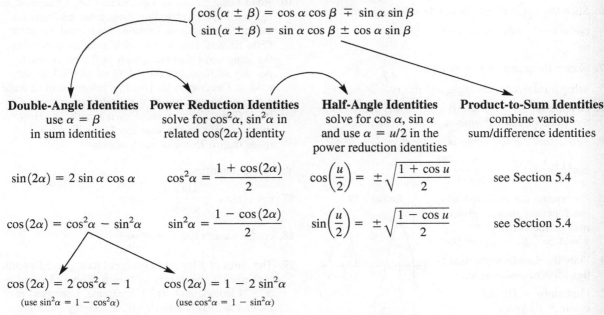

$$\begin{cases} \cos (\alpha \pm \beta) = \cos \alpha \cos \beta \mp \sin \alpha \sin \beta \\ \sin (\alpha \pm \beta) = \sin \alpha \cos \beta \pm \cos \alpha \sin \beta \end{cases}$$

**Double-Angle Identities**    **Power Reduction Identities**    **Half-Angle Identities**    **Product-to-Sum Identities**
use $\alpha = \beta$            solve for $\cos^2\alpha$, $\sin^2\alpha$ in        solve for $\cos \alpha$, $\sin \alpha$          combine various
in sum identities               related $\cos(2\alpha)$ identity        and use $\alpha = u/2$ in the          sum/difference identities
                                                                    power reduction identities

$$\sin(2\alpha) = 2\sin \alpha \cos \alpha \qquad \cos^2\alpha = \frac{1 + \cos(2\alpha)}{2} \qquad \cos\left(\frac{u}{2}\right) = \pm\sqrt{\frac{1 + \cos u}{2}} \qquad \text{see Section 5.4}$$

$$\cos(2\alpha) = \cos^2\alpha - \sin^2\alpha \qquad \sin^2\alpha = \frac{1 - \cos(2\alpha)}{2} \qquad \sin\left(\frac{u}{2}\right) = \pm\sqrt{\frac{1 - \cos u}{2}} \qquad \text{see Section 5.4}$$

$$\cos(2\alpha) = 2\cos^2\alpha - 1 \qquad \cos(2\alpha) = 1 - 2\sin^2\alpha$$

(use $\sin^2\alpha = 1 - \cos^2\alpha$)   (use $\cos^2\alpha = 1 - \sin^2\alpha$)

**Exercise 1:** Starting with the identity $\sin^2\alpha + \cos^2\alpha = 1$, derive the other two Pythagorean identities.

**Exercise 2:** Starting with the identity $\cos(\alpha \pm \beta) = \cos \alpha \cos \beta \mp \sin \alpha \sin \beta$, derive the double-angle identities for cosine.

## CUMULATIVE REVIEW CHAPTERS 1–5

**1.** Solve using a standard triangle.

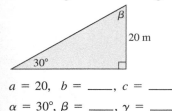

$a = 20$,  $b =$ _____,  $c =$ _____

$\alpha = 30°$, $\beta =$ _____, $\gamma =$ _____

**2.** Solve using trigonometric ratios.

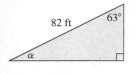

$a =$ _____,  $b =$ _____,  $c = 82$

$\alpha =$ _____,  $\beta = 63°$,  $\gamma =$ _____

**3.** State the three Pythagorean identities.

**4.** Given $\theta$ is in QIV and $\theta_r = 32°$, find the value of $\theta$.

**5.** The rollers on a conveyor belt have a radius of 6 in. and are turning at 300 rpm. How fast (in feet per second) is an object on the conveyor belt moving?

**6.** State the value of all six trig functions given
$\tan \alpha = -\dfrac{3}{4}$ with $\cos \alpha > 0$.

**7.** Sketch the graph of $y = 3\cos\left(2x - \dfrac{\pi}{4}\right)$
using a reference rectangle and the *rule of fourths*.

**8.** Given $\cos 53° \approx 0.6$ and $\cos 37° \approx 0.8$ approximate the value of $\cos 16°$ without using a calculator.

**9.** Verify that the following is an identity:

$$\cos^2\left(\frac{\alpha}{2}\right) = \frac{\sec \alpha + 2 + \cos \alpha}{2 \sec \alpha + 2}$$

**10.** Determine the equation of the function shown, given it is of the form
$y = A \cos[B(t + C)] + D$.

**Exercise 10**

**11.** State the double-angle identities for sine and cosine.

**12.** Find $\sin(\alpha + \beta)$ and $\cos(\alpha + \beta)$ given
$\cos \alpha = \dfrac{7}{25}$ in QIV and $\csc \beta = -\dfrac{13}{5}$ in QIII.

**13.** Use the sum identities to find exact values for $\sin 195°$ and $\cos 195°$.

**14.** Use a product-to-sum formula to find an exact value for $\cos\left(\dfrac{\pi}{12}\right)\sin\left(\dfrac{5\pi}{12}\right)$.

**15.** The approximate number of hours of daylight for Juneau, Alaska, is given month by month in the table to the right. Use the data to find an appropriate regression equation, then answer the following questions.

  **a.** Approximately how many daylight hours were there on April 15 ($t = 4.5$)?

  **b.** Approximate the dates between which there are over 15 hr of daylight.

| Month (Jan. → 1) | Daylight (hr) | Month (Jan. → 1) | Daylight (hr) |
|---|---|---|---|
| 1 | 5.5 | 7 | 18.1 |
| 2 | 8 | 8 | 17 |
| 3 | 11 | 9 | 14.5 |
| 4 | 13.5 | 10 | 12.5 |
| 5 | 16.5 | 11 | 9.5 |
| 6 | 18 | 12 | 7.5 |

**16.** Road Gang 52 out of Oklahoma City, Oklahoma, is responsible for rebuilding dangerous roadbeds for the rail line between Denton, Texas, and Arkansas City, Kansas. Due to favorable weather conditions, the gang can refurbish a high of 0.8 mi of track per day in June, but only 0.62 mi of track in the cold of December. (a) Use this information to build a sinusoidal equation that models the amount of track Gang 52 can rebuild each month. (b) How many months of the year can Gang 52 rebuild more than 0.75 mi of track per day?

Verify the identities.

**17.** $\cot x\left(\tan x - \dfrac{\sin x}{\cos^3 x}\right) = \tan^2 x$

**18.** $\cos^2 x - \csc^2 x \cos^2 x = -\dfrac{\cos^4 x}{\sin^2 x}$

**19.** The cities of Kiev and Leningrad have played significant roles in the history of Russia. Kiev is located at 50.3°N latitude and 30.3°E longitude. Leningrad is located at 59.6°N latitude and at roughly the same longitude. If the radius of the Earth is 6372 km, how many kilometers separate the two cities?

**20.** The planet Venus completes one orbit of the Sun in roughly 225 days. Find its linear velocity in miles per second if the radius of its orbit is approximately 67 million miles.

# Inverse Functions and Trigonometric Equations

# 6

# Inverse Functions and Trigonometric Equations

## CHAPTER CONNECTIONS

This chapter will unify much of what we've learned so far, and lead us to some intriguing, sophisticated, and surprising applications of trigonometry. Defining the trig functions (Chapters 1, 2, 3) helped us study a number of new relationships not possible using algebra alone. Their graphs (Chapter 4) gave us insights into how the functions are related to each other, and enabled a study of periodic phenomena. The identities (Chapter 5) were used to simplify complex expressions and to show how trig functions often work together to model natural events. One such "event" is a river's seasonal discharge rate, which tends to be greater during the annual snow melt. In this chapter, we'll learn how to predict the discharge rate during specific months of the year, information of great value to fisheries, oceanographers, and other scientists.

▶ This application appears as Exercises 45 and 46 in Section 6.4

## 6.1 | One-to-One and Inverse Functions

Consider the function $f(x) = 2x - 3$. If $f(x) = 7$, the equation becomes $2x - 3 = 7$, and the corresponding value of $x$ can be found using *inverse operations*. In this section, we introduce the concept of an *inverse function,* which can be viewed as a formula for finding $x$-values that correspond to *any* given value of $f(x)$.

### A. Identifying One-to-One Functions

The graphs of $y = 2x$ and $y = x^2$ are shown in Figures 6.1 and 6.2. The dashed, vertical lines clearly indicate both are functions, with each $x$-value corresponding to only one $y$. But the points on $y = 2x$ have one characteristic those from $y = x^2$ do not—*each y-value also corresponds to only one x* (for $y = x^2$, 4 corresponds to both $-2$ and 2). If each element from the range of a function corresponds to only one element of the domain, the function is said to be **one-to-one.**

**Figure 6.1**          **Figure 6.2**

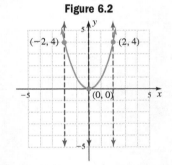

#### One-to-One Functions

A function $f$ is one-to-one if every element in the range corresponds to only one element of the domain.

In symbols,   if $f(x_1) = f(x_2)$, then $x_1 = x_2$, or
              if $x_1 \neq x_2$, then $f(x_1) \neq f(x_2)$.

From this definition we note the graph of a one-to-one function must not only pass a vertical line test (to show each $x$ corresponds to only one $y$), but also pass a **horizontal line test** (to show each $y$ corresponds to only one $x$).

#### Horizontal Line Test

If every horizontal line intersects the graph of a function in at most one point, the function is one-to-one.

Notice the graph of $y = 2x$ (Figure 6.3) passes the horizontal line test, while the graph of $y = x^2$ (Figure 6.4) does not.

**Figure 6.3**          **Figure 6.4**

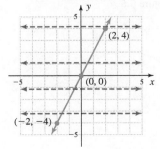
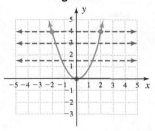

**EXAMPLE 1** ▶ Identifying One-to-One Functions

Use the horizontal line test to determine whether each graph is the graph of a one-to-one function.

a.
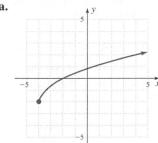

b.
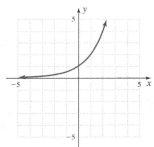

c.
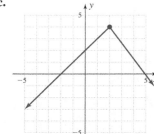

d.
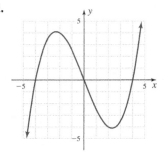

Solution ▶ A careful inspection shows all four graphs depict a function, since each passes the vertical line test. Only (a) and (b) pass the horizontal line test and are *one-to-one* functions.

**Now try Exercises 7 through 28 ▶**

☑ **A.** You've just learned how to identify one-to-one functions

If the function is given in ordered pair form, we simply check to see that no given second coordinate is paired with more than one first coordinate.

## B. Inverse Functions and Ordered Pairs

**Table 6.1**

| x | f(x) |
|----|------|
| −3 | −9 |
| 0 | −3 |
| 2 | 1 |
| 5 | 7 |
| 8 | 13 |

**Table 6.2**

| x | F(x) |
|----|------|
| −9 | −3 |
| −3 | 0 |
| 1 | 2 |
| 7 | 5 |
| 13 | 8 |

Consider the function $f(x) = 2x - 3$ and the solutions shown in Table 6.1. Figure 6.5 shows this function in diagram form (in blue), and illustrates that for each element of the domain, we *multiply by 2, then subtract 3*. An **inverse function** for $f$ is one that takes the result of these operations (elements of the range), and returns the original domain element. Figure 6.6 shows that function $F$ achieves this by "undoing" the operations in reverse order: *add 3, then divide by 2* (in red). A table of values for $F(x)$ is shown (Table 6.2).

**Figure 6.5**

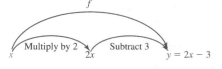

**Figure 6.6**

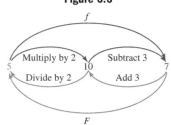

From this illustration we make the following observations regarding an inverse function, which we actually denote as $f^{-1}(x)$.

### Inverse Functions

If $f$ is a one-to-one function with ordered pairs $(a, b)$,
1. $f^{-1}(x)$ is a one-to-one function with ordered pairs $(b, a)$.
2. The range of $f$ will be the domain of $f^{-1}(x)$.
3. The domain of $f$ will be the range of $f^{-1}(x)$.

⚠ **CAUTION** ▶ The notation $f^{-1}(x)$ is simply a way of denoting an inverse function and has nothing to do with exponential properties. In particular, $f^{-1}(x)$ does *not* mean $\dfrac{1}{f(x)}$.

**EXAMPLE 2** ▶ **Finding the Inverse of a Function**

Find the inverse of each one-to-one function given:
a. $f(x) = \{(-4, 13), (-1, 7), (0, 5), (2, 1), (5, -5), (8, -11)\}$
b. $p(x) = -3x + 2$

Solution ▶ a. When a function is defined as a set of ordered pairs, the inverse function is found by simply interchanging the $x$- and $y$-coordinates:
$f^{-1}(x) = \{(13, -4), (7, -1), (5, 0), (1, 2), (-5, 5), (-11, 8)\}$.
b. Using diagrams similar to Figures 6.5 and 6.6, we reason that $p^{-1}(x)$ will subtract 2, then divide the result by $-3$: $p^{-1}(x) = \dfrac{x - 2}{-3}$. As a test, we find that $(-2, 8)$, $(0, 2)$, and $(3, -7)$ are solutions to $p(x)$, and note that $(8, -2)$, $(2, 0)$, and $(-7, 3)$ are indeed solutions to $p^{-1}(x)$.

☑ **B.** You've just learned how to explore inverse functions using ordered pairs

**Now try Exercises 29 through 40** ▶

## C. Finding Inverse Functions Using an Algebraic Method

**WORTHY OF NOTE**

If a function is *not* one-to-one, no inverse function exists since interchanging the $x$- and $y$-coordinates will result in a nonfunction. For instance, interchanging the coordinates of $(-2, 4)$ and $(2, 4)$ from $y = x^2$ results in $(4, -2)$ and $(4, 2)$, and we have one $x$-value being mapped to two $y$-values, in violation of the function definition.

The fact that interchanging $x$- and $y$-values helps determine an inverse function can be generalized to develop an **algebraic method** for finding inverses. Instead of interchanging *specific* $x$- and $y$-values, we actually interchange the $x$- and $y$-*variables,* then solve the equation for $y$. The process is summarized here.

### Finding an Inverse Function

1. Use $y$ instead of $f(x)$.
2. Interchange $x$ and $y$.
3. Solve the equation for $y$.
4. The result gives the inverse function: substitute $f^{-1}(x)$ for $y$.

In this process, it might seem like we're using the *same $y$* to represent two different functions. To see why there is actually no contradiction, **see Exercise 103.**

**EXAMPLE 3** ▶ **Finding Inverse Functions Algebraically**

Use the algebraic method to find the inverse function for
a. $f(x) = \sqrt[3]{x + 5}$        b. $g(x) = \dfrac{2x}{x + 1}$

Solution ▶  **a.**    $f(x) = \sqrt[3]{x + 5}$   given function

$y = \sqrt[3]{x + 5}$   use $y$ instead of $f(x)$

$x = \sqrt[3]{y + 5}$   interchange $x$ and $y$

$x^3 = y + 5$   cube both sides

$x^3 - 5 = y$   solve for $y$

$x^3 - 5 = f^{-1}(x)$   the result is $f^{-1}(x)$

For $f(x) = \sqrt[3]{x + 5},\ f^{-1}(x) = x^3 - 5$.

**b.**   $g(x) = \dfrac{2x}{x + 1}$   given function

$y = \dfrac{2x}{x + 1}$   use $y$ instead of $f(x)$

$x = \dfrac{2y}{y + 1}$   interchange $x$ and $y$

$xy + x = 2y$   multiply by $y + 1$ and distribute

$x = 2y - xy$   gather terms with $y$

$x = y(2 - x)$   factor

$\dfrac{x}{2 - x} = y$   solve for $y$

$\dfrac{x}{2 - x} = g^{-1}(x)$   the result is $g^{-1}(x)$

For $g(x) = \dfrac{2x}{x + 1},\ g^{-1}(x) = \dfrac{x}{2 - x}$.

**Now try Exercises 41 through 48 ▶**

In cases where a given function is *not* one-to-one, we can sometimes restrict the domain to create a function that *is,* and then determine an inverse. The restriction we use is arbitrary, and only requires that the result still produces all possible range values. For the most part, we simply choose a limited domain that seems convenient or reasonable.

**EXAMPLE 4 ▶**  **Restricting the Domain to Create a One-to-One Function**

Given $f(x) = (x - 4)^2$, restrict the domain to create a one-to-one function, then find $f^{-1}(x)$. State the domain and range of both resulting functions.

Solution ▶  The graph of $f$ is a parabola, opening upward with the vertex at $(4, 0)$. Restricting the domain to $x \geq 4$ (see figure) leaves only the "right branch" of the parabola, creating a one-to-one function without affecting the range, $y \in [0, \infty)$. For $f(x) = (x - 4)^2$, $x \geq 4$, we have

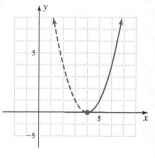

$f(x) = (x - 4)^2$   given function

$y = (x - 4)^2$   use $y$ instead of $f(x)$

$x = (y - 4)^2$   interchange $x$ and $y$

$\pm\sqrt{x} = y - 4$   take square roots

$\sqrt{x} + 4 = y$   solve for $y$, use $\sqrt{x}$ since $x \geq 4$

The result shows $f^{-1}(x) = \sqrt{x} + 4$, with domain $x \in [0, \infty)$ and range $y \in [4, \infty)$ (the domain of $f$ becomes the range of $f^{-1}$, and the range of $f$ becomes the domain of $f^{-1}$).

**Now try Exercises 49 through 54 ▶**

While we now have the ability to *find* the inverse of a function, we still lack a definitive method of *verifying* the inverse is correct. Actually, the diagrams in Figures 6.5 and 6.6 suggest just such a method. If we use the function $f$ itself as an input for $f^{-1}$, or the function $f^{-1}$ as an input for $f$, the end result should simply be $x$, as each function "undoes" the operations of the other. This is a composition of functions and using the notation for composition we have,

---

**Verifying Inverse Functions**

If $f$ is a one-to-one function, then the function $f^{-1}$ exists, where

$$(f \circ f^{-1})(x) = x \qquad \text{and} \qquad (f^{-1} \circ f)(x) = x$$

---

**EXAMPLE 5** ▶ **Finding and Verifying an Inverse Function**

Use the algebraic method to find the inverse function for $f(x) = \sqrt{x + 2}$. Then verify the inverse you found is correct.

**Solution** ▶ Since the graph of $f$ is the graph of $y = \sqrt{x}$ shifted 2 units left, we know $f$ is one-to-one with domain $x \in [-2, \infty)$ and range $y \in [0, \infty)$. This is important since the *domain and range values will be interchanged for the inverse function.* The domain of $f^{-1}$ will be $x \in [0, \infty)$ and its range $y \in [-2, \infty)$.

| | |
|---|---|
| $f(x) = \sqrt{x + 2}$ | given function; $x \geq -2$ |
| $y = \sqrt{x + 2}$ | use $y$ instead of $f(x)$ |
| $x = \sqrt{y + 2}$ | interchange $x$ and $y$ |
| $x^2 = y + 2$ | solve for $y$ (square both sides) |
| $x^2 - 2 = y$ | subtract 2 |
| $f^{-1}(x) = x^2 - 2$ | the result is $f^{-1}(x)$; $D: x \in [0, \infty)$, $R: y \in [-2, \infty)$ |

**Verify** ▶

| | |
|---|---|
| $(f \circ f^{-1})(x) = f[f^{-1}(x)]$ | $f^{-1}(x)$ is an input for $f$ |
| $= \sqrt{f^{-1}(x) + 2}$ | $f$ adds 2 to inputs, then takes the square root |
| $= \sqrt{(x^2 - 2) + 2}$ | substitute $x^2 - 2$ for $f^{-1}(x)$ |
| $= \sqrt{x^2}$ | simplify |
| $= x \checkmark$ | since the domain of $f^{-1}(x)$ is $x \in [0, \infty)$ |

**Verify** ▶

| | |
|---|---|
| $(f^{-1} \circ f)(x) = f^{-1}[f(x)]$ | $f(x)$ is an input for $f^{-1}$ |
| $= [f(x)]^2 - 2$ | $f^{-1}$ squares inputs, then subtracts 2 |
| $= [\sqrt{x + 2}]^2 - 2$ | substitute $\sqrt{x + 2}$ for $f(x)$ |
| $= x + 2 - 2$ | simplify |
| $= x \checkmark$ | result |

☑ **C.** You've just learned how to find inverse functions using an algebraic method

**Now try Exercises 55 through 80** ▶

## D. The Graph of a Function and Its Inverse

Graphing a function and its inverse on the same axes reveals an interesting and useful relationship—the graphs are reflections across the line $y = x$ (the identity function).

Consider the function $f(x) = 2x + 3$, and its inverse $f^{-1}(x) = \dfrac{x - 3}{2} = \dfrac{1}{2}x - \dfrac{3}{2}$. In Figure 6.7, the points $(1, 5)$, $(0, 3)$, $(-\frac{3}{2}, 0)$, and $(-4, -5)$ from $f$ (see Table 6.3) are graphed in blue, with the points $(5, 1)$, $(3, 0)$, $(0, -\frac{3}{2})$, and $(-5, -4)$ (see Table 6.4) from $f^{-1}$ graphed in red (note the $x$- and $y$-values are reversed). Graphing both lines illustrates this symmetry (Figure 6.8).

| Table 6.3 | |
|:---:|:---:|
| $x$ | $f(x)$ |
| 1 | 5 |
| 0 | 3 |
| $-\dfrac{3}{2}$ | 0 |
| $-4$ | $-5$ |

**Figure 6.7**

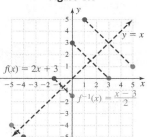

**Figure 6.8**

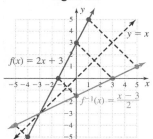

| Table 6.4 | |
|:---:|:---:|
| $x$ | $f^{-1}(x)$ |
| 5 | 1 |
| 3 | 0 |
| 0 | $-\dfrac{3}{2}$ |
| $-5$ | $-4$ |

**EXAMPLE 6** ▶ **Graphing a Function and Its Inverse**

In Example 5, we found the inverse function for $f(x) = \sqrt{x + 2}$ was $f^{-1}(x) = x^2 - 2, x \geq 0$. Graph these functions on the same axes and comment on how the graphs are related.

**Solution** ▶ The graph of $f$ is a square root function with initial point $(-2, 0)$, a $y$-intercept of $(0, \sqrt{2})$, and an $x$-intercept of $(-2, 0)$ (Figure 6.9 in blue). The graph of $x^2 - 2, x \geq 0$ is the right-hand branch of a parabola, with $y$-intercept at $(0, -2)$ and an $x$-intercept at $(\sqrt{2}, 0)$ (Figure 6.9 in red).

**Figure 6.9**

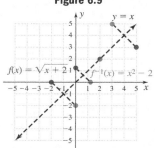

**Figure 6.10**

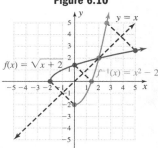

Connecting these points with a smooth curve indeed shows their graphs are symmetric to the line $y = x$ (Figure 6.10).

**Now try Exercises 81 through 88** ▶

**EXAMPLE 7** ▶ **Graphing a Function and Its Inverse**

Given the graph shown in Figure 6.11, use the grid in Figure 6.12 to draw a graph of the inverse function.

**Figure 6.11**

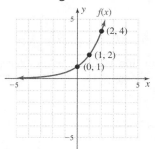

**Figure 6.12**

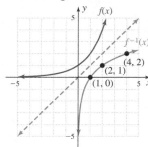

Solution ▶ From the graph, the domain of $f$ appears to be $x \in \mathbb{R}$ and the range is $y \in (0, \infty)$. This means the domain of $f^{-1}$ will be $x \in (0, \infty)$ and the range will be $y \in \mathbb{R}$. To sketch $f^{-1}$, draw the line $y = x$, interchange the $x$- and $y$-coordinates of the selected points, then plot these points and draw a smooth curve using the domain and range boundaries as a guide.

**Now try Exercises 89 through 94 ▶**

A summary of important points is given here.

---

**Functions and Inverse Functions**

1. If the graph of a function passes the horizontal line test, the function is one-to-one.
2. If a function $f$ is one-to-one, the function $f^{-1}$ exists.
3. The domain of $f$ is the range of $f^{-1}$, and the range of $f$ is the domain of $f^{-1}$.
4. For a function $f$ and its inverse $f^{-1}$, $(f \circ f^{-1})(x) = x$ and $(f^{-1} \circ f)(x) = x$.
5. The graphs of $f$ and $f^{-1}$ are symmetric with respect to the line $y = x$.

---

☑ **D. You've just learned how to graph a function and its inverse**

## E.  Applications of Inverse Functions

Our final example illustrates one of the many ways that inverse functions can be applied.

**EXAMPLE 8 ▶    Using Volume to Understand Inverse Functions**

The volume of an equipoise cylinder (height equal to diameter) is given by $v(x) = 2\pi x^3$ (since $h = d = 2r$), where $v(x)$ represents the volume in units cubed and $x$ represents the radius of the cylinder.

  a. Find the volume of such a cylinder if $x = 10$ ft.
  b. Find $v^{-1}(x)$, and discuss what the input and output variables represent.
  c. If a volume of $1024\pi$ ft³ is required, which formula would be easier to use to find the radius? What is this radius?

Solution ▶
  a.  $v(x) = 2\pi x^3$         given function
      $v(10) = 2\pi(10)^3$      substitute 10 for $x$
      $= 2000\pi$               $10^3 = 1000$, exact form

With a radius of 10 ft, the volume of the cylinder would be $2000\pi$ ft³.

  b.    $v(x) = 2\pi x^3$        given function
        $y = 2\pi x^3$           use $y$ instead of $v(x)$
        $x = 2\pi y^3$           interchange $x$ and $y$

        $\dfrac{x}{2\pi} = y^3$      solve for $y$

        $\sqrt[3]{\dfrac{x}{2\pi}} = y$      result

The inverse function is $v^{-1}(x) = \sqrt[3]{\dfrac{x}{2\pi}}$. In this case, the input $x$ is a given volume, and the output $v^{-1}(x)$ is the radius of an equipoise cylinder that will hold this volume.

**c.** Since the volume is known and we need the radius, using $v^{-1}(x) = \sqrt[3]{\dfrac{x}{2\pi}}$ would be more efficient.

$$v^{-1}(1024\pi) = \sqrt[3]{\dfrac{1024\pi}{2\pi}} \qquad \text{substitute } 1024\pi \text{ for } x \text{ in } v^{-1}(x)$$

$$= \sqrt[3]{512} \qquad \dfrac{2\pi}{2\pi} = 1$$

$$= 8 \qquad \text{result}$$

☑ **E.** You've just learned how to solve an application of inverse functions

The radius of the cylinder would be 8 ft.

**Now try Exercises 97 through 102 ▶**

---

## TECHNOLOGY HIGHLIGHT

### Investigating Inverse Functions

Many important ideas from this section can be illustrated using a graphing calculator. To begin, enter the function

$Y_1 = 2\sqrt[3]{x-2}$ and $Y_2 = \dfrac{x^3}{8} + 2$ (which appear to be inverse

functions) on the [Y=] screen, then press [ZOOM]
**5:ZSquare**. The graphs seem to be reflections across the line $y = x$ (Figure 6.13). To verify, use the [TABLE] feature with inputs $x = -2, -1, 0, 1, 2$, and 3. As shown in Figure 6.14, the points $(1, -2)$, $(2, 0)$, and $(3, 2)$ are on $Y_1$, and the points $(-2, 1)$, $(0, 2)$, and $(2, 3)$ are all on $Y_2$. While this seems convincing (the $x$- and $y$-coordinates are interchanged), the technology can actually *compose the two functions* to verify an inverse relationship. Function names $Y_1$ and $Y_2$ can be accessed using the [VARS] and [▶] keys, then pressing [ENTER]. After entering $Y_3 = Y_1(Y_2)$ and $Y_4 = Y_2(Y_1)$ on the [Y=] screen, we observe whether one function "undoes" the other using the TABLE feature (Figure 6.15).

**Figure 6.13**

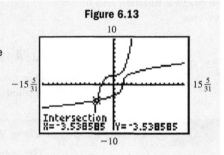

**Figure 6.14**

| X | Y₁ | Y₂ |
|---|------|-------|
| -2 | -3.175 | 1 |
| -1 | -2.884 | 1.875 |
| 0 | -2.52 | 2 |
| 1 | -2 | 2.125 |
| 2 | 0 | 3 |
| 3 | 2 | 5.375 |

X=

**Figure 6.15**

| X | Y₃ | Y₄ |
|---|----|----|
| -2 | -2 | -2 |
| -1 | -1 | -1 |
| 0 | 0 | 0 |
| 1 | 1 | 1 |
| 2 | 2 | 2 |
| 3 | 3 | 3 |

X=

For the functions given, (a) find $f^{-1}(x)$, then use your calculator to verify they are inverses by (b) using ordered pairs, (c) composing the functions, and (d) showing their graphs are symmetric to $y = x$.

**Exercise 1:** $f(x) = 2x + 1$          **Exercise 2:** $g(x) = x^2 + 1; x \geq 0$          **Exercise 3:** $h(x) = \dfrac{x}{x+1}$

## 6.1 EXERCISES

▶ **CONCEPTS AND VOCABULARY**

**Fill in each blank with the appropriate word or phrase. Carefully reread the section if needed.**

1. A function is one-to-one if each _____ coordinate corresponds to exactly _____ first coordinate.

2. If every _____ line intersects the graph of a function in at most _____ point, the function is one-to-one.

3. A certain function is defined by the ordered pairs $(-2, -11)$, $(0, -5)$, $(2, 1)$, and $(4, 19)$. The inverse function is _____.

4. To find $f^{-1}$ using the algebraic method, we (1) use _____ instead of $f(x)$, (2) _____ $x$ and $y$, (3) _____ for $y$, and (4) replace $y$ with $f^{-1}(x)$.

5. State true or false and explain why: *To show that g is the inverse function for f, simply show that* $(f \circ g)(x) = x$. Include an example in your response.

6. Discuss/Explain why no inverse function exists for $f(x) = (x + 3)^2$ and $g(x) = \sqrt{4 - x^2}$. How would the domain of each function have to be restricted to allow for an inverse function?

▶ **DEVELOPING YOUR SKILLS**

**Determine whether each graph given is the graph of a one-to-one function. If not, give examples of how the definition of one-to-oneness is violated.**

7.
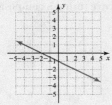

8.
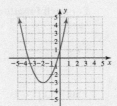

9.
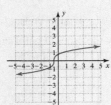

10.
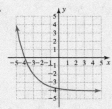

11.
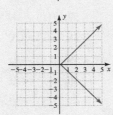

12.
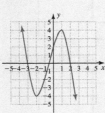

13.
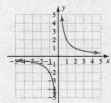

14.
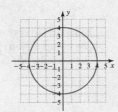

15.
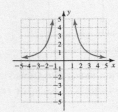

**Determine whether the functions given are one-to-one. If not, state why.**

**16.** $\{(-7, 4), (-1, 9), (0, 5), (-2, 1), (5, -5)\}$

**17.** $\{(9, 1), (-2, 7), (7, 4), (3, 9), (2, 7)\}$

**18.** $\{(-6, 1), (4, -9), (0, 11), (-2, 7), (-4, 5), (8, 1)\}$

**19.** $\{(-6, 2), (-3, 7), (8, 0), (12, -1), (2, -3), (1, 3)\}$

**Determine if the functions given are one-to-one by noting the function family to which each belongs and mentally picturing the shape of the graph. If a function is not one-to-one, discuss how the definition of one-to-oneness is violated.**

**20.** $f(x) = 3x - 5$      **21.** $g(x) = (x + 2)^3 - 1$

**22.** $h(x) = -|x - 4| + 3$      **23.** $p(t) = 3t^2 + 5$

**24.** $s(t) = \sqrt{2t - 1} + 5$      **25.** $r(t) = \sqrt[3]{t + 1} - 2$

**26.** $y = 3$      **27.** $y = -2x$      **28.** $y = x$

**For Exercises 29 to 32, find the inverse function of the one-to-one functions given.**

**29.** $f(x) = \{(-2, 1), (-1, 4), (0, 5), (2, 9), (5, 15)\}$

**30.** $g(x) = \{(-2, 30), (-1, 11), (0, 4), (1, 3), (2, 2)\}$

**31.** $v(x)$ is defined by the ordered pairs shown.

**32.** $w(x)$ is defined by the ordered pairs shown.

**Find the inverse function using diagrams similar to those illustrated in Example 2. Check the result using three test points.**

**33.** $f(x) = x + 5$      **34.** $g(x) = x - 4$

**35.** $p(x) = -\dfrac{4}{5}x$      **36.** $r(x) = \dfrac{3}{4}x$

**37.** $f(x) = 4x + 3$      **38.** $g(x) = 5x - 2$

**39.** $Y_1 = \sqrt[3]{x - 4}$      **40.** $Y_2 = \sqrt[3]{x + 2}$

**Find each function $f(x)$ given, (a) find any three ordered pair solutions $(a, b)$, then (b) algebraically compute $f^{-1}(x)$, and (c) verify the ordered pairs $(b, a)$ satisfy $f^{-1}(x)$.**

**41.** $f(x) = \sqrt[3]{x - 2}$      **42.** $f(x) = \sqrt[3]{x + 3}$

**43.** $f(x) = x^3 + 1$      **44.** $f(x) = x^3 - 2$

**45.** $f(x) = \dfrac{8}{x + 2}$      **46.** $f(x) = \dfrac{12}{x - 1}$

**47.** $f(x) = \dfrac{x}{x + 1}$      **48.** $f(x) = \dfrac{x + 2}{1 - x}$

**The functions given in Exercises 49 through 54 are not one-to-one. (a) Determine a domain restriction that preserves all range values, then state this domain and range. (b) Find the inverse function and state its domain and range.**

**49.** $f(x) = (x + 5)^2$      **50.** $g(x) = x^2 + 3$

**51.** $v(x) = \dfrac{8}{(x - 3)^2}$      **52.** $V(x) = \dfrac{4}{x^2} + 2$

**53.** $p(x) = (x + 4)^2 - 2$      **54.** $q(x) = \dfrac{4}{(x - 2)^2} + 1$

**For each function $f(x)$ given, prove (using a composition) that $g(x) = f^{-1}(x)$.**

**55.** $f(x) = -2x + 5, g(x) = \dfrac{x - 5}{-2}$

**56.** $f(x) = 3x - 4, g(x) = \dfrac{x + 4}{3}$

**57.** $f(x) = \sqrt[3]{x + 5}, g(x) = x^3 - 5$

**58.** $f(x) = \sqrt[3]{x - 4}, g(x) = x^3 + 4$

**59.** $f(x) = \frac{2}{3}x - 6, g(x) = \frac{3}{2}x + 9$

**60.** $f(x) = \frac{4}{5}x + 6, g(x) = \frac{5}{4}x - \frac{15}{2}$

**61.** $f(x) = x^2 - 3; x \geq 0, g(x) = \sqrt{x + 3}$

**62.** $f(x) = x^2 + 8; x \geq 0, g(x) = \sqrt{x - 8}$

**Find the inverse of each function $f(x)$ given, then prove (by composition) your inverse function is correct. Note the domain of $f$ is all real numbers.**

**63.** $f(x) = 3x - 5$      **64.** $f(x) = 5x + 4$

**65.** $f(x) = \dfrac{x - 5}{2}$      **66.** $f(x) = \dfrac{x + 4}{3}$

**67.** $f(x) = \frac{1}{2}x - 3$      **68.** $f(x) = \frac{2}{3}x + 1$

**69.** $f(x) = x^3 + 3$      **70.** $f(x) = x^3 - 4$

**71.** $f(x) = \sqrt[3]{2x + 1}$      **72.** $f(x) = \sqrt[3]{3x - 2}$

**73.** $f(x) = \dfrac{(x - 1)^3}{8}$      **74.** $f(x) = \dfrac{(x + 3)^3}{-27}$

Find the inverse of each function, then prove (by composition) your inverse function is correct. State the implied domain and range as you begin, and use these to state the domain and range of the inverse function.

**75.** $f(x) = \sqrt{3x + 2}$    **76.** $g(x) = \sqrt{2x - 5}$

**77.** $p(x) = 2\sqrt{x - 3}$    **78.** $q(x) = 4\sqrt{x + 1}$

**79.** $v(x) = x^2 + 3; x \geq 0$    **80.** $w(x) = x^2 - 1; x \geq 0$

Graph each function $f(x)$ and its inverse $f^{-1}(x)$ on the same grid and "dash-in" the line $y = x$. Note how the graphs are related. Then verify the "inverse function" relationship using a composition.

**81.** $f(x) = 4x + 1; f^{-1}(x) = \dfrac{x - 1}{4}$

**82.** $f(x) = 2x - 7; f^{-1}(x) = \dfrac{x + 7}{2}$

**83.** $f(x) = \sqrt[3]{x + 2}; f^{-1}(x) = x^3 - 2$

**84.** $f(x) = \sqrt[3]{x - 7}; f^{-1}(x) = x^3 + 7$

**85.** $f(x) = 0.2x + 1; f^{-1}(x) = 5x - 5$

**86.** $f(x) = \dfrac{2}{9}x + 4; f^{-1}(x) = \dfrac{9}{2}x - 18$

**87.** $f(x) = (x + 2)^2, x \geq -2; f^{-1}(x) = \sqrt{x} - 2$

**88.** $f(x) = (x - 3)^2, x \geq 3; f^{-1}(x) = \sqrt{x} + 3$

Determine the domain and range for each function whose graph is given, and use this information to state the domain and range of the inverse function. Then sketch in the line $y = x$, estimate the location of two or more points on the graph, and use these to graph $f^{-1}(x)$ on the same grid.

**89.** 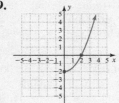    **90.**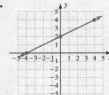

**91.** 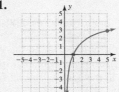    **92.**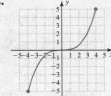

**93.** 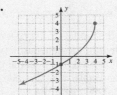    **94.**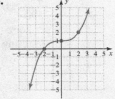

▶ **WORKING WITH FORMULAS**

**95. The height of a projected image:** $f(x) = \frac{1}{2}x - 8.5$

The height of an image projected on a screen by a projector is given by the formula shown, where $f(x)$ represents the actual height of the image on the projector (in centimeters) and $x$ is the distance of the projector from the screen (in centimeters). (a) When the projector is 80 cm from the screen, how large is the image? (b) Show that the inverse function is $f^{-1}(x) = 2x + 17$, then input your answer from part (a) and comment on the result. What information does the inverse function give?

**96. The radius of a sphere:** $r(x) = \sqrt[3]{\dfrac{3x}{4\pi}}$

In generic form, the radius of a sphere is given by the formula shown, where $r(x)$ represents the radius and $x$ represents the volume of the sphere in cubic units. (a) If a weather balloon that is roughly spherical holds 14,130 in³ of air, what is the radius of the balloon (use $\pi \approx 3.14$)? (b) Show that the inverse function is $r^{-1}(x) = \frac{4}{3}\pi x^3$, then input your answer from part (a) and comment on the result. What information does the inverse function give?

▶ **APPLICATIONS**

**97. Temperature and altitude:** The temperature (in degrees Fahrenheit) at a given altitude can be approximated by the function $f(x) = -\frac{7}{2}x + 59$, where $f(x)$ represents the temperature and $x$ represents the altitude in thousands of feet. (a) What is the approximate temperature at an altitude of 35,000 ft (normal cruising altitude for commercial airliners)? (b) Find $f^{-1}(x)$, and state what the independent and dependent variables represent. (c) If the temperature outside a weather balloon is $-18°$F, what is the approximate altitude of the balloon?

98. **Fines for speeding:** In some localities, there is a set formula to determine the amount of a fine for exceeding posted speed limits. Suppose the amount of the fine for exceeding a 50 mph speed limit was given by the function $f(x) = 12x - 560 \ (x > 50)$ where $f(x)$ represents the fine in dollars for a speed of $x$ mph. (a) What is the fine for traveling 65 mph through this speed zone? (b) Find $f^{-1}(x)$, and state what the independent and dependent variables represent. (c) If a fine of \$172 were assessed, how fast was the driver going through this speed zone?

99. **Effect of gravity:** Due to the effect of gravity, the distance an object has fallen after being dropped is given by the function $f(x) = 16x^2; \ x \geq 0$, where $f(x)$ represents the distance in feet after $x$ sec. (a) How far has the object fallen 3 sec after it has been dropped? (b) Find $f^{-1}(x)$, and state what the independent and dependent variables represent. (c) If the object is dropped from a height of 784 ft, how many seconds until it hits the ground (stops falling)?

100. **Area and radius:** In generic form, the area of a circle is given by $f(x) = \pi x^2$, where $f(x)$ represents the area in square units for a circle with radius $x$. (a) A pet dog is tethered to a stake in the backyard. If the tether is 10 ft long, how much area does the dog have to roam (use $\pi \approx 3.14$)? (b) Find $f^{-1}(x)$, and state what the independent and dependent variables represent. (c) If the owners want to allow the dog 1256 ft$^2$ of area to live and roam, how long a tether should be used?

101. **Volume of a cone:** In generic form, the volume of an equipoise cone (height equal to radius) is given by $f(x) = \frac{1}{3}\pi x^3$, where $f(x)$ represents the volume in units$^3$ and $x$ represents the height of the cone. (a) Find the volume of such a cone if $r = 30$ ft (use $\pi \approx 3.14$). (b) Find $f^{-1}(x)$, and state what the independent and dependent variables represent. (c) If the volume of water in the cone is 763.02 ft$^3$, how deep is the water at its deepest point?

102. **Wind power:** The power delivered by a certain wind-powered generator can be modeled by the function

    $f(x) = \dfrac{x^3}{2500}$, where $f(x)$ is the horsepower (hp) delivered by the generator and $x$ represents the speed of the wind

    in miles per hour. (a) Use the model to determine how much horsepower is generated by a 30 mph wind. (b) The person monitoring the output of the generators (wind generators are usually erected in large numbers) would like a function that gives the wind speed based on the horsepower readings on the gauges in the monitoring station. For this purpose, find $f^{-1}(x)$ and state what the independent and dependent variables represent. (c) If gauges show 25.6 hp is being generated, how fast is the wind blowing?

▶ **EXTENDING THE CONCEPT**

103. For a deeper understanding of the algebraic method for finding an inverse, suppose a function $f$ is defined as $f(x): \{(x, y)|y = 3x - 6\}$. We can then define the inverse as $f^{-1}: \{(x, y)|x = 3y - 6\}$, having interchanged $x$ and $y$ in the equation portion. The equation for $f^{-1}$ is not in standard form, but $(x, y)$ still represents all ordered pairs satisfying either equation. Solving for $y$ gives $f^{-1}: \left\{ (x, y)|y = \dfrac{x}{3} + 2 \right\}$, and demonstrates the role of steps 2, 3, and 4 of the method. (a) Find five ordered pairs that satisfy the equation for $f$, then (b) interchange their coordinates and show they satisfy the equation for $f^{-1}$.

104. The function $f(x) = \dfrac{1}{x}$ is one of the few functions that is its own inverse. This means the ordered pairs $(a, b)$ and $(b, a)$ must satisfy both $f$ and $f^{-1}$. (a) Find $f^{-1}$ using the algebraic method to verify that $f(x) = f^{-1}(x) = \dfrac{1}{x}$. (b) Graph the function $f(x) = \dfrac{1}{x}$ using a table of integers from $-4$ to 4. Note that for any ordered pair $(a, b)$ on $f$, the

ordered pair $(b, a)$ is also on $f$. (c) State where the graph of $y = x$ will intersect the graph of this function and discuss why.

105. By inspection, which of the following is the inverse function for $f(x) = \dfrac{2}{3}\left(x - \dfrac{1}{2}\right)^5 + \dfrac{4}{5}$?

    **a.** $f^{-1}(x) = \sqrt[5]{\dfrac{1}{2}\left(x - \dfrac{2}{3}\right)} - \dfrac{4}{5}$

    **b.** $f^{-1}(x) = \dfrac{3}{2}\sqrt[5]{(x - 2)} - \dfrac{5}{4}$

    **c.** $f^{-1}(x) = \dfrac{3}{2}\sqrt[5]{\left(x + \dfrac{1}{2}\right)} - \dfrac{5}{4}$

    **d.** $f^{-1}(x) = \sqrt[5]{\dfrac{3}{2}\left(x - \dfrac{4}{5}\right)} + \dfrac{1}{2}$

106. Suppose a function is defined as $f(x) = $ *the exponent that goes on 9 to obtain x*. For example, $f(81) = 2$ since 2 is the exponent that goes on 9 to obtain 81, and $f(3) = \frac{1}{2}$ since $\frac{1}{2}$ is the exponent that goes on 9 to obtain 3. Determine the value of each of the following:

    **a.** $f(1)$    **b.** $f(729)$    **c.** $f^{-1}(2)$    **d.** $f^{-1}\left(\dfrac{1}{2}\right)$

▶ **MAINTAINING YOUR SKILLS**

**107.** **(5.1)** Verify the following is an identity:
$\tan^2\theta \sin^2\theta = \tan^2\theta - \sin^2\theta$.

**108.** **(5.3)** Given $\tan(2\beta) = \dfrac{7}{24}$, with $2\beta$ in QI, use

double-angle formulas to find exact values for $\cos\beta$ and $\sin\beta$.

**109.** **(4.3)** Write the equation of the function graphed in two ways—in terms of a sine function then in terms of a cosine function.

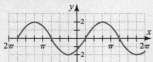

**110.** **(1.3)** Find $f(\theta)$ for all six trig functions, given $P(-8, 15)$ is on the terminal side of the angle.

**111.** **(2.3)** Standing 9 km (9000 meters) from the base of Mount Fuji (Japan), the angle of elevation to the summit is 22°46′. Is Mount Fuji taller than Mount Hood (Oregon), which stands 3428 m high?

**112.** **(3.2)** The area of a circular sector is $A = \dfrac{125\pi}{3}$ m².
If $r = 10$ m, what angle is subtended?

## 6.2 | The Inverse Trig Functions and Their Applications

### Learning Objectives

*In Section 6.2 you will learn how to:*

☐ **A.** Find and graph the inverse sine function and evaluate related expressions

☐ **B.** Find and graph the inverse cosine and tangent functions and evaluate related expressions

☐ **C.** Apply the definition and notation of inverse trig functions to simplify compositions

☐ **D.** Find and graph inverse functions for sec $x$, csc $x$, and cot $x$

☐ **E.** Solve applications involving inverse functions

While we usually associate the number $\pi$ with the features of a circle, it also occurs in some "interesting" places, such as the study of normal (bell) curves, Bessel functions, Stirling's formula, Fourier series, Laplace transforms, and infinite series. In much the same way, the trigonometric functions are surprisingly versatile, finding their way into a study of complex numbers and vectors, the simplification of algebraic expressions, and finding the area under certain curves—applications that are hugely important in a continuing study of mathematics. As you'll see, a study of the inverse trig functions helps support these fascinating applications.

### A. The Inverse Sine Function

In Section 6.1, we established that only one-to-one functions have an inverse. All six trig functions fail the horizontal line test and are not one-to-one as given. However, by suitably restricting the domain, a one-to-one function can be defined that makes finding an inverse possible. For the sine function, it seems natural to choose the interval $\left[ -\dfrac{\pi}{2}, \dfrac{\pi}{2} \right]$ since it is centrally located and the sine function attains all possible range values in this interval. A graph of $y = \sin x$ is shown in Figure 6.16, with the portion corresponding to this interval colored in red. Note the range is still $[-1, 1]$ (Figure 6.17).

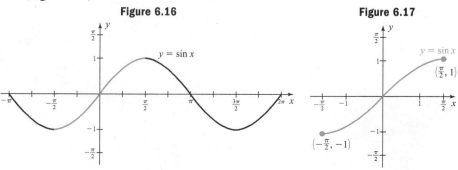

**Figure 6.16**      **Figure 6.17**

We can obtain an implicit equation for the inverse of $y = \sin x$ by interchanging $x$- and $y$-values, obtaining $x = \sin y$. By accepted convention, the *explicit* form of the inverse sine function is written $y = \sin^{-1}x$ or $y = \arcsin x$. Since domain and range values have been interchanged, the domain of $y = \sin^{-1}x$ is $[-1, 1]$ and the range is $\left[ -\dfrac{\pi}{2}, \dfrac{\pi}{2} \right]$. The graph of $y = \sin^{-1}x$ can be found by reflecting the portion in red across the line $y = x$ and using the endpoints of the domain and range (see Figure 6.18).

**Figure 6.18**

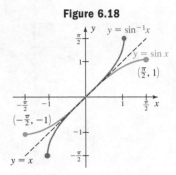

### The Inverse Sine Function

For $y = \sin x$ with domain $\left[ -\dfrac{\pi}{2}, \dfrac{\pi}{2} \right]$

and range $[-1, 1]$, the inverse sine function is

$$y = \sin^{-1}x \text{ or } y = \arcsin x,$$

with domain $[-1, 1]$ and range $\left[ -\dfrac{\pi}{2}, \dfrac{\pi}{2} \right]$.

$$y = \sin^{-1}x \text{ if and only if } \sin y = x$$

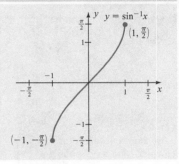

From the implicit form $x = \sin y$, we learn to interpret the inverse function as, "$y$ is the number or angle whose sine is $x$." Learning to read and interpret the explicit form in this way will be helpful. That is, $y = \sin^{-1}x$ means "$y$ is the number or angle whose sine is $x$."

$$y = \sin^{-1}x \Leftrightarrow x = \sin y \qquad x = \sin y \Leftrightarrow y = \sin^{-1}x$$

---

**EXAMPLE 1** ▶ **Evaluating $y = \sin^{-1}x$ Using Special Values**

Evaluate the inverse sine function for the values given:

**a.** $y = \sin^{-1}\left( \dfrac{\sqrt{3}}{2} \right)$     **b.** $y = \arcsin\left( -\dfrac{1}{2} \right)$     **c.** $y = \sin^{-1}(2)$

Solution ▶ For $x$ in $[-1, 1]$ and $y$ in $\left[ -\dfrac{\pi}{2}, \dfrac{\pi}{2} \right]$,

**a.** $y = \sin^{-1}\left( \dfrac{\sqrt{3}}{2} \right)$: $y$ is the number or angle whose sine is $\dfrac{\sqrt{3}}{2}$

$\Rightarrow \sin y = \dfrac{\sqrt{3}}{2}$, so $\sin^{-1}\left( \dfrac{\sqrt{3}}{2} \right) = \dfrac{\pi}{3}$.

**b.** $y = \arcsin\left( -\dfrac{1}{2} \right)$: $y$ is the arc or angle whose sine is $-\dfrac{1}{2}$

$\Rightarrow \sin y = -\dfrac{1}{2}$, so $\arcsin\left( -\dfrac{1}{2} \right) = -\dfrac{\pi}{6}$.

**c.** $y = \sin^{-1}(2)$: $y$ is the number or angle whose sine is 2

$\Rightarrow \sin y = 2$. Since 2 is not in $[-1, 1]$, $\sin^{-1}(2)$ is undefined.

Now try Exercises 7 through 12 ▶

**Table 6.5**

| $x$ | $\sin x$ |
|---|---|
| $-\frac{\pi}{2}$ | $-1$ |
| $-\frac{\pi}{3}$ | $-\frac{\sqrt{3}}{2}$ |
| $-\frac{\pi}{4}$ | $-\frac{\sqrt{2}}{2}$ |
| $-\frac{\pi}{6}$ | $-\frac{1}{2}$ |
| $0$ | $0$ |
| $\frac{\pi}{6}$ | $\frac{1}{2}$ |
| $\frac{\pi}{4}$ | $\frac{\sqrt{2}}{2}$ |
| $\frac{\pi}{3}$ | $\frac{\sqrt{3}}{2}$ |
| $\frac{\pi}{2}$ | $1$ |

In Examples 1(a) and 1(b), note that the equations $\sin y = \frac{\sqrt{3}}{2}$ and $\sin y = -\frac{1}{2}$ each have an infinite number of solutions, but only one solution in $\left[-\frac{\pi}{2}, \frac{\pi}{2}\right]$.

When $x$ is one of the standard values $\left(0, \frac{1}{2}, \frac{\sqrt{3}}{2}, 1, \text{ and so on}\right)$, $y = \sin^{-1}x$ can be evaluated by reading a standard table "in reverse." For $y = \arcsin(-1)$, we locate the number $-1$ in the right-hand column of Table 6.5, and note the "number or angle whose sine is $-1$," is $-\frac{\pi}{2}$. If $x$ is between $-1$ and $1$ but is not a standard value, we can use the $\sin^{-1}$ function on a calculator, which is most often the [2nd] or [INV] function for [SIN].

---

**EXAMPLE 2** ▶ **Evaluating $y = \sin^{-1}x$ Using a Calculator**

Evaluate each inverse sine function twice. First in radians rounded to four decimal places, then in degrees to the nearest tenth.

    **a.** $y = \sin^{-1}0.8492$          **b.** $y = \arcsin(-0.2317)$

**Solution** ▶ For $x$ in $[-1, 1]$, we evaluate $y = \sin^{-1}x$.

    **a.** $y = \sin^{-1}0.8492$: With the calculator in radian [MODE], use the keystrokes [2nd] [SIN] 0.8492 [ ) ] [ENTER]. We find $\sin^{-1}(0.8492) \approx 1.0145$ radians. In degree [MODE], the same sequence of keystrokes gives $\sin^{-1}(0.8492) \approx 58.1°$ (note that $1.0145$ rad $\approx 58.1°$).

    **b.** $y = \arcsin(-0.2317)$: In radian [MODE], we find $\sin^{-1}(-0.2317) \approx -0.2338$ rad. In degree [MODE], $\sin^{-1}(-0.2317) \approx -13.4°$.

**Now try Exercises 13 through 16** ▶

**WORTHY OF NOTE**

The $\sin^{-1}x$ notation for the inverse sine function is a carryover from the $f^{-1}(x)$ notation for a general inverse function, and likewise has nothing to do with the reciprocal of the function. The arcsin $x$ notation derives from our work in radians on the unit circle, where $y = \arcsin x$ can be interpreted as "$y$ is an arc whose sine is $x$."

From our work in Section 6.1, we know that if $f$ and $g$ are inverses, $(f \circ g)(x) = x$ and $(g \circ f)(x) = x$. This suggests the following properties.

---

**Inverse Function Properties for Sine**

For $f(x) = \sin x$ and $g(x) = \sin^{-1}x$:

    **I.** $(f \circ g)(x) = \sin(\sin^{-1}x) = x$ for $x$ in $[-1, 1]$

                      and

    **II.** $(g \circ f)(x) = \sin^{-1}(\sin x) = x$ for $x$ in $\left[-\frac{\pi}{2}, \frac{\pi}{2}\right]$

---

**EXAMPLE 3** ▶ **Evaluating Expressions Using Inverse Function Properties**

Evaluate each expression and verify the result on a calculator.

    **a.** $\sin\left[\sin^{-1}\left(\frac{1}{2}\right)\right]$        **b.** $\arcsin\left[\sin\left(\frac{\pi}{4}\right)\right]$        **c.** $\sin^{-1}\left[\sin\left(\frac{5\pi}{6}\right)\right]$

**Solution** ▶   **a.** $\sin\left[\sin^{-1}\left(\frac{1}{2}\right)\right] = \frac{1}{2}$, since $\frac{1}{2}$ is in $[-1, 1]$       Property I

          **b.** $\arcsin\left[\sin\left(\frac{\pi}{4}\right)\right] = \frac{\pi}{4}$, since $\frac{\pi}{4}$ is in $\left[-\frac{\pi}{2}, \frac{\pi}{2}\right]$       Property II

**c.** $\sin^{-1}\left[\sin\left(\dfrac{5\pi}{6}\right)\right] \neq \dfrac{5\pi}{6}$, since $\dfrac{5\pi}{6}$ is not in $\left[-\dfrac{\pi}{2}, \dfrac{\pi}{2}\right]$.

This doesn't mean the expression cannot be evaluated, only that we cannot use Property II. Since $\sin\left(\dfrac{5\pi}{6}\right) = \sin\left(\dfrac{\pi}{6}\right)$, $\sin^{-1}\left[\left(\sin\dfrac{5\pi}{6}\right)\right] = \sin^{-1}\left[\sin\left(\dfrac{\pi}{6}\right)\right] = \dfrac{\pi}{6}$.

The calculator verification for each is shown in Figures 6.19 and 6.20. Note $\dfrac{\pi}{6} \approx 0.5236$ and $\dfrac{\pi}{4} \approx 0.7854$.

**Figure 6.19**
**Parts (a) and (b)**

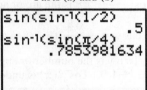

**Figure 6.20**
**Part (c)**

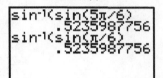

☑ **A.** You've just learned how to find and graph the inverse sine function and evaluate related expressions

**Now try Exercises 17 through 24** ▶

## B. The Inverse Cosine and Inverse Tangent Functions

Like the sine function, the cosine function is not one-to-one and its domain must also be restricted to develop an inverse function. For convenience we choose the interval $x \in [0, \pi]$ since it is again somewhat central and takes on all of its range values in this interval. A graph of the cosine function, with the interval corresponding to this interval shown in red, is given in Figure 6.21. Note the range is still $[-1, 1]$ (Figure 6.22).

**Figure 6.21**

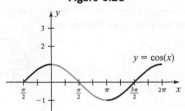

**Figure 6.22**

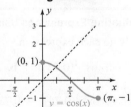

**Figure 6.23**

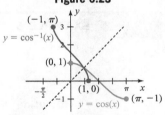

For the implicit equation of inverse cosine, $y = \cos x$ becomes $x = \cos y$, with the corresponding explicit forms being $y = \cos^{-1}x$ or $y = \arccos x$. By reflecting the graph of $y = \cos x$ across the line $y = x$, we obtain the graph of $y = \cos^{-1}x$ shown in Figure 6.23.

**The Inverse Cosine Function**

For $y = \cos x$ with domain $[0, \pi]$ and range $[-1, 1]$, the inverse cosine function is
$$y = \cos^{-1}x \text{ or } y = \arccos x$$
with domain $[-1, 1]$ and range $[0, \pi]$.
$$y = \cos^{-1}x \text{ if and only if } \cos y = x$$

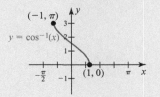

**EXAMPLE 4** ▶ **Evaluating $y = \cos^{-1}x$ Using Special Values**

Evaluate the inverse cosine for the values given:

**a.** $y = \cos^{-1}(0)$    **b.** $y = \arccos\left(-\dfrac{\sqrt{3}}{2}\right)$    **c.** $y = \cos^{-1}(\pi)$

**Solution** ▶ For $x$ in $[-1, 1]$ and $y$ in $[0, \pi]$,

**a.** $y = \cos^{-1}(0)$: $y$ is the number or angle whose cosine is $0 \Rightarrow \cos y = 0$.

This shows $\cos^{-1}(0) = \dfrac{\pi}{2}$.

**b.** $y = \arccos\left(-\dfrac{\sqrt{3}}{2}\right)$: $y$ is the arc or angle whose cosine is

$-\dfrac{\sqrt{3}}{2} \Rightarrow \cos y = -\dfrac{\sqrt{3}}{2}$. This shows $\arccos\left(-\dfrac{\sqrt{3}}{2}\right) = \dfrac{5\pi}{6}$.

**c.** $y = \cos^{-1}(\pi)$: $y$ is the number or angle whose cosine is $\pi \Rightarrow \cos y = \pi$.
Since $\pi \notin [-1, 1]$, $\cos^{-1}(\pi)$ is undefined.

**Now try Exercises 25 through 34** ▶

Knowing that $y = \cos x$ and $y = \cos^{-1}x$ are inverse functions enables us to state inverse function properties similar to those for sine.

**Inverse Function Properties for Cosine**

For $f(x) = \cos x$ and $g(x) = \cos^{-1}x$:

**I.** $(f \circ g)(x) = \cos(\cos^{-1}x) = x$ for $x$ in $[-1, 1]$

and

**II.** $(g \circ f)(x) = \cos^{-1}(\cos x) = x$ for $x$ in $[0, \pi]$

**EXAMPLE 5** ▶ **Evaluating Expressions Using Inverse Function Properties**

Evaluate each expression.

**a.** $\cos[\cos^{-1}(0.73)]$    **b.** $\arccos\left[\cos\left(\dfrac{\pi}{12}\right)\right]$    **c.** $\cos^{-1}\left[\cos\left(\dfrac{4\pi}{3}\right)\right]$

**Solution** ▶ **a.** $\cos[\cos^{-1}(0.73)] = 0.73$, since $0.73$ is in $[-1, 1]$   Property I

**b.** $\arccos\left[\cos\left(\dfrac{\pi}{12}\right)\right] = \dfrac{\pi}{12}$, since $\dfrac{\pi}{12}$ is in $[0, \pi]$   Property II

**c.** $\cos^{-1}\left[\cos\left(\dfrac{4\pi}{3}\right)\right] \neq \dfrac{4\pi}{3}$, since $\dfrac{4\pi}{3}$ is not in $[0, \pi]$.

This expression cannot be evaluated using Property II. Since

$\cos\left(\dfrac{4\pi}{3}\right) = \cos\left(\dfrac{2\pi}{3}\right)$, $\cos^{-1}\left[\cos\left(\dfrac{4\pi}{3}\right)\right] = \cos^{-1}\left[\cos\left(\dfrac{2\pi}{3}\right)\right] = \dfrac{2\pi}{3}$.

The results can also be verified using a calculator.

**Now try Exercises 35 through 42** ▶

For the tangent function, we likewise restrict the domain to obtain a one-to-one function, with the most common choice being $\left(-\dfrac{\pi}{2}, \dfrac{\pi}{2}\right)$. The corresponding range is $\mathbb{R}$. The *implicit* equation for the inverse tangent function is $x = \tan y$ with the explicit forms $y = \tan^{-1}x$ or $y = \arctan x$. With the domain and range interchanged, the domain of $y = \tan^{-1}x$ is $\mathbb{R}$, and the range is $\left(-\dfrac{\pi}{2}, \dfrac{\pi}{2}\right)$. The graph of $y = \tan x$ for $x$ in $\left(-\dfrac{\pi}{2}, \dfrac{\pi}{2}\right)$ is shown in red (Figure 6.24), with the inverse function $y = \tan^{-1}x$ shown in blue (Figure 6.25).

**Figure 6.24**

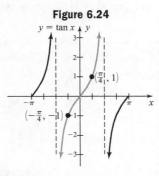

**Figure 6.25**

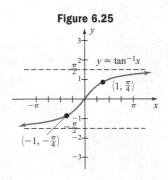

| The Inverse Tangent Function | Inverse Function Properties for Tangent |
|---|---|
| For $y = \tan x$ with domain $\left(-\dfrac{\pi}{2}, \dfrac{\pi}{2}\right)$ and range $\mathbb{R}$, the inverse tangent function is $$y = \tan^{-1}x \text{ or } y = \arctan x,$$ with domain $\mathbb{R}$ and range $\left(-\dfrac{\pi}{2}, \dfrac{\pi}{2}\right)$. $y = \tan^{-1}x$ **if and only if** $\tan y = x$ | For $f(x) = \tan x$ and $g(x) = \tan^{-1}x$: **I.** $(f \circ g)(x) = \tan(\tan^{-1}x) = x$ for $x$ in $\mathbb{R}$ and **II.** $(g \circ f)(x) = \tan^{-1}(\tan x) = x$ for $x$ in $\left(-\dfrac{\pi}{2}, \dfrac{\pi}{2}\right)$. |

**EXAMPLE 6** ▶ **Evaluating Expressions Involving Inverse Tangent**

Evaluate each expression.

    **a.** $\tan^{-1}(-\sqrt{3})$     **b.** $\arctan[\tan(-0.89)]$

**Solution** ▶ For $x$ in $\mathbb{R}$ and $y$ in $\left(-\dfrac{\pi}{2}, \dfrac{\pi}{2}\right)$,

☑ **B.** You've just learned how to find and graph the inverse cosine and tangent functions and evaluate related expressions

    **a.** $\tan^{-1}(-\sqrt{3}) = -\dfrac{\pi}{3}$, since $\tan\left(-\dfrac{\pi}{3}\right) = -\sqrt{3}$

    **b.** $\arctan[\tan(-0.89)] = -0.89$, since $-0.89$ is in $\left(-\dfrac{\pi}{2}, \dfrac{\pi}{2}\right)$    Property II

**Now try Exercises 43 through 52** ▶

## C.  Using the Inverse Trig Functions to Evaluate Compositions

In the context of angle measure, the expression $y = \sin^{-1}\left(-\dfrac{1}{2}\right)$ represents an angle—

the *angle y* whose sine is $-\dfrac{1}{2}$. It seems natural to ask, "What happens if we take the

tangent of this angle?" In other words, what does the expression $\tan\left[\sin^{-1}\left(-\dfrac{1}{2}\right)\right]$

mean? Similarly, if $y = \cos\left(\dfrac{\pi}{3}\right)$ represents a real number between $-1$ and $1$, how do

we compute $\sin^{-1}\left[\cos\left(\dfrac{\pi}{3}\right)\right]$? Expressions like these occur in many fields of study.

---

**EXAMPLE 7** ▶  **Simplifying Expressions Involving Inverse Trig Functions**

Simplify each expression:

  **a.** $\tan\left[\arcsin\left(-\dfrac{1}{2}\right)\right]$     **b.** $\sin^{-1}\left[\cos\left(\dfrac{\pi}{3}\right)\right]$

**Solution** ▶  **a.** In Example 1 we found $\arcsin\left(-\dfrac{1}{2}\right) = -\dfrac{\pi}{6}$. Substituting $-\dfrac{\pi}{6}$ for $\arcsin\left(-\dfrac{1}{2}\right)$

  gives $\tan\left(-\dfrac{\pi}{6}\right) = -\dfrac{\sqrt{3}}{3}$, showing $\tan\left[\arcsin\left(-\dfrac{1}{2}\right)\right] = -\dfrac{\sqrt{3}}{3}$.

  **b.** For $\sin^{-1}\left[\cos\left(\dfrac{\pi}{3}\right)\right]$, we begin with the inner function $\cos\left(\dfrac{\pi}{3}\right) = \dfrac{1}{2}$.

  Substituting $\dfrac{1}{2}$ for $\cos\left(\dfrac{\pi}{3}\right)$ gives $\sin^{-1}\left(\dfrac{1}{2}\right)$. With the appropriate checks

  satisfied we have $\sin^{-1}\left(\dfrac{1}{2}\right) = \dfrac{\pi}{6}$, showing $\sin^{-1}\left[\cos\left(\dfrac{\pi}{3}\right)\right] = \dfrac{\pi}{6}$.

**Now try Exercises 53 through 64** ▶

---

If the argument is not a special value and we need the answer in exact form, we can draw the triangle described by the inner expression using the definition of the trigonometric functions as ratios. In other words, for $\theta = \sin^{-1}\left(\dfrac{8}{17}\right)$, we draw a triangle with hypotenuse 17 and side 8 opposite $\theta$ to model the statement, "an angle whose sine is $\dfrac{8}{17} = \dfrac{\text{opp}}{\text{hyp}}$," (see Figure 6.26). Using the Pythagorean theorem, we find the adjacent side is 15 and can now name any of the other trig functions.

**Figure 6.26**

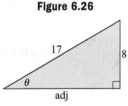

**EXAMPLE 8** ► **Using a Diagram to Evaluate an Expression Involving Inverse Trig Functions**

Evaluate the expression $\tan\left[\sin^{-1}\left(-\dfrac{8}{17}\right)\right]$.

**Solution** ► The expression $\tan\left[\sin^{-1}\left(-\dfrac{8}{17}\right)\right]$ is equivalent to $\tan\theta$,

where $\theta = \sin^{-1}\left(-\dfrac{8}{17}\right)$ with $\theta$ in

$\left[-\dfrac{\pi}{2}, \dfrac{\pi}{2}\right]$ (QIV or QI). For

$\sin\theta = -\dfrac{8}{17}$ ($\sin\theta < 0$), $\theta$ must be in

QIII or QIV. To satisfy both, $\theta$ must be in QIV. From the figure

we note $\tan\theta = -\dfrac{8}{15}$, showing $\tan\left[\sin^{-1}\left(-\dfrac{8}{17}\right)\right] = -\dfrac{8}{15}$.

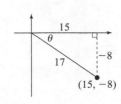

**WORTHY OF NOTE**

To verify the result of Example 8, we can actually find the value of $\sin^{-1}\left(-\dfrac{8}{17}\right)$ on a calculator, then take the tangent of the result. See the figure.

```
sin⁻¹(-8/17)
        -28.07248694
tan(Ans)
        -.5333333333
Ans▶Frac
              -8/15
```

**Now try Exercises 65 through 72 ►**

⚠ These ideas apply even when one side of the triangle is unknown. In other words, we can still draw a triangle for $\theta = \cos^{-1}\left(\dfrac{x}{\sqrt{x^2 + 16}}\right)$, since "$\theta$ is an angle whose

cosine is $\dfrac{x}{\sqrt{x^2 + 16}} = \dfrac{\text{adj}}{\text{hyp}}$."

**EXAMPLE 9** ► **Using a Diagram to Evaluate an Expression Involving Inverse Trig Functions**

Evaluate the expression $\tan\left[\cos^{-1}\left(\dfrac{x}{\sqrt{x^2 + 16}}\right)\right]$. Assume $x > 0$ and the inverse

function is defined for the expression given.

**Solution** ► Rewrite $\tan\left[\cos^{-1}\left(\dfrac{x}{\sqrt{x^2 + 16}}\right)\right]$ as $\tan\theta$, where

$\theta = \cos^{-1}\left(\dfrac{x}{\sqrt{x^2 + 16}}\right)$. Draw a triangle with

side $x$ adjacent to $\theta$ and a hypotenuse of $\sqrt{x^2 + 16}$. The Pythagorean theorem gives

$x^2 + \text{opp}^2 = (\sqrt{x^2 + 16})^2$, which leads to

$\text{opp}^2 = (x^2 + 16) - x^2$ giving $\text{opp} = \sqrt{16} = 4$. This shows

$\tan\theta = \tan\left[\cos^{-1}\left(\dfrac{x}{\sqrt{x^2 + 16}}\right)\right] = \dfrac{4}{x}$ (see the figure).

☑ **C. You've just learned how to apply the definition and notation of inverse trig functions to simplify compositions**

**Now try Exercises 73 through 76 ►**

## D. The Inverse Functions for Secant, Cosecant, and Cotangent

As with the other functions, we restrict the domain of the secant, cosecant, and cotangent functions to obtain a one-to-one function that is invertible (an inverse can be found). Once again the choice is arbitrary, and some domains are easier to work with than others in more advanced mathematics. For $y = \sec x$, we've chosen the "most

**Figure 6.27**
$y = \sec x$

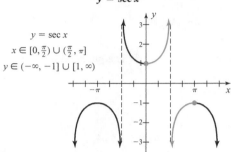

$y = \sec x$
$x \in [0, \frac{\pi}{2}) \cup (\frac{\pi}{2}, \pi]$
$y \in (-\infty, -1] \cup [1, \infty)$

**Figure 6.28**
$y = \sec^{-1}x$

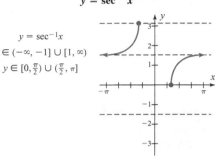

$y = \sec^{-1}x$
$x \in (-\infty, -1] \cup [1, \infty)$
$y \in [0, \frac{\pi}{2}) \cup (\frac{\pi}{2}, \pi]$

intuitive" restriction, one that seems more centrally located (nearer the origin). The graph of $y = \sec x$ is reproduced here, along with its inverse function (see Figures 6.27 and 6.28). The domain, range, and graphs of the functions $y = \csc^{-1}x$ and $y = \cot^{-1}x$ are asked for in the Exercises **(see Exercise 100).**

The functions $y = \sec^{-1}x$, $y = \csc^{-1}x$, and $y = \cot^{-1}x$ can be evaluated by noting their relationship to $y = \cos^{-1}x$, $y = \sin^{-1}x$, and $y = \tan^{-1}x$, respectively. For $y = \sec^{-1}x$, we have

<table>
<tr><td>$\sec y = x$</td><td>definition of inverse function</td></tr>
<tr><td>$\dfrac{1}{\sec y} = \dfrac{1}{x}$</td><td>property of reciprocals</td></tr>
<tr><td>$\cos y = \dfrac{1}{x}$</td><td>reciprocal ratio</td></tr>
<tr><td>$y = \cos^{-1}\left(\dfrac{1}{x}\right)$</td><td>rewrite using inverse function notation</td></tr>
<tr><td>$\sec^{-1}x = \cos^{-1}\left(\dfrac{1}{x}\right)$</td><td>substitute $\sec^{-1}x$ for $y$</td></tr>
</table>

In other words, to find the value of $y = \sec^{-1}x$, evaluate $y = \cos^{-1}\left(\dfrac{1}{x}\right)$, $|x| \geq 1$. Similarly, the expression $\csc^{-1}x$ can be evaluated using $\sin^{-1}\left(\dfrac{1}{x}\right)$, $|x| \geq 1$. The expression $\cot^{-1}x$ can likewise be evaluated using an inverse tangent function: $\cot^{-1}x = \tan^{-1}\left(\dfrac{1}{x}\right)$.

> **WORTHY OF NOTE**
>
> While the domains of $y = \cot^{-1}x$ and $y = \tan^{-1}x$ both include all real numbers, evaluating $\cot^{-1}x$ using $\tan^{-1}\left(\dfrac{1}{x}\right)$ involves the restriction $x \neq 0$. To maintain consistency, the equation $\cot^{-1}x = \dfrac{\pi}{2} - \tan^{-1}x$ is often used. The graph of $y = \dfrac{\pi}{2} - \tan^{-1}x$ is that of $y = \tan^{-1}x$ reflected across the x-axis and shifted $\dfrac{\pi}{2}$ units up, with the result identical to the graph of $y = \cot^{-1}x$.

---

**EXAMPLE 10** ▶ **Evaluating an Inverse Trig Function**

Evaluate using a calculator only if necessary:

    **a.** $\sec^{-1}\left(\dfrac{2}{\sqrt{3}}\right)$      **b.** $\cot^{-1}\left(\dfrac{\pi}{12}\right)$

Solution ▶     **a.** From our previous discussion, for $\sec^{-1}\left(\dfrac{2}{\sqrt{3}}\right)$, we evaluate $\cos^{-1}\left(\dfrac{\sqrt{3}}{2}\right)$.

        Since this is a standard value, no calculator is needed and the result is 30°.

    **b.** For $\cot^{-1}\left(\dfrac{\pi}{12}\right)$, find $\tan^{-1}\left(\dfrac{12}{\pi}\right)$ on a calculator:

        $\cot^{-1}\left(\dfrac{\pi}{12}\right) = \tan^{-1}\left(\dfrac{12}{\pi}\right) \approx 1.3147.$

☑ **D.** You've just learned how to find and graph inverse functions for sec $x$, csc $x$, and cot $x$

**Now try Exercises 77 through 86** ▶

A summary of the highlights from this section follows.

## Summary of Inverse Function Properties and Compositions

**1.** For $\sin x$ and $\sin^{-1}x$,

$\sin(\sin^{-1}x) = x$, for any $x$ in the interval $[-1, 1]$;

$\sin^{-1}(\sin x) = x$, for any $x$ in the interval $\left[-\dfrac{\pi}{2}, \dfrac{\pi}{2}\right]$

**3.** For $\tan x$ and $\tan^{-1}x$,

$\tan(\tan^{-1}x) = x$, for any real number $x$;

$\tan^{-1}(\tan x) = x$, for any $x$ in the interval $\left(-\dfrac{\pi}{2}, \dfrac{\pi}{2}\right)$

**2.** For $\cos x$ and $\cos^{-1}x$,

$\cos(\cos^{-1}x) = x$, for any $x$ in the interval $[-1, 1]$;

$\cos^{-1}(\cos x) = x$, for any $x$ in the interval $[0, \pi]$

**4.** To evaluate $\sec^{-1}x$, use $\cos^{-1}\left(\dfrac{1}{x}\right)$, $|x| \geq 1$;

for $\csc^{-1}x$, use $\sin^{-1}\left(\dfrac{1}{x}\right)$, $|x| \geq 1$;

for $\cot^{-1}x$, use $\dfrac{\pi}{2} - \tan^{-1}x$, for all real numbers $x$

## E. Applications of Inverse Trig Functions

We close this section with one example of the many ways that inverse functions can be applied.

**EXAMPLE 11** ▶ **Using Inverse Trig Functions to Find Viewing Angles**

Believe it or not, the drive-in movie theaters that were so popular in the 1950s are making a comeback! If you arrive early, you can park in one of the coveted "center spots," but if you arrive late, you might have to park very close and strain your neck to watch the movie. Surprisingly, the maximum viewing angle (not the most comfortable viewing angle in this case) is actually very close to the front. Assume the base of a 30-ft screen is 10 ft above eye level (see Figure 6.29).

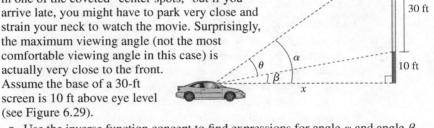

**Figure 6.29**

30 ft

10 ft

**a.** Use the inverse function concept to find expressions for angle $\alpha$ and angle $\beta$.

**b.** Use the result of Part (a) to find an expression for the *viewing angle* $\theta$.

**c.** Use a calculator to find the viewing angle $\theta$ (to tenths of a degree) for distances of 15, 25, 35, and 45 ft, then to determine the distance $x$ (to tenths of a foot) that maximizes the viewing angle.

Solution ▶ **a.** The side opposite $\beta$ is 10 ft, and we want to know $x$—the adjacent side. This suggests we use $\tan \beta = \dfrac{10}{x}$, giving $\beta = \tan^{-1}\left(\dfrac{10}{x}\right)$. In the same way, we find that $\alpha = \tan^{-1}\left(\dfrac{40}{x}\right)$.

**b.** From the diagram we note that $\theta = \alpha - \beta$, and substituting for $\alpha$ and $\beta$ directly gives $\theta = \tan^{-1}\left(\dfrac{40}{x}\right) - \tan^{-1}\left(\dfrac{10}{x}\right)$.

**c.** After we enter $Y_1 = \tan^{-1}\left(\dfrac{40}{x}\right) - \tan^{-1}\left(\dfrac{10}{x}\right)$, a graphing calculator gives

approximate viewing angles of 35.8 °, 36.2°, 32.9°, and 29.1°, for $x = 15$, 25, 35, and 45 ft, respectively. From these data, we note the distance $x$ that makes $\theta$ a maximum must be between 15 and 35 ft, and using [2nd] [TRACE] (CALC) **4:maximum** shows $\theta$ is a maximum of 36.9° at a distance of 20 ft from the screen (see Figure 6.30).

**Figure 6.30**

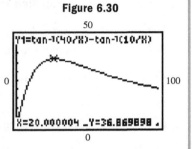

☑ **E.** You've just learned how to solve applications involving inverse functions

Now try Exercises 89 through 95 ▶

---

## TECHNOLOGY HIGHLIGHT

## More on Inverse Functions

The domain and range of the inverse functions for sine, cosine, and tangent are preprogrammed into most graphing calculators, making them an ideal tool for reinforcing the concepts involved. In particular, $\sin x = y$ implies that $\sin^{-1} y = x$ only if $-90° \le x \le 90°$ and $-1 \le y \le 1$. To illustrate this fact we'll use the TABLE feature of the grapher. Begin by using the TBLSET screen ( [2nd] [WINDOW]) to set TblStart = 90 with $\Delta$Tbl = −30. After placing the calculator in degree [MODE], go to the [Y=] screen and input $Y_1 = \sin x$, $Y_2 = \sin^{-1} x$, and $Y_3 = Y_2(Y_1)$ (the composition $Y_2 \circ Y_1$). Then disable $Y_2$ [turn it off—$Y_3$ will read it anyway) so that both $Y_1$ and $Y_3$ will be displayed simultaneously on the TABLE screen. Pressing [2nd] [GRAPH] brings up the TABLE shown in Figure 6.31, where we note the inputs are standard angles, the outputs in $Y_1$ are the (expected) standard values, and the outputs in $Y_3$ return the original standard values. Now scroll upward until 180° is at the top of the X column (Figure 6.32), and note that $Y_3$ continues to return standard angles from the interval $[-90°, 90°]$—a stark reminder that while the expression $\sin 150° = 0.5$, $\sin^{-1}(\sin 150°) \ne 150°$. Once again we note that while $\sin^{-1}(\sin 150°)$ can be evaluated, it cannot be evaluated directly using the inverse function properties. Use these ideas to complete the following exercises.

**Figure 6.31**

| X | Y₁ | Y₃ |
|---|---|---|
| **90** | 1 | 90 |
| 60 | .86603 | 60 |
| 30 | .5 | 30 |
| 0 | 0 | 0 |
| -30 | -.5 | -30 |
| -60 | -.866 | -60 |
| -90 | -1 | -90 |

X=90

**Figure 6.32**

| X | Y₁ | Y₃ |
|---|---|---|
| **180** | 0 | 0 |
| 150 | .5 | 30 |
| 120 | .86603 | 60 |
| 90 | 1 | 90 |
| 60 | .86603 | 60 |
| 30 | .5 | 30 |
| 0 | 0 | 0 |

X=180

**Exercise 1:**  Go through an exercise similar to the one here using $Y_1 = \cos x$ and $Y_2 = \cos^{-1} x$. Remember to modify the TBLSET to accommodate the restricted domain for cosine.

**Exercise 2:**  Complete parts (a) and (b) using the TABLE from Exercise 1. Complete parts (c) and (d) without a calculator.

**a.** $\cos^{-1}(\cos 150°)$                    **b.** $\cos^{-1}(\cos 210°)$

**c.** $\cos^{-1}(\cos 120°)$                    **d.** $\cos^{-1}(\cos 240°)$

## 6.2 EXERCISES

▶ **CONCEPTS AND VOCABULARY**

**Fill in each blank with the appropriate word or phrase. Carefully reread the section if needed.**

1. All six trigonometric functions fail the _____ _____ test and therefore are not _____ to _____ .

2. The two most common ways of writing the inverse function for $y = \sin x$ are _____ and _____ .

3. The domain for the inverse sine function is _____ and the range is _____ .

4. The domain for the inverse cosine function is _____ and the range is _____ .

5. Most calculators do not have a key for evaluating an expression like $\sec^{-1} 5$. Explain how it is done using the $\boxed{\cos}$ key.

6. Discuss/Explain what is meant by the *implicit form* of an inverse function and the *explicit form*. Give algebraic and trigonometric examples.

▶ **DEVELOPING YOUR SKILLS**

**The tables here show values of $\sin \theta$, $\cos \theta$, and $\tan \theta$ for $\theta \in [-180°$ to $210°]$. The restricted domain used to develop the inverse functions is shaded. Use the information from these tables to complete the exercises that follow.**

$y = \sin \theta$

| $\theta$ | $\sin \theta$ | $\theta$ | $\sin \theta$ |
|---|---|---|---|
| $-180°$ | $0$ | $30°$ | $\dfrac{1}{2}$ |
| $-150°$ | $-\dfrac{1}{2}$ | $60°$ | $\dfrac{\sqrt{3}}{2}$ |
| $-120°$ | $-\dfrac{\sqrt{3}}{2}$ | $90°$ | $1$ |
| $-90°$ | $-1$ | $120°$ | $\dfrac{\sqrt{3}}{2}$ |
| $-60°$ | $-\dfrac{\sqrt{3}}{2}$ | $150°$ | $\dfrac{1}{2}$ |
| $-30°$ | $-\dfrac{1}{2}$ | $180°$ | $0$ |
| $0$ | $0$ | $210°$ | $-\dfrac{1}{2}$ |

$y = \cos \theta$

| $\theta$ | $\cos \theta$ | $\theta$ | $\cos \theta$ |
|---|---|---|---|
| $-180°$ | $-1$ | $30°$ | $\dfrac{\sqrt{3}}{2}$ |
| $-150°$ | $-\dfrac{\sqrt{3}}{2}$ | $60°$ | $\dfrac{1}{2}$ |
| $-120°$ | $-\dfrac{1}{2}$ | $90°$ | $0$ |
| $-90°$ | $0$ | $120°$ | $-\dfrac{1}{2}$ |
| $-60°$ | $\dfrac{1}{2}$ | $150°$ | $-\dfrac{\sqrt{3}}{2}$ |
| $-30°$ | $\dfrac{\sqrt{3}}{2}$ | $180°$ | $-1$ |
| $0$ | $1$ | $210°$ | $-\dfrac{\sqrt{3}}{2}$ |

$y = \tan \theta$

| $\theta$ | $\tan \theta$ | $\theta$ | $\tan \theta$ |
|---|---|---|---|
| $-180°$ | $0$ | $30°$ | $\dfrac{\sqrt{3}}{3}$ |
| $-150°$ | $\dfrac{\sqrt{3}}{3}$ | $60°$ | $\sqrt{3}$ |
| $-120°$ | $\sqrt{3}$ | $90°$ | — |
| $-90°$ | — | $120°$ | $-\sqrt{3}$ |
| $-60°$ | $-\sqrt{3}$ | $150°$ | $-\dfrac{\sqrt{3}}{3}$ |
| $-30°$ | $-\dfrac{\sqrt{3}}{3}$ | $180°$ | $0$ |
| $0$ | $0$ | $210°$ | $\sqrt{3}$ |

**Use the preceding tables to fill in each blank (principal values only).**

7.

| | |
|---|---|
| $\sin 0 = 0$ | $\sin^{-1} 0 = $ ___ |
| $\sin\left(\dfrac{\pi}{6}\right) = $ ___ | $\arcsin\left(\dfrac{1}{2}\right) = \dfrac{\pi}{6}$ |
| $\sin\left(-\dfrac{5\pi}{6}\right) = -\dfrac{1}{2}$ | $\sin^{-1}\left(-\dfrac{1}{2}\right) = $ ___ |
| $\sin\left(-\dfrac{\pi}{2}\right) = -1$ | $\sin^{-1}(-1) = $ ___ |

8.

| | |
|---|---|
| $\sin \pi = 0$ | $\sin^{-1} 0 = $ ___ |
| $\sin 120° = \dfrac{\sqrt{3}}{2}$ | $\sin^{-1}\left(\dfrac{\sqrt{3}}{2}\right) = $ ___ |
| $\sin(-60°) = -\dfrac{\sqrt{3}}{2}$ | $\arcsin\left(-\dfrac{\sqrt{3}}{2}\right) = $ ___ |
| $\sin 180° = $ ___ | $\arcsin 0 = 0$ |

**Evaluate without the aid of calculators or tables,** *keeping the domain and range of each function in mind.* **Answer in radians.**

**9.** $\sin^{-1}\left(\dfrac{\sqrt{2}}{2}\right)$   **10.** $\arcsin\left(\dfrac{\sqrt{3}}{2}\right)$

**11.** $\sin^{-1}1$   **12.** $\arcsin\left(-\dfrac{1}{2}\right)$

**Evaluate using a calculator,** *keeping the domain and range of each function in mind.* **Answer in radians to the nearest ten-thousandth** *and* **in degrees to the nearest tenth.**

**13.** $\arcsin 0.8892$   **14.** $\arcsin\left(\dfrac{7}{8}\right)$

**15.** $\sin^{-1}\left(\dfrac{1}{\sqrt{7}}\right)$   **16.** $\sin^{-1}\left(\dfrac{1-\sqrt{5}}{2}\right)$

**Evaluate each expression.**

**17.** $\sin\left[\sin^{-1}\left(\dfrac{\sqrt{2}}{2}\right)\right]$   **18.** $\sin\left[\arcsin\left(\dfrac{\sqrt{3}}{2}\right)\right]$

**19.** $\arcsin\left[\sin\left(\dfrac{\pi}{3}\right)\right]$   **20.** $\sin^{-1}(\sin 30°)$

**21.** $\sin^{-1}(\sin 135°)$   **22.** $\arcsin\left[\sin\left(\dfrac{-2\pi}{3}\right)\right]$

**23.** $\sin(\sin^{-1}0.8205)$   **24.** $\sin\left[\arcsin\left(\dfrac{3}{5}\right)\right]$

**Use the tables given prior to Exercise 7 to fill in each blank (principal values only).**

**25.**

| $\cos 0 = 1$ | $\cos^{-1}1 = $ \_\_\_\_ |
|---|---|
| $\cos\left(\dfrac{\pi}{6}\right) = $ \_\_\_\_ | $\arccos\left(\dfrac{\sqrt{3}}{2}\right) = \dfrac{\pi}{6}$ |
| $\cos 120° = -\dfrac{1}{2}$ | $\arccos\left(-\dfrac{1}{2}\right) = $ \_\_\_\_ |
| $\cos \pi = -1$ | $\cos^{-1}(-1) = $ \_\_\_\_ |

**26.**

| $\cos(-60°) = \dfrac{1}{2}$ | $\cos^{-1}\left(\dfrac{1}{2}\right) = $ \_\_\_\_ |
|---|---|
| $\cos\left(-\dfrac{\pi}{6}\right) = \dfrac{\sqrt{3}}{2}$ | $\cos^{-1}\left(\dfrac{\sqrt{3}}{2}\right) = $ \_\_\_\_ |
| $\cos(-120°) = $ \_\_\_\_ | $\arccos\left(-\dfrac{1}{2}\right) = 120°$ |
| $\cos(2\pi) = 1$ | $\cos^{-1}1 = $ \_\_\_\_ |

**Evaluate without the aid of calculators or tables. Answer in radians.**

**27.** $\cos^{-1}\left(\dfrac{1}{2}\right)$   **28.** $\arccos\left(-\dfrac{\sqrt{3}}{2}\right)$

**29.** $\cos^{-1}(-1)$   **30.** $\arccos(0)$

**Evaluate using a calculator. Answer in radians to the nearest ten-thousandth, degrees to the nearest tenth.**

**31.** $\arccos 0.1352$   **32.** $\arccos\left(\dfrac{4}{7}\right)$

**33.** $\cos^{-1}\left(\dfrac{\sqrt{5}}{3}\right)$   **34.** $\cos^{-1}\left(\dfrac{\sqrt{6}-1}{5}\right)$

**Evaluate each expression.**

**35.** $\arccos\left[\cos\left(\dfrac{\pi}{4}\right)\right]$   **36.** $\cos^{-1}(\cos 60°)$

**37.** $\cos(\cos^{-1}0.5560)$   **38.** $\cos\left[\arccos\left(-\dfrac{8}{17}\right)\right]$

**39.** $\cos\left[\cos^{-1}\left(-\dfrac{\sqrt{2}}{2}\right)\right]$   **40.** $\cos\left[\arccos\left(\dfrac{\sqrt{3}}{2}\right)\right]$

**41.** $\cos^{-1}\left[\cos\left(\dfrac{5\pi}{4}\right)\right]$   **42.** $\arccos(\cos 44.2°)$

**Use the tables presented before Exercise 7 to fill in each blank. Convert from radians to degrees as needed.**

**43.**

| $\tan 0 = 0$ | $\tan^{-1}0 = $ \_\_\_\_ |
|---|---|
| $\tan\left(-\dfrac{\pi}{3}\right) = $ \_\_\_\_ | $\arctan(-\sqrt{3}) = -\dfrac{\pi}{3}$ |
| $\tan 30° = \dfrac{\sqrt{3}}{3}$ | $\arctan\left(\dfrac{\sqrt{3}}{3}\right) = $ \_\_\_\_ |
| $\tan\left(\dfrac{\pi}{3}\right) = $ \_\_\_\_ | $\tan^{-1}(\sqrt{3}) = $ \_\_\_\_ |

**44.**

| $\tan(-150°) = \dfrac{\sqrt{3}}{3}$ | $\tan^{-1}\left(\dfrac{\sqrt{3}}{3}\right) = $ \_\_\_\_ |
|---|---|
| $\tan \pi = 0$ | $\tan^{-1}0 = $ \_\_\_\_ |
| $\tan 120° = -\sqrt{3}$ | $\arctan(-\sqrt{3}) = $ \_\_\_\_ |
| $\tan\left(\dfrac{\pi}{4}\right) = $ \_\_\_\_ | $\arctan 1 = \dfrac{\pi}{4}$ |

**Evaluate without the aid of calculators or tables.**

**45.** $\tan^{-1}\left(-\dfrac{\sqrt{3}}{3}\right)$   **46.** $\arctan(-1)$

**47.** $\arctan(\sqrt{3})$   **48.** $\tan^{-1}0$

**Evaluate using a calculator,** *keeping the domain and range of each function in mind.* **Answer in radians to the nearest ten-thousandth** *and* **in degrees to the nearest tenth.**

**49.** $\tan^{-1}(-2.05)$          **50.** $\tan^{-1}(0.3267)$

**51.** $\arctan\left(\dfrac{29}{21}\right)$          **52.** $\arctan(-\sqrt{6})$

**Simplify each expression without using a calculator.**

**53.** $\sin^{-1}\left[\cos\left(\dfrac{2\pi}{3}\right)\right]$          **54.** $\cos^{-1}\left[\sin\left(-\dfrac{\pi}{3}\right)\right]$

**55.** $\tan\left[\arccos\left(\dfrac{\sqrt{3}}{2}\right)\right]$          **56.** $\sec\left[\arcsin\left(\dfrac{1}{2}\right)\right]$

**57.** $\csc\left[\sin^{-1}\left(\dfrac{\sqrt{2}}{2}\right)\right]$          **58.** $\cot\left[\cos^{-1}\left(-\dfrac{1}{2}\right)\right]$

**59.** $\arccos[\sin(-30°)]$          **60.** $\arcsin(\cos 135°)$

**Explain why the following expressions are not defined.**

**61.** $\tan(\sin^{-1}1)$          **62.** $\cot(\arccos 1)$

**63.** $\sin^{-1}\left[\csc\left(\dfrac{\pi}{4}\right)\right]$          **64.** $\cos^{-1}\left[\sec\left(\dfrac{2\pi}{3}\right)\right]$

**Use the diagrams shown to write the value of: (a) sin $\theta$, (b) cos $\theta$, and (c) tan $\theta$.**

**65.**           **66.**

**67.** 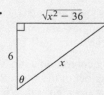          **68.**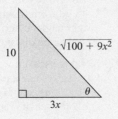

**Evaluate each expression by drawing a right triangle and labeling the sides.**

**69.** $\sin\left[\cos^{-1}\left(-\dfrac{7}{25}\right)\right]$          **70.** $\cos\left[\sin^{-1}\left(-\dfrac{11}{61}\right)\right]$

**71.** $\sin\left[\tan^{-1}\left(\dfrac{\sqrt{5}}{2}\right)\right]$          **72.** $\tan\left[\cos^{-1}\left(\dfrac{\sqrt{23}}{12}\right)\right]$

**73.** $\cot\left[\arcsin\left(\dfrac{3x}{5}\right)\right]$          **74.** $\tan\left[\operatorname{arcsec}\left(\dfrac{5}{2x}\right)\right]$

**75.** $\cos\left[\sin^{-1}\left(\dfrac{x}{\sqrt{12+x^2}}\right)\right]$

**76.** $\tan\left[\sec^{-1}\left(\dfrac{\sqrt{9+x^2}}{x}\right)\right]$

**Use the tables given prior to Exercise 7 to help fill in each blank.**

**77.**

| $\sec 0 = 1$ | $\sec^{-1}1 =$ \_\_\_\_ |
|---|---|
| $\sec\left(\dfrac{\pi}{3}\right) =$ \_\_\_\_ | $\operatorname{arcsec} 2 = \dfrac{\pi}{3}$ |
| $\sec(-30°) = \dfrac{2}{\sqrt{3}}$ | $\operatorname{arcsec}\left(\dfrac{2}{\sqrt{3}}\right) =$ \_\_\_\_ |
| $\sec(\pi) =$ \_\_\_\_ | $\sec^{-1}(-1) = \pi$ |

**78.**

| $\sec(-60°) = 2$ | $\operatorname{arcsec} 2 =$ \_\_\_\_ |
|---|---|
| $\sec\left(\dfrac{7\pi}{6}\right) = -\dfrac{2}{\sqrt{3}}$ | $\operatorname{arcsec}\left(-\dfrac{2}{\sqrt{3}}\right) =$ \_\_\_\_ |
| $\sec(-360°) = 1$ | $\operatorname{arcsec} 1 =$ \_\_\_\_ |
| $\sec(60°) =$ \_\_\_\_ | $\sec^{-1}(2) = 60°$ |

**Evaluate using a calculator only as necessary.**

**79.** $\operatorname{arccsc} 2$          **80.** $\csc^{-1}\left(-\dfrac{2}{\sqrt{3}}\right)$

**81.** $\cot^{-1}\sqrt{3}$          **82.** $\operatorname{arccot}(-1)$

**83.** $\operatorname{arcsec} 5.789$          **84.** $\cot^{-1}\left(-\dfrac{\sqrt{7}}{2}\right)$

**85.** $\sec^{-1}\sqrt{7}$          **86.** $\operatorname{arccsc} 2.9875$

▶ **WORKING WITH FORMULAS**

**87. The force normal to an object on an inclined plane:** $F_N = mg\cos\theta$

When an object is on an inclined plane, the **normal force** is the force acting perpendicular to the plane and away from the force of gravity, and is measured in a unit called **newtons (N)**. The magnitude of this force depends on the angle of incline of the plane according to the formula given, where $m$ is the mass of the object in kilograms and $g$ is the force of gravity (9.8 m/sec²). Given $m = 225$ g, find (a) $F_N$ for $\theta = 15°$ and $\theta = 45°$ and (b) $\theta$ for $F_N = 1$ N and $F_N = 2$ N.

**88. Heat flow on a cylindrical pipe:** $T = (T_0 - T_R) \sin\left(\dfrac{y}{\sqrt{x^2 + y^2}}\right) + T_R; y \geq 0$

When a circular pipe is exposed to a fan-driven source of heat, the temperature of the air reaching the pipe is greatest at the point nearest to the source (see diagram). As you move around the circumference of the pipe away from the source, the temperature of the air reaching the pipe gradually decreases. One possible model of this phenomenon is given by the formula shown, where $T$ is the temperature of the air at a point $(x, y)$ on the circumference of a pipe with outer radius $r = \sqrt{x^2 + y^2}$, $T_0$ is the temperature of the air at the source, and $T_R$ is the surrounding room temperature. Assuming $T_0 = 220°F$, $T_R = 72°$ and $r = 5$ cm: (a) Find the temperature of the air at the points $(0, 5)$, $(3, 4)$, $(4, 3)$, $(4.58, 2)$, and $(4.9, 1)$. (b) Why is the temperature decreasing for this sequence of points? (c) Simplify the formula using $r = 5$ and use it to find two points on the pipe's circumference where the temperature of the air is $113°$.

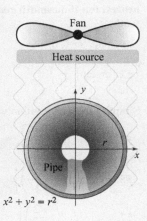

$x^2 + y^2 = r^2$

▶ **APPLICATIONS**

**89. Snowcone dimensions:** *Made in the Shade Snowcones* sells a colossal size cone that uses a conical cup holding 20 oz of ice and liquid. The cup is 20 cm tall and has a radius of 5.35 cm. Find the angle $\theta$ formed by a cross-section of the cup.

Exercise 89

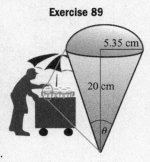

5.35 cm

20 cm

$\theta$

**90. Avalanche conditions:** Winter avalanches occur for many reasons, one being the slope of the mountain. Avalanches seem to occur most often for slopes between 35° and 60° (snow gradually slides off steeper slopes). The slopes at a local ski resort have an average rise of 2000 ft for each horizontal run of 2559 ft. Is this resort prone to avalanches? Find the angle $\theta$ and respond.

Exercise 90

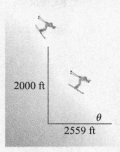

2000 ft

$\theta$

2559 ft

**91. Distance to hole:** A popular story on the PGA Tour has Gerry Yang, Tiger Woods' teammate at Stanford and occasional caddie, using the Pythagorean theorem to find the distance Tiger needed to reach a particular hole. Suppose you notice a marker in the ground stating that the straight-line distance from the marker to the hole ($H$) is 150 yd. If your ball $B$ is 48 yd from the marker ($M$) and angle $BMH$ is a right angle, determine the angle $\theta$ and *your* straight-line distance from the hole.

Exercise 91

$H$

150 yd

$M$

$\theta$

$B$    48 yd    Marker

**92. Ski jumps:** At a waterskiing contest on a large lake, skiers use a ramp rising out of the water that is 30 ft long and 10 ft high at the high end. What angle $\theta$ does the ramp make with the lake?

Exercise 92

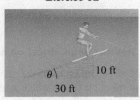

$\theta$    10 ft

30 ft

93. **Viewing angles for advertising:** A 25-ft-wide billboard is erected perpendicular to a straight highway, with the closer edge 50 ft away (see figure). Assume the advertisement on the billboard is most easily read when the viewing angle is 10.5° or more. (a) Use inverse functions to find an expression for the viewing angle $\theta$. (b) Use a calculator to help determine the distance $d$ (to tenths of a foot) for which the viewing angle is greater than 10.5°. (c) What distance $d$ maximizes this viewing angle?

**Exercise 93**

50 ft

25 ft

$d$

$\theta$

94. **Viewing angles at an art show:** At an art show, a painting 2.5 ft in height is hung on a wall so that its base is 1.5 ft above the eye level of an average viewer (see figure). (a) Use inverse functions to find expressions for angles $\alpha$ and $\beta$. (b) Use the result to find an expression for the *viewing angle* $\theta$. (c) Use a

**Exercise 94**

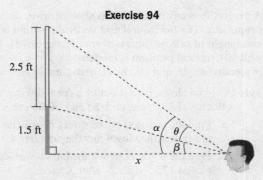

2.5 ft

1.5 ft

$\alpha$ $\theta$ $\beta$

$x$

calculator to help determine the distance $x$ (to tenths of a foot) that maximizes this viewing angle.

95. **Shooting angles and shots on goal:** A soccer player is on a breakaway and is dribbling just inside the right sideline toward the opposing goal (see figure). As the defense closes in, she has just a few seconds to decide when to shoot. (a) Use inverse functions to find an expression for the shooting angle $\theta$. (b) Use a calculator to help determine the distance $d$ (to tenths of a foot) that will maximize the shooting angle for the dimensions shown.

**Exercise 95**

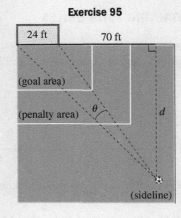

24 ft    70 ft

(goal area)

(penalty area) $\theta$   $d$

(sideline)

▶ **EXTENDING THE CONCEPT**

Consider a satellite orbiting at an altitude of $x$ mi above the Earth. The distance $d$ from the satellite to the horizon and the length $s$ of the corresponding arc of the Earth are shown in the diagram.

96. To find the distance $d$ we use the formula $d = \sqrt{2rx + x^2}$. (a) Show how this formula was developed using the Pythagorean theorem. (b) Find a formula for the angle $\theta$ in terms of $r$ and $x$, then a formula for the arc length $s$.

97. If the Earth has a radius of 3960 mi and the satellite is orbiting at an altitude of 150 mi, (a) what is the measure of angle $\theta$? (b) how much longer is $d$ than $s$?

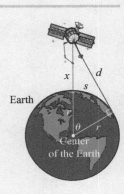

A projectile is any object that is shot, thrown, slung, or otherwise projected and has no continuing source of propulsion. The horizontal and vertical position of the projectile depends on its initial velocity, angle of projection, and height of release (air resistance is neglected). The horizontal position of the projectile is given by $x = v_0 \cos \theta \, t$, while its vertical position is modeled by $y = y_0 + v_0 \sin \theta \, t - 16t^2$, where $y_0$ is the height it is projected from, $\theta$ is the projection angle, and $t$ is the elapsed time in seconds.

**98.** A circus clown is shot out of a specially made cannon at an angle of 55°, with an initial velocity of 85 ft/sec, and the end of the cannon is 10 ft high.

   **a.** Find the position of the safety net (distance from the cannon and height from the ground) if the clown hits the net after 4.3 sec.

   **b.** Find the angle at which the clown was shot if the initial velocity was 75 ft/sec and the clown hits a net that is placed 175.5 ft away after 3.5 sec.

**99.** A winter ski jumper leaves the ski-jump with an initial velocity of 70 ft/sec at an angle of 10°. Assume the jump-off point has coordinates (0, 0).

   **a.** What is the horizontal position of the skier after 6 sec?

   **b.** What is the vertical position of the skier after 6 sec?

   **c.** What diagonal distance (down the mountain side) was traveled if the skier touched down after being airborne for 6 sec?

**Exercise 99**

**100.** Suppose the domain of $y = \csc x$ was restricted to $x \in \left[ -\dfrac{\pi}{2}, 0 \right) \cup \left( 0, \dfrac{\pi}{2} \right]$,

and the domain of $y = \cot x$ to $x \in (0, \pi)$. **(a)** Would these functions then be one-to-one? **(b)** What are the corresponding ranges? **(c)** State the domain and range of $y = \csc^{-1} x$ and $y = \cot^{-1} x$. **(d)** Graph each function.

▶ **MAINTAINING YOUR SKILLS**

**101.** (5.3) Use the triangle given with a double-angle identity to find the exact value of $\sin(2\theta)$.

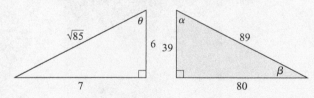

**102.** (5.2) Use the triangle given with a sum identity to find the exact value of $\sin(\alpha + \beta)$.

**103.** (3.2) Charlene just bought her daughter a battery operated jeep. If the wheels have a radius of 4 in.

and are turning at 3.5 revolutions per second at top speed, find the top speed of the vehicle in miles per hour, rounded to the nearest tenth.

**104.** (4.3) State the amplitude, period, and horizontal shift for $y = 5 \sin\left( 3x - \dfrac{\pi}{2} \right)$.

**105.** (1.3) Evaluate $\sin\theta$, $\cos\theta$, and $\tan\theta$ if the terminal side is along the line $y = \dfrac{12}{5} x$ with $\theta$ in QI.

**106.** (4.2) Explain how the graph of $y = \sec x$ is related to the graph of $y = \cos x$. Include a discussion of the domain and range of $y = \sec x$ and where the asymptotes occur.

**1.** The algebraic method for finding the inverse function for $f(x) = \tan x$ is illustrated here. The equation in (3) is called the _____ form of the inverse equation. The equation in (4) is called the _____ form.

| | | |
|---|---|---|
| (1) | $\tan x = f(x)$ | given function |
| (2) | $\tan x = y$ | use $y$ instead of $f(x)$ |
| (3) | $\tan y = x$ | interchange $x$ and $y$ |
| (4) | $y = \tan^{-1}x$ | solve for $y$ |
| (5) | $f^{-1}(x) = \tan^{-1}x$ | substitute $f^{-1}(x)$ for $y$ |

**2.** Determine whether the function given is one-to-one. If not, state why.

$\{(-3, 5), (-1, 11), (5, 12), (-2, 5), (1, -3)\}$

**3.** Find the inverse function of the one-to-one function given.

$f(x) = \{(-3, -14), (-1, -8), (5, 10), (-2, -11), (1, -2)\}$

**4.** Use the algebraic method to find the inverse function for $f(x) = 2^3\sqrt{2x + 1} + 3$, then verify your work using a composition.

**5.** The function $g(x) = |x + 3| - 2$ is not one-to-one. (a) State why. (b) Determine a domain restriction that preserves all range values and enables an inverse to be found, and (c) find an inverse function and state its domain and range. (*Hint:* Use the graph to determine the restriction and to help find the inverse.)

**6.** Comment on the third line in the following sequence. In particular, why does the "pattern" of inverses not hold in the third line?

$$\sin(60°) = \frac{\sqrt{3}}{2} \quad \rightarrow \quad \sin^{-1}\left(\frac{\sqrt{3}}{2}\right) = 60°$$

$$\sin(90°) = 1 \quad \rightarrow \quad \sin^{-1}(1) = 90°$$

$$\sin(120°) = \frac{\sqrt{3}}{2} \quad \rightarrow \quad \sin^{-1}\left(\frac{\sqrt{3}}{2}\right) = 60°(?)$$

**7.** Evaluate the following expressions without a calculator.

**a.** $\sec^{-1}(\sqrt{2})$

**b.** $\csc^{-1}\left(\dfrac{2}{\sqrt{3}}\right)$

**8.** Evaluate the following expressions without a calculator.

**a.** $\cos^{-1}\left[\cos\left(\dfrac{\pi}{6}\right)\right]$

**b.** $\cos^{-1}\left[\cos\left(\dfrac{7\pi}{6}\right)\right]$

**9.** Evaluate the following expressions with a calculator, keeping the domain and range of each function in mind. Answer in radians to the nearest tenth.

**a.** $\sin^{-1}(\sin 2.2)$

**b.** $\cos^{-1}(\cos 5.1)$

**10.** Evaluate the following expressions exactly by drawing the corresponding triangle.

**a.** $\cos\left[\tan^{-1}\left(\dfrac{13}{84}\right)\right]$

**b.** $\sec\left[\sin^{-1}\left(\dfrac{x}{\sqrt{x^2 + 49}}\right)\right]$

### The Domains of the Inverse Trig Functions

When working with the inverse trig functions, the most common difficulty students face is remembering and applying their respective domains and ranges. If we follow a few guiding principles when restricting the domain of the original function, there is no need to memorize six seemingly arbitrary intervals. Simply recall that the restricted domain of a trig function is the range of its inverse function, and the range of the original function is the domain of the inverse.

1.  **Know the graphs of the six basic trig functions.** The importance of this fundamental knowledge cannot be overstated. Without it, domain restrictions seem random and arbitrary.

2.  **The domain restriction should always include the interval $\left(0, \dfrac{\pi}{2}\right)$.** This ensures our domain will be "centrally located."

3.  **Select the nearest interval that includes all other range values.** This interval will be either $\left(-\dfrac{\pi}{2}, 0\right)$ or $\left(\dfrac{\pi}{2}, \pi\right)$. If both are possible (as in the case of $y = \tan t$), "keep the graph in one piece."

4.  **As necessary, include endpoints of these intervals to ensure that all possible range values are included.** The domain restriction must not only leave a graph that is one-to-one, it also must ensure all possible range values appear.

With these principles in mind, take another look at the graphs of the six trig functions.

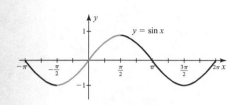

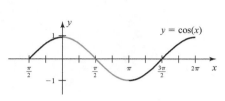

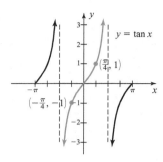

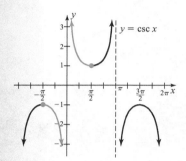

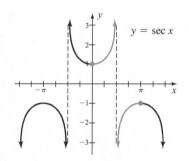

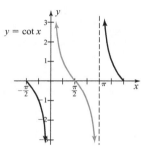

Note that while these domain restrictions are not necessarily used uniformly in subsequent mathematics courses, they do guide most calculators and our work here in trigonometry. That said, use the graphs and the four principles just mentioned to complete the following.

**Exercise 1:** Determine the domain and range of (a) $y = \csc^{-1} x$ and (b) $y = \cos^{-1} x$.

**Exercise 2:** Determine the domain and range of (a) $y = \cot^{-1} x$ and (b) $y = \sin^{-1} x$. For $y = \cot^{-1} x$, compare your answer to the Worthy of Note on p. 274.

## 6.3 | Solving Basic Trig Equations

### Learning Objectives

*In Section 6.3 you will learn how to:*

- ☐ **A.** Use a graph to gain information about principal roots, roots in $[0, 2\pi)$, and roots in $\mathbb{R}$

- ☐ **B.** Use inverse functions to solve trig equations for the principal root

- ☐ **C.** Solve trig equations for roots in $[0, 2\pi)$ or $[0°, 360°)$

- ☐ **D.** Solve trig equations for roots in $\mathbb{R}$

- ☐ **E.** Solve trig equations using fundamental identities

- ☐ **F.** Solve trig equations using graphing technology

In this section, we'll take the elements of basic equation solving and use them to help solve **trig equations,** or equations containing trigonometric functions. All of the algebraic techniques previously used can be applied to these equations, including the properties of equality and all forms of factoring (common terms, difference of squares, etc.). As with polynomial equations, we continue to be concerned with the *number of solutions* as well as with the *solutions themselves,* but there is one major difference. There is no "algebra" that can transform a function like $\sin x = \frac{1}{2}$ into $x = solution$. For that we rely on the inverse trig functions from Section 6.2.

### A. The Principal Root, Roots in $[0, 2\pi)$, and Real Roots

In a study of polynomial equations, making a connection between the degree of an equation, its graph, and its possible roots, helped give insights as to the number, location, and nature of the roots. Similarly, keeping graphs of basic trig functions *constantly* in mind helps you gain information regarding the solutions to trig equations. When solving trig equations, we refer to the solution found using $\sin^{-1}$, $\cos^{-1}$, and $\tan^{-1}$ as the **principal root.** You will alternatively be asked to find (1) the principal root, (2) solutions in $[0, 2\pi)$ or $[0°, 360°)$, or (3) solutions from the set of real numbers $\mathbb{R}$. For convenience, graphs of the basic sine, cosine, and tangent functions are repeated in Figures 6.33 through 6.35. Take a mental snapshot of them and keep them close at hand.

**Figure 6.33**

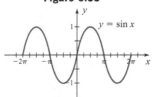

**Figure 6.34**

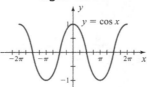

**Figure 6.35**

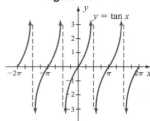

**EXAMPLE 1** ▶    **Visualizing Solutions Graphically**

Consider the equation $\sin x = \frac{2}{3}$. Using a graph of $y = \sin x$ and $y = \frac{2}{3}$,

**a.** State the quadrant of the principal root.

**b.** State the number of roots in $[0, 2\pi)$ and their quadrants.

**c.** Comment on the number of real roots.

**Solution** ▶    We begin by drawing a quick sketch of $y = \sin x$ and $y = \frac{2}{3}$, noting that solutions will occur where the graphs intersect.

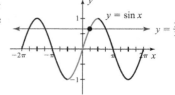

**a.** The sketch shows the principal root occurs between 0 and $\frac{\pi}{2}$ in QI.

**b.** For $[0, 2\pi)$ we note the graphs intersect twice and there will be two solutions in this interval.

**c.** Since the graphs of $y = \sin x$ and $y = \frac{2}{3}$ extend infinitely in both directions, they will intersect an infinite number of times—*but at regular intervals!* Once a root is found, adding integer multiples of $2\pi$ (the period of sine) to this root will give the location of additional roots.

**WORTHY OF NOTE**

Note that we refer to $\left(0, \frac{\pi}{2}\right)$ as Quadrant I or QI, regardless of whether we're discussing the unit circle or the graph of the function. In Example 1(b), the solutions correspond to those found in QI and QII on the unit circle, where $\sin x$ is also positive.

**Now try Exercises 7 through 10** ▶

When this process is applied to the equation $\tan x = -2$, the graph shows the principal root occurs between $-\frac{\pi}{2}$ and 0 in QIV on the unit circle (see Figure 6.36). In the interval $[0, 2\pi)$ the graphs intersect twice, in QII and QIV where $\tan x$ is negative (graphically—below the $x$-axis). As in Example 1, the graphs continue infinitely and will intersect an infinite number of times—*but again at regular intervals!* Once a root is found, adding integer multiples of $\pi$ (the period of tangent) to this root will give the location of other roots.

**Figure 6.36**

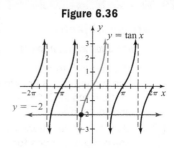

☑ **A.** You've just learned how to use a graph to gain information about principal roots, roots in $[0, 2\pi)$, and roots in ℝ

## B. Inverse Functions and Principal Roots

To solve equations having a single variable term, the basic goal is to isolate the variable term and apply the inverse function or operation. This is true for algebraic equations like $2x - 1 = 0, 2\sqrt{x} - 1 = 0$, or $2x^2 - 1 = 0$, and for trig equations like $2 \sin x - 1 = 0$. In each case we would add 1 to both sides, divide by 2, then apply the appropriate inverse. When the inverse trig functions are applied, the result is only the principal root and other solutions may exist depending on the interval under consideration.

**EXAMPLE 2** ▶ **Finding Principal Roots**

Find the principal root of $\sqrt{3}\tan x - 1 = 0$.

**Solution** ▶ We begin by isolating the variable term, then apply the inverse function.

$$\sqrt{3}\tan x - 1 = 0 \qquad \text{given equation}$$

$$\tan x = \frac{1}{\sqrt{3}} \qquad \text{add 1 and divide by } \sqrt{3}$$

$$\tan^{-1}(\tan x) = \tan^{-1}\left(\frac{1}{\sqrt{3}}\right) \qquad \text{apply inverse tangent to both sides}$$

$$x = \frac{\pi}{6} \qquad \text{result (exact form)}$$

**Now try Exercises 11 through 28** ▶

**Table 6.6**

| $\theta$ | $\sin\theta$ | $\cos\theta$ |
|---|---|---|
| 0 | 0 | 1 |
| $\dfrac{\pi}{6}$ | $\dfrac{1}{2}$ | $\dfrac{\sqrt{3}}{2}$ |
| $\dfrac{\pi}{4}$ | $\dfrac{\sqrt{2}}{2}$ | $\dfrac{\sqrt{2}}{2}$ |
| $\dfrac{\pi}{3}$ | $\dfrac{\sqrt{3}}{2}$ | $\dfrac{1}{2}$ |
| $\dfrac{\pi}{2}$ | 1 | 0 |

☑ **B. You've just learned how to use inverse functions to solve trig equations for the principal root**

Equations like the one in Example 2 demonstrate the need to be *very* familiar with the functions of a special angle. They are frequently used in equations and applications to ensure results don't get so messy they obscure the main ideas. For convenience, the values of $\sin\theta$ and $\cos\theta$ are repeated in Table 6.6 for $\theta \in \left[0, \frac{\pi}{2}\right]$. Using symmetry and the appropriate sign, the table can easily be extended to all values in $[0, 2\pi)$. Using the reciprocal and ratio relationships, values for the other trig functions can also be found.

## C. Solving Trig Equations for Roots in [0, 2π) or [0°, 360°)

To find multiple solutions to a trig equation, we simply take the reference angle of the principal root, and *use this angle to find all solutions* within a specified range. A mental image of the graph still guides us, and the standard table of values (also held in memory) allows for a quick solution to many equations.

**EXAMPLE 3** ▶ **Finding Solutions in [0, 2π)**

For $2\cos\theta + \sqrt{2} = 0$, find all solutions in $[0, 2\pi)$.

**Solution** ▶ Isolate the variable term, then apply the inverse function.

$$2\cos\theta + \sqrt{2} = 0 \qquad \text{given equation}$$

$$\cos\theta = -\frac{\sqrt{2}}{2} \qquad \text{subtract } \sqrt{2} \text{ and divide by 2}$$

$$\cos^{-1}(\cos\theta) = \cos^{-1}\left(-\frac{\sqrt{2}}{2}\right) \qquad \text{apply inverse cosine to both sides}$$

$$\theta = \frac{3\pi}{4} \qquad \text{result}$$

**WORTHY OF NOTE**

Note how the graph of a trig function displays the information regarding *quadrants*. From the graph of $y = \cos x$ we "read" that cosine is negative in QII and QIII [the lower "hump" of the graph is below the x-axis in $(\pi/2, 3\pi/2)$] and positive in QI and QIV [the graph is above the x-axis in the intervals $(0, \pi/2)$ and $(3\pi/2, 2\pi)$].

With $\frac{3\pi}{4}$ as the principal root, we know $\theta_r = \frac{\pi}{4}$. Since $\cos x$ is negative in QII and QIII, the second solution is $\frac{5\pi}{4}$. The second solution could also have been found from memory, recognition, or symmetry on the unit circle. Our (mental) graph verifies these are the only solutions in $[0, 2\pi)$.

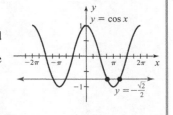

**Now try Exercises 29 through 34** ▶

**EXAMPLE 4** ▶ **Finding Solutions in [0, 2π)**

For $\tan^2 x - 1 = 0$, find all solutions in $[0, 2\pi)$.

**Solution** ▶ As with the other equations having a single variable term, we try to isolate this term or attempt a solution by factoring.

$$\tan^2 x - 1 = 0 \qquad \text{given equation}$$
$$\sqrt{\tan^2 x} = \pm\sqrt{1} \qquad \text{add 1 to both sides and take square roots}$$
$$\tan x = \pm 1 \qquad \text{result}$$

The algebra gives $\tan x = 1$ or $\tan x = -1$ and we solve each equation independently.

$$\tan x = 1 \qquad\qquad\qquad \tan x = -1$$
$$\tan^{-1}(\tan x) = \tan^{-1}(1) \qquad \tan^{-1}(\tan x) = \tan^{-1}(-1) \qquad \text{apply inverse tangent}$$
$$x = \frac{\pi}{4} \qquad\qquad\qquad x = -\frac{\pi}{4} \qquad \text{principal roots}$$

Of the principal roots, only $x = \dfrac{\pi}{4}$ is in the specified interval. With $\tan x$ positive in QI and QIII, a second solution is $\dfrac{5\pi}{4}$. While $x = -\dfrac{\pi}{4}$ is not in the interval, we still use it as a reference angle in QII and QIV (for $\tan x = -1$) and find the solutions $x = \dfrac{3\pi}{4}$ and $\dfrac{7\pi}{4}$. The four solutions are $x = \dfrac{\pi}{4}, \dfrac{3\pi}{4}, \dfrac{5\pi}{4}$, and $\dfrac{7\pi}{4}$, which is supported by the graph shown.

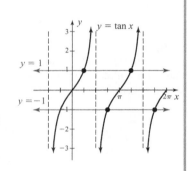

Now try Exercises 35 through 42 ▶

For any trig function that is not equal to a standard value, we can use a calculator to approximate the principal root or leave the result in exact form, and apply the same ideas to this root to find all solutions in the interval.

**EXAMPLE 5** ▶ **Finding Solutions in [0°, 360°)**

Find all solutions in $[0°, 360°)$ for $3\cos^2\theta + \cos\theta - 2 = 0$.

**Solution** ▶ Use a $u$-substitution to simplify the equation and help select an appropriate strategy. For $u = \cos\theta$, the equation becomes $3u^2 + u - 2 = 0$ and factoring seems the best approach. The factored form is $(u + 1)(3u - 2) = 0$, with solutions $u = -1$ and $u = \frac{2}{3}$. Re-substituting $\cos\theta$ for $u$ gives

$$\cos\theta = -1 \qquad\qquad\qquad \cos\theta = \frac{2}{3} \qquad \text{equations from factored form}$$

$$\cos^{-1}(\cos\theta) = \cos^{-1}(-1) \qquad \cos^{-1}(\cos\theta) = \cos^{-1}\left(\frac{2}{3}\right) \qquad \text{apply inverse cosine}$$

$$\theta = 180° \qquad\qquad\qquad \theta \approx 48.2° \qquad \text{principal roots}$$

☑ **C.** You've just learned how to solve trig equations for roots in [0, 2π) or [0°, 360°)

Both principal roots are in the specified interval. The first is quadrantal, the second was found using a calculator and is approximately 48.2°. With cos $\theta$ positive in QI and QIV, a second solution is $(360 - 48.2)° = 311.8°$. The three solutions are 48.2°, 180°, and 311.8° although only $\theta = 180°$ is exact.

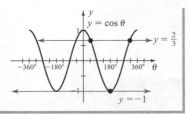

**Now try Exercises 43 through 50** ▶

## D. Solving Trig Equations for All Real Roots ($\mathbb{R}$)

As we noted, the intersections of a trig function with a horizontal line occur at regular, *predictable* intervals. This makes finding solutions from the set of real numbers a simple matter of extending the solutions we found in $[0, 2\pi)$ or $[0°, 360°)$. To illustrate, consider the solutions to Example 3. For $2 \cos \theta + \sqrt{2} = 0$, we found the solutions $\theta = \dfrac{3\pi}{4}$ and $\theta = \dfrac{5\pi}{4}$. For solutions in $\mathbb{R}$, we note the "predictable interval" between roots *is identical to the period of the function.* This means all real solutions will be represented by $\theta = \dfrac{3\pi}{4} + 2\pi k$ and $\theta = \dfrac{5\pi}{4} + 2\pi k$, $k \in \mathbb{Z}$ ($k$ is an integer). Both are illustrated in Figures 6.37 and 6.38 with the primary solution indicated with a "∗."

**Figure 6.37**

$\theta = \dfrac{3\pi}{4} + 2\pi k$

**Figure 6.38**

$\theta = \dfrac{5\pi}{4} + 2\pi k$

**EXAMPLE 6** ▶ **Finding Solutions in $\mathbb{R}$**

Find all real solutions to $\sqrt{3} \tan x - 1 = 0$.

**Solution** ▶ In Example 2 we found the principal root was $x = \dfrac{\pi}{6}$. Since the tangent function has a period of $\pi$, adding integer multiples of $\pi$ to this root will identify all solutions:

$x = \dfrac{\pi}{6} + \pi k$, $k \in \mathbb{Z}$, as illustrated here.

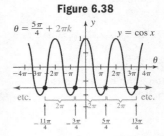

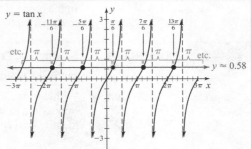

**Now try Exercises 51 through 56** ▶

These fundamental ideas can be extended to many different situations. When asked to find *all real solutions,* be sure you find all roots in a stipulated interval before naming solutions by applying the period of the function. For instance, $\cos x = 0$ has two solutions in $[0, 2\pi)$ $\left[ x = \dfrac{\pi}{2} \text{ and } x = \dfrac{3\pi}{2} \right]$, which we can quickly extend to find all real roots. But using $x = \cos^{-1} 0$ or a calculator limits us to the single (principal) root

$x = \dfrac{\pi}{2}$, and we'd miss all solutions stemming from $\dfrac{3\pi}{2}$. Note that solutions involving multiples of an angle (or fractional parts of an angle) should likewise be "handled with care," as in Example 7.

---

**EXAMPLE 7** ▶ **Finding Solutions in $\mathbb{R}$**

Find all real solutions to $2 \sin(2x) \cos x - \cos x = 0$.

**Solution** ▶ Since we have a common factor of $\cos x$, we begin by rewriting the equation as $\cos x[2 \sin(2x) - 1] = 0$ and solve using the zero factor property. The resulting equations are $\cos x = 0$ and $2 \sin(2x) - 1 = 0 \rightarrow \sin(2x) = \frac{1}{2}$.

$$\cos x = 0 \qquad \sin(2x) = \dfrac{1}{2} \quad \text{equations from factored form}$$

In $[0, 2\pi)$, $\cos x = 0$ has solutions $x = \dfrac{\pi}{2}$ and $x = \dfrac{3\pi}{2}$, giving $x = \dfrac{\pi}{2} + 2\pi k$ and $x = \dfrac{3\pi}{2} + 2\pi k$ as solutions in $\mathbb{R}$. Note these can actually be combined and written as $x = \dfrac{\pi}{2} + \pi k, \; k \in \mathbb{Z}$. The solution process for $\sin(2x) = \dfrac{1}{2}$ yields $2x = \dfrac{\pi}{6}$ and $2x = \dfrac{5\pi}{6}$. Since we seek all real roots, *we first extend each solution by $2\pi k$ before dividing by 2*, otherwise multiple solutions would be overlooked.

$$2x = \dfrac{\pi}{6} + 2\pi k \qquad\qquad 2x = \dfrac{5\pi}{6} + 2\pi k \quad \text{solutions from } \sin(2x) = \tfrac{1}{2}; \, k \in \mathbb{Z}$$

$$x = \dfrac{\pi}{12} + \pi k \qquad\qquad x = \dfrac{5\pi}{12} + \pi k \quad \text{divide by 2}$$

**Now try Exercises 57 through 66** ▶

**WORTHY OF NOTE**

When solving trig equations that involve arguments other than a single variable, a *u*-substitution is sometimes used. For Example 7, substituting *u* for $2x$ gives the equation $\sin u = \dfrac{1}{2}$, making it "easier to see" that $u = \dfrac{\pi}{6}$ (since $\dfrac{1}{2}$ is a special value), and therefore $2x = \dfrac{\pi}{6}$ and $x = \dfrac{\pi}{12}$.

☑ **D.** You've just learned how to solve trig equations for roots in $\mathbb{R}$

## E. Trig Equations and Trig Identities

In the process of solving trig equations, we sometimes employ fundamental identities to help simplify an equation, or to make factoring or some other method possible.

---

**EXAMPLE 8** ▶ **Solving Trig Equations Using an Identity**

Find all solutions in $[0°, 360°)$ for $\cos(2\theta) + \sin^2\theta - 3\cos\theta = 1$.

**Solution** ▶ With a mixture of functions, exponents, and arguments, the equation is almost impossible to solve as it stands. But we can eliminate the sine function using the identity $\cos(2\theta) = \cos^2\theta - \sin^2\theta$, leaving a quadratic equation in $\cos x$.

$$\cos(2\theta) + \sin^2\theta - 3\cos\theta = 1 \quad \text{given equation}$$
$$\cos^2\theta - \sin^2\theta + \sin^2\theta - 3\cos\theta = 1 \quad \text{substitute } \cos^2\theta - \sin^2\theta \text{ for } \cos(2\theta)$$
$$\cos^2\theta - 3\cos\theta = 1 \quad \text{combine like terms}$$
$$\cos^2\theta - 3\cos\theta - 1 = 0 \quad \text{subtract 1}$$

Let's substitute $u$ for $\cos\theta$ to give us a simpler view of the equation. This gives $u^2 - 3u - 1 = 0$, which is clearly not factorable over the integers. Using the quadratic formula with $a = 1$, $b = -3$, and $c = -1$ gives

$$u = \dfrac{3 \pm \sqrt{(-3)^2 - 4(1)(-1)}}{2(1)} \quad \text{quadratic formula in } u$$

$$= \dfrac{3 \pm \sqrt{13}}{2} \quad \text{simplified}$$

To four decimal places we have $u = 3.3028$ and $u = -0.3028$. To answer in terms of the original variable we re-substitute $\cos \theta$ for $u$, realizing that $\cos \theta \approx 3.3028$ has no solution, so solutions in $[0°, 360°)$ must be provided by $\cos \theta \approx -0.3028$ and occur in QII and QIII. The solutions are $\theta = \cos^{-1}(-0.3028) = 107.6°$ and $360° - 107.6° = 252.4°$ to the nearest tenth of a degree.

☑ **E. You've just learned how to solve trig equations using fundamental identities**

> **Now try Exercises 67 through 82** ▶

## F. Trig Equations and Graphing Technology

A majority of the trig equations you'll encounter in your studies can be solved using the ideas and methods presented here. But there are some equations that cannot be solved using standard methods because they mix polynomial functions (linear, quadratic, and so on) that can be solved using algebraic methods, with what are called **transcendental functions** (trigonometric, logarithmic, and so on). By definition, transcendental functions are those that *transcend* the reach of standard algebraic methods. These kinds of equations serve to highlight the value of graphing and calculating technology to today's problem solvers.

**EXAMPLE 9** ▶ **Solving Trig Equations Using Technology**

Use a graphing calculator in radian mode to find all real roots of

$2 \sin x + \dfrac{3x}{5} - 2 = 0$. Round solutions to four decimal places.

**Solution** ▶ When using graphing technology our initial concern is the size of the viewing window. After carefully entering the equation on the [ Y= ] screen, we note the term $2 \sin x$ will never be larger than 2 or less than $-2$ for any real number $x$. On the

other hand, the term $\dfrac{3x}{5}$ becomes larger for larger values of $x$, which would seem

to cause $2 \sin x + \dfrac{3x}{5}$ to "grow" as $x$ gets larger. We conclude the standard

window is a good place to start, and the resulting graph is shown in Figure 6.39.

**Figure 6.39**

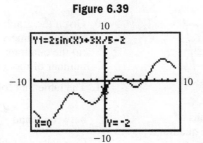

**Figure 6.40**

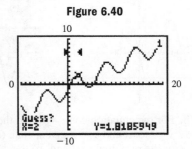

From this screen it appears there are three real roots, but to be sure none are hidden to the right, we extend the Xmax value to 20 (Figure 6.40). Using [ 2nd ] [ TRACE ] **(CALC) 2:zero,** we follow the prompts and enter a left bound of 0 (a number to the left of the zero) and a right bound of 2 (a number to the right of the zero—see Figure 6.40). If you can visually approximate the root, the calculator prompts you for a GUESS, otherwise just bypass the request by pressing [ ENTER ]. The smallest root is approximately $x = 0.8435$. Repeating this sequence we find the other roots are $x \approx 3.0593$ and $x \approx 5.5541$.

☑ **F. You've just learned how to solve trig equations using graphing technology**

> **Now try Exercises 83 through 88** ▶

 **6.3 EXERCISES**

▶ **CONCEPTS AND VOCABULARY**

**Fill in each blank with the appropriate word or phrase. Carefully reread the section if necessary.**

1. For simple equations, a mental graph will tell us the quadrant of the _____ root, the number of roots in _____ , and show a pattern for all _____ roots.

2. Solving trig equations is similar to solving algebraic equations, in that we first _____ the variable term, then apply the appropriate _____ function.

3. For $\sin x = \dfrac{\sqrt{2}}{2}$ the principal root is _____ , solutions in $[0, 2\pi)$ are _____ and _____ , and an expression for all real roots is _____ and _____ ; $k \in \mathbb{Z}$.

4. For $\tan x = -1$, the principal root is _____ , solutions in $[0, 2\pi)$ are _____ and _____ , and an expression for all real roots is _____ .

5. Discuss/Explain/Illustrate why $\tan x = \dfrac{3}{4}$ and $y = \cos x$ have two solutions in $[0, 2\pi)$, even though the period of $y = \tan x$ is $\pi$, while the period of $y = \cos x$ is $2\pi$.

6. The equation $\sin^2 x = \dfrac{1}{2}$ has four solutions in $[0, 2\pi)$. Explain how these solutions can be viewed as the vertices of a square inscribed in the unit circle.

▶ **DEVELOPING YOUR SKILLS**

7. For the equation $\sin x = -\dfrac{3}{4}$ and the graphs of $y = \sin x$ and $y = -\dfrac{3}{4}$ given, state (a) the quadrant of the principal root and (b) the number of roots in $[0, 2\pi)$.

**Exercise 7**

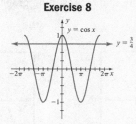

8. For the equation $\cos x = \dfrac{3}{4}$ and the graphs of $y = \cos x$ and $y = \dfrac{3}{4}$ given, state (a) the quadrant of the principal root and (b) the number of roots in $[0, 2\pi)$.

9. Given the graph $y = \tan x$ shown here, draw the horizontal line $y = -1.5$ and then for $\tan x = -1.5$, state (a) the quadrant of the principal root and (b) the number of roots in $[0, 2\pi)$.

**Exercise 9**

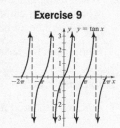

**Exercise 10**

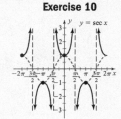

10. Given the graph of $y = \sec x$ shown, draw the horizontal line $y = \dfrac{5}{4}$ and then for $\sec x = \dfrac{5}{4}$, state (a) the quadrant of the principal root and (b) the number of roots in $[0, 2\pi)$.

11. The table that follows shows $\theta$ in multiples of $\dfrac{\pi}{6}$ between 0 and $\dfrac{4\pi}{3}$, with the values for $\sin \theta$ given.

    Complete the table without a calculator or references using your knowledge of the unit circle, the signs of $f(\theta)$ in each quadrant, memory/recognition, $\tan \theta = \dfrac{\sin \theta}{\cos \theta}$, and so on.

| **Exercise 11** | | | |
|---|---|---|---|
| $\theta$ | $\sin \theta$ | $\cos \theta$ | $\tan \theta$ |
| $0$ | $0$ | | |
| $\dfrac{\pi}{6}$ | $\dfrac{1}{2}$ | | |
| $\dfrac{\pi}{3}$ | $\dfrac{\sqrt{3}}{2}$ | | |
| $\dfrac{\pi}{2}$ | $1$ | | |
| $\dfrac{2\pi}{3}$ | $\dfrac{\sqrt{3}}{2}$ | | |
| $\dfrac{5\pi}{6}$ | $\dfrac{1}{2}$ | | |
| $\pi$ | $0$ | | |
| $\dfrac{7\pi}{6}$ | $-\dfrac{1}{2}$ | | |
| $\dfrac{4\pi}{3}$ | $-\dfrac{\sqrt{3}}{2}$ | | |

| **Exercise 12** | | | |
|---|---|---|---|
| $\theta$ | $\sin \theta$ | $\cos \theta$ | $\tan \theta$ |
| $0$ | | $1$ | |
| $\dfrac{\pi}{4}$ | | $\dfrac{\sqrt{2}}{2}$ | |
| $\dfrac{\pi}{2}$ | | $0$ | |
| $\dfrac{3\pi}{4}$ | | $-\dfrac{\sqrt{2}}{2}$ | |
| $\pi$ | | $-1$ | |
| $\dfrac{5\pi}{4}$ | | $-\dfrac{\sqrt{2}}{2}$ | |
| $\dfrac{3\pi}{2}$ | | $0$ | |
| $\dfrac{7\pi}{4}$ | | $\dfrac{\sqrt{2}}{2}$ | |
| $2\pi$ | | $1$ | |

**12.** The table shows $\theta$ in multiples of $\dfrac{\pi}{4}$ between 0 and $2\pi$, with the values for $\cos \theta$ given. Complete the table without a calculator or references using your knowledge of the unit circle, the signs of $f(\theta)$ in each quadrant, memory/recognition, $\tan \theta = \dfrac{\sin \theta}{\cos \theta}$, and so on.

**Find the principal root of each equation.**

**13.** $2 \cos x = \sqrt{2}$        **14.** $2 \sin x = -1$

**15.** $-4 \sin x = 2\sqrt{2}$        **16.** $-4 \cos x = 2\sqrt{3}$

**17.** $\sqrt{3} \tan x = 1$        **18.** $-2\sqrt{3} \tan x = 2$

**19.** $2\sqrt{3} \sin x = -3$        **20.** $-3\sqrt{2} \csc x = 6$

**21.** $-6 \cos x = 6$        **22.** $4 \sec x = -8$

**23.** $\dfrac{7}{8} \cos x = \dfrac{7}{16}$        **24.** $-\dfrac{5}{3} \sin x = \dfrac{5}{6}$

**25.** $2 = 4 \sin \theta$        **26.** $\pi \tan x = 0$

**27.** $-5\sqrt{3} = 10 \cos \theta$        **28.** $4\sqrt{3} = 4 \tan \theta$

**Find all solutions in $[0, 2\pi)$.**

**29.** $9 \sin x - 3.5 = 1$        **30.** $6.2 \cos x + 4 = 7.1$

**31.** $8 \tan x + 7\sqrt{3} = -\sqrt{3}$

**32.** $\dfrac{1}{2} \sec x - \dfrac{3}{4} = -\dfrac{7}{4}$        **33.** $\dfrac{2}{3} \cot x - \dfrac{5}{6} = -\dfrac{3}{2}$

**34.** $-110 \sin x = -55\sqrt{3}$        **35.** $4 \cos^2 x = 3$

**36.** $4 \sin^2 x = 1$        **37.** $-7 \tan^2 x = -21$

**38.** $3 \sec^2 x = 6$        **39.** $-4 \csc^2 x = -8$

**40.** $6\sqrt{3} \cos^2 x = 3\sqrt{3}$        **41.** $4\sqrt{2} \sin^2 x = 4\sqrt{2}$

**42.** $\dfrac{2}{3} \cos^2 x + \dfrac{5}{6} = \dfrac{4}{3}$

**Solve the following equations by factoring. State all real solutions in radians using the exact form where possible and rounded to four decimal places if the result is not a standard value.**

**43.** $3 \cos^2 \theta + 14 \cos \theta - 5 = 0$

**44.** $6 \tan^2 \theta - 2\sqrt{3} \tan \theta = 0$

**45.** $2 \cos x \sin x - \cos x = 0$

**46.** $2 \sin^2 x + 7 \sin x = 4$        **47.** $\sec^2 x - 6 \sec x = 16$

**48.** $2 \cos^3 x + \cos^2 x = 0$        **49.** $4 \sin^2 x - 1 = 0$

**50.** $4 \cos^2 x - 3 = 0$

**Find all real solutions. Note that identities are not required to solve these exercises.**

**51.** $-2 \sin x = \sqrt{2}$        **52.** $2 \cos x = 1$

**53.** $-4 \cos x = 2\sqrt{2}$        **54.** $4 \sin x = 2\sqrt{3}$

**55.** $\sqrt{3} \tan x = -\sqrt{3}$        **56.** $2\sqrt{3} \tan x = 2$

**57.** $6 \cos(2x) = -3$        **58.** $2 \sin(3x) = -\sqrt{2}$

**59.** $\sqrt{3} \tan(2x) = -\sqrt{3}$        **60.** $2\sqrt{3} \tan(3x) = 6$

**61.** $-2\sqrt{3} \cos\left(\dfrac{1}{3}x\right) = 2\sqrt{3}$

**62.** $-8 \sin\left(\dfrac{1}{2}x\right) = -4\sqrt{3}$

**63.** $\sqrt{2} \cos x \sin(2x) - 3 \cos x = 0$

**64.** $\sqrt{3} \sin x \tan(2x) - \sin x = 0$

**65.** $\cos(3x)\csc(2x) - 2 \cos(3x) = 0$

**66.** $\sqrt{3} \sin(2x)\sec(2x) - 2 \sin(2x) = 0$

**Solve each equation using calculator and inverse trig functions to determine the principal root (not by graphing). Clearly state (a) the principal root and (b) all real roots.**

**67.** $3 \cos x = 1$        **68.** $5 \sin x = -2$

**69.** $\sqrt{2} \sec x + 3 = 7$        **70.** $\sqrt{3} \csc x + 2 = 11$

**71.** $\dfrac{1}{2} \sin(2\theta) = \dfrac{1}{3}$        **72.** $\dfrac{2}{5} \cos(2\theta) = \dfrac{1}{4}$

**73.** $-5 \cos(2\theta) - 1 = 0$        **74.** $6 \sin(2\theta) - 3 = 2$

Solve the following equations using an identity. State all real solutions in radians using the exact form where possible and rounded to four decimal places if the result is not a standard value.

75. $\cos^2 x - \sin^2 x = \dfrac{1}{2}$

76. $4\sin^2 x - 4\cos^2 x = 2\sqrt{3}$

77. $2\cos\left(\dfrac{1}{2}x\right)\cos x - 2\sin\left(\dfrac{1}{2}x\right)\sin x = 1$

78. $\sqrt{2}\sin(2x)\cos(3x) + \sqrt{2}\sin(3x)\cos(2x) = 1$

79. $(\cos\theta + \sin\theta)^2 = 1$     80. $(\cos\theta + \sin\theta)^2 = 2$

81. $\cos(2\theta) + 2\sin^2\theta - 3\sin\theta = 0$

82. $3\sin(2\theta) - \cos^2(2\theta) - 1 = 0$

Find all roots in $[0, 2\pi)$ using a graphing calculator. State answers in radians rounded to four decimal places.

83. $5\cos x - x = 3$          84. $3\sin x + x = 4$

85. $\cos^2(2x) + x = 3$       86. $\sin^2(2x) + 2x = 1$

87. $x^2 + \sin(2x) = 1$       88. $\cos(2x) - x^2 = -5$

▶ WORKING WITH FORMULAS

89. **Range of a projectile: $R = \dfrac{5}{49}v^2\sin(2\theta)$**

The distance a projectile travels is called its range and is modeled by the formula shown, where $R$ is the range in meters, $v$ is the initial velocity in meters per second, and $\theta$ is the angle of release. Two friends are standing 16 m apart playing catch. If the first throw has an initial velocity of 15 m/sec, what *two* angles will ensure the ball travels the 16 m between the friends?

90. **Fine-tuning a golf swing: (club head to shoulder)$^2$ = (club length)$^2$ + (arm length)$^2$ − 2 (club length)(arm length)cos $\theta$**

A golf pro is taking specific measurements on a client's swing to help improve her game. If the angle $\theta$ is too small, the ball is hit late and "too thin" (you *top the ball*). If $\theta$ is too large, the ball is hit early and "too fat" (you *scoop the ball*). Approximate the angle $\theta$ formed by the club and the extended (left) arm using the given measurements and formula shown.

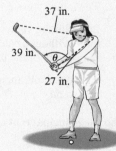

37 in.

39 in.

27 in.

▶ APPLICATIONS

**Acceleration due to gravity:** When a steel ball is released down an inclined plane, the rate of the ball's acceleration depends on the angle of incline. The acceleration can be approximated by the formula $A(\theta) = 9.8\sin\theta$, where $\theta$ is in degrees and the acceleration is measured in meters per second/per second. To the nearest tenth of a degree,

91. What angle produces an acceleration of 0 m/sec$^2$ when the ball is released? Explain why this is reasonable.

92. What angle produces an acceleration of 9.8 m/sec$^2$? What does this tell you about the acceleration due to gravity?

93. What angle produces an acceleration of 5 m/sec$^2$? Will the angle be larger or smaller for an acceleration of 4.5 m/sec$^2$?

94. Will an angle producing an acceleration of 2.5 m/sec$^2$ be one-half the angle required for an acceleration of 5 m/sec$^2$? Explore and discuss.

**Snell's law** states that when a ray of light passes from one medium into another, the sine of the angle of incidence $\alpha$ *varies directly with* the sine of the angle of refraction $\beta$ (see the figure). This phenomenon is modeled by the formula $\sin\alpha = k\sin\beta$, where $k$ is called the **index of refraction**. Note the angle $\theta$ is the angle at which the light strikes the surface, so that $\alpha = 90° - \theta$. Use this information to work Exercises 95 to 98.

**Exercises 95 to 98**

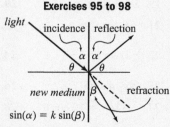

light  incidence | reflection

$\alpha$  $\alpha'$

$\theta$  $\theta$

*new medium*  $\beta$  refraction

$\sin(\alpha) = k\sin(\beta)$

95. A ray of light passes from air into water, striking the water at an angle of 55°. Find the angle of incidence $\alpha$ and the angle of refraction $\beta$, if the index of refraction for water is $k = 1.33$.

**96.** A ray of light passes from air into a diamond, striking the surface at an angle of 75°. Find the angle of incidence $\alpha$ and the angle of refraction $\beta$, if the index of refraction for a diamond is $k = 2.42$.

**97.** Find the index of refraction for ethyl alcohol if a beam of light strikes the surface of this medium at an angle of 40° and produces an angle of refraction $\beta = 34.3°$. Use this index to find the angle of incidence if a second beam of light created an angle of refraction measuring 15°.

**98.** Find the index of refraction for rutile (a type of mineral) if a beam of light strikes the surface of this medium at an angle of 30° and produces an angle of refraction $\beta = 18.7°$. Use this index to find the angle of incidence if a second beam of light created an angle of refraction measuring 10°.

**99. Roller coaster design:** As part of a science fair project, Hadra builds a scale model of a roller coaster using the equation
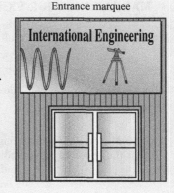
Loading platform

$y = 5 \sin\left(\dfrac{1}{2}x\right) + 7$, where $y$ is the height of the model in inches and $x$ is the distance from the "loading platform" in inches. (a) How high is the platform? (b) What distances from the platform does the model attain a height of 9.5 in.?

**100. Company logo:** Part of the logo for an engineering firm was modeled by a cosine function. The logo was then manufactured in steel and installed on the entrance marquee of the home office. The position and size of the logo is modeled by the function $y = 9 \cos x + 15$, where $y$ is the height of the graph above the base of the marquee in inches and

$x$ represents the distance from the edge of the marquee. Assume the graph begins flush with the edge. (a) How far above the base is the beginning of the cosine graph? (b) What distances from the edge does the graph attain a height of 19.5 in.?

Entrance marquee

International Engineering

**Geometry applications:** Solve Exercises 101 and 102 graphically using a calculator. For Exercise 101, give $\theta$ in radians rounded to four decimal places. For Exercise 102, answer in degrees to the nearest tenth of a degree.

**101.** The area of a circular segment (the shaded portion shown) is given by the formula $A = \dfrac{1}{2} r^2(\theta - \sin \theta)$, where $\theta$ is in radians. If the circle has a radius of 10 cm, find the angle $\theta$ that gives an area of 12 cm$^2$.

**102.** The perimeter of a trapezoid with parallel sides $B$ and $b$, altitude $h$, and base angles $\alpha$ and $\beta$ is given by the formula $P = B + b + h(\csc \alpha + \csc \beta)$. If $b = 30$ m, $B = 40$ m, $h = 10$ m, and $\alpha = 45°$, find the angle $\beta$ that gives a perimeter of 105 m.

▶ **EXTENDING THE CONCEPT**

**103.** Find all real solutions to $5 \cos x - x = -x$ in two ways. First use a calculator with $Y_1 = 5 \cos x - x$ and $Y_2 = -x$ to determine the regular intervals between points of intersection. Second, simplify by adding $x$ to both sides, and draw a quick sketch of the result to locate $x$-intercepts. Explain why both methods give the same result, even though the first presents you with a very different graph.

**104.** Once the fundamental ideas of solving a given family of equations is understood and practiced, a student usually begins to generalize them—making the numbers or symbols used in the equation irrelevant. (a) Use the inverse sine function to find the principal root of $y = A \sin(Bx - C) + D$, by solving for $x$ in terms of $y$, $A$, $B$, $C$, and $D$. (b) Solve the following equation using the techniques addressed in this section, and then using the "formula" from Part (a): $5 = 2 \sin\left(\dfrac{1}{2}x + \dfrac{\pi}{4}\right) + 3$.

Do the results agree?

▶ **MAINTAINING YOUR SKILLS**

**105. (1.3)** Find the value of all six trig functions given $\cos \theta = -\dfrac{5}{13}$ and $\tan \theta > 0$.

**106. (5.1)** Verify that the following is an identity:
$$\frac{\cot x + \tan x}{\csc x} = \sec x$$

**107. (2.3)** A road sign cautions truckers to slow down as the upcoming down hill roads have a $-12\%$ grade, meaning the ratio $\dfrac{\text{rise}}{\text{run}} = -0.12$. Find the angle of descent to the nearest tenth of a degree.

**108. (6.2)** Evaluate without using a calculator:

    **a.** $\tan\left[\sin^{-1}\left(-\dfrac{1}{2}\right)\right]$      **b.** $\sin\left[\tan^{-1}(-1)\right]$

**109. (4.3)** Write the equation of the function shown in two ways—first using a secant function, and second as a cosecant function.

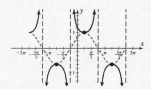

**110. (3.2)** The largest Ferris wheel in the world, located in Yokohama, Japan, has a radius of 50 m. To the nearest hundredth of a meter, how far does a seat on the rim travel as the wheel turns through $\theta = 292.5°$?

## 6.4 | Solving General Trig Equations and Applications

### Learning Objectives

*In Section 6.4 you will learn how to:*

☐ **A.** Use additional algebraic techniques to solve trig equations

☐ **B.** Solve trig equations using multiple angle, sum and difference, and sum-to-product identities

☐ **C.** Solve trig equations of the form $A \sin(Bx \pm C) \pm D = k$

☐ **D.** Use a combination of skills to model and solve a variety of applications

At this point you're likely beginning to understand the true value of trigonometry to the scientific world. Essentially, any phenomenon that is cyclic or periodic is beyond the reach of polynomial (and other) functions, and may require trig for an accurate understanding. And while there is an abundance of trig applications in oceanography, astronomy, meteorology, geology, zoology, and engineering, their value is not limited to the hard sciences. There are also rich applications in business and economics, and a growing number of modern artists are creating works based on attributes of the trig functions. In this section, we try to place some of these applications within your reach, with the exercise set offering an appealing variety from many of these fields.

### A. Trig Equations and Algebraic Methods

We begin this section with a follow-up to Section 6.3, by introducing trig equations that require slightly more sophisticated methods to work out a solution.

**EXAMPLE 1** ▶ **Solving a Trig Equation by Squaring Both Sides**

Find all solutions in $[0, 2\pi)$: $\sec x + \tan x = \sqrt{3}$.

**Solution** ▶ Our first instinct might be to rewrite the equation in terms of sine and cosine, but that simply leads to a similar equation that still has two different functions $[\sqrt{3} \cos x - \sin x = 1]$. Instead, we *square both sides* and see if the Pythagorean identity $1 + \tan^2 x = \sec^2 x$ will be of use. Prior to squaring, we separate the functions on opposite sides to avoid the mixed term $2 \tan x \sec x$.

$$\sec x + \tan x = \sqrt{3} \qquad \text{given equation}$$
$$(\sec x)^2 = (\sqrt{3} - \tan x)^2 \qquad \text{subtract } \tan x \text{ and square}$$
$$\sec^2 x = 3 - 2\sqrt{3} \tan x + \tan^2 x \qquad \text{result}$$

Since $\sec^2x = 1 + \tan^2x$, we substitute directly and obtain an equation in tangent alone.

$$1 + \tan^2x = 3 - 2\sqrt{3}\tan x + \tan^2x \qquad \text{substitute } 1 + \tan^2x \text{ for } \sec^2x$$

$$-2 = -2\sqrt{3}\tan x \qquad \text{simplify}$$

$$\frac{1}{\sqrt{3}} = \tan x \qquad \text{solve for } \tan x$$

$$\tan x > 0 \text{ in QI and QIII}$$

The proposed solutions are $x = \dfrac{\pi}{6}$ [QI] and $\dfrac{7\pi}{6}$ [QIII]. Since squaring an equation sometimes introduces extraneous roots, both should be checked in the original equation. The check shows only $x = \dfrac{\pi}{6}$ is a solution.

**Now try Exercises 7 through 12 ▶**

Here is one additional example that uses a factoring strategy commonly employed when an equation has more than three terms.

**EXAMPLE 2 ▶** **Solving a Trig Equation by Factoring**

Find all solutions in $[0°, 360°)$: $8\sin^2\theta\cos\theta - 2\cos\theta - 4\sin^2\theta + 1 = 0$.

**Solution ▶** The four terms in the equation share no common factors, so we attempt to factor by grouping. We could factor $2\cos\theta$ from the first two terms but instead elect to group the $\sin^2\theta$ terms and begin there.

$$8\sin^2\theta\cos\theta - 2\cos\theta - 4\sin^2\theta + 1 = 0 \qquad \text{given equation}$$

$$(8\sin^2\theta\cos\theta - 4\sin^2\theta) - (2\cos\theta - 1) = 0 \qquad \text{rearrange and group terms}$$

$$4\sin^2\theta(2\cos\theta - 1) - 1(2\cos\theta - 1) = 0 \qquad \text{remove common factors}$$

$$(2\cos\theta - 1)(4\sin^2\theta - 1) = 0 \qquad \text{remove common binomial factors}$$

Using the zero factor property, we write two equations and solve each independently.

| | |
|---|---|
| $2\cos\theta - 1 = 0$ | $4\sin^2\theta - 1 = 0$    resulting equations |
| $2\cos\theta = 1$ | $\sin^2\theta = \dfrac{1}{4}$    isolate variable term |
| $\cos\theta = \dfrac{1}{2}$ | $\sin\theta = \pm\dfrac{1}{2}$    solve |
| $\cos\theta > 0$ in QI and QIV | $\sin\theta > 0$ in QI and QII |
| $\theta = 60°, 300°$ | $\sin\theta < 0$ in QIII and QIV |
| | $\theta = 30°, 150°, 210°, 330°$    solutions |

☑ **A.** You've just learned how to use additional algebraic techniques to solve trig equations

Initially factoring $2\cos\theta$ from the first two terms and proceeding from there would have produced the same result.

**Now try Exercises 13 through 16 ▶**

## B. Solving Trig Equations Using Various Identities

To solve equations effectively, a student should strive to develop *all* of the necessary "tools." Certainly the underlying concepts and graphical connections are of primary importance, as are the related algebraic skills. But to solve *trig* equations effectively we must also have a ready command of commonly used identities. Observe how Example 3 combines a double-angle identity with factoring by grouping.

**EXAMPLE 3** ▶ **Using Identities and Algebra to Solve a Trig Equation**

Find all solutions in $[0, 2\pi)$: $3 \sin(2x) + 2 \sin x - 3 \cos x = 1$. Round solutions to four decimal places as necessary.

Solution ▶ Noting that one of the terms involves a double angle, we attempt to replace that term to make factoring a possibility. Using the double identity for sine, we have

$$3(2 \sin x \cos x) + 2 \sin x - 3 \cos x = 1 \qquad \text{substitute } 2 \sin x \cos x \text{ for } \sin (2x)$$
$$(6 \sin x \cos x + 2 \sin x) - (3 \cos x + 1) = 0 \qquad \text{set equal to zero and group terms}$$
$$2 \sin x(3 \cos x + 1) - 1(3 \cos x + 1) = 0 \qquad \text{factor using } 3 \cos x + 1$$
$$(3 \cos x + 1)(2 \sin x - 1) = 0 \qquad \text{common binomial factor}$$

Use the zero factor property to solve each equation independently.

$$3 \cos x + 1 = 0 \qquad\qquad 2 \sin x - 1 = 0 \qquad \text{resulting equations}$$
$$\cos x = -\frac{1}{3} \qquad\qquad \sin x = \frac{1}{2} \qquad \text{isolate variable term}$$
$$\cos x < 0 \text{ in QII and QIII} \qquad \sin x > 0 \text{ in QI and QII}$$
$$x \approx 1.9106, 4.3726 \qquad\qquad x = \frac{\pi}{6}, \frac{5\pi}{6} \qquad \text{solutions}$$

☑ **B.** You've just learned how to solve trig equations using multiple angle, sum and difference, and sum-to-product identities

Should you prefer the exact form, the solutions from the cosine equation could be written as $x = \cos^{-1}\left(-\frac{1}{3}\right)$ and $x = 2\pi - \cos^{-1}\left(-\frac{1}{3}\right)$.

**Now try Exercises 17 through 26** ▶

## C. Solving Equations of the Form $A \sin(Bx \pm C) \pm D = k$

You may remember equations of this form from Section 4.4. They actually occur quite frequently in the investigation of many natural phenomena and in the modeling of data from a periodic or seasonal context. Solving these equations requires a good combination of algebra skills with the fundamentals of trig.

**EXAMPLE 4** ▶ **Solving Equations That Involve Transformations**

Given $f(x) = 160 \sin\left(\frac{\pi}{3}x + \frac{\pi}{3}\right) + 320$ and $x \in [0, 2\pi)$, for what real numbers $x$ is $f(x)$ less than 240?

Solution ▶ We reason that to find values where $f(x) < 240$, we should begin by finding values where $f(x) = 240$. The result is

$$160 \sin\left(\frac{\pi}{3}x + \frac{\pi}{3}\right) + 320 = 240 \qquad \text{equation}$$
$$\sin\left(\frac{\pi}{3}x + \frac{\pi}{3}\right) = -0.5 \qquad \text{subtract 320 and divide by 160; isolate variable term}$$

At this point we elect to use a *u*-substitution for $\left(\dfrac{\pi}{3}x + \dfrac{\pi}{3}\right) = \dfrac{\pi}{3}(x + 1)$ to obtain a "clearer view."

$$\sin u = -0.5 \qquad \text{substitute } u \text{ for } \tfrac{\pi}{3}(x+1)$$

$$\sin u < 0 \text{ in QIII and QIV}$$

$$u = \frac{7\pi}{6} \qquad\qquad u = \frac{11\pi}{6} \qquad \text{solutions in } u$$

To complete the solution we re-substitute $\dfrac{\pi}{3}(x + 1)$ for *u* and solve.

$$\frac{\pi}{3}(x + 1) = \frac{7\pi}{6} \qquad \frac{\pi}{3}(x + 1) = \frac{11\pi}{6} \qquad \text{re-substitute } \tfrac{\pi}{3}(x+1) \text{ for } u$$

$$x + 1 = \frac{7}{2} \qquad\qquad x + 1 = \frac{11}{2} \qquad \text{multiply both sides by } \tfrac{3}{\pi}$$

$$x = 2.5 \qquad\qquad\quad x = 4.5 \qquad \text{solutions}$$

We now know $f(x) = 240$ when $x = 2.5$ and $x = 4.5$ but when will $f(x)$ be *less than* 240? By analyzing the equation, we find the function has period of

$$P = \frac{2\pi}{\frac{\pi}{3}} = 6$$ and is shifted to the left 1 unit. This would indicate the graph peaks

early in the interval $[0, 2\pi)$ with a "valley" in the interior. We conclude $f(x) < 240$ in the interval (2.5, 4.5).

☑ **C.** You've just learned how to solve trig equations of the form $A \sin(Bx \pm C) \pm D = k$

**Now try Exercises 27 through 30 ▶**

---

**GRAPHICAL SUPPORT**

Support for the result in Example 4 can be obtained by graphing the equation over the specified interval. Enter

$$Y_1 = 160 \sin\left(\frac{\pi}{3}x + \frac{\pi}{3}\right) + 320 \text{ on the } \boxed{Y =}$$

screen, then $Y_2 = 240$. After locating points of intersection, we note the graphs indeed verify that in the interval $[0, 2\pi)$, $f(x) < 240$ for $x \in (2.5, 4.5)$.

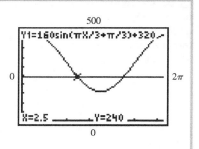

There is a mixed variety of equation types in **Exercises 31 through 40.**

## D. Applications Using Trigonometric Equations

Using characteristics of the trig functions, we can often generalize and extend many of the formulas that are familiar to you. For example, the formulas for the volume of a right circular cylinder and a right circular cone are well known, but what about the volume of a nonright figure (see Figure 6.41)? Here, trigonometry provides the answer, as the most general volume formula is $V = V_0 \sin \theta$, where $V_0$ is a "standard" volume formula and $\theta$ is the complement of angle of deflection (**see Exercises 43 and 44**).

As for other applications, consider the following from the environmental sciences. Natural scientists are very interested in the discharge rate of major rivers, as this gives an indication of rainfall over the inland area served by the river. In addition, the discharge rate has a large impact on the freshwater and saltwater zones found at the river's estuary (where it empties into the sea).

**Figure 6.41**

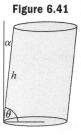

**EXAMPLE 5** ▶ **Solving an Equation Modeling the Discharge Rate of a River**

For May through November, the discharge rate of the Ganges River (Bangladesh)

can be modeled by $D(t) = 16{,}580 \sin\left(\dfrac{\pi}{3}t - \dfrac{2\pi}{3}\right) + 17{,}760$ where $t = 1$

represents May 1, and $D(t)$ is the discharge rate in m³/sec.

Source: Global River Discharge Database Project; www.rivdis.sr.unh.edu.

**a.** What is the discharge rate in mid-October?

**b.** For what months (within this interval) is the discharge rate over 26,050 m³/sec?

**Solution** ▶ **a.** To find the discharge rate in mid-October we simply evaluate the function at $t = 6.5$:

$$D(t) = 16{,}580 \sin\left(\frac{\pi}{3}t - \frac{2\pi}{3}\right) + 17{,}760 \qquad \text{given function}$$

$$D(6.5) = 16{,}580 \sin\left[\frac{\pi}{3}(6.5) - \frac{2\pi}{3}\right] + 17{,}760 \qquad \text{substitute 6.5 for } t$$

$$= 1180 \qquad \text{compute result on a calculator}$$

In mid-October the discharge rate is 1180 m³/sec.

**b.** We first find when the rate is *equal* to 26,050 m³/sec: $D(t) = 26{,}050$.

$$26{,}050 = 16{,}580 \sin\left(\frac{\pi}{3}t - \frac{2\pi}{3}\right) + 17{,}760 \qquad \text{substitute 26,050 for } D(t)$$

$$0.5 = \sin\left(\frac{\pi}{3}t - \frac{2\pi}{3}\right) \qquad \text{subtract 17,760; divide by 16,580}$$

Using a $u$-substitution for $\left(\dfrac{\pi}{3}t - \dfrac{2\pi}{3}\right)$ we obtain the equation

$$0.5 = \sin u$$
$$\sin u > 0 \text{ in QI and QII}$$

$$u = \frac{\pi}{6} \qquad\qquad u = \frac{5\pi}{6} \qquad \text{solutions in } u$$

To complete the solution we re-substitute $\left(\dfrac{\pi}{3}t - \dfrac{2\pi}{3}\right) = \dfrac{\pi}{3}(t-2)$ for $u$ and solve.

$$\frac{\pi}{3}(t-2) = \frac{\pi}{6} \qquad\qquad \frac{\pi}{3}(t-2) = \frac{5\pi}{6} \qquad \text{re-substitute } \frac{\pi}{3}(t-2) \text{ for } u$$

$$t - 2 = 0.5 \qquad\qquad t - 2 = 2.5 \qquad \text{multiply both sides by } \frac{3}{\pi}$$

$$t = 2.5 \qquad\qquad t = 4.5 \qquad \text{solutions}$$

The Ganges River will have a flow rate of over 26,050 m³/sec between mid-June (2.5) and mid-August (4.5).

**Now try Exercises 45 and 46** ▶

---

**GRAPHICAL SUPPORT**

To obtain a graphical view of the solution to Example 5(b), enter

$Y_1 = 16{,}580 \sin\left(\dfrac{\pi}{3}t - \dfrac{2\pi}{3}\right) + 17{,}760$ on the

Y= screen, then $Y_2 = 26{,}050$. To set
an appropriate window, note the amplitude is
16,580 and that the graph has been vertically
shifted by 17,760. Also note the $x$-axis
represents May through November. After
locating points of intersection, we note the
graphs verify that in the interval [1, 8]
$D(t) > 26{,}050$ for $t \in (2.5, 4.5)$.

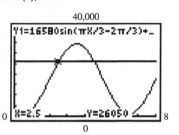

---

Our final application comes from the business/economics arena. Many businesses specialize in seasonal merchandise and run through cycles of high-sales/low-sales/high-sales/low-sales that are fairly regular from year to year. To even out the "feast or famine" effect, revenue projections need to be made and budgets set up.

**EXAMPLE 6** ▶ Joe's Water Sports sells boats, equipment for water skiing, camping supplies, and other supplies for water sports. Sales are great in summer but weak in winter. Revenue projections from day to day can be modeled by the function

$R(d) = 750 \sin\left(\dfrac{2\pi}{365}d - \dfrac{\pi}{2}\right) + 950$, where $R(d)$ is the daily revenue on the $d$th

day of the year ($d = 1 \rightarrow$ Jan 1).

**a.** Estimate the revenue for May 1.

**b.** For what days of the year is revenue over $1250?

Solution ▶ **a.** To find the revenue for May we evaluate $R(d)$ at
$d = (31 + 28 + 31 + 30 + 1) = 121$:

$$R(d) = 750 \sin\left(\frac{2\pi}{365}d - \frac{\pi}{2}\right) + 950 \qquad \text{given function}$$

$$R(121) = 750 \sin\left[\frac{2\pi}{365}(121) - \frac{\pi}{2}\right] + 950 \qquad \text{substitute 121 for } d$$

$$\approx \$1317.52 \qquad \text{result}$$

On May 1 the projected revenue is about $1317.52.

**b.** We first find when the amount of revenue is *equal* to $1250: $R(d) = 1250$.

$$1250 = 750 \sin\left(\frac{2\pi}{365}d - \frac{\pi}{2}\right) + 950 \qquad \text{substitute 1250 for } R(d)$$

$$0.4 = \sin\left(\frac{2\pi}{365}d - \frac{\pi}{2}\right) \qquad \text{subtract 950; divide by 750}$$

Using a $u$-substitution for $\left(\dfrac{2\pi}{365}d - \dfrac{\pi}{2}\right)$ we obtain the equation

$$0.4 = \sin u$$
$$\sin u > 0 \text{ in QI and QII}$$
$$u \approx 0.4115 \qquad\qquad u \approx 2.7301 \qquad \text{solutions in } u, \text{ rounded to four}$$
$$\text{decimal places}$$

To complete the solution we re-substitute $\dfrac{2\pi}{365}d - \dfrac{\pi}{2}$ for $u$ and solve.

$$\dfrac{2\pi}{365}d - \dfrac{\pi}{2} \approx 0.4115 \qquad \dfrac{2\pi}{365}d - \dfrac{\pi}{2} \approx 2.7301 \quad \text{re-substitute } \tfrac{2\pi}{365}d - \tfrac{\pi}{2} \text{ for } u$$

$$\dfrac{2\pi}{365}d \approx 1.9823 \qquad \dfrac{2\pi}{365}d \approx 4.3009 \quad \text{add } \tfrac{\pi}{2}$$

$$d \approx 115 \qquad t \approx 250 \quad \text{multiply by } \tfrac{365}{2\pi}$$

Joe's Water Sports will have revenue income of over $1250 between late April (day 115) and early September (day 250), during the summer swim season.

☑ **D.** You've just learned how to use a combination of skills to model and solve a variety of applications

**Now try Exercises 47 and 48** ▶

There is a variety of additional exercises in the Exercise Set. **See Exercises 49 through 54.**

## TECHNOLOGY HIGHLIGHT

## Window Size and Applications of the Trig Equations

As for graphical studies of other types of equations, setting an appropriate window size for trigonometric equations is a high priority. For applications involving sine and cosine functions, several things can be done to ensure a "good" window.

**Ymax, Ymin, and Yscl**

For equations of the form $y = A \sin(Bx - C) + D$, note the largest value that $\sin(Bx - C)$ can attain is 1, and the smallest is $-1$. This immediately tells us the largest value (Ymax) for $y$ is $A(1) + D$, and the smallest value for $y$ (Ymin) is $A(-1) + D$. However, to leave room for the calculator to display function names, TRACE values, and other information, we always add a "frame." Use this information to set Ymax, Ymin, and $\text{Yscl} = \dfrac{\text{Ymax} - \text{Ymin}}{10}$.

**Xmax, Xmin, and Xscl**

The values for Xmax, Xmin, and Xscl are always taken from the period of the function. For sine and cosine graphs, $P = \dfrac{2\pi}{B}$. If *any* period is sufficient we simply use Xmin = 0 and Xmax = $P$. If we want to see a primary interval, say where $\cos \theta$ begins at $y = A$ and ends at $y = A$, we set $(Bx - C) = 0$ and $(Bx - C) = 2\pi$ to find this interval. For Xscl, $\dfrac{P}{10}$ usually works well, but if the period is 12 and represents the months of the year, we would use $\dfrac{P}{12}$ as it places each month at a tick mark. Although scaling the axes is somewhat arbitrary, it should be used to improve the "readability" of a graph. We'll illustrate using the function $R(t) = 7500 \sin\left[\dfrac{\pi}{6}(t - 4.9)\right] + 8500$.

Enter the function as $Y_1 = 7500 \sin\left[\dfrac{\pi}{6}(X - 4.9)\right] + 8500$ on the Y= screen, then press WINDOW to begin setting the window size. For this example $A = 7500$, $B = \dfrac{\pi}{6}$, $C = \dfrac{4.9\pi}{6}$, and $D = 8500$.

$$\text{Ymax} = 7500(1) + 8500 = 16{,}000 \qquad \text{Xmax} = \dfrac{2\pi}{(\pi/6)} = 12$$

$$\text{Ymin} = 7500(-1) + 8500 = 1000 \qquad \text{Xmin} = 0$$

$$\text{Yscl} = 1500 \qquad \text{Xscl} = \dfrac{12}{12} = 1$$

The ⌐Y=⌐ screen, ⌐WINDOW⌐ screen, and ⌐GRAPH⌐ screen are shown in Figures 6.42, 6.43, and 6.44, respectively. Note that we have actually used a wider range of *y*-values than was necessary for our window, to ensure that the equation and displayed values do not obscure the graph.

**Figure 6.42**

**Figure 6.43**

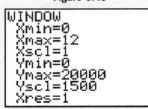

**Figure 6.44**

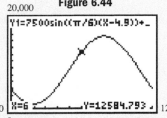

Use these ideas to complete the following exercises.

**Exercise 1:** Verify the results from Example 4.      **Exercise 2:** Verify the results from Example 5.

$$f(x) = 160 \sin\left(\frac{\pi}{3}x + \frac{\pi}{3}\right) + 320$$      $$D(t) = 16{,}580 \sin\left(\frac{\pi}{3}t - \frac{2\pi}{3}\right) + 17{,}760$$

# 6.4 EXERCISES

▶ **CONCEPTS AND VOCABULARY**

**Fill in each blank with the appropriate word or phrase. Carefully reread the section if needed.**

1. The three Pythagorean identities are _____ , _____ , and _____ .

2. When an equation contains two functions from a Pythagorean identity, sometimes _____ both sides will lead to a solution.

3. One strategy to solve equations with four terms and no common factors is _____ by _____ .

4. To combine two sine or cosine terms with different arguments, we can use the ___ to ___ formulas.

5. Regarding Example 5, discuss/explain how to determine the months of the year the discharge rate is *under* 26,050 m³/sec, using the solution set given.

6. Regarding Example 6, discuss/explain how to determine the months of the year the revenue projection is *under* $1250 using the solution set given.

▶ **DEVELOPING YOUR SKILLS**

**Solve each equation in $[0, 2\pi)$ using the method indicated. Round nonstandard values to four decimal places.**

• **Squaring both sides**

7. $\sin x + \cos x = \dfrac{\sqrt{6}}{2}$      8. $\cot x - \csc x = \sqrt{3}$

9. $\tan x - \sec x = -1$      10. $\sin x + \cos x = \sqrt{2}$

11. $\cos x + \sin x = \dfrac{4}{3}$      12. $\sec x + \tan x = 2$

• **Factor by grouping**

13. $\cot x \csc x - 2 \cot x - \csc x + 2 = 0$

14. $4 \sin x \cos x - 2\sqrt{3} \sin x - 2 \cos x + \sqrt{3} = 0$

15. $3 \tan^2 x \cos x - 3 \cos x + 2 = 2 \tan^2 x$

16. $4\sqrt{3} \sin^2 x \sec x - \sqrt{3} \sec x + 2 = 8 \sin^2 x$

• **Using identities**

17. $\dfrac{1 + \cot^2 x}{\cot^2 x} = 2$      18. $\dfrac{1 + \tan^2 x}{\tan^2 x} = \dfrac{4}{3}$

19. $3 \cos(2x) + 7 \sin x - 5 = 0$

20. $3 \cos(2x) - \cos x + 1 = 0$

**21.** $2\sin^2\left(\dfrac{x}{2}\right) - 3\cos\left(\dfrac{x}{2}\right) = 0$

**22.** $2\cos^2\left(\dfrac{x}{3}\right) + 3\sin\left(\dfrac{x}{3}\right) - 3 = 0$

**23.** $\cos(3x) + \cos(5x)\cos(2x) +$
$$\sin(5x)\sin(2x) - 1 = 0$$

**24.** $\sin(7x)\cos(4x) + \sin(5x) -$
$$\cos(7x)\sin(4x) + \cos x = 0$$

**25.** $\sec^4 x - 2\sec^2 x\,\tan^2 x + \tan^4 x = \tan^2 x$

**26.** $\tan^4 x - 2\sec^2 x\,\tan^2 x + \sec^4 x = \cot^2 x$

**State the period $P$ of each function and find all solutions in $[0, P)$. Round to four decimal places as needed.**

**27.** $250\sin\left(\dfrac{\pi}{6}x + \dfrac{\pi}{3}\right) - 125 = 0$

**28.** $-75\sqrt{2}\sec\left(\dfrac{\pi}{4}x + \dfrac{\pi}{6}\right) + 150 = 0$

**29.** $1235\cos\left(\dfrac{\pi}{12}x - \dfrac{\pi}{4}\right) + 772 = 1750$

**30.** $-0.075\sin\left(\dfrac{\pi}{2}x + \dfrac{\pi}{3}\right) - 0.023 = -0.068$

**Solve each equation in $[0, 2\pi)$ using any appropriate method. Round nonstandard values to four decimal places.**

**31.** $\cos x - \sin x = \dfrac{\sqrt{2}}{2}$

**32.** $5\sec^2 x - 2\tan x - 8 = 0$

**33.** $\dfrac{1 - \cos^2 x}{\tan^2 x} = \dfrac{\sqrt{3}}{2}$

**34.** $5\csc^2 x - 5\cot x - 5 = 0$

**35.** $\csc x + \cot x = 1$     **36.** $\dfrac{1 - \sin^2 x}{\cot^2 x} = \dfrac{\sqrt{2}}{2}$

**37.** $\sec x\cos\left(\dfrac{\pi}{2} - x\right) = -1$

**38.** $\sin\left(\dfrac{\pi}{2} - x\right)\csc x = \sqrt{3}$

**39.** $\sec^2 x\tan\left(\dfrac{\pi}{2} - x\right) = 4$

**40.** $2\tan\left(\dfrac{\pi}{2} - x\right)\sin^2 x = \dfrac{\sqrt{3}}{2}$

▶ **WORKING WITH FORMULAS**

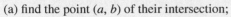

**41. The equation of a line in trigonometric form: $y = \dfrac{D - x\cos\theta}{\sin\theta}$**

The trigonometric form of a linear equation is given by the formula shown, where $D$ is the perpendicular distance from the origin to the line and $\theta$ is the angle between the perpendicular segment and the $x$-axis. For each pair of perpendicular lines given,

(a) find the point $(a, b)$ of their intersection;

(b) compute the distance $D = \sqrt{a^2 + b^2}$ and the angle $\theta = \tan^{-1}\left(\dfrac{b}{a}\right)$, and give the equation of the line in trigonometric form; and

(c) use the GRAPH or the 2nd GRAPH TABLE feature of a graphing calculator to verify that both equations name the same line.

    **I.** $L_1: y = -x + 5$     **II.** $L_1: y = -\dfrac{1}{2}x + 5$     **III.** $L_1: y = -\dfrac{\sqrt{3}}{3}x + \dfrac{4\sqrt{3}}{3}$

     $L_2: y = x$           $L_2: y = 2x$          $L_2: y = \sqrt{3}x$

**42. Rewriting $y = a\cos x + b\sin x$ as a single function: $y = k\sin(x + \theta)$**

Linear terms of sine and cosine can be rewritten as a single function using the formula shown, where

$k = \sqrt{a^2 + b^2}$ and $\theta = \sin^{-1}\left(\dfrac{a}{k}\right)$. Rewrite the equations given using these relationships and verify they are

equivalent using the GRAPH or the 2nd GRAPH TABLE feature of a graphing calculator:

    **a.** $y = 2\cos x + 2\sqrt{3}\sin x$        **b.** $y = 4\cos x + 3\sin x$

The ability to rewrite a trigonometric equation in simpler form has a tremendous number of applications in graphing, equation solving, working with identities, and solving applications.

▶ **APPLICATIONS**

43. **Volume of a cylinder:** The volume of a cylinder is given by the formula $V = \pi r^2 h \sin\theta$, where $r$ is the radius and $h$ is the height of the cylinder, and $\theta$ is the indicated complement of the angle of deflection $\alpha$. Note that when $\theta = \dfrac{\pi}{2}$, the formula becomes that of a right circular cylinder (if $\theta \neq \dfrac{\pi}{2}$, then $h$ is called the *slant height or lateral height* of the cylinder). An old farm silo is built in the form of a right circular cylinder with a radius of 10 ft and a height of 25 ft. After an earthquake, the silo became tilted with an angle of deflection $\alpha = 5°$. (a) Find the volume of the silo before the earthquake. (b) Find the volume of the silo after the earthquake. (c) What angle $\theta$ is required to bring the original volume of the silo down 2%?

**Exercise 43**

44. **Volume of a cone:** The volume of a cone is given by the formula $V = \dfrac{1}{3}\pi r^2 h \sin\theta$, where $r$ is the radius and $h$ is the height of the cone, and $\theta$ is the indicated complement of the angle of deflection $\alpha$. Note that when $\theta = \dfrac{\pi}{2}$, the formula becomes that of a right circular cone (if $\theta \neq \dfrac{\pi}{2}$, then $h$ is called the *slant height or lateral height* of the cone). As part of a sculpture exhibit, an artist is constructing three such structures each with a radius of 2 m and a slant height of 3 m. (a) Find the volume of the sculptures if the angle of deflection is $\alpha = 15°$. (b) What angle $\theta$ was used if the volume of each sculpture is 12 m³?

**Exercise 44**

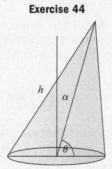

45. **River discharge rate:** For June through February, the discharge rate of the La Corcovada River (Venezuela) can be modeled by the function

$$D(t) = 36\sin\left(\frac{\pi}{4}t - \frac{9}{4}\right) + 44,$$ where t represents

the months of the year with $t = 1$ corresponding to June, and $D(t)$ is the discharge rate in cubic meters per second. (a) What is the discharge rate in mid-September? (b) For what months of the year is the discharge rate over 50 m³/sec?

*Source: Global River Discharge Database Project; www.rivdis.sr.unh.edu.*

46. **River discharge rate:** For February through June, the average monthly discharge of the Point Wolfe River (Canada) can be modeled by the function

$$D(t) = 4.6\sin\left(\frac{\pi}{2}t + 3\right) + 7.4,$$ where $t$ represents

the months of the year with $t = 1$ corresponding to February, and $D(t)$ is the discharge rate in cubic meters/second. (a) What is the discharge rate in mid-March ($t = 2.5$)? (b) For what months of the year is the discharge rate less than 7.5 m³/sec?

*Source: Global River Discharge Database Project; www.rivdis.sr.unh.edu.*

47. **Seasonal sales:** Hank's Heating Oil is a very seasonal enterprise, with sales in the winter far exceeding sales in the summer. Monthly sales for the company can be modeled by

$$S(x) = 1600\cos\left(\frac{\pi}{6}x - \frac{\pi}{12}\right) + 5100,$$ where $S(x)$

is the average sales in month $x$ ($x = 1 \rightarrow$ January). (a) What is the average sales amount for July? (b) For what months of the year are sales less than \$4000?

48. **Seasonal income:** As a roofing company employee, Mark's income fluctuates with the seasons and the availability of work. For the past several years his average monthly income could be approximated by

the function $I(m) = 2100\sin\left(\dfrac{\pi}{6}m - \dfrac{\pi}{2}\right) + 3520$,

where $I(m)$ represents income in month $m$ ($m = 1 \rightarrow$ January). (a) What is Mark's average monthly income in October? (b) For what months of the year is his average monthly income over \$4500?

49. **Seasonal ice thickness:** The average thickness of the ice covering an arctic lake can be modeled by

the function $T(x) = 9\cos\left(\dfrac{\pi}{6}x\right) + 15$, where $T(x)$ is

the average thickness in month $x$ ($x = 1 \rightarrow$ January). (a) How thick is the ice in mid-March? (b) For what months of the year is the ice at most 10.5 in. thick?

50. **Seasonal temperatures:** The function

$$T(x) = 19\sin\left(\frac{\pi}{6}x - \frac{\pi}{2}\right) + 53$$ models the average

monthly temperature of the water in a mountain stream, where $T(x)$ is the temperature (°F) of the water in month $x$ ($x = 1 \rightarrow$ January). (a) What is the temperature of the water in October? (b) What two months are most likely to give a temperature reading of 62°F? (c) For what months of the year is the temperature below 50°F?

**51. Coffee sales:** Coffee sales fluctuate with the weather, with a great deal more coffee sold in the winter than in the summer. For Joe's Diner, assume the function $G(x) = 21 \cos\left(\dfrac{2\pi}{365}x + \dfrac{\pi}{2}\right) + 29$ models daily coffee sales (for non-leap years), where $G(x)$ is the number of gallons sold and $x$ represents the days of the year ($x = 1 \rightarrow$ January 1). (a) How many gallons are projected to be sold on March 21? (b) For what days of the year are more than 40 gal of coffee sold?

**52. Park attendance:** Attendance at a popular state park varies with the weather, with a great deal more visitors coming in during the summer months. Assume daily attendance at the park can be modeled by the function $V(x) = 437 \cos\left(\dfrac{2\pi}{365}x - \pi\right) + 545$ (for non-leap years), where $V(x)$ gives the number of visitors on day $x$ ($x = 1 \rightarrow$ January 1). (a) Approximately how many people visited the park on November 1 ($11 \times 30.5 = 335.5$)? (b) For what days of the year are there more than 900 visitors?

**53. Exercise routine:** As part of his yearly physical, Manu Tuiosamoa's heart rate is closely monitored during a 12-min, cardiovascular exercise routine. His heart rate in beats per minute (bpm) is modeled by the function $B(x) = 58 \cos\left(\dfrac{\pi}{6}x + \pi\right) + 126$ where $x$ represents the duration of the workout in minutes. (a) What was his resting heart rate? (b) What was his heart rate 5 min into the workout? (c) At what times during the workout was his heart rate over 170 bpm?

**54. Exercise routine:** As part of her workout routine, Sara Lee programs her treadmill to begin at a slight initial grade (angle of incline), gradually increase to a maximum grade, then gradually decrease back to the original grade. For the duration of her workout, the grade is modeled by the function $G(x) = 3 \cos\left(\dfrac{\pi}{5}x - \pi\right) + 4$, where $G(x)$ is the percent grade $x$ minutes after the workout has begun. (a) What is the initial grade for her workout? (b) What is the grade at $x = 4$ min? (c) At $G(x) = 4.9\%$, how long has she been working out? (d) What is the duration of the treadmill workout?

▶ **EXTENDING THE CONCEPT**

 **55.** As we saw earlier, cosine is the cofunction of sine and each can be expressed in terms of the other: $\cos\left(\dfrac{\pi}{2} - \theta\right) = \sin\theta$ and $\sin\left(\dfrac{\pi}{2} - \theta\right) = \cos\theta$. This implies that either function can be used to model the phenomenon described in this section by adjusting the phase shift. By experimentation, (a) find a model using cosine that will produce results identical to the sine function in Exercise 50 and (b) find a model using sine that will produce results identical to the cosine function in Exercise 51.

**56.** Use multiple identities to find all real solutions for the equation given: $\sin(5x) + \sin(2x)\cos x + \cos(2x)\sin x = 0$.

**57.** A rectangular parallelepiped with square ends has 12 edges and six surfaces. If the sum of all edges is 176 cm and the total surface area is 1288 cm$^2$, find (a) the length of the diagonal of the parallelepiped (shown in bold) and (b) the angle the diagonal makes with the base (two answers are possible).

**Exercise 57**

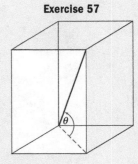

► **MAINTAINING YOUR SKILLS**

**58. (1.3)** Find $f(\theta)$ for all six trig functions, given $P(-51, 68)$ is on the terminal side.

**59. (6.2)** Draw a corresponding triangle to help write $\cos\left[\tan^{-1}\left(\dfrac{x}{6}\right)\right]$ in algebraic form.

**60. (5.3)** Use identities to evaluate $\cos(4x)$ exactly, given $\sin x = \dfrac{3}{5}$ and $\cos x = \dfrac{4}{5}$.

**61. (5.2)** If $\sin \alpha = \dfrac{\sqrt{2}}{2}$ and $\cos \beta = \dfrac{\sqrt{3}}{2}$, find the value of $\sin(\alpha + \beta)$ and the value of $\cos(\alpha + \beta)$.

**62. (4.1)** The graph of the function shown models one of the seven primary colors. Use the wavelength chart on page 149 to identify the color. The $x$-axis is marked in nanometers.

**Exercise 62**

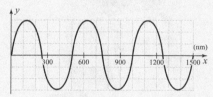

**63. (2.3)** The Sears Tower in Chicago, Illinois, remains one of the tallest structures in the world. The top of the roof reaches 1450 ft above the street below and the antenna extends an additional 280 ft into the air. Find the viewing angle $\theta$ for the antenna from a distance of 1000 ft (the angle formed from the base of the antenna to its top).

**Exercise 63**

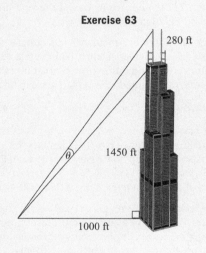

# SUMMARY AND CONCEPT REVIEW

## SECTION 6.1   One-to-One and Inverse Functions

### KEY CONCEPTS
- A function is one-to-one if each element of the range corresponds to a unique element of the domain.
- If every horizontal line intersects the graph of a function in at most one point, the function is one-to-one.
- If $f$ is a one-to-one function with ordered pairs $(a, b)$, then the inverse of $f$ exists and is that one-to-one function $f^{-1}$ with ordered pairs of the form $(b, a)$.
- The range of $f$ becomes the domain of $f^{-1}$, and the domain of $f$ becomes the range of $f^{-1}$.
- To find $f^{-1}$ using the algebraic method:
    1. Use $y$ instead of $f(x)$.         2. Interchange $x$ and $y$.
    3. Solve the equation for $y$.         4. Substitute $f^{-1}(x)$ for $y$.
- If $f$ is a one-to-one function, the inverse $f^{-1}$ exists, where $(f \circ f^{-1})(x) = x$ and $(f^{-1} \circ f)(x) = x$.
- The graphs of $f$ and $f^{-1}$ are symmetric with respect to the identity function $y = x$.

### EXERCISES
Determine whether the functions given are one-to-one by noting the function family to which each belongs and mentally picturing the shape of the graph.

**1.** $h(x) = -|x - 2| + 3$      **2.** $p(x) = 2x^2 + 7$      **3.** $s(x) = \sqrt{x - 1} + 5$

Find the inverse of each function given. Then show graphically and using composition that your inverse function is correct. State any necessary restrictions.

**4.** $f(x) = -3x + 2$      **5.** $f(x) = x^2 - 2, x \geq 0$      **6.** $f(x) = \sqrt{x - 1}$

Determine the domain and range for each function whose graph is given, and use this information to state the domain and range of the inverse function. Then sketch in the line $y = x$, estimate the location of three points on the graph, and use these to graph $f^{-1}(x)$ on the same grid.

**7.** 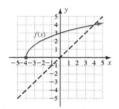      **8.** 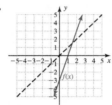      **9.**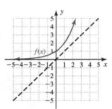

**10. Fines for overdue material:** Some libraries have set fees and penalties to discourage patrons from holding borrowed materials for an extended period. Suppose the fine for overdue DVDs is given by the function $f(t) = 0.15t + 2$, where $f(t)$ is the amount of the fine $t$ days after it is due. (a) What is the fine for keeping a DVD seven (7) extra days? (b) Find $f^{-1}(t)$, then input your answer from part (a) and comment on the result. (c) If a fine of \$3.80 was assessed, how many days was the DVD overdue?

## SECTION 6.2    The Inverse Trig Functions and Their Applications

### KEY CONCEPTS

- In order to create one-to-one functions, the domains of $y = \sin t$, $y = \cos t$, and $y = \tan t$ are restricted as follows:
  (a) $y = \sin t, t \in \left[ -\dfrac{\pi}{2}, \dfrac{\pi}{2} \right]$; (b) $y = \cos t, t \in [0, \pi]$; and (c) $y = \tan t; t \in \left( -\dfrac{\pi}{2}, \dfrac{\pi}{2} \right)$.
- For $y = \sin x$, the inverse function is given implicitly as $x = \sin y$ and explicitly as $y = \sin^{-1} x$ or $y = \arcsin x$.
- The expression $y = \sin^{-1} x$ is read, "$y$ is the angle or real number whose sine is $x$." The other inverse functions are similarly read/understood.
- For $y = \cos x$, the inverse function is given implicitly as $x = \cos y$ and explicitly as $y = \cos^{-1} x$ or $y = \arccos x$.
- For $y = \tan x$, the inverse function is given implicitly as $x = \tan y$ and explicitly as $y = \tan^{-1} x$ or $y = \arctan x$.
- The domains of $y = \sec x$, $y = \csc x$, and $y = \cot x$ are likewise restricted to create one-to-one functions:
  (a) $y = \sec t; t \in \left[ 0, \dfrac{\pi}{2} \right) \cup \left( \dfrac{\pi}{2}, \pi \right]$; (b) $y = \csc t, t \in \left[ -\dfrac{\pi}{2}, 0 \right) \cup \left( 0, \dfrac{\pi}{2} \right]$; and (c) $y = \cot t, t \in (0, \pi)$.
- In some applications, inverse functions occur in a composition with other trig functions, with the expression best evaluated by drawing a diagram using the ratio definition of the trig functions.
- To evaluate $y = \sec^{-1} t$, we use $y = \cos^{-1}\left( \dfrac{1}{t} \right)$; for $y = \cot^{-1} t$, use $\tan^{-1}\left( \dfrac{1}{t} \right)$; and so on.
- Trigonometric substitutions can be used to simplify certain algebraic expressions.

### EXERCISES

Evaluate without the aid of calculators or tables. State answers in both radians and degrees in exact form.

**11.** $y = \sin^{-1}\left( \dfrac{\sqrt{2}}{2} \right)$      **12.** $y = \csc^{-1} 2$      **13.** $y = \arccos\left( -\dfrac{\sqrt{3}}{2} \right)$

Evaluate the following using a calculator, *keeping the domain and range of each function in mind.* Answer in radians to the nearest ten-thousandth *and* in degrees to the nearest tenth. Some may be undefined.

**14.** $y = \tan^{-1} 4.3165$      **15.** $y = \sin^{-1} 0.8892$      **16.** $f(x) = \arccos\left( \dfrac{7}{8} \right)$

Evaluate the following without the aid of a calculator. Some may be undefined.

**17.** $\sin\left[\sin^{-1}\left(\dfrac{1}{2}\right)\right]$

**18.** $\operatorname{arcsec}\left[\sec\left(\dfrac{\pi}{4}\right)\right]$

**19.** $\cos(\cos^{-1}2)$

 Evaluate the following using a calculator. Some may be undefined.

**20.** $\sin^{-1}(\sin 1.0245)$

**21.** $\arccos[\cos(-60°)]$

**22.** $\cot^{-1}\left[\cot\left(\dfrac{11\pi}{4}\right)\right]$

Evaluate each expression by drawing a right triangle and labeling the sides.

**23.** $\sin\left[\cos^{-1}\left(\dfrac{12}{37}\right)\right]$

**24.** $\tan\left[\operatorname{arcsec}\left(\dfrac{7}{3x}\right)\right]$

**25.** $\cot\left[\sin^{-1}\left(\dfrac{x}{\sqrt{81+x^2}}\right)\right]$

Use an inverse function to solve the following equations for $\theta$ in terms of $x$.

**26.** $x = 5\cos\theta$

**27.** $7\sqrt{3}\sec\theta = x$

**28.** $x = 4\sin\left(\theta - \dfrac{\pi}{6}\right)$

## SECTION 6.3   Solving Basic Trig Equations

### KEY CONCEPTS

- When solving trig equations, we often consider either the principal root, roots in $[0, 2\pi)$, or all real roots.
- Keeping the graph of each function in mind helps to determine the desired solution set.
- After isolating the trigonometric term containing the variable, we solve by applying the appropriate inverse function, realizing the result is only the principal root.
- Once the principal root is found, roots in $[0, 2\pi)$ or all real roots can be found using reference angles and the period of the function under consideration.
- Trig identities can be used to obtain an equation that can be solved by factoring or other solution methods.

### EXERCISES

Solve each equation without the aid of a calculator (all solutions are standard values). Clearly state (a) the principal root; (b) all solutions in the interval $[0, 2\pi)$; and (c) all real roots.

**29.** $2\sin x = \sqrt{2}$

**30.** $3\sec x = -6$

**31.** $8\tan x + 7\sqrt{3} = -\sqrt{3}$

Solve using a calculator and the inverse trig functions (not by graphing). Clearly state (a) the principal root; (b) solutions in $[0, 2\pi)$; and (c) all real roots. Answer in radians to the nearest ten-thousandth as needed.

**32.** $9\cos x = 4$

**33.** $\dfrac{2}{5}\sin(2\theta) = \dfrac{1}{4}$

**34.** $\sqrt{2}\csc x + 3 = 7$

**35.** The area of a circular segment (the shaded portion shown in the diagram) is given by the formula $A = \dfrac{1}{2}r^2(\theta - \sin\theta)$, where $\theta$ is in radians. If the circle has a radius of 10 cm, find the angle $\theta$ that gives an area of 12 cm$^2$.

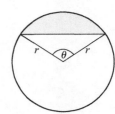

## SECTION 6.4   Solving General Trig Equations and Applications

### KEY CONCEPTS

- In addition to the basic solution methods from Section 6.3, additional strategies include squaring both sides, factoring by grouping, and using the full range of identities to simplify an equation.
- Many applications result in equations of the form $A\sin(Bx + C) + D = k$. To solve, isolate the factor $\sin(Bx + C)$ (subtract $D$ and divide by $A$), then apply the inverse function.
- Once the principal root is found, roots in $[0, 2\pi)$ or all real roots can be found using reference angles and the period of the function under consideration.

## EXERCISES

Find solutions in $[0, 2\pi)$ using the method indicated. Round nonstandard values to four decimal places.

**36. squaring both sides**

$$\sin x + \cos x = \frac{\sqrt{6}}{2}$$

**37. using identities**

$$3\cos(2x) + 7\sin x - 5 = 0$$

**38. factor by grouping**

$$4\sin x \cos x - 2\sqrt{3}\sin x - 2\cos x + \sqrt{3} = 0$$

**39. using any appropriate method**

$$\csc x + \cot x = 1$$

State the period $P$ of each function and find all solutions in $[0, P)$. Round to four decimal places as needed.

**40.** $-750\sin\left(\dfrac{\pi}{6}x + \dfrac{\pi}{2}\right) + 120 = 0$

**41.** $80\cos\left(\dfrac{\pi}{3}x + \dfrac{\pi}{4}\right) - 40\sqrt{2} = 0$

**42.** The revenue earned by Waipahu Joe's Tanning Lotions fluctuates with the seasons, with a great deal more lotion sold in the summer than in the winter. The function $R(x) = 15\sin\left(\dfrac{\pi}{6}x - \dfrac{\pi}{2}\right) + 30$ models the monthly sales of lotion nationwide, where $R(x)$ is the revenue in thousands of dollars and $x$ represents the months of the year ($x = 1 \to$ Jan). (a) How much revenue is projected for July? (b) For what months of the year does revenue exceed $37,000?

1. Given $f(x) = \dfrac{1}{(x + 2)^2}$, $x > -2$: (a) use the algebraic method to find the inverse function, (b) state the domain and range of $f^{-1}(x)$, and (c) verify your inverse is correct using a composition.

2. Determine the domain and range for the function $f$ whose graph is given, and use this information to state the domain and range of $f^{-1}$. Then sketch the line $y = x$ and sketch the graph of $y = f^{-1}(x)$ on the same grid.

**Exercise 2**

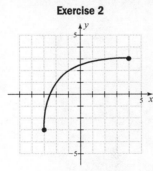

Solve the following equations for $x \in [0, 2\pi)$ without the aid of a calculator.

3. $-12 \sin x + 5 = 11$    4. $\dfrac{3}{4} \cos^2 x - \dfrac{1}{3} = \dfrac{1}{24}$

Evaluate each expression by drawing a right triangle and labeling the sides appropriately.

5. $\tan\left[\operatorname{arccsc}\left(\dfrac{10}{x}\right)\right]$    6. $\sin\left[\sec^{-1}\left(\dfrac{\sqrt{64 + x^2}}{x}\right)\right]$

7. Solve for $x$ in the interval $[0, 2\pi)$. Round to four decimal places as needed:

$$-100 \sin\left(\dfrac{\pi}{4}x - \dfrac{\pi}{6}\right) + 80 = 100$$

8. Without the aid of a calculator, find: (a) the principal roots, (b) all solutions in $[0, 2\pi)$, and (c) all real solutions: $(\cos x - 1)[2 \cos^2(x) - 1] = 0$.

9. For $g(x) = \sqrt{x - 1} + 2$, (a) state the domain and range, (b) find $g^{-1}(x)$ and state its domain and range, and (c) compute at least three ordered pairs $(a, b)$ for $g$ and show the ordered pairs $(b, a)$ are solutions to $g^{-1}$.

10. State the domain and range of the following functions from memory, using only a "mental picture" of the graphs of $y = \sin t$, $y = \cos t$, and $y = \tan t$.

    a. $f(t) = \sin^{-1}t$    b. $g(t) = \cos^{-1}t$
    c. $h(t) = \tan^{-1}t$

Evaluate without the aid of a calculator or tables. Answer in both radians and degrees.

11. $y = \operatorname{arcsec}(-\sqrt{2})$    12. $y = \sin^{-1}0$
13. $y = \arctan\sqrt{3}$

Use an inverse function to solve each equation for $\theta$ in terms of $x$.

**14.** $\dfrac{x}{10} = \tan\theta$        **15.** $2\sqrt{2}\csc\left(\theta - \dfrac{\pi}{4}\right) = x$

**16.** On a large clock, the distance from the tip of the hour hand to the base of the "12" can be approximated by the function

$$D(t) = \left| 8\sin\left(\dfrac{\pi t}{12}\right) \right| + 2,$$ where $D(t)$ is this distance

in feet at time $t$ in hours. Use this function to approximate (a) the time of day when the hand is 6 ft from the 12 and 10 ft from the 12 and (b) the distance between the tip and the 12 at 4:00. Check your answer graphically.

**17.** The figure shows a smaller pentagon inscribed within a larger pentagon. Find the measure of angle $\theta$ using the diagram and equation given:

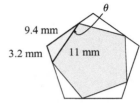

$$3.2^2 = 11^2 + 9.4^2 - 2(11)(9.4)\cos\theta$$

**18.** Given $100\sin t = 70$, use a calculator to find (a) the principal root, (b) all solutions in $[0, 2\pi)$, and (c) all real solutions. Round to the nearest ten-thousandth.

**19.** Use an identity to find all real solutions for $\cos(2\theta) + 2\sin^2\theta = -2\sin\theta$.

**20.** State the period $P$ of the function and find all exact solutions in $x \in [0, P)$, given

$$124\cos\left[\dfrac{\pi}{12}(x - 3)\right] + 82 = 144$$

1. For $f(x) = x^3$, the inverse function is $f^{-1}(x) = \sqrt[3]{x}$, but for $f(x) = x^2$, the inverse function is *not* $f^{-1}(x) = \sqrt{x}$. Explain why.

2. For $t$ in radians, the area of a circular sector is given by $A(t) = \frac{1}{2}r^2t$. (a) Find the area if $r = 10$ cm and $t = \frac{\pi}{4}$. (b) Use the algebraic method to find $A^{-1}(t)$, then substitute the result from part (a). What do you notice?

3. Sketch the graph of $y = \cos^{-1}x$ and state its domain and range.

4. Use a calculator to approximate the value of $y = \sec^{-1}(3)$ to four decimal places.

Evaluate without the aid of calculators or tables.

5. $y = \tan^{-1}\left(\dfrac{1}{\sqrt{3}}\right)$

6. $f(x) = \sin\left[\sin^{-1}\left(\dfrac{1}{2}\right)\right]$

7. $y = \arccos(\cos 30°)$

Evaluate the following. Answer in exact form, where possible.

8. $y = \sin^{-1}0.7528$

9. $y = \arctan(\tan 78.5°)$

10. $y = \sec^{-1}\left[\sec\left(\dfrac{7\pi}{24}\right)\right]$

Evaluate the expressions by drawing a right triangle and labeling the sides.

11. $\cos\left[\tan^{-1}\left(\dfrac{56}{33}\right)\right]$

12. $\cot\left[\cos^{-1}\left(\dfrac{x}{\sqrt{25 + x^2}}\right)\right]$

Solve without the aid of a calculator (all solutions are standard values). Clearly state (a) the principal root, (b) all solutions in the interval $[0, 2\pi)$, and (c) all real roots.

13. $8\cos x = -4\sqrt{2}$

14. $\sqrt{3}\sec x + 2 = 4$

Solve each equation using a calculator and inverse trig functions to find the principal root (not by graphing). Then state (a) the principal root, (b) all solutions in the interval $[0, 2\pi)$, and (c) all real roots.

15. $\dfrac{2}{3}\sin(2x) = \dfrac{1}{4}$

16. $-3\cos(2x) - 0.8 = 0$

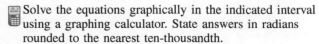 Solve the equations graphically in the indicated interval using a graphing calculator. State answers in radians rounded to the nearest ten-thousandth.

17. $3\cos(2x - 1) = \sin x$; $x \in [-\pi, \pi]$

18. $2\sqrt{x} - 1 = 3\cos^2 x$; $x \in [0, 2\pi)$

Solve the following equations for $x \in [0, 2\pi)$ using a combination of identities and/or factoring. State solutions in radians using the exact form, where possible.

**19.** $2 \sin x \sin(2x) + \sin(2x) = 0$

**20.** $(\cos x + \sin x)^2 = \dfrac{1}{2}$

Solve each equation in $[0, 2\pi)$ by squaring both sides, factoring, using identities or by using any appropriate method. Round nonstandard values to four decimal places.

**21.** $3 \sin(2x) + \cos x = 0$

**22.** $\dfrac{2}{3} \sin\left(2x - \dfrac{\pi}{6}\right) + \dfrac{3}{2} = \dfrac{5}{6}$

**23.** The revenue for Otake's Mower Repair is very seasonal, with business in the summer months far exceeding business in the winter months. Monthly revenue for the company can be modeled by the function $R(x) = 7.5 \cos\left(\dfrac{\pi}{6}x + \dfrac{4\pi}{3}\right) + 12.5$, where $R(x)$ is the average revenue (in thousands of dollars) for month $x$ ($x = 1 \rightarrow$ Jan). (a) What is the average revenue for September? (b) For what months of the year is revenue at least \$12,500?

**24.** State the domain and range of $f(x) = (x - 2)^2 - 3$ and determine if $f$ is a one-to-one function. If so, find its inverse. If not, restrict the domain of $f$ to create a one-to-one function, then find the inverse of this new function, including the domain and range.

**25.** Evaluate without the aid of calculators or tables.

$$\sin\left(\tan^{-1}\left\{\tan\left[\sec^{-1}\left(-\dfrac{2}{\sqrt{3}}\right)\right]\right\}\right)$$

## CALCULATOR EXPLORATION AND DISCOVERY

### Solving Equations Graphically Using a Graphing Calculator

The periodic behavior of the trig functions is often used to form a solution set, which can be very helpful when solutions are nonstandard values. In addition, some equations are very difficult to solve analytically, and even with the use of a graphing calculator a strong combination of analytical skills with technical skills is required to state the solution set. Consider the equation $5 \sin\left(\frac{1}{2}x\right) + 5 = \cot\left(\frac{1}{2}x\right)$. There appears to be no quick analytical solution, and the first attempt at a graphical solution holds some hidden surprises. Enter $Y_1 = 5 \sin\left(\frac{1}{2}x\right) + 5$ and $Y_2 = \dfrac{1}{\tan\left(\frac{1}{2}x\right)}$ on the  screen. Pressing ZOOM 7:ZTrig gives the screen shown in Figure 6.45, where we note there are at least

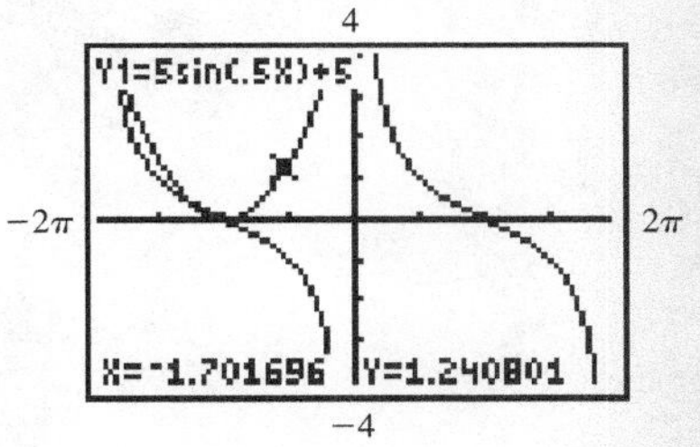

**Figure 6.45**

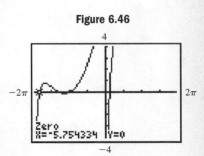

two and possibly three solutions, depending on how the sine graph "cuts" the cotangent graph. We are also uncertain as to whether the graphs intersect again between $-\frac{\pi}{2}$ and $\frac{\pi}{2}$. Increasing the maximum Y-value to Ymax = 8 shows they do indeed. But once again, are there now three or four solutions? In situations like this it is helpful to use the **Zeroes Method** for solving graphically, where we actually compute the difference between the two functions, looking for a difference of zero (meaning they intersect), with every $x$-intercept indicating an intersection point. On the Y= screen, disable $Y_1$ and $Y_2$ and enter $Y_3$ as $Y_1 - Y_2$. Pressing ZOOM 7:ZTrig at this point clearly shows that there are four solutions (Figure 6.46), which

**Figure 6.46**

can easily be found using 2nd CALC **2:zero:** $x \approx -5.7543$, $-4.0094$, $-3.1416$, and $0.3390$. To investigate solutions in $\mathbb{R}$, note the period of $Y_1$ is $P = \dfrac{2\pi}{\frac{1}{2}} = 4\pi$. On the 2nd WINDOW **(TBLSET)** screen, enter any one of the four solutions as the **TblStart** value, then set $\Delta$TBL to $\pi$, put the calculator in AUTO mode, and go to 2nd GRAPH **(TABLE)**. Scrolling through the TABLE shows this solution indeed repeats every $4\pi$ and we write the solution (to four decimal places) as

$x \approx -5.7543 + 4\pi k$ for all integers $k$. The other solutions are likewise found. Use these ideas to find all real solutions to the exercises that follow.

**Exercise 1:**    $(1 + \sin x)^2 + \cos(2x) = 4 \cos x(1 + \sin x)$      **Exercise 2:**    $4 \sin x = 2 \cos^2\left(\dfrac{x}{2}\right)$

## Trigonometric Equations and Inequalities

The ability to draw a quick graph of the trigonometric functions is a tremendous help in understanding equations and inequalities. A basic sketch can help reveal the number of solutions in $[0, 2\pi)$ and the quadrant of each solution. For non-standard angles, the value given by the inverse function can then be used as a basis for stating the solution set for all real numbers. We'll illustrate the process using a few simple examples, then generalize our observations to solve more realistic applications. Consider the function $f(x) = 2 \sin x + 1$, a sine wave with amplitude 2, and a vertical translation of $+1$. To find intervals in $[0, 2\pi)$ where $f(x) > 2.5$, we reason that $f$ has a maximum of $2(1) + 1 = 3$ and a minimum of $2(-1) + 1 = -1$, since $-1 \le \sin x \le 1$. With no phase shift and a standard period of $2\pi$, we can easily draw a quick sketch of $f$ by vertically translating $x$-intercepts and max/min points 1 unit up. After drawing the line $y = 2.5$ (see Figure 6.47), it appears there are two intersections in the interval, one in QI and one in QII. More importantly, it is clear that $f(x) > 2.5$ *between these two solutions*. Substituting 2.5 for $f(x)$ in $f(x) = 2 \sin x + 1$, we solve for $\sin x$ to obtain $\sin x = 0.75$, which we use to state the solution in exact form: $f(x) > 2.5$ for $x \in (\sin^{-1} 0.75, \pi - \sin^{-1} 0.75)$. In approximate form the solution interval is $x \in (0.85, 2.29)$. If the function involves a horizontal shift, the graphical analysis will reveal which intervals should be chosen to satisfy the given inequality.

**Figure 6.47**

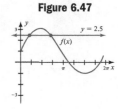

The basic ideas remain the same regardless of the complexity of the equation, and we illustrate by studying Example 6 from Section 6.4. Given the function $R(d) = 750 \sin\left(\dfrac{2\pi}{365} d - \dfrac{\pi}{2}\right) + 950$, we were asked to solve the inequality $R(d) > 1250$. Remember—our current goal is not a supremely accurate graph, just a sketch that will guide us to the solution using the inverse functions and the correct quadrants. Perhaps that greatest challenge is recalling that when $B \ne 1$, the horizontal shift is $-\dfrac{C}{B}$, but other than this a fairly accurate sketch can quickly be obtained.

---

**Illustration 1** ▶ Given $R(d) = 750 \sin\left(\dfrac{2\pi}{365} d - \dfrac{\pi}{2}\right) + 950$, find intervals in $[0, 365]$ where $R(d) > 1250$.

**Solution** ▶ This is a sine wave with a period of 365 days, an amplitude of 750, shifted $-\dfrac{C}{B} = 91.25$ units to the right and 950 units up. The maximum value will be 1700 and the minimum value will be 200. For convenience, scale the axes from 0 to 360 (as though the period were 360 days), and plot the $x$-intercepts and maximum/minimum values for a standard sine wave with amplitude 750 (by scaling the axes). Then shift these points about 90 units in the positive direction (to the right), and 950 units up, again using a scale that makes this convenient (see Figure 6.48). This sketch along with the graph of $y = 1250$ is sufficient to show that solutions to $R(d) = 1250$ occur early in the second quarter and late in the third quarter, with solutions to $R(d) > 1250$

**Figure 6.48**

occurring *between* these solutions. For $R(d) = 750 \sin\left(\dfrac{2\pi}{365} d - \dfrac{\pi}{2}\right) + 950$, we substitute 1250 for $R(d)$ and isolate the sine function, obtaining $\sin\left(\dfrac{2\pi}{365} d - \dfrac{\pi}{2}\right) = 0.4$, which leads to exact form solutions of $d = \left(\sin^{-1} 0.4 + \dfrac{\pi}{2}\right)\left(\dfrac{365}{2\pi}\right)$

and $d = \left(\pi - \sin^{-1} 0.4 + \dfrac{\pi}{2}\right)\left(\dfrac{365}{2\pi}\right)$. In approximate form the solution interval is $x \in [115, 250]$.

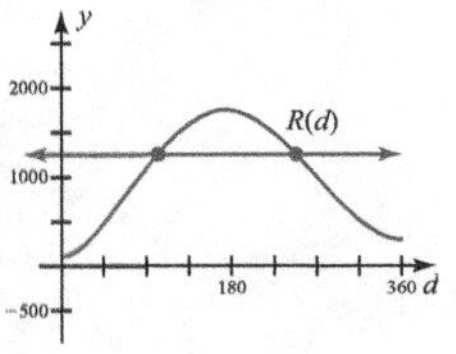

Practice with these ideas by finding solutions to the following inequalities in the intervals specified.

**Exercise 1:** $f(x) = 3 \sin x + 2; f(x) > 3.7; x \in [0, 2\pi)$

**Exercise 2:** $g(x) = 4 \sin\left(x - \dfrac{\pi}{3}\right) - 1; g(x) \le -2; x \in [0, 2\pi)$

**Exercise 3:** $h(x) = 125 \sin\left(\dfrac{\pi}{6}x - \dfrac{\pi}{2}\right) + 175; h(x) \le 150; x \in [0, 12)$

**Exercise 4:** $f(x) = 15{,}750 \sin\left(\dfrac{2\pi}{360}x - \dfrac{\pi}{4}\right) + 19{,}250; f(x) > 25{,}250; x \in [0, 360)$

1. Find $f(\theta)$ for all six trig functions, given $P(-13, 84)$ is on the terminal side with $\theta$ in QII.

2. Find the lengths of the missing sides.

**Exercise 2**
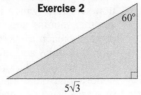

3. Convert $56°20'06''$ to (a) decimal degrees, and (b) radians (round to four places).

4. Verify $\left(-\dfrac{5}{6}, \dfrac{\sqrt{11}}{6}\right)$ is on the unit circle and use it to state the values $\sin t$, $\cos t$, and $\tan t$.

5. Standing 5 mi (26,400 ft) from the base of Mount Logan (Yukon), the angle of elevation to the summit is $36°56'$. How much taller is Mount McKinley (Alaska), which stands at 20,320 ft high?

6. The largest clock face in the world, located in Toi, Japan, has a diameter of 100 ft. To the nearest inch, how far does the tip of the minute hand travel from 1:05 P.M. to 1:37 P.M.? Assume the minute hand has a length of 50 ft.

7. Find all solutions in $[0, 2\pi)$. Round to four decimal places as needed: $3 \sin(2x) + \cos x = 0$.

8. The Petronas Towers in Malaysia are two of the tallest structures in the world. The top of the roof reaches 1483 ft above the street below and the stainless steel pinnacles extend an additional 241 ft into the air (see figure). Find the viewing angle $\theta$ for the pinnacles from a distance of 1000 ft (the angle formed from the base of the antennae to its top).

241 ft

1483 ft

$\theta$

1000 ft

9. A wheel with radius 45 cm is turning at 5 revolutions per second. Find the linear velocity of a point on the rim in kilometers per hour, rounded to the nearest tenth of a kilometer.

10. Find all real solutions to the equation
$$-2 \sin\left(\frac{\pi}{6}x\right) = \sqrt{3}$$

11. Evaluate without using a calculator:
$$\cos\left[\sin^{-1}\left(\frac{1}{2}\right)\right].$$

12. The Earth has a radius of 3960 mi. Tokyo, Japan, is located at 35.4°N latitude, very near the 139°E latitude line. Adelaide, Australia, is at 34.6°S latitude, and also very near 139°E latitude. How many miles separate the two cities?

13. The table shown gives the percentage of the Moon that is illuminated for the days of a particular month, at a given latitude. (a) Use a graphing calculator to find a sinusoidal regression model. (b) If this data applies to May, use the regression model to estimate the percent of the Moon that will be illuminated on June 7.

| Day | % Illum. | Day | % Illum. |
|-----|----------|-----|----------|
| 1   | 15       | 19  | 63       |
| 4   | 41       | 22  | 29       |
| 7   | 69       | 25  | 8        |
| 10  | 91       | 28  | 2        |
| 13  | 100      | 31  | 18       |
| 16  | 90       | —   | —        |

**14.** List the three Pythagorean identities and three identities equivalent to $\cos(2\theta)$.

**15.** For $f(x) = 325 \cos\left(\dfrac{\pi}{6}x - \dfrac{\pi}{2}\right) + 168$, what values of $x$ in $[0, 2\pi)$ satisfy $f(x) > 330.5$?

**16.** The revenue for Otake's Mower Repair is seasonal, with business in the summer months far exceeding business in the winter months. Monthly revenue for the company can be modeled by the function $R(x) = 7.5 \cos\left(\dfrac{\pi}{6}x + \pi\right) + 12.5$, where $R(x)$ is the average revenue (in thousands of dollars) for month $x (x = 1 \rightarrow \text{Jan})$. (a) What is the average revenue for October? (b) For what months of the year is revenue more than $16,250?

**17.** Use the triangle given to find the exact value of $\sin(2\theta)$.

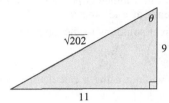

**18.** Write the equation of the function whose graph is given in terms of a sine function.

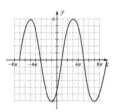

**19.** Verify that the following is an identity:
$$\frac{\cos x + 1}{\tan^2 x} = \frac{\cos x}{\sec x - 1}$$

**20.** The amount of waste product released by a manufacturing company varies according to its production schedule, which is much heavier during the summer months and lighter in the winter. Waste products reach a maximum of 32.5 tons in the month of July, and falls to a minimum of 21.7 tons in January $(t = 1)$. (a) Use this information to build a sinusoidal equation that models the amount of waste produced each month. (b) During what months of the year does output exceed 30 tons?

# Applications of
# Trigonometry

# Applications of Trigonometry

## CHAPTER CONNECTIONS

When an airline pilot charts a course, it's not as simple as pointing the airplane in the right direction. Wind currents must be taken into consideration, and compensated for by additional thrust or a change of heading that will help equalize the force of the wind and keep the plane flying in the desired direction. The effect of these forces working together can be modeled using a carefully drawn *vector diagram*, and with the aid of trigonometry, a pilot can easily determine any adjustments in navigation needed.

▶ This application appears as
Exercise 85 in Section 7.3.

## Learning Objectives

*In Section 7.1 you will learn how to:*

☐ **A.** Develop the law of sines and use it to solve ASA and AAS triangles

☐ **B.** Solve SSA triangles (the ambiguous case) using the law of sines

☐ **C.** Use the law of sines to solve applications

Many applications of trigonometry involve *oblique triangles*, or triangles that do not have a 90° angle. For example, suppose a trolley carries passengers from ground level up to a mountain chateau, as shown in Figure 7.1. Assuming the cable could be held taut, what is its approximate length? Can we also determine the slant height of the mountain? To answer questions like these, we'll develop techniques that enable us to solve acute and obtuse triangles using fundamental trigonometric relationships.

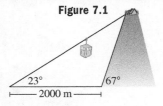

**Figure 7.1**

### A. The Law of Sines and Unique Solutions

Consider the oblique triangle *ABC* pictured in Figure 7.2. Since it is not a right triangle, it seems the trigonometric ratios studied earlier cannot be applied. But if we draw the altitude *h* (from vertex *B*), two right triangles are formed that *share a common side.* By applying the sine ratio to angles *A* and *C*, we can develop a relationship that will help us solve the triangle.

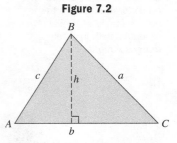

**Figure 7.2**

For $\angle A$ we have $\sin A = \dfrac{h}{c}$ or $h = c \sin A$. For

$\angle C$ we have $\sin C = \dfrac{h}{a}$ or $h = a \sin C$. Since both products are equal to *h*, the transitive property gives $c \sin A = a \sin C$, which leads to

$$c \sin A = a \sin C \quad \text{since } h = h$$

$$\frac{c \sin A}{ac} = \frac{a \sin C}{ac} \quad \text{divide by } ac$$

$$\frac{\sin A}{a} = \frac{\sin C}{c} \quad \text{simplify}$$

Using the same triangle and the altitude drawn from *C* (Figure 7.3), we note a similar relationship involving angles *A* and *B*: $\sin A = \dfrac{h}{b}$ or $h = b \sin A$, and

$\sin B = \dfrac{h}{a}$ or $h = a \sin B$. As before, we can then write $\dfrac{\sin A}{a} = \dfrac{\sin B}{b}$. If $\angle A$ is obtuse, the altitude *h* actually falls outside the triangle, as shown in Figure 7.4. In this case, consider that $\sin(180° - \alpha) = \sin \alpha$ from the difference formula for sines (Exercise 55, Section 5.2). In the figure we note $\sin(180° - \alpha) = \dfrac{h}{c} = \sin \alpha$, yielding $h = c \sin \alpha$

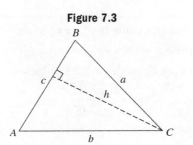

**Figure 7.3**

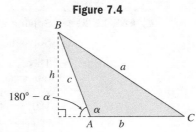

**Figure 7.4**

and the preceding relationship can now be stated using any pair of angles and corresponding sides. The result is called the **law of sines,** which is usually stated by combining the three possible proportions.

---

### The Law of Sines

For any triangle $ABC$, the ratio of the sine of an angle to the side opposite that angle is constant:

$$\frac{\sin A}{a} = \frac{\sin B}{b} = \frac{\sin C}{c}$$

---

**WORTHY OF NOTE**

The case where three angles are known (AAA) is not considered since we then have a family of similar triangles, with infinitely many solutions.

As a proportional relationship, the law requires that we have three parts in order to solve for the fourth. This suggests the following possibilities:

**1.** two angles and an included side (ASA)
**2.** two angles and a side opposite one of these angles (AAS)
**3.** two sides and an angle opposite one of these sides (SSA)
**4.** two sides and an included angle (SAS)
**5.** three sides (SSS)

Each of these possibilities is diagrammed in Figures 7.5 through 7.9.

**WORTHY OF NOTE**

When working with triangles, keeping these basic properties in mind will prevent errors and assist in their solution:

1. The angles must sum to 180°.
2. The combined length of any two sides must exceed the length of the third side.
3. Longer sides will be opposite larger angles.
4. The sine of an angle cannot be greater than 1.
5. For $y \in (0, 1)$, the equation $y = \sin \theta$ has two solutions in $(0°, 180°)$ that are supplements.

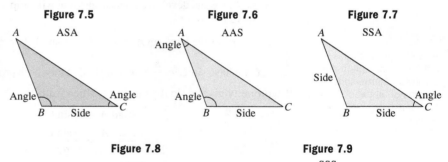

**Figure 7.5** — ASA          **Figure 7.6** — AAS          **Figure 7.7** — SSA

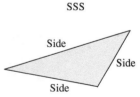

**Figure 7.8** — SAS          **Figure 7.9** — SSS

Since applying the law of sines requires we have a given side opposite a known angle, it cannot be used in the case of SAS or SSS triangles. These require the law of cosines, which we will develop in Section 7.2. In the case of ASA and AAS triangles, a unique triangle is formed since the measure of the third angle is fixed by the two angles given (they must sum to 180°) and the remaining sides must be of fixed length.

---

**EXAMPLE 1** ▶ **Solving a Triangle Using the Law of Sines**

Solve the triangle shown, and state your answer using a table.

**Solution** ▶ This is *not* a right triangle, so the standard ratios cannot be used. Since $\angle B$ and $\angle C$ are given, we know $\angle A = 180° - (110° + 32°) = 38°$. With $\angle A$ and side $a$, we have

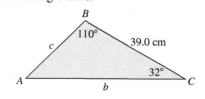

**WORTHY OF NOTE**

Although not a definitive check, always review the solution table to ensure the smallest side is opposite the smallest angle, the largest side is opposite the largest angle, and so on. If this is not the case, you should go back and check your work.

$$\frac{\sin A}{a} = \frac{\sin B}{b} \quad \text{law of sines applied to } \angle A \text{ and } \angle B$$

$$\frac{\sin 38°}{39} = \frac{\sin 110°}{b} \quad \text{substitute given values}$$

$$b \sin 38° = 39 \sin 110° \quad \text{multiply by } 39b$$

$$b = \frac{39 \sin 110°}{\sin 38°} \quad \text{divide by } \sin 38°$$

$$b \approx 59.5 \quad \text{result}$$

Repeating this procedure using $\frac{\sin A}{a} = \frac{\sin C}{c}$ shows side $c \approx 33.6$ cm. In table form we have

| Angles | Sides (cm) |
|---|---|
| $A = 38°$ | $\mathbf{a = 39.0}$ |
| $\mathbf{B = 110°}$ | $b \approx 59.5$ |
| $\mathbf{C = 32°}$ | $c \approx 33.6$ |

**A. You've just learned how to develop the law of sines and use it to solve ASA and AAS triangles**

Now try Exercises 7 through 24 ▶

## B. Solving SSA Triangles—The Ambiguous Case

Figure 7.10

To understand the concept of unique and nonunique solutions regarding the law of sines, consider an instructor who asks a large group of students to draw a triangle with sides of 15 and 12 units, and a nonincluded 25° angle. Unavoidably, three different solutions will be offered (see Figure 7.10). For the SSA case, there is some doubt as to the number of solutions possible, or whether a solution even exists.

To further understand why, consider a triangle with side $c = 30$ cm, $\angle A = 30°$, and side $a$ opposite the 30° angle (Figure 7.11—note the length of side $b$ is yet to be determined). From our work with 30-60-90 triangles, we know if $a = 15$ cm, it is exactly the length needed to form a right triangle (Figure 7.12).

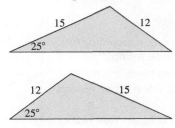

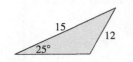

Figure 7.11

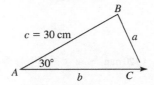

Figure 7.12

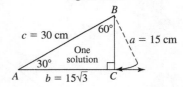

By varying the length of side $a$, we note three other possibilities. If side $a < 15$ cm, no triangle is possible since $a$ is too short to contact side $b$ (Figure 7.13), while if 15 cm $<$ side $a < 30$ cm, two triangles are possible since side $a$ will then intersect side $b$ at two points, $C_1$ and $C_2$ (Figure 7.14).

For future use, note that when two triangles are possible, angles $C_1$ and $C_2$ must be supplements since an isosceles triangle is formed. Finally, if side $a > 30$ cm, it will

Figure 7.13

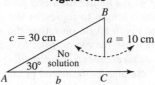

Figure 7.14

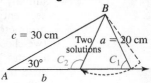

**Figure 7.15**

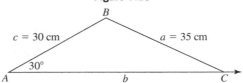

intersect side $b$ only once, forming the obtuse triangle shown in Figure 7.15, where we've assumed $a = 35$ cm. Since the final solution is in doubt until we do further work, the SSA case is called the **ambiguous case** of the law of sines.

---

**EXAMPLE 2** ▶ **Analyzing the Ambiguous Case of the Law of Sines**

Given triangle $ABC$ with $\angle A = 45°$ and side $c = 100\sqrt{2}$ mm,

**a.** What length for side $a$ will produce a right triangle where $\angle C = 90°$?

**b.** How many triangles can be formed if side $a = 90$ mm?

**c.** If side $a = 120$ mm, how many triangles can be formed?

**d.** If side $a = 145$ mm, how many triangles can be formed?

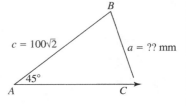

Solution ▶ **a.** Recognizing the sides of a 45-45-90 triangle are in proportion according to $1x:1x:\sqrt{2}x$, side $a$ must be 100 mm for a right triangle to be formed.

**b.** If $a = 90$ mm, it will be too short to contact side $b$ and no triangle is possible.

**c.** As shown in Figure 7.16, if $a = 120$ mm, it will contact side $b$ in two distinct places and two triangles are possible.

**d.** If $a = 145$ mm, it will contact side $b$ only once, since it is longer than side $c$ and will "miss" intersecting side $b$ a second time as it pivots around $\angle B$ (see Figure 7.17). One triangle is possible.

**Figure 7.16**            **Figure 7.17**

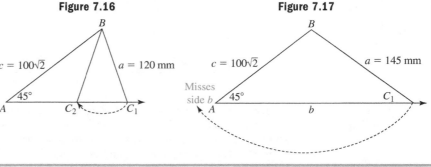

Now try Exercises 25 and 26 ▶

For a better understanding of the SSA (ambiguous) case, scaled drawings can initially be used along with a metric ruler and protractor. Begin with a horizontal line segment of undetermined length to represent the third (unknown) side, and use the protractor to draw the given angle on either the left or right side of this segment (we chose the left). Then use the metric ruler to draw an adjacent side of appropriate length, *choosing a scale that enables a complete diagram*. For instance, if the given sides are 3 ft and 5 ft, use 3 cm and 5 cm instead (1 cm = 1 ft). If the sides are 80 mi and 120 mi, use 8 cm and 12 cm (1 cm = 10 mi), and so on. Once the adjacent side is drawn, start at the free endpoint and draw a vertical segment to represent the remaining side. A careful sketch will often indicate whether none, one, or two triangles are possible (see the *Reinforcing Basic Concepts* feature on page 343).

---

**EXAMPLE 3** ▶ **Solving the Ambiguous Case of the Law of Sines**

Solve the triangle with side $b = 100$ ft, side $c = 60$ ft, and $\angle C = 28.0°$.

**Solution** ▶ Two sides and an angle opposite are given (SSA), and we draw a diagram to help determine the possibilities. Draw the horizontal segment of some length and use a protractor to mark $\angle C = 28°$. Then draw a segment 10 cm long (to represent $b = 100$ ft) as the adjacent side of the angle, with a vertical segment 6 cm long from the free end of $b$ (to represent $c = 60$ ft). It seems apparent that side $c$ will intersect the horizontal side in two places (see figure), and two triangles are possible. We apply the law of sines to solve the first triangle, whose features we'll note with a subscript of 1.

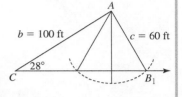

$$\frac{\sin B_1}{b} = \frac{\sin C}{c} \qquad \text{law of sines}$$

$$\frac{\sin B_1}{100} = \frac{\sin 28°}{60} \qquad \text{substitute}$$

$$\sin B_1 = \frac{5}{3} \sin 28° \qquad \text{solve for } \sin B_1$$

$$B_1 \approx 51.5° \qquad \text{apply arcsine}$$

Since $\angle B_1 + \angle B_2 = 180°$, we know $\angle B_2 \approx 128.5°$. These values give $100.5°$ and $23.5°$ as the measures of $\angle A_1$ and $\angle A_2$, respectively. By once again applying the law of sines to each triangle, we find side $a_1 \approx 125.7$ ft and $a_2 \approx 51.0$ ft. See Figure 7.18.

**WORTHY OF NOTE**

In Example 3, we found $\angle B_2$ using the property that states the angles must be supplements (see the isosceles triangle comment on bottom of page 318). We could also view $\angle B_1$ as a QI reference angle, which also gives a QII solution of $(180 - 51.5)° = 128.5°$.

| Angles | Sides (ft) |
|---|---|
| $A_1 \approx 100.5°$ | $a_1 \approx 125.7$ |
| $B_1 \approx 51.5°$ | $b = 100$ |
| $C = 28°$ | $c = 60$ |

| Angles | Sides (ft) |
|---|---|
| $A_2 \approx 23.5°$ | $a_2 \approx 51.0$ |
| $B_2 \approx 128.5°$ | $b = 100$ |
| $C = 28°$ | $c = 60$ |

**Figure 7.18**

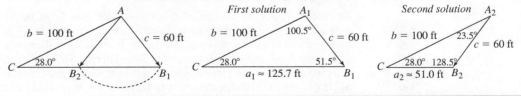

Now try Exercises 27 through 32 ▶

Admittedly, the scaled drawing approach has some drawbacks—it takes time to draw the diagrams and is of little use if the situation is a close call. It does, however, offer a deeper understanding of the subtleties involved in solving the SSA case. Instead of a scaled drawing, we can use a simple sketch *as a guide*, while keeping in mind the properties mentioned in the *Worthy of Note* on page 317.

EXAMPLE 4 ▶ **Solving the Ambiguous Case of the Law of Sines**

Solve the triangle with side $a = 220$ ft, side $b = 200$ ft, and $\angle A = 40°$.

Solution ▶ The information given is again SSA, and we apply the law of sines with this in mind.

$$\frac{\sin A}{a} = \frac{\sin B}{b} \qquad \text{law of sines}$$

$$\frac{\sin 40°}{220} = \frac{\sin B}{200} \qquad \text{substitute}$$

$$\sin B = \frac{200 \sin 40°}{220} \qquad \text{solve for } \sin B$$

$$B_1 \approx 35.7° \qquad \text{apply arcsine}$$

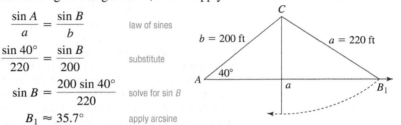

This is the solution from Quadrant I. The QII solution is about $(180 - 35.7)° = 144.3°$. At this point our solution tables have this form:

| Angles | Sides (ft) |
|---|---|
| $A = 40°$ | $a = 220$ |
| $B_1 \approx 35.7°$ | $b = 200$ |
| $C_1 =$ | $c_1 =$ |

| Angles | Sides (ft) |
|---|---|
| $A = 40°$ | $a = 220$ |
| $B_2 \approx 144.3°$ | $b = 200$ |
| $C_2 =$ | $c_2 =$ |

☑ **B. You've just learned how to solve SSA triangles (the ambiguous case) using the law of sines**

It seems reasonable to once again find the remaining angles and finish by reapplying the law of sines, but observe that the sum of the two angles from the second solution *already exceeds 180°*: $40° + 144.3° = 184.3°$! This means no second solution is possible (side $a$ is too long). We find that $C_1 \approx 104.3°$, and applying the law of sines gives a value of $c_1 \approx 331.7$ ft.

**Now try Exercises 33 through 44 ▶**

## C. Applications of the Law of Sines

As "ambiguous" as it is, the ambiguous case has a number of applications in engineering, astronomy, physics, and other areas. Here is an example from astronomy.

EXAMPLE 5 ▶ **Solving an Application of the Ambiguous Case—Planetary Distance**

The planet Venus can be seen from Earth with the naked eye, but as the diagram indicates, the position of Venus is uncertain (we are unable to tell if Venus is in the near position or the far position). Given the Earth is 93 million miles from the Sun and Venus is 67 million miles from the Sun, determine the closest and farthest possible distances that separate the planets in this alignment. Assume a viewing angle of $\theta \approx 18°$ and that the orbits of both planets are roughly circular.

Solution ▶ A close look at the information and diagram shows a SSA case. Begin by applying the law of sines where $E \to$ Earth, $V \to$ Venus, and $S \to$ Sun.

$$\frac{\sin E}{e} = \frac{\sin V}{v} \qquad \text{law of sines}$$

$$\frac{\sin 18°}{67} = \frac{\sin V}{93} \qquad \text{substitute given values}$$

$$\sin V = \frac{93 \sin 18°}{67} \qquad \text{solve for sin } V$$

$$V \approx 25.4° \qquad \text{apply arcsine}$$

This is the angle $V_1$ formed when Venus is farthest away. The angle $V_2$ at the closer distance is $180° - 25.4° = 154.6°$. At this point, our solution tables have this form:

| Angles | Sides ($10^6$ mi) |
|---|---|
| $E = 18°$ | $e = 67$ |
| $V_1 \approx 25.4°$ | $v = 93$ |
| $S_1 =$ | $s_1 =$ |

| Angles | Sides ($10^6$ mi) |
|---|---|
| $E = 18°$ | $e = 67$ |
| $V_2 = 154.6°$ | $v = 93$ |
| $S_2 =$ | $s_2 =$ |

For $S_1$ and $S_2$ we have $S_1 \approx 180° - (18° + 25.4°) = 136.6°$ (larger angle) and $S_2 \approx 180° - (18° + 154.6°) = 7.4°$ (smaller angle). Re-applying the law of sines for $s_1$ shows the farther distance between the planets is about 149 million miles. Solving for $s_2$ shows that the closer distance is approximately 28 million miles.

**Now try Exercises 47 and 48** ▶

---

**EXAMPLE 6** ▶ **Solving an Application of the Ambiguous Case — Radar Detection**

As shown in Figure 7.19, a radar ship is 30.0 mi off shore when a large fleet of ships leaves port at an angle of 43.0°.

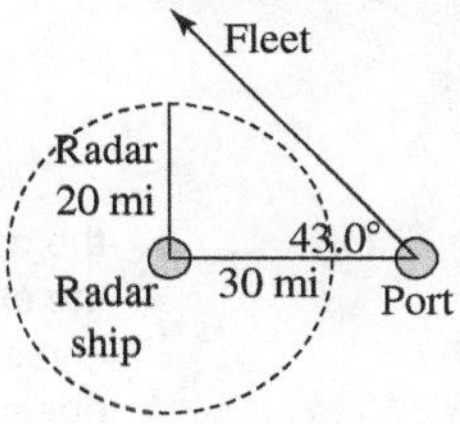

**a.** If the maximum range of the ship's radar is 20.0 mi, will the departing fleet be detected?

**b.** If the maximum range of the ship's radar is 25.0 mi, how far from port is the fleet when it is first detected?

**Figure 7.19**

**Solution** ▶ **a.** This is again the SSA (ambiguous) case. Applying the law of sines gives

$$\frac{\sin 43°}{20} = \frac{\sin \theta}{30} \qquad \text{law of sines}$$

$$\sin \theta = \frac{30 \sin 43°}{20} \qquad \text{solve for } \sin \theta$$

$$\sin \theta \approx 1.02299754 \qquad \text{result}$$

No triangle is possible and the departing fleet will not be detected.

**b.** If the radar has a range of 25.0 mi, the radar beam will intersect the projected course of the fleet in two places.

$$\frac{\sin 43°}{25} = \frac{\sin \theta}{30} \qquad \text{law of sines}$$

$$\sin \theta = \frac{30 \sin 43°}{25} \qquad \text{solve for } \sin \theta$$

$$\theta \approx 54.9° \qquad \text{apply arcsine}$$

**Figure 7.20**

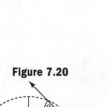

This is the acute angle $\theta$ related to the *farthest point* from port at which the fleet could be detected (see Figure 7.20). For the second triangle, we have $180° - 54.9° = 125.1°$ (the obtuse angle) giving a measure of $180° - (125.1° + 43°) = 11.9°$ for angle $\alpha$. For $d$ as the side opposite $\alpha$ we have

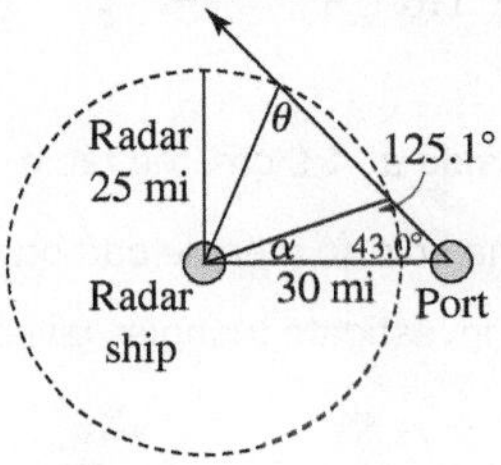

$$\frac{\sin 43°}{25} = \frac{\sin 11.9°}{d} \qquad \text{law of sines}$$

$$d = \frac{25 \sin 11.9°}{\sin 43°} \qquad \text{solve for } d$$

$$\approx 7.6 \qquad \text{simplify}$$

This shows the fleet is first detected about 7.6 mi from port.

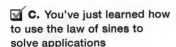 **C.** You've just learned how to use the law of sines to solve applications

**Now try Exercises 49 and 50** ▶

There are a number of additional, interesting applications in the exercise set (**see Exercises 51 through 70**).

## TECHNOLOGY HIGHLIGHT

## Using TABLES to Understand the Law of Sines

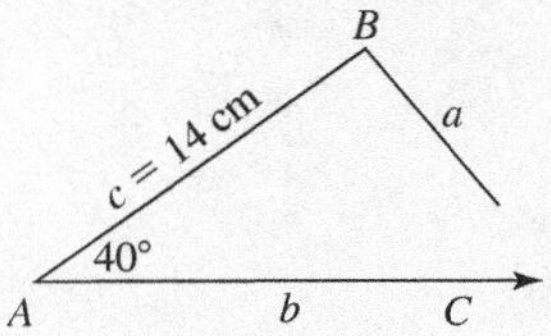

Using the TABLE feature of a graphing calculator can increase our understanding of the ambiguous case. Consider the "unfinished" $\triangle ABC$ shown in Figure 7.21, and the following questions:

**Figure 7.21**

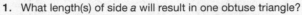

1.  What length(s) of side $a$ will result in one obtuse triangle?
2.  What length(s) of side $a$ will result in two triangles?
3.  What length(s) of side $a$ will result in one right triangle?

We can easily answer all three questions with the TABLE feature of a graphing calculator. Using the law of sines we have the following sequence:

$$\frac{\sin C}{14} = \frac{\sin 40°}{a}$$

$$\sin C = \frac{14 \sin 40°}{a}$$

$$C = \sin^{-1}\left(\frac{14 \sin 40°}{a}\right)$$

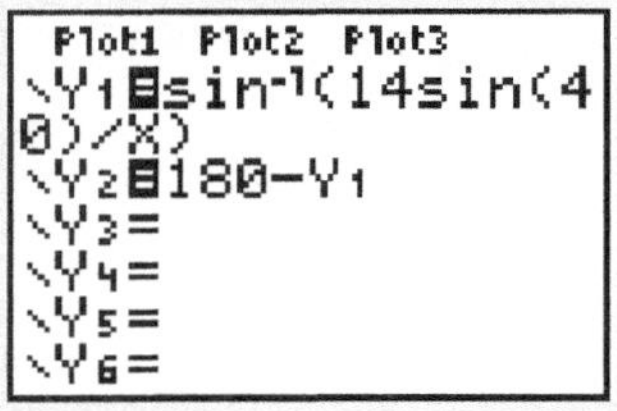

We can enter this expression for $\angle C$ as $Y_1$ on the [ Y= ] screen of the calculator (see Figure 7.22), then use the TABLE feature to evaluate the expression *for different lengths of side a*. The expression for $Y_2$ gives the second value for $\angle C$ if two triangles are possible. A casual observation shows that side $a$ must be 14 cm or longer to answer question 1. For $a > 14$ cm, side $a$ will intersect side $b$ one time (to the right) and miss side $b$ entirely (to the left) as it pivots at vertex $B$. To investigate other possibilities for side $a$, set up the TBLSET screen ( [ 2nd ] [ WINDOW ] ), as shown in Figure 7.23, which has us start at $a = 14$ and counting backward by 1's ($\Delta$Tbl $= -1$). Pressing [ 2nd ] [ GRAPH ] **(TABLE)** produces the TABLE shown in Figure 7.24. Note when $a = 14$, angle $C = 40°$ and an isosceles triangle is formed (base angles are equal). For $9 < x < 14$, two triangles are formed. Figure 7.25 shows the case where

**Figure 7.22**

```
Plot1  Plot2  Plot3
\Y1■sin⁻¹(14sin(4
0)/X)
\Y2■180-Y1
\Y3=
\Y4=
\Y5=
\Y6=
```

**Figure 7.23**

```
TABLE SETUP
 TblStart=14
 ∆Tbl=⁻1
Indpnt: Auto  Ask
Depend: Auto  Ask
```

**Figure 7.24**

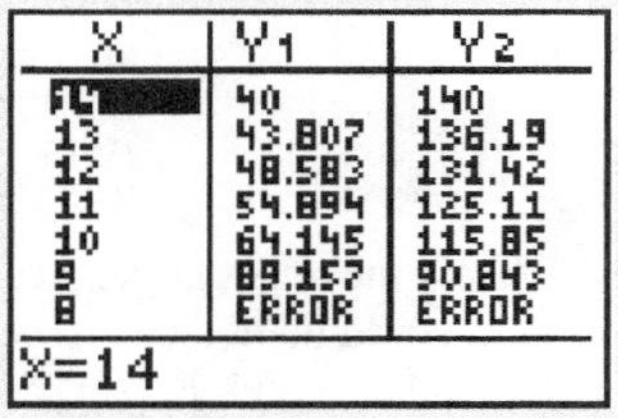

| X  | Y₁     | Y₂     |
|----|--------|--------|
| 14 | 40     | 140    |
| 13 | 43.807 | 136.19 |
| 12 | 48.583 | 131.42 |
| 11 | 54.894 | 125.11 |
| 10 | 64.145 | 115.85 |
| 9  | 89.157 | 90.843 |
| 8  | ERROR  | ERROR  |

X=14

**Figure 7.25**

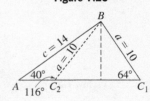

side $a \approx 10$ cm. When side $a \approx 9$ cm, a single right triangle is formed. When side $a < 9$ cm, the table returns an error message because the value of $\left[\dfrac{14 \sin 40°}{a}\right]$ is greater than one and no triangle can be formed. Use a diagram similar to the one shown and these ideas/methods to investigate triangles given the following conditions:

**Exercise 1:**   $\angle A = 35°$, side $c = 25$ mm, side $a = $ ____.
**Exercise 2:**   $\angle A = 30°$, side $c = 8$ in., side $a = $ ____.
**Exercise 3:**   $\angle C = 52°$, side $a = 27.5$ cm, side $c = $ ____.

## 7.1 EXERCISES

▶ **CONCEPTS AND VOCABULARY**

**Fill in each blank with the appropriate word or phrase. Carefully reread the section if needed.**

1. For the law of sines, if two sides and an angle opposite one side are given, this is referred to as the _____ case, since the solution is in doubt until further work.

2. Two inviolate properties of a triangle that can be used to help solve the ambiguous case are: (a) the angles must sum to _____ and (b) no sine ratio can exceed _____.

3. For positive $k$, the equation $\sin \theta = k$ has two solutions, one in Quadrant _____ and the other in Quadrant _____.

4. After a triangle is solved, you should always check to ensure that the _____ side is opposite the _____ angle.

5. In your own words, explain why the AAS case results in a unique solution while the SSA case does not. Give supporting diagrams.

6. Explain why no triangle is possible in each case:
   a. $A = 34°, B = 73°, C = 52°,$
      $a = 14', b = 22', c = 18'$
   b. $A = 42°, B = 57°, C = 81°,$
      $a = 7'', b = 9'', c = 22''$

▶ **DEVELOPING YOUR SKILLS**

**Solve each of the following equations for the unknown part (if possible). Round sides to the nearest hundredth and degrees to the nearest tenth.**

7. $\dfrac{\sin 32°}{15} = \dfrac{\sin 18.5°}{a}$

8. $\dfrac{\sin 52°}{b} = \dfrac{\sin 30°}{12}$

9. $\dfrac{\sin 63°}{21.9} = \dfrac{\sin C}{18.6}$

10. $\dfrac{\sin B}{3.14} = \dfrac{\sin 105°}{6.28}$

11. $\dfrac{\sin C}{48.5} = \dfrac{\sin 19°}{43.2}$

12. $\dfrac{\sin 38°}{125} = \dfrac{\sin B}{190}$

**Solve each triangle using the law of sines. If the law of sines cannot be used, state why. Draw and label a triangle or label the triangle given before you begin.**

13. side $a = 75$ cm
    $\angle A = 38°$
    $\angle B = 64°$

14. side $b = 385$ m
    $\angle B = 47°$
    $\angle A = 108°$

15. side $b = 10\sqrt{3}$ in.
    $\angle A = 30°$
    $\angle B = 60°$

16.
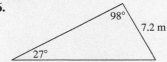

17.
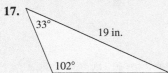

18.
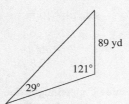

19. $\angle A = 45°$
    $\angle B = 45°$
    side $c = 15\sqrt{2}$ mi

20. $\angle A = 20.4°$
    side $c = 12.9$ mi
    $\angle B = 63.4°$

21. $\angle B = 103.4°$
    side $a = 42.7$ km
    $\angle C = 19.6°$

22.
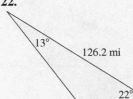

23.
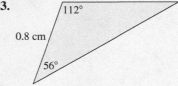

24.
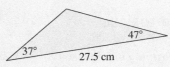

**Answer each question and justify your response using a diagram, but do not solve.**

25. Given △ABC with ∠A = 30° and side c = 20 cm, (a) what length for side a will produce a right triangle? (b) How many triangles can be formed if side a = 8 cm? (c) If side a = 12 cm, how many triangles can be formed? (d) If side a = 25 cm, how many triangles can be formed?

26. Given △ABC with ∠A = 60° and side c = 6√3 m, (a) what length for side a will produce a right triangle? (b) How many triangles can be formed if side a = 8 m? (c) If side a = 10 m, how many triangles can be formed? (d) If side a = 15 m, how many triangles can be formed?

**Solve using the law of sines and a scaled drawing. If two triangles exist, solve both completely.**

27. side b = 385 m
∠B = 67°
side a = 490 m

28. side a = 36.5 yd
∠B = 67°
side b = 12.9 yd

29. side c = 25.8 mi
∠A = 30°
side a = 12.9 mi

30. side c = 10√3 in.
∠A = 60°
side a = 15 in.

31. side c = 58 mi
∠C = 59°
side b = 67 mi

32. side b = 24.9 km
∠B = 45°
side a = 32.8 km

**Use the law of sines to determine if no triangle, one triangle, or two triangles can be formed from the diagrams given (diagrams *may not be to scale*), then solve. If two solutions exist, solve both completely. Note the arrowhead marks the side of undetermined length.**

33.
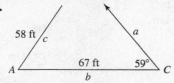

34.
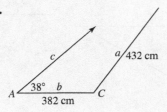

35.
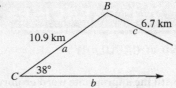

36.
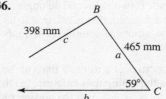

37.
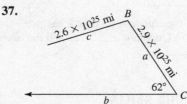

38.
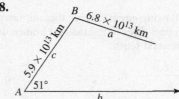

**For Exercises 39 to 44, assume the law of sines is being applied to solve a triangle. Solve for the unknown angle (if possible), then determine if a second angle (0° < θ < 180°) exists that also satisfies the proportion.**

39. $\dfrac{\sin A}{12} = \dfrac{\sin 48°}{27}$

40. $\dfrac{\sin 60°}{32} = \dfrac{\sin B}{9}$

41. $\dfrac{\sin 57°}{35.6} = \dfrac{\sin C}{40.2}$

42. $\dfrac{\sin B}{5.2} = \dfrac{\sin 65°}{4.9}$

43. $\dfrac{\sin A}{280} = \dfrac{\sin 15°}{52}$

44. $\dfrac{\sin 29°}{121} = \dfrac{\sin B}{321}$

▶ **WORKING WITH FORMULAS**

45. **Triple angle formula for sine: $\sin(3\theta) = 3\sin\theta - 4\sin^3\theta$**

Most students are familiar with the double-angle formula for sine: $\sin(2\theta) = 2\sin\theta\cos\theta$. The triple-angle formula for sine is given here. Use the formula to find an exact value for sin 135°, then verify the result using a reference angle.

**46. Radius of a circumscribed circle:** $R = \dfrac{b}{2 \sin B}$

Given $\triangle ABC$ is circumscribed by a circle of radius $R$, the radius of the circle can be found using the formula shown, where side $b$ is opposite angle $B$. Find the radius of the circle shown.

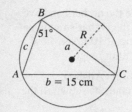

▶ **APPLICATIONS**

**47. Planetary distances:** In a solar system that parallels our own, the planet Sorus can be seen from a Class M planet with the naked eye, but as the diagram indicates, the position of Sorus is uncertain. Assume the orbits of both planets are roughly circular and that the viewing angle $\theta$ is about 20°. If the Class M planet is 82 million miles from its sun and Sorus is 51 million miles from this sun, determine the closest and farthest possible distances that separate the planets in this alignment.

**Exercise 47**

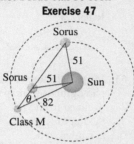

**48. Planetary distances:** In a solar system that parallels our own, the planet Cirrus can be seen from a Class M planet with the naked eye, but as the diagram indicates, the position of Cirrus is uncertain. Assume the orbits of both planets are roughly circular and that the viewing angle $\theta$ is about 15°. If the Class M planet is 105 million miles from its sun and Cirrus is 70 million miles from this sun, determine the closest and farthest possible distances that separate the planets in this alignment.

**Exercise 48**

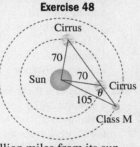

**49. Radar detection:** A radar ship is 15.0 mi off shore from a major port when a large fleet of ships leaves the port at the 35.0° angle shown. (a) If the maximum range of the ship's radar is 8.0 mi, will the departing fleet be detected? (b) If the maximum range of the ship's radar is 12 mi, how far from port is the fleet when it is first detected?

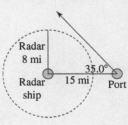

**50. Motion detection:** To notify environmentalists of the presence of big game, motion detectors are installed 200 yd from a watering hole. A pride of lions has just visited the hole and is leaving the area at the 29.0° angle shown. (a) If the maximum range of the motion detector is 90 yd, will the pride be detected? (b) If the maximum range of the motion detector is 120 yd, how far from the watering hole is the pride when first detected?

**Exercise 50**

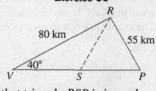

**51. Distance between cities:** The cities of Van Gogh, Rembrandt, Pissarro, and Seurat are situated as shown in the diagram. Assume that triangle $RSP$ is isosceles and use the law of sines to find the distance between Van Gogh and Seurat, and between Van Gogh and Pissarro.

**Exercise 51**

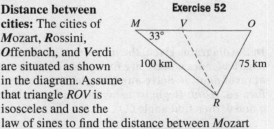

**52. Distance between cities:** The cities of Mozart, Rossini, Offenbach, and Verdi are situated as shown in the diagram. Assume that triangle $ROV$ is isosceles and use the law of sines to find the distance between Mozart and Verdi, and between Mozart and Offenbach.

**Exercise 52**

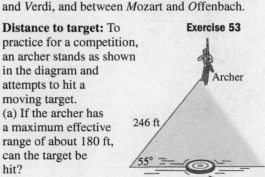

**53. Distance to target:** To practice for a competition, an archer stands as shown in the diagram and attempts to hit a moving target. (a) If the archer has a maximum effective range of about 180 ft, can the target be hit?

**Exercise 53**

(b) What is the shortest range the archer can have and still hit the target? (c) If the archer's range is 215 ft and the target is moving at 10 ft/sec, how many seconds is the target within range?

**54. Distance to target:** As part of an All-Star competition, a quarterback stands as shown in the diagram and attempts to hit a moving target with a football. (a) If the quarterback has a maximum effective range of about 35 yd, can the target be hit? (b) What is the shortest range the quarterback can have and still hit the target? (c) If the quarterback's range is 45 yd and the target is moving at 5 yd/sec, how many seconds is the target within range?

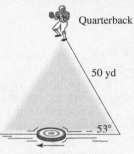

**In Exercises 55 and 56, three rods are attached via pivot joints so the rods can be manipulated to form a triangle. How many triangles can be formed if angle *B* must measure 26°? If one triangle, solve it. If two, solve both. Diagrams are not drawn to scale.**

**55.**

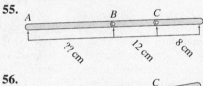

**56.**

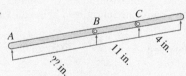

**In the diagrams given, the measure of angle *C* and the length of sides *a* and *c* are fixed. Side *c* can be rotated at pivot point *B*. Solve any triangles that can be formed. (*Hint:* Begin by using the grid to find lengths *a* and *c*, then find angle *C*.)**

**57.**

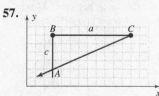

**58.**

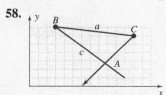

**Length of a rafter:** Determine the length of both roof rafters in the diagrams given.

**59.**

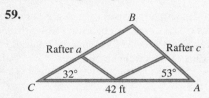

**60.**

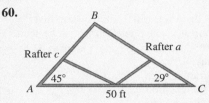

**61. Map distance:** A cartographer is using aerial photographs to prepare a map for publication. The distance from Sexton to Rhymes is known to be 27.2 km. Using a protractor, the map maker measures an angle of 96° from Sexton to Tarryson (a newly developed area) and an angle of 58° from Rhymes to Tarryson. Compute each unknown distance.

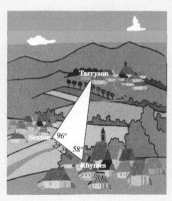

**62. Height of a fortress:** An ancient fortress is built on a steep hillside, with the base of the fortress walls making a 102° angle with the hill. At the moment the fortress casts a 112-ft shadow, the angle of elevation from the tip of the shadow to the top of the wall is 32°. What is the distance from the base of the fortress to the top of the tower?

**Exercise 62**

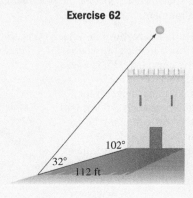

**63. Distance to a fire:** In Yellowstone Park, a fire is spotted by park rangers stationed in two towers that are known to be 5 mi apart. Using the line between them as a baseline, tower A reports the fire is at an angle of 39°, while tower B reports an angle of 58°. How far is the fire from the closer tower?

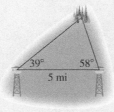

**64. Width of a canyon:** To find the distance across Waimea Canyon (on the island of Kauai), a surveyor marks a 1000-m baseline along the southern rim. Using a transit, she sights on a large rock formation on the north rim, and finds the angles indicated. How wide is the canyon from point *B* to point *C*?

**Exercise 64**

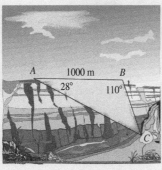

**65. Height of a blimp:** When the Good-Year Blimp is viewed from the field-level bleachers near the southern end-zone of a football stadium, the angle of elevation is 62°. From the field-level bleachers near the northern end-zone, the angle of elevation is 70°. Find the height of the blimp if the distance from the southern bleachers to the northern bleachers is 145 yd.

**Exercise 65**

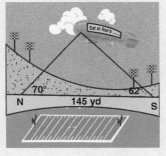

**66. Height of a blimp:** The rock-n-roll group *Pink Floyd* just finished their most recent tour and has moored their touring blimp at a hangar near the airport in Indianapolis, Indiana. From an unknown distance away, the angle of elevation is measured at 26.5°. After moving 110 yd closer, the angle of elevation has become 48.3°. At what height is the blimp moored?

**67. Circumscribed triangles:** A triangle is circumscribed within the upper semicircle drawn in the figure. Use the law of sines to solve the triangle given the measures shown. What is the diameter of the circle? What do you notice about the triangle?

**Exercises 67 and 68**

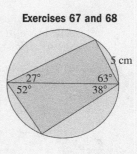

**68. Circumscribed triangles:** A triangle is circumscribed within the lower semicircle shown. Use the law of sines to solve the triangle given the measures shown. How long is the longer chord? What do you notice about the triangle?

**69. Height of a mountain:** Approaching from the west, a group of hikers notes the angle of elevation to the summit of a steep mountain is 35° at a distance of 1250 meters. Arriving at the base of the mountain, they estimate this side of the mountain has an average slope of 48°. (a) Find the slant height of the mountain's west side. (b) Find the slant height of the east side of the mountain, if the east side has an average slope of 65°. (c) How tall is the mountain?

**Exercise 69**

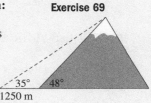

**70. Distance on a map:** Coffeyville and Liberal, Kansas, lie along the state's southern border and are roughly 298 mi apart. Olathe, Kansas, is very near the state's eastern border at an angle of 23° with Liberal and 72° with Coffeyville (using the southern border as one side of the angle). (a) Compute the distance between these cities. (b) What is the shortest (straight line) distance from Olathe to the southern border of Kansas?

**Exercise 70**

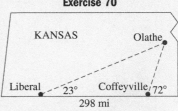

▶ **EXTENDING THE CONCEPT**

**71.** Solve the triangle shown in three ways—first by using the law of sines, second using right triangle trigonometry, and third using the standard 30-60-90 triangle. Was one method "easier" than the others? Use these connections to express the irrational number $\sqrt{3}$ as a quotient of two trigonometric functions of an angle. Can you find a similar expression for $\sqrt{2}$?

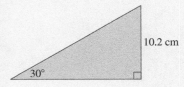

**72.** Use the law of sines and any needed identities to solve the triangle shown.

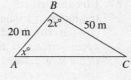

**73.** Similar to the law of sines, there is a *law of tangents*. The law says for any triangle *ABC*,

$$\frac{a + b}{a - b} = \frac{\tan\left[\frac{1}{2}(A + B)\right]}{\tan\left[\frac{1}{2}(A - B)\right]}.$$

Use the law of tangents to solve the triangle shown.

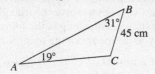

**74.** Lines $L_1$ and $L_2$ shown are parallel. The three triangles between these lines all share the same base (in bold). Explain why all three triangles must have the same area.

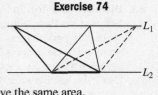

Exercise 74

**75.** A UFO is sighted on a direct line between the towns of Batesville and Cave City, sitting stationary in the sky. The towns are 13 mi apart as the crow flies. A student in Batesville calls a friend in Cave City and both take measurements of the angle of elevation: 35° from Batesville and 42° from Cave City. Suddenly the UFO zips across the sky at a level altitude heading directly for Cave City, then stops and hovers long enough for an additional measurement from Batesville: 24°. If the UFO was in motion for 1.2 sec, at what average speed (in mph) did it travel?

▶ **MAINTAINING YOUR SKILLS**

**76. (6.4)** Find all solutions to the equation $2 \sin x = \cos(2x)$

**77. (5.1)** Prove the given identity: $\tan^2 x - \sin^2 x = \tan^2 x \sin^2 x$

**78. (5.4)** Use sum-to-product formulas to verify that the following is an identity: $\cot x = \dfrac{\cos(3x) + \cos x}{\sin(3x) - \sin x}$

**79. (6.4)** Find all solutions in $[0, 2\pi)$: $2 \sin^2 x - 7 \sin x = -3$

**80. (3.2)** A Ferris wheel has a diameter of 50 ft. What is the linear distance a seat on the ferris wheel moves as the wheel rotates through an angle of 245°?

**81. (4.3)** Determine the equation of the graph shown, given it is of the form $y = A \tan(Bx \pm C)$.

Exercise 81

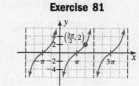

## 7.2 | The Law of Cosines; the Area of a Triangle

### Learning Objectives

*In Section 7.2 you will learn how to:*

☐ **A.** Apply the law of cosines when two sides and an included angle are known (SAS)

☐ **B.** Apply the law of cosines when three sides are known (SSS)

☐ **C.** Solve applications using the law of cosines

☐ **D.** Use trigonometry to find the area of a triangle

The distance formula $d = \sqrt{(x_2 - x_1)^2 + (y_2 - y_1)^2}$ is traditionally developed by placing two arbitrary points on a rectangular coordinate system and using the Pythagorean theorem. The relationship known as the *law of cosines* is developed in much the same way, but this time by using *three* arbitrary points (the vertices of a triangle). After giving the location of one vertex in trigonometric form, we obtain a formula that enables us to solve SSS and SAS triangles, which cannot be solved using the law of sines alone.

### A. The Law of Cosines and SAS Triangles

In situations where all three sides are known (but no angles), the law of sines cannot be applied. The same is true when two sides and the angle between them are known, since we must have an angle opposite one of the sides. In these two cases (Figure 7.26), side-side-side (**SSS**) and side-angle-side (**SAS**), we use the **law of cosines.**

**Figure 7.26**
Law of sines cannot be applied.

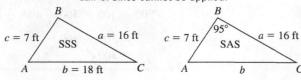

Keep in mind that the sum of any two sides of a triangle must be greater than the remaining side. For example, if $a = 7$, $B = 20$, and $C = 12$, no triangle is possible (see the figure).

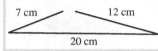

To solve these cases, it's evident we need additional insight on the unknown angles. Consider a general triangle $ABC$ on the rectangular coordinate system conveniently placed with vertex $A$ at the origin, side $c$ along the $x$-axis, and the vertex $C$ at some point $(x, y)$ in QI (Figure 7.27).

Note $\cos \theta = \dfrac{x}{b}$ giving $x = b \cos \theta$, and

$\sin \theta = \dfrac{y}{b}$ or $y = b \sin \theta$. This means we can

**Figure 7.27**

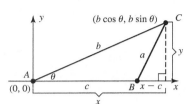

write the point $(x, y)$ as $(b \cos \theta, b \sin \theta)$ as shown, and use the Pythagorean theorem with side $x - c$ to find the length of side $a$ of the exterior, right triangle. It follows that

$$
\begin{aligned}
a^2 &= (x - c)^2 + y^2 & \text{Pythagorean theorem} \\
&= (b \cos \theta - c)^2 + (b \sin \theta)^2 & \text{substitute } b \cos \theta \text{ for } x \text{ and } b \sin \theta \text{ for } y \\
&= b^2\cos^2\theta - 2bc \cos \theta + c^2 + b^2\sin^2\theta & \text{square binomial, square term} \\
&= b^2\cos^2\theta + b^2\sin^2\theta + c^2 - 2bc \cos \theta & \text{rearrange terms} \\
&= b^2(\cos^2\theta + \sin^2\theta) + c^2 - 2bc \cos \theta & \text{factor out } b^2 \\
&= b^2 + c^2 - 2bc \cos \theta & \text{substitute 1 for } \cos^2\theta + \sin^2\theta
\end{aligned}
$$

We now have a formula relating all three sides and an included angle. Since the naming of the angles is purely arbitrary, the formula can be used in any of the three forms shown. For the derivation of the formula where $\angle B$ is acute, **see Exercise 60.**

**The Law of Cosines**

For any triangle $ABC$ and corresponding sides $a$, $b$, and $c$,
$$
\begin{aligned}
a^2 &= b^2 + c^2 - 2bc \cos A \\
b^2 &= a^2 + c^2 - 2ac \cos B \\
c^2 &= a^2 + b^2 - 2ab \cos C
\end{aligned}
$$
Note the relationship between the indicated angle and squared side.

In words, the law of cosines says that the square of any side is equal to the sums of the squares of the other two sides, minus twice their product times the cosine of the included angle. It is interesting to note that if the included angle is $90°$, the formula reduces to the Pythagorean theorem since $\cos 90° = 0$.

**EXAMPLE 1** ▶ **Verifying the Law of Cosines**

For the triangle shown, verify:
**a.** $c^2 = a^2 + b^2 - 2ab \cos C$
**b.** $b^2 = a^2 + c^2 - 2ac \cos B$

Solution ▶ Note the included angle $C$ is a right angle.
**a.** $c^2 = a^2 + b^2 - 2ab \cos C$
$20^2 = 10^2 + (10\sqrt{3})^2 - 2(10\sqrt{3})(10)\cos 90°$
$400 = 100 + 300 - 0$
$= 400\checkmark$

**b.** $b^2 = a^2 + c^2 - 2ac \cos B$
$(10\sqrt{3})^2 = 10^2 + 20^2 - 2(10)(20)\cos 60°$

$300 = 100 + 400 - 400\left(\dfrac{1}{2}\right)$

$= 500 - 200$
$= 300\checkmark$

**Now try Exercises 7 through 14** ▶

**CAUTION** ▶ When evaluating the law of cosines, a common error is to combine the coefficient of cos $\theta$ with the squared terms (the terms shown in blue): $a^2 = b^2 + c^2 - 2bc\cos A$. Be sure to use the correct order of operations when simplifying the expression.

Once additional information about the triangle is known, the law of sines can be used to complete the solution.

**EXAMPLE 2** ▶ **Solving a Triangle Using the Law of Cosines—SAS**

Solve the triangle shown. Write the solution in table form.

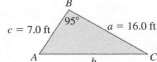

**Solution** ▶ The given information is SAS. Apply the law of cosines with respect to side $b$ and $\angle B$:

$b^2 = a^2 + c^2 - 2ac\cos B$      law of cosines with respect to $b$

$b^2 = (16)^2 + (7)^2 - 2(16)(7)\cos 95°$    substitute known values

$\phantom{b^2} \approx 324.522886$              simplify

$b \approx 18.0$                 $\sqrt{324.522886} \approx 18.0$

**WORTHY OF NOTE**

After using the law of cosines, we often use the law of sines to complete a solution. With a little foresight, we can avoid the ambiguous case—since the ambiguous case occurs only if $\theta$ *could be* obtuse (the largest angle of the triangle). After calculating the third side of a SAS triangle using the law of cosines, use the law of sines to find the smallest angle, since it cannot be obtuse.

We now have side $b$ opposite $\angle B$, and complete the solution using the law of sines, selecting the smaller angle to avoid the ambiguous case (we *could* apply the law of cosines again, if we chose).

$\dfrac{\sin C}{c} = \dfrac{\sin B}{b}$        law of sines applied to $\angle C$ and $\angle B$

$\dfrac{\sin C}{7} \approx \dfrac{\sin 95°}{18}$      substitute given values

$\sin C \approx 7 \cdot \dfrac{\sin 95°}{18}$      solve for $\sin C$

$C \approx \sin^{-1}\left(\dfrac{7\sin 95°}{18}\right)$    apply $\sin^{-1}$

$\phantom{C} \approx 22.8°$         result

☑ **A.** You've just learned how to apply the law of cosines when two sides and an included angle are known (SAS)

For the remaining angle, $\angle A$: $180° - (95° + 22.8°) = 62.2°$. The finished solution is shown in the table (given information is in bold).

| Angles | Sides (ft) |
|---|---|
| $A \approx 62.2°$ | $a = 16.0$ |
| $\mathbf{B = 95.0°}$ | $b \approx 18.0$ |
| $C \approx 22.8°$ | $c = 7.0$ |

**Now try Exercises 15 through 26** ▶

## B. The Law of Cosines and SSS Triangles

When three sides of a triangle are given, we use the law of cosines to find any one of the three angles. As a good practice, we first find the *largest* angle, or the angle opposite the largest side. This will ensure that the remaining two angles are acute, avoiding the ambiguous case if the law of sines is used to complete the solution.

**EXAMPLE 3** ▶ **Solving a Triangle Using the Law of Cosines—SSS**

Solve the triangle shown. Write the solution in table form, with angles rounded to tenths of a degree.

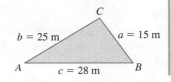

**Solution** ▶ The information is given as SSS. Since side $c$ is the longest side, we apply the law of cosines with respect to side $c$ and $\angle C$:

$$c^2 = a^2 + b^2 - 2ab \cos C \qquad \text{law of cosines with respect to } c$$
$$28^2 = (15)^2 + (25)^2 - 2(15)(25)\cos C \qquad \text{substitute known values}$$
$$784 = 850 - 750 \cos C \qquad \text{simplify}$$
$$-66 = -750 \cos C \qquad \text{isolate variable term}$$
$$0.088 = \cos C \qquad \text{divide}$$
$$\cos^{-1}0.088 = C \qquad \text{solve for } C$$
$$85.0° \approx C \qquad \text{result}$$

We now have $\angle C$ opposite side $c$ and finish up using the law of sines.

$$\frac{\sin A}{a} = \frac{\sin C}{c} \qquad \text{law of sines applied to } \angle A \text{ and } \angle C$$

$$\frac{\sin A}{15} \approx \frac{\sin 85°}{28} \qquad \text{substitute given values}$$

$$\sin A \approx 15 \cdot \frac{\sin 85°}{28} \qquad \text{solve for } \sin A$$

$$\approx 0.5336757311 \qquad \text{simplify}$$
$$A \approx \sin^{-1}0.5336757311 \qquad \text{solve for } A$$
$$\approx 32.3° \qquad \text{result}$$

**✓ B. You've just learned how to apply the law of cosines when three sides are known (SSS)**

Since the remaining angle must be acute, we compute it directly. $\angle B$: $180° - (85° + 32.3°) = 62.7°$. The finished solution is shown in the table, with the information originally given shown in bold.

| Angles | Sides (m) |
|--------|-----------|
| $A \approx 32.3°$ | $a = 15$ |
| $B \approx 62.7°$ | $b = 25$ |
| $C \approx 85°$ | $c = 28$ |

**Now try Exercises 27 through 34** ▶

## C. Applications Using the Law of Cosines

As with the law of sines, the law of cosines has a large number of applications from very diverse fields including geometry, navigation, surveying, and astronomy.

**EXAMPLE 4** ▶ **Solving an Application of the Law of Cosines—Geological Surveys**

A volcanologist needs to measure the distance across the base of an active volcano. Distance $AB$ is measured at 1.5 km, while distance $AC$ is 3.2 km. Using a theodolite (a sighting instrument used by surveyors), angle $BAC$ is found to be 95.7°. What is the distance across the base?

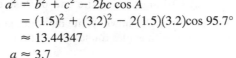

**Solution** ▶ The information is given as SAS. To find the distance $BC$ across the base of the volcano, we apply the law of cosines with respect to $\angle A$.

$$a^2 = b^2 + c^2 - 2bc \cos A \qquad \text{law of cosines with respect to } a$$
$$= (1.5)^2 + (3.2)^2 - 2(1.5)(3.2)\cos 95.7° \qquad \text{substitute known values}$$
$$\approx 13.44347 \qquad \text{simplify}$$
$$a \approx 3.7 \qquad \text{solve for } a$$

**✓ C. You've just learned how to solve applications using the law of cosines**

The volcano is approximately 3.7 km wide at its base.

**Now try Exercises 37 through 40** ▶

Recall from Section 2.3 that the *bearings* used by surveyors are stated as a number of degrees East or West from a due North or South orientation. *Headings* provide the same information, but are more commonly used in aerial and nautical navigation. They are stated simply as an *amount of rotation* from due north, in the clockwise direction ($0° \leq \theta < 360°$). For instance, the bearing N 25° W and a heading of 335° would indicate the same direction or course. **See Exercises 41 through 44.** A variety of additional applications of the law of cosines can be found in **Exercises 45 through 52.**

## D. Trigonometry and the Area of a Triangle

While you're likely familiar with the most common formula for a triangle's area, $A = \frac{1}{2}bh$, there are actually over 20 formulas for computing this area. Many involve basic trigonometric ideas, and we'll use some of these ideas to develop three additional formulas here.

For $A = \frac{1}{2}bh$, recall that $b$ represents the length of a designated base, and $h$ represents the length of the altitude drawn to that base (see Figure 7.28). If the height $h$ is unknown, but sides $a$ and $b$ with angle $C$ between them are known, $h$ can be found using $\sin C = \dfrac{h}{a}$, giving

$h = a \sin C$. Figure 7.29 indicates the same result is obtained if $C$ is obtuse, since $\sin(180° - C) = \sin C$. Substituting $a \sin C$ for $h$ in the formula $A = \frac{1}{2}bh$ gives $A = \frac{1}{2}ba \sin C$, or $A = \frac{1}{2}ab \sin C$ in more common form. Since naming the angles in a triangle is arbitrary, the formulas $A = \frac{1}{2}bc \sin A$ and $A = \frac{1}{2}ac \sin B$ can likewise be obtained.

**Figure 7.28**

**Figure 7.29**

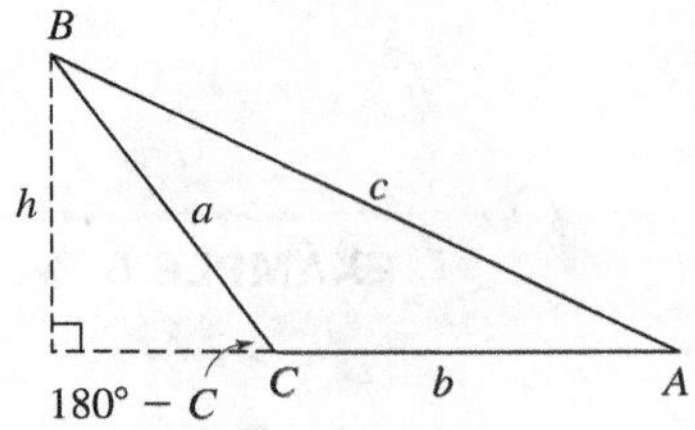

| **Area Given Two Sides and an Included Angle (SAS)** | | |
|---|---|---|
| **1.** $A = \dfrac{1}{2} ab \sin C$ | **2.** $A = \dfrac{1}{2} bc \sin A$ | **3.** $A = \dfrac{1}{2} ac \sin B$ |

In words, the formulas say the area of a triangle is equal to one-half the product of two sides times the sine of the angle between them.

**EXAMPLE 5** ▶ **Finding the Area of a Nonright Triangle**

Find the area of $\triangle ABC$, if $a = 16.2$ cm, $b = 25.6$ cm, and $C = 28.3°$.

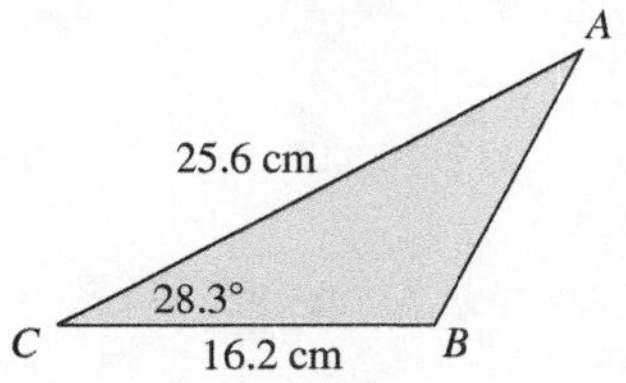

Solution ▶ Since sides $a$ and $b$ and angle $C$ are given, we apply the first formula.

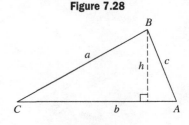

$$A = \frac{1}{2}ab \sin C \qquad \text{area formula}$$

$$= \frac{1}{2}(16.2)(25.6) \sin 28.3° \qquad \text{substitute 15.2 for } a, \text{ 25.6 for } b, \text{ and 28.3° for } C$$

$$\approx 98.3 \text{ cm}^2 \qquad \text{result}$$

The area of this triangle is approximately 98.3 cm².

Now try Exercises 53 and 54 ▶

Using these formulas, a second formula type requiring two angles and one side (AAS or ASA) can be developed. Solving for $b$ in $\mathcal{A} = \frac{1}{2}bc \sin A$ gives $b = \frac{2\mathcal{A}}{c \sin A}$. Likewise, solving for $a$ in $\mathcal{A} = \frac{1}{2}ac \sin B$ yields $a = \frac{2\mathcal{A}}{c \sin B}$. Substituting these for $b$ and $a$ in $\mathcal{A} = \frac{1}{2}ab \sin C$ gives

$$\mathcal{A} = \frac{1}{2} \cdot a \cdot b \cdot \sin C \qquad \text{given formula}$$

$$2\mathcal{A} = \frac{2\mathcal{A}}{c \sin B} \cdot \frac{2\mathcal{A}}{c \sin A} \cdot \sin C \qquad \text{substitute } \frac{2\mathcal{A}}{c \sin B} \text{ for } a, \frac{2\mathcal{A}}{c \sin A} \text{ for } b; \text{ multiply by 2}$$

$$c^2 \sin A \cdot \sin B = 2\mathcal{A} \cdot \sin C \qquad \text{multiply by } c \sin A \cdot c \sin B; \text{ divide by } 2\mathcal{A}$$

$$\frac{c^2 \sin A \sin B}{2 \sin C} = \mathcal{A} \qquad \text{solve for } \mathcal{A}$$

As with the previous formula, versions relying on side $a$ or side $b$ can also be found.

---

**Area Given Two Angles and Any Side (AAS/ASA)**

**1.** $\mathcal{A} = \dfrac{c^2 \cdot \sin A \cdot \sin B}{2 \sin C}$     **2.** $\mathcal{A} = \dfrac{a^2 \cdot \sin B \cdot \sin C}{2 \sin A}$     **3.** $\mathcal{A} = \dfrac{b^2 \cdot \sin A \cdot \sin C}{2 \sin B}$

---

**EXAMPLE 6** ▶ **Finding the Area of a Nonright Triangle**

Find the area of $\triangle ABC$ if $a = 34.5$ ft, $B = 87.9°$, and $C = 29.3°$.

Solution ▶ Since side $a$ is given, we apply the second version of the formula. First we find the measure of angle $A$, then make the appropriate substitutions:

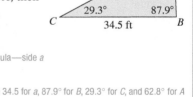

$$A = 180° - (87.9° + 29.3°) = 62.8°$$

$$\mathcal{A} = \frac{a^2 \sin B \sin C}{2 \sin A} \qquad \text{area formula—side } a$$

$$= \frac{(34.5)^2 \sin 87.9° \sin 29.3°}{2 \sin 62.8°} \qquad \text{substitute 34.5 for } a, 87.9° \text{ for } B, 29.3° \text{ for } C, \text{ and } 62.8° \text{ for } A$$

$$\approx 327.2 \text{ ft}^2 \qquad \text{simplify}$$

The area of this triangle is approximately $327.2 \text{ ft}^2$.

**Now try Exercises 55 and 56** ▶

Our final formula for a triangle's area is a useful addition to the other two, as it requires only the lengths of the three sides. The development of the formula requires only a Pythagorean identity and solving for the angle $C$ in the law of cosines, as follows.

$$a^2 + b^2 - 2ab \cos C = c^2 \qquad \text{law of cosines}$$

$$a^2 + b^2 - c^2 = 2ab \cos C \qquad \text{add } 2ab \cos C, \text{ subtract } c^2$$

$$\frac{a^2 + b^2 - c^2}{2ab} = \cos C \qquad \text{divide by } 2ab$$

Beginning with our first area formula, we then have

$$\mathcal{A} = \frac{1}{2}ab\sin C \qquad \text{previous area formula}$$

$$= \frac{1}{2}ab\sqrt{1-\cos^2 C} \qquad \sin^2 C + \cos^2 C = 1 \rightarrow \sin C = \sqrt{1-\cos^2 C}$$

$$= \frac{1}{2}ab\sqrt{1-\left(\frac{a^2+b^2-c^2}{2ab}\right)^2} \qquad \text{substitute } \frac{a^2+b^2+c^2}{2ab} \text{ for } \cos C$$

and can find the area of any triangle given its three sides. While the formula certainly serves this purpose, it is not so easy to use. By working algebraically and using the perimeter of the triangle, we can derive a more elegant version.

$$\mathcal{A}^2 = \frac{1}{4}a^2 b^2\left[1-\left(\frac{a^2+b^2-c^2}{2ab}\right)^2\right] \qquad \text{square both sides}$$

$$= \frac{1}{4}a^2 b^2\left[1+\left(\frac{a^2+b^2-c^2}{2ab}\right)\right]\left[1-\left(\frac{a^2+b^2-c^2}{2ab}\right)\right] \qquad \text{factor as a difference of squares}$$

$$= \frac{1}{4}a^2 b^2\left[\frac{2ab+a^2+b^2-c^2}{2ab}\right]\left[\frac{2ab-a^2-b^2+c^2}{2ab}\right] \qquad 1 = \frac{2ab}{2ab}; \text{ combine terms}$$

$$= \frac{1}{4}\left[\frac{(a^2+2ab+b^2)-c^2}{2}\right]\left[\frac{-(a^2-2ab+b^2)+c^2}{2}\right] \qquad \begin{array}{l}\text{rewrite/regroup} \\ \text{numerator; cancel } a^2 b^2\end{array}$$

$$= \frac{1}{16}\left[(a+b)^2-c^2\right]\left[c^2-(a-b)^2\right] \qquad \text{factor (binomial squares)}$$

$$= \frac{1}{16}(a+b+c)(a+b-c)(c+a-b)(c-a+b) \qquad \text{factor (difference of squares)}$$

For the perimeter $a+b+c=p$, we note the following relationships (subtract $2c$, $2b$, and $2a$ respectively, from both sides):

$$a+b-c=p-2c \qquad c+a-b=p-2b \qquad c-a+b=p-2a$$

and making the appropriate substitutions gives

$$\mathcal{A}^2 = \frac{1}{16}p(p-2c)(p-2b)(p-2a) \qquad \text{substitute}$$

While this would provide a usable formula for the area in terms of the perimeter, we can refine it further using the *semi*perimeter $s = \dfrac{a+b+c}{2} = \dfrac{p}{2}$. Since $\dfrac{1}{16} = \left(\dfrac{1}{2}\right)^4$, we can write the expression as

$$= \frac{p}{2}\left(\frac{p-2c}{2}\right)\left(\frac{p-2b}{2}\right)\left(\frac{p-2a}{2}\right) \qquad \text{rewrite expression}$$

$$= \frac{p}{2}\left(\frac{p}{2}-c\right)\left(\frac{p}{2}-b\right)\left(\frac{p}{2}-a\right) \qquad \text{simplify}$$

$$= s(s-c)(s-b)(s-a) \qquad \text{substitute } s \text{ for } \frac{p}{2}$$

Taking the square root of each side produces what is known as **Heron's formula.**

$$\mathcal{A} = \sqrt{s(s-a)(s-b)(s-c)} \qquad \text{Heron's formula}$$

### Heron's Formula

Given $\triangle ABC$ with sides $a$, $b$, and $c$ and semiperimeter $s = \dfrac{a + b + c}{2}$, the area of the triangle is

$$A = \sqrt{s(s - a)(s - b)(s - c)}$$

**EXAMPLE 7** ▶ **Solving an Application of Heron's Formula—Construction Planning**

A New York City developer wants to build condominiums on the triangular lot formed by Greenwich, Watts, and Canal Streets. How many square meters does the developer have to work with if the frontage along each street is approximately 34.1 m, 43.5 m, and 62.4 m, respectively?

**Solution** ▶ The perimeter of the lot is $p = 34.1 + 43.5 + 62.4 = 140$ m, so $s = 70$ m. By direct substitution we obtain

$$
\begin{aligned}
A &= \sqrt{s(s - a)(s - b)(s - c)} && \text{Heron's formula} \\
&= \sqrt{70(70 - 34.1)(70 - 43.5)(70 - 62.4)} && \text{substitute known values} \\
&= \sqrt{70(35.9)(26.5)(7.6)} && \text{simplify} \\
&= \sqrt{506,118.2} && \text{multiply} \\
&\approx 711.4 && \text{result}
\end{aligned}
$$

The developer has about 711.4 m² of land to work with.

**Now try Exercises 57 and 58** ▶

 **D.** You've just learned how to use trigonometry to find the area of a triangle

For a derivation of Heron's formula that does not depend on trigonometry, see Appendix VI.

## TECHNOLOGY HIGHLIGHT

### A Simple Program for the Law of Cosines (SSS)

Our website at www.mhhe.com/coburn has a number of interesting and useful features. In particular, there are some *Technology Extensions,* which are simple programs that may be of use in your study of Algebra and Trig. Writing programs tends to offer great insight as to how the various parts of a formula are related, and how the formula itself operates. You may notice that we've given this program a *descriptive* name, but the TI-84 Plus limits us to eight characters: SSSBYCOS (SSS by Cosines). The blank lines indicate that you should write the purpose and meaning of certain lines in the program, based on what is given elsewhere, or what you see as the output.

**PROGRAM:SSSBYCOS**

| | |
|---|---|
| **:ClrHome** | Clears the home screen, places cursor in upper left position |
| **:Disp "THIS PRGM SOLVES"** | Displays *THIS PRGM SOLVES* |
| **:Disp "SSS TRIANGLES"** | Displays *SSS TRIANGLES* |
| **:Disp "USING THE LAW"** | Displays *USING THE LAW* |
| **:Disp "OF COSINES"** | Displays *OF COSINES* |
| **:Pause:ClrHome** | Pauses execution, allows user to view results until $\boxed{\text{ENTER}}$ is pressed |

*—continued*

|  |  |
|---|---|
| :Disp "PLEASE ENTER" | |
| :Disp "THE LONGEST" | |
| :Disp "SIDE AS SIDE A" | |
| :Pause | |
| :Disp " " | Displays a blank line for formatting purposes |
| :Disp "THE 3 SIDES ARE:" | Displays *THE 3 SIDES ARE* |
| :Prompt A, B, C | Prompts user to input 3 lengths, stores them in A, B, and C |
| :ClrHome | |
| :$\cos^{-1}((A^2 - (B^2 + C^2))/(-2BC)) \to D$ | Computes the value of $\angle A$ and stores it in memory location D |
| :Disp "ANGLE A IS:" | Displays *ANGLE A IS:* |
| :round(D,1) $\to$ D | Rounds the value stored in D to one decimal, stores the new value |
| :Disp "D" | Displays the value now stored in memory location D |
| :Pause | |
| :$\sin^{-1}((B*\sin(D))/20) \to E$ | |
| :Disp "ANGLE B IS:" | |
| :round (E,1) $\to$ E | |
| :Disp "E" | |
| :Pause | |
| :$(180 - (A + B)) \to F$ | |
| :Disp "ANGLE C IS:" | |
| :round (F,1) $\to$ F | |
| :Disp "F" | |

**Exercise 1:** Using this program as a guide, write a program that will solve SAS triangles using the law of cosines.

## 7.2 EXERCISES

► CONCEPTS AND VOCABULARY

**Fill in each blank with the appropriate word or phrase. Carefully reread the section if needed.**

**1.** When the information given is SSS or SAS, the law of _____ is used to solve the triangle.

**2.** Write out which version of the law of cosines you would use to begin solving the triangle shown: _____
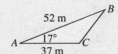

**3.** If the law of cosines is applied to a right triangle, the result is the same as the _____ theorem, since $\cos 90° = 0$.

**4.** Fill in the blank so that the law of cosines is complete: $c^2 = a^2 + b^2 - $ _____ $\cos C$

**5.** Solve the triangle in Exercise 2 using only the law of cosines, then by using the law of cosines followed by the law of sines. Which method was more efficient?

**6.** Begin with $a^2 = b^2 + c^2 - 2bc \cos A$ and write $\cos A$ in terms of $a$, $b$, and $c$ (solve for $\cos A$). Why must $b^2 + c^2 - a^2 < 2bc$ hold in order for a solution to exist?

▶ **DEVELOPING YOUR SKILLS**

**Determine whether the law of cosines can be used to begin the solution process for each triangle.**

**7.**

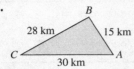

**8.**

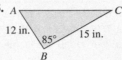

**9.**

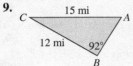

**10.**

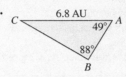

**11.**

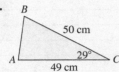

**12.**

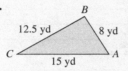

**For each triangle, verify all three forms of the law of cosines.**

**13.**

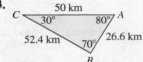

**14.**

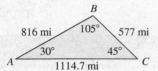

**Solve each of the following equations for the unknown part.**

**15.** $4^2 = 5^2 + 6^2 - 2(5)(6)\cos B$

**16.** $12.9^2 = 15.2^2 + 9.8^2 - 2(15.2)(9.8)\cos C$

**17.** $a^2 = 9^2 + 7^2 - 2(9)(7)\cos 52°$

**18.** $b^2 = 3.9^2 + 9.5^2 - 2(3.9)(9.5)\cos 30°$

**19.** $10^2 = 12^2 + 15^2 - 2(12)(15)\cos A$

**20.** $202^2 = 182^2 + 98^2 - 2(182)(98)\cos B$

**Solve each triangle using the law of cosines.**

**21.** side $a$ = 75 cm
  ∠$C$ = 38°
  side $b$ = 32 cm

**22.** side $b$ = 385 m
  ∠$C$ = 67°
  side $a$ = 490 m

**23.** side $c$ = 25.8 mi
  ∠$B$ = 30°
  side $a$ = 12.9 mi

**Solve using the law of cosines (if possible). Label each triangle appropriately before you begin.**

**24.**

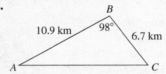

**25.**

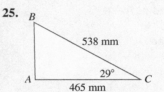

**26.**

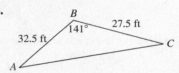

**27.** side $c = 10\sqrt{3}$ in.
  side $b = 6\sqrt{3}$ in.
  side $a = 15\sqrt{3}$ in.

**28.** side $a$ = 282 ft
  side $b$ = 129 ft
  side $c$ = 300 ft

**29.** side $a$ = 32.8 km
  side $b$ = 24.9 km
  side $c$ = 12.4 km

**30.**

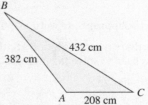

**31.**

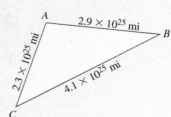

**32.**

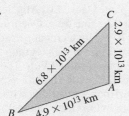

**33.** side $a = 12\sqrt{3}$ yd
side $b = 12.9$ yd
side $c = 9.2$ yd

**34.** side $a = 36.5$ AU
side $b = 12.9$ AU
side $c = 22$ AU

▶ **WORKING WITH FORMULAS**

**35. Alternative form for the law of cosines:**

$$\cos A = \frac{b^2 + c^2 - a^2}{2bc}$$

By solving the law of
cosines for the cosine of
the angle, the formula
can be written as shown.
Derive this formula (solve for $\cos \theta$), beginning
from $a^2 = b^2 + c^2 - 2bc \cos A$, then use this form
to begin the solution of the triangle given.

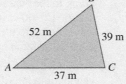

**36. The perimeter of a trapezoid:**
$$P = a + b + h(\csc \alpha + \csc \beta)$$

The perimeter of a
trapezoid can be
found using the
formula shown,
where $a$ and $b$
represent the
lengths of the parallel sides, $h$ is the height of the
trapezoid, and $\alpha$ and $\beta$ are the base angles. Find
the perimeter of Trapezoid Park (to the nearest
foot) if $a = 5000$ ft, $b = 7500$ ft, and $h = 2000$ ft,
with base angles $\alpha = 42°$ and $\beta = 78°$.

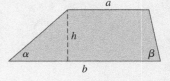

▶ **APPLICATIONS**

**37. Distance between cities:** The satellite Mercury II
measures its distance from Portland and from
Green Bay using radio waves as shown. Using an
on-board sighting device, the satellite determines
that $\angle M$ is 99°. How many miles is it from
Portland to Green Bay?

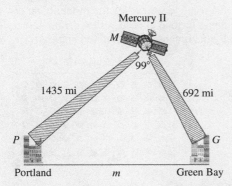

**38. Distance between cities:** Voyager VII measures its
distance from Los Angeles and from San Francisco
using radio waves as shown. Using an on-board
sighting device, the satellite determines $\angle V$ is 95°.
How many kilometers separate Los Angeles and
San Francisco?

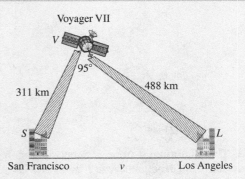

**39. Runway length:**
Surveyors are
measuring a large,
marshy area outside
of the city as part of a
feasibility study for
the construction of a
new airport. Using a
theodolite and the
markers shown gives the information indicated. If
the main runway must be at least 11,000 ft long,
and environmental concerns are satisfied, can the
airport be constructed at this site (recall that
1 mi = 5280 ft)?

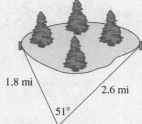

**40. Tunnel length:** An engineering firm decides to bid on a proposed tunnel through Harvest Mountain. In order to find the tunnel's length, the measurements shown are taken. (a) How long will the tunnel be? (b) Due to previous tunneling experience, the firm estimates a cost of $5000 per foot for boring through this type of rock and constructing the tunnel according to required specifications. If management insists on a 25% profit, what will be their minimum bid to the nearest hundred?

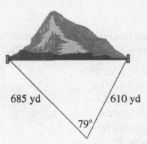

685 yd         610 yd

79°

**41. Trip planning:** A business executive is going to fly the corporate jet from Providence to College Cove. She calculates the distances shown using a map, with Mannerly Main for reference since it is due east of Providence. What is the measure of angle $P$? What heading should she set for this trip?

**Exercise 41**

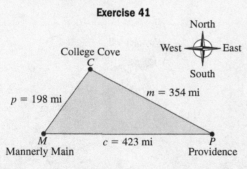

North

West        East

South

College Cove
$C$

$p = 198$ mi           $m = 354$ mi

$M$         $c = 423$ mi        $P$
Mannerly Main             Providence

**42. Trip planning:** A troop of Scouts is planning a hike from *M*ontgomery to *P*attonville. They calculate the distances shown using a map, using *B*radleyton for reference since it is due east of *M*ontgomery. What is the measure of angle *M*? What heading should they set for this trip?

**Exercise 42**

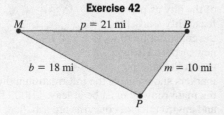

$M$       $p = 21$ mi       $B$

$b = 18$ mi        $m = 10$ mi

$P$

**43. Aerial distance:** Two planes leave Los Angeles International Airport at the same time. One travels due west (at heading 270°) with a cruising speed of 450 mph, going to Tokyo, Japan, with a group that seeks tranquility at the foot of Mount Fuji. The other travels at heading 225° with a cruising speed of 425 mph, going to Brisbane, Australia, with a group seeking adventure in the Great Outback. Approximate the distance between the planes after 5 hr of flight.

**44. Nautical distance:** Two ships leave Honolulu Harbor at the same time. One travels 15 knots (nautical miles per hour) at heading 150°, and is going to the Marquesas Islands (*Crosby, Stills, and Nash*). The other travels 12 knots at heading 200°, and is going to the Samoan Islands (*Samoa, le galu a tu*). How far apart are the two ships after 10 hr?

**45. Geoboard geometry:** A rubber band is placed on a geoboard (a board with all pegs 1 cm apart) as shown. Approximate the perimeter of the triangle formed by the rubber band *and* the angle formed at each vertex. (*Hint:* Use a standard triangle to find $\angle A$ and length $\overline{AB}$.)

**Exercise 45**

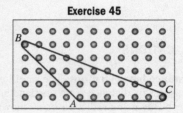

$B$

$C$

$A$

**46. Geoboard geometry:** A rubber band is placed on a geoboard as shown. Approximate the perimeter of the triangle formed by the rubber band *and* the angle formed at each vertex. (*Hint:* Use a Pythagorean triple, then find angle *A*.)

**Exercise 46**

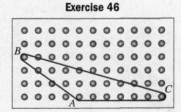

$B$

$C$

$A$

In Exercises 47 and 48, three rods are attached via pivot joints so the rods can be manipulated to form a triangle. Find the three angles of the triangle formed.

**47.**

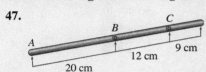

**48.**

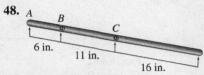

**49. Pentagon perimeter:** Find the perimeter of a regular *pentagon* that is circumscribed by a circle with radius $r = 10$ cm.

**Exercise 49**

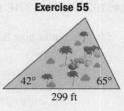

**50. Hexagon perimeter:** Find the perimeter of a regular *hexagon* that is circumscribed by a circle with radius $r = 15$ cm.

Solve the following triangles. Round sides and angles to the nearest tenth. (*Hint:* Use Pythagorean triples.)

**51.**

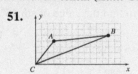

**52.**

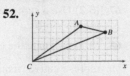

**53. Billboard design:** Creative Designs iNc. has designed a flashy, new billboard for one of its clients. Using a rectangular highway billboard measuring 20 ft by 30 ft, the primary advertising area is a triangle formed using the diagonal of the billboard as one side, and one-half the base as another (see figure). Use the dimensions given to find the angle $\alpha$ formed at the corner, then compute the area of the triangle using two sides and this included angle.

**Exercise 53**

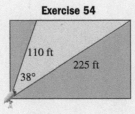

**54. Area caught by surveillance camera:** A stationary surveillance camera is set up to monitor activity in the parking lot of a shopping mall. If the camera has a 38° field of vision, how many square feet of the parking lot can it tape using the dimensions given?

**Exercise 54**

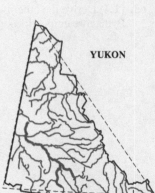

**55. Pricing for undeveloped lots:** Undeveloped land in a popular resort area is selling for $3,000,000/acre. Given the dimensions of the lot shown, (a) find what percent of a full acre is being purchased (to the nearest whole percent), and (b) compute the cost of the lot. Recall that 1 acre $= 43,560$ ft$^2$.

**Exercise 55**

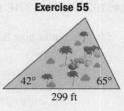

**56. Area of the Nile River Delta:** The Nile River Delta is one of the world's largest. The delta begins slightly up river from the Egyptian capitol (Cairo) and stretches along the Mediterranean from Alexandria in the west to Port Said in the east (over 240 km). Approximate the area of this rich agricultural region using the two triangles shown.

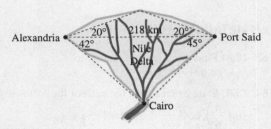

**57. Area of the Yukon Territory:** The Yukon Territory in northwest Canada is roughly triangular in shape with sides of 1289 km, 1063 km, and 922 km. What is the approximate area covered by this territory?

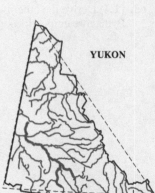

**58. Alternate method for computing area:** Referring to Exercise 53, since the dimensions of the billboard are known, all three sides of the triangle can actually be determined. Find the length of the sides rounded to the nearest whole, then use Heron's formula to find the area of the triangle. How close was your answer to that in Exercise 53?

▶ **EXTENDING THE CONCEPT**

**59.** No matter how hard I try, I cannot solve the triangle shown. Why?

**60.** In Figure 7.27 (page 330), note that if the *x*-coordinate of vertex *B* is greater than the *x*-coordinate of vertex *C*, ∠*B* becomes acute, and ∠*C* obtuse. How does this change the relationship between *x* and *c*? Verify the law of cosines remains unchanged.

**61.** For the triangle shown, verify that $c = b \cos A + a \cos B$, then use two different forms of the law of cosines to show this relationship holds for *any* triangle *ABC*.

**62.** Most students are familiar with this double-angle formula for cosine: $\cos(2\theta) = \cos^2\theta - \sin^2\theta$. The *triple* angle formula for cosine is $\cos(3\theta) = 4\cos^3\theta - 3\cos\theta$. Use the formula to find an exact value for cos 135°. Show that you get the same result as when using a reference angle.

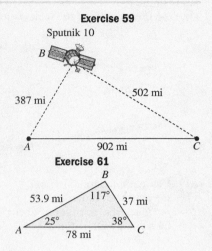

Exercise 59

Exercise 61

▶ **MAINTAINING YOUR SKILLS**

**63.** (6.3) Find the primary solution to: $-3\sec\theta + 7\sqrt{3} = 5\sqrt{3}$.

**64.** (3.3) State exact forms for each of the following: $\sin\left(\dfrac{\pi}{6}\right)$, $\cos\left(\dfrac{7\pi}{6}\right)$, and $\tan\left(\dfrac{\pi}{3}\right)$.

**65.** (1.4) Derive the other two common versions of the Pythagorean identities, given $\sin^2 x + \cos^2 x = 1$.

**66.** (1.4) Use fundamental identities to find the values of all six trig functions that satisfy the conditions $\sin x = -\dfrac{5}{13}$ and $\cos x > 0$.

**67.** (5.2) Use a sum identity to find the value of sin 75° in exact form.

**68.** (6.2) Evaluate the expression by drawing a representative triangle: $\csc\left[\tan^{-1}\left(\dfrac{55}{48}\right)\right]$.

## MID-CHAPTER CHECK

**1.** Beginning with $\dfrac{\sin A}{a} = \dfrac{\sin B}{b}$, solve for $\sin B$.

**2.** Given $b^2 = a^2 + c^2 - 2ac\cos B$, solve for $\cos B$.

Solve the triangles shown below using any appropriate method.

**3.**

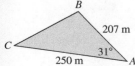

**4.**

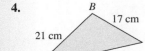

Solve the triangles described below using the law of sines. If more than one triangle exists, solve both.

**5.** $A = 44°$, $a = 2.1$ km, $c = 2.8$ km

**6.** $C = 27°$, $a = 70$ yd, $c = 100$ yd

**7.** A large highway sign is erected on a steep hillside that is inclined 45° from the horizontal. At 9:00 A.M. the sign casts a 75 ft shadow. Find the height of the sign if the angle of elevation (measured from a horizontal line) from the tip of the shadow to the top of the sign is 65°.

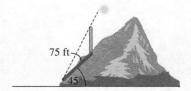

**8.** Modeled after an Egyptian obelisk, the Washington Monument (Washington, D.C.) is one of the tallest masonry buildings in the world. Find the height of the monument given the measurements shown (see the figure).

58° 70°
44 m

**9.** The circles shown here have radii of 4 cm, 9 cm, and 12 cm, and are tangent to each other. Find the angles formed by the line segments joining their centers.

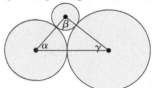
β
α
γ

**10.** On her delivery route, Judy drives 23 miles to **C**olumbus, then 17 mi to **D**rake, then back home to **B**alboa. Use the diagram given to find the distance from **D**rake to **B**alboa.

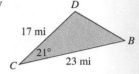
D
17 mi
B
21°
C
23 mi

REINFORCING BASIC CONCEPTS

## Scaled Drawings and the Laws of Sine and Cosine

In mathematics, there are few things as satisfying as the tactile verification of a concept or computation. In this *Reinforcing Basic Concepts,* we'll use scaled drawings to verify the relationships stated by the law of sines and the law of cosines. First, gather a blank sheet of paper, a ruler marked in centimeters/millimeters, and a protractor. When working with scale models, always measure and mark as carefully as possible. The greater the care, the better the results. For the first illustration (see Figure 7.30), we'll draw a 20-cm horizontal line segment near the bottom of the paper, then use the left endpoint to mark off a 35° angle. Draw the second side a length of 18 cm. Our first goal is to compute the length of the side needed to complete the triangle, then verify our computation by measurement. Since the current "triangle" is SAS, we use the law of cosines. Label the 35° as $\angle A$, the top vertex as $\angle B$, and the right endpoint as $\angle C$.

$$a^2 = b^2 + c^2 - 2bc \cos A \qquad \text{law of cosines with respect to } a$$
$$= (20)^2 + (18)^2 - 2(20)(18)\cos 35 \qquad \text{substitute known values}$$
$$\approx 724 - 589.8 \qquad \text{simplify (round to 10)}$$
$$= 134.2 \qquad \text{combine terms}$$
$$a \approx 11.6 \qquad \text{solve for } a$$

**Figure 7.30**

The computed length of side $a$ is approximately 11.6 cm, and if you took great care in drawing your diagram, you'll find the missing side is indeed very close to this length.

**Exercise 1:** Finish solving the triangle in Figure 7.30 using the law of sines. Once you've computed $\angle B$ and $\angle C$, measure these angles from the diagram using your protractor. How close was the computed measure to the actual measure?

For the second illustration (see Figure 7.31), draw *any arbitrary triangle* on a separate blank sheet, noting that the larger the triangle, the easier it is to measure the angles. After you've drawn it, measure the length of each side to the nearest millimeter (our triangle turned out to be 21.2 cm × 13.3 cm × 15.3 cm). Now use the law of cosines to find one angle, then the law of sines to solve the triangle. The computations for our triangle gave angles of 95.4°, 45.9°, and 38.7°. What angles did your computations give? Finally, use your protractor to measure the angles of the triangle you drew. With careful drawings, the measured results are often remarkably accurate!

**Figure 7.31**

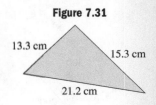

**Exercise 2:** Using sides of 18 cm and 15 cm, draw a 35° angle, a 50° angle, and a 70° angle, then complete each triangle by connecting the endpoints. Use the law of cosines to compute the length of this third side, then actually measure each one. Was the actual length close to the computed length?

## Learning Objectives

*In Section 7.3 you will learn how to:*

- ☐ **A.** Represent a vector quantity geometrically
- ☐ **B.** Represent a vector quantity graphically
- ☐ **C.** Perform defined operations on vectors
- ☐ **D.** Represent a vector quantity algebraically and find unit vectors
- ☐ **E.** Use vector diagrams to solve applications

The study of vectors is closely connected to the study of force, motion, velocity, and other related phenomena. Vectors enable us to quantify certain characteristics of these phenomena and to physically represent their magnitude and direction with a simple model. To quantify something means we assign it a relative numeric value for purposes of study and comparison. While very uncomplicated, this model turns out to be a powerful mathematical tool.

## A. The Notation and Geometry of Vectors

Measurements involving time, area, volume, energy, and temperature are called **scalar measurements** or **scalar quantities** because each can be adequately described by their magnitude alone and the appropriate unit or "scale." The related real number is simply called a **scalar.** Concepts that require more than a single quantity to describe their attributes are called **vector quantities.** Examples might include force, velocity, and displacement, which require knowing a magnitude *and* direction to describe them completely.

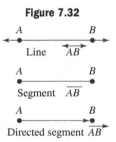

**Figure 7.32**

To begin our study, consider two identical airplanes flying at 300 mph, on a parallel course and in the same direction. Although we don't know how far apart they are, what direction they're flying, or if one is "ahead" of the other, we can still model, "300 mph on a parallel course," using **directed line segments** (Figure 7.32). Drawing these segments parallel with the arrowheads pointing the same way models the direction of flight, while drawing segments the *same length* indicates the velocities are equal. The directed segment used to represent a vector quantity is simply called a **vector.** In this case, the length of the vector models the **magnitude** of the velocity, while the arrowhead indicates the **direction** of travel. The origin of the segment is called the **initial point,** with the arrowhead pointing to the **terminal point.** Both are labeled using capital letters as shown in Figure 7.33 and we call this a *geometric representation* of the vectors.

**Figure 7.33**

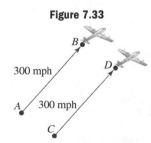

Vectors can be named using the initial and terminal points that define them (initial point first) as in $\overrightarrow{AB}$ and $\overrightarrow{CD}$, or using a bold, small case letter with the favorites being **v** (first letter of the word vector) and **u.** Other small case, bold letters can be used and subscripted vector names ($\mathbf{v}_1$, $\mathbf{v}_2$, $\mathbf{v}_3$, . . .) are also common. Two **vectors are equal** if they have the same magnitude and direction. For $\mathbf{u} = \overrightarrow{AB}$ and $\mathbf{v} = \overrightarrow{CD}$, we can say $\mathbf{u} = \mathbf{v}$ or $\overrightarrow{AB} = \overrightarrow{CD}$ since both airplanes are flying at the same speed and in the same direction (Figure 7.33).

**Figure 7.34**

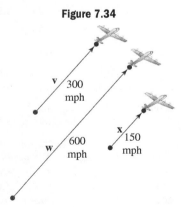

Based on these conventions, it seems reasonable to represent an airplane flying at 600 mph with a vector that is twice as long as **u** and **v,** and one flying at 150 mph with a vector that is half as long. If all planes are flying in the same direction on a parallel course, we can represent them geometrically as shown in Figure 7.34, and state that $\mathbf{w} = 2\mathbf{v}$, $\mathbf{x} = \frac{1}{2}\mathbf{v}$, and $\mathbf{w} = 4\mathbf{x}$. The multiplication of a vector by a constant is called **scalar multiplication,** since the product changes only the scale or size of the vector and not its direction.

**Figure 7.35**

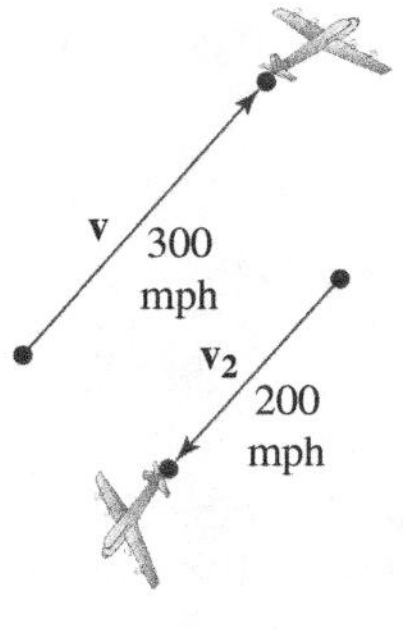

Finally, consider the airplane represented by vector $\mathbf{v}_2$, flying at 200 mph on a parallel course *but in the opposite direction* (see Figure 7.35). In this case, the directed segment will be $\frac{200}{300} = \frac{2}{3}$ as long as **v** and point in the opposite or "negative" direction. In perspective we can now state: $\mathbf{v}_2 = -\frac{2}{3}\mathbf{v}$, $\mathbf{v}_2 = -\frac{1}{3}\mathbf{w}$, $\mathbf{v}_2 = -\frac{4}{3}\mathbf{x}$, or any equivalent form of these equations.

<table>
<tr><td>**EXAMPLE 1** ▶</td><td>**Using Geometric Vectors to Model Forces Acting on a Point**</td></tr>
</table>

Two tugboats are attempting to free a barge that is stuck on a sand bar. One is pulling with a force of 2000 newtons (N) in a certain direction, the other is pulling with a force of 1500 N in a direction that is *perpendicular to the first*. Represent the situation geometrically using vectors.

Solution ▶  We could once again draw a vector of arbitrary length and let it represent the 2000-N force applied by the first tugboat. For better perspective, we can actually use a ruler and choose a convenient length, say 6 cm. We then represent the pulling force of the second tug with a vector that is $\frac{1500}{2000} = \frac{3}{4}$ as long (4.5 cm), drawn at a 90° angle with relation to the first. Note that many correct solutions are possible, depending on the direction of the first vector drawn.

☑ **A.** You've just learned how to represent a vector quantity geometrically

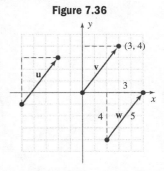

Now try Exercises 7 through 12 ▶

## B. Vectors and the Rectangular Coordinate System

Representing vectors geometrically (with a directed line segment) is fine for simple comparisons, but many applications involve numerous vectors acting on a single point or changes in a vector quantity over time. For these situations, a graphical representation in the coordinate plane helps to analyze this interaction. The only question is *where* to place the vector on the grid, and the answer is—it really doesn't matter. Consider the three vectors shown in Figure 7.36. From the initial point of each, counting four units in the vertical direction, then three units in the horizontal direction, puts us at the terminal point. This shows

**Figure 7.36**

the vectors are all 5 units long (since a 3-4-5 triangle is formed) and are all parallel (since slopes are equal: $\frac{\Delta y}{\Delta x} = \frac{4}{3}$). In other words, they are **equivalent vectors.**

Since a vector's location is unimportant, we can replace any given vector with a unique and equivalent vector whose initial point is (0, 0), called the **position vector.**

**Position Vectors**

For a vector **v** with initial point $(x_1, y_1)$ and terminal point $(x_2, y_2)$, the position vector for **v** is

$$\mathbf{v} = \langle x_2 - x_1, y_2 - y_1 \rangle,$$

an equivalent vector with initial point (0, 0) and terminal point $(x_2 - x_1, y_2, -y_1)$.

**WORTHY OF NOTE**

For vector **u**, the initial and terminal points are $(-5, -1)$ and $(-2, 3)$, respectively, yielding the position vector $\langle -2 - (-5), 3 - (-1) \rangle = \langle 3, 4 \rangle$ as before.

For instance, the initial and terminal points of vector **w** in Figure 7.36 are $(2, -4)$ and $(5, 0)$, respectively, with $(5 - 2, 0 - (-4)) = (3, 4)$. Since (3, 4) is also the terminal point of **v** (whose initial point is at the origin), **v** is the position vector for **u** and **w**. This observation also indicates that every geometric vector in the *xy*-plane corresponds to a unique ordered pair of real numbers $(a, b)$, with $a$ as the **horizontal component** and $b$ as the **vertical component** of the vector. As indicated, we denote the vector in

**component form** as $\langle a, b \rangle$, using the new notation to prevent confusing vector $\langle a, b \rangle$ with the ordered pair $(a, b)$. Finally, while each of the vectors in Figure 7.36 has a component form of $\langle 3, 4 \rangle$, the horizontal and vertical components can be read directly only from $\mathbf{v} = \langle 3, 4 \rangle$, giving it a distinct advantage.

---

**EXAMPLE 2** ▶ **Verifying the Components of a Position Vector**

Vector $\mathbf{v} = \langle 12, -5 \rangle$ has initial point $(-4, 3)$.
 **a.** Find the coordinates of the terminal point.
 **b.** Verify the position vector for $\mathbf{v}$ is $\langle 12, -5 \rangle$ and find its length.

**Solution** ▶ **a.** Since $\mathbf{v}$ has a horizontal component of 12 and a vertical component of $-5$, we add 12 to the $x$-coordinate and $-5$ to the $y$-coordinate of the initial point. This gives a terminal point of $(12 + (-4), -5 + 3) = (8, -2)$.

**b.** To verify we use the initial and terminal points to compute $\langle x_2 - x_1, y_2 - y_1 \rangle$, giving a position vector of $\langle 8 - (-4), -2 - 3 \rangle = \langle 12, -5 \rangle$. To find its length we can use either the Pythagorean theorem or simply note that a 5-12-13 Pythagorean triple is formed. Vector $\mathbf{v}$ has a length of 13 units.

Now try Exercises **13 through 20** ▶

---

For the remainder of this section, vector $\mathbf{v} = \langle a, b \rangle$ will refer to the unique position vector for all those equivalent to $\mathbf{v}$. Upon considering the graph of $\langle a, b \rangle$ (shown in QI for convenience in Figure 7.37), several things are immediately evident. The length or **magnitude** of the vector, which is denoted $|\mathbf{v}|$, can be determined using the Pythagorean theorem: $|\mathbf{v}| = \sqrt{a^2 + b^2}$. In addition, basic trigonometry shows the horizontal component can be found using $\cos \theta = \dfrac{a}{|\mathbf{v}|}$ or $a = |\mathbf{v}| \cos \theta$, with the vertical component being $\sin \theta = \dfrac{b}{|\mathbf{v}|}$ or $b = |\mathbf{v}| \sin \theta$. Finally, we note the angle $\theta$ can be determined using $\tan \theta = \dfrac{b}{a}$, or $\theta_r = \tan^{-1}\left|\dfrac{b}{a}\right|$ and the quadrant of $\mathbf{v}$.

**Figure 7.37**

---

**Vector Components in Trig Form**

For a position vector $\mathbf{v} = \langle a, b \rangle$ and angle $\theta$, we have

horizontal component: $a = |\mathbf{v}| \cos \theta$        vertical component: $b = |\mathbf{v}| \sin \theta$,

where    $\theta_r = \tan^{-1}\left|\dfrac{b}{a}\right|$ and

$|\mathbf{v}| = \sqrt{a^2 + b^2}$

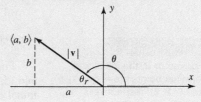

---

The ability to model characteristics of a vector using these equations is a huge benefit to solving applications, since we must often work out solutions using only the partial information given.

**EXAMPLE 3** ▶ **Finding the Magnitude and Direction Angle of a Vector**

For $\mathbf{v}_1 = \langle -2.5, -6 \rangle$ and $\mathbf{v}_2 = \langle 3\sqrt{3}, 3 \rangle$,

a. Graph each vector and name the quadrant where it is located.

b. Find their magnitudes.

c. Find the angle $\theta$ for each vector (round to tenths of a degree as needed).

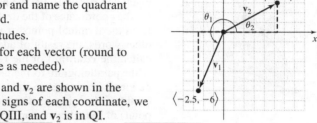

**Solution** ▶ a. The graphs of $\mathbf{v}_1$ and $\mathbf{v}_2$ are shown in the figure. Using the signs of each coordinate, we note that $\mathbf{v}_1$ is in QIII, and $\mathbf{v}_2$ is in QI.

b. $|\mathbf{v}_1| = \sqrt{(-2.5)^2 + (-6)^2}$            $|\mathbf{v}_2| = \sqrt{(3\sqrt{3})^2 + (3)^2}$

$\quad\quad = \sqrt{6.25 + 36}$                         $\quad\quad = \sqrt{27 + 9}$

$\quad\quad = \sqrt{42.25}$                              $\quad\quad = \sqrt{36}$

$\quad\quad = 6.5$                                        $\quad\quad = 6$

c. For $\mathbf{v}_1$: $\theta_r = \tan^{-1}\left|\dfrac{-6}{-2.5}\right|$            For $\mathbf{v}_2$: $\theta_r = \tan^{-1}\left|\dfrac{3}{3\sqrt{3}}\right|$

$\quad\quad\quad\quad = \tan^{-1}(2.4) \approx 67.4°$            $\quad\quad\quad\quad = \tan^{-1}\left(\dfrac{\sqrt{3}}{3}\right) = 30°$

In QIII, $\theta_1 \approx 247.4°$.                     In QI, $\theta_2 = 30°$.

**Now try Exercises 21 through 24** ▶

---

**EXAMPLE 4** ▶ **Finding the Horizontal and Vertical Components of a Vector**

The vector $\mathbf{v} = \langle a, b \rangle$ is in QIII, has a magnitude of $|\mathbf{v}| = 21$, and forms an angle of $25°$ with the negative $x$-axis (Figure 7.38). Find the horizontal and vertical components of the vector, rounded to tenths.

**Figure 7.38**

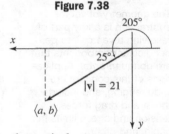

**Solution** ▶ Begin by graphing the vector and setting up the equations for its components. For $\theta_r = 25°$, $\theta = 205°$.

**Figure 7.39**

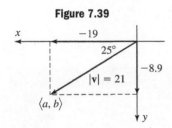

For the horizontal component:                    For the vertical component:

$\quad\quad a = |\mathbf{v}|\cos\theta$                        $\quad\quad b = |\mathbf{v}|\sin\theta$

$\quad\quad\quad = 21\cos 205°$                       $\quad\quad\quad = 21\sin 205°$

$\quad\quad\quad \approx -19$                         $\quad\quad\quad \approx -8.9$

With $\mathbf{v}$ in QIII, its component form is approximately $\langle -19, -8.9 \rangle$. As a check, we apply the Pythagorean theorem: $\sqrt{(-19)^2 + (-8.9)^2} \approx 21$ ✓. See Figure 7.39.

**Now try Exercises 25 through 30** ▶

☑ **B. You've just learned how to represent a vector quantity graphically**

## C. Operations on Vectors and Vector Properties

The operations defined for vectors have a close knit graphical representation. Consider a local park having a large pond with pathways around both sides, so that a park visitor can enjoy the view from either side. Suppose $\mathbf{v} = \langle 8, 2 \rangle$ is the position vector representing a person who decides to turn to the right at the pond, while $\mathbf{u} = \langle 2, 6 \rangle$ represents a person who decides to first turn left. At (8, 2) the first person

**Figure 7.40**

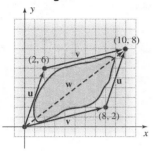

changes direction and walks to (10, 8) on the other side of the pond, while the second person arrives at (2, 6) and turns to head for (10, 8) as well. This is shown graphically in Figure 7.40 and demonstrates that (1) a parallelogram is formed (opposite sides equal and parallel), (2) the path taken is unimportant relative to the destination, and (3) the coordinates of the destination represent the *sum of corresponding coordinates* from the terminal points of **u** and **v**: (2, 6) + (8, 2) = (2 + 8, 6 + 2) = (10, 8). In other words, the result of adding **u** and **v** gives the new position vector **u** + **v** = **w**, called the **resultant** or the **resultant vector.** Note the resultant vector is a diagonal of the parallelogram formed. Geometrically or graphically, the addition of vectors can be viewed as a "tail-to-tip" combination of one with another, by shifting one vector (without changing its direction) so that its tail (initial point) is at the tip (terminal point) of the other vector. This is illustrated in Figures 7.41 through 7.43.

| **Figure 7.41** | **Figure 7.42** | **Figure 7.43** |
|:---:|:---:|:---:|
| **Given vectors u and v** | **Shift vector v** | **Shift vector u** |

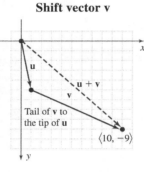
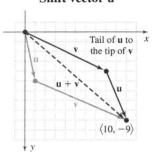

The geometry of vector subtraction is a key part of resolving a vector into perpendicular components that are nonquadrantal. Applications of this concept are wide ranging, and include thrust and drag forces, tension and stress limits in a cable, and others.

The subtraction of vectors can be understood as either **u** − **v** or **u** + (−**v**). Since the location of a vector is unimportant relative to the information it carries, vector subtraction can be interpreted as the *tip-to-tip diagonal* of the parallelogram from vector addition. In Figures 7.41 to 7.43, assume **u** = ⟨1, −5⟩ and **v** = ⟨9, −4⟩. Then **u** − **v** = ⟨1, −5⟩ − ⟨9, −4⟩ = ⟨1 − 9, −5 + 4⟩ giving the position vector ⟨−8, −1⟩. By repositioning this vector with its tail at the tip of **v**, we note the new vector points directly at **u**, forming the diagonal (see Figure 7.44). Scalar multiplication of vectors also has a graphical representation that corresponds to the geometric description given earlier.

**Figure 7.44**

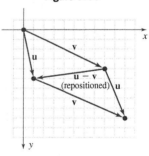

**Operations on Vectors**

Given vectors **u** = ⟨a, b⟩, **v** = ⟨c, d⟩, and a scalar k,

$$\textbf{1. } \mathbf{u} + \mathbf{v} = \langle a + c, b + d \rangle$$
$$\textbf{2. } \mathbf{u} - \mathbf{v} = \langle a - c, b - d \rangle$$
$$\textbf{3. } k\mathbf{u} = \langle ka, kb \rangle \text{ for } k \in \mathbb{R}$$

If $k > 0$, the new vector points in the same direction as **u**.
If $k < 0$, the new vector points in the opposite direction as **u**.

**EXAMPLE 5** ▶   **Representing Operations on Vectors Graphically**

Given $\mathbf{u} = \langle -3, -2 \rangle$ and $\mathbf{v} = \langle 4, -6 \rangle$ compute each of the following and represent the result graphically:

**a.** $-2\mathbf{u}$     **b.** $\dfrac{1}{2}\mathbf{v}$     **c.** $-2\mathbf{u} + \dfrac{1}{2}\mathbf{v}$

Note the relationship between part (c) and parts (a) and (b).

**Solution** ▶   **a.** $-2\mathbf{u} = -2\langle -3, -2 \rangle$          **b.** $\dfrac{1}{2}\mathbf{v} = \dfrac{1}{2}\langle 4, -6 \rangle$     **c.** $-2\mathbf{u} + \dfrac{1}{2}\mathbf{v} = \langle 6, 4 \rangle + \langle 2, -3 \rangle$

$= \langle 6, 4 \rangle$                                    $= \langle 2, -3 \rangle$                               $= \langle 8, 1 \rangle$

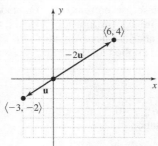 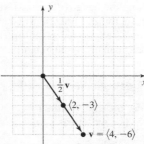 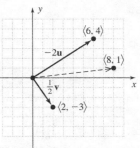

**Now try Exercises 31 through 48** ▶

The properties that guide operations on vectors closely resemble the familiar properties of real numbers. Note we define the zero vector $\mathbf{0} = \langle 0, 0 \rangle$ as one having no magnitude or direction.

---

**Properties of Vectors**

For vector quantities $\mathbf{u}$, $\mathbf{v}$, and $\mathbf{w}$ and real numbers $c$ and $k$,

**1.** $1\mathbf{u} = \mathbf{u}$                                     **2.** $0\mathbf{u} = \mathbf{0} = k\mathbf{0}$
**3.** $\mathbf{u} + \mathbf{v} = \mathbf{v} + \mathbf{u}$                            **4.** $\mathbf{u} - \mathbf{v} = \mathbf{u} + (-\mathbf{v})$
**5.** $(\mathbf{u} + \mathbf{v}) + \mathbf{w} = \mathbf{u} + (\mathbf{v} + \mathbf{w})$          **6.** $(ck)\mathbf{u} = c(k\mathbf{u}) = k(c\mathbf{u})$
**7.** $\mathbf{u} + \mathbf{0} = \mathbf{u}$                            **8.** $\mathbf{u} + (-\mathbf{u}) = \mathbf{0}$
**9.** $k(\mathbf{u} + \mathbf{v}) = k\mathbf{u} + k\mathbf{v}$                  **10.** $(c + k)\mathbf{u} = c\mathbf{u} + k\mathbf{u}$

---

**Proof of Property 3**

For $\mathbf{u} = \langle a, b \rangle$ and $\mathbf{v} = \langle c, d \rangle$, we have

$$\mathbf{u} + \mathbf{v} = \langle a, b \rangle + \langle c, d \rangle \quad \text{sum of } \mathbf{u} \text{ and } \mathbf{v}$$

$$= \langle a + c, b + d \rangle \quad \text{vector addition}$$

$$= \langle c + a, d + b \rangle \quad \text{commutative property}$$

$$= \langle c, d \rangle + \langle a, b \rangle \quad \text{vector addition}$$

☑ **C.** You've just learned how to perform defined operations on vectors

$$= \mathbf{v} + \mathbf{u} \quad \text{result}$$

Proofs of the other properties are similarly derived (see **Exercises 89 through 97**).

## D. Algebraic Vectors, Unit Vectors, and i, j Form

While the bold, small case **v** and the $\langle a, b\rangle$ notation for vectors has served us well, we now introduce an alternative form that is somewhat better suited to the **algebra of vectors,** and is used extensively in some of the physical sciences. Consider the vector $\langle 1, 0\rangle$, a vector 1 unit in length extending along the $x$-axis. It is called the **horizontal unit vector** and given the special designation **i** (not to be confused with the imaginary unit $i = \sqrt{-1}$). Likewise, the vector $\langle 0, 1\rangle$ is called the **vertical unit vector** and given the designation **j** (see Figure 7.45). Using scalar multiplication, the unit vector along the negative $x$-axis is $-$**i** and along the negative $y$-axis is $-$**j.** Similarly, the vector 4**i** represents a position vector 4 units long along the $x$-axis, and $-5$**j** represents a position vector 5 units long along the negative $y$-axis. Using these conventions, any nonquadrantal vector $\langle a, b\rangle$ can be written as a **linear combination** of **i** and **j,** with $a$ and $b$ expressed as multiples of **i** and **j,** respectively: $a\mathbf{i} + b\mathbf{j}$. These ideas can easily be generalized and applied to any vector.

**Figure 7.45**

**WORTHY OF NOTE**

Earlier we stated, "Two vectors are equal if they have the same magnitude and direction." Note that this means two vectors are equal if *their components are equal.*

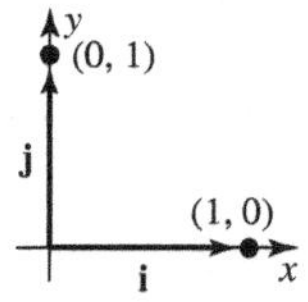

**Algebraic Vectors and i, j Form**

For the unit vectors $\mathbf{i} = \langle 1, 0\rangle$ and $\mathbf{j} = \langle 0, 1\rangle$, any arbitrary vector $\mathbf{v} = \langle a, b\rangle$ can be written as a linear combination of **i** and **j:**

$$\mathbf{v} = a\mathbf{i} + b\mathbf{j}$$

Graphically, **v** is being expressed as the resultant of a vector sum.

**EXAMPLE 6 ▶ Finding the Horizontal and Vertical Components of Algebraic Vectors**

Vector **u** is in QII, has a magnitude of 15, and makes an angle of 20° with the negative $x$-axis.

**a.** Graph the vector.

**b.** Find the horizontal and vertical components (round to one decimal place) then write **u** in component form.

**c.** Write **u** in terms of **i** and **j**.

**Solution ▶** **a.** The vector is graphed in Figure 7.46.

**Figure 7.46**

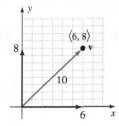

**b. Horizontal Component**

$$a = |\mathbf{v}|\cos\theta = 15\cos 160° \approx -14.1$$

**Vertical Component**

$$b = |\mathbf{v}|\sin\theta = 15\sin 160° \approx 5.1$$

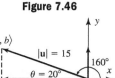

With the vector in QII, $\mathbf{u} = \langle -14.1, 5.1\rangle$ in component form.

**c.** In terms of **i** and **j** we have $\mathbf{u} = -14.1\mathbf{i} + 5.1\mathbf{j}$. See Figure 7.47.

**Figure 7.47**

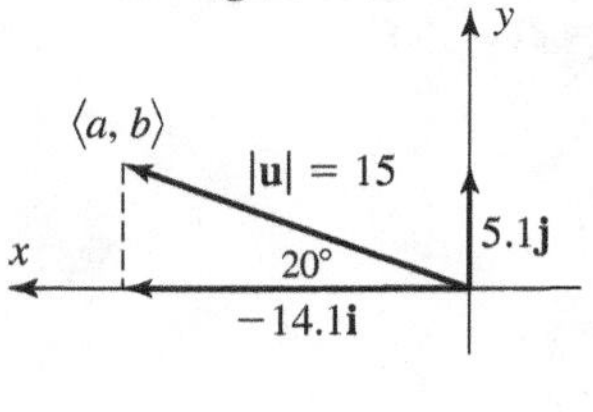

**Now try Exercises 49 through 62 ▶**

**Figure 7.48**

Some applications require that we find a nonhorizontal, nonvertical vector one unit in length, having the same direction as a given vector **v.** To understand how this is done, consider vector $\mathbf{v} = \langle 6, 8\rangle$. Using the Pythagorean theorem we find $|\mathbf{v}| = 10$, and can form a 6-8-10 triangle using the horizontal and vertical components (Figure 7.48). Knowing that similar triangles have sides that are proportional, we can find a unit vector in the same direction as **v** by dividing all three sides by 10, giving a triangle with sides $\frac{3}{5}$, $\frac{4}{5}$, and 1. The new vector **"u"** (along the hypotenuse) indeed points in the same direction since we have merely shortened **v,** and is a unit vector since $\left(\frac{3}{5}\right)^2 + \left(\frac{4}{5}\right)^2 \to \frac{9}{25} + \frac{16}{25} = 1$. In retrospect, we have divided the components of vector **v** by its magnitude |**v**| (or multiplied components by the reciprocal of |**v**|) to obtain the desired unit vector: $\dfrac{\mathbf{v}}{|\mathbf{v}|} = \dfrac{\langle 6, 8 \rangle}{10} = \left\langle \dfrac{6}{10}, \dfrac{8}{10} \right\rangle = \left\langle \dfrac{3}{5}, \dfrac{4}{5} \right\rangle$. In general we have the following:

---

### Unit Vectors

For any nonzero vector $\mathbf{v} = \langle a, b \rangle = a\mathbf{i} + b\mathbf{j}$, the vector

$$\mathbf{u} = \frac{\mathbf{v}}{|\mathbf{v}|} = \frac{a}{\sqrt{a^2 + b^2}}\mathbf{i} + \frac{b}{\sqrt{a^2 + b^2}}\mathbf{j}$$

is a unit vector in the same direction as **v.**

---

You are asked to verify this relationship in **Exercise 100.** In summary, for vector $\mathbf{v} = 6\mathbf{i} + 8\mathbf{j}$, we find $|\mathbf{v}| = \sqrt{6^2 + 8^2} = 10$, so the unit vector pointing in the same direction is $\dfrac{\mathbf{v}}{|\mathbf{v}|} = \dfrac{3}{5}\mathbf{i} + \dfrac{4}{5}\mathbf{j}$. **See Exercises 63 through 74.**

---

**EXAMPLE 7** ▶   **Using Unit Vectors to Find Coincident Vectors**

Vectors **u** and **v** form the 37° angle illustrated in the figure. Find the vector **w** (in red), which points in the same direction as **v** (is coincident with **v**) and forms the base of the right triangle shown.

**Solution** ▶   Using the Pythagorean theorem we find $|\mathbf{u}| \approx 7.3$ and $|\mathbf{v}| = 10$. Using the cosine of 37° the magnitude of **w** is then $|\mathbf{w}| \approx 7.3 \cos 37°$ or about 5.8. To ensure that **w** will point in the same direction as **v**, we simply multiply the 5.8 magnitude by the unit vector for **v**: $|\mathbf{w}| \dfrac{\mathbf{v}}{|\mathbf{v}|} \approx (5.8)\dfrac{\langle 8, 6 \rangle}{10} = (5.8)\langle 0.8, 0.6 \rangle$, and we find that $\mathbf{w} \approx \langle 4.6, 3.5 \rangle$. As a check we use the Pythagorean theorem: $\sqrt{4.6^2 + 3.5^2} = \sqrt{33.41} \approx 5.8$.

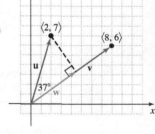

**WORTHY OF NOTE**

In this context, **w** is called the projection of **u** on **v**, an idea applied more extensively in Section 7.4

☑ **D.** You've just learned how to represent a vector quantity algebraically and find unit vectors

**Now try Exercises 75 through 78** ▶

## E. Vector Diagrams and Vector Applications

Applications of vectors are virtually unlimited, with many of these in the applied sciences. Here we'll look at two applications that are an extension of our work in this section. In Section 7.4 we'll see how vectors can be applied in a number of other creative and useful ways.

In Example 1, two tugboats were pulling on a barge to dislodge it from a sand bar, with the pulling force of each represented by a vector. Using our knowledge of vector components, vector addition, and **resultant forces** (a force exerted along the resultant), we can now determine the direction and magnitude of the resultant force if we know the angle formed by one of the vector forces and the barge.

**EXAMPLE 8** ▶  **Solving an Application of Vectors—Force Vectors Acting on a Barge**

Two tugboats are attempting to free a barge that is stuck on a sand bar, and are exerting the forces shown in Figure 7.49. Find the magnitude and direction of the resultant force.

**Figure 7.49**

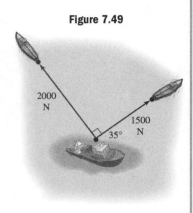

Solution ▶  Begin by orienting the diagram on a coordinate grid (see Figure 7.50). Since the angle between the vectors is 90°, we know the acute angle formed by the first tugboat and the $x$-axis is 55°. With this information, we can write each vector in "**i, j**" form and add the vectors to find the resultant.

For vector $\mathbf{v}_1$ (in QII):

| Horizontal Component | Vertical Component |
|---|---|
| $a = |\mathbf{v}_1|\cos\theta$ | $b = |\mathbf{v}_1|\sin\theta$ |
| $= 2000\cos 125°$ | $= 2000\sin 125°$ |
| $\approx -1147$ | $\approx 1638$ |

$$\mathbf{v}_1 \approx -1147\mathbf{i} + 1638\mathbf{j}$$

For vector $\mathbf{v}_2$ (in QI):

**Figure 7.50**

| Horizontal Component | Vertical Component |
|---|---|
| $a = |\mathbf{v}_2|\cos\theta$ | $b = |\mathbf{v}_2|\sin\theta$ |
| $= 1500\cos 35°$ | $= 1500\sin 35°$ |
| $\approx 1229$ | $\approx 860$ |

$$\mathbf{v}_2 \approx 1229\mathbf{i} + 860\mathbf{j}$$

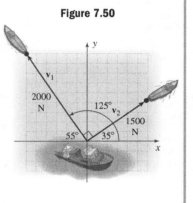

This gives a resultant of $\mathbf{v}_1 + \mathbf{v}_2 \approx (-1147\mathbf{i} + 1638\mathbf{j}) + (1229\mathbf{i} + 860\mathbf{j}) = 82\mathbf{i} + 2498\mathbf{j}$, with magnitude $|\mathbf{v}_1 + \mathbf{v}_2| \approx \sqrt{82^2 + 2498^2} \approx 2499$ N. To find the direction of the force, we have $\theta_r = \tan^{-1}\left|\dfrac{2498}{82}\right|$, or about 88°.

**Now try Exercises 81 and 82** ▶

It's worth noting that a single tugboat pulling at 88° with a force of 2499 N would have the same effect as the two tugs in the original diagram. In other words, the resultant vector $82\mathbf{i} + 2498\mathbf{j}$ truly represents the "result" of the two forces.

Knowing that the location of a vector is unimportant enables us to model and solve a great number of seemingly unrelated applications. Although the final example concerns aviation, **headings,** and crosswinds, the solution process has a striking similarity to the "tugboat" example just discussed. In navigation, headings involve a single angle, which is understood to be the amount of rotation from due north in the clockwise direction. Several headings are illustrated in Figures 7.51 through 7.54.

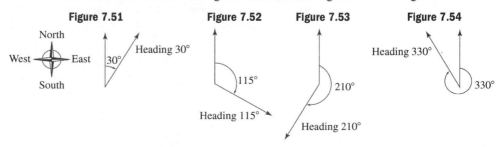

Figure 7.51    Figure 7.52    Figure 7.53    Figure 7.54

In order to keep an airplane on course, the captain must consider the direction and speed of any wind currents, since the plane's true course (relative to the ground) will be affected. Both the plane and the wind can be represented by vectors, with the plane's true course being the resultant vector.

---

**EXAMPLE 9** ▶ **Solving an Application of Vectors—Airplane Navigation**

An airplane is flying at 240 mph, heading 75°, when it suddenly encounters a strong, 60 mph wind blowing *from* the southwest, heading 10°. What is the actual course and speed of the plane (relative to the ground) as it flies through this wind?

**Solution** ▶ Begin by drawing a vector **p** to represent the speed and direction of the airplane (Figure 7.55). Since the heading is 75°, the angle between the vector and the *x*-axis must be 15°. For convenience (and because location is unimportant) we draw it as a position vector. Note the vector **w** representing the wind will be $\frac{60}{240} = \frac{1}{4}$ as long, and can also be drawn as a position vector—with an acute 80° angle. To find the resultant, we first find the components of each vector, then add. For vector **w** (in QI):

**Figure 7.55**

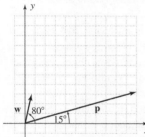

| Horizontal Component | Vertical Component |
|---|---|
| $a = |\mathbf{w}|\cos\theta$ | $b = |\mathbf{w}|\sin\theta$ |
| $= 60\cos 80°$ | $= 60\sin 80°$ |
| $\approx 10.4$ | $\approx 59.1$ |

$$\mathbf{w} \approx 10.4\mathbf{i} + 59.1\mathbf{j}$$

For vector **p** (in QI):

| Horizontal Component | Vertical Component |
|---|---|
| $a = |\mathbf{p}|\cos\theta$ | $b = |\mathbf{p}|\sin\theta$ |
| $= 240\cos 15°$ | $= 240\sin 15°$ |
| $= 231.8$ | $\approx 62.1$ |

$$\mathbf{p} \approx 231.8\mathbf{i} + 62.1\mathbf{j}$$

**Figure 7.56**

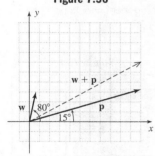

The resultant is $\mathbf{w} + \mathbf{p} \approx (10.4\mathbf{i} + 59.1\mathbf{j}) + (231.8\mathbf{i} + 62.1\mathbf{j}) = 242.2\mathbf{i} + 121.2\mathbf{j}$, with magnitude $|\mathbf{w} + \mathbf{p}| \approx \sqrt{(242.2)^2 + (121.2)^2} \approx 270.8$ mph (see Figure 7.56). To find the heading of the plane relative to the ground we use $\theta_r = \tan^{-1}\left|\frac{121.2}{242.2}\right|$, which shows $\theta_r \approx 26.6°$. The plane is flying on a course heading of $90° - 26.6° = 63.4°$ at a speed of about 270.8 mph relative to the ground. Note the airplane has actually "increased speed" due to the wind.

**Now try Exercises 83 through 86** ▶

---

**WORTHY OF NOTE**

Be aware that using the rounded values of intermediate calculations may cause slight variations in the final result. In Example 9, if we calculate **w** + **p** = $(60\cos 80° + 240\cos 15°)\mathbf{i}$ + $(60\sin 80° + 240\sin 15°)\mathbf{j}$, then find $|\mathbf{w} + \mathbf{p}|$, the result is actually closer to 270.9 mph.

Applications like those in Examples 8 and 9 can also be solved using what is called the **parallelogram method,** which takes its name from the tail-to-tip vector addition noted earlier (See Figure 7.57). The resultant will be a diagonal of the parallelogram, whose magnitude can be found using the law of cosines. For Example 9, we note the parallelogram has two acute angles of $(80 - 15)° = 65°$, and since the adjacent angles must sum to 180°, the obtuse angles must be 115°. Using the law of cosines,

**Figure 7.57**

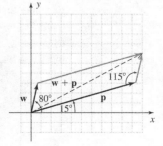

$$|\mathbf{w} + \mathbf{p}|^2 = \mathbf{p}^2 + \mathbf{w}^2 - 2\mathbf{pw}\cos 115° \qquad \text{law of cosines}$$
$$= 240^2 + 60^2 - 2(240)(60)\cos 115° \qquad \text{substitute 240 for } \mathbf{p}, \text{ 60 for } \mathbf{w}$$
$$= 73371.40594 \qquad \text{compute result}$$
$$|\mathbf{w} + \mathbf{p}| \approx 270.9 \qquad \text{take square roots}$$

✓ **E.** You've just learned how to use vector diagrams to solve applications

Note this answer is slightly more accurate, since there was no rounding until the final stage.

## TECHNOLOGY HIGHLIGHT

### Vector Components Given the Magnitude and the Angle $\theta$

The TABLE feature of a graphing calculator can help us find the horizontal and vertical components of any vector with ease. Consider the vector **v** shown in Figure 7.58, which has a magnitude of 9.5 with $\theta = 15°$. Knowing this magnitude is used in both computations, first store 9.5 in storage location A: 9.5 [STO →] [ALPHA] [MATH] . Next, enter the expressions for the horizontal and vertical components as $Y_1$ and $Y_2$ on the [Y =] screen (see Figure 7.59). Note that storing the magnitude 9.5 in memory will prevent our having to alter $Y_1$ and $Y_2$ as we apply these ideas to other values of $\theta$. As an additional check, note that $Y_3$ recomputes the magnitude of the vector using the components generated in $Y_1$ and $Y_2$. To access the function variables we press: [VARS] [ ► ] [ENTER] and select the desired function. Although our primary interest is the components for $\theta = 15°$, we use the TBLSET screen to begin at TblStart = 0, $\Delta$Tbl = 5, and have it count **AUTO**matically, so we can make additional observations. Pressing [2nd] [GRAPH] (**TABLE**) brings up the screen shown in Figure 7.60. As expected, at $\theta = 0°$ the horizontal component is the same as the magnitude and the vertical component is zero. At $\theta = 15°$ we have the components of the vector pictured in Figure 7.58, approximately $\langle 9.18, 2.46 \rangle$. If the angle were increased to $\theta = 30°$, a 30-60-90 triangle could be formed and one component should be $\sqrt{3}$ times the other. Sure enough, $\sqrt{3}(4.75) \approx 8.2272$.

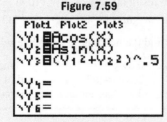

**Figure 7.58**

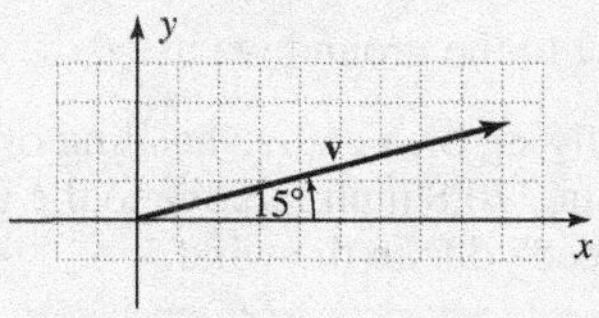

**Figure 7.59**

**Figure 7.60**

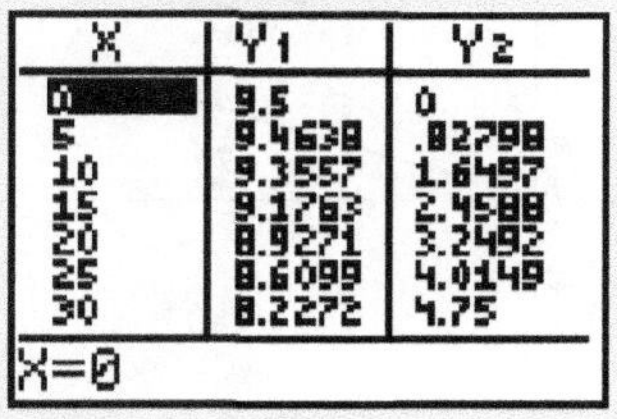

**Exercise 1:**  If $\theta = 45°$, what would you know about the lengths of the horizontal and vertical components? Scroll down to $\theta = 45°$ to verify.

**Exercise 2:**  If $\theta = 60°$, what would you know about the lengths of the horizontal and vertical components? Scroll down to $\theta = 60°$ to verify.

**Exercise 3:**  We used column $Y_3$ as a double check on the magnitude of **v** for any given $\theta$. What would this value be for $\theta = 45°$ and $\theta = 60°$? Press the right arrow [ ► ] to verify. What do you notice?

 **7.3 EXERCISES**

▶ **CONCEPTS AND VOCABULARY**

**Fill in each blank with the appropriate word or phrase. Carefully reread the section if needed.**

1. Measurements that can be described using a single number are called _____ quantities.

2. _____ quantities require more than a single number to describe their attributes. Examples are force, velocity, and displacement.

3. To represent a vector quantity geometrically we use a _____ _____ segment.

4. Two vectors are equal if they have the same _____ and _____.

5. Discuss/Explain the geometric interpretation of vector addition. Give several examples and illustrations.

6. Describe the process of finding a resultant vector given the magnitude and direction of two arbitrary vectors **u** and **v**. Follow-up with an example.

▶ **DEVELOPING YOUR SKILLS**

**Draw the comparative geometric vectors indicated.**

7. Three oceanic research vessels are traveling on a parallel course in the same direction, mapping the ocean floor. One ship is traveling at 12 knots (nautical miles per hour), one at 9 knots, and the third at 6 knots.

8. As part of family reunion activities, the Williams Clan is at a bowling alley and using three lanes. Being amateurs they all roll the ball straight on, aiming for the 1 pin. Grand Dad in Lane 1 rolls his ball at 50 ft/sec. Papa in Lane 2 lets it rip at 60 ft/sec, while Junior in Lane 3 can muster only 30 ft/sec.

9. Vector $v_1$ is a geometric vector representing a boat traveling at 20 knots. Vectors $v_2$, $v_3$, and $v_4$ are geometric vectors representing boats traveling at 10 knots, 15 knots, and 25 knots, respectively. Draw these vectors given that $v_2$ and $v_3$ are traveling the same direction and parallel to $v_1$, while $v_4$ is traveling in the opposite direction and parallel to $v_1$.

10. Vector $F_1$ is a geometric vector representing a force of 50 N. Vectors $F_2$, $F_3$, and $F_4$ are geometric vectors representing forces of 25 N, 35 N, and 65 N, respectively. Draw these vectors given that $F_2$ and $F_3$ are applied in the same direction and parallel to $F_1$, while $F_4$ is applied in the opposite direction and parallel to $F_1$.

**Represent each situation described using geometric vectors.**

11. Two tractors are pulling at a stump in an effort to clear land for more crops. The Massey-Ferguson is pulling with a force of 250 N, while the John Deere is pulling with a force of 210 N. The chains attached to the stump and each tractor form a 25° angle.

12. In an effort to get their mule up and plowing again, Jackson and Rupert are pulling on ropes attached to the mule's harness. Jackson pulls with 200 lb of force, while Rupert, who is really upset, pulls with 220 lb of force. The angle between their ropes is 16°.

**Draw the vector v indicated, then graph the equivalent position vector.**

13. initial point $(-3, 2)$; terminal point $(4, 5)$

14. initial point $(-4, -4)$; terminal point $(2, 3)$

15. initial point $(5, -3)$; terminal point $(-1, 2)$

16. initial point $(1, 4)$; terminal point $(-2, 2)$

**For each vector $v = \langle a, b \rangle$ and initial point $(x, y)$ given, find the coordinates of the terminal point and the length of the vector.**

17. $v = \langle 7, 2 \rangle$; initial point $(-2, -3)$

18. $v = \langle -6, 1 \rangle$; initial point $(5, -2)$

19. $v = \langle -3, -5 \rangle$; initial point $(2, 6)$

20. $v = \langle 8, -2 \rangle$; initial point $(-3, -5)$

For each position vector given, (a) graph the vector and name the quadrant, (b) compute its magnitude, and (c) find the acute angle $\theta$ formed by the vector and the nearest $x$-axis.

**21.** $\langle 8, 3 \rangle$          **22.** $\langle -7, 6 \rangle$

**23.** $\langle -2, -5 \rangle$      **24.** $\langle 8, -6 \rangle$

For Exercises 25 through 30, the magnitude of a vector is given, along with the quadrant of the terminal point and the angle it makes with the nearest $x$-axis. Find the horizontal and vertical components of each vector and write the result in component form.

**25.** $|\mathbf{v}| = 12; \theta = 25°;$ QII

**26.** $|\mathbf{u}| = 25; \theta = 32°;$ QIII

**27.** $|\mathbf{w}| = 140.5; \theta = 41°;$ QIV

**28.** $|\mathbf{p}| = 15; \theta = 65°;$ QI

**29.** $|\mathbf{q}| = 10; \theta = 15°;$ QIII

**30.** $|\mathbf{r}| = 4.75; \theta = 62°;$ QII

For each pair of vectors u and v given, compute (a) through (d) and illustrate the indicated operations graphically.

  **a. u + v**          **b. u − v**
  **c. 2u + 1.5v**      **d. u − 2v**

**31.** $\mathbf{u} = \langle 2, 3 \rangle; \mathbf{v} = \langle -3, 6 \rangle$

**32.** $\mathbf{u} = \langle -3, -4 \rangle; \mathbf{v} = \langle 0, 5 \rangle$

**33.** $\mathbf{u} = \langle 7, -2 \rangle; \mathbf{v} = \langle 1, 6 \rangle$

**34.** $\mathbf{u} = \langle -5, -3 \rangle; \mathbf{v} = \langle 6, -4 \rangle$

**35.** $\mathbf{u} = \langle -4, 2 \rangle; \mathbf{v} = \langle 1, 4 \rangle$

**36.** $\mathbf{u} = \langle 7, 3 \rangle; \mathbf{v} = \langle -7, 3 \rangle$

Use the graphs of vectors a, b, c, d, e, f, g, and h given to determine if the following statements are true or false.

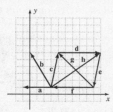

**37.** a + c = b          **38.** f − e = g

**39.** c + f = h          **40.** b + h = c

**41.** d − e = h          **42.** d + f = 0

For the vectors u and v shown, compute u + v and u − v and represent each result graphically.

**43.** 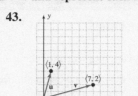      **44.**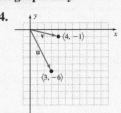

**45.** 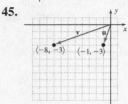      **46.**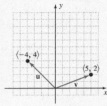

**47.** 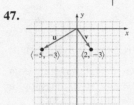      **48.**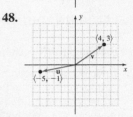

Graph each vector and write it as a linear combination of i and j. Then compute its magnitude.

**49.** $\mathbf{u} = \langle 8, 15 \rangle$      **50.** $\mathbf{v} = \langle -5, 12 \rangle$

**51.** $\mathbf{p} = \langle -3.2, -5.7 \rangle$      **52.** $\mathbf{q} = \langle 7.5, -3.4 \rangle$

For each vector here, $\theta_r$ represents the acute angle formed by the vector and the $x$-axis. (a) Graph each vector, (b) find the horizontal and vertical components and write the vector in component form, and (c) write the vector in i, j form. Round to the nearest tenth.

**53.** v in QIII, $|\mathbf{v}| = 12, \theta_r = 16°$

**54.** u in QII, $|\mathbf{u}| = 10.5, \theta_r = 25°$

**55.** w in QI, $|\mathbf{w}| = 9.5, \theta_r = 74.5°$

**56.** v in QIV, $|\mathbf{v}| = 20, \theta_r = 32.6°$

For vectors $v_1$ and $v_2$ given, compute the vector sums (a) through (d) and find the magnitude and direction of each resultant.

  **a.** $\mathbf{v}_1 + \mathbf{v}_2 = \mathbf{p}$       **b.** $\mathbf{v}_1 - \mathbf{v}_2 = \mathbf{q}$
  **c.** $2\mathbf{v}_1 + 1.5\mathbf{v}_2 = \mathbf{r}$    **d.** $\mathbf{v}_1 - 2\mathbf{v}_2 = \mathbf{s}$

**57.** $\mathbf{v}_1 = 2\mathbf{i} - 3\mathbf{j}; \mathbf{v}_2 = -4\mathbf{i} + 5\mathbf{j}$

**58.** $\mathbf{v}_1 = 7.8\mathbf{i} + 4.2\mathbf{j}; \mathbf{v}_2 = 5\mathbf{j}$

**59.** $\mathbf{v}_1 = 5\sqrt{2}\mathbf{i} + 7\mathbf{j}; \mathbf{v}_2 = -3\sqrt{2}\mathbf{i} - 5\mathbf{j}$

**60.** $v_1 = 6.8i - 9j$; $v_2 = -4i + 9j$

**61.** $v_1 = 12i + 4j$; $v_2 = -4i$

**62.** $v_1 = 2\sqrt{3}i - 6j$; $v_2 = -4\sqrt{3}i + 2j$

**Find a unit vector pointing in the same direction as the vector given. Verify that a unit vector was found.**

**63.** $u = \langle 7, 24 \rangle$       **64.** $v = \langle -15, 36 \rangle$

**65.** $p = \langle -20, 21 \rangle$       **66.** $q = \langle 12, -35 \rangle$

**67.** $20i - 21j$       **68.** $-4i - 7.5j$

**69.** $3.5i + 12j$       **70.** $-9.6i + 18j$

**71.** $v_1 = \langle 13, 3 \rangle$       **72.** $v_2 = \langle -4, 7 \rangle$

**73.** $6i + 11j$       **74.** $-2.5i + 7.2j$

**Vectors p and q form the angle indicated in each diagram. Find the vector r that points in the same direction as q and forms the base of the right triangle shown.**

**75.**
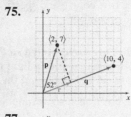

**76.**
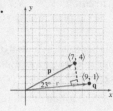

**77.**
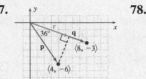

**78.**
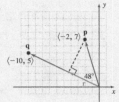

▶ **WORKING WITH FORMULAS**

**The magnitude of a vector in three dimensions:** $|v| = \sqrt{a^2 + b^2 + c^2}$

**79.** The magnitude of a vector in three dimensional space is given by the formula shown, where the components of the position vector **v** are $\langle a, b, c \rangle$. Find the magnitude of **v** if $v = \langle 5, 9, 10 \rangle$.

**80.** Find a cardboard box of any size and carefully measure its length, width, and height. Then use the given formula to find the magnitude of the box's diagonal. Verify your calculation by direct measurement.

▶ **APPLICATIONS**

**81. Tow forces:** A large van has careened off of the road into a ditch, and two tow trucks are attempting to winch it out. The cable from the first winch exerts a force of 900 lb, while the cable from the second exerts a force of 700 lb. Determine the angle $\theta$ for the first tow truck that will bring the van directly out of the ditch and along the line indicated.

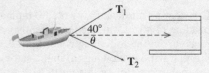

**82. Tow forces:** Two tugboats are pulling a large ship into dry dock. The first is pulling with a force of 1250 N and the second with a force of 1750 N. Determine the angle $\theta$ for the second tugboat that will keep the ship moving straight forward and into the dock.

**83. Projectile components:** An arrow is shot into the air at an angle of 37° with an initial velocity of 100 ft/sec. Compute the horizontal and vertical components of the representative vector.

**84. Projectile components:** A football is punted (kicked) into the air at an angle of 42° with an initial velocity of 20 m/sec. Compute the horizontal and vertical components of the representative vector.

**85. Headings and cross-winds:** An airplane is flying at 250 mph on a heading of 75°. There is a strong, 35 mph wind blowing from the southwest on a heading of 10°. What is the true course and speed of the plane (relative to the ground)?

**86. Headings and currents:** A cruise ship is traveling at 16 knots on a heading of 300°. There is a strong water current flowing at 6 knots from the northwest on a heading of 120°. What is the true course and speed of the cruise ship?

The lights used in a dentist's office are multijointed so they can be configured in multiple ways to accommodate various needs. As a simple model, consider such a light that has the three joints, as illustrated. The first segment has a length of 45 cm, the second is 40 cm in length, and the third is 35 cm.

**87.** If the joints of the light are positioned so a straight line is formed and the angle made with the horizontal is 15°, determine the approximate coordinates of the joint nearest the light.

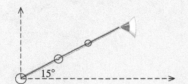

**88.** If the first segment is rotated 75° above horizontal, the second segment −30° (below the horizontal), and the third segment is parallel to the horizontal, determine the approximate coordinates of the joint nearest the light.

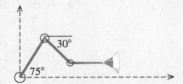

▶ **EXTENDING THE CONCEPT**

For the arbitrary vectors $\mathbf{u} = \langle a, b \rangle$, $\mathbf{v} = \langle c, d \rangle$, and $\mathbf{w} = \langle e, f \rangle$ and the scalars $c$ and $k$, prove the following vector properties using the properties of real numbers.

**89.** $1\mathbf{u} = \mathbf{u}$      **90.** $0\mathbf{u} = \mathbf{0} = k\mathbf{0}$

**91.** $\mathbf{u} - \mathbf{v} = \mathbf{u} + (-\mathbf{v})$

**92.** $(\mathbf{u} + \mathbf{v}) + \mathbf{w} = \mathbf{u} + (\mathbf{v} + \mathbf{w})$

**93.** $(ck)\mathbf{u} = c(k\mathbf{u}) = k(c\mathbf{u})$

**94.** $\mathbf{u} + \mathbf{0} = \mathbf{u}$      **95.** $\mathbf{u} + (-\mathbf{u}) = \mathbf{0}$

**96.** $k(\mathbf{u} + \mathbf{v}) = k\mathbf{u} + k\mathbf{v}$    **97.** $(c + k)\mathbf{u} = c\mathbf{u} + k\mathbf{u}$

**98.** Consider an airplane flying at 200 mph at a heading of 45°. Compute the groundspeed of the plane under the following conditions. A strong, 40-mph wind is blowing (a) in the same direction; (b) in the direction of due north (0°); (c) in the direction heading 315°; (d) in the direction heading 270°; and (e) in the direction heading 225°. What did you notice about the groundspeed for (a) and (b)? Explain why the plane's speed is greater than 200 mph for (a) and (b), but less than 200 mph for the others.

**99.** Show that the sum of the vectors given, which form the sides of a closed polygon, is the zero vector. Assume all vectors have integer coordinates and each tick mark is 1 unit.

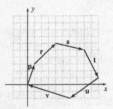

**100.** Verify that for $\mathbf{v} = a\mathbf{i} + b\mathbf{j}$ and
$$|\mathbf{v}| = \sqrt{a^2 + b^2}, \frac{\mathbf{v}}{|\mathbf{v}|} = 1.$$

(*Hint:* Create the vector $\mathbf{u} = \dfrac{\mathbf{v}}{|\mathbf{v}|}$ and find its magnitude.)

**101.** Referring to Exercises 87 and 88, suppose the dentist needed the pivot joint at the light (the furthest joint from the wall) to be at (80, 20) for a certain patient or procedure. Find at least one set of "joint angles" that will make this possible.

## ▶ MAINTAINING YOUR SKILLS

**102.** (2.3) Mt. Tortolas lies on the Argentine-Chilean border. When viewed from a distance of 5 mi, the angle of elevation to the top of the peak is 38°. How tall is Mount Tortolas? State your answer in feet.

**103.** (5.1) Prove the following is an identity:

$$2 \sec^2\theta = \frac{1}{1 + \sin\theta} + \frac{1}{1 - \sin\theta}$$

**104.** (4.3) Graph the function $y = 3 \sin\left(2x - \dfrac{\pi}{4}\right)$ using a reference rectangle and the *rule of fourths*.

**105.** (1.4) Use fundamental identities to find the values of all six trig functions that satisfy the conditions, $\sec x = \dfrac{13}{12}$ and $\sin x > 0$.

**106.** (7.2) The satellite Jupiter VII measures its distance from Denver and from Louisville using radio waves as shown. With an onboard sighting device, the satellite is able to determine that $\angle J$ is 98°. How many miles is it from Denver to Louisville?

**Exercise 106**

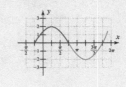

**107.** (4.3) Find the equation of the graph shown, (a) given it is of the form $y = A \sin(Bx \pm C)$ and (b) given it is of the form $y = A \cos(Bx \pm C)$.

In Section 7.3 we introduced the concept of a vector, with its geometric, graphical, and algebraic representations. We also looked at operations on vectors and employed vector diagrams to solve basic applications. In this section we introduce additional ideas that enable us to solve a variety of new applications, while laying a strong foundation for future studies.

## A. Vectors and Equilibrium

Much like the intuitive meaning of the word, vector forces are in **equilibrium** when they "counterbalance" each other. The simplest example is two vector forces of equal magnitude acting on the same point but in opposite directions. Similar to a tug-of-war with both sides equally matched, no one wins. If vector $\mathbf{F}_1$ has a magnitude of 500 lb in the positive direction, $\mathbf{F}_1 = \langle 500, 0 \rangle$ would need vector $\mathbf{F}_2 = \langle -500, 0 \rangle$ to counter it. If the forces are nonquadrantal, we intuitively sense the components must still sum to zero, and that $\mathbf{F}_3 = \langle 600, -200 \rangle$ would need $\mathbf{F}_4 = \langle -600, 200 \rangle$ for equilibrium to occur (see Figure 7.61). In other words, two vectors are in equilibrium when their sum is

**Figure 7.61**

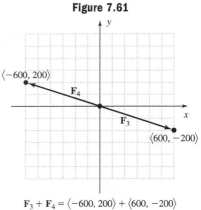

$$\mathbf{F}_3 + \mathbf{F}_4 = \langle -600, 200 \rangle + \langle 600, -200 \rangle$$
$$= \langle 0, 0 \rangle = \mathbf{0}$$

the zero vector **0.** If the forces have unequal magnitudes or do not pull in opposite directions, recall a resultant vector $\mathbf{F} = \mathbf{F}_a + \mathbf{F}_b$ can be found that represents the combined force. Equilibrium will then occur by adding the vector $-1(\mathbf{F})$ and this vector is sometimes called the **equilibriant.**

These ideas can be extended to include any number of vector forces acting on the same point. In general, we have the following:

---

**Vectors and Equilibrium**

Given vectors $\mathbf{F}_1, \mathbf{F}_2, \ldots, \mathbf{F}_n$ acting on a point $P$,
1. The resultant vector is $\mathbf{F} = \mathbf{F}_1 + \mathbf{F}_2 + \cdots + \mathbf{F}_n$.
2. Equilibrium for these forces requires the vector $-1\mathbf{F}$, where $\mathbf{F} + (-1\mathbf{F}) = \mathbf{0}$.

---

**EXAMPLE 1** ▶ **Finding the Equilibriant for Vector Forces**

Two force vectors $\mathbf{F}_1$ and $\mathbf{F}_2$ act on the point $P$ as shown. Find a force $\mathbf{F}_3$ so equilibrium will occur, and sketch it on the grid.

Solution ▶ Begin by finding the horizontal and vertical components of each vector. For $\mathbf{F}_1$ we have $\langle -4.5 \cos 64°, 4.5 \sin 64° \rangle \approx \langle -2.0, 4.0 \rangle$, and for $\mathbf{F}_2$ we have $\langle 6.3 \cos 18°, 6.3 \sin 18° \rangle \approx \langle 6.0, 1.9 \rangle$. The resultant vector is $\mathbf{F} = \mathbf{F}_1 + \mathbf{F}_2 = \langle 4.0, 5.9 \rangle$, meaning equilibrium will occur by applying the force $-1\mathbf{F} = \langle -4.0, -5.9 \rangle$ (see figure).

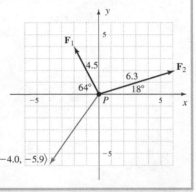

☑ **A.** You've just learned how to use vectors to investigate forces in equilibrium

Now try Exercises 7 through 20 ▶

## B. The Component of u along v: comp$_v$u

As in Example 1, many simple applications involve position vectors where the angle and horizontal/vertical components are known or can easily be found. In these situations, the components are often quadrantal, that is, they lie along the $x$- and $y$-axes and meet at a right angle. Many other applications require us to find components of a vector that are nonquadrantal, with one of the components parallel to, or lying along a second vector. Given vectors **u** and **v,** as shown in Figure 7.62, we symbolize the component of **u** that lies along **v** as comp$_v$u, noting its value is simply $|\mathbf{u}|\cos\theta$ since

 $\cos\theta = \dfrac{\text{adj}}{\text{hyp}} = \dfrac{\text{comp}_v\text{u}}{|\mathbf{u}|}$. As the diagrams further indicate, comp$_v$u $= |\mathbf{u}|\cos\theta$ regardless

**Figure 7.62**

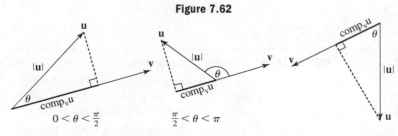

of how the vectors are oriented. Note that even when the components of a vector do not lie along the $x$- or $y$-axes, they are still **orthogonal** (meet at a 90° angle).

It is important to note that comp$_v$u is a *scalar quantity* (not a vector), giving only the magnitude of this component (the **vector projection** of **u** along **v** is studied later in this section). From these developments we make the following observations regarding the angle $\theta$ at which vectors **u** and **v** meet:

> ### Vectors and the Component of u Along v
>
> Given vectors **u** and **v,** which meet at an angle $\theta$,
>   **1.** $\text{comp}_v\mathbf{u} = |\mathbf{u}|\cos\theta$.
>   **2.** If $0° < \theta < 90°$, $\text{comp}_v\mathbf{u} > 0$; if $90° < \theta < 180°$, $\text{comp}_v\mathbf{u} < 0$.
>   **3.** If $\theta = 0°$, **u** and **v** have the same direction and $\text{comp}_v\mathbf{u} = |\mathbf{u}|$.
>   **4.** If $\theta = 90°$, **u** and **v** are orthogonal and $\text{comp}_v\mathbf{u} = 0$.
>   **5.** If $\theta = 180°$, **u** and **v** have opposite directions and $\text{comp}_v\mathbf{u} = -|\mathbf{u}|$.

**EXAMPLE 2** ▶ **Finding the Component of Vector G Along Vector v**

Given the vectors **G** and **v** with $|\mathbf{G}| = 850$ lb as shown in the figure, find $\text{comp}_v\mathbf{G}$.

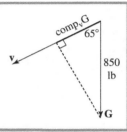

**Solution** ▶ Using $|\mathbf{G}|\cos\theta = \text{comp}_v\mathbf{G}$ we have $850\cos 65° \approx 359$ lb. The component of **G** along **v** is about 359 pounds.

**Now try Exercises 21 through 26** ▶

One interesting application of equilibrium and $\text{comp}_v\mathbf{u}$ involves the force of gravity acting on an object placed on a ramp or an inclined plane. The greater the incline, the greater the tendency of the object to slide down the plane (for this study, we assume there is no friction between the object and the plane). While the force of gravity continues to pull straight downward (represented by the vector **G** in Figure 7.63), **G** is now the resultant of a force acting parallel to the plane along vector **v** (causing the object to slide) and a force acting perpendicular to the plane along vector **p** (causing the object to press against the plane). If we knew the component of **G** along **v** (indicated by the shorter, bold segment), we would know the force required to keep the object stationary as the two forces must be opposites. Note that **G** forms a right angle with the base of the inclined plane (see Figure 7.64), meaning that $\alpha$ and $\beta$ must be complementary angles. Also note that since the location of a vector is unimportant, vector **p** has been repositioned for clarity.

**Figure 7.63**                           **Figure 7.64**

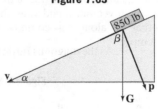                       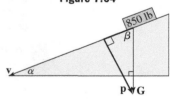

**EXAMPLE 3A** ▶ **Finding Components of Force for an Object on a Ramp**

A 850-lb object is sitting on a ramp that is inclined at 25°. Find the force needed to hold the object stationary (in equilibrium).

**Solution** ▶ Given $\alpha = 25°$, we know $\beta = 65°$. This means the component of **G** along the inclined plane is $\text{comp}_v\mathbf{G} = 850\cos 65°$ or about 359 lb. A force of 359 lb is required to keep the object from sliding down the incline (compare to Example 2).

**EXAMPLE 3B** ▶ A winch is being used to haul a 2000-lb block of granite up a ramp that is inclined at 15°. If the winch has a maximum tow rating of 500 lb, will it be successful?

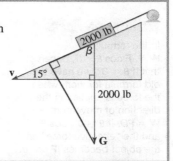

Solution ▶ We again need the component of **G** along the inclined plane: $comp_v G = 2000 \cos 75° \approx 518$ lb. Since the capacity of the winch is exceeded, the attempt will likely not be successful.

☑ **B.** You've just learned how to find the components of one vector along another

Now try Exercises 27 through 30 ▶

## C. Vector Applications Involving Work

Figure 7.65

Figure 7.66

In common, everyday usage, **work** is understood to involve the exertion of energy or force to move an object a certain distance. For example, digging a ditch is hard work and involves moving dirt (exerting a force) from the trench to the bankside (over a certain distance). In an office, moving a filing cabinet likewise involves work. If the filing cabinet is heavier, or the distance it needs to be moved is greater, more work is required to move it (Figures 7.65 and 7.66).

To determine how much work was done by each person, we need to quantify the concept. Consider a constant force **F**, applied to move an object a distance *D in the same direction as the force*. In this case, work is defined as the product of the force applied and the distance the object is moved: Work = Force × Distance or $W = |\mathbf{F}|D$. If the force is given in pounds and the distance in feet, the amount of work is measured in a unit called **foot-pounds** (ft-lb). If the force is in newtons and the distance in meters, the amount of work is measured in **Newton-meters** (N-m).

**EXAMPLE 4** ▶ **Solving Applications of Vectors—Work and Force Parallel to the Direction of Movement**

While rearranging the office, Carrie must apply a force of 55.8 N to relocate a filing cabinet 4.5 m, while Bernard applies a 77.5 N force to move a second cabinet 3.2 m. Who did the most work?

Solution ▶ For Carrie: $W = |\mathbf{F}|D$           For Bernard: $W = |\mathbf{F}|D$
$\qquad = (55.8)(4.5)$                 $\qquad = (77.5)(3.2)$
$\qquad = 251.1$ N-m              $\qquad = 248$ N-m

Carrie did $251.1 - 248 = 3.1$ N-m more work than Bernard.

Now try Exercises 31 and 32 ▶

In many applications of work, the force **F** is not applied parallel to the direction of movement, as illustrated in Figures 7.67 and 7.68.

In calculating the amount of work done, the general concept of force × distance is preserved, *but only the component of force in the direction of movement is used.*

Figure 7.67

Figure 7.68

In terms of the component forces discussed earlier, if **F** is a constant force applied at angle $\theta$ to the direction of movement, the amount of work done is *the component of force along D times the distance the object is moved.*

**Force Vectors and Work *W***

Given a force **F** applied in the direction of movement at the acute angle $\theta$ to an object, and *D* the distance it is moved,

$$W = |\mathbf{F}|\cos \theta \times D$$

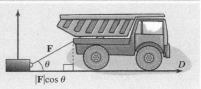

**EXAMPLE 5** ▶ **Solving an Application of Vectors—Work and Force Applied at Angle $\theta$ to the Direction of Movement**

To help move heavy pieces of furniture across the floor, movers sometime employ a body harness similar to that used for a plow horse. A mover applies a constant 200-lb force to drag a piano 100 ft down a long hallway and into another room. If the straps make a 40° angle with the direction of movement, find the amount of work performed.

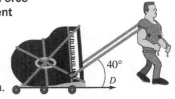

Solution ▶ The component of force in the direction of movement is 200 cos 40° or about 153 lb. The amount of work done is $W \approx 153(100) = 15{,}300$ ft-lb.

**Now try Exercises 35 through 40** ▶

These ideas can be generalized to include work problems where the component of force in the direction of motion is along a *nonhorizontal* vector **v.** Consider Example 6.

**EXAMPLE 6** ▶ **Solving an Application of Vectors—Forces Along a Nonhorizontal Vector**

The force vector $\mathbf{F} = \langle 5, 12 \rangle$ moves an object along the vector $\mathbf{v} = \langle 15.44, 2 \rangle$ as shown. Find the amount of work required to move the object along the entire length of **v.** Assume force is in pounds and distance in feet.

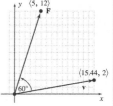

Solution ▶ To begin, we first determine the angle between the vectors.

In this case we have $\theta = \tan^{-1}\left|\dfrac{12}{5}\right| - \tan^{-1}\left|\dfrac{2}{15.44}\right| \approx 60°$.

For $|\mathbf{F}| = 13$ (5-12-13 triangle), the component of force in the direction of motion is $\text{comp}_v\mathbf{F} = 13 \cos 60° = 6.5$. With $|\mathbf{v}| = \sqrt{(15.44)^2 + (2)^2} \approx 15.57$, the work required is $W = \text{comp}_v\mathbf{F} \times |\mathbf{v}|$ or $(6.5)(15.57) \approx 101.2$ ft-lb.

☑ **C. You've just learned how to solve applications involving work**

**Now try Exercises 41 through 44** ▶

## D. Dot Products and the Angle Between Two Vectors

When the component of force in the direction of motion lies along a *nonhorizontal* vector (as in Example 6), the work performed can actually be computed more efficiently using an operation called the **dot product.** For any two vectors **u** and **v,** the dot product $\mathbf{u} \cdot \mathbf{v}$ is equivalent to $\text{comp}_v\mathbf{u} \times |\mathbf{v}|$, yet is much easier to compute (for the proof of $\mathbf{u} \cdot \mathbf{v} = \text{comp}_v\mathbf{u} \times |\mathbf{v}|$, see Appendix VI). The operation is defined as follows:

### The Dot Product $\mathbf{u} \cdot \mathbf{v}$

Given vectors $\mathbf{u} = \langle a, b \rangle$ and $\mathbf{v} = \langle c, d \rangle$, $\mathbf{u} \cdot \mathbf{v} = \langle a, b \rangle \cdot \langle c, d \rangle = ac + bd$. In words, it is the *real number* found by taking the sum of corresponding component products.

**EXAMPLE 7** ▶ **Using the Dot Product to Determine Force Along a Nonhorizontal Vector**

Verify the answer to Example 6 using the dot product $\mathbf{u} \cdot \mathbf{v}$.

Solution ▶ For $\mathbf{u} = \langle 5, 12 \rangle$ and $\mathbf{v} = \langle 15.44, 2 \rangle$, we have $\mathbf{u} \cdot \mathbf{v} = \langle 5, 12 \rangle \cdot \langle 15.44, 2 \rangle$ giving $5(15.44) + 12(2) = 101.2$. The result is 101.2, as in Example 6.

**Now try Exercises 45 through 48** ▶

Note that dot products can also be used in the simpler case where the direction of motion is along a horizontal distance (Examples 4 and 5). While the dot product offers a powerful and efficient way to compute the work performed, it has many other applications; for example, to find the angle between two vectors. Consider that for any two vectors $\mathbf{u}$ and $\mathbf{v}$, $\mathbf{u} \cdot \mathbf{v} = |\mathbf{u}|\cos \theta \times |\mathbf{v}|$, leading directly to $\cos \theta = \dfrac{\mathbf{u}}{|\mathbf{u}|} \cdot \dfrac{\mathbf{v}}{|\mathbf{v}|}$ (solve for $\cos \theta$).

In summary,

### The Angle $\theta$ Between Two Vectors

Given the nonzero vectors $\mathbf{u}$ and $\mathbf{v}$:
$$\cos \theta = \frac{\mathbf{u}}{|\mathbf{u}|} \cdot \frac{\mathbf{v}}{|\mathbf{v}|} \quad \text{and} \quad \theta = \cos^{-1}\left(\frac{\mathbf{u}}{|\mathbf{u}|} \cdot \frac{\mathbf{v}}{|\mathbf{v}|}\right)$$

**Figure 7.69**

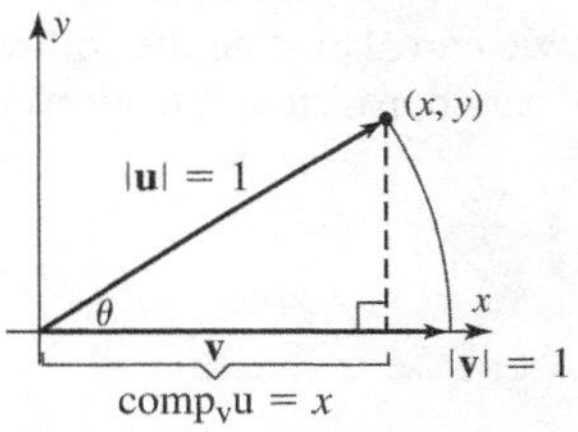

In the special case where $\mathbf{u}$ *and* $\mathbf{v}$ *are unit vectors*, this simplifies to $\cos \theta = \mathbf{u} \cdot \mathbf{v}$ since $|\mathbf{u}| = |\mathbf{v}| = 1$. This relationship is shown in Figure 7.69. The dot product $\mathbf{u} \cdot \mathbf{v}$ gives $\text{comp}_{\mathbf{v}}\mathbf{u} \times |\mathbf{v}|$, but $|\mathbf{v}| = 1$ and the component of $\mathbf{u}$ along $\mathbf{v}$ is simply the adjacent side of a right triangle whose hypotenuse is 1. Hence $\mathbf{u} \cdot \mathbf{v} = \cos \theta$.

**EXAMPLE 8** ▶ **Determining the Angle Between Two Vectors**

Find the angle between the vectors given.
a. $\mathbf{u} = \langle -3, 4 \rangle$; $\mathbf{v} = \langle 5, 12 \rangle$     b. $\mathbf{v}_1 = 2\mathbf{i} - 3\mathbf{j}$; $\mathbf{v}_2 = 6\mathbf{i} + 4\mathbf{j}$

Solution ▶
a. $\cos \theta = \dfrac{\mathbf{u}}{|\mathbf{u}|} \cdot \dfrac{\mathbf{v}}{|\mathbf{v}|}$

$= \left\langle \dfrac{-3}{5}, \dfrac{4}{5} \right\rangle \cdot \left\langle \dfrac{5}{13}, \dfrac{12}{13} \right\rangle$

$= \dfrac{-15}{65} + \dfrac{48}{65}$

$= \dfrac{33}{65}$

$\theta = \cos^{-1}\left(\dfrac{33}{65}\right)$

$\approx 59.5°$

b. $\cos \theta = \dfrac{\mathbf{v}_1}{|\mathbf{v}_1|} \cdot \dfrac{\mathbf{v}_2}{|\mathbf{v}_2|}$

$= \left\langle \dfrac{2}{\sqrt{13}}, \dfrac{-3}{\sqrt{13}} \right\rangle \cdot \left\langle \dfrac{6}{\sqrt{52}}, \dfrac{4}{\sqrt{52}} \right\rangle$

$= \dfrac{12}{\sqrt{676}} + \dfrac{-12}{\sqrt{676}}$

$= \dfrac{0}{26} = 0$

$\theta = \cos^{-1} 0$

$= 90°$

**Now try Exercises 49 through 66** ▶

Note we have implicitly shown that if $\mathbf{u} \cdot \mathbf{v} = 0$, then $\mathbf{u}$ is orthogonal to $\mathbf{v}$. As with other vector operations, recognizing certain properties of the dot product will enable us to work with them more efficiently.

---

**Properties of the Dot Product**

Given vectors $\mathbf{u}$, $\mathbf{v}$, and $\mathbf{w}$ and a constant $k$,

1. $\mathbf{u} \cdot \mathbf{v} = \mathbf{v} \cdot \mathbf{u}$
2. $\mathbf{u} \cdot \mathbf{u} = |\mathbf{u}|^2$
3. $\mathbf{w} \cdot (\mathbf{u} + \mathbf{v}) = \mathbf{w} \cdot \mathbf{u} + \mathbf{w} \cdot \mathbf{v}$
4. $k(\mathbf{u} \cdot \mathbf{v}) = k\mathbf{u} \cdot \mathbf{v} = \mathbf{u} \cdot k\mathbf{v}$
5. $\mathbf{0} \cdot \mathbf{u} = \mathbf{u} \cdot \mathbf{0} = 0$
6. $\dfrac{\mathbf{u}}{|\mathbf{u}|} \cdot \dfrac{\mathbf{v}}{|\mathbf{v}|} = \dfrac{\mathbf{u} \cdot \mathbf{v}}{|\mathbf{u}||\mathbf{v}|}$

---

Property 6 offers an alternative to unit vectors when finding $\cos\theta$—the dot product of the vectors can be computed first, and the result divided by the product of their magnitudes: $\cos\theta = \dfrac{\mathbf{u} \cdot \mathbf{v}}{|\mathbf{u}||\mathbf{v}|}$. Proofs of the first two properties are given here. Proofs of the others have a similar development **(see Exercises 79 through 82).** For any two nonzero vectors $\mathbf{u} = \langle a, b \rangle$ and $\mathbf{v} = \langle c, d \rangle$:

Property 1: $\mathbf{u} \cdot \mathbf{v} = \langle a, b \rangle \cdot \langle c, d \rangle$
$= ac + bd$
$= ca + db$
$= \langle c, d \rangle \cdot \langle a, b \rangle$
$= \mathbf{v} \cdot \mathbf{u}$

Property 2: $\mathbf{u} \cdot \mathbf{u} = \langle a, b \rangle \cdot \langle a, b \rangle$
$= a^2 + b^2$
$= |\mathbf{u}|^2$
(since $|\mathbf{u}| = \sqrt{a^2 + b^2}$)

Using $\text{comp}_\mathbf{v}\mathbf{u} = |\mathbf{u}|\cos\theta$ and $\mathbf{u} \cdot \mathbf{v} = \text{comp}_\mathbf{v}\mathbf{u} \times |\mathbf{v}|$, we can also state the following relationships, which give us some flexibility on how we approach applications of the dot product.

For any two vectors $\mathbf{u} = \langle a, b \rangle$ and $\mathbf{v} = \langle c, d \rangle$:

(1) $\mathbf{u} \cdot \mathbf{v} = ac + bd$      standard computation of the dot product

(2) $\mathbf{u} \cdot \mathbf{v} = |\mathbf{u}|\cos\theta \times |\mathbf{v}|$      alternative computation of the dot product

(3) $\mathbf{u} \cdot \mathbf{v} = \text{comp}_\mathbf{v}\mathbf{u} \times |\mathbf{v}|$      replace $|\mathbf{u}|\cos\theta$ in (2) with $\text{comp}_\mathbf{v}\mathbf{u}$

(4) $\dfrac{\mathbf{u} \cdot \mathbf{v}}{|\mathbf{u}||\mathbf{v}|} = \cos\theta$      divide (2) by scalars $|\mathbf{u}|$ and $|\mathbf{v}|$

(5) $\dfrac{\mathbf{u} \cdot \mathbf{v}}{|\mathbf{v}|} = \text{comp}_\mathbf{v}\mathbf{u}$      divide (3) by $|\mathbf{v}|$

✓ **D.** You've just learned how to compute dot products and the angle between two vectors

## E. Vector Projections and Orthogonal Components

In work problems and other simple applications, it is enough to find and apply $\text{comp}_\mathbf{v}\mathbf{u}$ (Figure 7.70). However, applications involving thrust and drag forces, tension and stress limits in a cable, electronic circuits, and cartoon animations often require that we also find the *vector form of* $\text{comp}_\mathbf{v}\mathbf{u}$. This is called the **projection** of $\mathbf{u}$ along $\mathbf{v}$ or **proj$_\mathbf{v}$u**, and is a vector in the same direction of $\mathbf{v}$ with magnitude $\text{comp}_\mathbf{v}\mathbf{u}$ (Figures 7.71 and 7.72).

**Figure 7.70**

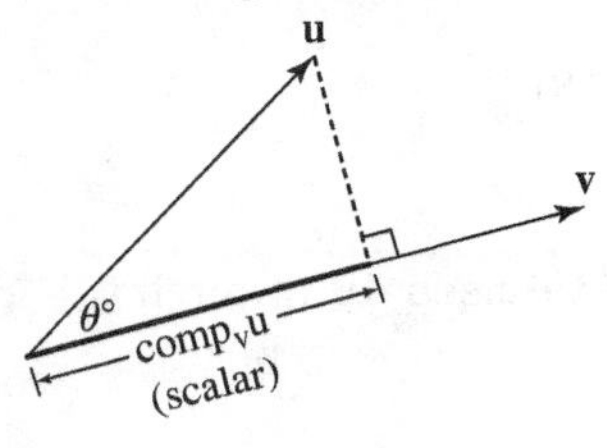

**Figure 7.71**

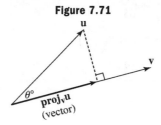

**Figure 7.72**

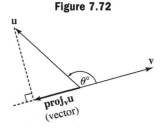

By its design, the unit vector $\dfrac{\mathbf{v}}{|\mathbf{v}|}$ has a length of one and points in the same direction as

$\mathbf{v}$, so $\mathbf{proj_v u}$ can be computed as $\text{comp}_v \mathbf{u} \times \dfrac{\mathbf{v}}{|\mathbf{v}|}$ (see Example 7, Section 7.3). Using

equation (5) from page 365 and the properties shown earlier, an alternative formula for $\mathbf{proj_v u}$ can be found that is usually easier to simplify:

$$\mathbf{proj_v u} = \text{comp}_v \mathbf{u} \times \frac{\mathbf{v}}{|\mathbf{v}|} \qquad \text{definition of a projection}$$

$$= \frac{\mathbf{u} \cdot \mathbf{v}}{|\mathbf{v}|} \times \frac{\mathbf{v}}{|\mathbf{v}|} \qquad \text{substitute } \frac{\mathbf{u} \cdot \mathbf{v}}{|\mathbf{v}|} \text{ for } \text{comp}_v \mathbf{u}$$

$$= \frac{\mathbf{u} \cdot \mathbf{v}}{|\mathbf{v}|^2} \times \mathbf{v} \qquad \text{rewrite factors}$$

### Vector Projections

Given vectors $\mathbf{u}$ and $\mathbf{v}$, the projection of $\mathbf{u}$ along $\mathbf{v}$ is the *vector*

$$\mathbf{proj_v u} = \left( \frac{\mathbf{u} \cdot \mathbf{v}}{|\mathbf{v}|^2} \right) \mathbf{v}$$

**EXAMPLE 9A** ▶  **Finding the Projection of One Vector Along Another**

Given $\mathbf{u} = \langle -7, 1 \rangle$ and $\mathbf{v} = \langle 6, 6 \rangle$, find $\mathbf{proj_v u}$.

**Solution** ▶  To begin, find $\mathbf{u} \cdot \mathbf{v}$ and $|\mathbf{v}|$.

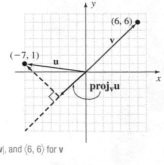

$$\mathbf{u} \cdot \mathbf{v} = \langle -7, 1 \rangle \cdot \langle 6, 6 \rangle \qquad\qquad |\mathbf{v}| = \sqrt{6^2 + 6^2}$$
$$= -42 + 6 \qquad\qquad\qquad\qquad = \sqrt{72}$$
$$= -36 \qquad\qquad\qquad\qquad\qquad = 6\sqrt{2}$$

$$\mathbf{proj_v u} = \left( \frac{\mathbf{u} \cdot \mathbf{v}}{|\mathbf{v}|^2} \right) \mathbf{v} \qquad \text{projection of } \mathbf{u} \text{ along } \mathbf{v}$$

$$= \left( \frac{-36}{72} \right) \langle 6, 6 \rangle \qquad \text{substitute } -36 \text{ for } \mathbf{u} \cdot \mathbf{v}, \sqrt{72} \text{ for } |\mathbf{v}|, \text{ and } \langle 6, 6 \rangle \text{ for } \mathbf{v}$$

$$= \langle -3, -3 \rangle \qquad \text{result}$$

**WORTHY OF NOTE**

Note that $\mathbf{u_2} = \mathbf{u} - \mathbf{u_1}$ is the shorter diagonal of the parallelogram formed by the vectors $\mathbf{u}$ and $\mathbf{u_1} = \mathbf{proj_v u}$. This can also be seen in the graph supplied for Example 9B.

A useful consequence of computing $\mathbf{proj_v u}$ is we can then **resolve** the vector $\mathbf{u}$ into **orthogonal components** *that need not be quadrantal.* One component will be parallel to $\mathbf{v}$ and the other perpendicular to $\mathbf{v}$ (the dashed line in the diagram in Example 9A). In general terms, this means we can write $\mathbf{u}$ as the vector sum $\mathbf{u_1} + \mathbf{u_2}$, where $\mathbf{u_1} = \mathbf{proj_v u}$ and $\mathbf{u_2} = \mathbf{u} - \mathbf{u_1}$ (note $\mathbf{u_1} \| \mathbf{v}$).

### Resolving a Vector into Orthogonal Components

Given vectors $\mathbf{u}$, $\mathbf{v}$, and $\mathbf{proj_v u}$, $\mathbf{u}$ can be resolved into the orthogonal components $\mathbf{u_1}$ and $\mathbf{u_2}$, where $\mathbf{u} = \mathbf{u_1} + \mathbf{u_2}$, $\mathbf{u_1} = \mathbf{proj_v u}$, and $\mathbf{u_2} = \mathbf{u} - \mathbf{u_1}$.

**EXAMPLE 9B** ▶  Resolving a Vector into Orthogonal Components

Given $\mathbf{u} = \langle 2, 8 \rangle$ and $\mathbf{v} = \langle 8, 6 \rangle$, resolve $\mathbf{u}$ into orthogonal components $\mathbf{u_1}$ and $\mathbf{u_2}$, where $\mathbf{u_1} \| \mathbf{v}$ and $\mathbf{u_2} \perp \mathbf{v}$. Also verify $\mathbf{u_1} \perp \mathbf{u_2}$.

Solution ▶ Once again, begin by finding $\mathbf{u} \cdot \mathbf{v}$ and $|\mathbf{v}|$.

$$\mathbf{u} \cdot \mathbf{v} = \langle 2, 8 \rangle \cdot \langle 8, 6 \rangle \qquad\qquad |\mathbf{v}| = \sqrt{8^2 + 6^2}$$
$$= 16 + 48 \qquad\qquad\qquad\qquad = \sqrt{100}$$
$$= 64 \qquad\qquad\qquad\qquad\qquad = 10$$

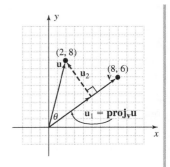

$$\mathbf{proj_v u} = \left(\frac{\mathbf{u} \cdot \mathbf{v}}{|\mathbf{v}|^2}\right)\mathbf{v} \qquad \text{projection of } \mathbf{u} \text{ along } \mathbf{v}$$

$$= \left(\frac{64}{100}\right)\langle 8, 6 \rangle \qquad \begin{array}{l}\text{substitute 64 for } \mathbf{u} \cdot \mathbf{v}, \text{ 10 for} \\ |\mathbf{v}|, \text{ and } \langle 8, 6 \rangle \text{ for } \mathbf{v}\end{array}$$

$$= \langle 5.12, 3.84 \rangle \qquad \text{result}$$

☑ **E.** You've just learned how to find the projection of one vector along another and resolve a vector into orthogonal components

For $\mathbf{proj_v u} = \mathbf{u}_1 = \langle 5.12, 3.84 \rangle$, we have $\mathbf{u}_2 = \mathbf{u} - \mathbf{u}_1 = \langle 2, 8 \rangle - \langle 5.12, 3.84 \rangle = \langle -3.12, 4.16 \rangle$. To verify $\mathbf{u}_1 \perp \mathbf{u}_2$, we need only show $\mathbf{u}_1 \cdot \mathbf{u}_2 = 0$:

$$\mathbf{u}_1 \cdot \mathbf{u}_2 = \langle 5.12, 3.84 \rangle \cdot \langle -3.12, 4.16 \rangle$$
$$= (5.12)(-3.12) + (3.84)(4.16)$$
$$= 0 ✓$$

**Now try Exercises 67 through 72** ▶

## F. Vectors and the Height of a Projectile

Our final application of vectors involves **projectile motion.** A projectile is any object that is thrown or projected upward, with no source of propulsion to sustain its motion. In this case, the only force acting on the projectile is gravity (air resistance is neglected), so the maximum height and the range of the projectile depend solely on its initial velocity and the angle $\theta$ at which it is projected. In a college algebra course, the equation $y = v_0 t - 16t^2$ is developed to model the height in feet (at time $t$) of a projectile thrown vertically upward with initial velocity of $v_0$ feet per second. Here, we'll modify the equation slightly to take into account that the object is now moving horizontally as well as vertically. As you can see in Figure 7.73, the vector $\mathbf{v}$ representing the initial velocity, as well as the velocity vector at other times, can easily be decomposed into horizontal and vertical components. This will enable us to find a more general relationship for the position of the projectile. For now, we'll let $\mathbf{v}_y$ represent the component of velocity in the vertical ($y$) direction, and $\mathbf{v}_x$ represent the component of velocity in the horizontal ($x$) direction. Since gravity acts only in the vertical (and negative) direction, the horizontal component of the velocity remains constant at $\mathbf{v}_x = |\mathbf{v}|\cos\theta$. Using $D = RT$, the $x$-coordinate of the projectile at time $t$ is $x = (|\mathbf{v}|\cos\theta)t$. For the vertical component $\mathbf{v}_y$ we use the projectile equation developed earlier, *substituting* $|\mathbf{v}|\sin\theta$ *for* $v_0$, since the angle of projection is no longer 90°. This gives the $y$-coordinate at time $t$ as $y = v_0 t - 16t^2 = (|\mathbf{v}|\sin\theta)t - 16t^2$.

**Figure 7.73**

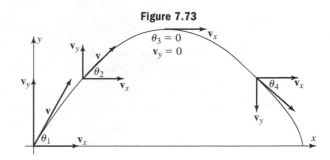

---

### Projectile Motion

Given an object is projected upward from the origin with initial velocity $|\mathbf{v}|$ at angle $\theta$.
The $x$-coordinate of its position at time $t$ is $x = (|\mathbf{v}|\cos\theta)t$.
The $y$-coordinate of its position at time $t$ is $y = (|\mathbf{v}|\sin\theta)t - 16t^2$.

---

**EXAMPLE 10** ▶ **Solving an Application of Vectors—Projectile Motion**

An arrow is shot upward with an initial velocity of 150 ft/sec at an angle of 50°.
a. Find the position of the arrow after 2 sec.
b. How many seconds does it take to reach a height of 190 ft?

**Solution** ▶ a. Using the preceding equations yields these coordinates for its position at $t = 2$:

$$x = (|\mathbf{v}|\cos\theta)t \qquad\qquad y = (|\mathbf{v}|\sin\theta)t - 16t^2$$
$$= (150\cos 50°)(2) \qquad\quad = (150\sin 50°)(2) - 16(2)^2$$
$$\approx 193 \qquad\qquad\qquad\quad \approx 166$$

The arrow has traveled a horizontal distance of about 193 ft and is 166 ft high.

b. To find the time required to reach 190 ft in height, set the equation for the $y$ coordinate equal to 190, which yields a quadratic equation in $t$:

$$y = (|\mathbf{v}|\sin\theta)t - 16t^2 \qquad \text{equation for } y$$
$$190 = (150\sin 50°)t - 16t^2 \qquad \text{substitute 150 for } |\mathbf{v}| \text{ and 50° for } \theta$$
$$0 \approx -16t^2 + 115t - 190 \qquad 150\sin 50 \approx 115$$

Using the quadratic formula we find that $t \approx 2.6$ sec and $t \approx 4.6$ sec are solutions. This makes sense, since the arrow reaches a given height once on the way up and again on the way down, as long as it hasn't reached its maximum height.

☑ **F.** You've just learned how to use vectors to develop an equation for nonvertical projectile motion and solve related applications

**Now try Exercises 73 through 78** ▶

For more on projectile motion, see the *Calculator Exploration and Discovery* feature at the end of this chapter.

---

## TECHNOLOGY HIGHLIGHT

### The Magnitude and Reference Angle of a Vector

As you've seen in this chapter, a vector can be written or named in the component form $\langle a, b \rangle$ or in terms of its magnitude and direction. The vector $\langle 5\sqrt{3}, 5 \rangle$ is equal to the position vector with magnitude 10 and angle $\theta = 30°$, since $10\cos 30° = 5\sqrt{3}$ and $10\sin 30° = 5$. Many calculators use "$r$" (instead of $|\mathbf{v}|$) for the magnitude of a vector. When the magnitude and angle of a vector are written in the form $(r, \theta)$ we say the vector is written in **polar form.** Most graphing calculators offer features that enable a quick conversion from the component form $\langle a, b \rangle$ of a vector to its polar form $(r, \theta)$ and vice versa. On the TI-84 Plus, these features are accessed using [2nd] [APPS] **(ANGLE).** As you can see from the screen in Figure 7.74, we are interested in options 5 through 8 (press the up arrow [▲] to bring option 8 into view). Option **5:R ▶ Pr(** takes the Rectangular coordinates and returns the magnitude **r** of the **P**olar Coordinates. Option **6:R ▶ Pθ(** returns the angle of the **P**olar form. Option **7:P ▶ Rx(** takes the **P**olar form $(r, \theta)$ of the vector and returns the

**Figure 7.74**

```
ANGLE
2↑°
3:r
4:▶DMS
5:R▶Pr(
6:R▶Pθ(
7:P▶Rx(
8▶P▶Ry(
```

*—continued*

horizontal component of the **Rectangular** form. As you might expect, option **8:P ▶ Ry(** takes the **Polar** form $(r, \theta)$ of the vector and returns the vertical component of the **Rectangular** form. To verify the previous illustration for $\langle 5\sqrt{3}, 5 \rangle$, we CLEAR the home screen and press 2nd APPS 5 to access the desired option and enter the components as **5:R ▶ Pr**$(5\sqrt{3}, 5)$. Pressing ENTER gives a magnitude 10, as expected (Figure 7.75).

**Figure 7.75**

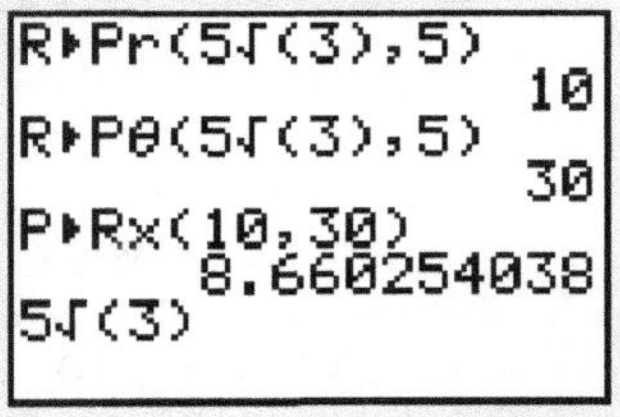

```
R▶Pr(5√(3),5)
                    10
R▶Pθ(5√(3),5)
                    30
P▶Rx(10,30)
           8.660254038
5√(3)
```

**Exercise 1:** Use your calculator to write the vector $\langle 5\sqrt{2}, 5\sqrt{2} \rangle$ in polar form. Check the result by converting manually.

**Exercise 2:** Use your calculator to write the vector $(r, \theta) = \langle 20\sqrt{2}, 45 \rangle$ in rectangular form. Check the result by converting manually.

---

## 7.4 EXERCISES

### ▶ CONCEPTS AND VOCABULARY

**Fill in each blank with the appropriate word or phrase. Carefully reread the section if needed.**

1. Vector forces are in _____ when they counterbalance each other. Such vectors have a sum of _____.

2. The component of a vector **u** along another vector **v** is written notationally as _____, and is computed as _____.

3. Two vectors that meet at a right angle are said to be _____.

4. The component of **u** along **v** is a _____ quantity. The projection of **u** along **v** is a _____.

5. Explain/Discuss exactly what information the dot product of two vectors gives us. Illustrate with a few examples.

6. Compare and contrast the projectile equations $y = v_0 t - 16t^2$ and $y = (v_0 \sin \theta)t - 16t^2$. Discuss similarities/differences using illustrative examples.

### ▶ DEVELOPING YOUR SKILLS

**The force vectors given are acting on a common point $P$. Find an additional force vector so that equilibrium takes place.**

7. $\mathbf{F}_1 = \langle -8, -3 \rangle$; $\mathbf{F}_2 = \langle 2, -5 \rangle$

8. $\mathbf{F}_1 = \langle -2, 7 \rangle$; $\mathbf{F}_2 = \langle 5, 3 \rangle$

9. $\mathbf{F}_1 = \langle -2, -7 \rangle$; $\mathbf{F}_2 = \langle 2, -7 \rangle$; $\mathbf{F}_3 = \langle 5, 4 \rangle$

10. $\mathbf{F}_1 = \langle -3, 10 \rangle$; $\mathbf{F}_2 = \langle -10, 3 \rangle$; $\mathbf{F}_3 = \langle -9, -2 \rangle$

11. $\mathbf{F}_1 = 5\mathbf{i} - 2\mathbf{j}$; $\mathbf{F}_2 = \mathbf{i} + 10\mathbf{j}$

12. $\mathbf{F}_1 = -7\mathbf{i} + 6\mathbf{j}$; $\mathbf{F}_2 = -8\mathbf{i} - 3\mathbf{j}$

13. $\mathbf{F}_1 = 2.5\mathbf{i} + 4.7\mathbf{j}$; $\mathbf{F}_2 = -0.3\mathbf{i} + 6.9\mathbf{j}$; $\mathbf{F}_3 = -12\mathbf{j}$

14. $\mathbf{F}_1 = 3\sqrt{2}\mathbf{i} - 2\sqrt{3}\mathbf{j}$; $\mathbf{F}_2 = -2\mathbf{i} + 7\mathbf{j}$; $\mathbf{F}_3 = 5\mathbf{i} + 2\sqrt{3}\mathbf{j}$

15.

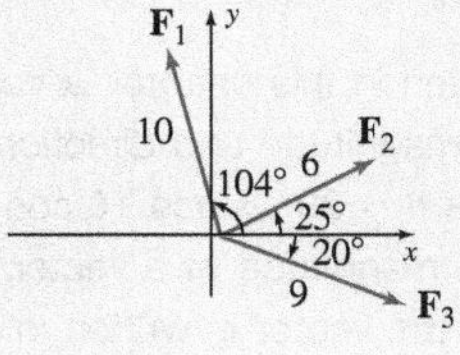

16.

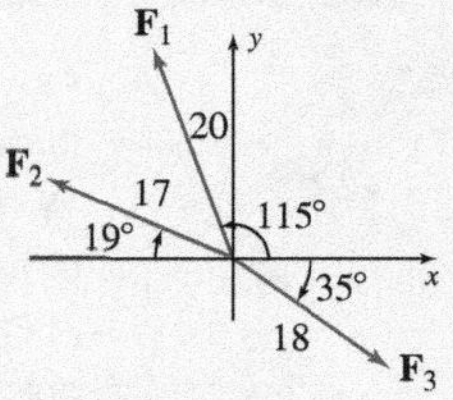

17. The force vectors $\mathbf{F}_1$ and $\mathbf{F}_2$ are simultaneously acting on a point $P$. Find a third vector $\mathbf{F}_3$ so that equilibrium takes place if $\mathbf{F}_1 = \langle 19, 10 \rangle$ and $\mathbf{F}_2 = \langle 5, 17 \rangle$.

18. The force vectors $\mathbf{F}_1$, $\mathbf{F}_2$, and $\mathbf{F}_3$ are simultaneously acting on a point $P$. Find a fourth vector $\mathbf{F}_4$ so that equilibrium takes place if $\mathbf{F}_1 = \langle -12, 2 \rangle$, $\mathbf{F}_2 = \langle -6, 17 \rangle$, and $\mathbf{F}_3 = \langle 3, 15 \rangle$.

19. A new "Survivor" game involves a three-team tug-of-war. Teams 1 and 2 are pulling with the magnitude and at the angles indicated in the diagram. If the teams are currently in a stalemate, find the magnitude and angle of the rope held by team 3.

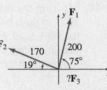

20. Three cowhands have roped a wild stallion and are attempting to hold him steady. The first and second cowhands are pulling with the magnitude and at the angles indicated in the diagram. If the stallion is held fast by the three cowhands, find the magnitude and angle of the rope from the third cowhand.

**Find the component of u along v (compute comp$_v$u) for the vectors u and v given.**

21.

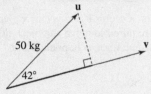

22.

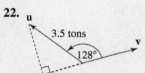

23.

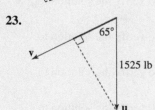

24.

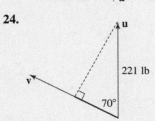

25.

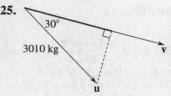

26.

2 tons

**Determine the missing component of static equilibrium.**

27. A 500-lb crate is sitting on a ramp that is inclined at 35°. Find the force needed to hold the object stationary.

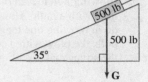

28. A 1200-lb skiff is being pulled from a lake, using a boat ramp inclined at 20°. Find the minimum force needed to dock the skiff.

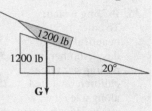

29. A 325-kg carton is sitting on a ramp, held stationary by 225 kg of tension in a restraining rope. Find the ramps's angle of incline.

30. A heavy dump truck is being winched up a ramp with an 18° incline. Approximate the weight of the truck if the winch is working at its maximum capacity of 1.75 tons and the truck is barely moving.

**Determine the amount of work done.**

31. While rearranging the patio furniture, Rick has to push the weighted base of the umbrella stand 15 m. If he uses a constant force of 75 N, how much work did he do?

32. Vinny's car just broke down in the middle of the road. Luckily, a buddy is with him and offers to steer if Vinny will get out and push. If he pushes with a constant force of 185 N to move the car 30 m, how much work did he do?

▶ **WORKING WITH FORMULAS**

The range of a projectile: $R = \dfrac{v^2 \sin\theta \cos\theta}{16}$

**33.** The range of a projected object (total horizontal distance traveled) is given by the formula shown, where $v$ is the initial velocity and $\theta$ is the angle at which it is projected. If an arrow leaves the bow traveling 175 ft/sec at an angle of 45°, what horizontal distance will it travel?

**34.** A collegiate javelin thrower releases the javelin at a 40° angle, with an initial velocity of about 95 ft/sec. If the NCAA record is 280 ft, will this throw break the record? What is the smallest angle of release that will break this record? If the javelin were released at the optimum 45°, by how many feet would the record be broken?

▶ **APPLICATIONS**

**35. Plowing a field:** An old-time farmer is plowing his field with a mule. How much work does the mule do in plowing one length of a field 300 ft long, if it pulls the plow with a constant force of 250 lb and the straps make a 30° angle with the horizontal.

**36. Pulling a sled:**
To enjoy a beautiful snowy day, a mother is pulling her three children on a sled along a level  street. How much work (play) is done if the street is 100 ft long and she pulls with a constant force of 55 lb with the tow-rope making an angle of 32° with the street?

**37. Tough-man contest:** As part of a "tough-man" contest, participants are required to pull a bus along a level street for 100 ft. If one contestant did 45,000 ft-lb of work to accomplish the task and the straps used made an angle of 5° with the street, find the tension in the strap during the pull.

**38. Moving supplies:** An arctic explorer is hauling supplies from the supply hut to her tent, a distance of 150 ft, in a sled she is dragging behind her. If 9000 ft-lb of work was done and the straps used made an angle of 25° with the snow-covered ground, find the tension in the strap during the task.

**39. Wheelbarrow rides:** To break up the monotony of a long, hot, boring Saturday, a father decides to (carefully) give his kids a ride in a wheelbarrow. He applies a force of 30 N to move the "load" 100 m, then stops to rest. Find the amount of work done if the wheelbarrow makes an angle of 20° with level ground while in motion.

**40. Mowing the lawn:** A home owner applies a force of 40 N to push her lawn mower back and forth across the back yard. Find the amount of work done if the yard is 50 m long, requires 24 passes to get the lawn mowed, and the mower arm makes an angle of 39° with the level ground.

**Force vectors:** For the force vector **F** and vector **v** given, find the amount of work required to move an object along the entire length of **v**. Assume force is in pounds and distance in feet.

**41.** $\mathbf{F} = \langle 15, 10 \rangle;\ \mathbf{v} = \langle 50, 5 \rangle$

**42.** $\mathbf{F} = \langle -5, 12 \rangle;\ \mathbf{v} = \langle -25, 10 \rangle$

**43.** $\mathbf{F} = \langle 8, 2 \rangle;\ \mathbf{v} = \langle 15, -1 \rangle$

**44.** $\mathbf{F} = \langle 15, -3 \rangle;\ \mathbf{v} = \langle 24, -20 \rangle$

**45.** Use the dot product to verify the solution to Exercise 41.

**46.** Use the dot product to verify the solution to Exercise 42.

**47.** Use the dot product to verify the solution to Exercise 43.

**48.** Use the dot product to verify the solution to Exercise 44.

**For each pair of vectors given, (a) compute the dot product p · q and (b) find the angle between the vectors to the nearest tenth of a degree.**

49. $p = \langle 5, 2 \rangle$; $q = \langle 3, 7 \rangle$

50. $p = \langle -3, 6 \rangle$; $q = \langle 2, -5 \rangle$

51. $p = -2i + 3j$; $q = -6i - 4j$

52. $p = -4i + 3j$; $q = -6i - 8j$

53. $p = 7\sqrt{2}i - 3j$; $q = 2\sqrt{2}i + 9j$

54. $p = \sqrt{2}i - 3j$; $q = 3\sqrt{2}i + 5j$

**Determine if the pair of vectors given are orthogonal.**

55. $u = \langle 7, -2 \rangle$; $v = \langle 4, 14 \rangle$

56. $u = \langle -3.5, 2.1 \rangle$; $v = \langle -6, -10 \rangle$

57. $u = \langle -6, -3 \rangle$; $v = \langle -8, 15 \rangle$

58. $u = \langle -5, 4 \rangle$; $v = \langle -9, -11 \rangle$

59. $u = -2i - 6j$; $v = 9i - 3j$

60. $u = 3\sqrt{2}i - 2j$; $v = 2\sqrt{2}i + 6j$

**Find comp$_v$u for the vectors u and v given.**

61. $u = \langle 3, 5 \rangle$; $v = \langle 7, 1 \rangle$

62. $u = \langle 3, 5 \rangle$; $v = \langle -7, 1 \rangle$

63. $u = -7i + 4j$; $v = -10j$

64. $u = 8i$; $v = 10i + 3j$

65. $u = 7\sqrt{2}i - 3j$; $v = 6i + 5\sqrt{3}j$

66. $u = -3\sqrt{2}i + 6j$; $v = 2i + 5\sqrt{5}j$

**For each pair of vectors given, (a) find the projection of u along v (compute proj$_v$u) and (b) resolve u into vectors u$_1$ and u$_2$, where u$_1 \parallel$v and u$_2 \perp$v.**

67. $u = \langle 2, 6 \rangle$; $v = \langle 8, 3 \rangle$

68. $u = \langle -3, 8 \rangle$; $v = \langle -12, 3 \rangle$

69. $u = \langle -2, -8 \rangle$; $v = \langle -6, 1 \rangle$

70. $u = \langle -4.2, 3 \rangle$; $v = \langle -5, -8.3 \rangle$

71. $u = 10i + 5j$; $v = 12i + 2j$

72. $u = -3i - 9j$; $v = 5i - 3j$

**Projectile motion:** A projectile is launched from a catapult with the initial velocity $v_0$ and angle $\theta$ indicated. Find (a) the position of the object after 3 sec and (b) the time required to reach a height of 250 ft.

73. $v_0 = 250$ ft/sec; $\theta = 60°$

74. $v_0 = 300$ ft/sec; $\theta = 55°$

75. $v_0 = 200$ ft/sec; $\theta = 45°$

76. $v_0 = 500$ ft/sec; $\theta = 70°$

77. At the circus, a "human cannon ball" is shot from a large cannon with an initial velocity of 90 ft/sec at an angle of 65° from the horizontal. How high is the acrobat after 1.2 sec? How long until the acrobat is again at this same height?

78. A center fielder runs down a long hit by an opposing batter and whirls to throw the ball to the infield to keep the hitter to a double. If the initial velocity of the throw is 130 ft/sec and the ball is released at an angle of 30° with level ground, how high is the ball after 1.5 sec? How long until the ball again reaches this same height?

▶ **EXTENDING THE CONCEPT**

For the arbitrary vectors $u = \langle a, b \rangle$, $v = \langle c, d \rangle$, and $w = \langle e, f \rangle$ and the scalar $k$, prove the following vector properties using the properties of real numbers.

79. $w \cdot (u + v) = w \cdot u + w \cdot v$

80. $k(u \cdot v) = ku \cdot v = u \cdot kv$

81. $0 \cdot u = u \cdot 0 = 0$

82. $\dfrac{u}{|u|} \cdot \dfrac{v}{|v|} = \dfrac{u \cdot v}{|u||v|}$

83. As alternative to $\cos \theta = \dfrac{u \cdot v}{|u||v|}$ for finding the angle between two vectors, the equation $\tan \theta = \dfrac{m_2 - m_1}{1 + m_2 m_1}$ can be used, where $m_1$ and $m_2$ represent the slopes of the vectors. Find the angle between the vectors $1i + 5j$ and $5i + 2j$ using each equation and comment on which you found more efficient. Then see if you can find a geometric connection between the two equations.

84. Use the equations for the horizontal and vertical components of the projected object's position to obtain the equation of trajectory $y = (\tan \theta)x - \dfrac{16}{v^2\cos^2\theta}x^2$. This is a quadratic equation in $x$. What can you say about its graph? Include comments about the concavity, $x$-intercepts, maximum height, and so on.

▶ **MAINTAINING YOUR SKILLS**

**85. (7.1)** Solve using the law of sines.

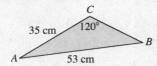

**86. (7.2)** Solve using the law of cosines.

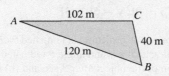

**87. (6.2)** Draw the graph of $y = \sin^{-1}x$ and state the domain and range of the function.

**88. (6.4)** Use a sum identity to find all solutions in $[0, 2\pi)$. Answer in exact form.
$\sin(2x)\cos x + \cos(2x)\sin x = 0.5$

**89. (5.3)** Use a half-angle identity to find the value of $\sin 15°$ and $\cos 75°$ in exact form. What do you notice?

**90. (2.3)** From the top of a 1000-ft cliff to a hut in the valley below, the angle of depression is 27°. How far is the hut from the foot of the cliff?

## SECTION 7.1   Oblique Triangles and the Law of Sines

### KEY CONCEPTS

- In any triangle, the ratio of the sine of an angle to its opposite side is constant: $\dfrac{\sin A}{a} = \dfrac{\sin B}{b} = \dfrac{\sin C}{c}$.
- The law of sines requires a known angle, a side opposite this angle, and an additional side or angle, hence cannot be applied for SSS and SAS triangles.
- For AAS and ASA triangles, the law of sines yields a unique solution.
- When given two sides of a triangle and an angle opposite one of these sides (SSA), the number of solutions is *in doubt,* giving rise to the designation, "the ambiguous case."
- SSA triangles may have no solution, one solution, or two solutions, depending on the length of the side opposite the given angle.
- When solving triangles, always remember:
  - The sum of all angles must be 180°: $\angle A + \angle B + \angle C = 180°$.
  - The sum of any two sides must exceed the length of the remaining side.
  - Longer sides are opposite larger angles.
  - $k = \sin^{-1}\theta$ has no solution for $|k| > 1$.
  - $k = \sin^{-1}\theta$ has two solutions in $[0°, 360°)$ for $0 < |k| < 1$.

### EXERCISES

Solve the following triangles.

1.
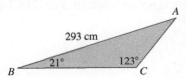

2.
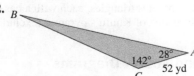

3. A tree is growing vertically on a hillside. Find the height of the tree if it makes an angle of 110° with the hillside and the angle of elevation from the base of the hill to the top of the tree is 25° at a distance of 70 ft.

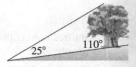

**4.** Find two values of $\theta$ that will make the equation true: $\dfrac{\sin \theta}{14} = \dfrac{\sin 50°}{31}$.

**5.** Solve using the law of sines. If two solutions exist, find both (figure not drawn to scale).

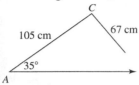

**6.** Jasmine is flying her tethered, gas-powered airplane at a local park, where a group of bystanders is watching from a distance of 60 ft, as shown. If the tether has a radius of 35 ft and one of the bystanders walks away at an angle of 40°, will he get hit by the plane? What is the smallest angle of exit he could take (to the nearest whole) without being struck by Jasmine's plane?

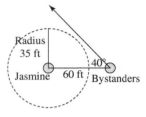

## SECTION 7.2   The Law of Cosines; the Area of a Triangle

**KEY CONCEPTS**

- The law of cosines is used to solve SSS and SAS triangles.
- The law of cosines states that in any triangle, the square of any side is equal to the sums of the squares of the other two sides, minus twice their product times the cosine of the included angle:

$$a^2 = b^2 + c^2 - 2bc \cos A$$

- When using the law of cosines to solve a SSS triangle, always begin with the largest angle or the angle opposite the largest side.
- The area of a nonright triangle can be found using the following formulas. The choice of formula depends on the information given.

  - two sides $a$ and $b$ with included angle $C$

    $$A = \frac{1}{2}ab \sin C$$

  - two angles $A$ and $B$ with included side $c$

    $$A = \frac{c^2 \sin A \sin B}{2 \sin C}$$

  - three sides $a$, $b$, and $c$ with $s = \dfrac{a + b + c}{2}$

    $$A = \sqrt{s(s - a)(s - b)(s - c)}$$

**EXERCISES**

**7.** Solve for $B$: $9^2 = 12^2 + 15^2 - 2(12)(15) \cos B$

**8.** Use the law of cosines to find the missing side.

**9.** While preparing for the day's orienteering meet, Rick finds that the distances between the first three markers he wants to pick up are 1250 yd, 1820 yd, and 720 yd. Find the measure of each angle in the triangle formed so that Rick is sure to find all three markers.

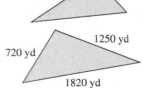

**10.** The Great Pyramid of Giza, also known as Khufu's pyramid, is the sole remaining member of the Seven Wonders of the Ancient World. It was built as a tomb for the Egyptian pharaoh Khufu from the fourth dynasty. This square pyramid is made up of four isosceles triangles, each with a base of 230.0 m and a slant height of about 218.7 m. Approximate the total surface area of Khufu's pyramid (excluding the base).

## SECTION 7.3   Vectors and Vector Diagrams

**KEY CONCEPTS**

- Quantities/concepts that can be described using a single number are called scalar quantities. Examples are time, perimeter, area, volume, energy, temperature, weight, and so on.
- Quantities/concepts that require more than a single number to describe their attributes are called vector quantities. Examples are force, velocity, displacement, pressure, and so on.

- Vectors can be represented using directed line segments to indicate magnitude and direction. The origin of the segment is called the initial point, with the arrowhead pointing to the terminal point. When used solely for comparative analysis, they are called geometric vectors.
- Two vectors are equal if they have the same magnitude and direction.
- Vectors can be represented graphically in the $xy$-plane by naming the initial and terminal points of the vector or by giving the magnitude and angle of the related position vector [initial point at $(0, 0)$].
- For a vector with initial point $(x_1, y_1)$ and terminal point $(x_2, y_2)$, the related position vector can be written in the component form $\langle a, b \rangle$, where $a = x_2 - x_1$ and $b = y_2 - y_1$.
- For a vector written in the component form $\langle a, b \rangle$, $a$ is called the horizontal component and $b$ is called the vertical component of the vector.
- For vector $\mathbf{v} = \langle a, b \rangle$, the magnitude of $\mathbf{v}$ is $|\mathbf{v}| = \sqrt{a^2 + b^2}$.
- Vector components can also be written in trigonometric form. See page 346.
- For $\mathbf{u} = \langle a, b \rangle$, $\mathbf{v} = \langle c, d \rangle$, and any scalar $k$, we have the following operations defined:

$$\mathbf{u} + \mathbf{v} = \langle a + c, b + d \rangle \qquad \mathbf{u} - \mathbf{v} = \langle a - c, b - d \rangle \qquad k\mathbf{u} = \langle ka, kb \rangle \text{ for } k \in \mathbb{R}$$

  If $k > 0$, the new vector has the same direction as $\mathbf{u}$; $k < 0$, the opposite direction.
- Vectors can be written in algebraic form using $\mathbf{i}, \mathbf{j}$ notation, where $\mathbf{i}$ is an $x$-axis unit vector and $\mathbf{j}$ is a $y$-axis unit vector. The vector $\langle a, b \rangle$ is written as a linear combination of $\mathbf{i}$ and $\mathbf{j}$: $\langle a, b \rangle = a\mathbf{i} + b\mathbf{j}$.
- For any nonzero vector $\mathbf{v}$, vector $\mathbf{u} = \dfrac{\mathbf{v}}{|\mathbf{v}|}$ is a unit vector in the same direction as $\mathbf{v}$.
- In aviation and shipping, the heading of a ship or plane is understood to be the amount of rotation from due north in the clockwise direction.

### EXERCISES

**11.** Graph the vector $\mathbf{v} = \langle 9, 5 \rangle$, then compute its magnitude and direction angle.

**12.** Write the vector $\mathbf{u} = \langle -8, 3 \rangle$ in $\mathbf{i}, \mathbf{j}$ form and compute its magnitude and direction angle.

**13.** Approximate the horizontal and vertical components of the vector $\mathbf{u}$, where $|\mathbf{u}| = 18$ and $\theta = 52°$.

**14.** Compute $2\mathbf{u} + \mathbf{v}$, then find the magnitude and direction of the resultant: $\mathbf{u} = \langle -3, -5 \rangle$ and $\mathbf{v} = \langle 2, 8 \rangle$.

**15.** Find a unit vector that points in the same direction as $\mathbf{u} = 7\mathbf{i} + 12\mathbf{j}$.

**16.** Without computing, if $\mathbf{u} = \langle -9, 2 \rangle$ and $\mathbf{v} = \langle 2, 8 \rangle$, will the resultant sum lie in Quadrant I or II? Why?

**17.** It's once again time for the Great River Race, a $\frac{1}{2}$-mi swim across the Panache River. If Karl fails to take the river's 1-mph current into account and he swims the race at 3 mph, how far from the finish marker does he end up when he makes it to the other side?

**Exercise 18**

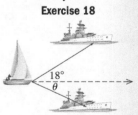

**18.** Two Coast Guard vessels are towing a large yacht into port. The first is pulling with a force of 928 N and the second with a force of 850 N. Determine the angle $\theta$ for the second Coast Guard vessel that will keep the ship moving safely in a straight line.

## SECTION 7.4    Vector Applications and the Dot Product

### KEY CONCEPTS

- Vector forces are in equilibrium when the sum of their components is the zero vector.
- When the components of vector $\mathbf{u}$ are nonquadrantal, with one of its components lying along vector $\mathbf{v}$, we call this component the "component of $\mathbf{u}$ along $\mathbf{v}$" or $\text{comp}_\mathbf{v}\mathbf{u}$.
- For vectors $\mathbf{u}$ and $\mathbf{v}$, $\text{comp}_\mathbf{v}\mathbf{u} = |\mathbf{u}|\cos\theta$, where $\theta$ is the angle between $\mathbf{u}$ and $\mathbf{v}$.
- Work done is computed as the product of the constant force $\mathbf{F}$ applied, times the distance $D$ the force is applied: $W = |\mathbf{F}| \cdot D$.
- If force is not applied parallel to the direction of movement, only the component of the force in the direction of movement is used in the computation of work. If $\mathbf{u}$ is a force vector not parallel to the direction of vector $\mathbf{v}$, the equation becomes $W = \text{comp}_\mathbf{v}\mathbf{u} \cdot |\mathbf{v}|$.

- For vectors $\mathbf{u} = \langle a, b \rangle$ and $\mathbf{v} = \langle c, d \rangle$, the dot product $\mathbf{u} \cdot \mathbf{v}$ is defined as the scalar $ac + bd$.
- The dot product $\mathbf{u} \cdot \mathbf{v}$ is equivalent to $\text{comp}_\mathbf{u}\mathbf{v} \cdot |\mathbf{v}|$ and to $|\mathbf{u}||\mathbf{v}|\cos\theta$.
- The angle between two vectors can be computed using $\cos\theta = \dfrac{\mathbf{u}}{|\mathbf{u}|} \cdot \dfrac{\mathbf{v}}{|\mathbf{v}|} = \dfrac{\mathbf{u} \cdot \mathbf{v}}{|\mathbf{u}||\mathbf{v}|}$.
- Given vectors $\mathbf{u}$ and $\mathbf{v}$, the projection of $\mathbf{u}$ along $\mathbf{v}$ is the *vector* $\text{proj}_\mathbf{v}\mathbf{u}$ defined by $\text{proj}_\mathbf{v}\mathbf{u} = \left(\dfrac{\mathbf{u} \cdot \mathbf{v}}{|\mathbf{v}|^2}\right)\mathbf{v}$.
- Given vectors $\mathbf{u}$ and $\mathbf{v}$ and $\text{proj}_\mathbf{v}\mathbf{u}$, $\mathbf{u}$ can be resolved into the orthogonal components $\mathbf{u}_1$ and $\mathbf{u}_2$ where $\mathbf{u} = \mathbf{u}_1 + \mathbf{u}_2$, $\mathbf{u}_1 = \text{proj}_\mathbf{v}\mathbf{u}$, and $\mathbf{u}_2 = \mathbf{u} - \mathbf{u}_1$.
- The horizontal distance $x$ a projectile travels in $t$ seconds is $x = (|\mathbf{v}|\cos\theta)t$.
- The vertical height $y$ of a projectile after $t$ seconds is $y = (|\mathbf{v}|\sin\theta)t - 16t^2$, where $|\mathbf{v}|$ is the magnitude of the initial velocity, and $\theta$ is the angle of projection.

## EXERCISES

19. For the force vectors $\mathbf{F}_1$ and $\mathbf{F}_2$ given, find the resultant and an additional force vector so that equilibrium takes place: $\mathbf{F}_1 = \langle -20, 70 \rangle$; $\mathbf{F}_2 = \langle 45, 53 \rangle$.

20. Find $\text{comp}_\mathbf{v}\mathbf{u}$ for $\mathbf{u} = -12\mathbf{i} - 16\mathbf{j}$ and $\mathbf{v} = 19\mathbf{i} - 13\mathbf{j}$.

21. Find the component $d$ that ensures vectors $\mathbf{u}$ and $\mathbf{v}$ are orthogonal: $\mathbf{u} = \langle 2, 9 \rangle$ and $\mathbf{v} = \langle -18, d \rangle$.

22. Compute $\mathbf{p} \cdot \mathbf{q}$ and find the angle between them: $\mathbf{p} = \langle -5, -2 \rangle$; $\mathbf{q} = \langle 4, -7 \rangle$.

23. Given force vector $\mathbf{F} = \langle 50, 15 \rangle$ and $\mathbf{v} = \langle 85, 6 \rangle$, find the work required to move an object along the entire length of $\mathbf{v}$. Assume force is in pounds and distance in feet.

24. A 650-lb crate is sitting on a ramp that is inclined at 40°. Find the force needed to hold the crate stationary.

25. An arctic explorer is hauling supplies from the supply hut to her tent, a distance of 120 ft, in a sled she is dragging behind her. If the straps used make an angle of 25° with the snow-covered ground and she pulls with a constant force of 75 lb, find the amount of work done.

**Exercise 24**

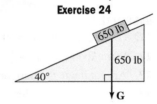

26. A projectile is launched from a sling-shot with an initial velocity of $v_0 = 280$ ft/sec at an angle of $\theta = 50°$. Find (a) the position of the object after 1.5 sec and (b) the time required to reach a height of 150 ft.

Solve each triangle using either the law of sines or law of cosines (whichever is appropriate) then find the area of each.

**1.**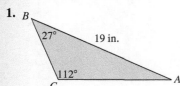

**2.**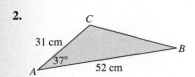

**3.** Find the horizontal and vertical components of the vector **u**, where $|\mathbf{u}| = 21$ and $\theta = 40°$.

**4.** Compute $2\mathbf{u} + \mathbf{v}$, then find the magnitude and direction of the resultant: $\mathbf{u} = \langle 6, -3 \rangle$, $\mathbf{v} = \langle -2, 8 \rangle$.

**5.** Find the height of a flagpole that sits atop a hill, if it makes an angle of 122° with the hillside, and the angle of elevation between the side of the hill to the top of the flagpole is 35° at a distance of 120 ft.

**6.** A 900-lb crate is sitting on a ramp that is inclined at 28°. Find the force needed to hold the object stationary.

**Exercise 6**

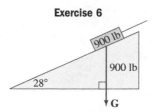

**7.** A jet plane is flying at 750 mph on a heading of 30°. There is a strong, 50-mph wind blowing from due south (heading 0°). What is the true course and speed of the plane (relative to the ground)?

**8.** Graph the vector $\mathbf{v} = \langle -8, 5 \rangle$, then compute its magnitude and direction.

**9.** Solve using the law of sines. If two solutions exist, find both.

**Exercise 9**

**10.** A local Outdoors Club sponsors a treasure hunt activity for its members, and has placed surprise packages at the corners of the triangular park shown. Find the measure of each angle to help club members find their way to the treasure.

**Exercise 10**

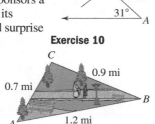

**11.** As part of a lab demonstrating centrifugal and centripetal forces, a physics teacher is whirling a tethered weight above her head while a group of students looks on from a distance of 20 ft as shown. If the tether has a radius of 10 ft and a student departs at the 35° angle shown, will the student be struck by the weight? What is the smallest angle of exit the student could take (to the nearest whole) without being struck by the whirling weight?

**12.** Given the vectors $\mathbf{p} = \langle -5, 2 \rangle$ and $\mathbf{q} = \langle 4, 7 \rangle$, use the dot product $\mathbf{p} \cdot \mathbf{q}$ to find the angle between them.

**13.** On a large world map, if you connect the cities of Honolulu, Hawaii, San Francisco, California, and Tokyo, Japan, on a map, a triangle is formed. Find the distance (a) from Honolulu to Tokyo and (b) from Honolulu to San Francisco, given the angle at the Honolulu vertex is 108.4°, the angle at the San Francisco vertex is 45.5°, and the distance between Tokyo and San Francisco is 5142 mi.

**14.** Solve for A to the nearest hundredth of a degree:
$12^2 = 5^2 + 10^2 - 2(5)(10) \cos A$

**15.** Two tractors are dragging a large, fallen tree into the brush pile that's being prepared for a large Fourth of July bonfire. The first is pulling with a force of 418 N and the second with a force of 320 N. Determine the angle $\theta$ for the second tractor that will keep the tree headed straight for the brush pile.

**16.** Find the unit vector pointing in the same direction as $11\mathbf{i} - 60\mathbf{j}$.

**17.** Given the vectors $\mathbf{u} = -12\mathbf{i} - 16\mathbf{j}$ and $\mathbf{v} = 19\mathbf{i} - 13\mathbf{j}$, find $\text{comp}_v\mathbf{u}$ and $\text{proj}_v\mathbf{u}$.

**18.** Find the area of the triangular park in Exercise 10.

**19.** Find the coordinates of the terminal point of the vector $\langle 5, -2 \rangle$ given its initial point is (−3, 1).

**20.** Find the measure of the smallest angle in a triangle whose sides measure 1.1 m, 1.2 m, and 1.3 m. Round to the nearest hundredth of a degree.

1. Within the Kilimanjaro Game Reserve, a fire is spotted by park rangers stationed in two towers known to be 10 mi apart. Using the line between them as a baseline, tower A reports the fire is at an angle of 39°, while tower B reports an angle of 68°. How far is the fire from the closer tower?

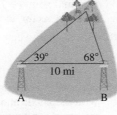

2. At the circus, Mac and Joe are watching a high-wire act from first-row seats on opposite sides of the center ring. Find the height of the performing acrobat at the instant Mac measures an angle of elevation of 68° while Joe measures an angle of 72°. Assume Mac and Joe are 100 ft apart.

**Exercise 2**

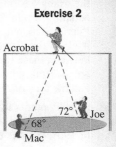

3. Three rods are attached via two joints and shaped into a triangle. How many triangles can be formed if the angle at the joint B must measure 20°? If two triangles can be formed, solve both.

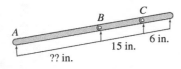

4. Jackie and Sam are rounding up cattle in the brush country, and are communicating via walkie-talkie. Jackie is at the water hole and Sam is at Dead Oak, which are 6 mi apart. Sam finds some strays and heads them home at the 32° indicated. (a) If the maximum range of Jackie's unit is 3 mi, will she be able to communicate with Sam as he heads home? (b) If the maximum range were 4 mi, how far from Dead Oak is Sam when he is first contacted by Jackie?

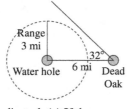

5. As part of an All-Star competition, a group of soccer players (forwards) stand where shown in the diagram and attempt to hit a moving target with a two-handed overhead pass. If a player has a maximum effective range of approximately (a) 25 yd, can the target be hit? (b) about 28 yd, how many "effective" throws can be made? (c) 35 yd and the target is moving at 5 yd/sec, how many seconds is the target within range?

**Exercise 5**

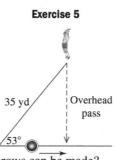

6. The summit of Triangle Peak can only be reached from one side, using a trail straight up the side that is approximately 3.5 mi long. If the mountain is 5 mi wide at its base and the trail makes a 24° angle with the horizontal, (a) what is the approximate length of the opposing side? (b) How tall is the peak (in feet)?

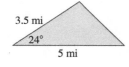

7. The Bermuda Triangle is generally thought to be the triangle formed by Miami, Florida, San Juan, Puerto Rico, and Bermuda itself. If the distances between these locations are the 1025 mi, 1020 mi, and 977 mi indicated, find the measure of each angle and the area of the Bermuda Triangle.

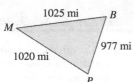

8. A helicopter is flying at 90 mph on a heading of 40°. A 20-mph wind is blowing from the NE on a heading of 190°. What is the true course and speed of the helicopter relative to the ground? Draw a diagram as part of your solution.

9. Two mules walking along a river bank are pulling a heavy barge up river. The first is pulling with a force of 250 N and the second with a force of 210 N. Determine the angle $\theta$ for the second mule that will ensure the barge stays midriver and does not collide with the shore.

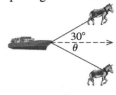

10. Along a production line, various tools are attached to the ceiling with a multijointed arm so that workers can draw one down, position it for use, then move it up out of the way for the next tool (see the diagram). If the first segment is 100 cm, the second is 75 cm, and the third is 50 cm, determine the approximate coordinates of the last joint.

**Exercise 10**

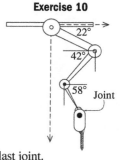

11. Three ranch hands have roped a run-away steer and are attempting to hold him steady. The first and second ranch hands are pulling with the magnitude and at the angles indicated in the diagram. If the steer is held fast by the efforts of all three, find the magnitude of the tension and angle of the rope from the third cowhand.

12. For $\mathbf{u} = \langle -9, 5 \rangle$ and $\mathbf{v} = \langle -2, 6 \rangle$, (a) compute the angle between $\mathbf{u}$ and $\mathbf{v}$; (b) find the projection of $\mathbf{u}$ along $\mathbf{v}$ (find $\mathbf{proj_v u}$); and (c) resolve $\mathbf{u}$ into vectors $\mathbf{u}_1$ and $\mathbf{u}_2$, where $\mathbf{u}_1 \parallel \mathbf{v}$ and $\mathbf{u}_2 \perp \mathbf{v}$.

13. A lacrosse player flips a long pass to a teammate way down field who is near the opponent's goal. If the initial velocity of the pass is 110 ft/sec and the ball is released at an angle of 50° with level ground, how high is the ball after 2 sec? How long until the ball again reaches this same height?

14. Write an expression for $C$ in the law of cosines:
$$c^2 = a^2 + b^2 - 2ab \cos C$$

15. Given vector $\mathbf{v}$ has initial point $(13, -9)$ and terminal point $(-7, -3)$, find (a) the equivalent position vector and (b) $|\mathbf{v}|$.

16. Find the unit vector pointing in the same direction as $\frac{5}{4}\mathbf{i} + \frac{3}{2}\mathbf{j}$.

17. A position vector $\mathbf{v}$ in QII makes an angle of 35° with the $x$-axis and has magnitude of 8. Write the vector in component form, rounded to the nearest tenth.

18. John is carefully pulling his boat out of the garage onto the driveway by hand. The driveway slopes downward at an angle of 4° and he is pulling the boat upward at an angle of 11°. (a) Write an equation for the work done if he pulls the boat $x$ ft down the driveway, using a constant force of $p$ lb. (b) Use the equation to determine how much work is done if he pulls the boat 20 ft with a constant force of 80 lb?

19. For the force vector $\mathbf{F} = -8\mathbf{i} + 7\mathbf{j}$ and vector $\mathbf{v} = 2\mathbf{i} + 9\mathbf{j}$, (a) find the angle between $\mathbf{F}$ and $\mathbf{v}$ and (b) find the amount of work required to move an object along the entire length of $\mathbf{v}$. Assume force is in pounds and distance in feet.

20. Due to its huge biodiversity, preserving Southeast Asia's Coral Triangle has become a top priority for conservationists. Stretching from the northern Philippines ($P$), south through Borneo ($B$) to the Lesser Sunda Islands ($L$), then eastward to the Solomon Islands ($S$), this area is home to over 75% of all coral species known. Use the triangle formulas from section 7.2 to help find the total area of this natural wonderland, given the dimensions shown.

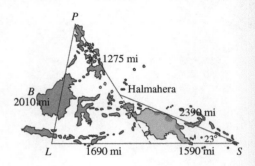

## Investigating Projectile Motion

There are two important aspects of projectile motion that were not discussed earlier, the **range** of the projectile and the **optimum angle** $\theta$ that will maximize this range. Both can be explored using the equations for the horizontal and vertical components of the projectile's position: horizontal $\rightarrow (|\mathbf{v}|\cos\theta)t$ and vertical $\rightarrow (|\mathbf{v}|\sin\theta)t - 16t^2$. In Example 10 of Section 7.4, an arrow was shot from a bow with initial velocity $|\mathbf{v}| = 150$ ft/sec at an angle of $\theta = 50°$. Enter the equations above on the  screen as $Y_1$ and $Y_2$, using these values (Figure 7.76). Then set up the TABLE using TblStart = 0, $\Delta$Tbl = 0.5 and the AUTO mode. The resulting table is shown in Figure 7.77, where $Y_1$ represents the horizontal distance the arrow has traveled, and $Y_2$ represents the height of the arrow. To find the *range* of the arrow, scroll downward ▼ until the height ($Y_2$) shows a value that is less than or equal to zero (the arrow has hit the ground). As Figure 7.78 shows, this happens somewhere between $t = 7$ and $t = 7.5$ sec. We could now change the TBLSET settings to TblStart = 0 and $\Delta$Tbl = 0.1 to get a better approximation of the time the arrow is in flight (it's just less than 7.2 sec) and the horizontal range of the arrow (about 692.4 ft), but our main interest is how to *compute these values exactly*. We begin with the equation for the arrow's vertical position $y = (|\mathbf{v}|\sin\theta)t - 16t^2$. Since the object returns to Earth when $y = 0$, we substitute 0 for $y$ and factor out $t$: $0 = t(|\mathbf{v}|\sin\theta - 16t)$. Solving for $t$ gives $t = 0$ or $t = \dfrac{|\mathbf{v}|\sin\theta}{16}$. Since the component of velocity in the horizontal direction is $|\mathbf{v}|\cos\theta$, the basic distance relationship $D = r \cdot t$ gives the horizontal range of $R = |\mathbf{v}|\cos\theta \cdot \dfrac{|\mathbf{v}|\sin\theta}{16}$ or $\dfrac{|\mathbf{v}|^2\sin\theta\cos\theta}{16}$. Checking the values given for the arrow ($|\mathbf{v}| = 150$ ft/sec and $\theta = 50°$) verifies the range is $R \approx 692.4$. But what about the *maximum possible range* for the arrow? Using $|\mathbf{v}| = 150$ for $R$ results in an equation in theta only: $R(\theta) = \dfrac{150^2\sin\theta\cos\theta}{16}$, which we can enter as $Y_3$ and investigate

for various $\theta$. After carefully entering $R(\theta)$ as $Y_3$ and resetting TBLSET to TblStart = 30 and $\Delta$Tbl = 5, the TABLE in Figure 7.79 shows a maximum range of about 703 ft at 45°. Resetting TBLSET to TblStart = 40 and $\Delta$Tbl = 1 verifies this fact.

**Figure 7.76**

```
Plot1  Plot2  Plot3
\Y1 ◻150cos(50)X
\Y2 ◻150sin(50)X-
16X²
\Y3 =
\Y4 =
\Y5 =
\Y6 =
```

**Figure 7.77**

| X | Y₁ | Y₂ |
|---|-----|------|
| 0 | 0 | 0 |
| .5 | 48.209 | 53.453 |
| 1 | 96.418 | 98.907 |
| 1.5 | 144.63 | 136.36 |
| 2 | 192.84 | 165.81 |
| 2.5 | 241.05 | 187.27 |
| 3 | 289.26 | 200.72 |

X=0

**Figure 7.78**

| X | Y₁ | Y₂ |
|---|-----|------|
| 5 | 482.09 | 174.53 |
| 5.5 | 530.3 | 147.99 |
| 6 | 578.51 | 113.44 |
| 6.5 | 626.72 | 70.893 |
| 7 | 674.93 | 20.347 |
| 7.5 | 723.14 | -38.2 |
| 8 | 771.35 | -104.7 |

X=7.5

For each of the following exercises, find (a) the height of the projectile after 1.75 sec, (b) the maximum height of the projectile, (c) the range of the projectile, and (d) the number of seconds the projectile is airborne.

**Exercise 1:** A javelin is thrown with an initial velocity of 85 ft/sec at an angle of 42°.

**Exercise 2:** A cannon ball is shot with an initial velocity of 1120 ft/sec at an angle of 30°.

**Exercise 3:** A baseball is hit with an initial velocity of 120 ft/sec at an angle of 50°. Will it clear the center field fence, 10 ft high and 375 ft away?

**Exercise 4:** A field goal (American football) is kicked with an initial velocity of 65 ft/sec at an angle of 35°. Will it clear the crossbar, 10 ft high and 40 yd away?

**Figure 7.79**

| X | Y₃ |
|---|---|
| 30 | 608.92 |
| 35 | 660.72 |
| 40 | 692.44 |
| 45 | 703.13 |
| 50 | 692.44 |
| 55 | 660.72 |
| 60 | 608.92 |

X=30

## STRENGTHENING CORE SKILLS

### Vectors and Static Equilibrium

In Sections 7.3 and 7.4, the concepts of vector forces, resultant forces, and equilibrium were studied extensively. A nice extension of these concepts involves what is called **static equilibrium.** Assuming that only coplanar forces are acting on an object, the object is said to be in static equilibrium if *the sum of all vector forces acting on it is **0**.* This implies that the object is stationary, since the forces all counterbalance each other. The methods involved are simple and direct, with a wonderful connection to the systems of equations you've likely seen previously. Consider the following example.

**Illustration 1** ▶  As part of their training, prospective FBI agents must move hand-over-hand across a rope strung between two towers. An agent-in-training weighing 180 lb is two-thirds of the way across, causing the rope to deflect from the horizontal at the angles shown. What is the tension in each part of the rope at this point?

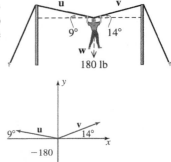

**Solution** ▶  We have three concurrent forces acting on the point where the agent grasps the rope. Begin by drawing a vector diagram and computing the components of each force, using the **i, j** notation. Note that $\mathbf{w} = -180\mathbf{j}$.

$$\mathbf{u} = -|\mathbf{u}|\cos(9°)\mathbf{i} + |\mathbf{u}|\sin(9°)\mathbf{j}$$
$$\approx -0.9877|\mathbf{u}|\mathbf{i} + 0.1564|\mathbf{u}|\mathbf{j}$$
$$\mathbf{v} = |\mathbf{v}|\cos(14°)\mathbf{i} + |\mathbf{v}|\sin(14°)\mathbf{j}$$
$$\approx 0.9703|\mathbf{v}|\mathbf{i} + 0.2419|\mathbf{v}|\mathbf{j}$$

For equilibrium, all vector forces must sum to the zero vector: $\mathbf{u} + \mathbf{v} + \mathbf{w} = 0$, which results in the following equation: $-0.9877|\mathbf{u}|\mathbf{i} + 0.1564|\mathbf{u}|\mathbf{j} + 0.9703|\mathbf{v}|\mathbf{i} + 0.2419|\mathbf{v}|\mathbf{j} - 180\mathbf{j} = 0\mathbf{i} + 0\mathbf{j}$. Factoring out **i** and **j** from the left-hand side yields $(-0.9877|\mathbf{u}| + 0.9703|\mathbf{v}|)\mathbf{i} + (0.1564|\mathbf{u}| + 0.2419|\mathbf{v}| - 180)\mathbf{j} = 0\mathbf{i} + 0\mathbf{j}$. Since any two vectors are equal only when corresponding components are equal, we obtain a system in the two variables

$$|\mathbf{u}| \text{ and } |\mathbf{v}| : \begin{cases} -0.9877|\mathbf{u}| + 0.9703|\mathbf{v}|) = 0 \\ 0.1564|\mathbf{u}| + 0.2419|\mathbf{v}| - 180 = 0 \end{cases}.$$

Solving the system using matrix equations and a calculator (or any desired method), gives $|\mathbf{u}| \approx 447$ lb and $|\mathbf{v}| \approx 455$ lb.

At first it may seem surprising that the vector forces (tension) in each part of the rope are so much greater than the 180 lb the agent weighs. But with a 180-lb object hanging from the middle of the rope, the tension required to keep the rope taut (with small angles of deflection) must be very great. This should become more obvious to you after you work Exercise 2.

**Exercise 1:** A 500-lb crate is suspended by two ropes attached to the ceiling rafters. Find the tension in each rope.

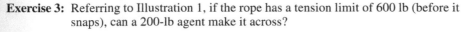

**Exercise 2:** Two people team up to carry a 150-lb weight by passing a rope through an eyelet in the object. Find the tension in each rope.

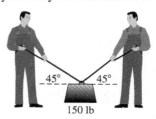

**Exercise 3:** Referring to Illustration 1, if the rope has a tension limit of 600 lb (before it snaps), can a 200-lb agent make it across?

## CUMULATIVE REVIEW CHAPTERS 1–7

**1.** Solve using a standard triangle.

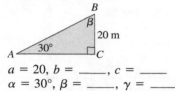

$a = 20$, $b =$ _____, $c =$ _____
$\alpha = 30°$, $\beta =$ _____, $\gamma =$ _____

**2.** Solve using trigonometric ratios.

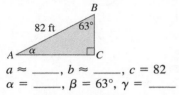

$a \approx$ _____, $b \approx$ _____, $c = 82$
$\alpha =$ _____, $\beta = 63°$, $\gamma =$ _____

**3.** Solve for $t$: $A\cos(Bt + C) - D = 0$

**4.** For a complex number $a + bi$, (a) verify the sum of a complex number and its conjugate is a real number, and (b) verify the product of a complex number and its conjugate is a real number.

**5.** State the value of all six trig functions given $\tan \alpha = -\dfrac{3}{4}$ with $\cos \alpha > 0$.

**6.** Sketch the graph of $y = 3\cos\left(\dfrac{\pi}{6}x - \dfrac{\pi}{3}\right)$ using a reference rectangle and the *rule of fourths*.

**7.** State each related identity:

   **a.** $\sin(2\alpha)$      **b.** $\sin\left(\dfrac{\alpha}{2}\right)$      **c.** $\sin(\alpha + \beta)$

**8.** State the domain and range of each function:

   **a.** $y = \sin^{-1}t$      **b.** $y = \cos^{-1}t$      **c.** $y = \tan^{-1}t$

**9.** Given $\cos 53° \approx 0.6$ and $\cos 72° \approx 0.3$, approximate the value of $\cos 19°$ and $\cos 125°$ without using a calculator.

**10.** Find all real values of $x$ that satisfy the equation $\sqrt{3} + 2\sin(2x) = 2\sqrt{3}$. State the answer in degrees.

**11.** The approximate number of daylight hours for Juneau, Alaska (58° N latitude), is given in the table. Use the data to find an appropriate regression equation, then answer the following:

   **a.** Approximately how many daylight hours were there on April 15 ($t = 4.5$)?

**b.** Approximate the dates between which there are over 15 hr of daylight.

Source: Alaskan Alternative Energy @ www.absak.com/design/sunhours.

| Month (Jan → 1) | Daylight (hours) | Month (Jan → 1) | Daylight (hours) |
|---|---|---|---|
| 1 | 6.5 | 7 | 18.1 |
| 2 | 8.3 | 8 | 16.5 |
| 3 | 10.5 | 9 | 14.0 |
| 4 | 13.2 | 10 | 11.5 |
| 5 | 15.7 | 11 | 9.0 |
| 6 | 17.8 | 12 | 6.9 |

**12.** Verify that $\csc^2 t + \sec^2 t = \csc^2 t\sec^2 t$ is an identity.

**13.** Verify that the following is an identity:
$$\frac{2\cos^2\theta}{\csc^2\theta} + \frac{2\sin^2\theta}{\sec^2\theta} = \sin^2(2\theta)$$

Solve each triangle using the law of sines or the law of cosines, whichever is appropriate.

**14.**

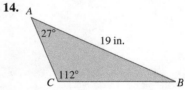

**15.**

**16.** A mountain climber has slipped off the edge of a cliff, and his partner is attempting to pull him 30 ft up the face of the cliff and back onto the plateau. If the rope makes an angle of 10° with the plateau and she must pull with a force of 200 lb to make headway, how much work is done to save the fallen climber?

**17.** A 900-lb crate is sitting on a ramp that is inclined at 28°. Find the force needed to hold the object stationary.

**Exercise 17**

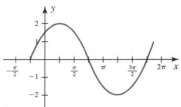

**18.** A jet plane is flying at 750 mph on a heading of 30°. There is a strong, 50-mph wind blowing from due south (heading of 0°). What is the true course and speed of the plane (relative to the ground)?

**19.** Use the dot product to find the angle $\theta$ between the vectors $\langle -3, 8 \rangle$ and $\langle 7, 6 \rangle$.

**20.** The graph given is of the form $y = A \sin(Bx \pm C)$. Find the values of $A$, $B$, and $C$.

**Exercise 20**

# Trigonometric Connections
to Algebra

# Trigonometric Connections to Algebra

## CHAPTER OUTLINE

## CHAPTER CONNECTIONS

While surprising to some, there are a number of "natural connections" between a study of algebra and a study of trigonometry. As the study of complex numbers matured, it was found that they could be represented in trigonometric form, leading to vastly simplified methods of computing powers and roots. Trigonometry also offers essential alternatives to using points (x, y) for graphing algebraic relations. While the use of rectangular coordinates is much more widely known, *polar graphs* and graphs using *parametric equations* bring a higher level of simplicity in certain instances where a graph is required. Cathedral windows like the one shown here are just one place where the beauty and intricacy of polar graphs can be appreciated.

▶ The graphs shown appear as Exercises 73 and 81 in Section 8.4

8

## Learning Objectives

*In Section 8.1 you will learn how to:*

☐ **A.** Identify and simplify imaginary and complex numbers

☐ **B.** Add and subtract complex numbers

☐ **C.** Multiply complex numbers and find powers of $i$

☐ **D.** Divide complex numbers

For centuries, even the most prominent mathematicians refused to work with equations like $x^2 + 1 = 0$. Using the principal of square roots gave the "solutions" $x = \sqrt{-1}$ and $x = -\sqrt{-1}$, which they found baffling and mysterious, since there is no real number whose square is $-1$. In this section, we'll see how this "mystery" was finally resolved.

## A. Identifying and Simplifying Imaginary and Complex Numbers

The equation $x^2 = -1$ has no real solutions, since the square of any real number is positive. But if we apply the principle of square roots we get $x = \sqrt{-1}$ and $x = -\sqrt{-1}$, which seem to check when substituted into the original equation:

$$x^2 + 1 = 0 \qquad \text{original equation}$$

(1)
$$(\sqrt{-1})^2 + 1 = 0 \qquad \text{substitute } \sqrt{-1} \text{ for } x$$
$$-1 + 1 = 0 \checkmark \qquad \text{answer "checks"}$$

(2)
$$(-\sqrt{-1})^2 + 1 = 0 \qquad \text{substitute } -\sqrt{-1} \text{ for } x$$
$$-1 + 1 = 0 \checkmark \qquad \text{answer "checks"}$$

This observation likely played a part in prompting Renaissance mathematicians to study such numbers in greater depth, as they reasoned that while these were not *real number* solutions, they must be *solutions of a new and different kind*. Their study eventually resulted in the introduction of the set of **imaginary numbers** and the **imaginary unit $i$,** as follows.

### Imaginary Numbers and the Imaginary Unit

- Imaginary numbers are those of the form $\sqrt{-k}$, where $k$ is a positive real number.
- The imaginary unit $i$ represents the number whose square is $-1$:

$$i^2 = -1 \text{ and } i = \sqrt{-1}$$

**WORTHY OF NOTE**

It was René Descartes (in 1637) who first used the term *imaginary* to describe these numbers; Leonhard Euler (in 1777) who introduced the letter $i$ to represent $\sqrt{-1}$; and Carl F. Gauss (in 1831) who first used the phrase *complex number* to describe solutions that had both a real number part and an imaginary part. For more on complex numbers and their story, see www.mhhe.com/coburn

As a convenience to understanding and working with imaginary numbers, we rewrite them in terms of $i$, allowing that the product property of radicals ($\sqrt{AB} = \sqrt{A}\sqrt{B}$) still applies if *only one* of the radicands is negative. For $\sqrt{-3}$, we have $\sqrt{-1 \cdot 3} = \sqrt{-1}\sqrt{3} = i\sqrt{3}$. In general, we simply state the following property.

### Rewriting Imaginary Numbers

- For any positive real number $k$,

$$\sqrt{-k} = i\sqrt{k}.$$

For $\sqrt{-20}$ we have

$$\sqrt{-20} = i\sqrt{20}$$
$$= i\sqrt{4 \cdot 5}$$
$$= 2i\sqrt{5}$$

and we say the expression has been *simplified and written in terms of i*. Note that we've written the result with the unit "$i$" *in front of the radical* to prevent it being interpreted as being *under the radical*. In symbols, $2i\sqrt{5} = 2\sqrt{5}i \neq 2\sqrt{5i}$.

The solutions to $x^2 = -1$ also serve to illustrate that for $k > 0$, there are two solutions to $x^2 = -k$, namely, $i\sqrt{k}$ and $-i\sqrt{k}$. In other words, every negative number has two square roots, one positive and one negative. The first of these, $i\sqrt{k}$, is called the **principal square root** of $-k$.

**EXAMPLE 1 ▶ Simplifying Imaginary Numbers**

Rewrite the imaginary numbers in terms of $i$ and simplify if possible.

**a.** $\sqrt{-7}$      **b.** $\sqrt{-81}$      **c.** $\sqrt{-24}$      **d.** $-3\sqrt{-16}$

**Solution ▶**

**a.** $\sqrt{-7} = i\sqrt{7}$               **b.** $\sqrt{-81} = i\sqrt{81}$
                                                     $= 9i$

**c.** $\sqrt{-24} = i\sqrt{24}$            **d.** $-3\sqrt{-16} = -3i\sqrt{16}$
            $= i\sqrt{4 \cdot 6}$                             $= -3i(4)$
            $= 2i\sqrt{6}$                               $= -12i$

**Now try Exercises 7 through 12 ▶**

**EXAMPLE 2 ▶ Writing an Expression in Terms of $i$**

The numbers $x = \dfrac{-6 + \sqrt{-16}}{2}$ and $x = \dfrac{-6 - \sqrt{-16}}{2}$ are not real, but are known to be solutions of $x^2 + 6x + 13 = 0$. Simplify $\dfrac{-6 + \sqrt{-16}}{2}$.

**Solution ▶** Using the $i$ notation, we have

$$\frac{-6 + \sqrt{-16}}{2} = \frac{-6 + i\sqrt{16}}{2} \qquad \text{write in } i \text{ notation}$$

$$= \frac{-6 + 4i}{2} \qquad \text{simplify}$$

$$= \frac{2(-3 + 2i)}{2} \qquad \text{factor numerator}$$

$$= -3 + 2i \qquad \text{reduce}$$

**Now try Exercises 13 through 16 ▶**

**WORTHY OF NOTE**

The expression $\dfrac{-6 + 4i}{2}$ from the solution of Example 2 can also be simplified by rewriting it as two separate terms, then simplifying each term:
$\dfrac{-6 + 4i}{2} = \dfrac{-6}{2} + \dfrac{4i}{2}$
$= -3 + 2i.$

The result in Example 2 contains both a **real number part** $(-3)$ and an **imaginary part** $(2i)$. Numbers of this type are called **complex numbers.**

**Complex Numbers**

Complex numbers are numbers that can be written in the form $a + bi$, where $a$ and $b$ are real numbers and $i = \sqrt{-1}$.

The expression $a + bi$ is called the **standard form** of a complex number. From this definition we note that all real numbers are also complex numbers, since $a + 0i$ is complex with $b = 0$. In addition, all imaginary numbers are complex numbers, since $0 + bi$ is a complex number with $a = 0$.

**EXAMPLE 3 ▶ Writing Complex Numbers in Standard Form**

Write each complex number in the form $a + bi$, and identify the values of $a$ and $b$.

**a.** $2 + \sqrt{-49}$      **b.** $\sqrt{-12}$      **c.** $7$      **d.** $\dfrac{4 + 3\sqrt{-25}}{20}$

**Solution ▶**

**a.** $2 + \sqrt{-49} = 2 + i\sqrt{49}$          **b.** $\sqrt{-12} = 0 + i\sqrt{12}$
                 $= 2 + 7i$                         $= 0 + 2i\sqrt{3}$
              $a = 2, b = 7$                    $a = 0, b = 2\sqrt{3}$

**c.** $7 = 7 + 0i$
$a = 7, b = 0$

**d.** $\dfrac{4 + 3\sqrt{-25}}{20} = \dfrac{4 + 3i\sqrt{25}}{20}$

$= \dfrac{4 + 15i}{20}$

$= \dfrac{1}{5} + \dfrac{3}{4}i$

$a = \dfrac{1}{5}, b = \dfrac{3}{4}$

**Now try Exercises 17 through 24 ▶**

☑ **A.** You've just learned how to identify and simplify imaginary and complex numbers

Complex numbers complete the development of our "numerical landscape." Sets of numbers and their relationships are represented in Figure 8.1, which shows how some sets of numbers are nested within larger sets and highlights the fact that complex numbers consist of a real number part (any number within the orange rectangle), and an imaginary number part (any number within the yellow rectangle).

**Figure 8.1**

$\mathbb{C}$ (complex): Numbers of the form $a + bi$, where $a, b \in \mathbb{R}$ and $i = \sqrt{-1}$.

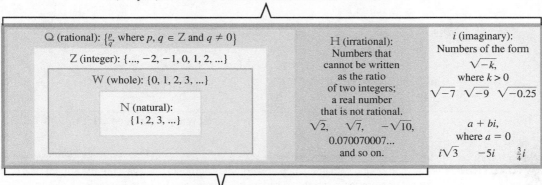

$\mathbb{R}$ (real): All rational and irrational numbers: $a + bi$, where $a \in \mathbb{R}$ and $b = 0$.

## B. Adding and Subtracting Complex Numbers

The sum and difference of two polynomials is computed by identifying and combining like terms. The sum or difference of two complex numbers is computed in a similar way, by adding the real number parts from each, and the imaginary parts from each. Notice in Example 4 that the commutative, associative, and distributive properties also apply to complex numbers.

**EXAMPLE 4 ▶    Adding and Subtracting Complex Numbers**

Perform the indicated operation and write the result in $a + bi$ form.

**a.** $(2 + 3i) + (-5 + 2i)$        **b.** $(-5 - 4i) - (-2 - \sqrt{2}i)$

**Solution ▶**

| | | |
|---|---|---|
| **a.** $(2 + 3i) + (-5 + 2i)$ | original sum | **b.** $(-5 - 4i) - (-2 - \sqrt{2}i)$ |
| $= 2 + 3i + (-5) + 2i$ | distribute | $= -5 - 4i + 2 + \sqrt{2}i$ |
| $= 2 + (-5) + 3i + 2i$ | commute terms | $= -5 + 2 + (-4i) + \sqrt{2}i$ |
| $= [2 + (-5)] + (3i + 2i)$ | group like terms | $= (-5 + 2) + [(-4i) + \sqrt{2}i]$ |
| $= -3 + 5i$ | result | $= -3 + (-4 + \sqrt{2})i$ |

original difference, distribute, commute terms, group like terms, result

☑ **B.** You've just learned how to add and subtract complex numbers

**Now try Exercises 25 through 30 ▶**

## C. Multiplying Complex Numbers; Powers of $i$

The product of two complex numbers is computed using the distributive property and the F-O-I-L process in the same way we apply these to binomials. If any result gives a factor of $i^2$, remember that $i^2 = -1$.

---

**EXAMPLE 5** ▶   **Multiplying Complex Numbers**

Find the indicated product and write the answer in $a + bi$ form.

    **a.** $\sqrt{-4}\sqrt{-9}$            **b.** $\sqrt{-6}\,(2 + \sqrt{-3})$

    **c.** $(6 - 5i)(4 + i)$       **d.** $(2 + 3i)(2 - 3i)$

**Solution** ▶   **a.** $\sqrt{-4}\sqrt{-9}$                         **b.** $\sqrt{-6}\,(2 + \sqrt{-3})$

          $= i\sqrt{4} \cdot i\sqrt{9}$   rewrite in terms of $i$           $= i\sqrt{6}(2 + i\sqrt{3})$   rewrite in terms of $i$

          $= 2i \cdot 3i$            simplify                 $= 2i\sqrt{6} + i^2\sqrt{18}$   distribute

          $= 6i^2$              multiply                $= 2i\sqrt{6} + (-1)\sqrt{9}\sqrt{2}$   $i^2 = -1$

          $= -6 + 0i$    result ($i^2 = -1$)           $= 2i\sqrt{6} - 3\sqrt{2}$   simplify

                                                        $= -3\sqrt{2} + 2i\sqrt{6}$   standard form

    **c.** $(6 - 5i)(4 + i)$                      **d.** $(2 + 3i)(2 - 3i)$

       $= (6)(4) + 6i + (-5i)(4) + (-5i)(i)$  F-O-I-L     $= (2)^2 - (3i)^2$   $(A + B)(A - B) = A^2 - B^2$

       $= 24 + 6i + (-20i) + (-5)i^2$     $i \cdot i = i^2$         $= 4 - 9i^2$       $(3i)^2 = 9i^2$

       $= 24 + 6i + (-20i) + (-5)(-1)$   $i^2 = -1$      $= 4 - 9(-1)$     $i^2 = -1$

       $= 29 - 14i$                       result            $= 13 + 0i$     result

**Now try Exercises 31 through 48** ▶

---

⚠ **CAUTION** ▶   When computing with imaginary and complex numbers, always write the square root of a negative number in terms of $i$ before you begin, as shown in Examples 5(a) and 5(b). Otherwise we get conflicting results, since $\sqrt{-4}\sqrt{-9} = \sqrt{36} = 6$ if we multiply the radicands first, which is an incorrect result because the original factors were imaginary. **See Exercise 80.**

---

Recall that expressions $2x + 5$ and $2x - 5$ are called binomial conjugates. In the same way, $a + bi$ and $a - bi$ are called **complex conjugates.** From Example 5(d), we note that the *product* of the complex number $a + bi$ with its complex conjugate $a - bi$ *is a real number.* This relationship is useful when rationalizing expressions with a complex number in the denominator, and we generalize the result as follows:

**WORTHY OF NOTE**

Notice that the product of a complex number and its conjugate also gives us a method for *factoring the sum of two squares* using complex numbers! For the expression $x^2 + 4$, the factored form would be $(x + 2i)(x - 2i)$. For more on this idea, **see Exercise 79.**

**Product of Complex Conjugates**

For a complex number $a + bi$ and its conjugate $a - bi$,
their product $(a + bi)(a - bi)$ is the real number $a^2 + b^2$;

$$(a + bi)(a - bi) = a^2 + b^2$$

Showing that $(a + bi)(a - bi) = a^2 + b^2$ is left as an exercise (**see Exercise 79**), but from here on, when asked to compute the product of complex conjugates, simply refer to the formula as illustrated here: $(-3 + 5i)(-3 - 5i) = (-3)^2 + 5^2$ or 34.

These operations on complex numbers enable us to verify complex solutions by substitution, in the same way we verify solutions for real numbers. In Example 2 we stated that $x = -3 + 2i$ was one solution to $x^2 + 6x + 13 = 0$. This is verified here.

**EXAMPLE 6** ▶ **Checking a Complex Root by Substitution**

Verify that $x = -3 + 2i$ is a solution to $x^2 + 6x + 13 = 0$.

Solution ▶

$$x^2 + 6x + 13 = 0 \quad \text{original equation}$$
$$(-3 + 2i)^2 + 6(-3 + 2i) + 13 = 0 \quad \text{substitute } -3 + 2i \text{ for } x$$
$$(-3)^2 + 2(-3)(2i) + (2i)^2 - 18 + 12i + 13 = 0 \quad \text{square and distribute}$$
$$9 - 12i + 4i^2 + 12i - 5 = 0 \quad \text{simplify}$$
$$9 + (-4) - 5 = 0 \quad \text{combine terms } (12i - 12i = 0; i^2 = -1)$$
$$0 = 0 ✔$$

**Now try Exercises 49 through 56** ▶

**EXAMPLE 7** ▶ **Checking a Complex Root by Substitution**

Show that $x = 2 - i\sqrt{3}$ is a solution of $x^2 - 4x = -7$.

Solution ▶

$$x^2 - 4x = -7 \quad \text{original equation}$$
$$(2 - i\sqrt{3})^2 - 4(2 - i\sqrt{3}) = -7 \quad \text{substitute } 2 - i\sqrt{3} \text{ for } x$$
$$4 - 4i\sqrt{3} + (i\sqrt{3})^2 - 8 + 4i\sqrt{3} = -7 \quad \text{square and distribute}$$
$$4 - 4i\sqrt{3} - 3 - 8 + 4i\sqrt{3} = -7 \quad (i\sqrt{3})^2 = -3$$
$$-7 = -7 ✔ \quad \text{solution checks}$$

**Now try Exercises 57 through 60** ▶

The imaginary unit $i$ has another interesting and useful property. Since $i = \sqrt{-1}$ and $i^2 = -1$, we know that $i^3 = i^2 \cdot i = (-1)i = -i$ and $i^4 = (i^2)^2 = 1$. We can now simplify any *higher power of i* by rewriting the expression in terms of $i^4$.

$$i^5 = i^4 \cdot i = i$$
$$i^6 = i^4 \cdot i^2 = -1$$
$$i^7 = i^4 \cdot i^3 = -i$$
$$i^8 = (i^4)^2 = 1$$

Since the powers of $i$ "cycle through" the four values $i, -1, -i$ and 1, we reduce higher powers using the power property of exponents and $i^4 = 1$. Essentially, we divide the exponent on $i$ by 4, then use the remainder to compute the value of the expression. For $i^{35}$, $35 \div 4 = 8$ remainder 3, showing $i^{35} = (i^4)^8 \cdot i^3 = -i$.

**EXAMPLE 8** ▶ **Simplifying Higher Powers of i**

Simplify:

    **a.** $i^{22}$      **b.** $i^{28}$      **c.** $i^{57}$      **d.** $i^{75}$

Solution ▶   **a.** $i^{22} = (i^4)^5 \cdot (i^2)$      **b.** $i^{28} = (i^4)^7$
               $= (1)^5(-1)$            $= (1)^7$
               $= -1$               $= 1$

☑ **C.** You've just learned how to multiply complex numbers and find powers of $i$

**c.** $i^{57} = (i^4)^{14} \cdot i$
$= (1)^{14} i$
$= i$

**d.** $i^{75} = (i^4)^{18} \cdot (i^3)$
$= (1)^{18}(-i)$
$= -i$

**Now try Exercises 61 and 62 ▶**

## D. Division of Complex Numbers

Since $i = \sqrt{-1}$, expressions like $\dfrac{3 - i}{2 + i}$ actually have a radical in the denominator. To divide complex numbers, we simply rationalize the denominator using a *complex conjugate*.

**EXAMPLE 9 ▶**  **Dividing Complex Numbers**

Divide and write each result in $a + bi$ form.

**a.** $\dfrac{2}{5 - 3i}$ **b.** $\dfrac{3 - i}{2 + i}$ **c.** $\dfrac{6 + \sqrt{-36}}{3 + \sqrt{-9}}$

**Solution ▶**  **a.** $\dfrac{2}{5 - 3i} = \dfrac{2}{5 - 3i} \cdot \dfrac{5 + 3i}{5 + 3i}$

$= \dfrac{2(5 + 3i)}{5^2 + 3^2}$

$= \dfrac{10 + 6i}{34}$

$= \dfrac{10}{34} + \dfrac{6}{34}i$

$= \dfrac{5}{17} + \dfrac{3}{17}i$

**b.** $\dfrac{3 - i}{2 + i} = \dfrac{3 - i}{2 + i} \cdot \dfrac{2 - i}{2 - i}$

$= \dfrac{6 - 3i - 2i + i^2}{2^2 + 1^2}$

$= \dfrac{6 - 5i + (-1)}{5}$

$= \dfrac{5 - 5i}{5} = \dfrac{5}{5} - \dfrac{5i}{5}$

$= 1 - i$

**c.** $\dfrac{6 + \sqrt{-36}}{3 + \sqrt{-9}} = \dfrac{6 + i\sqrt{36}}{3 + i\sqrt{9}}$   convert to $i$ notation

$= \dfrac{6 + 6i}{3 + 3i}$   simplify

The expression can be further simplified by reducing common factors.

$= \dfrac{6(1 + i)}{3(1 + i)} = 2$   factor and reduce

**Now try Exercises 63 through 68 ▶**

Operations on complex numbers can be checked using inverse operations, just as we do for real numbers. To check the answer $1 - i$ from Example 9(b), we multiply it by the divisor:

$$(1 - i)(2 + i) = 2 + i - 2i - i^2$$
$$= 2 - i - (-1)$$
$$= 2 - i + 1$$
$$= 3 - i \checkmark$$    Several checks are asked for in the exercises.

☑ **D.** You've just learned how to divide complex numbers

## TECHNOLOGY HIGHLIGHT

### Graphing Calculators and Operations on Complex Numbers

Virtually all graphing calculators have the ability to find imaginary and complex roots, as well as perform operations on complex numbers. To use this capability on the TI-84 Plus, we first put the calculator in $a + bi$ mode. Press the [MODE] key (next to the [2nd] key) and the screen shown in Figure 8.2 appears. On the third line from the bottom, note the calculator may be in "Real" mode. To change to "$a + bi$" mode, simply navigate the cursor down to this line using the down arrow, then overlay the "$a + bi$" selection using the right arrow and press the [ENTER] key. The calculator is now in complex number mode. Press [2nd] [MODE] (QUIT) to return to the home screen. To compute the product $(-2 - 3i)(5 + 4i)$, enter the expression on the home screen exactly as it is written. The number "$i$" is located above the decimal point on the bottom row. After pressing [ENTER] the result $2 - 23i$ immediately appears. Compute the product by hand to see if results match.

**Figure 8.2**

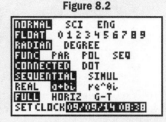

**Exercise 1:** Use a graphing calculator to compute the sum $(-2 + \sqrt{-108}) + (5 - \sqrt{-192})$. Note the result is in approximate form. Compute the sum by hand in exact form and compare the results.

**Exercise 2:** Use a graphing calculator to compute the product $(-3 + 7i)(4 - 5i)$. Then compute the product by hand and compare results. Check your answer using complex number division.

**Exercise 3:** Use a graphing calculator to compute the quotient $(2i)/(3 + i)$. Then compute the quotient by hand and compare results. Check your answer using multiplication.

## 8.1 EXERCISES

### ▶ CONCEPTS AND VOCABULARY

**Fill in each blank with the appropriate word or phrase. Carefully reread the section, if necessary.**

1. Given the complex number $3 + 2i$, its complex conjugate is _____.

2. The product $(3 + 2i)(3 - 2i)$ gives the real number _____.

3. If the expression $\dfrac{4 + 6i\sqrt{2}}{2}$ is written in the standard form $a + bi$, then $a =$ _____ and $b =$ _____.

4. For $i = \sqrt{-1}$, $i^2 =$ ___, $i^4 =$ ___, $i^6 =$ ___, and $i^8 =$ ___, $i^3 =$ ___, $i^5 =$ ___, $i^7 =$ ___, and $i^9 =$ ___.

5. Discuss/Explain which is correct:
   a. $\sqrt{-4} \cdot \sqrt{-9} = \sqrt{(-4)(-9)} = \sqrt{36} = 6$
   b. $\sqrt{-4} \cdot \sqrt{-9} = 2i \cdot 3i = 6i^2 = -6$

6. Compare/Contrast the product $(1 + \sqrt{2})(1 - \sqrt{3})$ with the product $(1 + i\sqrt{2})(1 - i\sqrt{3})$. What is the same? What is different?

### ▶ DEVELOPING YOUR SKILLS

**Simplify each radical (if possible). If imaginary, rewrite in terms of $i$ and simplify.**

7. a. $\sqrt{-16}$      b. $\sqrt{-49}$
   c. $\sqrt{27}$       d. $\sqrt{72}$

8. a. $\sqrt{-81}$      b. $\sqrt{-169}$
   c. $\sqrt{64}$       d. $\sqrt{98}$

9. a. $-\sqrt{-18}$     b. $-\sqrt{-50}$
   c. $3\sqrt{-25}$     d. $2\sqrt{-9}$

10. a. $-\sqrt{-32}$     b. $-\sqrt{-75}$
    c. $3\sqrt{-144}$    d. $2\sqrt{-81}$

11. a. $\sqrt{-19}$     b. $\sqrt{-31}$

    c. $\sqrt{\dfrac{-12}{25}}$     d. $\sqrt{\dfrac{-9}{32}}$

12. a. $\sqrt{-17}$     b. $\sqrt{-53}$

    c. $\sqrt{\dfrac{-45}{36}}$     d. $\sqrt{\dfrac{-49}{75}}$

**Write each complex number in the standard form $a + bi$ and clearly identify the values of $a$ and $b$.**

13. a. $\dfrac{2 + \sqrt{-4}}{2}$     b. $\dfrac{6 + \sqrt{-27}}{3}$

14. a. $\dfrac{16 - \sqrt{-8}}{2}$    b. $\dfrac{4 + 3\sqrt{-20}}{2}$

15. a. $\dfrac{8 + \sqrt{-16}}{2}$    b. $\dfrac{10 - \sqrt{-50}}{5}$

16. a. $\dfrac{6 - \sqrt{-72}}{4}$    b. $\dfrac{12 + \sqrt{-200}}{8}$

17. a. $5$     b. $3i$

18. a. $-2$     b. $-4i$

19. a. $2\sqrt{-81}$     b. $\dfrac{\sqrt{-32}}{8}$

20. a. $-3\sqrt{-36}$     b. $\dfrac{\sqrt{-75}}{15}$

21. a. $4 + \sqrt{-50}$     b. $-5 + \sqrt{-27}$

22. a. $-2 + \sqrt{-48}$     b. $7 + \sqrt{-75}$

23. a. $\dfrac{14 + \sqrt{-98}}{8}$     b. $\dfrac{5 + \sqrt{-250}}{10}$

24. a. $\dfrac{21 + \sqrt{-63}}{12}$     b. $\dfrac{8 + \sqrt{-27}}{6}$

**Perform the addition or subtraction. Write the result in $a + bi$ form.**

25. a. $(12 - \sqrt{-4}) + (7 + \sqrt{-9})$
    b. $(3 + \sqrt{-25}) + (-1 - \sqrt{-81})$
    c. $(11 + \sqrt{-108}) - (2 - \sqrt{-48})$

26. a. $(-7 - \sqrt{-72}) + (8 + \sqrt{-50})$
    b. $(\sqrt{3} + \sqrt{-2}) - (\sqrt{12} + \sqrt{-8})$
    c. $(\sqrt{20} - \sqrt{-3}) + (\sqrt{5} - \sqrt{-12})$

27. a. $(2 + 3i) + (-5 - i)$
    b. $(5 - 2i) + (3 + 2i)$
    c. $(6 - 5i) - (4 + 3i)$

28. a. $(-2 + 5i) + (3 - i)$
    b. $(7 - 4i) - (2 - 3i)$
    c. $(2.5 - 3.1i) + (4.3 + 2.4i)$

29. a. $(3.7 + 6.1i) - (1 + 5.9i)$
    b. $\left(8 + \dfrac{3}{4}i\right) - \left(-7 + \dfrac{2}{3}i\right)$
    c. $\left(-6 - \dfrac{5}{8}i\right) + \left(4 + \dfrac{1}{2}i\right)$

30. a. $(9.4 - 8.7i) - (6.5 + 4.1i)$
    b. $\left(3 + \dfrac{3}{5}i\right) - \left(-11 + \dfrac{7}{15}i\right)$
    c. $\left(-4 - \dfrac{5}{6}i\right) + \left(13 + \dfrac{3}{8}i\right)$

**Multiply and write your answer in $a + bi$ form.**

31. a. $5i(-3i)$     b. $(4i)(-4i)$

32. a. $3(2 - 3i)$     b. $-7(3 + 5i)$

33. a. $-7i(5 - 3i)$     b. $6i(-3 + 7i)$

34. a. $(-4 - 2i)(3 + 2i)$   b. $(2 - 3i)(-5 + i)$

35. a. $(-3 + 2i)(2 + 3i)$   b. $(3 + 2i)(1 + i)$

36. a. $(5 + 2i)(-7 + 3i)$   b. $(4 - i)(7 + 2i)$

**For each complex number, name the complex conjugate. Then find the product.**

37. a. $4 + 5i$     b. $3 - i\sqrt{2}$

38. a. $2 - i$     b. $-1 + i\sqrt{5}$

39. a. $7i$     b. $\dfrac{1}{2} - \dfrac{2}{3}i$

40. a. $-5i$     b. $\dfrac{3}{4} + \dfrac{1}{5}i$

**Compute the special products and write your answer in $a + bi$ form.**

41. a. $(4 - 5i)(4 + 5i)$
    b. $(7 - 5i)(7 + 5i)$

42. a. $(-2 - 7i)(-2 + 7i)$
    b. $(2 + i)(2 - i)$

43. a. $(3 - i\sqrt{2})(3 + i\sqrt{2})$
    b. $(\tfrac{1}{6} + \tfrac{2}{3}i)(\tfrac{1}{6} - \tfrac{2}{3}i)$

44. a. $(5 + i\sqrt{3})(5 - i\sqrt{3})$
    b. $(\tfrac{1}{2} + \tfrac{3}{4}i)(\tfrac{1}{2} - \tfrac{3}{4}i)$

45. a. $(2 + 3i)^2$     b. $(3 - 4i)^2$

46. a. $(2 - i)^2$     b. $(3 - i)^2$

47. a. $(-2 + 5i)^2$     b. $(3 + i\sqrt{2})^2$

48. a. $(-2 - 5i)^2$     b. $(2 - i\sqrt{3})^2$

Use substitution to determine if the value shown is a solution to the given equation.

**49.** $x^2 + 36 = 0; x = -6$

**50.** $x^2 + 16 = 0; x = -4$

**51.** $x^2 + 49 = 0; x = -7i$

**52.** $x^2 + 25 = 0; x = -5i$

**53.** $(x - 3)^2 = -9; x = 3 - 3i$

**54.** $(x + 1)^2 = -4; x = -1 + 2i$

**55.** $x^2 - 2x + 5 = 0; x = 1 - 2i$

**56.** $x^2 + 6x + 13 = 0; x = -3 + 2i$

**57.** $x^2 - 4x + 9 = 0; x = 2 + i\sqrt{5}$

**58.** $x^2 - 2x + 4 = 0; x = 1 - \sqrt{3}i$

**59.** Show that $x = 1 + 4i$ is a solution to $x^2 - 2x + 17 = 0$. Then show its complex conjugate $1 - 4i$ is also a solution.

**60.** Show that $x = 2 - 3\sqrt{2}i$ is a solution to $x^2 - 4x + 22 = 0$. Then show its complex conjugate $2 + 3\sqrt{2}i$ is also a solution.

Simplify using powers of $i$.

**61. a.** $i^{48}$    **b.** $i^{26}$    **c.** $i^{39}$    **d.** $i^{53}$

**62. a.** $i^{36}$    **b.** $i^{50}$    **c.** $i^{19}$    **d.** $i^{65}$

Divide and write your answer in $a + bi$ form. Check your answer using multiplication.

**63. a.** $\dfrac{-2}{\sqrt{-49}}$    **b.** $\dfrac{4}{\sqrt{-25}}$

**64. a.** $\dfrac{2}{1 - \sqrt{-4}}$    **b.** $\dfrac{3}{2 + \sqrt{-9}}$

**65. a.** $\dfrac{7}{3 + 2i}$    **b.** $\dfrac{-5}{2 - 3i}$

**66. a.** $\dfrac{6}{1 + 3i}$    **b.** $\dfrac{7}{7 - 2i}$

**67. a.** $\dfrac{3 + 4i}{4i}$    **b.** $\dfrac{2 - 3i}{3i}$

**68. a.** $\dfrac{-4 + 8i}{2 - 4i}$    **b.** $\dfrac{3 - 2i}{-6 + 4i}$

▶ **WORKING WITH FORMULAS**

**69. Absolute value of a complex number:**
$|a + bi| = \sqrt{a^2 + b^2}$

The absolute value of any complex number $a + bi$ (sometimes called the *modulus* of the number) is computed by taking the square root of the sum of the squares of $a$ and $b$. Find the absolute value of the given complex numbers.

   **a.** $|2 + 3i|$       **b.** $|4 - 3i|$
   **c.** $|3 + \sqrt{2}\,i|$

**70. Binomial cubes:**
$(A + B)^3 = A^3 + 3A^2B + 3AB^2 + B^3$

The cube of any binomial can be found using the formula shown, where $A$ and $B$ are the terms of the binomial. Use the formula to compute $(1 - 2i)^3$ (note $A = 1$ and $B = -2i$).

▶ **APPLICATIONS**

**71. Dawn of imaginary numbers:** In a day when imaginary numbers were imperfectly understood, Girolamo Cardano (1501–1576) once posed the problem, "Find two numbers that have a sum of 10 and whose product is 40." In other words, $A + B = 10$ and $AB = 40$. Although the solution is routine today, at the time the problem posed an enormous challenge. Verify that $A = 5 + \sqrt{15}i$ and $B = 5 - \sqrt{15}i$ satisfy these conditions.

**72. Verifying calculations using $i$:** Suppose Cardano had said, "Find two numbers that have a sum of 4 and a product of 7" (see Exercise 71). Verify that $A = 2 + \sqrt{3}i$ and $B = 2 - \sqrt{3}i$ satisfy these conditions.

Although it may seem odd, imaginary numbers have several applications in the real world. Many of these involve a study of electrical circuits, in particular *alternating current* or AC circuits. Briefly, the components of an AC circuit are current $I$ (in amperes), voltage $V$ (in volts), and the impedance $Z$ (in ohms). The impedance of an electrical circuit is a measure of the total opposition to the flow of current through the circuit and is calculated as $Z = R + iX_L - iX_C$ where $R$ represents a pure resistance, $X_C$ represents the capacitance, and $X_L$ represents the inductance. Each of these is also measured in ohms (symbolized by $\Omega$).

**73.** Find the impedance $Z$ if $R = 7\ \Omega$, $X_L = 6\ \Omega$, and $X_C = 11\ \Omega$.

**74.** Find the impedance $Z$ if $R = 9.2\ \Omega$, $X_L = 5.6\ \Omega$, and $X_C = 8.3\ \Omega$.

The voltage $V$ across any element in an AC circuit is calculated as a product of the current $I$ and the impedance $Z$: $V = IZ$.

**75.** Find the voltage in a circuit with current $I = 3 - 2i$ amperes and an impedance of $Z = 5 + 5i\ \Omega$.

**76.** Find the voltage in a circuit with current $I = 2 - 3i$ amperes and an impedance of $Z = 4 + 2i\ \Omega$.

For an AC circuit wired in parallel, the total impedance (in ohms) is given by $Z = \dfrac{Z_1 Z_2}{Z_1 + Z_2}$, where $Z_1$ and $Z_2$ represent the impedance in each branch of the circuit.

**77.** Find the total impedance $Z$ if $Z_1 = 1 + 2i$ and $Z_2 = 3 - 2i$.

**78.** Find the total impedance $Z$ if $Z_1 = 3 - i$ and $Z_2 = 2 + i$.

▶ **EXTENDING THE CONCEPT**

**79.** Up to this point, we've said that expressions like $x^2 - 9$ and $p^2 - 7$ are factorable:

$$x^2 - 9 = (x + 3)(x - 3) \quad \text{and}$$
$$p^2 - 7 = (p + \sqrt{7})(p - \sqrt{7}),$$

while $x^2 + 9$ and $p^2 + 7$ are prime. More correctly, we should state that $x^2 + 9$ and $p^2 + 7$ are nonfactorable *using real numbers,* since they actually *can* be factored if complex numbers are used. From $(a + bi)(a - bi) = a^2 + b^2$ we note $a^2 + b^2 = (a + bi)(a - bi)$, showing

$$x^2 + 9 = (x + 3i)(x - 3i) \quad \text{and}$$
$$p^2 + 7 = (p + i\sqrt{7})(p - i\sqrt{7}).$$

Use this idea to factor the following.

**a.** $x^2 + 36$  **b.** $m^2 + 3$

**c.** $n^2 + 12$  **d.** $4x^2 + 49$

**80.** In this section, we noted that the product property of radicals $\sqrt{AB} = \sqrt{A}\sqrt{B}$, can still be applied when at most one of the factors is negative. So what happens if *both* are negative? First consider the

expression $\sqrt{-4 \cdot -25}$. What happens if you first multiply in the radicand, then compute the square root? Next consider the product $\sqrt{-4} \cdot \sqrt{-25}$. Rewrite each factor using the $i$ notation, then compute the product. Do you get the same result as before? What can you say about $\sqrt{-4 \cdot -25}$ and $\sqrt{-4} \cdot \sqrt{-25}$?

**81.** Simplify the expression $i^{17}(3 - 4i) - 3i^3(1 + 2i)^2$.

**82.** While it is a simple concept for real numbers, the square root of a complex number is much more involved due to the interplay between its real and imaginary parts. For $z = a + bi$ the square root of $z$ can be found using the formula:

$$\sqrt{z} = \frac{\sqrt{2}}{2}(\sqrt{|z| + a} \pm i\sqrt{|z| - a}),$$ where the sign

is chosen to match the sign of $b$ (see Exercise 69). Use the formula to find the square root of each complex number, then check by squaring.

**a.** $z = -7 + 24i$  **b.** $z = 5 - 12i$

**c.** $z = 4 + 3i$

▶ **MAINTAINING YOUR SKILLS**

**83. (7.4)** Find the angle $\theta$ between the vectors $\mathbf{u} = \langle -2, 9 \rangle$ and $\mathbf{v} = \langle 6, 5 \rangle$.

**84. (6.4)** Find all real solutions to $2\sin(2\theta) + \sqrt{3} = 0$.

**85. (5.1)** Prove the following identity:

$$1 + \sin\theta = \frac{\cos^2\theta}{1 - \sin\theta}.$$

**86. (4.3)** Graph the function using a reference rectangle and the *rule of fourths:*

$$y = 3\cos\left(2\theta - \frac{\pi}{4}\right)$$

**87. (7.2)** Solve the triangle shown, then compute its perimeter and area.

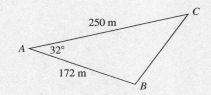

**88. (7.3)** A plane is flying 200 mph at heading 30°, with a 40 mph wind blowing from the west. Find the true course and speed of the plane.

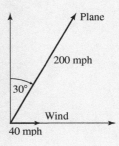

# 8.2 | Complex Numbers in Trigonometric Form

## Learning Objectives

*In Section 8.2 you will learn how to:*

- ☐ **A.** Graph a complex number
- ☐ **B.** Write a complex number in trigonometric form
- ☐ **C.** Convert from trigonometric form to rectangular form
- ☐ **D.** Interpret products and quotients geometrically
- ☐ **E.** Compute products and quotients in trigonometric form
- ☐ **F.** Solve applications involving complex numbers (optional)

Once the set of complex numbers became recognized and defined, the related basic operations matured very quickly. With little modification—sums, differences, products, quotients, and powers all lent themselves fairly well to the algebraic techniques used for real numbers. But roots of complex numbers did not yield so easily and additional tools and techniques were needed. Writing complex numbers in trigonometric form enables us to find complex roots (Section 8.3) and in some cases, makes computing products, quotients, and powers more efficient.

## A. Graphing Complex Numbers

In previous sections, we defined a vector quantity as one that required more than a single component to describe its attributes. The complex number $z = a + bi$ certainly fits this description, since both a real number "component" and an imaginary "component" are needed to define it. In many respects, we can treat complex numbers in the same way we treated vectors and in fact, there is much we can learn from this connection.

Since both axes in the $xy$-plane have real number values, it's not possible to graph a complex number in $\mathbb{R}$ (the real plane). However, in the same way we used the $x$-axis for the horizontal component of a vector and the $y$-axis for the vertical,

**WORTHY OF NOTE**

Surprisingly, the study of complex numbers matured much earlier than the study of vectors, and using directed line segments to represent complex numbers actually preceded their application to a vector quantity.

we can let the $x$-axis represent the real valued part of a complex number and the $y$-axis the imaginary part. The result is called the **complex plane** $\mathbb{C}$. Every point $(a, b)$ in $\mathbb{C}$ can be associated with a complex number $a + bi$, and any complex number $a + bi$ can be associated with a point $(a, b)$ in $\mathbb{C}$ (Figure 8.3). The point $(a, b)$ can also be regarded as the terminal point of a position vector representing the complex number, generally named using the letter $z$.

**Figure 8.3**

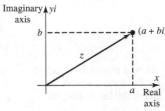

**EXAMPLE 1** ▶ **Graphing Complex Numbers**

Graph the complex numbers below on the same complex plane.

**a.** $z_1 = -2 - 6i$      **b.** $z_2 = 5 + 4i$

**c.** $z_3 = 5$      **d.** $z_4 = 4i$

**Solution** ▶ The graph of each complex number is shown in the figure.

Now try Exercises 7 through 10 ▶

In Example 1, you likely noticed that from a vector perspective, $z_2$ is the "resultant vector" for the sum $z_3 + z_4$. To investigate further, consider $z_1 = (2 + 3i)$, $z_2 = (-5 + 2i)$, and the sum $z_1 + z_2 = z$ shown in Figure 8.4. The figure helps to confirm that the sum of complex numbers can be illustrated geometrically using the parallelogram (tail-to-tip) method employed for vectors in Section 7.3.

☑ **A.** You've just learned how to graph a complex number

**B. Complex Numbers in Trigonometric Form**

**Figure 8.4**

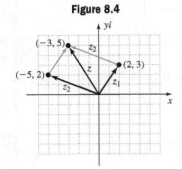

The complex number $z = a + bi$ is said to be in **rectangular form** since it can be graphed using the rectangular coordinates of the complex plane. Complex numbers can also be written in **trigonometric form**. Similar to how $|x|$ represents the distance between the real number $x$ and zero, $|z|$ represents the distance between $(a, b)$ and the origin in the complex plane, and is computed as $|z| = \sqrt{a^2 + b^2}$. With any nonzero $z$, we can also associate an angle $\theta$, which is the angle in standard position whose terminal side coincides with the graph of $z$. If we let $r$ represent $|z|$, Figure 8.5 shows $\cos\theta = \dfrac{a}{r}$ and

**Figure 8.5**

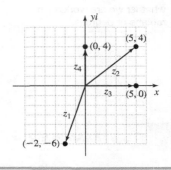

$\sin\theta = \dfrac{b}{r}$, yielding $r\cos\theta = a$ and $r\sin\theta = b$. The appropriate substitutions into $a + bi$ give the trigonometric form:

$$z = a + bi$$
$$= r\cos\theta + r\sin\theta \cdot i$$

Factoring out $r$ and writing the imaginary unit as the lead factor of $\sin\theta$ gives the relationship in its more common form, $z = r(\cos\theta + i\sin\theta)$, where $\tan\theta = \dfrac{b}{a}$.

**WORTHY OF NOTE**

While it is true the trigonometric form can more generally be written as $z = r[\cos(\theta + 2\pi k) + i\sin(\theta + 2\pi k)]$ for $k \in \mathbb{Z}$, the result is identical for any integer $k$ and we will select $\theta$ so that $0 \le \theta < 2\pi$ or $0° \le \theta < 360°$, depending on whether we are working in radians or degrees.

---

**The Trigonometric Form of a Complex Number**

For the complex number $z = a + bi$ and angle $\theta$ shown, $z = r(\cos\theta + i\sin\theta)$ is the trigonometric form of $z$, where $r = \sqrt{a^2 + b^2}$, and $\tan\theta = \dfrac{b}{a}; a \neq 0$.

- $r = |z|$ represents the magnitude of $z$ (also called the **modulus**).
- $\theta$ is often referred to as the **argument** of $z$.

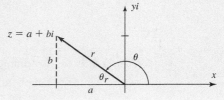

Be sure to note that for $\tan\theta = \dfrac{b}{a}$, $\tan^{-1}\left|\dfrac{b}{a}\right|$ is equal to $\theta_r$ (the reference angle for $\theta$) and the value of $\theta$ will ultimately *depend on the quadrant of $z$*.

---

**EXAMPLE 2** ▶ **Converting a Complex Number from Rectangular to Trigonometric Form**

State the quadrant of the complex number, then write each in trigonometric form.

    **a.** $z_1 = -2 - 2i$             **b.** $z_2 = 6 + 2i$

**Solution** ▶ Knowing that modulus $r$ and angle $\theta$ are needed for the trigonometric form, we first determine these values. Once again, to find the correct value of $\theta$, *it's important to note the quadrant of the complex number.*

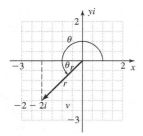

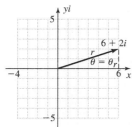

**a.** $z_1 = -2 - 2i$; QIII

$$r = \sqrt{(-2)^2 + (-2)^2}$$
$$= \sqrt{8} = 2\sqrt{2}$$

$$\theta_r = \tan^{-1}\left|\frac{-2}{-2}\right|$$

$$= \tan^{-1}(1)$$

$$= \frac{\pi}{4}$$

with $z_1$ in QIII, $\theta = \dfrac{5\pi}{4}$.

$$z_1 = 2\sqrt{2}\left[\cos\left(\frac{5\pi}{4}\right) + i\sin\left(\frac{5\pi}{4}\right)\right]$$

See the figure.

**b.** $z = 6 + 2i$; QI

$$r = \sqrt{(6)^2 + (2)^2}$$
$$= \sqrt{40} = 2\sqrt{10}$$

$$\theta_r = \tan^{-1}\left|\frac{2}{6}\right|$$

$$= \tan^{-1}\left(\frac{1}{3}\right)$$

$z$ is in QI, so $\theta = \tan^{-1}\left(\dfrac{1}{3}\right)$

$$z = 2\sqrt{10}\left(\cos\left[\tan^{-1}\left(\frac{1}{3}\right)\right] + i\sin\left[\tan^{-1}\left(\frac{1}{3}\right)\right]\right)$$

**Now try Exercises 11 through 26** ▶

**☑ B.** You've just learned how to write a complex number in trigonometric form

---

**WORTHY OF NOTE**

Using the triangle diagrams from Section 6.2,

$\cos\left[\tan^{-1}\left(\dfrac{1}{3}\right)\right]$ and

$\sin\left[\tan^{-1}\left(\dfrac{1}{3}\right)\right]$ can easily be

evaluated and used to verify

$2\sqrt{10}\, \text{cis}\left[\tan^{-1}\left(\dfrac{1}{3}\right)\right] = 6 + 2i.$

---

Since the angle $\theta$ is repeated for both cosine and sine, we often use an abbreviated notation for the trigonometric form, called "cis" (sis) notation: $z = r(\cos\theta + i\sin\theta) = r\,\text{cis}\,\theta$. The results of Example 2(a) and 2(b) would then be written $z = 2\sqrt{2}\,\text{cis}\left(\dfrac{5\pi}{4}\right)$ and $z = 2\sqrt{10}\,\text{cis}\left[\tan^{-1}\left(\dfrac{1}{3}\right)\right]$, respectively.

As in Example 2b, when $\theta_r = \tan^{-1}\left|\dfrac{b}{a}\right|$ is not a standard angle we can either answer in exact form as shown, or use a four-decimal-place approximation: $2\sqrt{10}\,\text{cis}(0.3218)$.

## C. Converting from Trigonometric Form to Rectangular Form

Converting from trigonometric form back to rectangular form is simply a matter of evaluating $r\,\text{cis}\,\theta$. This can be done regardless of whether $\theta$ is a standard angle or in the form $\tan^{-1}\left(\dfrac{b}{a}\right)$, since in the latter case we can construct a right triangle with side $b$ opposite $\theta$ and side $a$ adjacent $\theta$, and find the needed values as in Section 6.2.

---

**EXAMPLE 3 ▶  Converting a Complex Number from Trigonometric to Rectangular Form**

Graph the following complex numbers, then write them in rectangular form.

  **a.** $z = 12\,\text{cis}\left(\dfrac{\pi}{6}\right)$              **b.** $z = 13\,\text{cis}\left[\tan^{-1}\left(\dfrac{5}{12}\right)\right]$

**Solution ▶  a.** We have $r = 12$ and $\theta = \dfrac{\pi}{6}$, which yields the graph in Figure 8.6. In the nonabbreviated form we have $z = 12\left[\cos\left(\dfrac{\pi}{6}\right) + i\sin\left(\dfrac{\pi}{6}\right)\right]$. Evaluating within the brackets gives $z = 12\left[\dfrac{\sqrt{3}}{2} + \dfrac{1}{2}i\right] = 6\sqrt{3} + 6i.$

**Figure 8.6**

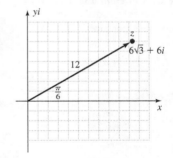

  **b.** For $r = 13$ and $\theta = \tan^{-1}\left(\dfrac{5}{12}\right)$, we have the graph shown in Figure 8.7. Here we obtain the rectangular form directly from the diagram with $z = 12 + 5i$. Verify by noting that for $\theta = \tan^{-1}\left(\dfrac{5}{12}\right)$, $\cos\theta = \dfrac{12}{13}$, and $\sin\theta = \dfrac{5}{13}$, meaning

$z = 13(\cos\theta + i\sin\theta) =$

$13\left[\dfrac{12}{13} + \dfrac{5}{13}i\right] = 12 + 5i.$

**Figure 8.7**

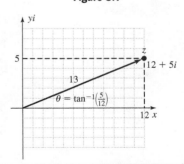

**☑ C.** You've just learned how to convert from trigonometric form to rectangular form

**Now try Exercises 27 through 34 ▶**

## D. Interpreting Products and Quotients Geometrically

The multiplication and division of complex numbers has some geometric connections that can help us understand their computation in trigonometric form. Note the relationship between the modulus and argument of the following product, with the moduli (plural of modulus) and arguments from each factor.

---

**EXAMPLE 4** ▶ **Noting Graphical Connections for the Product of Two Complex Numbers**

For $z_1 = 3 + 3i$ and $z_2 = 0 + 2i$,

**a.** Graph the complex numbers and compute their moduli and arguments.

**b.** Compute and graph the product $z_1z_2$ and find its modulus and argument. Discuss any connections you see between the factors and the resulting product.

**Solution** ▶ **a.** The graphs of $z_1$ and $z_2$ are shown in the figure. For the modulus and argument we have:

$$z_1 = 3 + 3i; \quad \text{QI} \qquad z_2 = 0 + 2i; \quad \text{(quadrantal)}$$
$$r = \sqrt{(3)^2 + (3)^2} \qquad r = 2 \text{ directly}$$
$$= \sqrt{18} = 3\sqrt{2} \qquad \theta = 90° \text{ directly}$$
$$\theta = \tan^{-1}1$$
$$\Rightarrow \theta = 45°$$

**b.** The product $z_1z_2$ is $(3 + 3i)(2i) = -6 + 6i$, which is in QII. The modulus is
$$\sqrt{(-6)^2 + (6)^2} = \sqrt{72} = 6\sqrt{2}, \text{ with}$$
$\theta_r = \tan^{-1}|-1| = 45°$ and an argument $\theta = 135°$ (QII). Note the product of the two moduli *is equal to the modulus of the final product:* $2 \cdot 3\sqrt{2} = 6\sqrt{2}$. Also note that the sum of the arguments for $z_1$ and $z_2$ *is equal to the argument of the product:* $45° + 90° = 135°$!

☑ **D.** You've just learned how to interpret products and quotients geometrically

---

Now try Exercises 35 and 36 ▶

A similar geometric connection exists for the division of complex numbers. This connection is explored in **Exercises 37 and 38** of the exercise set.

## E. Products and Quotients in Trigonometric Form

The connections in Example 4 are not a coincidence, and can be proven to hold for all complex numbers. Consider any two nonzero complex numbers $z_1 = r_1 (\cos \alpha + i \sin \alpha)$ and $z_2 = r_2(\cos \beta + i \sin \beta)$. For the product $z_1z_2$ we have

$z_1z_2 = r_1(\cos \alpha + i \sin \alpha) \, r_2(\cos \beta + i \sin \beta)$     product in trig form

$\quad = r_1r_2[(\cos \alpha + i \sin \alpha)(\cos \beta + i \sin \beta)]$     rearrange factors

$\quad = r_1r_2[\cos \alpha \cos \beta + i \sin \beta \cos \alpha + i \sin \alpha \cos \beta + i^2\sin \alpha \sin \beta]$     F-O-I-L

$\quad = r_1r_2[(\cos \alpha \cos \beta - \sin \alpha \sin \beta) + i(\sin \beta \cos \alpha + \sin \alpha \cos \beta)]$     commute
terms; $i^2 = -1$

$\quad = r_1r_2[\cos(\alpha + \beta) + i \sin(\alpha + \beta)]$     use sum/difference identities for sine/cosine

In words, the proof says that to *multiply* complex numbers in trigonometric form, we *multiply* the moduli and *add* the arguments. For *division*, we *divide* the moduli and *subtract* the arguments. The proof for division resembles that for multiplication and is asked for in **Exercise 71.**

### Products and Quotients of Complex Numbers in Trigonometric Form

For the complex numbers $z_1 = r_1(\cos \alpha + i \sin \alpha)$ and
$$z_2 = r_2(\cos \beta + i \sin \beta),$$
$$z_1 z_2 = r_1 r_2 [\cos(\alpha + \beta) + i \sin(\alpha + \beta)]$$
and
$$\frac{z_1}{z_2} = \frac{r_1}{r_2}[\cos(\alpha - \beta) + i \sin(\alpha - \beta)], z_2 \neq 0.$$

---

**EXAMPLE 5** ▶ **Multiplying Complex Numbers in Trigonometric Form**

For $z_1 = -3 + \sqrt{3}i$ and $z_2 = \sqrt{3} + 1i$,

**a.** Write $z_1$ and $z_2$ in trigonometric form and compute $z_1 z_2$.

**b.** Compute the quotient $\dfrac{z_1}{z_2}$ in trigonometric form.

**c.** Verify the product using the rectangular form.

Solution ▶ **a.** For $z_1$ in QII we find $r = 2\sqrt{3}$ and $\theta = 150°$, for $z_2$ in QI, $r = 2$ and $\theta = 30°$. In trigonometric form,

$z_1 = 2\sqrt{3}(\cos 150° + i \sin 150°)$ and
$z_2 = 2(\cos 30° + i \sin 30°)$:
$$z_1 z_2 = 2\sqrt{3}(\cos 150° + i \sin 150°) \cdot 2(\cos 30° + i \sin 30°)$$
$$= 2\sqrt{3} \cdot 2[\cos(150° + 30°) + i \sin(150° + 30°)] \quad \text{multiply moduli, add arguments}$$
$$= 4\sqrt{3}(\cos 180° + i \sin 180°)$$
$$= 4\sqrt{3}(-1 + 0i)$$
$$= -4\sqrt{3}$$

**b.** $\dfrac{z_1}{z_2} = \dfrac{2\sqrt{3}(\cos 150° + i \sin 150°)}{2(\cos 30° + i \sin 30°)}$
$$= \sqrt{3}[\cos(150° - 30°) + i \sin(150° - 30°)] \quad \text{divide moduli, subtract arguments}$$
$$= \sqrt{3}(\cos 120° + i \sin 120°)$$
$$= \sqrt{3}\left(-\frac{1}{2} + \frac{\sqrt{3}}{2}i\right)$$
$$= -\frac{\sqrt{3}}{2} + \frac{3}{2}i$$

**c.** $z_1 z_2 = (-3 + \sqrt{3}i)(\sqrt{3} + 1i)$
$$= -3\sqrt{3} - 3i + 3i + \sqrt{3}i^2$$
$$= -4\sqrt{3}$$

**Now try Exercises 39 through 42** ▶

---

Converting to trigonometric form for multiplication and division seems too clumsy for practical use, as we can often compute these results more efficiently in rectangular form. However, this approach leads to powers and roots of complex numbers, *an indispensable part of advanced equation solving,* and these are not easily found in rectangular form. In any case, note that the power and simplicity of computing products/quotients in trigonometric form is highly magnified when the complex numbers are *given in trig form:*

☑ **E.** You've just learned how to compute products and quotients in trigonometric form

$$(12 \text{ cis } 50°)(3 \text{ cis } 20°) = 36 \text{ cis } 70° \qquad \frac{12 \text{ cis } 50°}{3 \text{ cis } 20°} = 4 \text{ cis } 30°$$

**See Exercises 43 through 50.**

## F. (Optional) Applications of Complex Numbers

Somewhat surprisingly, complex numbers have several applications in the real world. Many of these involve a study of electricity, and in particular **AC (alternating current) circuits.**

In simplistic terms, when an armature (molded wire) is rotated in a uniform magnetic field, a voltage $V$ is generated that depends on the strength of the field. As the armature is rotated, the voltage varies between a maximum and a minimum value, with the amount of voltage modeled by $V(\theta) = V_{max}\sin(B\theta)$, with $\theta$ in degrees. Here, $V_{max}$ represents the maximum voltage attained, and the

**Figure 8.8**

Magnetic flux

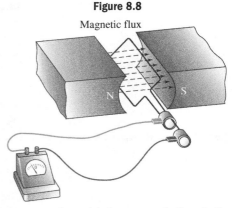

input variable $\theta$ represents the angle the armature makes with the **magnetic flux,** indicated in Figure 8.8 by the dashed arrows between the magnets.

When the armature is perpendicular to the flux, we say $\theta = 0°$. At $\theta = 0°$ and $\theta = 180°$, no voltage is produced, while at $\theta = 90°$ and $\theta = 270°$, the voltage reaches its maximum and minimum values, respectively (hence the name *alternating current*). Many electric dryers and other large appliances are labeled as 220 volt (V) appliances, but use an alternating current that varies from 311 V to $-311$ V (see *Worthy of Note*). This means when $\theta = 52°$, $V(52°) = 311\sin(52°) = 245$ V is being generated. In practical applications, we use time $t$ as the independent variable, rather than the angle of the armature. These large appliances usually operate with a frequency of 60 cycles per second, or 1 cycle every $\dfrac{1}{60}$ of a second $\left(P = \dfrac{1}{60}\right)$. Using $B = \dfrac{2\pi}{P}$, we obtain $B = 120\pi$ and our equation model becomes $V(t) = 311\sin(120\pi t)$ with $t$ in radians. This variation in voltage is an excellent example of a simple harmonic model.

**WORTHY OF NOTE**

You may have wondered why we're using an amplitude of 311 for a 220-V appliance. Due to the nature of the sine wave, the average value of an alternating current is always zero and gives no useful information about the voltage generated. Instead, the root-mean-square (rms) of the voltage is given on most appliances. While the maximum voltage is 311 V, the rms voltage is

$\dfrac{311}{\sqrt{2}} \approx 220$ V. **See Exercise 72.**

---

**EXAMPLE 6** ▶ **Analyzing Alternating Current Using Trigonometry**

Use the equation $V(t) = 311\sin(120\pi t)$ to:

    **a.** Create a table of values illustrating the voltage produced every thousandth of a second for the first half-cycle $\left(t = \dfrac{1}{120} \approx 0.008\right)$.

    **b.** Use a graphing calculator to find the times $t$ in this half-cycle when 160 V is being produced.

**Solution** ▶ **a.** Starting at $t = 0$ and using increments of 0.001 sec produces the table shown.

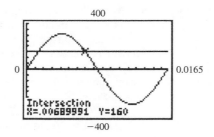

| Time $t$ | Voltage |
|:---:|:---:|
| 0 | 0 |
| 0.001 | 114.5 |
| 0.002 | 212.9 |
| 0.003 | 281.4 |
| 0.004 | 310.4 |
| 0.005 | 295.8 |
| 0.006 | 239.6 |
| 0.007 | 149.8 |
| 0.008 | 39.0 |

**b.** From the table we note $V(t) = 160$ when $t \in (0.001, 0.002)$ and $t \in (0.006, 0.007)$. Using the intersection of graphs method places these values at $t \approx 0.0014$ and $t \approx 0.0069$ (see graph).

Now try Exercises 53 and 54 ▶

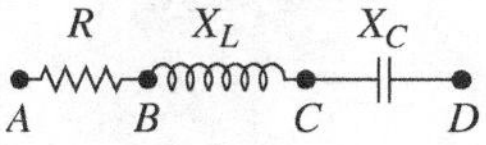

**Figure 8.10**

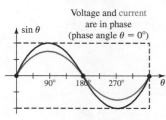

Voltage and current are in phase (phase angle $\theta = 0°$)

The chief components of AC circuits are **voltage** ($V$) and **current** ($I$). Due to the nature of how the current is generated, $V$ and $I$ can be modeled by sine functions. Other characteristics of electricity include pure **resistance** ($R$), **inductive reactance** ($X_L$), and **capacitive reactance** ($X_C$) (see Figure 8.9). Each of these is measured in a unit called ohms ($\Omega$), while current $I$ is measured in amperes (A), and voltages are measured in volts (V). These components of electricity *are related by fixed and inherent traits,* which include the following: (1) voltage across a resistor is always *in phase* with the current, meaning the phase shift or **phase angle** between them is 0° (Figure 8.10); (2) voltage across an inductor *leads the current* by 90° (Figure 8.11); (3) voltage across a capacitor *lags the current* by 90° (Figure 8.12); and (4) voltage is equal to the product of the current times the resistance or reactance: $V = IR$, $V = IX_L$, and $V = IX_C$.

**Figure 8.9**

$R \quad X_L \quad X_C$

●-ⱳⱳⱳ-●-ⱱⱱⱱⱱⱱ-●-╫-●
$A \quad B \quad C \quad D$

**Figure 8.11**

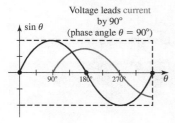

Voltage leads current by 90° (phase angle $\theta = 90°$)

Different combinations of $R$, $X_L$, and $X_C$ in a combined (series) circuit alter the phase angle and the resulting voltage. Since voltage across a resistance is always in phase with the current (trait 1), we can model the resistance as a vector along the positive real axis (since the phase angle is 0°). For traits (2) and (3), $X_L$ is modeled on the positive imaginary axis since voltage leads current by 90°, and $X_C$ on the negative imaginary axis since voltage lags current by 90° (see Figure 8.13). These natural characteristics make the complex plane *a perfect fit for describing the characteristics of the circuit.*

**Figure 8.13**

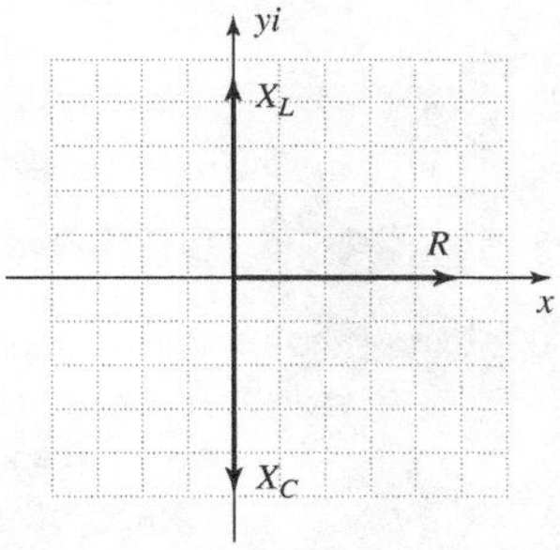

$yi$

$X_L$

$R$

$x$

$X_C$

**Figure 8.12**

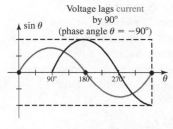

Voltage lags current by 90° (phase angle $\theta = -90°$)

Consider a series circuit (Figure 8.9), where $R = 12\ \Omega$, $X_L = 9\ \Omega$, and $X_C = 4\ \Omega$. For a current of $I = 2$ amps through this circuit, the voltage across each individual element would be $V_R = (2)(12) = 24$ V ($A$ to $B$), $V_L = (2)(9) = 18$ V ($B$ to $C$), and $V_C = (2)(4) = 8$ V ($C$ to $D$). However, the resulting voltage across this circuit *cannot be an arithmetic sum,* since $R$ is real, while $X_L$ and $X_C$ are represented by imaginary numbers. The joint effect of resistance ($R$) and reactance ($X_L$, $X_C$) in a circuit is called the **impedance,** denoted by the letter $Z$, and is a measure of the total resistance to the flow of electrons. It is computed $Z = R + X_L j - X_C j$ (see *Worthy of Note*), due to the phase angle relationship of the voltage in each element ($X_L$ and $X_C$ point in opposite directions, hence the subtraction). The expression for $Z$ is more commonly written $R + (X_L - X_C)j$, where we more clearly note $Z$ *is a complex number* whose magnitude and angle with the x-axis can be found as before:

**WORTHY OF NOTE**

While mathematicians generally use the symbol $i$ to represent $\sqrt{-1}$, the "$i$" is used in other fields to represent an electric current so the symbol $j = \sqrt{-1}$ is used instead. In conformance with this convention, we will temporarily use $j$ for $\sqrt{-1}$ as well.

$$|Z| = \sqrt{R^2 + (X_L - X_C)^2} \text{ and } \theta_r = \tan^{-1}\left(\frac{X_L - X_C}{R}\right).$$ The angle $\theta$ represents the phase angle between the voltage and current brought about by this combination of elements. The resulting voltage of the circuit is then calculated as the product of the current with the magnitude of the impedance, or $V_{RLC} = I|Z|$ ($Z$ is also measured in ohms, $\Omega$).

**EXAMPLE 7 ▶ Finding the Impedence and Phase Angle of the Current in a Circuit**

For the circuit diagrammed in the figure, (a) find the magnitude of $Z$, the phase angle between current and voltage, and write the result in trigonometric form; and (b) find the total voltage across this circuit.

Solution ▶ **a.** Using the values given, we find

$$Z = R + (X_L - X_C)j$$
$$= 12 + (9 - 4)j$$
$$= 12 + 5j \text{ (QI)}:$$

This gives a magnitude of

$$|Z| = \sqrt{(12)^2 + (5)^2} = \sqrt{169} = 13 \ \Omega, \text{ with a phase angle of}$$

$$\theta = \tan^{-1}\left(\frac{5}{12}\right) \approx 22.6° \text{ (voltage leads the current by about 22.6°)}.$$

In trigonometric form $Z \approx 13 \text{ cis } 22.6°$.

$R$   $X_L$   $X_C$

$A$ 12Ω $B$   9Ω   $C$ 4Ω $D$

☑ **F. You have just learned how to solve applications involving complex numbers**

**b.** With $I = 2$ amps, the total voltage across this circuit is

$$V_{RLC} = I|Z| = 2(13) = 26 \text{ V}.$$

Now try Exercises 55 through 70 ▶

## TECHNOLOGY HIGHLIGHT

### Graphing Calculators and Complex Numbers

With a graphing calculator in "$a + bi$" mode, we have the ability to confirm and extend many of the results obtained in this section. To find the argument of a complex number using the calculator, press MATH then ▶ ▶ to get to the **CPX** (complex) submenu (Figure 8.14). Option "**4:angle(**" displays the angle (argument) of the complex number entered. This option can also find the argument for a product or quotient if entered in that form. Let's use the calculator to verify that for the product of complex numbers, we add the arguments of each factor. We'll use $z_1 = 2 + 3i$ and $z_2 = 8 + 2i$ for this purpose. Results are displayed on the screen in Figure 8.15, where we note that arguments do indeed sum to $\approx 70.35°$. Note that option "**5:abs(**" can be used to find the modulus of a complex number.

**Figure 8.14**          **Figure 8.15**

```
MATH NUM CPX PRB
1▐conj(
2:real(
3:imag(
4:angle(
5:abs(
6:▶Rect
7:▶Polar
```

```
angle(2+3i)
          56.30993247
angle(8+2i)
          14.03624347
angle((2+3i)(8+2
i))
          70.34617594
```

**Exercise 1:** Use $z_1 = 2 + 3i$ and $z_2 = 8 + 2i$ and a graphing calculator to confirm that for the quotient of complex numbers, we subtract the arguments of each factor.

**Exercise 2:** Create two complex numbers on your own, one with $\alpha = 45°$ and another with $\beta = 30°$. $\left(\text{Hint: Use } \tan^{-1}\frac{b}{a}.\right)$ Use these numbers and your graphing calculator to verify the moduli and argument relationships for products and quotients.

**Exercise 3:** Compute the product $(87 - 87i)(-187.5 + 62.5\sqrt{3}i)$ by hand, then once again using the trigonometric form. Comment on what you notice.

 **8.2 EXERCISES**

## ▶ CONCEPTS AND VOCABULARY

**Fill in each blank with the appropriate word or phrase. Carefully reread the section if needed.**

1. For a complex number written in the form $z = r(\cos\theta + i\sin\theta)$, $r$ is called the _____ and $\theta$ is called the _____.

2. The complex number $z = 2\left[\cos\left(\dfrac{\pi}{4}\right) + i\sin\left(\dfrac{\pi}{4}\right)\right]$ can be written as the abbreviated "cis" notation as _____.

3. To multiply complex numbers in trigonometric form, we _____ the moduli and _____ the arguments.

4. To divide complex numbers in trigonometric form, we _____ the moduli and _____ the arguments.

5. Write $z = -1 - \sqrt{3}i$ in trigonometric form and explain why the argument is $\theta = 240°$ instead of $60°$ as indicated by your calculator.

6. Discuss the similarities between finding the components of a vector and writing a complex number in trigonometric form.

## ▶ DEVELOPING YOUR SKILLS

**Graph the complex numbers $z_1$, $z_2$, and $z_3$ given, then express one as the sum of the other two.**

7. $z_1 = 7 + 2i$
   $z_2 = 8 + 6i$
   $z_3 = 1 + 4i$

8. $z_1 = 2 + 7i$
   $z_2 = 3 + 4i$
   $z_3 = -1 + 3i$

9. $z_1 = -2 - 5i$
   $z_2 = 1 - 7i$
   $z_3 = 3 - 2i$

10. $z_1 = -2 + 6i$
    $z_2 = 7 - 2i$
    $z_3 = 5 + 4i$

**State the quadrant of each complex number, then write it in trigonometric form. For Exercises 11 through 14, answer in degrees. For 15 through 18, answer in radians.**

11. $-2 - 2i$

12. $7 - 7i$

13. $-5\sqrt{3} - 5i$

14. $2 - 2\sqrt{3}i$

15. $-3\sqrt{2} + 3\sqrt{2}i$

16. $5\sqrt{7} - 5\sqrt{7}i$

17. $4\sqrt{3} - 4i$

18. $-6 + 6\sqrt{3}i$

**Write each complex number in trigonometric form. For Exercises 19 through 22, answer in degrees using both an exact form and an approximate form, rounding to tenths. For 23 through 26, answer in radians using both an exact form and an approximate form, rounding to four decimal places.**

19. $8 + 6i$

20. $-9 + 12i$

21. $-5 - 12i$

22. $-8 + 15i$

23. $6 + 17.5i$

24. $30 - 5.5i$

25. $-6 + 10i$

26. $12 - 4i$

**Graph each complex number using its trigonometric form, then convert each to rectangular form.**

27. $2\,\text{cis}\left(\dfrac{\pi}{4}\right)$

28. $12\,\text{cis}\left(\dfrac{\pi}{6}\right)$

29. $4\sqrt{3}\,\text{cis}\left(\dfrac{\pi}{3}\right)$

30. $5\sqrt{3}\,\text{cis}\left(\dfrac{7\pi}{6}\right)$

31. $17\,\text{cis}\left[\tan^{-1}\left(\dfrac{15}{8}\right)\right]$

32. $10\,\text{cis}\left[\tan^{-1}\left(\dfrac{3}{4}\right)\right]$

33. $6\,\text{cis}\left[\pi - \tan^{-1}\left(\dfrac{5}{\sqrt{11}}\right)\right]$

34. $4\,\text{cis}\left[\pi + \tan^{-1}\left(\dfrac{\sqrt{7}}{3}\right)\right]$

**For the complex numbers $z_1$ and $z_2$ given, find their moduli $r_1$ and $r_2$ and arguments $\theta_1$ and $\theta_2$. Then compute their *product* in rectangular form. For modulus $r$ and argument $\theta$ of the product, verify that $r_1 r_2 = r$ and $\theta_1 + \theta_2 = \theta$.**

35. $z_1 = -2 + 2i$;   $z_2 = 3 + 3i$

36. $z_1 = 1 + \sqrt{3}i$;   $z_2 = 3 + \sqrt{3}i$

For the complex numbers $z_1$ and $z_2$ given, find their moduli $r_1$ and $r_2$ and arguments $\theta_1$ and $\theta_2$. Then compute their *quotient* in rectangular form. For modulus $r$ and argument $\theta$ of the quotient, verify that $\frac{r_1}{r_2} = r$ and $\theta_1 - \theta_2 = \theta$.

**37.** $z_1 = \sqrt{3} + i$;   $z_2 = 1 + \sqrt{3}i$

**38.** $z_1 = -\sqrt{3} + i$;   $z_2 = 3 + 0i$

Compute the product $z_1z_2$ and quotient $\frac{z_1}{z_2}$ using the trigonometric form. Answer in exact rectangular form where possible, otherwise round all values to two decimal places.

**39.** $z_1 = -4\sqrt{3} + 4i$
   $z_2 = \frac{3\sqrt{3}}{2} + \frac{3}{2}i$

**40.** $z_1 = \frac{5\sqrt{3}}{2} + \frac{5}{2}i$
   $z_2 = 0 + 6i$

**41.** $z_1 = -2\sqrt{3} + 0i$
   $z_2 = -\frac{21}{2} + \frac{7i\sqrt{3}}{2}$

**42.** $z_1 = 0 - 6i\sqrt{2}$
   $z_2 = \frac{3\sqrt{2}}{2} + \frac{3i\sqrt{6}}{2}$

**43.** $z_1 = 9\left[\cos\left(\frac{\pi}{15}\right) + i\sin\left(\frac{\pi}{15}\right)\right]$

$z_2 = 1.8\left[\cos\left(\frac{2\pi}{3}\right) + i\sin\left(\frac{2\pi}{3}\right)\right]$

**44.** $z_1 = 2\left[\cos\left(\frac{3\pi}{5}\right) + i\sin\left(\frac{3\pi}{5}\right)\right]$

$z_2 = 8.4\left[\cos\left(\frac{\pi}{5}\right) + i\sin\left(\frac{\pi}{5}\right)\right]$

**45.** $z_1 = 10(\cos 60° + i\sin 60°)$
   $z_2 = 4(\cos 30° + i\sin 30°)$

**46.** $z_1 = 7(\cos 120° + i\sin 120°)$
   $z_2 = 2(\cos 300° + i\sin 300°)$

**47.** $z_1 = 5\sqrt{2}$ cis $210°$
   $z_2 = 2\sqrt{2}$ cis $30°$

**48.** $z_1 = 5\sqrt{3}$ cis $240°$
   $z_2 = \sqrt{3}$ cis $90°$

**49.** $z_1 = 6$ cis $82°$
   $z_2 = 1.5$ cis $27°$

**50.** $z_1 = 1.6$ cis $59°$
   $z_2 = 8$ cis $275°$

▶ **WORKING WITH FORMULAS**

**51. Equilateral triangles in the complex plane:**
$u^2 + v^2 + w^2 = uv + uw + vw$

If the line segments connecting the complex numbers $u$, $v$, and $w$ form the vertices of an equilateral triangle, the formula shown holds true. Verify that $u = 2 + \sqrt{3}i$, $v = 10 + \sqrt{3}i$, and $w = 6 + 5\sqrt{3}i$ form the vertices of an equilateral triangle using the distance formula, then verify the formula given.

**52. The cube of a complex number:**
$(A + B)^3 = A^3 + 3A^2B + 3AB^2 + B^3$

The cube of any binomial can be found using the formula here, where $A$ and $B$ are the terms of the binomial. Use the formula to compute the cube of $1 - 2i$ (note $A = 1$ and $B = -2i$).

▶ **APPLICATIONS**

**53. Electric current:** In the United States, electric power is supplied to homes and offices via a "120 V circuit," using an alternating current that varies from 170 V to $-170$ V, at a frequency of 60 cycles/sec. (a) Write the voltage equation for U.S. households, (b) create a table of values illustrating the voltage produced every thousandth of a second for the first half-cycle, and (c) find the first time $t$ in this half-cycle when exactly 140 V is being produced.

**54. Electric current:** While the electricity supplied in Europe is still not quite uniform, most countries employ 230-V circuits, using an alternating current that varies from 325 V to $-325$ V. However, the frequency is only *50 cycles per second*. (a) Write the voltage equation for these European countries, (b) create a table of values illustrating the voltage produced every thousandth of a second for the first half-cycle, and (c) find the first time $t$ in this half-cycle when exactly 215 V is being produced.

**AC circuits:** For the circuits indicated in Exercises 55 through 60, (a) find the magnitude of $Z$, the phase angle between current and voltage, and write the result in trigonometric form; and (b) find the total voltage across this circuit. Recall $Z = R + (X_L - X_C)j$ and $|Z| = \sqrt{R^2 + (X_L - X_C)^2}$.

**55.** $R = 15\ \Omega$, $X_L = 12\ \Omega$, and $X_C = 4\ \Omega$, with $I = 3$ A

**56.** $R = 24\ \Omega$, $X_L = 12\ \Omega$, and $X_C = 5\ \Omega$, with $I = 2.5$ A

**Exercises 55 through 58**

**57.** $R = 7\,\Omega$, $X_L = 6\,\Omega$, and $X_C = 11\,\Omega$, with $I = 1.8$ A

**58.** $R = 9.2\,\Omega$, $X_L = 5.6\,\Omega$, and $X_C = 8.3\,\Omega$, with $I = 2.0$ A

**59.** $R = 12\,\Omega$ and $X_L = 5\,\Omega$, with $I = 1.7$ A

**60.** $R = 35\,\Omega$ and $X_L = 12\,\Omega$, with $I = 4$ A

**Exercises 59 and 60**

**AC circuits—voltage:** The current $I$ and the impedance $Z$ for certain AC circuits are given. Write $I$ and $Z$ in trigonometric form and find the voltage in each circuit. Recall $V = IZ$.

**61.** $I = \sqrt{3} + 1j$ A and $Z = 5 + 5j\,\Omega$

**62.** $I = \sqrt{3} - 1j$ A and $Z = 2 + 2j\,\Omega$

**63.** $I = 3 - 2j$ A and $Z = 2 + 3.75j\,\Omega$

**64.** $I = 4 + 3j$ A and $Z = 2 - 4j\,\Omega$

**AC circuits—current:** If the voltage and impedance are known, the current $I$ in the circuit is calculated as the quotient $I = \dfrac{V}{Z}$. Write $V$ and $Z$ in trigonometric form to find the current in each circuit.

**65.** $V = 2 + 2\sqrt{3}j$ and $Z = 4 - 4j\,\Omega$

**66.** $V = 4\sqrt{3} - 4j$ and $Z = 1 - 1j\,\Omega$

**67.** $V = 3 - 4j$ and $Z = 4 + 7.5j\,\Omega$

**68.** $V = 2.8 + 9.6j$ and $Z = 1.4 - 4.8j\,\Omega$

**Parallel circuits:** For AC circuits *wired in parallel*, the total impedance is given by $Z = \dfrac{Z_1 Z_2}{Z_1 + Z_2}$, where $Z_1$ and $Z_2$ represent the impedance in each branch. Find the total impedance for the values given. Compute the product in the numerator using trigonometric form, and the sum in the denominator in rectangular form.

**69.** $Z_1 = 1 + 2j$ and $Z_2 = 3 - 2j$

**70.** $Z_1 = 3 - j$ and $Z_2 = 2 + j$

▶ **EXTENDING THE CONCEPT**

**71.** Verify/prove that for the complex numbers
$z_1 = r_1(\cos\alpha + i\sin\alpha)$ and
$z_2 = r_2(\cos\beta + i\sin\beta)$,
$\dfrac{z_1}{z_2} = \dfrac{r_1}{r_2}\left[\cos(\alpha - \beta) + i\sin(\alpha - \beta)\right].$

**72.** Using the Internet, a trade manual, or some other resource, find the voltage and frequency at which electricity is supplied to most of Japan (oddly enough—two different frequencies are in common use). As in Example 6, the voltage given will likely be the root-mean-square (rms) voltage. Use the information to find the true voltage and the equation model for voltage in most of Japan.

**73.** Recall that two lines are perpendicular if their slopes have a product of $-1$. For the directed line segment representing the complex number $z_1 = 7 + 24i$, find complex numbers $z_2$ and $z_3$ whose directed line segments are perpendicular to $z_1$ and have a magnitude one-fifth as large.

**74.** The magnitude of the impedance is
$|Z| = \sqrt{R^2 + (X_L - X_C)^2}$. If $R$, $X_L$, and $X_C$ are all nonzero, what conditions would make the magnitude of $Z$ as small as possible?

▶ **MAINTAINING YOUR SKILLS**

**75. (6.4)** Solve for $x \in [0, 2\pi)$:

$$350 = 750\sin\left(2x - \frac{\pi}{4}\right) - 25$$

**76. (5.3)** Write $\cos 15°$ in exact form using (a) a half angle identity and (b) a difference identity. Verify the results obtained are equivalent.

**77. (5.1)** Verify the following is an identity:
$$\frac{1 + \cos\alpha}{1 - \cos\alpha} = \frac{\sec\alpha + 1}{\sec\alpha - 1}$$

**78. (3.1)** For $24°12'36''$, (a) determine its complement, (b) convert the complement to decimal degrees, and (c) convert the complement to radians.

**79. (7.1)** A ship is spotted by two observation posts that are 4 mi apart. Using the line between them for reference, the first post reports the ship is at an angle of 41°, while the second reports an angle of 63°, as shown. How far is the ship from the closest post?

**Exercises 79**

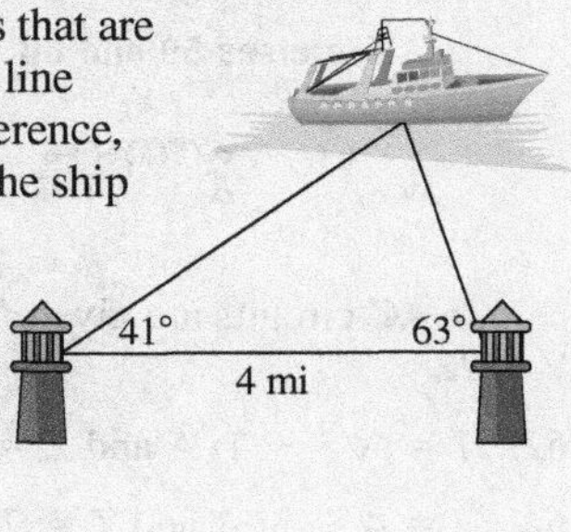

41°        63°

4 mi

**80. (7.3)** Two tugboats are pulling a large ship into dry dock. The first is pulling with a force of 1500 N and the second with a force of 1800 N. Determine the angle $\theta$ for the second tugboat that will keep the ship moving straight forward and into the dock.

**Exercises 80**

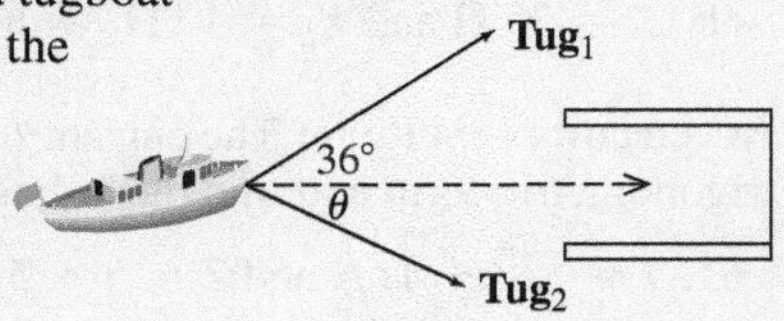

Tug₁

36°
$\theta$

Tug₂

The material in this section represents some of the most significant developments in the history of mathematics. After hundreds of years of struggle, mathematical scientists had not only come to recognize the existence of complex numbers, but were able to make operations on them commonplace and routine. This allowed for the unification of many ideas related to the study of polynomial equations, and answered questions that had puzzled scientists from many different fields for centuries. In this section, we will look at two fairly simple theorems that actually represent over 1000 years in the evolution of mathematical thought.

### A. De Moivre's Theorem

Having found acceptable means for applying the four basic operations to complex numbers, our attention naturally shifts to the computation of powers and roots. Without them, we'd remain wholly unable to offer complete solutions to polynomial equations and find solutions for many applications. The computation of powers, squares, and cubes offer little challenge, as they can be computed easily using the formula for binomial squares $[(A + B)^2 = A^2 + 2AB + B^2]$ or by applying the **binomial theorem.** For larger powers, the binomial theorem becomes too time consuming and a more efficient method is desired. The key here is to use the trigonometric form of the complex number. In Section 8.2, we noted the product of two complex numbers involved multiplying their moduli and adding their arguments:

For $z_1 = r_1(\cos \theta_1 + i \sin \theta_1)$ and $z_2 = r_2(\cos \theta_2 + i \sin \theta_2)$ we have
$$z_1 z_2 = r_1 r_2 [\cos(\theta_1 + \theta_2) + i \sin(\theta_1 + \theta_2)]$$

For the square of a complex number, $r_1 = r_2$ and $\theta_1 = \theta_2$. Using $\theta$ itself yields
$$z^2 = r^2[\cos(\theta + \theta) + i \sin(\theta + \theta)]$$
$$= r^2[\cos(2\theta) + i \sin(2\theta)]$$

Multiplying this result by $z = r(\cos \theta + i \sin \theta)$ to compute $z^3$ gives
$$r^2[\cos(2\theta) + i \sin(2\theta)] \, r(\cos \theta + i \sin \theta) = r^3[\cos(2\theta + \theta) + i \sin(2\theta + \theta)]$$
$$= r^3[\cos(3\theta) + i \sin(3\theta)].$$

The result can be extended further and generalized into **De Moivre's theorem.**

**WORTHY OF NOTE**

Sometimes the argument of cosine and sine becomes very large after applying De Moivre's theorem. In these cases, we use the fact that $\theta = \theta \pm 360°k$ and $\theta = \theta \pm 2\pi k$ represent coterminal angles for integers $k$, and use the coterminal angle $\theta$ where $0° \leq \theta < 360°$ or $0 \leq \theta < 2\pi$.

### De Moivre's Theorem

For any positive integer $n$, and $z = r(\cos \theta + i \sin \theta)$,
$$z^n = r^n[\cos(n\theta) + i \sin(n\theta)]$$

For a proof of the theorem where $n$ is an integer and $n \geq 1$, see Appendix VI.

**EXAMPLE 1** ▶ **Using De Moivre's Theorem to Compute the Power of a Complex Number**
Use De Moivre's theorem to compute $z^9$, given $z = -\frac{1}{2} - \frac{1}{2}i$.

**Solution** ▶ Here we have $r = \sqrt{\left(-\frac{1}{2}\right)^2 + \left(-\frac{1}{2}\right)^2} = \frac{\sqrt{2}}{2}$. With $z$ in QIII, $\tan\theta = 1$ yields $\theta = \frac{5\pi}{4}$. The trigonometric form is $z = \frac{\sqrt{2}}{2}\left[\cos\left(\frac{5\pi}{4}\right) + i\sin\left(\frac{5\pi}{4}\right)\right]$ and applying the theorem with $n = 9$ gives

$$z^9 = \left(\frac{\sqrt{2}}{2}\right)^9\left[\cos\left(9 \cdot \frac{5\pi}{4}\right) + i\sin\left(9 \cdot \frac{5\pi}{4}\right)\right] \qquad \text{De Moivre's theorem}$$

$$= \frac{\sqrt{2}}{32}\left[\cos\left(\frac{45\pi}{4}\right) + i\sin\left(\frac{45\pi}{4}\right)\right] \qquad \text{simplify}$$

$$= \frac{\sqrt{2}}{32}\left[\cos\left(\frac{5\pi}{4}\right) + i\sin\left(\frac{5\pi}{4}\right)\right] \qquad \text{coterminal angles}$$

$$= \frac{\sqrt{2}}{32}\left(-\frac{\sqrt{2}}{2} - \frac{\sqrt{2}}{2}i\right) \qquad \text{evaluate functions}$$

$$= -\frac{1}{32} - \frac{1}{32}i \qquad \text{result}$$

**Now try Exercises 7 through 14** ▶

As with products and quotients, if the complex number is *given* in trigonometric form, computing any power of the number is both elegant and efficient. For instance, if $z = 2\,\text{cis}\,40°$, then $z^4 = 16\,\text{cis}\,160°$. **See Exercises 15 through 18.**

For cases where $\theta$ is not a standard angle, De Moivre's theorem requires an intriguing application of the skills developed in Chapter 5, including the use of multiple angle identities and working from a right triangle drawn relative to $\theta_r = \tan^{-1}\left|\frac{b}{a}\right|$. **See Exercises 53 and 54.**

☑ **A.** You've just learned how to use De Moivre's theorem to raise complex numbers to any power

## B. Checking Solutions to Polynomial Equations

One application of De Moivre's theorem is checking the complex roots of a polynomial, as in Example 2.

**EXAMPLE 2** ▶ **Using De Moivre's Theorem to Check Solutions to a Polynomial Equation**
Use De Moivre's theorem to show that $z = -2 - 2i$ is a solution to $z^4 - 3z^3 - 38z^2 - 128z - 144 = 0$.

**Solution** ▶ We will apply the theorem to the third and fourth degree terms, and compute the square directly. Since $z$ is in QIII, the trigonometric form is $z = 2\sqrt{2}\,\text{cis}\,225°$. In the following illustration, note that $900°$ and $180°$ are coterminal, as are $675°$ and $315°$.

$$(-2 - 2i)^4 \qquad\qquad (-2 - 2i)^3 \qquad\qquad (-2 - 2i)^2$$

$$= (2\sqrt{2})^4\text{cis}(4 \cdot 225°) \qquad = (2\sqrt{2})^3\text{cis}(3 \cdot 225°) \qquad = 4 + 8i + (2i)^2$$

$$= (2\sqrt{2})^4\text{cis}\,900° \qquad\quad = (2\sqrt{2})^3\text{cis}\,675° \qquad\quad = 4 + 8i + 4i^2$$

$$= 64\,\text{cis}\,180° \qquad\qquad\quad = (2\sqrt{2})^3\text{cis}\,315° \qquad\quad = 4 + 8i - 4$$

$$= 64(-1 + 0i) \qquad\qquad = 16\sqrt{2}\left(\frac{\sqrt{2}}{2} - \frac{\sqrt{2}}{2}i\right) \qquad = 0 + 8i$$

$$= -64 \qquad\qquad\qquad\quad = 16 - 16i \qquad\qquad\qquad = 8i$$

Substituting back into the original equation gives

$$1z^4 - 3z^3 - 38z^2 - 128z - 144 = 0$$
$$1(-64) - 3(16 - 16i) - 38(8i) - 128(-2 - 2i) - 144 = 0$$
$$-64 - 48 + 48i - 304i + 256 + 256i - 144 = 0$$
$$(-64 - 48 + 256 - 144) + (48 - 304 + 256)i = 0$$
$$0 = 0 \checkmark$$

**Now try Exercises 19 through 26** ▶

☑ **B. You've just learned to use De Moivre's theorem to check solutions to polynomial equations**

Regarding Example 2, we know from a study of algebra that complex roots must occur in conjugate pairs, meaning $-2 + 2i$ is also a root. This equation actually has two real and two complex roots, with $z = 9$ and $z = -2$ being the two real roots.

## C. The *n*th Roots Theorem

Having looked at De Moivre's theorem, which raises a complex number to any power, we now consider the **nth roots theorem,** which will compute the *n*th roots of a complex number. If we allow that De Moivre's theorem also holds for rational values $\frac{1}{n}$, instead of only the integers *n* illustrated previously, the formula for computing an *n*th root would be a direct result:

$$z^{\frac{1}{n}} = r^{\frac{1}{n}}\left[\cos\left(\frac{1}{n}\theta\right) + i\sin\left(\frac{1}{n}\theta\right)\right] \quad \text{replace } n \text{ with } \frac{1}{n} \text{ in De Moivre's theorem}$$
$$= \sqrt[n]{r}\left[\cos\left(\frac{\theta}{n}\right) + i\sin\left(\frac{\theta}{n}\right)\right] \quad \text{simplify}$$

However, this formula would *find only the principal nth root*! In other words, periodic solutions would be ignored. As in Section 8.2, it's worth noting the most general form of a complex number is $z = r[\cos(\theta + 360°k) + i\sin(\theta + 360°k)]$, for $k \in \mathbb{Z}$. When De Moivre's theorem is applied to this form for *integers n*, we obtain $z^n = r^n[\cos(n\theta + 360°kn) + i\sin(n\theta + 360°kn)]$, which returns a result identical to $r^n[\cos(n\theta) + i\sin(n\theta)]$. However, for the rational exponent $\frac{1}{n}$, the general form takes additional solutions into account and will return all *n*, *n*th roots.

$$z^{\frac{1}{n}} = r^{\frac{1}{n}}\left\{\cos\left[\frac{1}{n}(\theta + 360°k)\right] + i\sin\left[\frac{1}{n}(\theta + 360°k)\right]\right\} \quad \begin{array}{l}\text{De Moivre's} \\ \text{theorem for rational} \\ \text{exponents}\end{array}$$
$$= \sqrt[n]{r}\left[\cos\left(\frac{\theta}{n} + \frac{360°k}{n}\right) + i\sin\left(\frac{\theta}{n} + \frac{360°k}{n}\right)\right] \quad \text{simplify}$$

### The *n*th Roots Theorem

For $z = r(\cos\theta + i\sin\theta)$, a positive integer *n*, and $r \in \mathbb{R}$, $z$ has exactly *n* distinct *n*th roots determined by

$$\sqrt[n]{z} = \sqrt[n]{r}\left[\cos\left(\frac{\theta}{n} + \frac{360°k}{n}\right) + i\sin\left(\frac{\theta}{n} + \frac{360°k}{n}\right)\right]$$

where $k = 0, 1, 2, \ldots, n - 1$.

For ease of computation, it helps to note that once the argument for the principal root is found using $k = 0$, $\dfrac{\theta}{n} + \dfrac{360°k}{n}$ simply adds $\dfrac{360°}{n}$ $\left(\text{or } \dfrac{2\pi}{n}\right)$ to the previous argument for $k = 1, 2, 3, \ldots, n - 1$.

In Example 3 you're asked to find the three cube roots of 1, also called the **cube roots of unity,** and graph the results. The *n*th roots of unity play a significant role in the solution of many polynomial equations. For an in-depth study of this connection, visit www.mhhe.com/coburn and go to **Section 8.7: Trigonometry, Complex Numbers, and Cubic Equations.**

---

**EXAMPLE 3** ▶ **Finding *n*th Roots**

Use the *n*th roots theorem to solve the equation $x^3 - 1 = 0$. Write the results in rectangular form and graph.

**Solution** ▶ From $x^3 - 1 = 0$, we have $x^3 = 1$ and must find the three cube roots of unity. As before, we begin in trigonometric form: $1 + 0i = 1(\cos 0° + i \sin 0°)$ since $\theta = \tan^{-1}(0) = 0°$. With $n = 3$, $r = 1$, and $\theta = 0°$, we have $\sqrt[3]{r} = \sqrt[3]{1} = 1$, and $\dfrac{0°}{3} + \dfrac{360°k}{3} = 0° + 120°k$. The principal

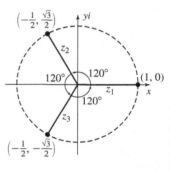

root ($k = 0$) is $z_0 = 1(\cos 0° + i \sin 0°) = 1$. Adding 120° to each previous argument, we find the other roots are

$$z_1 = 1(\cos 120° + i \sin 120°)$$
$$z_2 = 1(\cos 240° + i \sin 240°).$$

In rectangular form these are $-\dfrac{1}{2} + \dfrac{\sqrt{3}}{2}i$, and $-\dfrac{1}{2} - \dfrac{\sqrt{3}}{2}i$, as shown in the figure.

**Now try Exercises 27 through 40 ▶**

---

**EXAMPLE 4** ▶ **Finding *n*th Roots**

Use the *n*th roots theorem to find the five fifth roots of $z = 16\sqrt{3} + 16i$.

**Solution** ▶ In trigonometric form, $16\sqrt{3} + 16i = 32(\cos 30° + i \sin 30°)$ since $\theta = \tan^{-1}\left(\dfrac{16}{16\sqrt{3}}\right) = 30°$. With $n = 5$, $r = 32$, and $\theta = 30°$, we have $\sqrt[5]{r} = \sqrt[5]{32} = 2$, and $\dfrac{30°}{5} + \dfrac{360°k}{5} = 6° + 72°k$. The principal root is $z_0 = 2(\cos 6° + i \sin 6°)$.

Adding 72° to each previous argument, we find the other four roots are

$$z_1 = 2(\cos 78° + i \sin 78°) \qquad z_2 = 2(\cos 150° + i \sin 150°)$$
$$z_3 = 2(\cos 222° + i \sin 222°) \qquad z_4 = 2(\cos 294° + i \sin 294°)$$

**Now try Exercises 41 through 44 ▶**

Of the five roots in Example 4, only $z_2 = 2(\cos 150° + i \sin 150°)$ uses a standard angle. Applying De Moivre's theorem with $n = 5$ gives $(2 \operatorname{cis} 150°)^5 = 32 \operatorname{cis} 750° = 32 \operatorname{cis} 30°$ or $16\sqrt{3} + 16i$.✓ **See Exercise 48.**

**Figure 8.16**

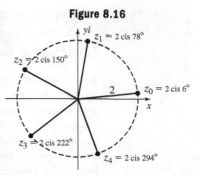

As a consequence of the arguments in a solution being uniformly separated by $\dfrac{360°}{n}$, the graphs of complex roots are equally spaced about a circle of radius $r$. The five fifth roots from Example 3 are shown in Figure 8.16 (note each argument differs by 72°).

For additional insight into roots of complex numbers, we reason that the $n$th roots of a complex number must also be complex. To find the four fourth roots of $z = 8 + 8\sqrt{3}i = 16(\cos 60° + i \sin 60°)$, we seek a number of the form $r(\cos \alpha + i \sin \alpha)$ such that $[r(\cos \alpha + i \sin \alpha)]^4 = 16(\cos 60° + i \sin 60°)$. Applying De Moivre's theorem to the left-hand side and equating equivalent parts we obtain

$$r^4[\cos(4\alpha) + i \sin(4\alpha)] = 16(\cos 60° + i \sin 60°), \text{ which leads to}$$
$$r^4 = 16 \text{ and}$$
$$4\alpha = 60°$$

From this it is obvious that $r = 2$, but as with similar equations solved in Chapter 6, the equation $4\alpha = 60°$ has multiple solutions. To find them, we first add $360°k$ to $60°$, *then* solve for $\alpha$.

$$4\alpha = 60° + 360°k \quad \text{add } 360°k$$
$$\alpha = \frac{60° + 360°k}{4} \quad \text{divide by 4}$$
$$= 15° + 90°k \quad \text{result}$$

For convenience, we start with $k = 0, 1, 2$, and so on, which leads to

For $k = 0$:  $\alpha = 15° + 90°(0)$     For $k = 1$:  $\alpha = 15° + 90°(1)$
$= 15°$                                     $= 105°$
For $k = 2$:  $\alpha = 15° + 90°(2)$     For $k = 3$:  $\alpha = 15° + 90°(3)$
$= 195°$                                    $= 285°$

At this point it should strike us that we have four roots—exactly the number required. Indeed, using $k = 4$ gives $\alpha = 15° + 90°(4) = 375°$, which is coterminal with the $15°$ obtained when $k = 0$. Hence, the four fourth roots are

$$z_0 = 2(\cos 15° + i \sin 15°) \qquad z_1 = 2(\cos 105° + i \sin 105°)$$
$$z_2 = 2(\cos 195° + i \sin 195°) \qquad z_3 = 2(\cos 285° + i \sin 285°).$$

The check for these solutions is asked for in **Exercise 47.**

As a final note, it must have struck the mathematicians who pioneered these discoveries with some amazement that complex numbers and the trigonometric functions should be so closely related. The amazement must have been all the more profound upon discovering an additional connection between complex numbers and *exponential functions*. For more on these connections, see the Strengthening Core Skills feature at the end of this chapter or visit www.mhhe.com/coburn and review **Section 8.6: Complex Numbers in Exponential Form.**

☑ **C.** You've just learned how to use the $n$th roots theorem to find the $n$th roots of a complex number

## TECHNOLOGY HIGHLIGHT

## Templates, Graphing Calculators, and Complex Numbers

To work efficiently with larger expressions on a graphing calculator, it helps to set up a general template that can repeatedly be recalled and reused. For De Moivre's theorem, different complex numbers will give different values for *n, r,* and $\theta$. Generally *n* and *r* will consist of a single digit, but $\theta$ will often have one, two, or three digits so we set the template to accommodate this fact. After clearing the home screen, we enter the generic template R^N*(cos(N*$\theta$) + *i* sin(N*$\theta$)) as in Figure 8.17, store the value of $\theta$, then recall the expression each time we wish to use it. For *n*th roots we enter N$\sqrt[x]{}$R*(cos($\theta$/N + 360K/N) + *i* sin($\theta$/N + 360K/N)). In either case we can recall and overwrite the values to use the formula (as in Example 1 here), or store values in N, R, $\theta$, and K to use the formula as it stands (as in Example 2).

**Figure 8.17**

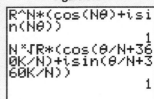

**EXAMPLE 1**  Use the template above for De Moivre's theorem and your graphing calculator to find the value of $(2\sqrt{3} - 2i)^6$.

Solution:  In this case the complex number is $z = 2\sqrt{3} - 2i$ (in QIV) with $n = 6, r = 4,$ and $\theta = -30°$. Storing $-30$ in location $\theta$ ($-30$ STO → ALPHA 3), we recall the expression for De Moivre's theorem and enter/overwrite N and R. Here, $z^6 = -4096$. See Figure 8.18.

**Figure 8.18**

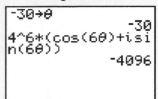

**EXAMPLE 2**  Use the template above for the *n*th roots theorem and the storage/recall abilities of your graphing calculator to find the three cube roots of $z = -2 - 2i$.

Solution:  The complex number $z = -2 - 2i$ (in QIII) yields $r = \sqrt{8}$ and $\theta = 225°$. With $n = 3$ and $k = 0$ to begin, we store these values in their respective locations: $\sqrt{8}$ STO → ALPHA × for R, 3 STO → ALPHA LOG for N, 225 STO → ALPHA 3 for $\theta$, and 0 STO → ALPHA ( for K (see Figure 8.19). Recalling the template for *n*th roots and pressing ENTER gives $z_0 = 0.3660254038 + 1.366025404i$. Changing the value of *k* to $k = 1$ and $k = 2$ gives $z_1 = -1.366025404 - 0.3660254038i$, with $z_2 = 1 - i$.

**Figure 8.19**

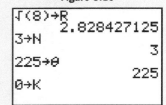

**Exercise 1:**  Use the appropriate template to find the three cube roots of unity, $z = 1 + 0i \left(\text{note } \dfrac{\sqrt{3}}{2} \approx 0.8660\right)$.

**Exercise 2:**  Use the appropriate template to find $z^3$, given $z = 1 - \sqrt{3}i$.

## 8.3 EXERCISES

▶ **CONCEPTS AND VOCABULARY**

**Fill in each blank with the appropriate word or phrase. Carefully reread the section if needed.**

1. For $z = r(\cos \theta + i \sin \theta)$, $z^5$ is computed as _____ according to _____ theorem.

2. If $z = 6i$, then *z* raised to an _____ power will be real and *z* raised to an _____ power will be _____ since $\theta = $ _____.

3. One application of De Moivre's theorem is to check _____ solutions to a polynomial equation.

4. The $n$th roots of a complex number are equally spaced on a circle of radius $r$, since their arguments all differ by _____ degrees or _____ radians.

5. From Example 4, go ahead and compute the value of $z_5$, $z_6$, and $z_7$. What do you notice? Discuss how this reaffirms that there are exactly $n$, $n$th roots.

6. Use a calculator to find $(1 - 3i)^4$. Then use it again to find the fourth root of the result. What do you notice? Explain the discrepancy and then resolve it using the $n$th roots theorem to find all four roots.

## ▶ DEVELOPING YOUR SKILLS

**Use De Moivre's theorem to compute the following. Clearly state the value of $r$, $n$, and $\theta$ before you begin.**

7. $(3 + 3i)^4$

8. $(-2 + 2i)^6$

9. $(-1 + \sqrt{3}i)^3$

10. $(\sqrt{3} - i)^3$

11. $\left(\dfrac{1}{2} - \dfrac{\sqrt{3}}{2}i\right)^5$

12. $\left(-\dfrac{\sqrt{3}}{2} + \dfrac{1}{2}i\right)^6$

13. $\left(\dfrac{\sqrt{2}}{2} - \dfrac{\sqrt{2}}{2}i\right)^6$

14. $\left(-\dfrac{\sqrt{2}}{2} + \dfrac{\sqrt{2}}{2}i\right)^5$

15. $(4 \operatorname{cis} 330°)^3$

16. $(4 \operatorname{cis} 300°)^3$

17. $\left(\dfrac{\sqrt{2}}{2} \operatorname{cis} 135°\right)^5$

18. $\left(\dfrac{\sqrt{2}}{2} \operatorname{cis} 135°\right)^8$

**Use De Moivre's theorem to verify the solution given for each polynomial equation.**

19. $z^4 + 3z^3 - 6z^2 + 12z - 40 = 0$; $z = 2i$

20. $z^4 - z^3 + 7z^2 - 9z - 18 = 0$; $z = -3i$

21. $z^4 + 6z^3 + 19z^2 + 6z + 18 = 0$; $z = -3 - 3i$

22. $2z^4 + 3z^3 - 4z^2 + 2z + 12 = 0$; $z = 1 - i$

23. $z^5 + z^4 - 4z^3 - 4z^2 + 16z + 16 = 0$; $z = \sqrt{3} - i$

24. $z^5 + z^4 - 16z^3 - 16z^2 + 256z + 256 = 0$; $z = 2\sqrt{3} + 2i$

25. $z^4 - 4z^3 + 7z^2 - 6z - 10 = 0$; $z = 1 + 2i$

26. $z^4 - 2z^3 - 7z^2 + 28z + 52 = 0$; $z = 3 - 2i$

**Find the $n$th roots indicated by writing and solving the related equation.**

27. five fifth roots of unity

28. six sixth roots of unity

29. five fifth roots of 243

30. three cube roots of 8

31. three cube roots of $-27i$

32. five fifth roots of $32i$

**Solve each equation using the $n$th roots theorem.**

33. $x^5 - 32 = 0$

34. $x^5 - 243 = 0$

35. $x^3 - 27i = 0$

36. $x^3 + 64i = 0$

37. $x^5 - \sqrt{2} - \sqrt{2}i = 0$

38. $x^5 - 1 + \sqrt{3}i = 0$

39. Solve the equation $x^3 - 1 = 0$ by factoring it as the difference of cubes and applying the quadratic formula. Compare results to those obtained in Example 3.

40. Use the $n$th roots theorem to find the four fourth roots of unity, then find all solutions to $x^4 - 1 = 0$ by factoring it as a difference of squares. What do you notice?

**Use the nth roots theorem to find the $n$th roots. Clearly state $r$, $n$, and $\theta$ (from the trigonometric form of $z$) as you begin. Answer in exact form when possible, otherwise use a four decimal place approximation.**

41. four fourth roots of $-8 + 8\sqrt{3}i$

42. five fifth roots of $16 - 16\sqrt{3}i$

43. four fourth roots of $-7 - 7i$

44. three cube roots of $9 + 9i$

## ▶ WORKING WITH FORMULAS

**The discriminant of a cubic equation:** $D = \dfrac{4p^3 + 27q^2}{108}$

For cubic equations of the form $z^3 + pz + q = 0$, where $p$ and $q$ are real numbers, one solution has the form

$z = \sqrt[3]{-\dfrac{q}{2} + \sqrt{D}} + \sqrt[3]{-\dfrac{q}{2} - \sqrt{D}}$, where $D$ is called the discriminant. Compute the value of $D$ for the cubic

equations given, then use the nth roots theorem to find the three cube roots of $-\dfrac{q}{2} + \sqrt{D}$ and $-\dfrac{q}{2} - \sqrt{D}$ in

trigonometric form (also see Exercises 55 and 56).

**45.** $z^3 - 6z + 4 = 0$                                **46.** $z^3 - 12z - 8 = 0$

## ▶ APPLICATIONS

**47. Powers and roots:** Just after Example 4, the four fourth roots of $z = 8 + 8\sqrt{3}i$ were given as

$z_0 = 2(\cos 15° + i \sin 15°)$

$z_1 = 2(\cos 105° + i \sin 105°)$

$z_2 = 2(\cos 195° + i \sin 195°)$

$z_3 = 2(\cos 285° + i \sin 285°)$.

Verify these are the four fourth roots of $z = 8 + 8\sqrt{3}i$ using a calculator and De Moivre's theorem.

**48. Powers and roots:** In Example 4 we found the five fifth roots of $z = 16\sqrt{3} + 16i$ were

$z_0 = 2(\cos 6° + i \sin 6°)$

$z_1 = 2(\cos 78° + i \sin 78°)$

$z_2 = 2(\cos 150° + i \sin 150°)$

$z_3 = 2(\cos 222° + i \sin 222°)$

$z_4 = 2(\cos 294° + i \sin 294°)$

Verify these are the five fifth roots of $16\sqrt{3} + 16i$ using a calculator and De Moivre's theorem.

**Electrical circuits:** For an AC circuit with three branches wired in parallel, the total impedance is given by

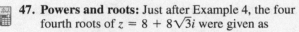

$Z_T = \dfrac{Z_1 Z_2 Z_3}{Z_1 Z_2 + Z_1 Z_3 + Z_2 Z_3}$, where $Z_1$, $Z_2$, and $Z_3$ represent the impedance in each branch of the circuit. If the impedance

in each branch is identical, $Z_1 = Z_2 = Z_3 = Z$, and the numerator becomes $Z^3$ and the denominator becomes $3Z^2$, (a) use De Moivre's theorem to calculate the numerator and denominator for each value of $Z$ given, (b) find the total impedance by

computing the quotient $\dfrac{Z^3}{3Z^2}$, and (c) verify your result is identical to $\dfrac{Z}{3}$.

**49.** $Z = 3 + 4j$ in all three branches                    **50.** $Z = 5\sqrt{3} + 5j$ in all three branches

## ▶ EXTENDING THE CONCEPT

In Chapter 5, you were asked to verify that $\sin(3\theta) = 3 \sin \theta - 4 \sin^3\theta$ and $\cos(4\theta) = 8 \cos^2\theta - 8 \cos^2\theta + 1$ were

identities (Section 5.3, Exercises 21 and 22). For $z = 3 + \sqrt{7}i$, verify $|z| = 4$ and $\theta = \tan^{-1}\!\left(\dfrac{\sqrt{7}}{3}\right)$, then draw a right

triangle with $\sqrt{7}$ opposite $\theta$ and 3 adjacent to $\theta$. Discuss how this right triangle and the identities given can be used in conjunction with De Moivre's theorem to find the exact value of the powers given (also see Exercises 53 and 54).

**51.** $(3 + \sqrt{7}i)^3$                                **52.** $(3 + \sqrt{7}i)^4$

For cases where $\theta$ is not a standard angle, working toward an exact answer using De Moivre's theorem requires the use of multiple angle identities and drawing the right triangle related to $\theta = \tan^{-1}\left|\dfrac{b}{a}\right|$. For Exercises 53 and 54, use De Moivre's theorem to compute the complex powers by (a) constructing the related right triangle for $\theta$, (b) evaluating $\sin(4\theta)$ using two applications of double-angle identities, and (c) evaluating $\cos(4\theta)$ using a Pythagorean identity and the computed value of $\sin(4\theta)$.

**53.** $z = (1 + 2i)^4$

**54.** $(2 + \sqrt{5}i)^4$

The solutions to the cubic equations in Exercises 45 and 46 (repeated as the equations in Exercises 55 and 56) can be found by adding the cube roots of $-\dfrac{q}{2} + \sqrt{D}$ and $-\dfrac{q}{2} - \sqrt{D}$ that have arguments summing to 360°.

**55.** Find the roots of $z^3 - 6z + 4 = 0$

**56.** Find the roots of $z^3 - 12z - 8 = 0$

▶ **MAINTAINING YOUR SKILLS**

**57.** (8.1) In AC (alternating current) circuits, the current $I$ is computed as the quotient of the voltage $V$ and the impedance Z: $I = \dfrac{V}{Z}$. (a) Find the amount of current given $V = 14 - 5i$ and $Z = 3 - 2i$. (b) Verify your answer by showing $ZI = V$.

**58.** (6.2) Using her calculator, Julia finds that $\sin 120° = \dfrac{\sqrt{3}}{2}$ but $\sin^{-1}\left(\dfrac{\sqrt{3}}{2}\right) \neq 120°$. Explain why.

**59.** (5.1) Prove the following is an identity:
$$\frac{\tan^2 x}{\sec x + 1} = \frac{1 - \cos x}{\cos x}$$

**60.** (8.2) Convert $z = 4 - 4i$ to trigonometric form.

**61.** (1.1) Solve the triangle shown using a 30-60-90 standard triangle.

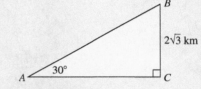

**62.** (2.2) Solve the triangle given. Round lengths to hundredths of a meter.

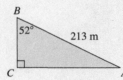

1. Find the sum and product of the complex numbers $2 + 3i$ and $2 - 3i$. Comment on what you notice.

2. Determine the quotient: $\dfrac{2 + 3i}{3 - 2i}$

3. Check by substitution: Is $x = 1 + 2i$ a solution to $x^2 - 2x + 5 = 0$?

4. State the quadrant of each complex number, then write it in trigonometric form in degrees rounded to the nearest tenth (when necessary).
   a. $-4 + 4\sqrt{3}i$   b. $-12 - 9i$

5. Convert the following complex numbers to rectangular form.
   a. $3\sqrt{2}\,\mathrm{cis}\left(\dfrac{\pi}{4}\right)$   b. $2\sqrt{3}\,\mathrm{cis}\left(\dfrac{11\pi}{6}\right)$

6. Given $z_1 = 0 - 5i$ and $z_2 = 2 - 2\sqrt{3}i$, compute the product $z_1 z_2$ using the trigonometric form. Answer in degrees.

7. Given $z_1 = -3 + 3i$ and $z_2 = 5\sqrt{3} + 5i$, compute the quotient $\dfrac{z_1}{z_2}$ using the trigonometric form. Answer in radians.

8. Use De Moivre's theorem to find the value of $(-2 + 2i)^5$.

9. Use the $n$th roots theorem to find the five fifth roots of $-32$. Leave your answer in degree trigonometric form.

10. Use the $n$th roots theorem to find all solutions (real and complex) to $x^3 - 729 = 0$.

## REINFORCING BASIC CONCEPTS

### More on the Imaginary Unit

It would be hard to overstate the importance of the multiplicative identity "1" (the real number unit) to a study of the real numbers. Much of its utility is based on the fact that multiplication by 1 does not change the magnitude of a given quantity. After a study of complex numbers, it might seem natural to wonder if there are any similarities between the imaginary unit "$i$" and the real number unit "1." In a spirit of exploration, we begin by computing the product of $z_1 = 2 + 3i$ and the imaginary unit.

$$z_1 \cdot i = (2 + 3i)(i) \qquad \text{substitute } 2 + 3i \text{ for } z_1$$
$$= 2i + 3i^2 \qquad \text{distribute}$$
$$= 2i + 3(-1) \qquad \text{substitute } -1 \text{ for } i^2$$
$$= -3 + 2i \qquad \text{multiply and rearrange terms}$$

At first, the investigation appears to be a dead end. But a closer look reveals that multiplying $z_1$ by the imaginary unit likewise does not change its magnitude, only its orientation, due to the causal interplay between the real and imaginary parts. For $z_1 = 2 + 3i$ and $z_2 = -3 + 2i$ we have $|z_1| = \sqrt{2^2 + 3^2} = \sqrt{13}$, and $|z_2| = \sqrt{(-3)^2 + 2^2} = \sqrt{13}$. Further, from the graphs of $z_1$ and $z_2$ in the complex plane, we note that $z_2$ is a *90° counterclockwise rotation* of $z_1$. In fact, it turns out that the product of any complex number $z$ and the imaginary unit yields a 90° counterclockwise rotation of $z$, on a central circle of radius $|z|$. To see why, consider $i = 0 + 1i = 1 \operatorname{cis}(90°)$ and $z = a + bi = |z| \operatorname{cis} \theta$. From the standard method of multiplying complex numbers, if $z_1 = |z_1| \operatorname{cis} \alpha$ and $z_2 = |z_2| \operatorname{cis} \beta$, then $z_1 z_2 = |z_1 z_2| \operatorname{cis}(\alpha + \beta)$.

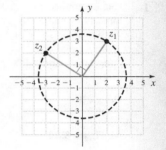

$$zi = (|z| \operatorname{cis} \theta)(1 \operatorname{cis} 90°) \qquad \text{trigonometric form}$$
$$= |z| (1) \operatorname{cis}(\theta + 90°) \qquad \text{multiply magnitudes, add arguments}$$
$$= |z| \operatorname{cis}(\theta + 90°) \qquad \text{result}$$

By combining this with the preceding result, we note the following:

1. If $|z_1| = 1$, then $|z_1 z_2| = |z_2|$.
2. If $|z_1| = 1$, then $z_1 z_2$ corresponds to a rotation of $z_2$ by $\alpha°$.

If these are true, we have an alternative method of finding the $n$th roots of a complex number, if any one of them is known. These and other ideas are explored in the following exercises.

**Exercise 1:** Based on these observations, what is the effect of multiplying any complex number $z$ by $i^2$, $i^3$, or $i^4$?

**Exercise 2:** Verify $z_1 = 2 + 3i$ is a fourth root of $z = -119 - 120i$. Recalling that the $n$th roots of a complex number are separated by $\left(\dfrac{360}{n}\right)^°$, the four fourth roots of $z$ must be 90° apart. Use the preceding observations and multiplication by $i$ to find the other three roots.

**Exercise 3:** For $z = 0 + 1i$, we noted $|z| = 1$ and $\theta = 90°$. (a) Find the magnitude and angle $\theta$ for $z = \dfrac{\sqrt{2}}{2} + \dfrac{\sqrt{2}}{2}i$, and (b) use what you find along with our previous observations to find all solutions to $z^8 = 256$, given $2i$ is a solution.

**Exercise 4:** (a) Describe the set of all complex numbers whose magnitude is 1. (b) Considering your answers to Exercises 2 and 3, find the unique complex number whose product with any complex number $z$ amounts to rotating $z$ counterclockwise 120°, and (c) use what you observe to find the remaining third roots of $-8i$, given $2i$ is a root.

## Learning Objectives

*In Section 8.4 you will learn how to:*

☐ **A.** Plot points given in polar form

☐ **B.** Express a point in polar form

☐ **C.** Convert between polar form and rectangular form

☐ **D.** Sketch basic polar graphs using an *r*-value analysis

☐ **E.** Use symmetry and families of curves to write a polar equation given a polar graph or information about the graph

One of the most enduring goals of mathematics is to express relations with the greatest possible simplicity and ease of use. For $\dfrac{\tan\theta - \cot\theta}{\tan^2\theta - \cot^2\theta} = \sin\theta\cos\theta$, we would definitely prefer working with $\sin\theta\cos\theta$, although the expressions are equivalent. Similarly, we would prefer computing $(3 + \sqrt{3}i)^6$ in trigonometric form rather than algebraic form—and would quickly find the result is $-1728$. In just this way, many equations and graphs are easier to work with in **polar form** rather than rectangular form. In rectangular form, a circle of radius 2 centered at $(0, 2)$ has the equation $x^2 + (y - 2)^2 = 4$. In polar form, the equation of the same circle is simply $r = 4\sin\theta$. As you'll see, polar coordinates offer an alternative method for plotting points and graphing relations.

## A. Plotting Points Using Polar Coordinates

Suppose a Coast Guard station receives a distress call from a stranded boat. The boater could attempt to give the location in rectangular form, but this might require imposing an arbitrary coordinate grid on an uneven shoreline, using uncertain points of reference. However, if the radio message said, "We're stranded 4 miles out, bearing 60°," the Coast Guard could immediately locate the boat and send help. In **polar coordinates,** "4 miles out, bearing 60°" would simply be written $(r, \theta) = (4, 30°)$, with $r$ representing the distance from the station and $\theta > 0$ measured from a horizontal axis in the counterclockwise direction as before (see Figure 8.20). If we placed the scenario on a rectangular grid (assuming a straight shoreline), the coordinates of the boat would be $(2\sqrt{3}, 2)$ using basic trigonometry. As you see, the **polar coordinate system** uses angles and distances to locate a point in the plane. In this example, the Coast Guard station would be considered the **pole** or origin, with the *x*-axis as the **polar axis** or axis of reference (Figure 8.21). A distinctive feature of polar coordinates is that *we allow r to be negative,* in which case $P(r, \theta)$ is the point $|r|$ units from the pole in a direction opposite (180°) to that of $\theta$ (Figure 8.22). For convenience, polar graph paper is often used when working with polar coordinates. It consists of a series of concentric circles that share the same center and have integer radii. The standard angles are marked off in multiples of $\dfrac{\pi}{12} = 15°$ depending on whether you're working in radians or degrees (Figure 8.23). To plot the point $P(r, \theta)$, go a distance of $|r|$ at 0° then move $\theta°$ counterclockwise along a circle of radius $r$. If $r > 0$, plot a point at that location (you're finished). If $r < 0$, the point is plotted on a circle of the same radius, but 180° in the opposite direction.

**Figure 8.20**

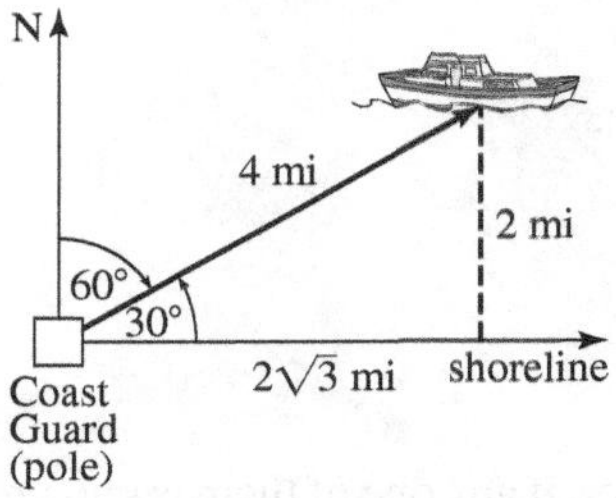

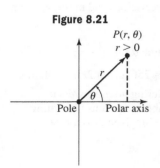

**Figure 8.21**

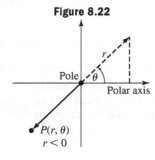

**Figure 8.22**

**Figure 8.23**

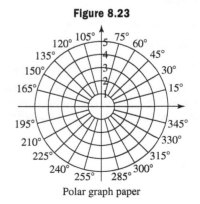

Polar graph paper

**EXAMPLE 1** ▶ **Plotting Points in Polar Coordinates**

Plot each point $P(r, \theta)$ given:

$$A(4, 45°); B(-5, 135°); C(-3, -30°); D\left(2, \frac{2\pi}{3}\right); E\left(-5, \frac{\pi}{3}\right); \text{ and } F\left(3, -\frac{\pi}{6}\right).$$

Solution ▶ For $A(4, 45°)$ go 4 units at $0°$, then rotate $45°$ counterclockwise and plot point $A$. For $B(-5, 135°)$, move $|-5| = 5$ units at $0°$, rotate $135°$, then actually plot point $B$ $180°$ in the opposite direction, as shown. Point $C(-3, -30°)$ is plotted by moving $|-3| = 3$ units at $0°$, rotating $-30°$, then plotting point $C$ $180°$ in the opposite direction (since $r < 0$). See Figure 8.24. The points $D\left(2, \frac{2\pi}{3}\right), E\left(-5, \frac{\pi}{3}\right)$, and $F\left(3, -\frac{\pi}{6}\right)$ are plotted on the grid in Figure 8.25.

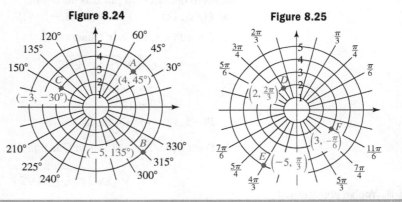

Figure 8.24                                    Figure 8.25

Now try Exercises 7 through 22 ▶

While plotting the points $B(-5, 135°)$ and $F\left(3, -\frac{\pi}{6}\right)$, you likely noticed that the coordinates of a point in polar coordinates are not unique. For $B(-5, 135°)$ it appears more natural to name the location $(5, 315°)$, while for $F\left(3, -\frac{\pi}{6}\right)$, the expression $\left(3, \frac{11\pi}{6}\right)$ is just as reasonable. In fact, for any point $P(r, \theta)$ in polar coordinates, $P(r, \theta \pm 2\pi)$ and $P(-r, \theta \pm \pi)$ name the same location. **See Exercises 23 through 36.**

☑ **A.** You've just learned how to plot points given in polar form

## B. Expressing a Point in Polar Coordinates

Conversions between rectangular and polar coordinates is a simple application of skills from previous sections, and closely resembles the conversion from the rectangular form to the trigonometric form of a complex number. To make the connection, we first assume $r > 0$ with $\theta$ in Quadrant II (see Figure 8.26). In rectangular form, the coordinates of the point are simply $(x, y)$, with the lengths of $x$ and $y$ forming the sides of a right triangle. The distance $r$ from the origin to point $P$ resembles the modulus of a complex number and is computed in the same way: $r = \sqrt{x^2 + y^2}$. As long as $x \neq 0$, we have $\theta_r = \tan^{-1}\left|\frac{y}{x}\right|$, noting $\theta_r$ is a reference

Figure 8.26

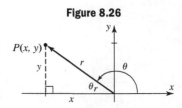

angle if the terminal side is not in Quadrant I. If needed, refer to Section 3.4 for a review of reference arcs and reference angles.

### Converting from Rectangular to Polar Coordinates

Any point $P(x, y)$ in rectangular coordinates can be represented as $P(r, \theta)$ in polar coordinates, where $r = \sqrt{x^2 + y^2}$ and $\theta_r = \tan^{-1}\left|\dfrac{y}{x}\right|$, $x \neq 0$.

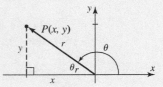

---

**EXAMPLE 2** ▶ **Converting a Point from Rectangular Form to Polar Form**

Convert from rectangular to polar form, with $r > 0$ and $0° \leq \theta < 360°$ (round values to one decimal place as needed).

**a.** $P(-5, 12)$          **b.** $P(3\sqrt{2}, -3\sqrt{2})$

Solution ▶ **a.** Point $P(-5, 12)$ is in Quadrant II.

$$r = \sqrt{(-5)^2 + 12^2} \qquad \theta_r = \tan^{-1}\left(\frac{12}{5}\right)$$
$$= \sqrt{169} \qquad\qquad \theta_r \approx 67.4°$$
$$= 13 \qquad\qquad\quad \theta \approx 112.6°$$
$$P(-5, 12) \rightarrow P(13, 112.6°)$$

**b.** Point $P(3\sqrt{2}, -3\sqrt{2})$ is in Quadrant IV.

$$r = \sqrt{(3\sqrt{2})^2 + (-3\sqrt{2})^2} \qquad \theta_r = \tan^{-1}\left(\frac{3\sqrt{2}}{3\sqrt{2}}\right)$$
$$= \sqrt{36} \qquad\qquad\qquad \theta_r = 45°$$
$$= 6 \qquad\qquad\qquad\quad \theta = 315°$$
$$P(3\sqrt{2}, -3\sqrt{2}) \rightarrow P(6, 315°)$$

☑ **B.** You've just learned how to express a point in polar form

Now try Exercises 37 through 44 ▶

## C. Converting Between Polar Coordinates and Rectangular Coordinates

The conversion from polar form to rectangular form is likewise straightforward. From Figure 8.27 we again note $\cos \theta = \dfrac{x}{r}$ and $\sin \theta = \dfrac{y}{r}$, giving $x = r\cos \theta$ and $y = r \sin \theta$. The conversion simply consists of making these substitutions and simplifying.

**Figure 8.27**

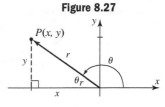

### Converting from Polar to Rectangular Coordinates

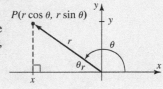

Any point $P(r, \theta)$ in polar coordinates can be represented as $P(x, y)$ in rectangular coordinates, where $x = r \cos \theta$ and $y = r \sin \theta$.

**EXAMPLE 3** ▶ **Converting a Point from Polar Form to Rectangular Form**

Convert from polar to rectangular form (round values to one decimal place as needed).

**a.** $P\left(12, \dfrac{5\pi}{3}\right)$       **b.** $P(6, 240°)$

**Solution** ▶ **a.** Point $P\left(12, \dfrac{5\pi}{3}\right)$ is in Quadrant IV.

$$x = r\cos\theta \qquad\qquad y = r\sin\theta$$
$$= 12\cos\left(\frac{5\pi}{3}\right) \qquad = 12\sin\left(\frac{5\pi}{3}\right)$$
$$= 12\left(\frac{1}{2}\right) \qquad\qquad = 12\left(\frac{-\sqrt{3}}{2}\right)$$
$$= 6 \qquad\qquad\qquad = -6\sqrt{3}$$

$$P\left(12, \frac{5\pi}{3}\right) \rightarrow P(6, -6\sqrt{3}) \approx P(6, -10.4)$$

**b.** Point $P(6, 240°)$ is in Quadrant III.

$$x = 6\cos 240° \qquad\qquad y = 6\sin 240°$$
$$= 6\left(-\frac{1}{2}\right) \qquad\qquad = 6\left(\frac{-\sqrt{3}}{2}\right)$$
$$= -3 \qquad\qquad\qquad = -3\sqrt{3}$$

$$P(6, 240°) \rightarrow P(-3, -3\sqrt{3}) \approx P(-3, -5.2)$$

**Now try Exercises 45 through 52** ▶

Using the relationships $x = r\cos\theta$ and $y = r\sin\theta$, we can convert an equation given in rectangular form, to an equivalent equation in polar form.

**EXAMPLE 4** ▶ **Converting an Equation from Rectangular Form to Polar Form**

Convert the following equations to polar form.

**a.** $x^2 + y^2 = 16$       **b.** $y = \dfrac{1}{x}$

**Solution** ▶ **a.** The graph of this equation is a circle of radius 4 centered at the origin.

$$x^2 + y^2 = 16 \quad \text{given equation}$$
$$(r\cos\theta)^2 + (r\sin\theta)^2 = 16 \quad \text{substitute } r\cos\theta \text{ for } x \text{ and } r\sin\theta \text{ for } y$$
$$r^2\cos^2\theta + r^2\sin^2\theta = 16 \quad \text{expand squares}$$
$$r^2(\cos^2\theta + \sin^2\theta) = 16 \quad \text{factor out } r^2 \text{ on the left}$$
$$r^2(1) = 16 \quad \text{Pythagorean identity, } \cos^2\theta + \sin^2\theta = 1$$
$$r^2 = 16 \quad \text{simplify}$$
$$r = 4 \quad \text{square root of both sides}$$

In polar form, the equation of this circle is expressed simply as $r = 4$.

**b.** For this rational function, we proceed as before, simplifying with algebra and trigonometric identities.

$$y = \frac{1}{x} \qquad \text{given equation}$$

$$r \sin \theta = \frac{1}{r \cos \theta} \qquad \text{substitute } r \cos \theta \text{ for } x \text{ and } r \sin \theta \text{ for } y$$

$$(r \sin \theta)(r \cos \theta) = 1 \qquad \text{multiply both sides by } r \cos \theta$$

$$r^2 \sin \theta \cos \theta = 1 \qquad \text{reorder terms}$$

$$2r^2 \sin \theta \cos \theta = 2 \qquad \text{multiply both sides by 2}$$

$$r^2 \sin 2\theta = 2 \qquad \text{double angle identity: } 2 \sin \theta \cos \theta = \sin 2\theta$$

**WORTHY OF NOTE**

Note in Part b of Example 4, the equation was actually simpler in rectangular coordinates.

Multiplying both sides by 2 enabled us to use a double-angle identity and express the rational function in polar form as $r^2 \sin 2\theta = 2$. Note the similarity to rectangular coordinates, where there are many different forms in which an equation may be written.

> **Now try Exercises 53 through 60 ▶**

Converting an equation given in polar form to rectangular form relies primarily on the relationships $x = r \cos \theta$, $y = r \sin \theta$, $\tan \theta = \dfrac{y}{x}$, and $x^2 + y^2 = r^2$. With experience, you will become familiar with various "tricks of the trade," which include

1. Multiplying both sides of an equation by $r$ to yield terms of $r \cos \theta$ or $r \sin \theta$.
2. Taking the tangent of both sides.
3. Squaring both sides of an equation to yield $r^2$.

---

**EXAMPLE 5 ▶**   **Converting an Equation from Polar Form to Rectangular Form**
Convert the following equations to rectangular form.

**a.** $\theta = \dfrac{\pi}{4}$     **b.** $r = 4 \sin \theta$

**Solution ▶**   **a.** With $\theta$ isolated on the left side, we must introduce a trig function.

$$\theta = \frac{\pi}{4} \qquad \text{given equation}$$

$$\tan \theta = \tan \frac{\pi}{4} \qquad \text{take tangent of both sides}$$

$$\frac{y}{x} = 1 \qquad \text{substitute } \frac{y}{x} \text{ for } \tan \theta; \tan \frac{\pi}{4} = 1$$

$$y = x \qquad \text{multiply both sides by } x$$

In rectangular form, we recognize the equation $y = x$ as a line with slope 1 passing through the origin.

**b.** Hoping to use the relationship $y = r \sin \theta$, we proceed as follows:

$$r = 4 \sin \theta \qquad \text{given equation}$$

$$r^2 = 4r \sin \theta \qquad \text{multiply both sides by } r$$

$$x^2 + y^2 = 4y \qquad \text{substitute } x^2 + y^2 \text{ for } r^2 \text{ and } y \text{ for } r \sin \theta$$

Using algebra, we can write the equation $x^2 + y^2 = 4y$ as $x^2 + (y - 2)^2 = 4$, which is the standard form of a circle with center (0, 2) and radius 2.

> **Now try Exercises 61 through 68 ▶**

**☑ C. You've just learned how to convert between polar form and rectangular form**

While squaring both sides of the equation in Example 5(b) would also have yielded $r^2$ on the left, the right would have become $16 \sin^2\theta$, which does not easily convert to rectangular form. Often, you will need to try various approaches before finding one that works.

### D. Basic Polar Graphs and *r*-Value Analysis

To really understand polar graphs, an intuitive sense of how they're developed is needed. Polar equations are generally stated in terms of $r$ and trigonometric functions of $\theta$, with $\theta$ being the input value and $r$ being the output value. First, it helps to view the length $r$ as the long second hand of a clock, but extending an equal distance in both directions from center (Figure 8.28). This "second hand" ticks around the face of the clock in the counterclockwise direction, with the angular measure of each tick being $\dfrac{\pi}{12}$ radians $= 15°$. As each angle "ticks by," we locate a point somewhere along the radius, depending on whether $r$ is positive or negative, and plot it on the face of the clock before going on to the next tick. For the purposes of this study, we will allow that all polar graphs are continuous and smooth curves, without presenting a formal proof.

**Figure 8.28**

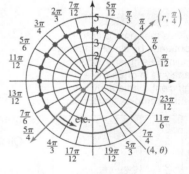

---

**EXAMPLE 6 ▶**    **Graphing Basic Polar Equations**

Graph the polar equations.

    **a.** $r = 4$        **b.** $\theta = \dfrac{\pi}{4}$

**Solution ▶**    **a.** For $r = 4$, we're plotting all points of the form $(4, \theta)$ where $r$ has a constant value and $\theta$ varies. As the second hand "ticks around the polar grid," we plot all points a distance of 4 units from the pole. As you might imagine, the graph is a circle with radius 4. See Example 4(a).

       **b.** For $\theta = \dfrac{\pi}{4}$, all points have the form $\left(r, \dfrac{\pi}{4}\right)$ with $\dfrac{\pi}{4}$ constant and $r$ varying. In this case, the "second hand" is frozen at $\dfrac{\pi}{4}$, and we plot any selection of $r$-values, producing the straight line shown in the figure. See Example 5(a).

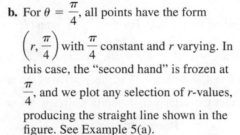

**Now try Exercises 69 through 72 ▶**

---

To develop an "intuitive sense" that allows for the efficient graphing of more sophisticated equations, we use a technique called **r-value analysis.** This technique basically takes advantage of the predictable patterns in $r = \sin\theta$ and $r = \cos\theta$ taken from their graphs, including the zeros and maximum/minimum values.

We begin with the $r$-value analysis for $r = \sin\theta$, using the graph shown in Figure 8.29. Note the analysis occurs in the four colored parts corresponding to Quadrants I, II, III, and IV, and that the maximum value of $|\sin\theta| = 1$.

**Figure 8.29**

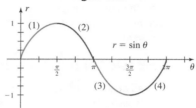

1. As $\theta$ moves from 0 to $\dfrac{\pi}{2}$, $\sin \theta$ is positive and $|\sin \theta|$ increases from 0 to 1.

   $\Rightarrow$ for $r = \sin \theta$, $r$ is increasing

2. As $\theta$ moves from $\dfrac{\pi}{2}$ to $\pi$, $\sin \theta$ is positive and $|\sin \theta|$ decreases from 1 to 0.

   $\Rightarrow$ for $r = \sin \theta$, $r$ is decreasing

3. As $\theta$ moves from $\pi$ to $\dfrac{3\pi}{2}$, $\sin \theta$ is negative and $|\sin \theta|$ increases from 0 to 1.

   $\Rightarrow$ for $r = \sin \theta$, $r$ is increasing

4. As $\theta$ moves from $\dfrac{3\pi}{2}$ to $2\pi$, $\sin \theta$ is negative and $|\sin \theta|$ decreases from 1 to 0.

   $\Rightarrow$ for $r = \sin \theta$, $r$ is decreasing

In summary, note that the value of $|r|$ goes through four cycles, two where it is increasing from 0 to 1 (in red), and two where it is decreasing from 1 to 0 (in blue).

**WORTHY OF NOTE**

It is important to remember that if $r < 0$, the related point on the graph is $|r|$ units from center, 180° *in the opposite direction:* $(-r, \theta) \rightarrow (r, \theta + 180°)$. In addition, students are encouraged not to use a table of values, a conversion to rectangular coordinates, or a graphing calculator until after the *r*-value analysis.

---

**EXAMPLE 7 ▶   Graphing Polar Equations Using an *r*-Value Analysis**

Sketch the graph of $r = 4 \sin \theta$ using an *r*-value analysis.

**Solution ▶**   Begin by noting that $r = 0$ at $\theta = 0$, and will increase from 0 to 4 as the clock "ticks" from 0 to $\dfrac{\pi}{2}$, since $\sin \theta$ is increasing from 0 to 1. (1) For $\theta = \dfrac{\pi}{6}, \dfrac{\pi}{4}$, and $\dfrac{\pi}{3}$, $r = 2$, $r \approx 2.8$, and $r \approx 3.5$, respectively (at $\theta = \dfrac{\pi}{2}$, $r = 4$). See Figure 8.30.

(2) As $\theta$ continues "ticking" from $\dfrac{\pi}{2}$ to $\pi$, $|r|$ decreases from 4 to 0, since $\sin \theta$ is decreasing from 1 to 0. For $\theta = \dfrac{2\pi}{3}, \dfrac{3\pi}{4}$, and $\dfrac{5\pi}{6}$, $r \approx 3.5$, $r \approx 2.8$, and $r = 2$, respectively (at $\theta = \pi$, $r = 0$). See Figure 8.31. (3) From $\pi$ to $\dfrac{3\pi}{2}$, $|r|$ increases from 0 to 4, but since $r < 0$, this portion of the graph is reflected back into Quadrant I, overlapping the portion already drawn from 0 to $\dfrac{\pi}{2}$.

**WORTHY OF NOTE**

While the same graph is obtained by simply plotting points, using an *r*-value analysis is often more efficient, particularly with more complex equations.

| $\theta$ | $r = 4 \sin \theta$ |
|---|---|
| 0 | 0 |
| $\dfrac{\pi}{6}$ | 2 |
| $\dfrac{\pi}{4}$ | $2\sqrt{2} \approx 2.8$ |
| $\dfrac{\pi}{3}$ | $2\sqrt{3} \approx 3.5$ |
| $\dfrac{\pi}{2}$ | 4 |
| $\dfrac{2\pi}{3}$ | $2\sqrt{3} \approx 3.5$ |
| $\dfrac{3\pi}{4}$ | $2\sqrt{2} \approx 2.8$ |
| $\dfrac{5\pi}{6}$ | 2 |
| $\pi$ | 0 |

**Figure 8.30**

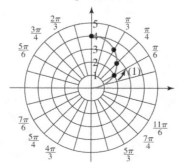

**Figure 8.31**

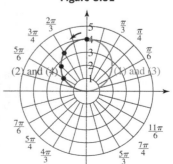

(4) From $\frac{3\pi}{2}$ to $2\pi$, $|r|$ decreases from 4 to 0, overlapping the portion drawn from $\frac{\pi}{2}$ to $\pi$. We conclude the graph is a closed figure limited to Quadrants I and II as shown in Figure 8.31. This is a circle with radius 2, centered at (0, 2) [see Example 5(b)]. In summary:

$$r = 4\sin\theta$$

| $\theta$ | 0 to $\frac{\pi}{2}$ | $\frac{\pi}{2}$ to $\pi$ | $\pi$ to $\frac{3\pi}{2}$ | $\frac{3\pi}{2}$ to $2\pi$ |
|---|---|---|---|---|
| $|r|$ | 0 to 4 | 4 to 0 | 0 to 4 | 4 to 0 |

**Now try Exercises 73 and 74** ▶

Although it takes some effort, $r$-value analysis offers an efficient way to graph polar equations, and gives a better understanding of graphing in polar coordinates. In addition, it often enables you to sketch the graph with a minimum number of calculations and plotted points. As you continue using the technique, it will help to have Figure 8.29 in plain view for quick reference, as well as the corresponding analysis of $y = \cos\theta$ for polar graphs involving cosine (**see Exercise 114**).

**EXAMPLE 8** ▶ **Graphing Polar Equations Using an *r*-Value Analysis**

Sketch the graph of $r = 2 + 2\sin\theta$ using an $r$-value analysis.

**Solution** ▶ Since the minimum value of $\sin\theta$ is $-1$, we note that $r$ will always be greater than or equal to zero. At $\theta = 0$, $r$ has a value of 2 ($\sin 0 = 0$), and will increase from 2 to 4 as the clock "ticks" from 0 to $\frac{\pi}{2}$ ($\sin\theta$ is positive and $|\sin\theta|$ is increasing).

From $\frac{\pi}{2}$ to $\pi$, $r$ decreases from 4 to 2 ($\sin\theta$ is positive and $|\sin\theta|$ is decreasing).

From $\pi$ to $\frac{3\pi}{2}$, $r$ decreases from 2 to 0 ($\sin\theta$ is negative and $|\sin\theta|$ is increasing);

and from $\frac{3\pi}{2}$ to $2\pi$, $r$ increases from 0 to 2 ($\sin\theta$ is negative and $|\sin\theta|$ is decreasing). We conclude the graph is a closed figure containing the points (2, 0), $\left(4, \frac{\pi}{2}\right)$, (2, $\pi$), and $\left(0, \frac{3\pi}{2}\right)$. Noting that $\theta = \frac{\pi}{6}$ and $\theta = \frac{5\pi}{6}$ will produce integer values, we evaluate $r = 2 + 2\sin\theta$ and obtain the additional points $\left(3, \frac{\pi}{6}\right)$ and $\left(3, \frac{5\pi}{6}\right)$. Using these points and the $r$-value analysis produces the graph shown here, called a **cardioid** (from the limaçon family of curves). In summary we have:

| $\theta$ | $r = 2 + 2\sin\theta$ |
|---|---|
| (1) 0 to $\frac{\pi}{2}$ | 2 to 4 |
| (2) $\frac{\pi}{2}$ to $\pi$ | 4 to 2 |
| (3) $\pi$ to $\frac{3\pi}{2}$ | 2 to 0 |
| (4) $\frac{3\pi}{2}$ to $2\pi$ | 0 to 2 |

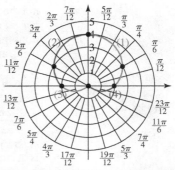

☑ **D.** You've just learned how to sketch basic polar graphs using an $r$-value analysis

**Now try Exercises 75 through 78** ▶

### E. Symmetry and Families of Polar Graphs

Even with a careful *r*-value analysis, some polar graphs require a good deal of effort to produce. In many cases, symmetry can be a big help, as can recognizing certain families of equations and their related graphs. As with other forms of graphing, gathering this information beforehand will enable you to graph relations with a smaller number of plotted points. Figures 8.32 to 8.35 offer some examples of symmetry for polar graphs.

**Figure 8.32**
Vertical-axis symmetry:
$r = -2 - 2\sin\theta$

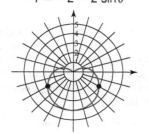

**Figure 8.33**
Polar-axis symmetry:
$r = 5\cos\theta$

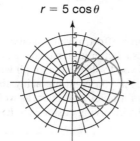

**Figure 8.34**
Polar symmetry:
$r = 5\sin(2\theta)$

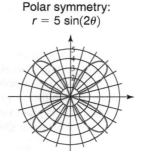

**Figure 8.35**
Polar symmetry:
$r^2 = 25\cos(2\theta)$

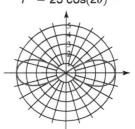

**WORTHY OF NOTE**

In mathematics we refer to the tests for polar symmetry as *sufficient but not necessary conditions*. The tests are *sufficient* to show symmetry (if the test is satisfied, the graph must be symmetric), but the tests are *not necessary* to show symmetry (the graph may be symmetric even if the test is not satisfied).

The tests for symmetry in polar coordinates bear a strong resemblance to those for rectangular coordinates, but there is a major difference. Since there are many different ways to name a point in polar coordinates, a polar graph may actually exhibit a form of symmetry without satisfying the related test. In other words, the tests are *sufficient* to establish symmetry, but not *necessary*.

The formal tests for symmetry are explored in **Exercises 116 to 118.** For our purposes, we'll rely on a somewhat narrower view, one that is actually a synthesis of our observations here and our previous experience with the sine and cosine.

**Symmetry for Graphs of Certain Polar Equations**

Given the polar equation $r = f(\theta)$,
1. If $f(\theta)$ represents an expression in terms of sine(s), the graph will be symmetric to $\theta = \dfrac{\pi}{2}$: $(r, \theta)$ and $(r, \pi - \theta)$ are on the graph.

2. If $f(\theta)$ represents an expression in terms of cosine(s), the graph will be symmetric to $\theta = 0$: $(r, \theta)$ and $(r, -\theta)$ are on the graph.

While the fundamental ideas from Examples 7 and 8 go a long way toward graphing other polar equations, our discussion would not be complete without a review of the *period* of sine and cosine. Many polar equations have factors of $\sin(n\theta)$ or $\cos(n\theta)$ in them, and it helps to recall the period formula $P = \dfrac{2\pi}{n}$. Comparing $r = 4\sin\theta$ from

**Figure 8.36**

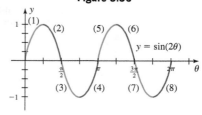

Example 7 with $r = 4\sin(2\theta)$, we note the period of sine changes from $P = 2\pi$ to $P = \dfrac{2\pi}{2} = \pi$, *meaning there will be twice as many cycles* and $|r|$ will now go through *eight* cycles—four where $|\sin(2\theta)|$ is increasing from 0 to 1 (in red), and four where it is decreasing from 1 to 0 (in blue). See Figure 8.36.

**EXAMPLE 9** ▶ **Sketching Polar Graphs Using Symmetry and *r*-Values**

Sketch the graph of $r = 4 \sin(2\theta)$ using symmetry and an *r*-value analysis.

Solution ▶ Since *r* is expressed in terms of sine, the graph will be symmetric to $\theta = \dfrac{\pi}{2}$. We note that $r = 0$ at $\theta = \dfrac{n\pi}{2}$, where *n* is any integer, and the graph will go through the pole at these points. This also tells us the graph will be a closed figure. From the graph of $\sin(2\theta)$ in Figure 8.36, we see $|\sin(2\theta)| = 1$ at $\theta = \dfrac{\pi}{4}, \dfrac{3\pi}{4}, \dfrac{5\pi}{4}$, and $\dfrac{7\pi}{4}$, so the graph will include the points $\left(4, \dfrac{\pi}{4}\right), \left(-4, \dfrac{3\pi}{4}\right), \left(4, \dfrac{5\pi}{4}\right)$, and $\left(-4, \dfrac{7\pi}{4}\right)$. Only the analysis of the first four cycles is given next, since the remainder of the graph can be drawn using symmetry.

| | Cycle | *r*-Value Analysis | Location of Graph |
|---|---|---|---|
| (1) | 0 to $\dfrac{\pi}{4}$ | $|r|$ increases from 0 to 4 | QI ($r > 0$) |
| (2) | $\dfrac{\pi}{4}$ to $\dfrac{\pi}{2}$ | $|r|$ decreases from 4 to 0 | QI ($r > 0$) |
| (3) | $\dfrac{\pi}{2}$ to $\dfrac{3\pi}{4}$ | $|r|$ increases from 0 to 4 | QIV ($r < 0$) |
| (4) | $\dfrac{3\pi}{4}$ to $\pi$ | $|r|$ decreases from 4 to 0 | QIV ($r < 0$) |

**Table 8.1**

| $\theta$ | $r = 4 \sin(2\theta)$ |
|---|---|
| 0 | 0 |
| $\dfrac{\pi}{6}$ | $2\sqrt{3} \approx 3.5$ |
| $\dfrac{\pi}{4}$ | 4 |
| $\dfrac{\pi}{3}$ | $2\sqrt{3} \approx 3.5$ |
| $\dfrac{\pi}{2}$ | 0 |
| $\dfrac{2\pi}{3}$ | $-2\sqrt{3} \approx -3.5$ |
| $\dfrac{3\pi}{4}$ | $-4$ |
| $\dfrac{5\pi}{6}$ | $-2\sqrt{3} \approx -3.5$ |
| $\pi$ | 0 |

Plotting the points and applying the *r*-value analysis with the symmetry involved produces the graph in the figure, called a **four-leaf rose**. At any time during this process, additional points such as those shown in Table 8.1 can be calculated to "round-out" the graph.

$r = 4 \sin(2\theta)$

| $\theta$ | $|r|$ |
|---|---|
| 0 to $\dfrac{\pi}{4}$ | 0 to 4 |
| $\dfrac{\pi}{4}$ to $\dfrac{\pi}{2}$ | 4 to 0 |
| $\dfrac{\pi}{2}$ to $\dfrac{3\pi}{4}$ | 0 to 4 |
| $\dfrac{3\pi}{4}$ to $\pi$ | 4 to 0 |

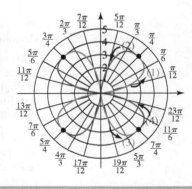

Now try Exercises 79 through 86 ▶

**Graphing Polar Equations**

To assist the process of graphing polar equations:
1. Carefully note any symmetries you can use.
2. Have graphs of $y = \sin(n\theta)$ and $y = \cos(n\theta)$ in view for quick reference.
3. Use these graphs to analyze the value of *r* as the "clock ticks" around the polar grid: (a) determine the max/min *r*-values and write them in polar form, and (b) determine the polar-axis intercepts and write them in polar form.
4. Plot the points, then use the *r*-value analysis and any symmetries to complete the graph.

Similar to polynomial graphs, polar graphs come in numerous shapes and varieties, yet many of them share common characteristics and can be organized into certain families. Some of the more common families are illustrated in Appendix VII, and give the general equation and related graph for common family members. Also included are characteristics of certain graphs that will enable you to develop the polar equation given its graph or information about its graph. For further investigations using a graphing calculator, **see Exercises 87 through 92.**

**EXAMPLE 10** ▶ **Graphing a Limaçon Using Stated Conditions**

Find the equation of the polar curve satisfying the given conditions, then sketch the graph: limaçon, symmetric to $\theta = 90°$, with $a = 2$ and $b = -3$.

Solution ▶ The general equation of a limaçon symmetric to $\theta = 90°$ is $r = a + b \sin \theta$, so our desired equation is $r = 2 - 3 \sin \theta$. Since $|a| < |b|$, the limaçon has an inner loop of length $3 - 2 = 1$ and a maximum distance from the origin of $2 + 3 = 5$. The polar-axis intercepts are $(2, 0°)$ and $(2, 180°)$. With $b < 0$, the graph is reflected across the polar axis (facing "downward"). The complete graph is shown in the figure.

| $\theta$ | $r = 2 - 3 \sin \theta$ |
|---|---|
| 0° | 2 |
| 45° | $\approx -0.1$ |
| 90° | $-1$ |
| 135° | $\approx -0.1$ |
| 180° | 2 |
| 225° | $\approx 4.1$ |
| 270° | 5 |
| 315° | $\approx 4.1$ |
| 360° | 2 |

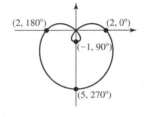

Now try Exercises 95 through 110 ▶

**EXAMPLE 11** ▶ **Modeling the Flight Path of a Scavenger Bird**

Scavenger birds sometimes fly over dead or dying animals (called carrion) in a "figure-eight" formation, closely resembling the graph of a lemniscate. Suppose the flight path of one of these birds was plotted and found to contain the polar coordinates $(81, 0°)$ and $(0, 45°)$. Find the equation of the lemniscate. If the bird lands at the point $(r, 136°)$, how far is it from the carrion? Assume $r$ is in yards.

Solution ▶ Since $(81, 0°)$ is a point on the graph, the lemniscate is symmetric to the polar axis and the general equation is $r^2 = a^2 \cos(2\theta)$. The point $(81, 0°)$ indicates $a = 81$, hence the equation is $r^2 = 6561 \cos(2\theta)$. At $\theta = 136°$ we have $r^2 = 6561 \cos 272°$, and the bird has landed $r \approx 15$ yd away.

| $\theta$ | $r = \sqrt{6561 \cos(2\theta)}$ |
|---|---|
| 0° | 81 |
| 30° | $\approx 57.3$ |
| 60° | error |
| 90° | error |
| 120° | error |
| 150° | $\approx 57.3$ |
| 180° | 81 |

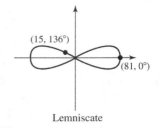

Lemniscate

Now try Exercises 111 through 113 ▶

You've likely been wondering how the different families of polar graphs were named. The roses are easy to figure as each graph has a flower-like appearance. The limaçon (pronounced li-ma-sawn) family takes its name from the Latin words *limax* or *lamacis,* meaning "snail." With some imagination, these graphs do have the appearance of a snail shell. The cardioids are a subset of the limaçon family and are so named due to their obvious resemblance to the human heart. In fact, the name stems from the Greek *kardia* meaning heart, and many derivative words are still in common use (a cardiologist is one who specializes in a study of the heart). Finally, there is the lemniscate family, a name derived from the Latin *lemniscus,* which describes a certain kind of ribbon. Once again, a little creativity enables us to make the connection between ribbons, bows, and the shape of this graph.

☑ **E.** You've just learned how to use symmetry and families of curves to write a polar equation given a polar graph or information about the graph

## TECHNOLOGY HIGHLIGHT

### Polar and Rectangular Coordinates (and Symmetry) on a Graphing Calculator

Most graphing calculators are programmed to evaluate and graph four kinds of relations—functions, sequences, polar equations, and parametric equations. This is the reason the "default" variable key X,T,θ,n is embossed with four different input variables. The X is used for functions, T for parametric equations, $\theta$ for polar equations, and $n$ for relations defined by a sequence. To change the operating mode of the calculator, press the MODE key, highlight the desired operating mode, and press ENTER (Figure 8.37). In this case, our main interest is polar equations. Note the Y= screen obtained while in **Pol** (polar mode) is similar to that obtained in **Func** (function mode), except the dependent variable is now $r_i$ instead of $\mathbf{Y}_i$ (Figure 8.38). In addition, a $\theta$ now appears when the variable key X,T,θ,n is pressed, rather than an X as when in function mode. Verify by entering the equation from Example 7, $r_1 = 4 \sin \theta$, as shown. Since polar graphs are by nature different from polynomial graphs, the WINDOW screen also takes on a different appearance (Figure 8.39). We can still set a desired window size or use the ZOOM options as before, and we can also state the desired interval for $\theta$, and indicate the interval between plotted points using $\theta$ step. The standard settings ( ZOOM 6) are shown in Figure 8.39. Knowing that the graph of $r_1$ is a circle of radius 4 centered at (0, 2), we set the window appropriately to obtain the GRAPH shown in Figure 8.40.

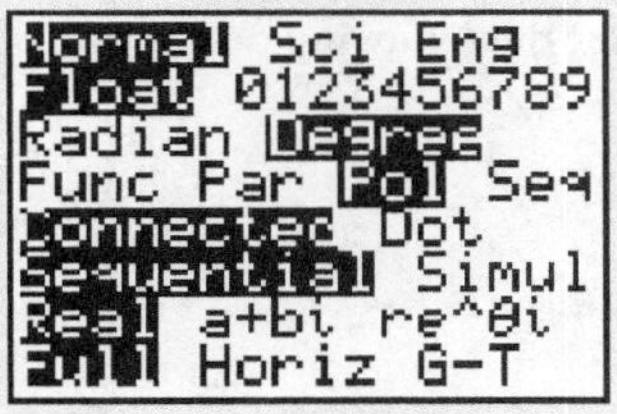

Figure 8.37

Normal Sci Eng
Float 0123456789
Radian Degree
Func Par Pol Seq
Connected Dot
Sequential Simul
Real a+bi re^θi
Full Horiz G-T

Figure 8.38

Plot1 Plot2 Plot3
\r1=4sin(θ)
\r2=
\r3=
\r4=
\r5=
\r6=

Figure 8.39

WINDOW
θmin=0
θmax=360
θstep=7.5
Xmin=-10
Xmax=10
Xscl=1
↓Ymin=-10

Figure 8.40

4.5
1
−4.7
4.7
θ=45
X=2
Y=2
−1.5

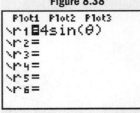

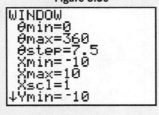

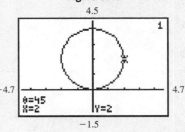

**Exercise 1:** Graph $r_1 = 4 \sin \theta$ three more times, using $\theta$step = 15, $\theta$step = 45, and $\theta$step = 60. What do you notice?

**Exercise 2:** Graph $r_1 = 2 + 4 \cos\left(\frac{\theta}{2}\right)$ on the standard screen ( ZOOM 6). It appears that only one-half of the graph is drawn. Can you determine why? Graph this equation three more times using $\theta$max = 540, $\theta$max = 630, and $\theta$max = 720. What do you notice?

**Exercise 3:** Graph $r_1 = 4 \sin(n\theta)$ for $n$ = 3, 4, 5, and 6. What pattern do you see? Verify using $r_1 = 4 \cos(n\theta)$.

## 8.4 EXERCISES

▶ CONCEPTS AND VOCABULARY

**Fill in each blank with the appropriate word or phrase. Carefully reread the section if needed.**

1. The point $(r, \theta)$ is said to be written in _____ coordinates.

2. In polar coordinates, the origin is called the _____ and the horizontal axis is called the _____ axis.

3. The point $(4, 135°)$ is located in Q _____, while $(-4, 135°)$ is located in Q _____.

4. If a polar equation is given in terms of cosine, the graph will be symmetric to _____.

5. Write out the procedure for plotting points in polar coordinates, as though you were explaining the process to a friend.

6. Discuss the graph of $r = 6 \cos \theta$ in terms of an $r$-value analysis, using $y = \cos \theta$ and a color-coded graph.

▶ DEVELOPING YOUR SKILLS

**Plot the following points using polar graph paper.**

7. $\left(4, \dfrac{\pi}{2}\right)$    8. $\left(3, \dfrac{3\pi}{2}\right)$    9. $\left(2, \dfrac{5\pi}{4}\right)$

10. $\left(4.5, -\dfrac{\pi}{3}\right)$    11. $\left(-5, \dfrac{5\pi}{6}\right)$    12. $\left(-4, \dfrac{7\pi}{4}\right)$

13. $\left(-3, -\dfrac{2\pi}{3}\right)$    14. $\left(-4, -\dfrac{\pi}{4}\right)$

**Express the points shown using polar coordinates with $\theta$ in radians, $0 \le \theta < 2\pi$ and $r > 0$.**

15.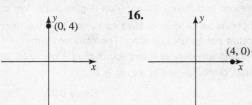

16.

17.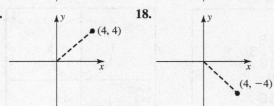

18.

19.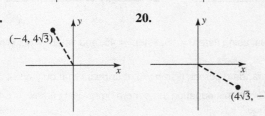

20.

21.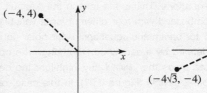

22.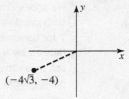

**List three alternative ways the given points can be expressed in polar coordinates using $r > 0, r < 0$, and $\theta \in [-2\pi, 2\pi)$.**

23. $\left(3\sqrt{2}, \dfrac{3\pi}{4}\right)$    24. $\left(4\sqrt{3}, -\dfrac{5\pi}{3}\right)$

25. $\left(-2, \dfrac{11\pi}{6}\right)$    26. $\left(-3, -\dfrac{7\pi}{6}\right)$

**Match each $(r, \theta)$ given to one of the points $A, B, C,$ or $D$ shown.**

**Exercise 27–36**

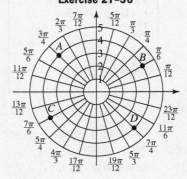

27. $\left(4, -\dfrac{5\pi}{6}\right)$    28. $\left(4, -\dfrac{5\pi}{4}\right)$

**29.** $\left(-4, \dfrac{\pi}{6}\right)$       **30.** $\left(-4, \dfrac{3\pi}{4}\right)$

**31.** $\left(-4, -\dfrac{5\pi}{4}\right)$       **32.** $\left(-4, -\dfrac{\pi}{4}\right)$

**33.** $\left(4, \dfrac{13\pi}{6}\right)$       **34.** $\left(4, \dfrac{19\pi}{6}\right)$

**35.** $\left(-4, -\dfrac{21\pi}{4}\right)$       **36.** $\left(4, -\dfrac{35\pi}{6}\right)$

**Convert from rectangular coordinates to polar coordinates. A diagram may help.**

**37.** $(-8, 0)$       **38.** $(0, -7)$

**39.** $(4, 4)$       **40.** $(4\sqrt{3}, 4)$

**41.** $(5\sqrt{2}, 5\sqrt{2})$       **42.** $(6, -6\sqrt{3})$

**43.** $(-5, -12)$       **44.** $(-3.5, 12)$

**Convert from polar coordinates to rectangular coordinates. A diagram may help.**

**45.** $(8, 45°)$       **46.** $(6, 60°)$

**47.** $\left(4, \dfrac{3\pi}{4}\right)$       **48.** $\left(5, \dfrac{5\pi}{6}\right)$

**49.** $\left(-2, \dfrac{7\pi}{6}\right)$       **50.** $\left(-10, \dfrac{4\pi}{3}\right)$

**51.** $(-5, -135°)$       **52.** $(-4, -30°)$

**Convert the following equations to polar form.**

**53.** $x^2 = 25 - y^2$       **54.** $y = \sqrt{3}x$

**55.** $x = \dfrac{3}{y}$       **56.** $6xy = 1$

**57.** $y = 3x^2 + x$       **58.** $y^2 = 5x$

**59.** $x^2 - y^2 = x^4 + 2x^2y^2 + y^4$

**60.** $x^2 - y^2 = 2xy$

**Convert the following equations to rectangular form.**

**61.** $r = 6 \cos \theta$       **62.** $r = 2 \sin \theta$

**63.** $r = 2 \sec \theta$       **64.** $r = -3 \csc \theta$

**65.** $r = \sqrt{r \cos \theta - 1}$       **66.** $r \sin \theta = r\sqrt{\cos 2\theta}$

**67.** $r = \dfrac{1}{1 + \sin \theta}$       **68.** $r = \dfrac{6}{2 + 4 \sin \theta}$

**Sketch each polar graph using an $r$-value analysis (a table may help), symmetry, and any convenient points.**

**69.** $r = 5$       **70.** $r = 6$

**71.** $\theta = \dfrac{\pi}{6}$       **72.** $\theta = -\dfrac{3\pi}{4}$

**73.** $r = 4 \cos \theta$       **74.** $r = 2 \sin \theta$

**75.** $r = 3 + 3 \sin \theta$       **76.** $r = 2 + 2 \cos \theta$

**77.** $r = 2 - 4 \sin \theta$       **78.** $r = 1 - 2 \cos \theta$

**79.** $r = 5 \cos(2\theta)$       **80.** $r = 3 \sin(4\theta)$

**81.** $r = 4 \sin 2\theta$       **82.** $r = 6 \cos(5\theta)$

**83.** $r^2 = 9 \sin(2\theta)$       **84.** $r^2 = 16 \cos(2\theta)$

**85.** $r = 4 \sin\left(\dfrac{\theta}{2}\right)$       **86.** $r = 6 \cos\left(\dfrac{\theta}{2}\right)$

**Use a graphing calculator in polar mode to produce the following polar graphs.**

**87.** $r = 4\sqrt{1 - \sin^2\theta}$, *a hippopede*

**88.** $r = 3 + \csc \theta$, *a conchoid*

**89.** $r = 2 \cos \theta \cot \theta$, *a cissoid*

**90.** $r = \cot \theta$, *a kappa curve*

**91.** $r = 8 \sin \theta \cos^2\theta$, *a bifoliate*

**92.** $r = 8 \cos \theta(4 \sin^2\theta - 2)$, *a folium*

▶ **WORKING WITH FORMULAS**

**93. The midpoint formula in polar coordinates:**
$$M = \left(\frac{r \cos \alpha + R \cos \beta}{2}, \frac{r \sin \alpha + R \sin \beta}{2}\right)$$

The midpoint of a line segment connecting the points $(r, \alpha)$ and $(R, \beta)$ in polar coordinates can be found using the formula shown. Find the midpoint of the line segment between $(r, \alpha) = (6, 45°)$ and $(R, \beta) = (8, 30°)$, then convert these points to rectangular coordinates and find the midpoint using the "standard" formula. Do the results match?

**94. The distance formula in polar coordinates:**
$$d = \sqrt{R^2 + r^2 - 2Rr \cos(\alpha - \beta)}$$

Using the law of cosines, it can be shown that the distance between the points $(R, \alpha)$ and $(r, \beta)$ in polar coordinates is given by the formula indicated. Use the formula to find the distance between $(R, \alpha) = (6, 45°)$ and $(r, \beta) = (8, 30°)$, then convert these to rectangular coordinates and compute the distance between them using the "standard" formula. Do the results match?

▶ **APPLICATIONS**

**Polar graphs:** Find the equation of a polar graph satisfying the given conditions, then sketch the graph.

**95.** limaçon, symmetric to polar axis, $a = 4$ and $b = 4$

**96.** rose, four petals, two petals symmetric to the polar axis, $a = 6$

**97.** rose, five petals, one petal symmetric to the polar axis, $a = 4$

**98.** limaçon, symmetric to $\theta = \dfrac{\pi}{2}$, $a = 2$ and $b = 4$

**99.** lemniscate, $a = 4$ through $(\pi, 4)$

**100.** lemniscate, $a = 8$ through $\left(8, \dfrac{\pi}{4}\right)$

**101.** circle, symmetric to $\theta = \dfrac{\pi}{2}$, center at $\left(2, \dfrac{\pi}{2}\right)$, containing $\left(2, \dfrac{\pi}{6}\right)$

**102.** circle, symmetric to polar axis, through $(6, \pi)$

**Matching:** Match each graph to its equation a through h, which follow. Justify your answers.

**103.** 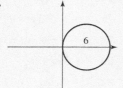 **104.** 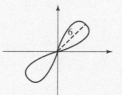 **105.** 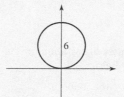 **106.**

**107.** 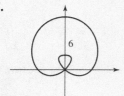 **108.** 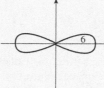 **109.** 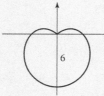 **110.**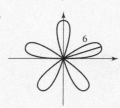

**a.** $r = 6 \cos \theta$    **b.** $r = 3 - 3 \sin \theta$    **c.** $r = 6 \cos(4\theta)$    **d.** $r^2 = 36 \cos(2\theta)$

**e.** $r^2 = 36 \sin(2\theta)$    **f.** $r = 2 + 4 \sin \theta$    **g.** $r = 6 \sin \theta$    **h.** $r = 6 \sin(5\theta)$

**111. Figure eights:** Waiting for help to arrive on foot, a light plane is circling over some stranded hikers using a "figure eight" formation, closely resembling the graph of a lemniscate. Suppose the flight path of the plane was plotted (using the hikers as the origin) and found to contain the polar coordinates (7200, 45°) and (0, 90°) with $r$ in meters. Find the equation of the lemniscate.

**112. Animal territories:** Territorial animals often prowl the borders of their territory, marking the boundaries with various bodily excretions. Suppose the territory of one such animal was limaçon shaped, with the pole representing the den of the animal. Find the polar equation defining the animal's territory if markings are left at (750, 0°), (1000, 90°), and (750, 180°). Assume $r$ is in meters.

**113. Prop manufacturing:** The propellers for a toy boat are manufactured by stamping out a rose with $n$ petals and then bending each blade. If the manufacturer wants propellers with five blades and a radius of 15 mm, what two polar equations will satisfy these specifications?

**114. Polar curves and cosine:** Do a complete $r$-value analysis for graphing polar curves involving cosine. Include a color-coded graph showing the relationship between $r$ and $\theta$, similar to the analysis for sines that preceded Example 8.

▶ **EXTENDING THE CONCEPT**

**115.** The polar graph $r = a\theta$ is called the *Spiral of Archimedes*. Consider the spiral $r = \frac{1}{2}\theta$. As this graph spirals around the origin, what is the distance between each positive, polar intercept? In QI, what is the distance between consecutive branches of the spiral each time it intersects $\theta = \frac{\pi}{4}$? What is the distance between consecutive branches of the spiral at $\theta = \frac{\pi}{2}$? What can you conclude?

As mentioned in the exposition, tests for symmetry of polar graphs are sufficient to show symmetry (if the test is satisfied, the graph must be symmetric), but the tests are not necessary to show symmetry (the graph may be symmetric even if the test is not satisfied). For $r = f(\theta)$, the formal tests for the symmetry are: (1) the graph will be symmetric to the polar axis if $f(\theta) = f(-\theta)$; (2) the graph will be symmetric to the line $\theta = \frac{\pi}{2}$ if $f(\pi - \theta) = f(\theta)$; and (3) the graph will be symmetric to the pole if $f(\theta) = -f(\theta)$.

**116.** Sketch the graph of $r = 4\sin(2\theta)$. Show the equation fails the first test, yet the graph is still symmetric to the polar axis.

**117.** Why is the graph of every lemniscate symmetric to the pole?

**118.** Verify that the graph of every limaçon of the form $r = a + b\cos\theta$ is symmetric to the polar axis.

**119.** The graphs of $r = a\sin(n\theta)$ and $r = a\cos(n\theta)$ are from the rose family of polar graphs. If $n$ is odd, there are $n$ petals in the rose, and if $n$ is even, there are $2n$ petals. An interesting extension of this fact is that the $n$ petals enclose exactly 25% of the area of the circumscribed circle, and the $2n$ petals enclose exactly 50%. Find the area within the boundaries of the rose defined by $r = 6\sin(5\theta)$.

▶ **MAINTAINING YOUR SKILLS**

**120.** (1.3) Find the value of all six trig functions given $\sin\theta = -\frac{5}{13}$ and $\sec\theta > 0$.

**121.** (5.1) Verify that the following is an identity:
$$\frac{\cos x}{1 - \sin x} = \frac{1 + \sin x}{\cos x}$$

**122.** (7.4) Find the angle $\theta$ between the vectors $\mathbf{u} = -12\mathbf{i} + 5\mathbf{j}$ and $\mathbf{v} = -2\mathbf{i} + 10\mathbf{j}$.

**123.** (8.2) Which complex number has the greater absolute value: $z_1 = 15 + 1i$ or $z_2 = 13 + 9i$?

**124.** (4.3) The graph of $f(x) = A\sin(Bx + C)$ is shown here. Find the value of $A$, $B$, and $C$ given that $f\left(\frac{3\pi}{8}\right) = -3$.

**Exercise 124**

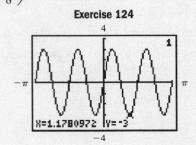

**125.** (2.2) The blueprint for a ride at Wet Willy's Water Park is pictured here. Find the entire length $L$ of the slide given the dimensions and angles indicated.

**Exercise 125**

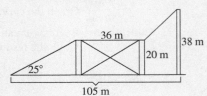

## Learning Objectives

*In Section 8.5 you will learn how to:*

☐ **A.** Sketch the graph of a parametric equation

☐ **B.** Write parametric equations in rectangular form

☐ **C.** Graph curves from the cycloid family

☐ **D.** Solve applications involving parametric equations

A large portion of the mathematics curriculum is devoted to functions, due to their overall importance and widespread applicability. But there are a host of applications for which nonfunctions are a more natural fit. In this section, we show that many *non-functions* can be expressed as **parametric equations,** where each is actually a function. These equations can be appreciated for the diversity and versatility they bring to the mathematical spectrum.

## A. Sketching a Curve Defined Parametrically

Suppose you were given the set of points in the table here, and asked to come up with an equation model for the data. To begin, you might plot the points to see if any patterns or clues emerge, but in this case the result seems to be a curve we've never seen before (see Figure 8.41).

**Figure 8.41**

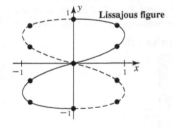

| $x$ | 0 | $\dfrac{\sqrt{3}}{2}$ | $\dfrac{\sqrt{3}}{2}$ | 0 | $-\dfrac{\sqrt{3}}{2}$ | $-\dfrac{\sqrt{3}}{2}$ | 0 |
| --- | --- | --- | --- | --- | --- | --- | --- |
| $y$ | 1 | $\dfrac{\sqrt{3}}{2}$ | $\dfrac{1}{2}$ | 0 | $-\dfrac{1}{2}$ | $-\dfrac{\sqrt{3}}{2}$ | $-1$ |

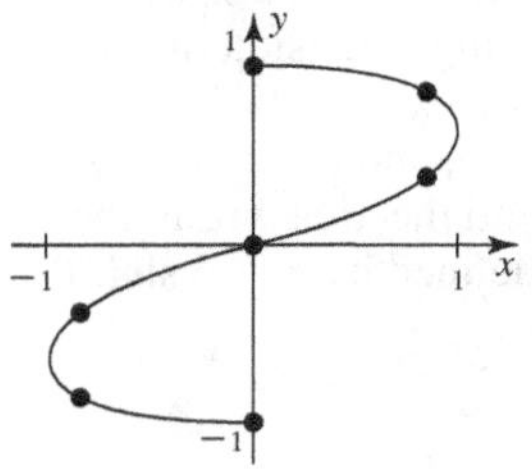

You also might consider running a regression on the data, but it's not possible since the graph is obviously not a function. However, a closer look at the data reveals the $y$-values could be modeled *independently of the x-values* by a cosine function, $y = \cos t$ for $t \in [0, \pi]$. This observation leads to a closer look at the $x$-values, which we find could be modeled by a sine function over the same interval, namely, $x = \sin(2t)$ for $t \in [0, \pi]$. These two functions combine to name all points on this curve, and both use the independent variable $t$ called a **parameter.** The functions $x = \sin(2t)$ and $y = \cos t$ are called the parametric equations for this curve. The complete curve, shown in Figure 8.42, is called a **Lissajous figure,** or a closed graph (coincident beginning and ending points) that crosses itself to form two or more loops. Note that since the maximum value of $x$ and $y$ is 1 (the amplitude of each function), the entire figure will fit within a $2 \times 2$ rectangle centered at the origin. This observation can often be used to help sketch parametric graphs with trigonometric parameters. In general, parametric equations can take many forms, including polynomial, exponential, trigonometric, and other forms.

**Figure 8.42**

Lissajous figure

### Parametric Equations

Given the set of points $P(x, y)$ such that $x = f(t)$ and $y = g(t)$, where $f$ and $g$ are both defined on an interval of the domain, the equations $x = f(t)$ and $y = g(t)$ are called parametric equations, with parameter $t$.

**EXAMPLE 1** ▶ **Graphing a Parametric Curve Where $f$ and $g$ Are Algebraic**

Graph the curve defined by the parametric equations $x = t^2 - 3$ and $y = 2t + 1$.

Solution ▶ Begin by creating a table of values using $t \in [-3, 3]$. After plotting ordered pairs $(x, y)$, the result appears to be a parabola, opening to the right.

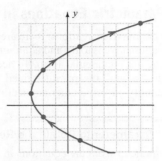

| $t$ | $x = t^2 - 3$ | $y = 2t + 1$ |
|-----|---------------|--------------|
| −3  | 6             | −5           |
| −2  | 1             | −3           |
| −1  | −2            | −1           |
| 0   | −3            | 1            |
| 1   | −2            | 3            |
| 2   | 1             | 5            |
| 3   | 6             | 7            |

**Now try Exercises 7 through 12, Part a ▶**

If the parameter is a trig function, we'll often use standard angles as inputs to simplify calculations and the period of the function(s) to help sketch the resulting graph. Also note that successive values of $t$ give rise to a directional evolution of the graph, meaning the curve is traced out in a direction dictated by the points that correspond to the next value of $t$. The arrows drawn along the graph illustrate this direction, also known as the **orientation** of the graph.

**EXAMPLE 2 ▶**    **Graphing a Parametric Curve Where f and g Are Trig Functions**

Graph the curve defined by the parametric equations $x = 2 \cos t$ and $y = 4 \sin t$.

**Solution ▶**    Using standard angle inputs and knowing the maximum value of any $x$- and $y$-coordinate will be 2 and 4, respectively, we begin computing and graphing a few points. After going from 0 to $\pi$, we note the graph appears to be a vertical ellipse. This is verified using standard values from $\pi$ to $2\pi$. Plotting the points and connecting them with a smooth curve produces the ellipse shown in the figure.

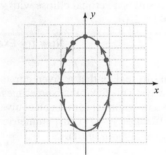

| $t$ | $x = 2 \cos t$ | $y = 4 \sin t$ |
|-----|----------------|----------------|
| 0   | 2              | 0              |
| $\dfrac{\pi}{6}$ | $\sqrt{3}$ | 2 |
| $\dfrac{\pi}{3}$ | 1 | $2\sqrt{3}$ |
| $\dfrac{\pi}{2}$ | 0 | 4 |
| $\dfrac{2\pi}{3}$ | −1 | $2\sqrt{3}$ |
| $\dfrac{5\pi}{6}$ | $-\sqrt{3}$ | 2 |
| $\pi$ | −2 | 0 |

**Now try Exercises 13 through 18, Part a ▶**

☑ **A.** You've just learned how to sketch the graph of a parametric equation

Note the ellipse has a counterclockwise orientation.

## B. Writing Parametric Equations in Rectangular Form

When graphing parametric equations, there are sometimes alternatives to simply plotting points. One alternative is to try and *eliminate the parameter*, writing the parametric equations in standard, rectangular form. To accomplish this we use some connection that allows us to "rejoin" the parameterized equations, such as variable $t$ itself, a trigonometric identity, or some other connection.

---

**EXAMPLE 3** ▶ **Eliminating the Parameter to Obtain the Rectangular Form**

Eliminate the parameter from the equations in Example 1: $x = t^2 - 3$ and $y = 2t + 1$.

**Solution** ▶ Solving for $t$ in the second equation gives $t = \dfrac{y - 1}{2}$, which we then substitute into the first. The result is $x = \left(\dfrac{y - 1}{2}\right)^2 - 3 = \dfrac{1}{4}(y - 1)^2 - 3$. Notice this is indeed a horizontal parabola, opening to the right, with vertex at $(-3, 1)$.

**Now try Exercises 7 through 12, Part b ▶**

---

**EXAMPLE 4** ▶ **Eliminating the Parameter to Obtain the Rectangular Form**

Eliminate the parameter from the equations in Example 2: $x = 2 \cos t$ and $y = 4 \sin t$.

**Solution** ▶ Instead of trying to solve for $t$, we note the parametrized equations involve sine and cosine functions with the same argument $(t)$, and opt to use the identity $\cos^2 t + \sin^2 t = 1$. Squaring both equations and solving for $\cos^2 t$ and $\sin^2 t$ yields $\dfrac{x^2}{4} = \cos^2 t$ and $\dfrac{y^2}{16} = \sin^2 t$. This shows $\cos^2 t + \sin^2 t = \dfrac{x^2}{4} + \dfrac{y^2}{16} = 1$, and as we suspected—the result is a vertical ellipse with vertices at $(0, \pm4)$ and endpoints of the minor axis at $(\pm2, 0)$.

**Now try Exercises 13 through 18, Part b ▶**

---

It's important to realize that a given curve can be represented parametrically in infinitely many ways. This flexibility sometimes enables us to simplify the given form, or to write a given polynomial form in an equivalent nonpolynomial form. The easiest way to write the function $y = f(x)$ in parametric form is $x = t$; $y = f(t)$, which is valid *as long as $t$ is in the domain of $f(t)$.*

---

**EXAMPLE 5** ▶ **Writing an Equation in Terms of Various Parameters**

Write the equation $y = 4(x - 3)^2 + 1$ in three different parametric forms.

**Solution** ▶ **1.** If we let $x = t$, we have $y = 4(t - 3)^2 + 1$.

**2.** Letting $x = t + 3$ simplifies the related equation for $y$, and we begin to see some of the advantages of using a parameter: $x = t + 3$; $y = 4t^2 + 1$.

**3.** As a third alternative, we can let $x = \dfrac{1}{2}\tan t + 3$, which gives

☑ **B. You've just learned how to write parametric equations in rectangular form**

$$x = \frac{1}{2}\tan t + 3; \quad y = 4\left(\frac{1}{2}\tan t\right)^2 + 1 = \tan^2 t + 1 \text{ or } y = \sec^2 t.$$

**Now try Exercises 19 through 26 ▶**

## C. Graphing Curves from the Cycloid Family

The **cycloids** are an important family of curves, and are used extensively to solve what are called **brachistochrone** applications. The name comes from the Greek *brakhus,* meaning short, and *khronos,* meaning time, and deal with finding the path along which a weight will fall in the shortest time possible. Cycloids are an excellent example of why parametric equations are important, as it's very difficult to name them in rectangular form. Consider a point fixed to the circumference of a wheel as it rolls from left to right. If we trace the path of the point as the wheel rolls, the resulting curve is a cycloid. Figure 8.43 shows the location of the point every one-quarter turn.

**Figure 8.43**

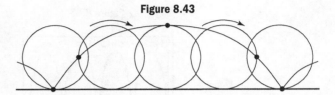

By superimposing a coordinate grid on the diagram in Figure 8.43, we can construct parametric equations that will produce the graph. This is done by developing equations for the location of a point $P(x, y)$ on the circumference of a circle with center $(h, k)$, as the circle rotates through angle $t$. After a rotation of $t$ rad, the $x$-coordinate of $P(x, y)$ is $x = h - a$ (Figure 8.44), and the $y$-coordinate is $y = k - b$. Using a right triangle with the radius as the hypotenuse, we find $\sin t = \dfrac{a}{r}$ and $\cos t = \dfrac{b}{r}$, giving $a = r \sin t$ and $b = r \cos t$. Substituting into $x = h - a$ and $y = k - b$ yields $x = h - r \sin t$ and $y = k - r \cos t$. Since the circle has radius $r$, we know $k = r$ (the "height" of the center is constantly $k = r$). The arc length subtended by $t$ is the same as the distance $h$ (see Figure 8.44), meaning $h = rt$ ($t$ in radians) Substituting $rt$ for $h$ and $r$ for $k$ in the equations $x = h - r \sin t$ and $y = k - r \cos t$, gives the equation of the cycloid in parametric form: $x = rt - r \sin t$ and $y = r - r \cos t$, sometimes written $x = r(t - \sin t)$ and $y = r(1 - \cos t)$.

**Figure 8.44**

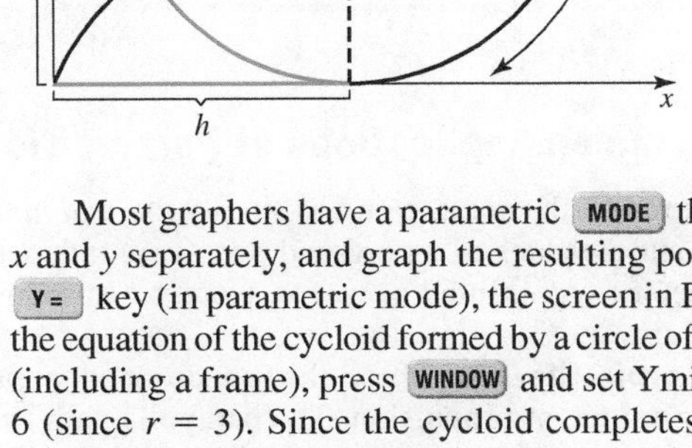

**Figure 8.45**

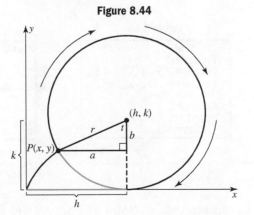

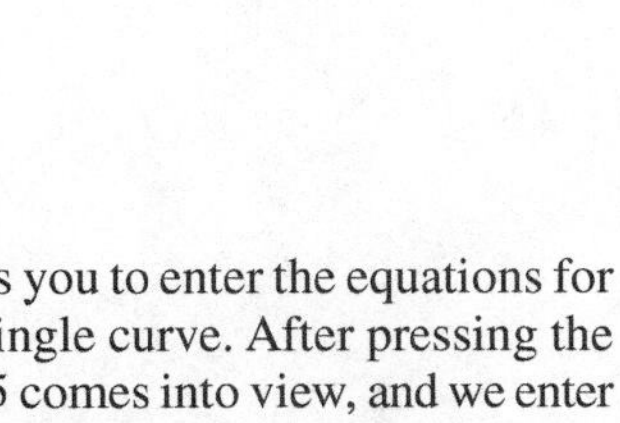

Most graphers have a parametric [**MODE**] that enables you to enter the equations for $x$ and $y$ separately, and graph the resulting points as a single curve. After pressing the [**Y=**] key (in parametric mode), the screen in Figure 8.45 comes into view, and we enter the equation of the cycloid formed by a circle of radius $r = 3$. To set the viewing window (including a frame), press [**WINDOW**] and set Ymin $= -1$ and Ymax at slightly more than 6 (since $r = 3$). Since the cycloid completes one cycle every $2\pi r$, we set Xmax at $2\pi rn$, where $n$ is the number of cycles we'd like to see. In this case, we set it for four

**Figure 8.46**

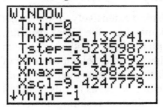

cycles $(2\pi)(3)(4) = 24\pi$ (Figure 8.46). With $r = 3$ we can set Xscl at $3(2\pi) = 6\pi \approx 18.8$ to tick each cycle, or Xscl $= 3\pi \approx 9.4$ to tick each half cycle (Figure 8.46). For parametric equations, we must also specify a range of values for $t$, which we set at Tmin $= 0$, Tmax $= 8\pi \approx 25.1$ for the four cycles, and Tstep $= \dfrac{\pi}{6} \approx 0.52$ (Tstep controls the number of points plotted and joined to form the curve). The window settings and resulting graph are shown in Figure 8.47, which doesn't look much like a cycloid because the current settings do not produce a square viewing window. Using  ZOOM  **5:ZSquare** (and changing Yscl) produces the graph shown in Figure 8.48, which looks much more like the cycloid we expected.

**Figure 8.47**

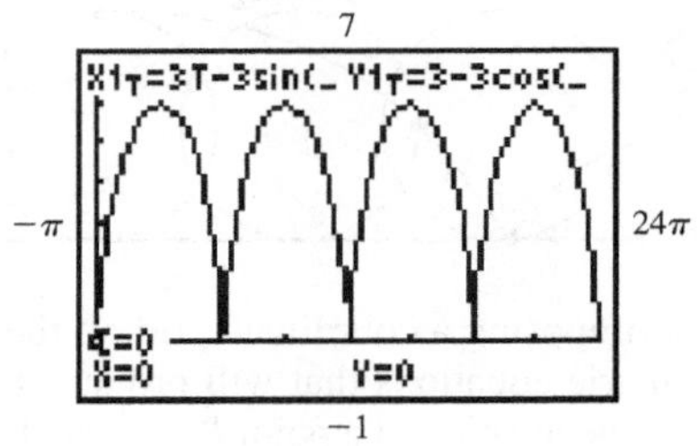

**Figure 8.48**

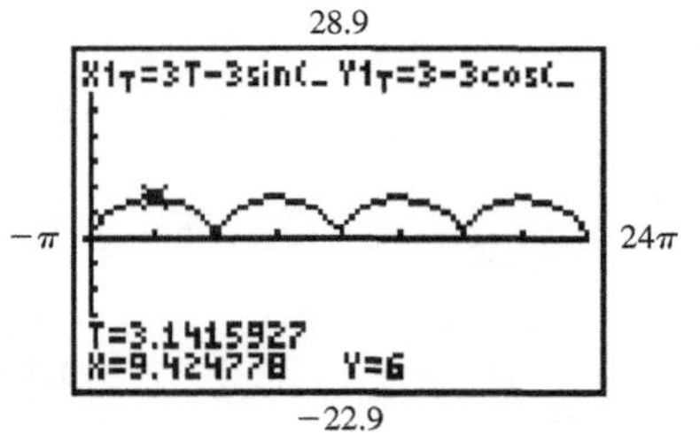

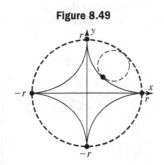

---

**EXAMPLE 6** ▶  **Using Technology to Graph a Cycloid**

Use a graphing calculator to graph the curve defined by the equations $x = 3\cos^3 t$ and $y = 3\sin^3 t$, called a **hypocycloid with four cusps.**

Solution ▶  A hypocycloid is a curve traced out by the path of a point on the circumference of a circle as it rolls *inside a larger circle* of radius $r$ (see Figure 8.49). Here $r = 3$ and we set Xmax and Ymax accordingly. Knowing ahead of time the hypocycloid will have four cusps, we set Tmax $= 4(2\pi) \approx 25.13$ to show all four. The window settings used and the resulting graph are shown in Figures 8.50 and 8.51.

**Figure 8.49**

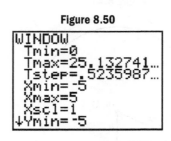

**Figure 8.50**

**Figure 8.51**

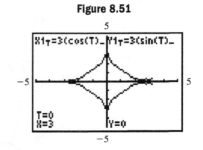

☑ **C.** You've just learned how to graph curves from the cycloid family

Now try Exercises 27 through 35 ▶

## D. Common Applications of Parametric Equations

In Example 1 the parameter was simply the *real number t*, which enabled us to model the *x*- and *y*-values of an ordered pair $(x, y)$ independently. In Examples 2 and 6, the parameter $t$ represented an *angle*. Here we introduce yet another kind of parameter, that of *time t.*

A **projectile** is any object thrown, dropped, or projected in some way with no continuing source of propulsion. The parabolic path traced out by the projectile (assuming negligible air resistance) was fully developed in Section 7.4. It is stated again here in parametric terms. For the projectile's location $P(x, y)$ and any time $t$ in seconds, the $x$-coordinate (horizontal distance from point of projection) is given by $x = v_0 t \cos \theta$, where $v_0$ is the initial velocity in feet per second and $t$ is the time in seconds. The $y$-coordinate (vertical height) is $y = v_0 t \sin \theta - 16t^2$.

**EXAMPLE 7 ▶ Using Parametric Equations in Projectile Applications**

As part of a circus act, Karl the Human Cannonball is shot out of a specially designed cannon at an angle of 40° with an initial velocity of 120 ft/sec. Use a graphing calculator to graph the resulting parametric curve. Then use the graph to determine how high the Ring Master must place a circular ring for Karl to be shot through at the maximum height of his trajectory, and how far away the net must be placed to catch Karl.

**Solution ▶** The information given leads to the equations $x = 120t \cos 40°$ and $y = 120t \sin 40° - 16t^2$. Enter these equations on the Y= screen of your calculator, remembering to reset the MODE to degrees (circus clowns may not know or understand radians). To set the window size, we can use trial and error, or estimate using $\theta = 45°$ (instead of 40°) and an estimate for $t$ (the time that Karl will stay aloft). With $t = 6$ we get estimates of $x = 120(6)\left(\frac{\sqrt{2}}{2}\right) = 360\sqrt{2}$ for the horizontal distance. To find a range for $y$, use $t = 3$ since the maximum height of the parabolic path will occur halfway through the flight. This gives an estimate of $120(3)\left(\frac{\sqrt{2}}{2}\right) - 16(9) = 180\sqrt{2} - 144$ for $y$. The results are shown in Figures 8.52 and 8.53. Using the TRACE feature or 2nd GRAPH (**TABLE**) feature, we find the center of the net used to catch Karl should be set at a distance of about 440 ft from the cannon, and the ring should be located 220 ft from the cannon at a height of about 93 ft.

**Figure 8.52**

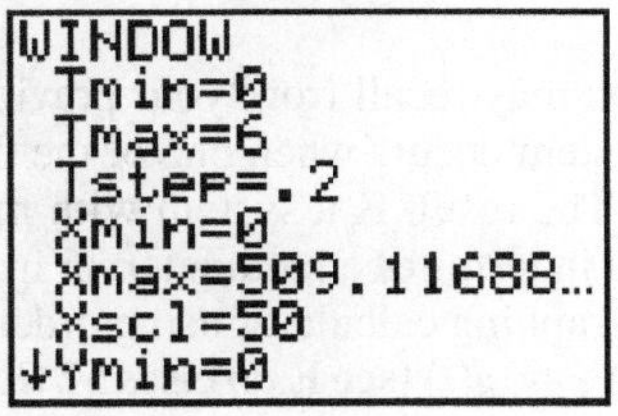

WINDOW
Tmin=0
Tmax=6
Tstep=.2
Xmin=0
Xmax=509.11688...
Xscl=50
↓Ymin=0

**Figure 8.53**

100
X1T=120Tcos_ Y1T=120Tsin(_
0
509
T=2.4
X=220.6208 Y=92.962832
0

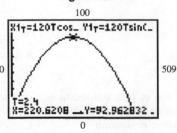

**Now try Exercises 46 through 49 ▶**

It is well known that planets orbit the Sun in elliptical paths. While we're able to model their orbits in both rectangular and polar form, neither of these forms can give a true picture of the *direction they travel.* This gives parametric forms a great advantage, in that they can model the shape of the orbit, *while also indicating the direction of travel.* We illustrate in Example 8 using a "planet" with a very simple orbit.

**EXAMPLE 8** ▶ **Modeling Elliptical Orbits Parametrically**

The elliptical orbit of a certain planet is defined parametrically as $x = 4 \sin t$ and $y = -3 \cos t$. Graph the orbit and verify that for increasing values of $t$, the planet orbits in a counterclockwise direction.

Solution ▶ Eliminating the parameter as in Example 4, we obtain the equation $\dfrac{x^2}{16} + \dfrac{y^2}{9} = 1$, or the equation of an ellipse with center at $(0, 0)$, major axis of length 8, and minor axis of length 6. The path of the planet is traced out by the ordered pairs $(x, y)$ generated by the parametric equations, shown in the table for $t \in [0, \pi]$. Starting at $t = 0$, $P(x, y)$ begins at $(0, -3)$ with $x$ and $y$ both increasing until $t = \dfrac{\pi}{2}$. Then from $t = \dfrac{\pi}{2}$ to $t = \pi$, $y$ continues to increase as $x$ decreases, indicating a counterclockwise orbit in this case. The orbit is illustrated in the figure.

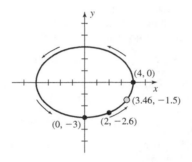

| $t$ | $x = 4 \sin t$ | $y = -3 \cos t$ |
|---|---|---|
| $0$ | $0$ | $-3$ |
| $\dfrac{\pi}{6}$ | $2$ | $-2.6$ |
| $\dfrac{\pi}{3}$ | $3.46$ | $-1.5$ |
| $\dfrac{\pi}{2}$ | $4$ | $0$ |
| $\dfrac{2\pi}{3}$ | $3.46$ | $1.5$ |
| $\dfrac{5\pi}{6}$ | $2$ | $2.6$ |
| $\pi$ | $0$ | $3$ |

Now try Exercises 50 and 51 ▶

Finally, you may recall from your previous work with linear $3 \times 3$ systems, that a dependent system occurs when one of the three equations is a linear combination of the other two. The result is a system with more variables than equations, with solutions expressed in terms of a parameter, or in *parametric form*. These solutions can be explored on a graphing calculator using ordered triples of the form $(t, f(t), g(t))$, where $Y_1 = f(t)$ and $Y_2 = g(t)$ **(see Exercises 52 through 55)**. For more information, see the *Calculator Exploration and Discovery* feature on page 448.

☑ **D.** You've just learned how to solve applications involving parametric equations

## TECHNOLOGY HIGHLIGHT

### Exploring Parametric Graphs

Most graphing calculators have features that make it easy (and fun) to explore parametric equations by using a circular cursor to trace the path of the plotted points, as they are generated by the equations. This can be used to illustrate the path of a projectile, the distance of a runner, or the orbit of a planet. Operations can also be applied to the parameter T to give the effect of "speed" (the points from one set of equations are plotted faster than the points of a second set). To help illustrate their use, consider again the simple, elliptical orbit of a planet in Example 8. Physics tells us the closer a planet is to the Sun, the faster its orbit. In fact, the orbital speed of Mercury is about twice that of Mars and about 10 times as fast as the dwarf planet Pluto (29.8, 15, and 2.9 mi/sec,

*—continued*

respectively). With this information, we can explore a number of interesting questions. On the [Y=] screen, let the orbits of Planet 1 and Planet 2 be modeled parametrically by the equations shown in Figure 8.54. Since the orbit of Planet 1 is "smaller" (closer to the Sun), we have T-values growing at a rate that is *four times as fast* as for Planet 2. Notice to the far left of $X_{1T}$, there is a symbol that looks like an old key "−0." By moving the cursor to the far left of the equation, you can change how the graph will look by repeatedly pressing [ENTER]. With this symbol in view, the calculator will trace

**Figure 8.54**

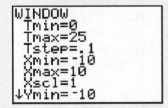

out the curve with a circular cursor, which in this case represents the planets as they orbit (be sure you are in simultaneous [MODE]). Setting the window as in Figure 8.55 and pressing [GRAPH] produces Figure 8.56, which displays their elliptical paths as they race around the Sun. Notice the inner planet has already completed one orbit while the outer planet has just completed one-fourth of an orbit.

**Figure 8.55**

**Figure 8.56**

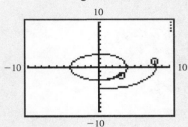

**Exercise 1:** Verify that the inner planet completes four orbits for every single orbit of the outer planet.

**Exercise 2:** Suppose that due to some cosmic interference, the orbit of the faster planet begins to decay at a rate of $T^{0.84}$ (replace T with $T^{0.84}$ in both equations for the inner planet). By observation, about how many orbits did the inner planet make for the first revolution of the outer planet? What is the ratio of orbits for the next complete orbit of the outer planet?

## 8.5 EXERCISES

### ▶ CONCEPTS AND VOCABULARY

**Fill in each blank with the appropriate word or phrase. Carefully reread the section if needed.**

1. When the coordinates of a point $(x, y)$ are generated independently using $x = f(t)$ and $y = g(t)$, $t$ is called a(n) _____.

2. The equations $x = f(t)$ and $y = g(t)$ used to generate the ordered pairs $(x, y)$ are called _____ equations.

3. Parametric equations can both graph a curve *and* indicate the _____ traveled by a point on the curve.

4. To write parametric equations in rectangular form, we must _____ the parameter to write a single equation.

5. Discuss the connection between solutions to dependent systems and the parametric equations studied in this section.

6. In your own words, explain and illustrate the process used to develop the equation of a cycloid. Illustrate with a specific example.

▶ **DEVELOPING YOUR SKILLS**

For Exercises 7 through 18, (a) graph the curves defined by the parametric equations using the specified interval and identify the graph (if possible) and (b) eliminate the parameter (Exercises 7 to 16 only) and write the corresponding rectangular form.

**7.** $x = t + 2; t \in [-3, 3]$
$y = t^2 - 1$

**8.** $x = t - 3; t \in [-5, 5]$
$y = 2 - 0.5t^2$

**9.** $x = (2 - t)^2; t \in [0, 5]$
$y = (t - 3)^2$

**10.** $x = t^3 - 3; t \in [-2, 2.5]$
$y = t^2 + 1$

**11.** $x = \dfrac{5}{t}, t \neq 0; t \in [-3.5, 3.5]$
$y = t^2$

**12.** $x = \dfrac{t^3}{10}; t \in [-5, 5]$
$y = |t|$

**13.** $x = 4 \cos t; t \in [0, 2\pi)$
$y = 3 \sin t$

**14.** $x = 2 \sin t; t \in [0, 2\pi)$
$y = -3 \cos t$

**15.** $x = 4 \sin(2t); t \in [0, 2\pi)$
$y = 6 \cos t$

**16.** $x = 4 \cos(2t); t \in \left[\dfrac{\pi}{2}, \dfrac{3\pi}{2}\right]$

$y = 6 \sin t$

**17.** $x = \dfrac{-3}{\tan t}; t \in (0, \pi)$
$y = 5 \sin(2t)$

**18.** $x = \tan^2 t; t \neq \dfrac{\pi}{2}, t \in [0, \pi]$

$y = 3 \cos t$

Write each function in three different parametric forms by altering the parameter. For Exercises 19–22 use at least one trigonometric form, restricting the domain as needed.

**19.** $y = 3x - 2$       **20.** $y = 0.5x + 6$

**21.** $y = (x + 3)^2 + 1$       **22.** $y = 2(x - 5)^2 - 1$

**23.** $y = \tan^2(x - 2) + 1$   **24.** $y = \sin(2x - 1)$

**25.** Use a graphing calculator or computer to verify that the parametric equations from Example 5 all produce the same graph.

**26.** Use a graphing calculator or computer to verify that your parametric equations from Exercise 21 all produce the same graph.

The curves defined by the following parametric equations are from the cycloid family. (a) Use a graphing calculator or computer to draw the graph and (b) use the graph to approximate all $x$- and $y$-intercepts, and maximum and minimum values to one decimal place.

**27.** $x = 8 \cos t + 2 \cos(4t), y = 8 \sin t - 2 \sin(4t)$, hypocycloid (5-cusp)

**28.** $x = 8 \cos t + 4 \cos(2t), y = 8 \sin t - 4 \sin(2t)$, hypocycloid (3-cusp)

**29.** $x = \dfrac{2}{\tan t}, y = 8 \sin t \cos t$, serpentine curve

**30.** $x = 8 \sin^2 t, y = \dfrac{8 \sin^3 t}{\cos t}$, cissoid of Diocles

**31.** $x = 2(\cos t + t \sin t), y = 2(\sin t - t \cos t)$, involute of a circle

**32.** $4x = (16 - 36)\cos^3 t, 6y = (16 - 36)\sin^3 t$, evolute of an ellipse

**33.** $x = 3t - \sin t, y = 3 - \cos t$, curtate cycloid

**34.** $x = t - 3 \sin t, y = 1 - 3 \cos t$, prolate cycloid

**35.** $x = 2[3 \cos t - \cos(3t)], y = 2[3 \sin t - \sin(3t)]$, nephroid

Use a graphing calculator or computer to draw the following parametrically defined graphs, called Lissajous figures (Exercise 37 is a scaled version of the initial example from this section). Then find the dimensions of the rectangle necessary to frame the figure and state the number of times the graph crosses itself.

**36.** $x = 6 \sin(3t)$       **37.** $x = 6 \sin(2t)$
$y = 8 \cos t$                $y = 8 \cos t$

**38.** $x = 8 \sin(4t)$       **39.** $x = 5 \sin(7t)$
$y = 10 \cos t$               $y = 7 \cos(4t)$

**40.** $x = 8 \sin(4t)$       **41.** $x = 10 \sin(1.5t)$
$y = 10 \cos(3t)$             $y = 10 \cos(2.5t)$

**42.** Use a graphing calculator to experiment with parametric equations of the form $x = A \sin(mt)$ and $y = B \cos(nt)$. Try different values of $A$, $B$, $m$, and $n$, then discuss their effect on the Lissajous figures.

**43.** Use a graphing calculator to experiment with parametric equations of the form $x = \dfrac{a}{\tan t}$ and $y = b \sin t \cos t$. Try different values of $a$ and $b$, then discuss their effect on the resulting graph, called a serpentine curve. Also see Exercise 29.

## ▶ WORKING WITH FORMULAS

**44. The Folium of Descartes:**

$$x(t) = \frac{3kt}{1 + t^3};\ y(t) = \frac{3kt^2}{1 + t^3}$$

The Folium of Descartes is a parametric curve developed by Descartes in order to test the ability of Fermat to find its maximum and minimum values.

  **a.** Graph the curve on a graphing calculator with $k = 1$ using a reduced window ( ZOOM 4), with Tmin = −6, Tmax = 6, and Tstep = 0.1. Locate the coordinates of the tip of the folium (the loop).

  **b.** This graph actually has a discontinuity (a break in the graph). At what value of $t$ does this occur?

  **c.** Experiment with different values of $k$ and generalize its effect on the basic graph.

**45. The Witch of Agnesi:** $x(t) = 2kt;\ y(t) = \dfrac{2k}{1 + t^2}$

The Witch of Agnesi is a parametric curve named by Maria Agnesi in 1748. Some believe various translations confused the Italian word for *witch* with a similar word that means curve, or turning. In any case, the name stuck. The curve can also be stated in trigonometric form: $x(t) = 2k \cot t$ and $y = 2k \sin^2 t$.

  **a.** Graph the curve with $k = 1$ on a calculator or computer on a reduced window ( ZOOM 4) using both of the forms shown with Tmin = −6, Tmax = 6, and Tstep = 0.1. Try to determine the maximum value.

  **b.** Explain why the *x*-axis is a horizontal asymptote.

  **c.** Experiment with different values of $k$ and generalize its effect on the basic graph.

## ▶ APPLICATIONS

**Model each application using parametric equations, then solve using the GRAPH and TRACE features of a graphing calculator.**

**46. Archery competition:** At an archery contest, a large circular target 5 ft in diameter is laid flat on the ground with the bull's-eye exactly 180 yd (540 ft) away from the archers. Marion draws her bow and shoots an arrow at an angle of 25° above horizontal with an initial velocity of 150 ft/sec (assume the archers are standing in a depression and the arrow is shot from ground level). (a) What was the maximum height of the arrow? (b) Does the arrow hit the target? (c) What is the distance between Marion's arrow and the bull's-eye after the arrow hits?

**47. Football competition:** As part of their contribution to charity, a group of college quarterbacks participate in a contest. The object is to throw a football through a hoop whose center is 30 ft high and 25 yd (75 ft) away, trying to hit a stationary (circular) target laid on the ground with the center 56 yd (168 ft) away. The hoop and target both have a diameter of 4 ft. On his turn, Lance throws the football at an angle of 36° with an initial velocity of 75 ft/sec. (a) Does the football make it through the hoop? (b) Does the ball hit the target? (c) What is the approximate distance between the football and the center of the target when the ball hits the ground?

**48. Walk-off home run:** It's the bottom of the ninth, two outs, the count is full, and the bases are loaded with the opposing team ahead 5 to 2. The home team has Heavy Harley, their best hitter at the plate;  the opposition has Raymond the Rocket on the mound. Here's the pitch . . . it's hit . . . a long fly ball to left-center field! If the ball left the bat at an angle of 30° with an initial velocity of 112 ft/sec, will it clear the home run fence, 9 ft high and 320 ft away?

**49. Last-second win:** It's fourth-and-long, late in the fourth quarter of the homecoming football game, with the home team trailing 29 to 27. The coach elects to kick a field goal, even though the goal posts are 50 yd (150 ft) away from the spot of the kick. If the ball leaves the kicker's foot at an angle of 29° with an initial velocity of 80 ft/sec, and the kick is "true," will the home team win (does the ball clear the 10-ft high cross bar)?

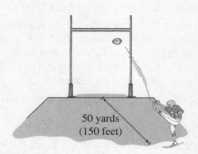

50 yards
(150 feet)

**50. Particle motion:** The motion of a particle is modeled by the parametric equations

$$\begin{cases} x = 5t - 2t^2 \\ y = 3t - 2 \end{cases}$$ . Between $t = 0$ and $t = 1$, is the

particle moving to the right or to the left? Is the particle moving upward or downward?

**51. Electron motion:** The motion of an electron as it orbits the nucleus is modeled by the parametric

equations $\begin{cases} x = 6 \cos t \\ y = 2 \sin t \end{cases}$ with $t$ in radians. Between

$t = 2$ and $t = 3$, is the electron moving to the right or to the left? Is the electron moving upward or downward?

**Systems applications:** Solve the following systems using elimination. If the system is dependent, write the general solution in parametric form and use a calculator to generate several solutions.

**52.** $\begin{cases} 2x - y + 3z = -3 \\ 3x + 2y - z = 4 \\ 8x + 3y + z = 5 \end{cases}$    **53.** $\begin{cases} x - 5y + z = 3 \\ 5x + y - 7z = -9 \\ 2x + 3y - 4z = -6 \end{cases}$

**54.** $\begin{cases} -5x - 3z = -1 \\ x + 2y - 2z = -3 \\ -2x + 6y - 9z = -10 \end{cases}$

**55.** $\begin{cases} x + y - 5z = -4 \\ 2y - 3z = -1 \\ x - 3y + z = -3 \end{cases}$

**56. Regressions and parameters:** Draw a scatter-plot of the data given in the table. Note that connecting the points with a smooth curve will not result in a function, so a standard regression cannot be run on the data. Now consider the $x$-values alone—what do you notice? Find a sinusoidal model for the $x$-values, using $T = 0, 1, 2, 3, \ldots, 8$. Use the same inputs to run some form of regression on the $y$-values, then use the results to form the "best-fit" parametric equations for this data (use L1 for T, L2 for the $x$-values, and L3 for the $y$-values). With your calculator in parametric **MODE**, enter the equations as $X_{1T}$ and $Y_{1T}$, then graph these along with the scatterplot (L2, L3) to see the finished result. Use the **TABLE** feature of your calculator to comment on the accuracy of the model.

| x | y |
|---|---|
| 0 | 0 |
| $\sqrt{2}$ | 0.25 |
| 2 | 2 |
| $\sqrt{2}$ | 6.75 |
| 0 | 16 |
| $-\sqrt{2}$ | 31.25 |
| $-2$ | 54 |
| $-\sqrt{2}$ | 85.75 |
| 0 | 128 |

**57. Regressions and parameters:** Draw a scatter-plot of the data given in the table, and connect the points with a smooth curve. The result is a function, but no standard regression seems to give an accurate model. The $x$-values alone are actually generated by an exponential function. Run a regression on these values using $T = 0, 1, 2, 3, \ldots, 8$ as inputs to find the exponential model. Then use the same inputs to run some form of regression on the $y$-values and use the results to form the "best-fit" parametric equations for this data (use L1 for T, L2 for the $x$-values, and L3 for the $y$-values). With your calculator in parametric **MODE**, enter the equations as $X_{1T}$ and $Y_{1T}$, then graph these along with the scatterplot (L2, L3) to see the finished result. Use the **TABLE** feature of your calculator to comment on the accuracy of the model.

| x | y |
|---|---|
| 1 | 0 |
| 1.2247 | $-1.75$ |
| 1.5 | $-3$ |
| 1.8371 | $-3.75$ |
| 2.25 | $-4$ |
| 2.7557 | $-3.75$ |
| 3.375 | $-3$ |
| 4.1335 | $-1.75$ |
| 5.0625 | 0 |

▶ **EXTENDING THE CONCEPT**

**58.** What is the difference between an *epicycloid,* a *hypercycloid,* and a *hypocycloid*? Do a word study on the prefixes *epi-, hyper-,* and *hypo-,* and see how their meanings match with the mathematical figures graphed in Exercises 27 to 35. To what other shapes or figures are these prefixes applied?

**59.** The motion of a particle in a certain medium is modeled by the parametric equations $\begin{cases} x = 6\sin(4t) \\ y = 8\cos t \end{cases}$. Initially, use only the ⟨2nd⟩ ⟨GRAPH⟩ **(TABLE)** feature of your calculator (not the graph) to name the intervals for which the particle is moving (a) to the left and upward and (b) to the left and downward. Answer to the nearest tenth (set $\Delta$Tbl = 0.1). Is it *possible* for this particle to collide with another particle in this medium whose movement is modeled by $\begin{cases} x = 3\cos t + 7 \\ y = 2\sin t + 2 \end{cases}$? Discuss why or why not.

**60.** Write the function $y = \dfrac{1}{2}(x + 3)^2 - 1$ in parametric form using the substitution $x = 2\cos t - 3$ and the appropriate double-angle identity. Is the result equivalent to the original function? Why or why not?

▶ **MAINTAINING YOUR SKILLS**

**61.** **(7.3)** A ship is traveling at 12 mph on a heading of 315°, when it encounters a 3-mph current with a heading of 30°. Find the true course and speed of the ship as it travels through the current.

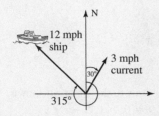

**62.** **(4.3)** Use the graph shown to write an equation of the form $y = A\sec(Bx + C)$.

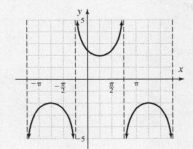

**63.** **(5.2)** Use a sum or difference identity to write the value of cos 105° in exact form.

**64.** **(6.4)** Find all values of $x \in [0, 2\pi)$ that make the equation true: $1560 = 250\sin\left(2x - \dfrac{\pi}{6}\right) + 1735$. Round to four decimal places as needed.

**65.** **(7.1)** Determine the number of triangles that can be formed from the dimensions given here. If two triangles exist, solve both.

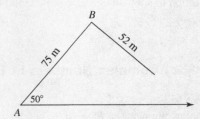

**66.** **(3.2)** The wheels on a motorcycle are rotating at 1000 rpm. If they have a 12-in. radius, how fast is the motorcycle traveling in miles per hour?

# SUMMARY AND CONCEPT REVIEW

## SECTION 8.1    Complex Numbers

### KEY CONCEPTS

- The italicized $i$ represents the number whose square is $-1$. This means $i^2 = -1$ and $i = \sqrt{-1}$.
- Larger powers of $i$ can be simplified using $i^4 = 1$.
- For $k > 0$, $\sqrt{-k} = i\sqrt{k}$ and we say the expression has been *written in terms of i.*
- The standard form of a *complex number* is $a + bi$, where $a$ is the *real number part* and $bi$ is the *imaginary number part.*
- To add or subtract complex numbers, combine the like terms.
- For any complex number $a + bi$, its *complex conjugate* is $a - bi$.
- The *product* of a complex number and its conjugate is a real number.
- The commutative, associative, and distributive properties also apply to complex numbers and are used to perform basic operations.
- To multiply complex numbers, use the F-O-I-L method and simplify.
- To find a *quotient* of complex numbers, multiply the numerator and denominator by the conjugate of the denominator.

### EXERCISES

Simplify each expression and write the result in standard form.

**1.** $\sqrt{-72}$            **2.** $6\sqrt{-48}$          **3.** $\dfrac{-10 + \sqrt{-50}}{5}$

**4.** $\sqrt{3}\sqrt{-6}$          **5.** $i^{57}$

Perform the operation indicated and write the result in standard form.

**6.** $(5 + 2i)^2$          **7.** $\dfrac{5i}{1 - 2i}$          **8.** $(-3 + 5i) - (2 - 2i)$

**9.** $(2 + 3i)(2 - 3i)$        **10.** $4i(-3 + 5i)$

Use substitution to show the given complex number and its conjugate are solutions to the equation shown.

**11.** $x^2 - 9 = -34; x = 5i$                **12.** $x^2 - 4x + 9 = 0; x = 2 + i\sqrt{5}$

## SECTION 8.2    Complex Numbers in Trigonometric Form

### KEY CONCEPTS

- A complex number $a + bi = (a, b)$ can be written in trigonometric form by noting (from its graph) that $a = r\cos\theta$ and $b = r\sin\theta$: $a + bi = r(\cos\theta + i\sin\theta)$.

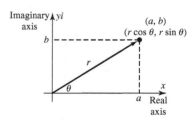

- The angle $\theta$ is called the argument of $z$ and $r$ is called the modulus of $z$.
- The argument of a complex number $z$ is not unique, since any rotation of $\theta + 2\pi k$ ($k$ an integer) will yield a coterminal angle.
- To convert from trigonometric to rectangular form, evaluate $\cos\theta$ and $\sin\theta$ and multiply by the modulus.
- To multiply complex numbers in trig form, multiply the moduli and add the arguments. To divide complex numbers in trig form, divide the moduli and subtract the arguments.
- Complex numbers have numerous real-world applications, particularly in a study of AC electrical circuits.

- The impedance of an AC circuit is given as $Z = R + j(X_L - X_C)$, where $R$ is a pure resistance, $X_C$ is the capacitive reactance, $X_L$ is the inductive reactance, and $j = \sqrt{-1}$.
- $Z$ is a complex number with magnitude $|Z| = \sqrt{R^2 + (X_L - X_C)^2}$ and phase angle $\theta = \tan^{-1}\left(\dfrac{X_L - X_C}{R}\right)$ ($\theta$ represents the angle between the voltage and current).
- In an AC circuit, voltage $V = IZ$; current $I = \dfrac{V}{Z}$.

**EXERCISES**

**13.** Write in trigonometric form: $z = -1 - \sqrt{3}i$

**14.** Write in rectangular form: $z = 3\sqrt{2}\left[\operatorname{cis}\left(\dfrac{\pi}{4}\right)\right]$

**15.** Graph in the complex plane: $z = 5(\cos 30° + i \sin 30°)$

**16.** For $z_1 = 8 \operatorname{cis}\left(\dfrac{\pi}{4}\right)$ and $z_2 = 2 \operatorname{cis}\left(\dfrac{\pi}{6}\right)$, compute $z_1 z_2$ and $\dfrac{z_1}{z_2}$.

**17.** Find the current $I$ in a circuit where $V = 4\sqrt{3} - 4j$ and $Z = 1 - \sqrt{3}j \ \Omega$.

**18.** In the $V_{RLC}$ series circuit shown, $R = 10 \ \Omega$, $X_L = 8 \ \Omega$, and $X_C = 5 \ \Omega$. Find the magnitude of $Z$ and the phase angle between current and voltage. Express the result in trigonometric form.

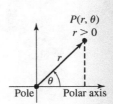

## SECTION 8.3   De Moivre's Theorem and the Theorem on $n$th Roots

**KEY CONCEPTS**

- For complex number $z = r(\cos \theta + i \sin \theta)$, $z^n = r^n[\cos(n\theta) + i \sin(n\theta)]$ (De Moivre's theorem).
- De Moivre's theorem can be used to check complex solutions of polynomial equations.
- For complex number $z = r(\cos \theta + i \sin \theta)$, $\sqrt[n]{z} = \sqrt[n]{r}\left[\cos\left(\dfrac{\theta}{n} + \dfrac{2\pi k}{n}\right) + i \sin\left(\dfrac{\theta}{n} + \dfrac{2\pi k}{n}\right)\right]$, for $k = 1, 2, 3, \ldots, n - 1$ ($n$th roots theorem).
- The $n$th roots of a complex number are equally spaced around a circle of radius $r$ in the complex plane.

**EXERCISES**

**19.** Use De Moivre's theorem to compute the value of $(-1 + i\sqrt{3})^5$.

**20.** Use De Moivre's theorem to verify that $z = 1 - i$ is a solution of $z^4 + z^3 - 2z^2 + 2z + 4 = 0$.

**21.** Use the $n$th roots theorem to find the three cube roots of $125i$.

**22.** Solve the equation using the $n$th roots theorem: $x^3 - 216 = 0$.

**23.** Given that $z = 2 + 2i$ is a fourth root of $-64$, state the other three roots.

**24.** Solve using the quadratic formula and the $n$th roots theorem: $z^4 + 6z^2 + 25 = 0$.

**25.** Use De Moivre's theorem to verify the three roots of $125i$ found in Exercise 21.

## SECTION 8.4   Polar Coordinates, Equations, and Graphs

**KEY CONCEPTS**

- In polar coordinates, the location of a point in the plane is denoted $(r, \theta)$, where $r$ is the distance to the point from the origin or *pole*, and $\theta$ is the angle between a stipulated polar axis and a ray containing $P$.
- In the polar coordinate system, the location $(r, \theta)$ of a point is not unique for two reasons: (1) the angles $\theta$ and $\theta + 2\pi n$ are coterminal ($n$ an integer), and (2) $r$ may be negative.

- The point $P(r, \theta)$ can be converted to $P(x, y)$ in rectangular coordinates where $x = r \cos \theta$ and $y = r \sin \theta$.
- The point $P(x, y)$ in rectangular coordinates can be converted to $P(r, \theta)$ in polar coordinates, where $r = \sqrt{x^2 + y^2}$ and $\theta_r = \tan^{-1}\left|\dfrac{y}{x}\right|$.
- To sketch a polar graph, we view the length $r$ as being along the second hand of a clock, ticking in a counterclockwise direction. Each "tick" is $\dfrac{\pi}{12}$ rad or 15°. For each tick we locate a point on the radius and plot it on the face of the clock before going on.
- For graphing, we also apply an "$r$-value" analysis, which looks where $r$ is increasing, decreasing, zero, maximized, and/or minimized.
- If the polar equation is given in terms of sines, the graph will be symmetric to $\theta = \dfrac{\pi}{2}$.
- If the polar equation is given in terms of cosines, the graph will be symmetric to the polar axis.
- The graphs of several common polar equations are given in Appendix VII.

## EXERCISES
Sketch using an $r$-value analysis (include a table), symmetry, and any convenient points.

**26.** $r = 5 \sin \theta$    **27.** $r = 4 + 4 \cos \theta$    **28.** $r = 2 + 4 \cos \theta$    **29.** $r = 8 \sin(2\theta)$

## SECTION 8.5   Parametric Equations and Graphs

### KEY CONCEPTS
- If we consider the set of points $P(x, y)$ such that the $x$-values are generated by $f(t)$ and the $y$-values are generated by $g(t)$ (assuming $f$ and $g$ are both defined on an interval of the domain), the equations $x = f(t)$ and $y = g(t)$ are called parametric equations, with parameter $t$.
- Parametric equations can be converted to rectangular form by eliminating the parameter. This can sometimes be done by solving for $t$ in one equation and substituting in the other, or by using trigonometric forms.
- A function can be written in parametric form many different ways, by altering the parameter or using trigonometric identities.
- The cycloids are an important family of curves, with equations $x = r(t - \sin t)$ and $y = r(1 - \cos t)$.
- The solutions to dependent systems of equations are often expression in parametric form, with the points $P(x, y)$ given by the parametric equations generating solutions to the system.

### EXERCISES
Graph the curves defined by the parametric equations over the specified interval and identify the graph. Then eliminate the parameter and write the corresponding rectangular form.

**30.** $x = t - 4$: $t \in [-3, 3]$:   **31.** $x = (2 - t)^2$: $t \in [0, 5]$:   **32.** $x = -3 \sin t$: $t \in [0, 2\pi)$:
$y = -2t^2 + 3$          $y = (t - 3)^2$                $y = 4 \cos t$

**33.** Write the function in three different forms by altering the parameter: $y = 2(x - 5)^2 - 1$

**34.** Use a graphing calculator to graph the Lissajous figure indicated, then state the size of the rectangle needed to frame it: $x = 4 \sin(5t)$; $y = 8 \cos t$

1. Perform the operations indicated.

   a. $\sqrt{-18} + \sqrt{-50}$    b. $(1 - 2i)^2$

   c. $\dfrac{3i}{1 + i}$    d. $(2 + i\sqrt{3})(2 - i\sqrt{3})$

2. a. Graph the complex number using the rectangular form, then convert to trigonometric form: $z = 4 - 4i$.

   b. Graph the complex number using the trigonometric form, then convert to rectangular form: $z = 6(\cos 120° + i \sin 120°)$.

**3. a.** Verify that $z = 4 - 5i$ *and* its conjugate are solutions to $z^2 - 8z + 41 = 0$.

   **b.** Solve using the quadratic formula:
   $z^2 - 6iz + 7 = 0$

**4.** Given $z_1 = 8(\cos 45° + i \sin 45°)$ and $z_2 = 4(\cos 15° + i \sin 15°)$ compute:

   **a.** the product $z_1 z_2$       **b.** the quotient $\dfrac{z_1}{z_2}$

**5.** Find the result using De Moivre's theorem: $(2\sqrt{3} - 2i)^6$.

**6.** Use the $n$th roots theorem to find the four fourth roots of $-2 + 2i\sqrt{3}$.

**7.** The impedance of an AC circuit is $Z = R + j(X_L - X_C)$. The voltage across the circuit is $V_{RLC} = I|Z|$. Given $R = 12\ \Omega$, $X_L = 15.2\ \Omega$, and $X_C = 9.4\ \Omega$, write $Z$ in trigonometric form and find the voltage in the circuit if the current is $I = 6.5$ A.

**8.** Graph the curve defined by the parametric equations given, using the interval $t \in [0, 10]$. Then identify the graph: $x = (t - 2)^2$, $y = (t - 4)^2$

**9.** Plot the polar coordinates given, then convert to rectangular coordinates.

   **a.** $\left(3.5, \dfrac{2\pi}{3}\right)$       **b.** $\left(-4, \dfrac{5\pi}{4}\right)$

**10.** Match each equation to its corresponding graph. Justify each response.

   **(i)** $r = 3.5 + \cos\theta$
   **(ii)** $r^2 = 20.25 \sin(-2\theta)$
   **(iii)** $r = 4.5 \cos\theta$

   **a.**

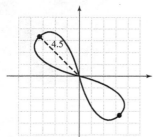

   **b.**

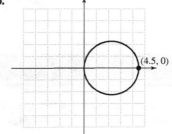

(4.5, 0)

   **c.**

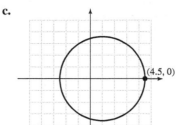

(4.5, 0)

**11.** In the design of their corporate headquarters, Centurion Computing includes a seven-leaf rose in a large foyer, with a fountain in the center. Each of the leaves is 5 m long (when measured from the center of the fountain), and will hold flower beds for carefully chosen perennials. The rose is to be symmetric to a vertical axis, with the leaf bisected by $\theta = \dfrac{\pi}{2}$ pointing directly to the elevators. Find the equation of the rose in polar form.

**12.** Find the quotient in trigonometric form:
$z_1 = 3 + \sqrt{3}i$ and $z_2 = \sqrt{3} + 3i$

**13.** Write the parametric equations in rectangular form:
$x = 3 \cos T$
$y = -4 \sin T$

**14.** Simplify the following expressions:

   **a.** $i^{29}$        **b.** $i^{66}$
   **c.** $i^{136}$       **d.** $i^{87}$

**15.** Use De Moivre's theorem to verify $-\dfrac{5\sqrt{2}}{2} - \dfrac{5\sqrt{2}}{2}i$

   is a solution for $\dfrac{1}{25}z^4 + z^2 + 25 - 25i = 0$

**16.** Find the equation of a lemniscate with $a = 10$ through (100, 0).

**17.** Eliminate the parameter from $x = 3 \cos t$ and $y = 3 \sin t$.

**18.** Evaluate $(3 - 4i)^3$. Express your answer in rectangular form.

**19.** Find the eight eighth roots of unity.

**20.** At the end of the football game, Ismael throws a "Hail Mary" pass to Martin, who in turn scores the winning touchdown. If the football leaves Ismael's hand at an angle of 50° with an initial velocity of 65 ft/sec, how far down the field does it travel through the air?

# PRACTICE TEST

Simplify each expression.

**1.** $\dfrac{-8 + \sqrt{-20}}{6}$    **2.** $i^{39}$

**3.** Given $x = \dfrac{1}{2} + \dfrac{\sqrt{3}}{2}i$ and $y = \dfrac{1}{2} - \dfrac{\sqrt{3}}{2}i$ find

   **a.** $x + y$    **b.** $x - y$    **c.** $xy$

**4.** Compute the quotient: $\dfrac{3i}{1 - i}$.

**5.** Find the product: $(3i + 5)(5 - 3i)$.

**6.** Show $x = 2 - 3i$ is a solution of $x^2 - 4x + 13 = 0$.

**7.** Compute the quotient $\dfrac{z_1}{z_2}$, given

   $z_1 = 6\sqrt{5}\,\text{cis}\left(\dfrac{\pi}{8}\right)$ and $z_2 = 3\sqrt{5}\,\text{cis}\left(\dfrac{\pi}{12}\right)$.

**8.** Compute the product $z = z_1 z_2$ in trigonometric form, then verify $|z_1||z_2| = |z|$ and $\theta_1 + \theta_2 = \theta$:
$z_1 = -6 + 6i;\ z_2 = 4 - 4\sqrt{3}i$

**9.** The impedance of an AC circuit is $Z = R + j(X_L - X_C)$. The voltage across the circuit is $V_{RLC} = I|Z|$. Given $R = 18\ \Omega$, $X_L = 6.1\ \Omega$, and $X_C = 1.4\ \Omega$, express $Z$ in trigonometric form and find the voltage in the circuit if the current is $I = 2.5$ A.

**10.** Use De Moivre's theorem to compute the value of $(\sqrt{3} - i)^4$.

**11.** Use De Moivre's theorem to verify $2 + 2\sqrt{3}i$ is a solution to $z^5 + 3z^3 + 64z^2 + 192 = 0$.

**12.** Use the $n$th roots theorem to solve $x^3 - 125i = 0$.

**13.** Solve using $u$-substitution, the quadratic formula, and the $n$th roots theorem: $z^4 - 6z^2 + 58 = 0$.

Graph each polar equation.

**14.** $r = 3 + 3\cos\theta$    **15.** $r = 4 + 8\cos\theta$

**16.** $r = 6\sin(2\theta)$

For Exercises 17 and 18, identify and graph each conic section from the parametric equations given. Then remove the parameter and convert to rectangular form.

**17.** $x = 4\sin t$     **18.** $x = (t - 3)^2 + 1$
    $y = 5\cos t$          $y = t + 2$

**19.** Use a graphing calculator to graph the cycloid, then identify the maximum and minimum values, and the period. $x = 4T - 4\sin T$, $y = 4 - 4\cos T$

**20.** The soccer match is tied, with time running out. In a desperate attempt to win, the opposing coach pulls his goalie and substitutes a forward. Suddenly, Marques gets a break-away and has an open shot at the empty net, 165 ft away. If the kick is on-line and leaves his foot at an angle of 28° with an initial velocity of 80 ft/sec, is the ball likely to go in the net and score the winning goal?

## CALCULATOR EXPLORATION AND DISCOVERY

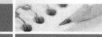

### Parametric Equations and Dependent Systems

As mentioned in Section 8.5, solutions to a linearly dependent system of equations can be represented parametrically. Consider the following illustration.

**Illustration 1** ▶ Solve using elimination: $\begin{cases} 3x - 2y + z = -1 \\ 2x + y - z = 5 \\ 10x - 2y = 8 \end{cases}$

**Solution** ▶ Using R1, we'll target $z$ in R2, since R3 has no $z$-term.

$$\begin{cases} 3x - 2y + z = -1 & \text{R1} \\ 2x + y - z = 5 & \text{R2} \\ 10x - 2y = 8 & \text{R3} \end{cases}$$

R1 + R2 eliminates the $z$-term from R2, yielding a new R2: $5x - y = 4$, and we obtain the equivalent system shown.

$$\begin{cases} 3x - 2y + z = -1 \\ 2x + y - z = 5 \\ 10x - 2y = 8 \end{cases} \xrightarrow[\text{R3} \rightarrow \text{R3}]{\text{R1} + \text{R2} \rightarrow \text{R2}} \begin{cases} 3x - 2y + z = -1 \\ 5x - y = 4 \\ 10x - 2y = 8 \end{cases}$$

To finish, we use $-2R2 + R3$ to eliminate the $y$-term in R3, but this *also eliminates all other terms*:

$$
\begin{array}{r}
-2R2 \\
+ \\
\underline{R3}
\end{array}
\left\{
\begin{array}{r}
-10x + 2y = -8 \\
\underline{10x - 2y = \phantom{-}8} \\
0 = \phantom{-}0
\end{array}
\right. \quad \text{result}
$$

Since R3 = 2R2, the system is linearly dependent and equivalent to $\begin{cases} 3x - 2y + z = -1 \\ 5x - y = 4 \end{cases}$. For a solution, we express the remaining equations in terms of a common variable, called the parameter. For R2 we have $y = 5x - 4$, and substituting $5x - 4$ for $y$ in R1 we can also write $z$ in terms of $x$:

$$
\begin{array}{rl}
3x - \phantom{2(}2y\phantom{)} + z = \phantom{-}-1 & \text{R1} \\
3x - 2(5x - 4) + z = \phantom{-}-1 & \text{substitute } 5x - 4 \text{ for } y \\
z = 7x - 9 & \text{simplify and solve for } z
\end{array}
$$

The general solution is $(x, 5x - 4, 7x - 9)$. In cases of linear dependence, it is common practice to express the solution in terms of a new parameter, with $t$ being a common choice. The solution to the original system is any triple satisfying $(t, 5t - 4, 7t - 9)$. We can actually enter this solution in parametric form using our calculator, with $X_{1T} = 5T - 4$, $Y_{1T} = 7T - 9$, and T as the parameter (Figure 8.57). Since the slope of both parameterized lines is very steep, window settings are a concern. Using $T \in [-10, 10]$, with $x \in [-50, 50]$ and $y \in [-50, 50]$ will display a large number of the possible solutions (Figure 8.58). The graph is shown in Figure 8.59, with the TRACE feature being used to view various possibilities. The solution illustrated in Figure 8.59 is the ordered triple $(3, 11, 12)$.

**Figure 8.57**

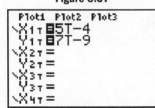

**Figure 8.58**

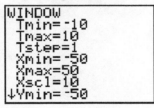

**Figure 8.59**

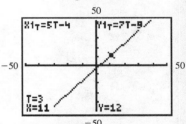

Solve each system using elimination. If the system is linearly dependent, write the general solution in parametric form and use a calculator to generate several solutions. Many representations are possible.

**Exercise 1:** $\begin{cases} 2x - y - z = -1 \\ -3x + 2y + z = 4 \\ 3x - 3y = -9 \end{cases}$    **Exercise 2:** $\begin{cases} -x + y + 2z = 1 \\ 2x - 3y - 3z = 1 \\ 4x - 7y - 5z = 5 \end{cases}$

**Complex Numbers, Sum and Difference Identities, and Euler's Formula**

### Sum and Difference Identities

In Section 8.2, we used the sum and difference identities to establish the process for multiplying and dividing complex numbers in trigonometric form. As a result, we can use multiplication and division of complex numbers to recall the sum and difference identities. If we let $z_1 = \text{cis } \alpha$ and $z_2 = \text{cis } \beta$ (note $r_1 = r_2 = 1$), we proceed as follows:

$$z_1 z_2 = \text{cis } \alpha \text{ cis } \beta \qquad \text{substitute cis } \alpha \text{ for } z_1 \text{ and cis } \beta \text{ for } z_2$$
$$= \text{cis}(\alpha + \beta) \qquad \text{multiplication of complex numbers in trig form}$$
$$= \cos(\alpha + \beta) + i\sin(\alpha + \beta) \qquad \text{expand cis notation}$$

Alternatively, we could have directly multiplied the complex numbers in trigonometric form.

$$
\begin{aligned}
z_1 z_2 &= \operatorname{cis} \alpha \operatorname{cis} \beta && \text{as before} \\
&= (\cos \alpha + i \sin \alpha)(\cos \beta + i \sin \beta) && \text{expand cis notation} \\
&= \cos \alpha \cos \beta + i \cos \alpha \sin \beta \\
&\quad + i \sin \alpha \cos \beta + i^2 \sin \alpha \sin \beta && \text{F-O-I-L} \\
&= \cos \alpha \cos \beta - \sin \alpha \sin \beta && \text{rearrange terms} \\
&\quad + i\,(\cos \alpha \sin \beta + \sin \alpha \cos \beta)
\end{aligned}
$$

Consider the last line of each expression of $z_1 z_2$. Since the real and imaginary parts of the product $z_1 z_2$ must be equal regardless of how it is written, we have two of the sum identities:

$$
\cos(\alpha + \beta) = \cos \alpha \cos \beta - \sin \alpha \sin \beta
$$
$$
\sin(\alpha + \beta) = \cos \alpha \sin \beta + \sin \alpha \cos \beta
$$

In Exercise 1, you will produce two of the difference identities using the division of complex numbers.

## Euler's Formula

As mentioned in Section 8.3, one of the more fascinating discoveries involving complex numbers was that they can also be expressed in *exponential form*. While several mathematicians were aware of the relationship, it was Leonard Euler who first published the formula in its current form, and the formula still bears his name.

---

**Euler's Formula**

For any real number $x$,
$$
e^{ix} = \cos x + i \sin x
$$

---

Although the formula appears imposing and uses the imaginary unit as an exponent, these exponential terms retain the same properties as real number exponents. This greatly facilitates the computation of products, quotients, and powers of complex numbers, and relieves much of the tedium encountered when using the trigonometric form. Using Euler's formula we can rewrite the trigonometric form of a complex number as follows:

$$
\begin{aligned}
z &= r(\cos \theta + i \sin \theta) && \text{trigonometric form} \\
&= re^{i\theta} && \text{substitute } e^{i\theta} \text{ for } \cos \theta + i \sin \theta
\end{aligned}
$$

In Example 5 from Section 8.2, we were given $z_1 = -3 + \sqrt{3}i$ and $z_2 = \sqrt{3} + 1i$.

In trigonometric form, we have $z_1 = 2\sqrt{3} \operatorname{cis}\left(\dfrac{5\pi}{6}\right)$ and $z_2 = 2 \operatorname{cis}\left(\dfrac{\pi}{6}\right)$, and using

Euler's formula we obtain the exponential form: $z_1 = 2\sqrt{3}e^{i\left(\frac{5\pi}{6}\right)}$ and $z_2 = 2e^{i\left(\frac{\pi}{6}\right)}$. In this form, computing the product $z_1 z_2$ requires only the application of the product property of exponents.

$$
\begin{aligned}
z_1 z_2 &= \left[2\sqrt{3}e^{i\left(\frac{5\pi}{6}\right)}\right]\left[2e^{i\left(\frac{\pi}{6}\right)}\right] && \text{substitute } 2\sqrt{3}e^{i\left(\frac{5\pi}{6}\right)} \text{ for } z_1 \text{ and } 2e^{i\left(\frac{\pi}{6}\right)} \text{ for } z_2 \\
&= (2\sqrt{3} \cdot 2)\left[e^{i\left(\frac{5\pi}{6}\right)}e^{i\left(\frac{\pi}{6}\right)}\right] && \text{rearrange terms} \\
&= 4\sqrt{3}e^{i\left(\frac{5\pi}{6}\right) + i\left(\frac{\pi}{6}\right)} && \text{product property of exponents} \\
&= 4\sqrt{3}e^{i\pi} && \dfrac{5\pi}{6} + \dfrac{\pi}{6} = \pi
\end{aligned}
$$

**WORTHY OF NOTE**

Euler's formula gives us a more concise version of the preceding procedure for recalling the sum and difference identities:
$$
e^{i(\alpha + \beta)} = e^{i\alpha}e^{i\beta}
$$

Using the formula to convert this result back into trigonometric form yields the following sequence, and the same result as before.

$$= 4\sqrt{3}(\cos \pi + i \sin \pi) \quad \text{Euler's formula, } e^{i\pi} = \cos \pi + i \sin \pi$$

$$= 4\sqrt{3}(-1 + 0i) \quad \cos \pi = -1, \sin \pi = 0$$

$$= -4\sqrt{3} \quad \text{simplify}$$

**Exercise 1:** Given $z_1 = \text{cis } \alpha$ and $z_2 = \text{cis } \beta$, evaluate $\dfrac{z_1}{z_2}$ in two different ways to verify the difference identities.

**Exercise 2:** Given $z_1 = \text{cis } 225°$ and $z_2 = \text{cis } 300°$, perform the following:

**a.** Compute the product $z_1 z_2$ in trigonometric form.

**b.** Express $z_1$ and $z_2$ in rectangular form and compute $z_1 z_2$ directly.

**c.** Use your answers to Parts (a) and (b) to determine $\cos 525°$ and $\sin 525°$.

**d.** Use a sum identity to verify your results from Part (c).

**e.** Use a calculator to verify your results from Part (c).

**Exercise 3:** Use the exponential form of $z_1 = -3 + \sqrt{3}i$ and $z_2 = \sqrt{3} + 1i$ to compute $\dfrac{z_1}{z_2}$. Answer in exact rectangular form and compare your answer to Example 5(b) from Section 8.2.

**Exercise 4:** Use the exponential form of $z_1 = 4 \text{ cis}\left(\dfrac{\pi}{5}\right)$ and $z_2 = 2 \text{ cis}\left(\dfrac{3\pi}{10}\right)$ to compute $z_1 z_2$. Answer in exact rectangular form.

**Exercise 5:** Use the exponential form of $z = 3 \text{ cis } 137°$ to compute $z^4$. Answer in rectangular form rounded to two decimal places.

Solve each equation.

**1.** $-6 \tan x = 2\sqrt{3}$

**2.** $\dfrac{\sin 27°}{18} = \dfrac{\sin x}{35}$

**3.** $25 \sin\left(\dfrac{\pi}{3}x - \dfrac{\pi}{6}\right) + 3 = 15.5$

**4.** $619^2 = 450^2 + 325^2 - 2(450)(325)\cos\theta$

Graph each relation. Include and label vertices, $x$- and $y$-intercepts, asymptotes, and other features as applicable.

**5.** At 2000 m from the base of a mountain, the angle of elevation to its peak is 40°. If the slope of the mountain itself is 72°, how tall is the mountain?

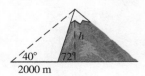

**6.** Solve the equation for $x \in [0, 360°)$: $|\tan x| = \sqrt{3}$.

**7.** Find $\sin(2t)$ and $\cos(2t)$ given $\cos t = \dfrac{12}{13}$ with $t$ in Quadrant IV.

**8.** $y = -2\cos\left(x - \dfrac{\pi}{4}\right) + 1$

**9.** $r = 4\cos(2\theta)$

**10.** $x = 2\sin t$
$y = \tan t$

**11.** Use the dot product to find the angle between the vectors $\mathbf{u} = \langle -4, 5 \rangle$ and $\mathbf{v} = \langle 3, 7 \rangle$.

**12.** Solve using a standard triangle (no trig).

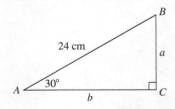

**13.** Find the area of the triangle shown.

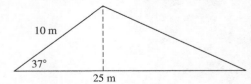

**14.** Verify the following is an identity:
$(\cos\theta + \sin\theta)^2 = 1 + \sin(2\theta)$

**15.** For what values of $\theta \in [0, 2\pi)$ is the following relation not defined?

$$\sec\theta - \cot\theta = \dfrac{\cos\theta}{1 + \sin\theta}$$

16. Convert $\gamma = 2.426$ to degrees, rounded to the nearest tenth.

17. Name an angle coterminal with $\alpha = 32°$ and one coterminal with $\beta = 0.7169$.

18. An arc is subtended by $\theta = 125°$. If the circle has a radius of 6 ft, how long is the arc?

19. What is the area of the circular sector described in Exercise 18?

20. A child's bicycle has wheels with an 8-in. radius that are rotating at 300 rpm (revolutions per minute). (a) Find the angular velocity of the wheels and, (b) the linear velocity of the bicycle in miles per hour.

21. When viewed from a distance of 100 yd, the angle of elevation from the canyon floor to the top of the canyon is 52°. How tall are the canyon walls?

22. Starting with $\sin^2\theta + \cos^2\theta = 1$, derive the Pythagorean identities involving sec/tan and csc/cot.

23. Starting with $\cos(2\theta) = \cos^2\theta - \sin^2\theta$, use a Pythagorean identity to derive two other forms of the double angle formula for cosine.

24. Use a sum/difference identity to find the value of $\sin 15°$ and $\sin 105°$ in exact form.

25. Write in terms of a single sine function:
$$\sin\left(\frac{\pi}{8}\right)\cos\left(\frac{\pi}{12}\right) - \cos\left(\frac{\pi}{8}\right)\sin\left(\frac{\pi}{12}\right)$$

26. A mover applies a constant force of $18\sqrt{3}$ N at 30° to move a piano 15 m. How much work was done?

To notify nature enthusiasts of the presence of nocturnal animals, a motion detector is installed 20 m from a watering hole. A rare brown hyena (*Hyaena brunnea*) just made a midnight visit to the hole and is leaving the area at the 32° angle shown.

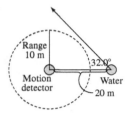

27. If the maximum range of the motion detector is 10 m, will the hyena be detected?

28. If the maximum range of the motion detector is 12 m, how far from the watering hole is the hyena when it is first detected?

29. Given $z = 1 - \sqrt{3}i$, use De Moivre's theorem to calculate the value of $z^4$.

30. Use the $n$th roots theorem to find the four fourth roots of $-8 + 8\sqrt{3}i$.

# Appendix

# APPENDIX I

# Exponential and Logarithmic Functions

## APPENDIX OUTLINE

---

## A | Exponential Functions

### Learning Objectives

*In Section A you will learn how to:*

☐ **A.** Evaluate an exponential function

☐ **B.** Graph general exponential functions

☐ **C.** Graph base-*e* exponential functions

☐ **D.** Solve exponential equations and applications

*Demographics* is the statistical study of human populations. In this section, we introduce the family of *exponential functions,* which are widely used to model population growth or decline with additional applications in science, engineering, and many other fields. As with other functions, we begin with a study of the graph and its characteristics.

### A. Evaluating Exponential Functions

In the boomtowns of the old west, it was not uncommon for a town to double in size every year (at least for a time) as the lure of gold drew more and more people westward. When this type of growth is modeled using mathematics, exponents play a lead role. Suppose the town of Goldsboro had 1000 residents when gold was first discovered. After 1 yr the population doubled to 2000 residents. The next year it doubled again to 4000, then

again to 8000, then to 16,000 and so on. You probably recognize the digits in blue as powers of two (indicating the population is *doubling*), with each one multiplied by 1000 (the initial population). This suggests we can model the relationship using

$$P(x) = 1000 \cdot 2^x$$

where $P(x)$ is the population after $x$ yr. Further, we can evaluate this function, called an **exponential function,** for *fractional parts of a year* using rational exponents. The population of Goldsboro one-and-a-half years after the gold rush was

$$P\left(\frac{3}{2}\right) = 1000 \cdot 2^{\frac{3}{2}}$$
$$= 1000 \cdot (\sqrt{2})^3$$
$$\approx 2828 \text{ people}$$

To properly understand the exponential function and its graph requires that we evaluate $f(x) = 2^x$ even when $x$ is *irrational*. For example, what does $2^{\sqrt{5}}$ mean? While the technical details require calculus, it can be shown that successive approximations of $2^{\sqrt{5}}$ as in $2^{2.2360}$, $2^{2.23606}$, $2^{2.23236067}$, . . . approach a unique real number, and $f(x) = 2^x$ exists for all real numbers $x$.

In general, exponential functions are defined as follows.

**Exponential Functions**

For $b > 0$, $b \neq 1$, and all real numbers $x$,
$$f(x) = b^x$$
defines the base $b$ exponential function.

Limiting $b$ to positive values ensures that outputs will be real numbers, and the restriction $b \neq 1$ is needed since $y = 1^x$ is a constant function (1 raised to *any* power is still 1). Specifically note the domain of an exponential function is *all real numbers*, and that all of the familiar properties of exponents still hold. A summary of these properties follows.

**Exponential Properties**

For real numbers $a$, $b$, $m$, and $n$, with $a, b > 0$,

$$b^m \cdot b^n = b^{m+n} \qquad \frac{b^m}{b^n} = b^{m-n} \qquad (b^m)^n = b^{mn}$$

$$(ab)^n = a^n \cdot b^n \qquad b^{-n} = \frac{1}{b^n} \qquad \left(\frac{b}{a}\right)^{-n} = \left(\frac{a}{b}\right)^n$$

**EXAMPLE 1** ▶ **Evaluating Exponential Functions**

Evaluate each exponential function for $x = 2$, $x = -1$, $x = \frac{1}{2}$, and $x = \pi$. Use a calculator for $x = \pi$, rounding to five decimal places.

**a.** $f(x) = 4^x$      **b.** $g(x) = \left(\dfrac{4}{9}\right)^x$

Solution ▶ **a.** For $f(x) = 4^x$,      **b.** For $g(x) = \left(\dfrac{4}{9}\right)^x$,

$$f(2) = 4^2 = 16 \qquad\qquad g(2) = \left(\frac{4}{9}\right)^2 = \frac{16}{81}$$

$$f(-1) = 4^{-1} = \frac{1}{4} \qquad\qquad g(-1) = \left(\frac{4}{9}\right)^{-1} = \frac{9}{4}$$

$$f\left(\frac{1}{2}\right) = 4^{\frac{1}{2}} = \sqrt{4} = 2 \qquad g\left(\frac{1}{2}\right) = \left(\frac{4}{9}\right)^{\frac{1}{2}} = \sqrt{\frac{4}{9}} = \frac{2}{3}$$

$$f(\pi) = 4^{\pi} \approx 77.88023 \qquad g(\pi) = \left(\frac{4}{9}\right)^{\pi} \approx 0.07827$$

☑ **A. You've just learned how to evaluate an exponential function**

Now try Exercises 7 through 12 ▶

## B. Graphing Exponential Functions

To gain a better understanding of exponential functions, we'll graph examples of $y = b^x$ and note some of the characteristic features. Since $b \neq 1$, it seems reasonable that we graph one exponential function where $b > 1$ and one where $0 < b < 1$.

**EXAMPLE 2** ▶ **Graphing Exponential Functions with $b > 1$**

Graph $y = 2^x$ using a table of values.

**Solution** ▶ To get an idea of the graph's shape we'll use integer values from $-3$ to 3 in our table, then draw the graph as a continuous curve, since the function is defined for all real numbers.

| $x$ | $y = 2^x$ |
|-----|-----------|
| $-3$ | $2^{-3} = \frac{1}{8}$ |
| $-2$ | $2^{-2} = \frac{1}{4}$ |
| $-1$ | $2^{-1} = \frac{1}{2}$ |
| $0$ | $2^0 = 1$ |
| $1$ | $2^1 = 2$ |
| $2$ | $2^2 = 4$ |
| $3$ | $2^3 = 8$ |

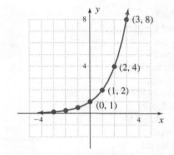

**Now try Exercises 13 and 14 ▶**

**WORTHY OF NOTE**

As in Example 2, functions that are increasing for all $x \in D$ are said to be **monotonically increasing** or simply **monotonic functions.** The function in Example 3 is monotonically decreasing.

Several important observations can now be made. First note the $x$-axis (the line $y = 0$) is a horizontal asymptote for the function, because as $x \to -\infty$, $y \to 0$. Second, the function is increasing over its entire domain, giving the function a range of $y \in (0, \infty)$.

**EXAMPLE 3** ▶ **Graphing Exponential Functions with $0 < b < 1$**

Graph $y = \left(\frac{1}{2}\right)^x$ using a table of values.

**Solution** ▶ Using properties of exponents, we can write $\left(\frac{1}{2}\right)^x$ as $\left(\frac{2}{1}\right)^{-x} = 2^{-x}$. Again using integers from $-3$ to 3, we plot the ordered pairs and draw a continuous curve.

| $x$ | $y = 2^{-x}$ |
|-----|--------------|
| $-3$ | $2^{-(-3)} = 2^3 = 8$ |
| $-2$ | $2^{-(-2)} = 2^2 = 4$ |
| $-1$ | $2^{-(-1)} = 2^1 = 2$ |
| $0$ | $2^0 = 1$ |
| $1$ | $2^{-1} = \frac{1}{2}$ |
| $2$ | $2^{-2} = \frac{1}{4}$ |
| $3$ | $2^{-3} = \frac{1}{8}$ |

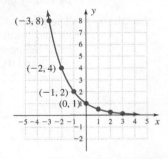

**Now try Exercises 15 and 16 ▶**

We note this graph is also asymptotic to the $x$-axis, but *decreasing on its domain.* In addition, both $y = 2^x$ and $y = 2^{-x} = \left(\frac{1}{2}\right)^x$ have a $y$-intercept of (0, 1) (which we expect since any base to the zero power is 1) and both are one-to-one, which suggests that an inverse function can be found. Finally, observe that $y = b^{-x}$ is *a reflection of $y = b^x$ across the y-axis,* a property that indicates these basic graphs might also be transformed in other ways (see Appendix II). The characteristics of exponential functions are summarized here:

$f(x) = b^x, b > 0$ and $b \neq 1$

- one-to-one function
- domain: $x \in \mathbb{R}$
- increasing if $b > 1$

- $y$-intercept $(0, 1)$
- range: $y \in (0, \infty)$
- decreasing if $0 < b < 1$

- asymptotic to the $x$-axis (the line $y = 0$)

**Figure AI.1**

**Figure AI.2**

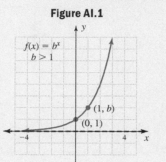
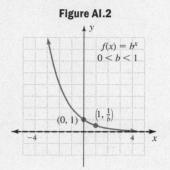

Just as the graph of a quadratic function maintains its parabolic shape regardless of the transformations applied, exponential functions will also maintain their general shape and features. Any sum or difference applied to the basic function ($y = b^x \pm k$ vs. $y = b^x$) will cause a vertical shift in the same direction as the sign, and any change to input values ($y = b^{x+h}$ vs. $y = b^x$) will cause a horizontal shift in a direction opposite the sign.

**EXAMPLE 4** ▶ **Graphing Exponential Functions Using Transformations**

Graph $F(x) = 2^{x-1} + 2$ using transformations of the basic function $f(x) = 2^x$ (not by simply plotting points). Clearly state what transformations are applied.

Solution ▶ The graph of $F$ is that of the basic function $y = 2^x$ shifted 1 unit right and 2 units up. With this in mind the horizontal asymptote shifts from $y = 0$ to $y = 2$ and $(0, 1)$ shifts to $(1, 3)$. The $y$-intercept of $F$ is at $(0, 2.5)$.

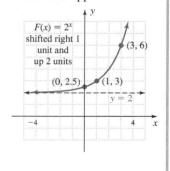

$$F(0) = 2^{(0)-1} + 2$$
$$= 2^{-1} + 2$$
$$= \frac{1}{2} + 2$$
$$= 2.5$$

☑ **B.** You've just learned how to graph general exponential functions

To help sketch a more accurate graph, the additional point $(3, 6)$ is used: $F(3) = 6$.

Now try Exercises 17 through 38 ▶

## C. The Base-$e$ Exponential Function: $f(x) = e^x$

In nature, exponential growth occurs when the rate of change in a population's growth, is in constant proportion to its current size. Using the rate of change notation, $\dfrac{\Delta P}{\Delta t} = kP$, where $k$ is a constant. For the city of Goldsboro, we know the population at time $t$ is given by $P(t) = 1000 \cdot 2^t$, but have no information on this value of $k$ (**see Exercise 96**). We can actually rewrite this function, and other exponential functions, using a base that gives the value of $k$ directly and without having to apply the difference quotient. This new base is an irrational number, symbolized by the letter $e$ and defined as follows.

**The Number e**

For $x > 0$,

$$\text{as } x \to \infty, \left(1 + \frac{1}{x}\right)^x \to e$$

In words, $e$ is the number that $\left(1 + \dfrac{1}{x}\right)^x$ approaches as $x$ becomes infinitely large.

It has been proven that as $x$ grows without bound, $\left(1 + \dfrac{1}{x}\right)^x$ indeed approaches the unique, irrational number that we have named $e$ (**see Exercise 97**). Table AI.1 gives approximate values of the expression for selected values of $x$, and shows $e \approx 2.71828$ to five decimal places.

The result is the base-$e$ **exponential function:** $f(x) = e^x$, also called the **natural exponential function.** Instead of having to enter a decimal approximation when computing with $e$, most calculators have an "$e^x$" key, usually as the [2nd] function for the key marked [LN]. To find the value of $e^2$, use the keystrokes [2nd] [LN] 2 [ ) ] [ENTER], and the calculator display should read 7.389056099. Note the calculator supplies the left parenthesis for the exponent, and you must supply the right.

**Table AI.1**

| $x$ | $(1 + \frac{1}{x})^x$ |
|---|---|
| 1 | 2 |
| 10 | 2.59 |
| 100 | 2.705 |
| 1000 | 2.7169 |
| 10,000 | 2.71815 |
| 100,000 | 2.718268 |
| 1,000,000 | 2.7182804 |
| 10,000,000 | 2.71828169 |

---

**EXAMPLE 5** ▶ **Evaluating the Natural Exponential Function**

Use a calculator to evaluate $f(x) = e^x$ for the values of $x$ given. Round to six decimal places as needed.

    **a.** $f(3)$     **b.** $f(1)$     **c.** $f(0)$     **d.** $f(\frac{1}{2})$

Solution ▶   **a.** $f(3) = e^3 \approx 20.085537$     **b.** $f(1) = e^1 \approx 2.718282$

        **c.** $f(0) = e^0 = 1$ (exactly)    **d.** $f(\frac{1}{2}) = e^{\frac{1}{2}} \approx 1.648721$

Now try Exercises 39 through 46 ▶

Although $e$ is an irrational number, the graph of $y = e^x$ behaves in exactly the same way and has the same characteristics as other exponential graphs. Figure AI.3 shows this graph on the same grid as $y = 2^x$ and $y = 3^x$. As we might expect, all three graphs are increasing, have an asymptote at $y = 0$, and contain the point $(0, 1)$, with the graph of $y = e^x$ "between" the other two. The domain for all three functions, as with all basic exponential functions, is $x \in (-\infty, \infty)$ with range $y \in (0, \infty)$. The same transformations discussed in Appendix II can be applied to the graph of $y = e^x$.

**Figure AI.3**

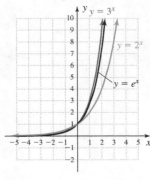

**EXAMPLE 6** ▶  **Graphing Exponential Functions Using a Transformation**

Graph $f(x) = e^{x+1} - 2$ using transformations of $y = e^x$. Clearly state the transformations applied.

**Solution** ▶  The graph of $f$ is the same as $y = e^x$, shifted 1 unit left and 2 units down. The point $(0, 1)$ becomes $(-1, -1)$, and the horizontal asymptote becomes $y = -2$. As the basic shape of the graph is known, we compute $f(1) \approx 5.4$, and complete the graph as shown.

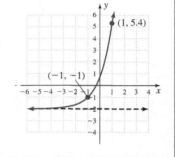

☑ **C.** You've just learned how to graph base-$e$ exponential functions

Now try Exercises 47 through 52 ▶

## D. Solving Exponential Equations Using the Uniqueness Property

Since exponential functions are one-to-one, we can solve equations where each side is an exponential term with the identical base. This is because one-to-oneness guarantees a unique solution to the equation.

Exponential functions are very different from the power functions. For power functions, the base is variable and the exponent is constant: $y = x^b$, while for exponential functions the *exponent is a variable* and the *base is constant:* $y = b^x$.

**Exponential Equations and the Uniqueness Property**

For all real numbers $m$, $n$, and $b$, where $b > 0$ and $b \neq 1$,

$$\text{If } b^m = b^n,$$
$$\text{then } m = n.$$

Equal bases imply exponents are equal.

The equation $2^x = 32$ can be written as $2^x = 2^5$, and we note $x = 5$ is a solution. Although $3^x = 32$ can be written as $3^x = 2^5$, the bases are not alike and the solution to this equation must wait until additional tools are developed in Appendix I.C.

**EXAMPLE 7** ▶  **Solving Exponential Equations**

Solve the exponential equations using the uniqueness property.

   **a.** $3^{2x-1} = 81$         **b.** $25^{-2x} = 125^{x+7}$

   **c.** $\left(\frac{1}{6}\right)^{-3x-2} = 36^{x+1}$     **d.** $e^x e^2 = \dfrac{e^4}{e^{x+1}}$

**Solution** ▶  **a.**  $\quad 3^{2x-1} = 81$      given

$\qquad\qquad 3^{2x-1} = 3^4$      rewrite using base 3

$\qquad\Rightarrow 2x - 1 = 4$      uniqueness property

$\qquad\qquad\quad x = \dfrac{5}{2}$      solve for $x$

**Check** ▶  $\qquad 3^{2x-1} = 81$      given

$\qquad 3^{2\left(\frac{5}{2}\right)-1} = 81$      substitute $\frac{5}{2}$ for $x$

$\qquad\quad 3^{5-1} = 81$      simplify

$\qquad\qquad 3^4 = 81$      result checks

$\qquad\qquad 81 = 81 \checkmark$

The remaining checks are left to the student.

**b.**

$$25^{-2x} = 125^{x+7}$$    given

$$(5^2)^{-2x} = (5^3)^{x+7}$$    rewrite using base 5

$$5^{-4x} = 5^{3x+21}$$    power property of exponents

$$\Rightarrow -4x = 3x + 21$$    uniqueness property

$$x = -3$$    solve for x

**c.**

$$\left(\frac{1}{6}\right)^{-3x-2} = 36^{x+1}$$    given

$$(6^{-1})^{-3x-2} = (6^2)^{x+1}$$    rewrite using base 6

$$6^{3x+2} = 6^{2x+2}$$    power property of exponents

$$\Rightarrow 3x + 2 = 2x + 2$$    uniqueness property

$$x = 0$$    solve for x

**d.**

$$e^x e^2 = \frac{e^4}{e^{x+1}}$$    given

$$e^{x+2} = e^{4-(x+1)}$$    product property; quotient property

$$e^{x+2} = e^{3-x}$$    simplify

$$\Rightarrow x + 2 = 3 - x$$    uniqueness property

$$2x = 1$$    add x, subtract 2

$$x = \frac{1}{2}$$    solve for x

**Now try Exercises 53 through 72 ▶**

One very practical application of the natural exponential function involves **Newton's law of cooling.** This law or formula models the temperature of an object as it cools down, as when a pizza is removed from the oven and placed on the kitchen counter. The function model is

$$T(x) = T_R + (T_0 - T_R)e^{kx}, k < 0$$

where $T_0$ represents the initial temperature of the object, $T_R$ represents the temperature of the room or surrounding medium, $T(x)$ is the temperature of the object $x$ min later, and $k$ is the cooling rate as determined by the nature and physical properties of the object.

**EXAMPLE 8 ▶**   **Applying an Exponential Function—Newton's Law of Cooling**

A pizza is taken from a 425°F oven and placed on the counter to cool. If the temperature in the kitchen is 75°F, and the cooling rate for this type of pizza is $k = -0.35$,

**a.** What is the temperature (to the nearest degree) of the pizza 2 min later?

**b.** To the nearest minute, how long until the pizza has cooled to a temperature below 90°F?

**c.** If Zack and Raef like to eat their pizza at a temperature of about 110°F, how many minutes should they wait to "dig in"?

**Solution ▶**   Begin by substituting the given values to obtain the equation model:

$$T(x) = T_R + (T_0 - T_R)e^{kx}$$    general equation model

$$= 75 + (425 - 75)e^{-0.35x}$$    substitute 75 for $T_R$, 425 for $T_0$, and $-0.35$ for $k$

$$= 75 + 350e^{-0.35x}$$    simplify

For part (a) we simply find $T(2)$:

**a.** $T(2) = 75 + 350e^{-0.35(2)}$    substitute 2 for x

$$\approx 249$$    result

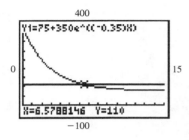

Two minutes later, the temperature of the pizza is near 249°.

**b.** Using the [TABLE] feature of a graphing calculator shows the pizza reaches a temperature of just under 90° after 9 min: $T(9) \approx 90°F$.

**c.** We elect to use the intersection of graphs method (see the *Technology Highlight* on this page). After setting an appropriate window, we enter $Y_1 = 75 + 350e^{-0.35x}$ and $Y_2 = 110$, then press [2nd] [CALC] option **5: intersect.** After pressing [ENTER] three times, the coordinates of the point of intersection appear at the bottom of the screen: $x \approx 6.6$, $y = 110$. It appears the boys should wait about $6\frac{1}{2}$ min for the pizza to cool.

**Now try Exercises 75 and 76 ▶**

Another common application of exponential functions involves appreciation (as when an item grows in value over time), and depreciation (as when tools and equipment decrease in value over time).

---

**EXAMPLE 9 ▶**   **Applications of Exponential Functions—Depreciation**

For insurance purposes, it is estimated that large household appliances lose $\frac{1}{5}$ of their value each year. The current value can then be modeled by the function $V(t) = V_0(\frac{4}{5})^t$, where $V_0$ is the initial value and $V(t)$ represents the value after $t$ years. How many years does it take a washing machine that cost \$625 new, to depreciate to a value of \$256?

**Solution ▶**   For this exercise, $V_0 = \$625$ and $V(t) = \$256$. The formula yields

$$V(t) = V_0\left(\frac{4}{5}\right)^t \qquad \text{given}$$

$$256 = 625\left(\frac{4}{5}\right)^t \qquad \text{substitute known values}$$

$$\frac{256}{625} = \left(\frac{4}{5}\right)^t \qquad \text{divide by 625}$$

$$\left(\frac{4}{5}\right)^4 = \left(\frac{4}{5}\right)^t \qquad \text{equate bases } \frac{256}{625} = \left(\frac{4}{5}\right)^4$$

$$\Rightarrow 4 = t \qquad \text{Uniqueness Property}$$

After 4 yr, the washing machine's value has dropped to \$256.

**Now try Exercises 77 through 90 ▶**

☑ **D.** You've just learned how to solve exponential equations and applications

There are a number of additional applications of exponential functions in the Exercise Set.

---

## TECHNOLOGY HIGHLIGHT

### Solving Exponential Equations Graphically

In this section, we showed the exponential function $f(x) = b^x$ was defined for all real numbers and was a one-to-one function. This is important because it establishes that equations like $2^x = 7$ must have a solution, even if $x$ is not rational. In fact, since $2^2 = 4$ and $2^3 = 8$, the following inequalities indicate the solution must be between 2 and 3.

$$4 < 7 < 8 \qquad \text{7 is between 4 and 8}$$

$$2^2 < 2^x < 2^3 \qquad \text{replace 4 with } 2^2 \text{, 8 with } 2^3$$

$$\Rightarrow 2 < x < 3 \qquad \text{x must be between 2 and 3}$$

*—continued*

Until we develop an inverse for exponential functions, we are unable to solve many of these equations in exact form. We can, however, get a very close approximation using a graphing calculator. For the equation $2^x = 7$, enter $Y_1 = 2^x$ and $Y_2 = 7$ on the [ Y = ] screen. Then press [ ZOOM ] 6 to graph both functions (see Figure AI.4). To find the point of intersection, press [ 2nd ] [ TRACE ] (CALC) and select option **5: intersect,** then press [ ENTER ] *three* times (to identify the intersecting functions and bypass "Guess"). The x- and y-coordinates of the point of intersection will appear at the bottom of the screen, with the x-coordinate being the solution. As you can see, x is indeed between 2 and 3. Solve the following equations. First estimate the answer by bounding it between two integers, then solve the equation graphically. Adjust the viewing window as needed.

**Figure AI.4**

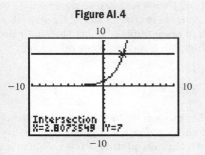

**Exercise 1:** $3^x = 22$       **Exercise 2:** $2^x = 0.125$

**Exercise 3:** $e^{x-1} = 9$       **Exercise 4:** $e^{0.5x} = 0.1x^3$

## A EXERCISES

▶ **CONCEPTS AND VOCABULARY**

**Fill in each blank with the appropriate word or phrase. Carefully reread the section if needed.**

1. An exponential function is one of the form $y =$ _____, where _____ $> 0$, _____ $\neq 1$, and _____ is any real number.

2. The domain of $y = b^x$ is all _____, and the range is $y \in$ _____. Further, as $x \to -\infty$, $y$ _____.

3. For exponential functions of the form $y = ab^x$, the y-intercept is (0, _____), since $b^0 =$ _____ for any real number $b$.

4. If each side of an equation can be written as an exponential term with the same base, the equation can be solved using the _____ _____.

5. State true or false and explain why: $y = b^x$ is always increasing if $0 < b < 1$.

6. Discuss/Explain the statement, "For $k > 0$, the y-intercept of $y = ab^x + k$ is $(0, a + k)$."

▶ **DEVELOPING YOUR SKILLS**

 **Use a calculator (as needed) to evaluate each function as indicated. Round answers to thousandths.**

7. $P(t) = 2500 \cdot 4^t$;
$t = 2, t = \frac{1}{2}, t = \frac{3}{2}$,
$t = \sqrt{3}$

8. $Q(t) = 5000 \cdot 8^t$;
$t = 2, t = \frac{1}{3}, t = \frac{5}{3}$,
$t = 5$

9. $f(x) = 0.5 \cdot 10^x$;
$x = 3, x = \frac{1}{2}, x = \frac{2}{3}$,
$x = \sqrt{7}$

10. $g(x) = 0.8 \cdot 5^x$;
$x = 4, x = \frac{1}{4}, x = \frac{4}{5}$,
$x = \pi$

11. $V(n) = 10{,}000(\frac{2}{3})^n$;
$n = 0, n = 4, n = 4.7$,
$n = 5$

12. $W(m) = 3300(\frac{4}{5})^m$;
$m = 0, m = 5, m = 7.2$,
$m = 10$

**Graph each function using a table of values and integer inputs between −3 and 3. Clearly label the y-intercept and one additional point, then indicate whether the function is increasing or decreasing.**

**13.** $y = 3^x$          **14.** $y = 4^x$

**15.** $y = \left(\frac{1}{3}\right)^x$       **16.** $y = \left(\frac{1}{4}\right)^x$

**Graph each of the following functions by *translating the basic function* $y = b^x$, sketching the asymptote, and strategically plotting a few points to round out the graph. Clearly state the basic function and what shifts are applied.**

**17.** $y = 3^x + 2$       **18.** $y = 3^x - 3$

**19.** $y = 3^{x+3}$        **20.** $y = 3^{x-2}$

**21.** $y = 2^{-x}$         **22.** $y = 3^{-x}$

**23.** $y = 2^{-x} + 3$      **24.** $y = 3^{-x} - 2$

**25.** $y = 2^{x+1} - 3$     **26.** $y = 3^{x-2} + 1$

**27.** $y = \left(\frac{1}{3}\right)^x + 1$     **28.** $y = \left(\frac{1}{3}\right)^x - 4$

**29.** $y = \left(\frac{1}{3}\right)^{x-2}$      **30.** $y = \left(\frac{1}{3}\right)^{x+2}$

**31.** $f(x) = \left(\frac{1}{3}\right)^x - 2$    **32.** $g(x) = \left(\frac{1}{3}\right)^x + 2$

**Match each graph to the correct exponential equation.**

**33.** $y = 5^{-x}$          **34.** $y = 4^{-x}$

**35.** $y = 3^{-x+1}$       **36.** $y = 3^{-x} + 1$

**37.** $y = 2^{x+1} - 2$     **38.** $y = 2^{x+2} - 1$

**a.**
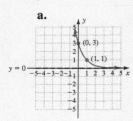

**b.**
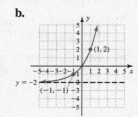

**c.**
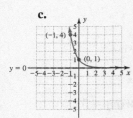

**d.**
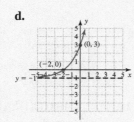

**e.**
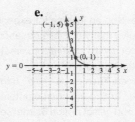

**f.**
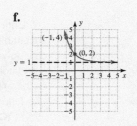

**Use a calculator to evaluate each expression, rounded to six decimal places.**

**39.** $e^1$            **40.** $e^0$

**41.** $e^2$            **42.** $e^5$

**43.** $e^{1.5}$          **44.** $e^{-3.2}$

**45.** $e^{\sqrt{2}}$          **46.** $e^{\pi}$

**Graph each exponential function.**

**47.** $f(x) = e^{x+3} - 2$     **48.** $g(x) = e^{x-2} + 1$

**49.** $r(t) = -e^t + 2$       **50.** $s(t) = -e^{t+2}$

**51.** $p(x) = e^{-x+2} - 1$    **52.** $q(x) = e^{-x-1} + 2$

**Solve each exponential equation and check your answer by substituting into the original equation.**

**53.** $10^x = 1000$        **54.** $144 = 12^x$

**55.** $25^x = 125$         **56.** $81 = 27^x$

**57.** $8^{x+2} = 32$         **58.** $9^{x-1} = 27$

**59.** $32^x = 16^{x+1}$      **60.** $100^{x+2} = 1000^x$

**61.** $\left(\frac{1}{5}\right)^x = 125$      **62.** $\left(\frac{1}{4}\right)^x = 64$

**63.** $\left(\frac{1}{3}\right)^{2x} = 9^{x-6}$    **64.** $\left(\frac{1}{2}\right)^{3x} = 8^{x-2}$

**65.** $\left(\frac{1}{9}\right)^{x-5} = 3^{3x}$    **66.** $2^{-2x} = \left(\frac{1}{32}\right)^{x-3}$

**67.** $25^{3x} = 125^{x-2}$     **68.** $27^{2x+4} = 9^{4x}$

**69.** $\dfrac{e^4}{e^{2-x}} = e^3 e$       **70.** $e^x(e^x + e) = \dfrac{e^x + e^{3x}}{e^{-x}}$

**71.** $\left(e^{2x-4}\right)^3 = \dfrac{e^{x+5}}{e^2}$    **72.** $e^x e^{x+3} = \left(e^{x+2}\right)^3$

▶ **WORKING WITH FORMULAS**

**73. The growth of bacteria:** $P(t) = 1000 \cdot 3^t$

If the initial population of a common bacterium is 1000 and the population triples every day, its population is given by the formula shown, where $P(t)$ is the total population after $t$ days. (a) Find the total population 12 hr, 1 day, $1\frac{1}{2}$ days, and 2 days later. (b) Do the outputs show the population is tripling every 24 hr (1 day)? (c) Explain why this is an increasing function. (d) Graph the function using an appropriate scale.

**74. Spinners with numbers 1–4:** $P(x) = (\frac{1}{4})^x$

Games that involve moving pieces around a board using a fair spinner are fairly common. If the spinner has the numbers 1 through 4, the probability that any one number is spun repeatedly is given by the formula shown, where $x$ represents the number of spins and $P(x)$ represents the probability the same number results $x$ times. (a) What is the probability that the first player spins a 2? (b) What is the probability that all four players spin a 2? (c) Explain why this is a decreasing function.

▶ **APPLICATIONS**

Use Newton's law of cooling to complete Exercises 75 and 76: $T(x) = T_R + (T_0 - T_R)e^{kx}$.

**75. Cold party drinks:** Janae was late getting ready for the party, and the liters of soft drinks she bought were still at room temperature (73°F) with guests due to arrive in 15 min. If she puts these in her freezer at −10°F, will the drinks be cold enough (35°F) for her guests? Assume $k \approx -0.031$.

**76. Warm party drinks:** Newton's law of cooling applies equally well if the "cooling is negative," meaning the object is taken from a colder medium and placed in a warmer one. If a can of soft drink is taken from a 35°F cooler and placed in a room where the temperature is 75°F, how long will it take the drink to warm to 65°F? Assume $k \approx -0.031$.

**77. Depreciation:**

The financial analyst for a large construction firm estimates that its heavy equipment loses one-fifth of its value each year. The current value of the equipment is then modeled by the function $V(t) = V_0(\frac{4}{5})^t$, where $V_0$ represents the initial value, $t$ is in years, and $V(t)$ represents the value after $t$ years. (a) How much is a large earthmover worth after 1 yr if it cost $125 thousand new? (b) How many years does it take for the earthmover to depreciate to a value of $64 thousand?

**78. Depreciation:** Photocopiers have become a critical part of the operation of many businesses, and due to their heavy use they can depreciate in value very quickly. If a copier loses $\frac{3}{8}$ of its value each year,

the current value of the copier can be modeled by the function $V(t) = V_0(\frac{5}{8})^t$, where $V_0$ represents the initial value, $t$ is in years, and $V(t)$ represents the value after $t$ yr. (a) How much is this copier worth after one year if it cost $64 thousand new? (b) How many years does it take for the copier to depreciate to a value of $25 thousand?

**79. Depreciation:** Margaret Madison, DDS, estimates that her dental equipment loses one-sixth of its value each year. (a) Determine the value of an x-ray machine after 5 yr if it cost $216 thousand new, and (b) determine how long until the machine is worth less than $125 thousand.

**80. Exponential decay:** The groundskeeper of a local high school estimates that due to heavy usage by the baseball and softball teams, the pitcher's mound loses one-fifth of its height every month. (a) Determine the height of the mound after 3 months if it was 25 cm to begin, and (b) determine how long until the pitcher's mound is less than 16 cm high (meaning it must be rebuilt).

81. **Exponential growth:** Similar to a small town doubling in size after a discovery of gold, a business that develops a product in high demand has the potential for doubling its revenue each year for a number of years. The revenue would be modeled by the function $R(t) = R_0 2^t$, where $R_0$ represents the initial revenue, and $R(t)$ represents the revenue after $t$ years. (a) How much revenue is being generated after 4 yr, if the company's initial revenue was $2.5 million? (b) How many years does it take for the business to be generating $320 million in revenue?

82. **Exponential growth:** If a company's revenue grows at a rate of 150% per year (rather than doubling as in Exercise 81), the revenue would be modeled by the function $R(t) = R_0(\frac{3}{2})^t$, where $R_0$ represents the initial revenue, and $R(t)$ represents the revenue after $t$ years. (a) How much revenue is being generated after 3 yr, if the company's initial revenue was $256 thousand? (b) How long until the business is generating $1944 thousand in revenue? (*Hint:* Reduce the fraction.)

**Photochromatic sunglasses:** Sunglasses that darken in sunlight (photochromatic sunglasses) contain millions of molecules of a substance known as *silver halide*. The molecules are transparent indoors in the absence of ultraviolent (UV) light. Outdoors, UV light from the sun causes the molecules to change shape, darkening the lenses in response to the intensity of the UV light. For certain lenses, the function $T(x) = 0.85^x$ models the transparency of the lenses (as a percentage) based on a UV index $x$. Find the transparency (to the nearest percent), if the lenses are exposed to

83. sunlight with a UV index of 7 (a high exposure).

84. sunlight with a UV index of 5.5 (a moderate exposure).

85. Given that a UV index of 11 is very high and most individuals should stay indoors, what is the minimum transparency percentage for these lenses?

86. Use trial-and-error to determine the UV index when the lenses are 50% transparent.

**Modeling inflation:** Assuming the rate of inflation is 5% per year, the predicted price of an item can be modeled by the function $P(t) = P_0(1.05)^t$, where $P_0$ represents the initial price of the item and $t$ is in years. Use this information to solve Exercises 87 and 88.

87. What will the price of a new car be in the year 2010, if it cost $20,000 in the year 2000?

88. What will the price of a gallon of milk be in the year 2010, if it cost $2.95 in the year 2000? Round to the nearest cent.

**Modeling radioactive decay:** The half-life of a radioactive substance is the time required for half an initial amount of the substance to disappear through decay. The amount of the substance remaining is given by the formula $Q(t) = Q_0(\frac{1}{2})^{\frac{t}{h}}$, where $h$ is the half-life, $t$ represents the elapsed time, and $Q(t)$ represents the amount that remains ($t$ and $h$ must have the same unit of time). Use this information to solve Exercises 89 and 90.

89. Some isotopes of the substance known as thorium have a half-life of only 8 min. (a) If 64 grams are initially present, how many grams (g) of the substance remain after 24 min? (b) How many minutes until only 1 gram (g) of the substance remains?

90. Some isotopes of sodium have a half-life of about 16 hr. (a) If 128 g are initially present, how many grams of the substance remain after 2 days (48 hr)? (b) How many hours until only 1 g of the substance remains?

▶ **EXTENDING THE CONCEPT**

91. If $10^{2x} = 25$, what is the value of $10^{-x}$?

92. If $5^{3x} = 27$, what is the value of $5^{2x}$?

93. If $3^{0.5x} = 5$, what is the value of $3^{x+1}$?

94. If $\left(\frac{1}{2}\right)^{x+1} = \frac{1}{3}$, what is the value of $\left(\frac{1}{2}\right)^{-x}$?

95. The formula $f(x) = (\frac{1}{2})^x$ gives the probability that "$x$" number of flips result in heads (or tails). First determine the probability that 20 flips results in *20 heads in a row*. Then use the Internet or some other resource to determine the probability of winning a state lottery (expressed as a decimal). Which has the greater probability? Were you surprised?

**The growth rate constant that governs an exponential function was introduced on page A-4.**

**96.** In later sections, we will easily be able to find the growth constant $k$ for Goldsboro, where $P(t) = 1000 \cdot 2^t$. For now we'll approximate its value using the rate of change formula on a very small interval of the domain. From the definition of an exponential function, $\dfrac{\Delta P}{\Delta t} = kP(t)$. Since $k$ is constant, we can choose any value of $t$, say

$t = 4$. For $h = 0.0001$, we have $\dfrac{1000 \cdot 2^{4+0.0001} - 1000 \cdot 2^4}{0.0001} = k \cdot P(4)$

(a) Use the equation shown to solve for $k$ (round to thousandths). (b) Show that $k$ is constant by completing the same exercise for $t = 2$ and $t = 6$. (c) Verify that $P(t) = 1000 \cdot 2^t$ and $P(t) = 1000e^{kt}$ give approximately the same results.

**97.** As we analyze the expression $\left(1 + \dfrac{1}{x}\right)^x$, we notice a battle (of sorts) takes place between the base $\left(1 + \dfrac{1}{x}\right)$ and

the exponent $x$. As $x \to \infty$, $\dfrac{1}{x}$ becomes infinitely small, but the exponent becomes infinitely large. So what happens? The answer is best understood by computing a series of *average rates of change,* using the intervals given here. Using the tools of Calculus, it can be shown that this rate of change becomes infinitely small, and that the "battle" ends at the irrational number $e$. In other words, $e$ is an upper bound on the value of this expression, regardless of how large $x$ becomes.

  **a.** Use a calculator to find the average rate of change for $y = \left(1 + \dfrac{1}{x}\right)^x$ in these intervals:  $[1, 1.01]$, $[4, 4.01]$, $[10, 10.01]$, and $[20, 20.01]$. What do you notice?

  **b.** What is the smallest integer value for $x$ that gives the value of $e$ correct to four decimal places?

  **c.** Use a graphing calculator to graph this function on a window size of $x \in [0, 25]$ and $y \in [0, 3]$. Does the graph seem to support the statements above?

## B | Logarithms and Logarithmic Functions

### Learning Objectives

*In Section B you will learn how to:*

☐ **A.** Write exponential equations in logarithmic form

☐ **B.** Find common logarithms and natural logarithms

☐ **C.** Graph logarithmic functions

☐ **D.** Find the domain of a logarithmic function

☐ **E.** Solve applications of logarithmic functions

A **transcendental function** is one whose solutions are beyond or *transcend* the methods applied to polynomial functions. The exponential function and its inverse, called the logarithmic function, are transcendental functions. In this section, we'll use the concept of an inverse to develop an understanding of the logarithmic function, which has numerous applications that include measuring pH levels, sound and earthquake intensities, barometric pressure, and other natural phenomena.

### A. Exponential Equations and Logarithmic Form

While exponential functions have a large number of significant applications, we can't appreciate their full value until we develop the inverse function. Without it, we're unable to solve all but the simplest equations, of the type encountered in Appendix I.A Using the fact that $f(x) = b^x$ is one-to-one, we have the following:

  **1.** The function $f^{-1}(x)$ must exist.
  **2.** We can graph $f^{-1}(x)$ by interchanging the $x$- and $y$-coordinates of points from $f(x)$.
  **3.** The domain of $f(x)$ will become the range of $f^{-1}(x)$.
  **4.** The range of $f(x)$ will become the domain of $f^{-1}(x)$.
  **5.** The graph of $f^{-1}(x)$ will be a reflection of $f(x)$ across the line $y = x$.

Table AI.2 contains selected values for $f(x) = 2^x$. The values for $f^{-1}(x)$ in Table AI.3 were found by interchanging $x$- and $y$-coordinates. Both functions were then graphed using these values.

**Table AI.2**

$f(x): y = 2^x$

| $x$ | $y$ |
|---|---|
| $-3$ | $\frac{1}{8}$ |
| $-2$ | $\frac{1}{4}$ |
| $-1$ | $\frac{1}{2}$ |
| $0$ | $1$ |
| $1$ | $2$ |
| $2$ | $4$ |
| $3$ | $8$ |

**Table AI.3**

$f^{-1}(x): x = 2^y$

| $x$ | $y = f^{-1}(x)$ |
|---|---|
| $\frac{1}{8}$ | $-3$ |
| $\frac{1}{4}$ | $-2$ |
| $\frac{1}{2}$ | $-1$ |
| $1$ | $0$ |
| $2$ | $1$ |
| $4$ | $2$ |
| $8$ | $3$ |

**Figure AI.5**

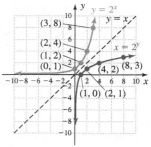

The interchange of $x$ and $y$ and the graphs in Figure AI.5 show that $f^{-1}(x)$ has an $x$-intercept of $(1, 0)$, a vertical asymptote at $x = 0$, a domain of $x \in (0, \infty)$, and a range of $y \in (-\infty, \infty)$. To find *an equation* for $f^{-1}(x)$, we'll attempt to use the algebraic approach employed in Section 6.1. For $f(x) = 2^x$,

**1.** use $y$ instead of $f(x)$: $y = 2^x$.
**2.** interchange $x$ and $y$: $x = 2^y$.

At this point we have an *implicit* equation for the inverse function, but no algebraic operations that enable us to solve *explicitly* for $y$ in terms of $x$. Instead, we write $x = 2^y$ in function form by noting that "$y$ is the exponent that goes on base 2 to obtain $x$." In the language of mathematics, this phrase is represented by $y = \log_2 x$ and is called a **logarithmic function** with base 2. For example, from Table AI.3 we have: $-3$ is the exponent that goes on base 2 to get $\frac{1}{8}$, and this is written $-3 = \log_2 \frac{1}{8}$ since $2^{-3} = \frac{1}{8}$.

For $y = b^x$, $x = b^y \rightarrow y = \log_b x$ is the inverse function, and is read, "$y$ is the logarithm base $b$ of $x$." For this new function, we must always keep in mind what $y$ *represents*—$y$ is an exponent. In fact, *$y$ is the exponent that goes on base $b$ to obtain $x$: $y = \log_b x$.*

**Logarithmic Functions**

For positive numbers $x$ and $b$, with $b \neq 1$,
$$y = \log_b x \text{ if and only if } x = b^y$$
The function $f(x) = \log_b x$ is a logarithmic function with base $b$. The expression $\log_b x$ is simply called a logarithm, and represents the exponent on $b$ that yields $x$.

Finally, note the equations $x = b^y$ and $y = \log_b x$ are equivalent. We say that $x = b^y$ is the **exponential form** of the equation, whereas $y = \log_b x$ is written in **logarithmic form.**

**EXAMPLE 1** ▶ **Converting from Logarithmic Form to Exponential Form**

Write each equation in words, then in exponential form.

**a.** $3 = \log_2 8$   **b.** $1 = \log_{10} 10$   **c.** $0 = \log_e 1$   **d.** $-2 = \log_3(\frac{1}{9})$

Solution ▶ **a.** $3 = \log_2 8 \rightarrow 3$ is the exponent on base 2 to obtain 8: $2^3 = 8$.
**b.** $1 = \log_{10} 10 \rightarrow 1$ is the exponent on base 10 to obtain 10: $10^1 = 10$.
**c.** $0 = \log_e 1 \rightarrow 0$ is the exponent on base $e$ to obtain 1: $e^0 = 1$.
**d.** $-2 = \log_3(\frac{1}{9}) \rightarrow -2$ is the exponent on base 3 to obtain $\frac{1}{9}$: $3^{-2} = \frac{1}{9}$.

Now try Exercises 7 through 22 ▶

To convert from exponential form to logarithmic form, note the exponent on the base and read from there. For $5^3 = 125$, "3 is the exponent that goes on base 5 to obtain 125," or *3 is the logarithm base 5 of 125*: $3 = \log_5 125$.

**EXAMPLE 2** ▶ **Converting from Exponential Form to Logarithmic Form**

Write each equation in words, then in logarithmic form.

**a.** $10^3 = 1000$   **b.** $2^{-1} = \frac{1}{2}$   **c.** $e^2 \approx 7.389$   **d.** $9^{\frac{3}{2}} = 27$

Solution ▶ **a.** $10^3 = 1000 \rightarrow 3$ is the exponent on base 10 to obtain 1000, or
3 is the logarithm base 10 of 1000: $3 = \log_{10} 1000$.
**b.** $2^{-1} = \frac{1}{2} \rightarrow -1$ is the exponent on base 2 to obtain $\frac{1}{2}$, or
$-1$ is the logarithm base 2 of $\frac{1}{2}$: $-1 = \log_2(\frac{1}{2})$.
**c.** $e^2 \approx 7.389 \rightarrow 2$ is the exponent on base $e$ to obtain 7.389, or
2 is the logarithm base $e$ of 7.389: $2 \approx \log_e 7.389$.
**d.** $9^{\frac{3}{2}} = 27 \rightarrow \frac{3}{2}$ is the exponent on base 9 to obtain 27, or
$\frac{3}{2}$ is the logarithm base 9 of 27: $\frac{3}{2} = \log_9 27$.

☑ **A.** You've just learned how to write exponential equations in logarithmic form

Now try Exercises 23 through 38 ▶

## B. Finding Common Logarithms and Natural Logarithms

Of all possible bases for $\log_b x$, the most common are base 10 (likely due to our base-10 number system), and base $e$ (due to the advantages it offers in advanced courses). The expression $\log_{10} x$ is called a **common logarithm,** and we simply write $\log x$ for $\log_{10} x$. The expression $\log_e x$ is called a **natural logarithm,** and is written in abbreviated form as $\ln x$.

Some logarithms are easy to evaluate. For example, $\log 100 = 2$ since $10^2 = 100$, and $\log \frac{1}{100} = -2$ since $10^{-2} = \frac{1}{100}$. But what about the expressions $\log 850$ and $\ln 4$? Because logarithmic functions are continuous on their domains, a value exists for $\log 850$ and the equation $10^x = 850$ must have a solution. Further, the inequalities

$$\log 100 < \log 850 < \log 1000$$
$$2 < \log 850 < 3$$

tell us that $\log 850$ must be between 2 and 3. Fortunately, modern calculators can compute base-10 and base-$e$ logarithms instantly, often with nine-decimal-place accuracy. For log 850, press ⬛ LOG, then input 850 and press ⬛ ENTER. The display should read 2.929418926. We can also use the calculator to verify $10^{2.929418926} = 850$ (see Figure AI.6). For ln 4, press the ⬛ LN key, then input 4 and press ⬛ ENTER to obtain 1.386294361. Figure AI.7 verifies that $e^{1.386294361} = 4$.

**WORTHY OF NOTE**

Since base-10 logarithms occur so frequently, we usually use only log $x$ to represent $\log_{10} x$. We do something similar with square roots. Technically, the "square root of $x$" should be written $\sqrt[2]{x}$. However, square roots are so common we often leave off the two, assuming that if no index is written, an index of two is intended.

**Figure AI.6**

```
log(850)
           2.929418926
10^Ans
                     850
```

**Figure AI.7**

```
ln(4)
           1.386294361
e^(Ans)
                      4
```

---

**EXAMPLE 3** ▶ **Finding the Value of a Logarithm**

Determine the value of each logarithm without using a calculator:

a. $\log_2 8$     b. $\log_5(\frac{1}{25})$     c. $\log_e e$     d. $\log_{10}\sqrt{10}$

**Solution** ▶ a. $\log_2 8$ represents the exponent on 2 to obtain 8: $\log_2 8 = 3$, since $2^3 = 8$.
b. $\log_5(\frac{1}{25})$ represents the exponent on 5 to obtain $\frac{1}{25}$: $\log_5\frac{1}{25} = -2$, since $5^{-2} = \frac{1}{25}$.
c. $\log_e e$ represents the exponent on $e$ to obtain $e$: $\log_e e = 1$, since $e^1 = e$.
d. $\log_{10}\sqrt{10}$ represents the exponent on 10 to obtain $\sqrt{10}$: $\log_{10}\sqrt{10} = \frac{1}{2}$, since $10^{\frac{1}{2}} = \sqrt{10}$.

**Now try Exercises 39 through 50 ▶**

---

**EXAMPLE 4** ▶ **Using a Calculator to Find Logarithms**

Use a calculator to evaluate each logarithmic expression. Verify the result.

a. log 1857     b. log 0.258     c. ln 3.592

**Solution** ▶ a. log 1857 = 3.268811904,         c. ln 3.592 ≈ 1.27870915
$10^{3.268811904} = 1857$ ✓        $e^{1.27870915} \approx 3.592$ ✓

☑ **B.** You've just learned how to find common logarithms and natural logarithms

b. log 0.258 = −0.588380294,
$10^{-0.588380294} = 0.258$ ✓

**Now try Exercises 51 through 58 ▶**

## C. Graphing Logarithmic Functions

For convenience and ease of calculation, our first examples of logarithmic graphs are done using base-2 logarithms. However, the basic shape of a logarithmic graph remains unchanged regardless of the base used, and transformations can be applied to $y = \log_b(x)$ for any value of $b$. For $y = a\log(x \pm h) \pm k$, $a$ continues to govern stretches, compressions, and vertical reflections, the graph will shift horizontally $h$ units opposite the sign, and shift $k$ units vertically in the same direction as the sign. Our earlier graph of $y = \log_2 x$ was completed using $x = 2^y$ as the inverse function for $y = 2^x$ (Figure AI.5). For reference, the graph is repeated in Figure AI.8.

**WORTHY OF NOTE**

As with the basic graphs, logarithmic graphs maintain the same characteristics when transformations are applied, and these graphs *should be added to your collection of basic functions,* ready for recall or analysis as the situation requires.

**Figure AI.8**

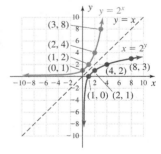

**EXAMPLE 5** ▶ **Graphing Logarithmic Functions Using Transformations**

Graph $f(x) = \log_2(x - 3) + 1$ using transformations of $y = \log_2 x$ (not by simply plotting points). Clearly state what transformations are applied.

**Solution** ▶ The graph of $f$ is the same as that of $y = \log_2 x$, shifted 3 units right and 1 unit up. The vertical asymptote will be at $x = 3$ and the point $(1, 0)$ from the basic graph becomes $(1 + 3, 0 + 1) = (4, 1)$. Knowing the graph's basic shape, we compute one additional point using $x = 7$:

**Figure AI.9**

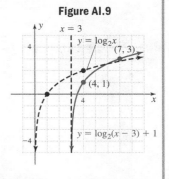

$$f(7) = \log_2(7 - 3) + 1$$
$$= \log_2 4 + 1$$
$$= 2 + 1$$
$$= 3$$

The point $(7, 3)$ is on the graph, shown in Figure AI.9.

**Now try Exercises 59 through 62** ▶

As with the exponential functions, much can be learned from graphs of logarithmic functions and a summary of important characteristics is given here.

---

$f(x) = \log_b x$, $b > 0$ and $b \neq 1$

- one-to-one function
- domain: $x \in (0, \infty)$
- increasing if $b > 1$

- $x$-intercept $(1, 0)$
- range: $y \in \mathbb{R}$
- decreasing if $0 < b < 1$

- asymptotic to the $y$-axis (the line $x = 0$)

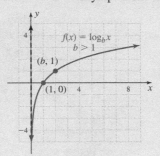 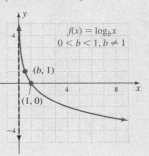

---

**EXAMPLE 6** ▶ **Graphing Logarithmic Functions Using Transformations**

Graph $g(x) = -\ln(x + 2)$ using transformations of $y = \ln x$ (not by simply plotting points). Clearly state what transformations are applied.

**Solution** ▶ The graph of $g$ is the same as $y = \ln x$, shifted 2 units left, then reflected across the $x$-axis. The vertical asymptote will be at $x = -2$, and the point $(1, 0)$ from the basic function becomes $(-1, 0)$. To complete the graph we compute $f(6)$:

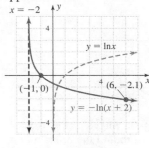

**WORTHY OF NOTE**

Accurate graphs can actually be drawn for logarithms of *any base* using what is called the change-of-base formula, introduced in Appendix I.C

$$f(6) = -\ln(6 + 2)$$
$$= -\ln 8$$
$$\approx -2.1 \text{ (using a calculator).}$$

☑ **C.** You've just learned how to graph logarithmic functions

The point $(6, -2.1)$ is on the graph shown in the figure.

**Now try Exercises 63 through 72** ▶

## D. Finding the Domain of a Logarithmic Function

Examples 5 and 6 illustrate how the domain of a logarithmic function can change when certain transformations are applied. Since the domain consists of *positive* real numbers, the argument of a logarithmic function must be greater than zero. This means finding the domain often consists of solving various inequalities.

**EXAMPLE 7** ▶ **Finding the Domain of a Logarithmic Function**

Determine the domain of each function.

**a.** $p(x) = \log_2(2x + 3)$        **b.** $q(x) = \log_5(x^2 - 2x)$

**c.** $r(x) = \log\left(\dfrac{3 - x}{x + 3}\right)$        **d.** $f(x) = \ln|x - 2|$

**Solution** ▶ Begin by writing the argument of each logarithmic function as a greater than inequality.

**a.** Solving $2x + 3 > 0$ for $x$ gives $x > -\frac{3}{2}$, and the domain of $p$ is $x \in (-\frac{3}{2}, \infty)$.

**b.** For $x^2 - 2x > 0$, we note $y = x^2 - 2x$ is a parabola, opening upward, with zeroes at $x = 0$ and $x = 2$ (see Figure AI.10). This means $x^2 - 2x$ will be positive for $x < 0$ and $x > 2$. The domain of $q$ is $x \in (-\infty, 0) \cup (2, \infty)$.

**Figure AI.10**

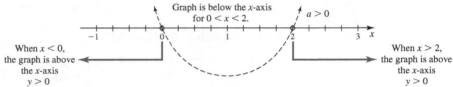

Graph is below the $x$-axis for $0 < x < 2$.     $a > 0$

When $x < 0$, the graph is above the $x$-axis $y > 0$

When $x > 2$, the graph is above the $x$-axis $y > 0$

**c.** For $\dfrac{3 - x}{x + 3} > 0$, we note $y = \dfrac{3 - x}{x + 3}$ has a zero at $x = 3$, and a vertical asymptote at $x = -3$. Outputs are positive when $x = 0$ (see Figure AI.11), so $y$ is positive in the interval $(-3, 3)$ and negative elsewhere. The domain of $r$ is $x \in (-3, 3)$.

**Figure AI.11**

When $-3 < x < 3$, $y > 0$ (interval test)

When $x < -3, y < 0$        When $x > 3, y < 0$

**d.** For $|x - 2| > 0$, we note $y = |x - 2|$ is the graph of $y = |x|$ shifted 2 units right, with its vertex at $(2, 0)$. The graph is positive for all $x$, except at $x = 2$. The domain of $f$ is $x \in (-\infty, 2) \cup (2, \infty)$.

**Now try Exercises 73 through 78** ▶

**GRAPHICAL SUPPORT**

The domain for $r(x) = \log_{10}\left(\dfrac{3 - x}{x + 3}\right)$ from Example 7(c) can be confirmed using the [ LOG ] key on a graphing calculator. Use the key to enter the equation as $Y_1$ on the [ Y= ] screen, then graph the function using the [ ZOOM ] **4:ZDecimal** option. Both the graph and TABLE feature help to confirm the domain is $x \in (-3, 3)$.

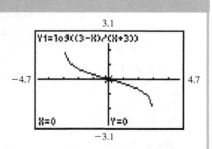

✓ **D.** You've just learned how to find the domain of a logarithmic function

# E. Applications of Logarithms

As we use mathematics to model the real world, there are times when the range of outcomes is so large that using a linear scale would be hard to manage. For example, compared to a whisper—the scream of a jet engine may be up to *ten billion times* louder. Similar ranges exist in the measurement of earthquakes, light, acidity, and voltage. In lieu of a linear scale, logarithms are used where each whole number increase in magnitude represents a tenfold increase in the intensity. For earthquake intensities (a measure of the wave energy produced by the quake), units called **magnitudes** (or **Richter values**) are used. Earthquakes with a magnitude of 6.5 or more often cause significant damage, while the slightest earthquakes have magnitudes near 1 and are barely perceptible. The magnitude of the intensity $M(I)$ is given by $M(I) = \log\left(\dfrac{I}{I_0}\right)$ where $I$ is the measured intensity and $I_0$ represents a minimum or **reference intensity.** The value of $I$ is often given as a multiple of this reference intensity.

---

**EXAMPLE 8A** ▶ **Finding the Magnitude of an Earthquake**

Find the magnitude of an earthquake (rounded to hundredths) with the intensities given.

    **a.** $I = 4000I_0$     **b.** $I = 8{,}252{,}000I_0$

**Solution** ▶   **a.** $\quad M(I) = \log\left(\dfrac{I}{I_0}\right)$             magnitude equation

$$M(4000I_0) = \log\left(\dfrac{4000I_0}{I_0}\right) \quad\quad \text{substitute } 4000I_0 \text{ for } I$$

$$= \log 4000 \quad\quad\quad\quad \text{simplify}$$

$$\approx 3.60 \quad\quad\quad\quad\quad \text{result}$$

The earthquake had a magnitude of 3.6.

    **b.** $\quad\quad M(I) = \log\left(\dfrac{I}{I_0}\right)$           magnitude equation

$$M(8{,}252{,}000I_0) = \log\left(\dfrac{8{,}252{,}000I_0}{I_0}\right) \quad \text{substitute } 8{,}252{,}000 \, I_0 \text{ for } I$$

$$= \log 8{,}252{,}000 \quad\quad \text{simplify}$$

$$\approx 6.92 \quad\quad\quad\quad\quad \text{result}$$

The earthquake had a magnitude of about 6.92.

---

**EXAMPLE 8B** ▶ **Comparing Earthquake Intensity to the Reference Intensity**

How many times more intense than the reference intensity $I_0$ is an earthquake with a magnitude of 6.7?

**Solution** ▶        $M(I) = \log\left(\dfrac{I}{I_0}\right)$        magnitude equation

$$6.7 = \log\left(\dfrac{I}{I_0}\right) \quad\quad \text{substitute 6.7 for } M(I)$$

$$10^{6.7} = \left(\dfrac{I}{I_0}\right) \quad\quad \text{exponential form}$$

$$I = 10^{6.7}I_0 \quad\quad\quad \text{solve for } I$$

$$I = 5{,}011{,}872I_0 \quad\quad 10^{6.7} \approx 5{,}011{,}872$$

An earthquake of magnitude 6.7 is over 5 million times more intense than the reference intensity.

**EXAMPLE 8C** ▶ **Comparing Earthquake Intensities**

The Great San Francisco Earthquake of 1906 left over 800 dead, did $80,000,000 in damage (see photo), and had an estimated magnitude of 7.7. The 2004 Indian Ocean earthquake, which had a magnitude of approximately 9.2, triggered a series of deadly tsunamis and was responsible for nearly 300,000 casualties. How much more intense was the 2004 quake?

**Solution** ▶ To find the intensity of each quake, substitute the given magnitude for $M(I)$ and solve for $I$:

$$M(I) = \log\left(\frac{I}{I_0}\right) \quad \text{magnitude equation} \qquad M(I) = \log\left(\frac{I}{I_0}\right)$$

$$7.7 = \log\left(\frac{I}{I_0}\right) \quad \text{substitute for } M(I) \qquad 9.2 = \log\left(\frac{I}{I_0}\right)$$

$$10^{7.7} = \left(\frac{I}{I_0}\right) \quad \text{exponential form} \qquad 10^{9.2} = \left(\frac{I}{I_0}\right)$$

$$10^{7.7}I_0 = I \quad \text{solve for } I \qquad 10^{9.2}I_0 = I$$

Using these intensities, we find that the Indian Ocean quake was $\frac{10^{9.2}}{10^{7.7}} = 10^{1.5} \approx 31.6$ times more intense.

**Now try Exercises 81 through 90** ▶

A second application of logarithmic functions involves the relationship between altitude and barometric pressure. The altitude or height above sea level can be determined by the formula $H = (30T + 8000)\ln\left(\frac{P_0}{P}\right)$, where $H$ is the altitude in meters for a temperature $T$ in degrees Celsius, $P$ is the barometric pressure at a given altitude in units called **centimeters of mercury** (cmHg), and $P_0$ is the barometric pressure at sea level: 76 cmHg.

**EXAMPLE 9** ▶ **Using Logarithms to Determine Altitude**

Hikers at the summit of Mt. Shasta in northern California take a pressure reading of 45.1 cmHg at a temperature of 9°C. How high is Mt. Shasta?

**Solution** ▶ For this exercise, $P_0 = 76$, $P = 45.1$, and $T = 9$. The formula yields

$$H = (30T + 8000)\ln\left(\frac{P_0}{P}\right) \quad \text{given formula}$$

$$= [30(9) + 8000]\ln\left(\frac{76}{45.1}\right) \quad \text{substitute given values}$$

$$= 8270\ln\left(\frac{76}{45.1}\right) \quad \text{simplify}$$

$$\approx 4316 \quad \text{result}$$

Mt. Shasta is about 4316 m high.

**Now try Exercises 91 through 94** ▶

Our final application shows the versatility of logarithmic functions, and their value as a real-world model. Large advertising agencies are well aware that after a new ad campaign, sales will increase rapidly as more people become aware of the product. Continued advertising will give the new product additional market share, but once the "newness" wears off and the competition begins responding, sales tend to taper off—regardless of any additional amount spent on ads. This phenomenon can be modeled by the function

$$S(d) = k + a \ln d,$$

where $S(d)$ is the number of expected sales after $d$ dollars are spent, and $a$ and $k$ are constants related to product type and market size.

---

**EXAMPLE 10** ▶ **Using Logarithms for Marketing Strategies**

Market research has shown that sales of the MusicMaster, a new system for downloading and playing music, can be approximated by the equation $S(d) = 2500 + 250 \ln d$, where $S(d)$ is the number of sales after $d$ thousand dollars is spent on advertising.

   **a.** What sales volume is expected if the advertising budget is \$40,000?

   **b.** If the company needs to sell 3500 units to begin making a profit, how much should be spent on advertising?

   **c.** To gain a firm hold on market share, the company is willing to continue spending on advertising up to a point where only 3 additional sales are gained for each \$1000 spent, in other words, $\dfrac{\Delta S}{\Delta d} = \dfrac{3}{1}$. Verify that spending between \$83,200 and \$83,300 puts them very close to this goal.

Solution ▶    **a.** For sales volume, we simply evaluate the function for $d = 40$ ($d$ in thousands):

$$
\begin{aligned}
S(d) &= 2500 + 250 \ln d &&\text{given equation}\\
S(40) &= 2500 + 250 \ln 40 &&\text{substitute 40 for } d\\
&\approx 2500 + 922 &&250 \ln 40 \approx 922\\
&= 3422
\end{aligned}
$$

Spending \$40,000 on advertising will generate approximately 3422 sales.

   **b.** To find the advertising budget needed, we substitute number of sales and solve for $d$.

$$
\begin{aligned}
S(d) &= 2500 + 250 \ln d &&\text{given equation}\\
3500 &= 2500 + 250 \ln d &&\text{substitute 3500 for } S(d)\\
1000 &= 250 \ln d &&\text{subtract 2500}\\
4 &= \ln d &&\text{divide by 250}\\
e^4 &= d &&\text{exponential form}\\
54.598 &\approx d &&e^4 \approx 54.598
\end{aligned}
$$

About \$54,600 should be spent in order to sell 3500 units.

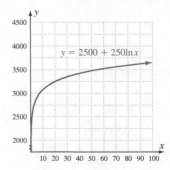

**c.** To verify, we calculate the average rate of change on the interval [83.2, 83.3].

$$\frac{\Delta S}{\Delta d} = \frac{S(d_2) - S(d_1)}{d_2 - d_1}$$    formula for average rate of change

$$= \frac{S(83.3) - S(83.2)}{83.3 - 83.2}$$    substitute 83.3 for $d_2$ and 83.2 for $d_1$

$$\approx \frac{3605.6 - 3605.3}{0.1}$$    evaluate $S$(83.3) and $S$(83.2)

$$= 3$$

The average rate of change in this interval is very close to $\frac{3}{1}$.

 **E.** You've just learned how to solve applications of logarithmic functions

**Now try Exercises 95 and 96** ▶

## B EXERCISES

▶ **CONCEPTS AND VOCABULARY**

**Fill in each blank with the appropriate word or phrase. Carefully reread the section if needed.**

1. A logarithmic function is of the form $y = $ _____, where ____ $> 0$, ____ $\neq 1$ and inputs are _____ than zero.

2. The range of $y = \log_b x$ is all _____ _____, and the domain is $x \in$ _____. Further, as $x \to 0$, $y \to$ ___.

3. For logarithmic functions of the form $y = \log_b x$, the x-intercept is _____, since $\log_b 1 = $ ____.

4. The function $y = \log_b x$ is an increasing function if _____, and a decreasing function if _____.

5. What number does the expression $\log_2 32$ represent? Discuss/Explain how $\log_2 32 = \log_2 2^5$ justifies this fact.

6. Explain how the graph of $Y = \log_b(x - 3)$ can be obtained from $y = \log_b x$. Where is the "new" x-intercept? Where is the new asymptote?

▶ **DEVELOPING YOUR SKILLS**

**Write each equation in exponential form.**

7. $3 = \log_2 8$

8. $2 = \log_3 9$

9. $-1 = \log_7 \frac{1}{7}$

10. $-3 = \log_e \frac{1}{e^3}$

11. $0 = \log_9 1$

12. $0 = \log_e 1$

13. $\frac{1}{3} = \log_8 2$

14. $\frac{1}{2} = \log_{81} 9$

15. $1 = \log_2 2$

16. $1 = \log_e e$

17. $\log_7 49 = 2$

18. $\log_4 16 = 2$

19. $\log_{10} 100 = 2$

20. $\log_{10} 10,000 = 4$

21. $\log_e(54.598) \approx 4$

22. $\log_{10} 0.001 = -3$

**Write each equation in logarithmic form.**

23. $4^3 = 64$

24. $e^3 \approx 20.086$

25. $3^{-2} = \frac{1}{9}$

26. $2^{-3} = \frac{1}{8}$

27. $e^0 = 1$

28. $8^0 = 1$

29. $\left(\frac{1}{3}\right)^{-3} = 27$

30. $\left(\frac{1}{5}\right)^{-2} = 25$

31. $10^3 = 1000$

32. $e^1 = e$

33. $10^{-2} = \frac{1}{100}$

34. $10^{-5} = \frac{1}{100,000}$

35. $4^{\frac{3}{2}} = 8$

36. $e^{\frac{3}{4}} \approx 2.117$

37. $4^{\frac{-3}{2}} = \frac{1}{8}$

38. $27^{\frac{-2}{3}} = \frac{1}{9}$

**Determine the value of each logarithm without using a calculator.**

39. $\log_4 4$

40. $\log_9 9$

41. $\log_{11} 121$

42. $\log_{12} 144$

**43.** $\log_e e$

**44.** $\log_e e^2$

**45.** $\log_4 2$

**46.** $\log_{81} 9$

**47.** $\log_7 \frac{1}{49}$

**48.** $\log_9 \frac{1}{81}$

**49.** $\log_e \frac{1}{e^2}$

**50.** $\log_e \frac{1}{\sqrt{e}}$

**Use a calculator to evaluate each expression, rounded to four decimal places.**

**51.** $\log 50$

**52.** $\log 47$

**53.** $\ln 1.6$

**54.** $\ln 0.75$

**55.** $\ln 225$

**56.** $\ln 381$

**57.** $\log \sqrt{37}$

**58.** $\log 4\pi$

**Graph each function *using transformations* of $y = \log_b x$ and strategically plotting a few points. Clearly state the transformations applied.**

**59.** $f(x) = \log_2 x + 3$

**60.** $g(x) = \log_2(x - 2)$

**61.** $h(x) = \log_2(x - 2) + 3$

**62.** $p(x) = \log_3 x - 2$

**63.** $q(x) = \ln(x + 1)$

**64.** $r(x) = \ln(x + 1) - 2$

**65.** $Y_1 = -\ln(x + 1)$

**66.** $Y_2 = -\ln x + 2$

**Use the transformation equation $y = af(x \pm h) \pm k$ and the asymptotes and intercept(s) of the parent function to match each equation to one of the graphs given.**

**67.** $y = \log_b(x + 2)$

**68.** $y = 2\log_b x$

**69.** $y = 1 - \log_b x$

**70.** $y = \log_b x - 1$

**71.** $y = \log_b x + 2$

**72.** $y = -\log_b x$

I.
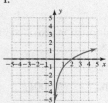

II.
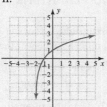

III.
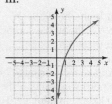

IV.
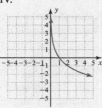

V.
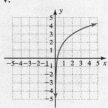

VI.
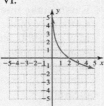

**Determine the domain of the following functions.**

**73.** $y = \log_6\left(\dfrac{x + 1}{x - 3}\right)$

**74.** $y = \ln\left(\dfrac{x - 2}{x + 3}\right)$

**75.** $y = \log_5 \sqrt{2x - 3}$

**76.** $y = \ln\sqrt{5 - 3x}$

**77.** $y = \log(9 - x^2)$

**78.** $y = \ln(9x - x^2)$

▶ **WORKING THE FORMULAS**

**79. pH level:** $f(x) = -\log_{10} x$

The pH level of a solution indicates the concentration of hydrogen ($H^+$) ions in a unit called *moles per liter*. The pH level $f(x)$ is given by the formula shown, where $x$ is the ion concentration (given in scientific notation). A solution with pH $< 7$ is called an acid (lemon juice: pH $\approx 2$), and a solution with pH $> 7$ is called a base (household ammonia: pH $\approx 11$). Use the formula to determine the pH level of tomato juice if $x = 7.94 \times 10^{-5}$ moles per liter. Is this an acid or base solution?

**80. Time required for an investment to double:**
$$T(r) = \frac{\log 2}{\log(1 + r)}$$

The time required for an investment to double in value is given by the formula shown, where $r$ represents the interest rate (expressed as a decimal) and $T(r)$ gives the years required. How long would it take an investment to double if the interest rate were (a) 5%, (b) 8%, (c) 12%?

▶ **APPLICATIONS**

**Earthquake intensity:** Use the information provided in Example 8 to answer the following.

**81.** Find the value of $M(I)$ given

    **a.** $I = 50{,}000I_0$    and    **b.** $I = 75{,}000I_0$.

**82.** Find the intensity $I$ of the earthquake given

    **a.** $M(I) = 3.2$    and    **b.** $M(I) = 8.1$.

**83. Earthquake intensity:** On June 25, 1989, an earthquake with magnitude 6.2 shook the southeast side of the Island of Hawaii (near Kalapana), causing some $1,000,000 in damage. On October 15, 2006, an earthquake measuring 6.7 on the Richter scale shook the northwest side of the island, causing over $100,000,000 in damage. How much more intense was the 2006 quake?

**84. Earthquake intensity:** The most intense earthquake of the modern era occurred in Chile on May 22, 1960, and measured 9.5 on the Richter scale. How many times more intense was this earthquake, than the quake that hit Northern Sumatra (Indonesia) on March 28, 2005, and measured 8.7?

**Brightness of a star:** The brightness or intensity $I$ of a star as perceived by the naked eye is measured in units called *magnitudes*. The brightest stars have magnitude $1\ [M(I) = 1]$ and the dimmest have magnitude $6\ [M(I) = 6]$. The magnitude of a star is given by the equation $M(I) = 6 - 2.5 \cdot \log\left(\dfrac{I}{I_0}\right)$, where $I$ is the actual intensity of light from the star and $I_0$ is the faintest light visible to the human eye, called the reference intensity. The intensity $I$ is often given as a multiple of this reference intensity.

**85.** Find the value of $M(I)$ given

    **a.** $I = 27I_0$    and    **b.** $I = 85I_0$.

**86.** Find the intensity $I$ of a star given

    **a.** $M(I) = 1.6$    and    **b.** $M(I) = 5.2$.

**Intensity of sound:** The intensity of sound as perceived by the human ear is measured in units called decibels (dB). The loudest sounds that can be withstood without damage to the eardrum are in the 120- to 130-dB range, while a whisper may measure in the 15- to 20-dB range. Decibel measure is given by the equation $D(I) = 10\log\left(\dfrac{I}{I_0}\right)$, where $I$ is the actual intensity of the sound and $I_0$ is the faintest sound perceptible by the human ear—called the reference intensity. The intensity $I$ is often given as a multiple of this reference intensity, but often the constant $10^{-16}$ (watts per cm$^2$; W/cm$^2$) is used as the threshold of audibility.

**87.** Find the value of $D(I)$ given

    **a.** $I = 10^{-14}$    and    **b.** $I = 10^{-4}$.

**88.** Find the intensity $I$ of the sound given

    **a.** $D(I) = 83$    and    **b.** $D(I) = 125$.

**89. Sound intensity of a hair dryer:** Every morning (it seems), Jose is awakened by the mind-jarring, ear-jamming sound of his daughter's hair dryer (75 dB). He knew he was exaggerating, but told her (many times) of how it reminded him of his railroad days, when the air compressor for the pneumatic tools was running (110 dB). In fact, how many times more intense was the sound of the air compressor compared to the sound of the hair dryer?

**90. Sound intensity of a busy street:** The decibel level of noisy, downtown traffic has been estimated at 87 dB, while the laughter and banter at a loud party might be in the 60 dB range. How many times more intense is the sound of the downtown traffic?

The *barometric equation* $H = (30T + 8000)\ln\left(\dfrac{P_0}{P}\right)$ was discussed in Example 9.

**91. Temperature and atmospheric pressure:** Determine the height of Mount McKinley (Alaska), if the temperature at the summit is $-10°C$, with a barometric reading of 34 cmHg.

**92. Temperature and atmospheric pressure:** A large passenger plane is flying cross-country. The instruments on board show an air temperature of $3°C$, with a barometric pressure of 22 cmHg. What is the altitude of the plane?

**93. Altitude and atmospheric pressure:** By definition, a mountain pass is a low point between two mountains. Passes may be very short with steep slopes, or as large as a valley between two peaks. Perhaps the highest drivable pass in the world is the Semo La pass in central Tibet. At its highest elevation, a temperature reading of $8°C$ was taken, along with a barometer reading of 39.3 cmHg. (a) Approximately how high is the Semo La pass? (b) While traveling up to this pass, an elevation marker is seen. If the barometer reading was 47.1 cmHg at a temperature of $12°C$, what height did the marker give?

**94. Altitude and atmospheric pressure:** Hikers on Mt. Everest take successive readings of 35 cmHg at 5°C and 30 cmHg at −10°C. (a) How far up the mountain are they at each reading? (b) Approximate the height of Mt. Everest if the temperature at the summit is −27°C and the barometric pressure is 22.2 cmHg.

**95. Marketing budgets:** An advertising agency has determined the number of items sold by a certain client is modeled by the equation $N(A) = 1500 + 315 \ln A$, where $N(A)$ represents the number of sales after spending $A$ thousands of dollars on advertising. Determine the approximate number of items sold on an advertising budget of (a) $10,000; (b) $50,000. (c) Use the TABLE feature of a calculator to estimate how large a budget is needed (to the nearest $500 dollars) to sell 3000 items. (d) This company is willing to continue advertising as long as eight additional sales are gained for every $1000 spent: $\dfrac{\Delta N}{\Delta A} = \dfrac{8}{1}$. Show this occurs by spending between $39,300 to $39,400.

**96. Sports promotions:** The accountants for a major boxing promoter have determined that the number of pay-per-view subscriptions sold to their championship bouts can be modeled by the function $N(d) = 15,000 + 5850 \ln d$, where $N(d)$ represents the number of subscriptions sold after spending $d$ thousand dollars on promotional activities. Determine the number of subscriptions sold if (a) $50,000 and (b) $100,000 is spent. (c) Use the TABLE feature of a calculator to estimate how much should be spent (to the nearest $1000 dollars) to sell over 50,000 subscriptions. (d) This promoter is willing to continue promotional spending as long as 14 additional subscriptions are sold for every $1000 spent: $\dfrac{\Delta N}{\Delta d} = \dfrac{14}{1}$. Show this occurs by spending between $417,800 and $417,900.

**97. Home ventilation:** In the construction of new housing, there is considerable emphasis placed on correct ventilation. If too little outdoor air enters a home, pollutants can sometimes accumulate to levels that pose a health risk. For homes of various sizes, ventilation requirements have been established and are based on floor area and the number of bedrooms. For a three-bedroom home, the relationship can be modeled by the function $C(x) = 42 \ln x - 270$, where $C(x)$ represents the number of cubic feet of air per minute (cfm) that should be exchanged with outside air in a home with floor area $x$ (in square feet). (a) How many cfm of exchanged air are needed for a three-bedroom home with a floor area of 2500 ft²? (b) If a three-bedroom home is being mechanically ventilated by a system with 40 cfm capacity, what is the square footage of the home, assuming it is built to code?

**98. Runway takeoff distance:** Many will remember the August 27, 2006, crash of a commuter jet at Lexington's Blue Grass Airport, that was mistakenly trying to take off on a runway that was just too short. Forty-nine lives were lost. The

minimum required length of a runway depends on the maximum allowable takeoff weight (mtw) of a specific plane. This relationship can be approximated by the function $L(x) = 2085 \ln x - 14,900$, where $L(x)$ represents the required length of a runway in feet, for a plane with $x$ mtw in pounds.

   **a.** The Airbus-320 has a 169,750 lb mtw. What minimum runway length is required for takeoff?

   **b.** A Learjet 30 model requires a runway of 5550 ft to takeoff safely. What is its mtw?

**Memory retention:** Under certain conditions, a person's retention of random facts can be modeled by the equation $P(x) = 95 - 14 \log_2 x$, where $P(x)$ is the percentage of those facts retained after $x$ number of days. Find the percentage of facts a person might retain after:

**99. a.** 1 day       **b.** 4 days       **c.** 16 days

**100. a.** 32 days     **b.** 64 days     **c.** 78 days

**101. pH level:** Use the formula given in Exercise 79 to determine the pH level of black coffee if $x = 5.1 \times 10^{-5}$ moles per liter. Is black coffee considered an acid or base solution?

**102.** The length of time required for an amount of money to *triple* is given by the formula

$$T(r) = \frac{\log 3}{\log(1 + r)} \text{ (refer to Exercise 80). Construct}$$

a table of values to help estimate what interest rate is needed for an investment to triple in nine years.

▶ **EXTENDING THE CONCEPT**

**103.** Many texts and reference books give estimates of the noise level (in decibels dB) of common sounds. Through reading and research, try to locate or approximate where the following sounds would fall along this scale. In addition, determine at what point pain or ear damage begins to occur.

    **a.** threshold of audibility    **b.** lawn mower

    **c.** whisper               **d.** loud rock concert

    **e.** lively party          **f.** jet engine

**104.** Determine the value of $x$ that makes the equation true: $\log_3[\log_3(\log_3 x)] = 0$.

**105.** Find the value of each expression without using a calculator.

    **a.** $\log_{64}\frac{1}{16}$     **b.** $\log_{\frac{4}{9}}\frac{27}{8}$     **c.** $\log_{0.25}32$

**106.** Suppose you and I represent two different numbers. Is the following cryptogram true or false? *The log of me base me is one and the log of you base you is one, but the log of you base me is equal to the log of me base you turned upside down.*

## MID-CHAPTER CHECK

**1.** Write the following in logarithmic form.

    **a.** $27^{\frac{2}{3}} = 9$            **b.** $81^{\frac{5}{4}} = 243$

**2.** Write the following in exponential form.

    **a.** $\log_8 32 = \frac{5}{3}$       **b.** $\log_{1296}6 = 0.25$

**3.** Solve each equation for the unknown:

    **a.** $4^{2x} = 32^{x-1}$       **b.** $\left(\frac{1}{3}\right)^{4b} = 9^{2b-5}$

**4.** Solve each equation for the unknown:

    **a.** $\log_{27}x = \frac{1}{3}$       **b.** $\log_b 125 = 3$

 **5.** The homes in a popular neighborhood are growing in value according to the formula $V(t) = V_0\left(\frac{9}{8}\right)^t$, where $t$ is the time in years, $V_0$ is the purchase price of the home, and $V(t)$ is the current value of the home. (a) In 3 yr, how much will a $50,000 home be worth? (b) Use the TABLE feature of your calculator to estimate how many years (to the nearest year) until the home doubles in value.

**6.** The graph of the function $f(x) = 5^x$ has been shifted right 3 units, up 2 units, and stretched by a factor of 4. What is the equation of the resulting function?

**7.** Gianni is ready to dig into a steaming plate of gnocchi, but at 200°F it is too hot to eat. The temperature in the room is 75°F and the cooling rate for this pasta is $k = -0.28$. (a) What is the temperature (to the nearest degree) of the gnocchi 3 min later? (b) Use the TABLE feature of your calculator to estimate (to the nearest minute) when the gnocchi has cooled to 105°.

**8.** Write the following equations in logarithmic form, then verify the result on a calculator.

    **a.** $81 = 3^4$            **b.** $e^4 \approx 54.598$

**9.** Write the following equations in exponential form, then verify the result on a calculator.

    **a.** $\frac{2}{3} = \log_{27}9$       **b.** $1.4 \approx \ln 4.0552$

**10.** On August 15, 2007, an earthquake measuring 8.0 on the Richter scale struck coastal Peru. On October 17, 1989, right before Game 3 of the World Series between the Oakland A's and the San Francisco Giants, the Loma Prieta earthquake, measuring 7.1 on the Richter scale, struck the San Francisco Bay area. How much more intense was the Peruvian earthquake?

## REINFORCING BASIC CONCEPTS

### Linear and Logarithmic Scales

The use of logarithmic scales as a tool of measurement is primarily due to the range of values for the phenomenon being measured. For instance, time is generally measured on a linear scale, and for short periods a linear scale is appropriate. For the time line in Figure AI.12, each tick-mark *represents 1 unit,* and the time line can display a period of 10 yr.

However, the scale would be useless in a study of world history or geology. If we scale the number line logarithmically, each tick-mark *represents a power of 10* (Figure AI.13) and a scale of the same length can now display a time period of 10 billion years.

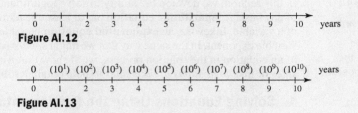

**Figure AI.12**

**Figure AI.13**

In much the same way, logarithmic measures are needed in a study of sound and earthquake intensity, as the scream of a jet engine is over 1 billion times more intense than the threshold of hearing, and the most destructive earthquakes are billions of times stronger than the slightest earth movement that can be felt. Figures AI.14 and AI.15 show logarithmic scales for measuring sound in decibels (1 bel = 10 decibels) and earthquake intensity in Richter values (or magnitudes).

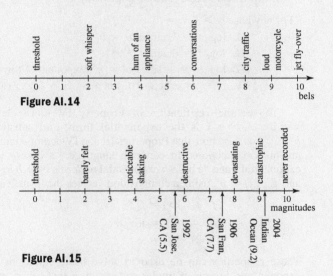

**Figure AI.14**

**Figure AI.15**

As you view these scales, remember that each unit increase represents a power of 10. For instance, the 1906 San Francisco earthquake was $7.7 - 5.5 = 2.2$ magnitudes greater than the San Jose quake of 1992, meaning it was $10^{2.2} \approx 158$ *times more intense*. Use this information to complete the following exercises. Determine how many times more intense the first sound is compared to the second.

**Exercise 1:** jet engine: 14 bels; rock concert: 11.8 bels

**Exercise 2:** pneumatic hammer: 11.2 bels; heavy lawn mower: 8.5 bels

**Exercise 3:** train horn: 7.5 bels; soft music: 3.4 bels

Determine how many times more intense the first quake was compared to the second.

**Exercise 4:** Great Chilean (1960): magnitude 9.5; Kobe, Japan (1995): magnitude 6.9

**Exercise 5:** Northern Sumatra (2004): magnitude 9.1; Southern Greece (2008): magnitude 4.5

# C | Properties of Logarithms; Solving Exponential/Logarithmic Equations

## Learning Objectives

*In Section C you will learn how to:*

☐ **A.** Solve logarithmic equations using the fundamental properties of logarithms

☐ **B.** Apply the product, quotient, and power properties of logarithms

☐ **C.** Solve general logarithmic and exponential equations

☐ **D.** Solve applications involving logistic, exponential, and logarithmic functions

In this section, we develop the ability to solve logarithmic and exponential equations of any base. A **logarithmic equation** has at least one term that involves the logarithm of a variable. Likewise, an **exponential equation** has at least one term that involves a variable exponent. In the same way that we might *square both sides* or *divide both sides* of an equation in the solution process, we'll show that we can also *exponentiate both sides* or *take logarithms of both sides* to help obtain a solution.

## A. Solving Equations Using the Fundamental Properties of Logarithms

In Appendix I.B, we converted expressions from exponential form to logarithmic form using the basic definition: $x = b^y \Leftrightarrow y = \log_b x$. This relationship reveals the following four properties:

### Fundamental Properties of Logarithms

For any base $b > 0$, $b \neq 1$,

    **I.** $\log_b b = 1$, since $b^1 = b$

    **II.** $\log_b 1 = 0$, since $b^0 = 1$

    **III.** $\log_b b^x = x$, since $b^x = b^x$ (exponential form)

    **IV.** $b^{\log_b x} = x$ $(x > 0)$, since $\log_b x = \log_b x$ (logarithmic form)

To see the verification of Property IV more clearly, again note that for $y = \log_b x$, $b^y = x$ is the exponential form, and substituting $\log_b x$ for $y$ yields $b^{\log_b x} = x$. Also note that Properties III and IV demonstrate that $y = \log_b x$ and $y = b^x$ are inverse functions. In common language, "a base-$b$ logarithm *undoes* a base-$b$ exponential," and "a base-$b$ exponential *undoes* a base-$b$ logarithm." For $f(x) = \log_b x$ and $f^{-1}(x) = b^x$, using a composition verifies the inverse relationship:

$$(f \circ f^{-1})(x) = f[f^{-1}(x)] \qquad (f^{-1} \circ f)(x) = f^{-1}[f(x)]$$
$$= \log_b b^x \qquad\qquad\qquad = b^{\log_b x}$$
$$= x \qquad\qquad\qquad\qquad = x$$

These properties can be used to solve basic equations involving logarithms and exponentials. For the examples and exercises that follow, note that if $\log_b x = k$, then $b^{\log_b x} = b^k$ and we say that we have *exponentiated* both sides.

---

**EXAMPLE 1** ▶ **Solving Basic Logarithmic Equations**

Solve each equation by applying fundamental properties. Answer in exact form and approximate form using a calculator (round to 1000ths).

    **a.** $\ln x = 2$    **b.** $-0.52 = \log x$

**Solution** ▶   **a.**    $\ln x = 2$        given

              $e^{\ln x} = e^2$    exponentiate both sides

                  $x = e^2$    Property IV (exact form)

                 $x \approx 7.389$    approximate form

    **b.**    $-0.52 = \log x$    given

        $10^{-0.52} = 10^{\log x}$    exponentiate both sides

        $10^{-0.52} = x$    Property IV (exact form)

          $0.302 \approx x$    approximate form

**Now try Exercises 7 through 10** ▶

Note that exponentiating both sides of the equation produced the same result as simply writing the original equation in exponential form, and either approach can be used.

---

**EXAMPLE 2** ▶ **Solving Basic Exponential Equations**

Solve each equation by applying fundamental properties. Answer in exact form and approximate form using a calculator (round to 1000ths).

    **a.** $e^x = 167$      **b.** $10^x = 8.223$

Solution ▶   **a.**

      $e^x = 167$      given

    $\ln e^x = \ln 167$      take natural log of both sides

      $x = \ln 167$      Property III (exact form)

      $x \approx 5.118$      approximate form

  **b.**

      $10^x = 8.223$      given

  $\log 10^x = \log 8.223$      take common log of both sides

      $x = \log 8.223$      Property III (exact form)

      $x \approx 0.915$      approximate form

**Now try Exercises 11 through 14** ▶

---

Similar to our previous observation, taking the logarithm of both sides produced the same result as writing the original equation in logarithmic form, and either approach can be used.

If an equation has a single logarithmic or exponential term (base 10 or base $e$), the equation can be solved by isolating this term and applying one of the fundamental properties.

---

**EXAMPLE 3** ▶ **Solving Exponential Equations**

Solve each equation. Write answers in exact form and approximate form to four decimal places.

    **a.** $10^x - 29 = 51$      **b.** $3e^{x+1} - 5 = 7$

Solution ▶   **a.** $10^x - 29 = 51$    given

          $10^x = 80$    add 29

Since the left-hand side is base 10, we apply a common logarithm.

    $\log 10^x = \log 80$      take the common log of both sides

        $x = \log 80$      Property III (exact form)

        $x \approx 1.9031$      approximate form

  **b.** $3e^{x+1} - 5 = 7$    given

      $3e^{x+1} = 12$    add 5

       $e^{x+1} = 4$    divide by 3

Since the left-hand side is base $e$, we apply a natural logarithm.

    $\ln e^{x+1} = \ln 4$      take the natural log of both sides

      $x + 1 = \ln 4$      Property III

          $x = \ln 4 - 1$      solve for $x$ (exact form)

          $x \approx 0.3863$      approximate form

**Now try Exercises 15 through 20** ▶

**WORTHY OF NOTE**

To check solutions using a calculator, we can **STO ▸** (store) the exact result in storage location **X,T,θ,n** (the function variable $x$) and simply enter the original equation on the home screen. The figure shows this verification for Example 3(b).

```
ln(4)-1→X
            .3862943611
3e^(X+1)-5
                       7
```

**EXAMPLE 4** ▶ **Solving Logarithmic Equations**

Solve each equation. Write answers in exact form and approximate form to four decimal places.

**a.** $2 \log(7x) + 1 = 4$    **b.** $-4 \ln(x + 1) - 5 = 7$

Solution ▶    **a.**

| | |
|---|---|
| $2 \log(7x) + 1 = 4$ | given |
| $2 \log(7x) = 3$ | subtract 1 |
| $\log(7x) = \dfrac{3}{2}$ | divide by 2 |
| $7x = 10^{\frac{3}{2}}$ | exponential form |
| $x = \dfrac{10^{\frac{3}{2}}}{7}$ | divide by 7 (exact form) |
| $x \approx 4.5175$ | approximate form |

**b.**

| | |
|---|---|
| $-4 \ln(x + 1) - 5 = 7$ | given |
| $-4 \ln(x + 1) = 12$ | add 5 |
| $\ln(x + 1) = -3$ | divide by $-4$ |
| $x + 1 = e^{-3}$ | exponential form |
| $x = e^{-3} - 1$ | subtract 1 (exact form) |
| $x \approx -0.9502$ | approximate form |

Now try Exercises 21 through 26 ▶

**GRAPHICAL SUPPORT**

Solutions can be also checked using the intersection of graphs method. For Example 4(a), enter $Y_1 = 2 \log(7x) + 1$ and $Y_2 = 4$ on the [Y=] screen. From the domain of the function and the expected answer, we set a window that includes only Quadrant I. Use the keystrokes [2nd] [TRACE] (CALC) 5:intersect, and identify each graph by pressing [ENTER] 3 times. The calculator will find the point of intersection and display it at the bottom of the screen.

☑ **A.** You've just learned how to solve logarithmic equations using the fundamental properties of logarithms

## B. The Product, Quotient, and Power Properties of Logarithms

Generally speaking, equation solving involves simplifying the equation, isolating a variable term on one side, and applying an inverse to solve for the unknown. For logarithmic equations such as $\log x + \log(x + 3) = 1$, we must find a way to combine the terms on the left, before we can work toward a solution. This requires a further exploration of logarithmic properties.

Due to the close connection between exponents and logarithms, their properties are very similar. To illustrate, we'll use terms that can all be written in the form $2^x$, and write the equations $8 \cdot 4 = 32$, $\frac{8}{4} = 2$, and $8^2 = 64$ in both exponential form and logarithmic form.

*The exponents from a product are added:*

exponential form:    $2^3 \cdot 2^2 = 2^{3+2}$

logarithmic form:    $\log_2(8 \cdot 4) = \log_2 8 + \log_2 4$

*The exponents from a quotient are subtracted:*

exponential form:    $\dfrac{2^3}{2^2} = 2^{3-2}$

logarithmic form:    $\log_2\left(\dfrac{8}{4}\right) = \log_2 8 - \log_2 4$

| | | |
|---|---|---|
| *The exponents from a power are multiplied:* | exponential form: | $(2^3)^2 = 2^{3 \cdot 2}$ |
| | logarithmic form: | $\log_2 8^2 = 2 \cdot \log_2 8$ |

Each illustration can be generalized and applied with any base $b$.

### Properties of Logarithms

Give $M$, $N$, and $b \neq 1$ are *positive* real numbers, and *any* real number $p$.

**Product Property**

$$\log_b(MN) = \log_b M + \log_b N$$

The log of a product is a sum of logarithms.

**Quotient Property**

$$\log_b\left(\frac{M}{N}\right) = \log_b M - \log_b N$$

The log of a quotient is a difference of logarithms.

**Power Property**

$$\log_b M^p = p\log_b M$$

The log of a quantity to a power is the power times the log of the quantity.

## Proof of the Product Property

*Given $M$, $N$, and $b \neq 1$ are positive real numbers, $\log_b(MN) = \log_b M + \log_b N$.*

For $P = \log_b M$ and $Q = \log_b N$, we have $b^P = M$ and $b^Q = N$ in exponential form. It follows that

$$
\begin{aligned}
\log_b(MN) &= \log_b(b^P b^Q) && \text{substitute } b^P \text{ for } M \text{ and } b^Q \text{ for } N \\
&= \log_b(b^{P+Q}) && \text{properties of exponents} \\
&= P + Q && \text{log property 3} \\
&= \log_b M + \log_b N && \text{substitute } \log_b M \text{ for } P \text{ and } \log_b N \text{ for } Q
\end{aligned}
$$

## Proof of the Quotient Property

*Given $M$, $N$, and $b \neq 1$ are positive real numbers, $\log_b\left(\frac{M}{N}\right) = \log_b M - \log_b N$.*

For $P = \log_b M$ and $Q = \log_b N$, we have $b^P = M$ and $b^Q = N$ in exponential form. It follows that

$$
\begin{aligned}
\log_b\left(\frac{M}{N}\right) &= \log_b\left(\frac{b^P}{b^Q}\right) && \text{substitute } b^P \text{ for } M \text{ and } b^Q \text{ for } N \\
&= \log_b(b^{P-Q}) && \text{properties of exponents} \\
&= P - Q && \text{log property 3} \\
&= \log_b M - \log_b N && \text{substitute } \log_b M \text{ for } P \text{ and } \log_b N \text{ for } Q
\end{aligned}
$$

## Proof of the Power Property

*Given $M$ and $b \neq 1$ are positive real numbers and any real number $x$, $\log_b M^x = x\log_b M$.*

For $P = \log_b M$, we have $b^P = M$ in exponential form. It follows that

$$
\begin{aligned}
\log_b(M)^x &= \log_b(b^P)^x && \text{substitute } b^P \text{ for } M \\
&= \log_b(b^{Px}) && \text{properties of exponents} \\
&= Px && \text{log property 3} \\
&= (\log_b M)x && \text{substitute } \log_b M \text{ for } P \\
&= x\log_b M && \text{rewrite factors}
\end{aligned}
$$

> ⚠ **CAUTION** ▶ It's very important that you read and understand these properties correctly. For instance, note that $\log_b(M + N) \neq \log_b M + \log_b N$, and $\log_b\left(\dfrac{M}{N}\right) \neq \dfrac{\log_b M}{\log_b N}$. In the first case, it might help to compare the statement $f(x + 3)$ with $f(x) + f(3)$. The first represents a horizontal shift of the graph 3 units left, the second is a vertical shift of $f(x)$ by $f(3)$ units. In particular, $f(x + 3) \neq f(x) + f(3)$.

In many cases, these properties are applied to consolidate logarithmic terms in preparation for equation solving.

**EXAMPLE 5** ▶ **Rewriting Expressions Using Logarithmic Properties**

Use the properties of logarithms to write each expression as a single term.
   **a.** $\log_2 7 + \log_2 5$     **b.** $2 \ln x + \ln(x + 6)$     **c.** $\ln(x + 2) - \ln x$

Solution ▶   **a.** $\log_2 7 + \log_2 5 = \log_2(7 \cdot 5)$   product property
                       $= \log_2 35$   simplify
   **b.** $2 \ln x + \ln(x + 6) = \ln x^2 + \ln(x + 6)$   power property
                       $= \ln[x^2(x + 6)]$   product property
                       $= \ln[x^3 + 6x^2]$   simplify
   **c.** $\ln(x + 2) - \ln x = \ln\left(\dfrac{x + 2}{x}\right)$   quotient property

**Now try Exercises 27 through 42** ▶

**EXAMPLE 6** ▶ **Rewriting Logarithmic Expressions Using the Power Property**

Use the power property of logarithms to rewrite each term as a product.
   **a.** $\ln 5^x$     **b.** $\log 32^{x+2}$     **c.** $\log \sqrt{x}$

Solution ▶   **a.** $\ln 5^x = x \ln 5$   power property
   **b.** $\log 32^{x+2} = (x + 2)\log 32$   power property (note use of parentheses)
   **c.** $\log \sqrt{x} = \log x^{\frac{1}{2}}$   write radical using a rational exponent
                       $= \dfrac{1}{2} \log x$   power property

**Now try Exercises 43 through 50** ▶

> ⚠ **CAUTION** ▶ Note from Example 6(b) that parentheses *must be used* whenever the exponent is a sum or difference. There is a huge difference between $(x + 2)\log 32$ and $x + 2 \log 32$.

In other cases, these properties help rewrite an expression so that certain procedures can be applied more easily. Example 7 actually lays the foundation for more advanced work in mathematics.

**EXAMPLE 7** ▶ **Rewriting Expressions Using Logarithmic Properties**

Use the properties of logarithms to write the following expressions as a sum or difference of simple logarithmic terms.
   **a.** $\log(x^2 z)$     **b.** $\ln\sqrt{\dfrac{x}{x + 5}}$     **c.** $\ln\left[\dfrac{e\sqrt{x^2 + 1}}{(2x + 5)^3}\right]$

Solution ▶   **a.** $\log(x^2 z) = \log x^2 + \log z$        product property
                    $= 2\log x + \log z$        power property

**b.** $\ln\sqrt{\dfrac{x}{x+5}} = \ln\left(\dfrac{x}{x+5}\right)^{\frac{1}{2}}$        write radical using a rational exponent

$\qquad\qquad = \dfrac{1}{2}\ln\left(\dfrac{x}{x+5}\right)$        power property

$\qquad\qquad = \dfrac{1}{2}[\ln x - \ln(x+5)]$        quotient property

**c.** $\ln\left[\dfrac{e\sqrt{x^2+1}}{(2x+5)^3}\right] = \ln\left[\dfrac{e(x^2+1)^{\frac{1}{2}}}{(2x+5)^3}\right]$        write radical using a rational exponent

$\qquad\qquad = \ln[e(x^2+1)^{\frac{1}{2}}] - \ln(2x+5)^3$        quotient property

$\qquad\qquad = \ln e + \ln(x^2+1)^{\frac{1}{2}} - \ln(2x+3)^3$        product property

$\qquad\qquad = 1 + \dfrac{1}{2}\ln(x^2+1) - 3\ln(2x+3)$        power property

**Now try Exercises 51 through 60 ▶**

Although base-10 and base-$e$ logarithms dominate the mathematical landscape, there are many practical applications that use other bases. Fortunately, a formula exists that will convert any given base into either base 10 or base $e$. It's called the **change-of-base formula.**

### Change-of-Base Formula

For the positive real numbers $M$, $a$, and $b$, with $a, b \neq 1$,

$$\log_b M = \frac{\log M}{\log b}\qquad\qquad \log_b M = \frac{\ln M}{\ln b}\qquad\qquad \log_b M = \frac{\log_a M}{\log_a b}$$

base 10                         base $e$                         arbitrary base $a$

### Proof of the Change-of-Base Formula:

For $y = \log_b M$, we have $b^y = M$ in exponential form. It follows that

$$\log_a(b^y) = \log_a M \qquad \text{take base-}a\text{ logarithm of both sides}$$
$$y\log_a b = \log_a M \qquad \text{power property of logarithms}$$
$$y = \frac{\log_a M}{\log_a b} \qquad \text{divide by } \log_a b$$
$$\log_b M = \frac{\log_a M}{\log_a b} \qquad \text{substitute } \log_b M \text{ for } y$$

**EXAMPLE 8 ▶   Using the Change-of-Base Formula to Evaluate Expressions**

Find the value of each expression using the change-of-base formula. Answer in exact form and approximate form using nine digits, then *verify the result* using the original base.

**a.** $\log_3 29$        **b.** $\log_5 3.6$

Solution ▶   **a.** $\log_3 29 = \dfrac{\log 29}{\log 3}$        **b.** $\log_5 3.6 = \dfrac{\ln 3.6}{\ln 5}$

$\qquad\qquad = 3.065044752$        $\qquad\qquad = 0.795888947$

Check ▶   $3^{3.065044752} = 29 \checkmark$        $5^{0.795888947} = 3.6 \checkmark$

**Now try Exercises 61 through 72 ▶**

The change-of-base formula can also be used to study and graph logarithmic functions of *any* base. For $y = \log_b x$, the right-hand expression is simply rewritten using the formula and the equivalent function is $y = \dfrac{\log x}{\log b}$. The new function can then be evaluated as in Example 8, or used to study the graph of $y = \log_b x$ for any base $b$.

## C. Solving Logarithmic Equations

One of the most common mistakes in solving exponential and logarithmic equations is to apply the inverse function too early—before the equation has been simplified. Furthermore, since the domain of $y = \log_b x$ is $x > 0$, logarithmic equations can sometimes produce **extraneous roots,** and checking all answers is a good practice. We'll illustrate by solving the equation mentioned earlier: $\log x + \log(x + 3) = 1$.

**EXAMPLE 9** ▶ **Solving a Logarithmic Equation**

Solve for $x$ and check your answer: $\log x + \log(x + 3) = 1$.

**Solution** ▶
$$\log x + \log(x + 3) = 1 \quad \text{original equation}$$
$$\log[x(x + 3)] = 1 \quad \text{product property}$$
$$x^2 + 3x = 10^1 \quad \text{exponential form, distribute } x$$
$$x^2 + 3x - 10 = 0 \quad \text{set equal to 0}$$
$$(x + 5)(x - 2) = 0 \quad \text{factor}$$
$$x = -5 \text{ or } x = 2 \quad \text{result}$$

**Check** ▶ The "solution" $x = -5$ is outside the domain and is discarded. For $x = 2$,
$$\log x + \log(x + 3) = 1 \quad \text{original equation}$$
$$\log 2 + \log(2 + 3) = 1 \quad \text{substitute 2 for } x$$
$$\log 2 + \log 5 = 1 \quad \text{simplify}$$
$$\log(2 \cdot 5) = 1 \quad \text{product property}$$
$$\log 10 = 1 \checkmark \quad \text{Property I}$$

**Now try Exercises 73 through 80** ▶

As an alternative check, you could also use a calculator to verify $\log 2 + \log 5 = 1$ directly.

If the simplified form of an equation yields a logarithmic term on both sides, the **uniqueness property of logarithms** provides an efficient way to work toward a solution. Since logarithmic functions are one-to-one, we have

**The Uniqueness Property of Logarithms**

For positive real numbers $m$, $n$, and $b \neq 1$,
$$\text{If } \log_b m = \log_b n, \quad \text{then } m = n$$
Equal bases imply equal arguments.

**EXAMPLE 10** ▶ **Solving Logarithmic Equations Using the Uniqueness Property**

Solve each equation using the uniqueness property.
**a.** $\log(x + 2) = \log 7 + \log x$    **b.** $\ln 87 - \ln x = \ln 29$

**Solution ▶**

**a.** $\log(x + 2) = \log 7 + \log x$

$\log(x + 2) = \log 7x$      properties of logarithms

$x + 2 = 7x$      uniqueness property

$2 = 6x$      solve for $x$

$\dfrac{1}{3} = x$      result

**b.** $\ln 87 - \ln x = \ln 29$

$\ln\left(\dfrac{87}{x}\right) = \ln 29$

$\dfrac{87}{x} = 29$

$87 = 29x$

$3 = x$

> **WORTHY OF NOTE**
>
> The uniqueness property can also be viewed as exponentiating both sides using the appropriate base, then applying Property IV.

The checks are left to the student.

**Now try Exercises 81 through 86 ▶**

Often the solution may depend on using a variety of algebraic skills in addition to logarithmic or exponential properties.

**EXAMPLE 11 ▶**    **Solving Logarithmic Equations**

Solve each equation and check your answers.

     **a.** $\ln(x + 7) - 2\ln 5 = 0.9$      **b.** $\log(x + 12) - \log x = \log(x + 9)$

**Solution ▶**

**a.** $\ln(x + 7) - 2\ln 5 = 0.9$      given

$\ln(x + 7) - \ln 5^2 = 0.9$      power property

$\ln\left(\dfrac{x + 7}{25}\right) = 0.9$      quotient property

$\dfrac{x + 7}{25} = e^{0.9}$      exponential form

$x + 7 = 25e^{0.9}$      clear denominator

$x = 25e^{0.9} - 7$      solve for $x$ (exact form)

$x \approx 54.49$      approximate form (to 100ths)

**Check:**     $\ln(x + 7) - 2\ln 5 = 0.9$      original equation

$\ln(54.49 + 7) - 2\ln 5 \approx 0.9$      substitute 54.49 for $x$

$\ln 61.49 - 2\ln 5 \approx 0.9$      simplify

$0.9 \approx 0.9$ ✓      result checks

**b.** $\log(x + 12) - \log x = \log(x + 9)$      given equation

$\log\left(\dfrac{x + 12}{x}\right) = \log(x + 9)$      quotient property

$\dfrac{x + 12}{x} = x + 9$      uniqueness property

$x + 12 = x^2 + 9x$      clear denominator

$0 = x^2 + 8x - 12$      set equal to 0

> **WORTHY OF NOTE**
>
> If all digits given by your calculator are used in the check, a calculator will generally produce "exact" answers. Try using the solution $x = 54.49007778$ in Example 11(a) by substituting directly, or by storing the result of the original computation and using your home screen.

The equation is not factorable, and the quadratic formula must be used.

$x = \dfrac{-b \pm \sqrt{b^2 - 4ac}}{2a}$      quadratic formula

$= \dfrac{-8 \pm \sqrt{(8)^2 - 4(1)(-12)}}{2(1)}$      substitute 1 for $a$, 8 for $b$, −12 for $c$

$= \dfrac{-8 \pm \sqrt{112}}{2} = \dfrac{-8 \pm 4\sqrt{7}}{2}$      simplify

$= -4 \pm 2\sqrt{7}$      result

Substitution shows $x = -4 + 2\sqrt{7}$ ($x \approx 1.29150$) checks, but substituting $-4 - 2\sqrt{7}$ for $x$ gives $\log(2.7085) - \log(-9.2915) = \log(-0.2915)$ and two of the three terms do not represent real numbers ($x = -4 - 2\sqrt{7}$ is an extraneous root).

**Now try Exercises 87 through 102** ▶

---

**GRAPHICAL SUPPORT**

Logarithmic equations can also be checked using the intersection of graphs method. For Example 11(b), we first enter $\log(x + 12) - \log x$ as $Y_1$ and $\log(x + 9)$ as $Y_2$ on the [Y =] screen. Using [2nd] [TRACE] (CALC) **5:intersect**, we find the graphs intersect at $x = 1.2915026$, and that *this is the only solution* (knowing the graph's basic shape, we conclude they cannot intersect again).

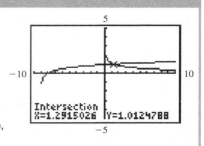

---

⚠ **CAUTION** ▶ Be careful not to dismiss or discard a possible solution simply because it's negative. For the equation $\log(-6 - x) = 1$, $x = -16$ is the solution (the domain here allows negative numbers: $-6 - x > 0$ yields $x < -6$ as the domain). In general, when a logarithmic equation has multiple solutions, all solutions should be checked.

---

Solving exponential equations likewise involves isolating an exponential term on one side, or writing the equation where exponential terms of like base occur on each side. The latter case can be solved using the uniqueness property. If the exponential base is neither 10 nor $e$, logarithms of either base can be used along with the Power Property to solve the equation.

**EXAMPLE 12** ▶ **Solving an Exponential Equation Using Base 10 or Base e**

Solve the exponential equation. Answer in both exact form, and approximate form to four decimal places: $4^{3x} - 1 = 8$

**Solution** ▶ $4^{3x} - 1 = 8$    given equation

$4^{3x} = 9$    add 1

The left-hand side is neither base 10 or base $e$, so the choice is arbitrary. Here we chose base 10 to solve.

$\log 4^{3x} = \log 9$    take logarithm base 10 of both sides

$3x \log 4 = \log 9$    power property

$x = \dfrac{\log 9}{3 \log 4}$    divide by 3 log 4 (exact form)

$x \approx 0.5283$    approximate form

**Now try Exercises 103 through 106** ▶

**WORTHY OF NOTE**

The equation $\log 4^{3x} = \log 9$ from Example 12, can actually be solved using the change-of-base property, by taking logarithms base 4 of both sides.

$\log_4 4^{3x} = \log_4 9$    logarithms base 4

$3x = \dfrac{\log 9}{\log 4}$    Property III; change-of-base property

$x = \dfrac{\log 9}{3 \log 4}$    divide by 3

In some cases, two exponential terms with *unlike* bases may be involved. Here again, either common logs or natural logs can be used, but be sure to distinguish between constant terms like *ln 5* and variable terms like *x ln 5*. As with all equations, the goal is to isolate the *variable terms* on one side, with all constant terms on the other.

**EXAMPLE 13** ▶ **Solving an Exponential Equation with Unlike Bases**

Solve the exponential equation $5^{x+1} = 6^{2x}$.

**Solution** ▶  $5^{x+1} = 6^{2x}$   original equation

Begin by taking the natural log of both sides:

$$\ln(5^{x+1}) = \ln(6^{2x}) \qquad \text{apply base-}e\text{ logarithms}$$
$$(x+1)\ln 5 = 2x\ln 6 \qquad \text{power property}$$
$$x\ln 5 + \ln 5 = 2x\ln 6 \qquad \text{distribute}$$
$$\ln 5 = 2x\ln 6 - x\ln 5 \qquad \text{variable terms to one side}$$
$$\ln 5 = x(2\ln 6 - \ln 5) \qquad \text{factor out } x$$
$$\frac{\ln 5}{2\ln 6 - \ln 5} = x \qquad \text{solve for } x \text{ (exact form)}$$
$$0.8153 \approx x \qquad \text{approximate form}$$

☑ **C.** You've just learned how to solve general logarithmic and exponential equations

The solution can be checked on a calculator.

Now try Exercises 107 through 110 ▶

## D. Applications of Logistic, Exponential, and Logarithmic Functions

Applications of exponential and logarithmic functions take many different forms and it would be impossible to illustrate them all. As you work through the exercises, try to adopt a "big picture" approach, applying the general principles illustrated here to other applications. Some may have been introduced in previous sections. The difference here is that we can now *solve for the independent variable,* instead of simply evaluating the relationships.

In applications involving the **logistic growth** of animal populations, the initial stage of growth is virtually exponential, but due to limitations on food, space, or other resources, growth slows and at some point it reaches a limit. In business, the same principle applies to the logistic growth of sales or profits, due to market saturation. In these cases, the exponential term appears in the denominator of a quotient, and we "clear denominators" to begin the solution process.

**EXAMPLE 14** ▶ **Solving a Logistics Equation**

A small business makes a new discovery and begins an aggressive advertising campaign, confident they can capture 66% of the market in a short period of time. They anticipate their market share will be modeled by the function

$M(t) = \dfrac{66}{1 + 10e^{-0.05t}}$, where $M(t)$ represents the percentage after $t$ days. Use this

function to answer the following.

   **a.** What was the company's initial market share ($t = 0$)? What will their market share be 30 days later?

   **b.** How long will it take the company to reach a 60% market share?

Solution ▶  **a.** $M(t) = \dfrac{66}{1 + 10e^{-0.05t}}$    given

$M(0) = \dfrac{66}{1 + 10e^{-0.05(0)}}$    substitute 0 for $t$

$= \dfrac{66}{11}$    simplify

$= 6$    result

The company originally had only a 6% market share.

$M(30) = \dfrac{66}{1 + 10e^{-0.05(30)}}$    substitute 30 for $t$

$= \dfrac{66}{1 + 10e^{-1.5}}$    simplify

$\approx 20.4$    result

After 30 days, they will hold a 20.4% market share.

**b.** For Part b, we replace $M(t)$ with 60 and solve for $t$.

$60 = \dfrac{66}{1 + 10e^{-0.05t}}$    given

$60(1 + 10e^{-0.05t}) = 66$    multiply by $1 + 10e^{-0.05t}$

$1 + 10e^{-0.05t} = 1.1$    divide by 60

$10e^{-0.05t} = 0.1$    subtract 1

$e^{-0.05t} = 0.01$    divide by 10

$\ln e^{-0.05t} = \ln 0.01$    apply base-$e$ logarithms

$-0.05t = \ln 0.01$    Property III

$t = \dfrac{\ln 0.01}{-0.05}$    solve for $t$ (exact form)

$\approx 92$    approximate form

According to this model, the company will reach a 60% market share in about 92 days.

Now try Exercises 111 through 116 ▶

Earlier we used the barometric equation $H = (30T + 8000) \ln\left(\dfrac{P_0}{P}\right)$ to find an altitude $H$, given a temperature and the atmospheric (barometric) pressure in centimeters of mercury (cmHg). Using the tools from this section, we are now able to find the atmospheric pressure for a given altitude and temperature.

**EXAMPLE 15** ▶  **Using Logarithms to Determine Atmospheric Pressure**

Suppose a group of climbers has just scaled Mt. Rainier, the highest mountain of the Cascade Range in western Washington State. If the mountain is about 4395 m high and the temperature at the summit is $-22.5°C$, what is the atmospheric pressure at this altitude? The pressure at sea level is $P_0 = 76$ cmHg.

Solution ▶

$$H = (30T + 8000) \ln\left(\frac{P_0}{P}\right)$$    given

$$4395 = [30(-22.5) + 8000] \ln\left(\frac{76}{P}\right)$$    substitute 4395 for $H$, 76 for $P_0$, and $-22.5$ for $T$

$$4395 = 7325 \ln\left(\frac{76}{P}\right)$$    simplify

$$0.6 = \ln\left(\frac{76}{P}\right)$$    divide by 7325

$$e^{0.6} = \frac{76}{P}$$    exponential form

$$Pe^{0.6} = 76$$    multiply by $P$

$$P = \frac{76}{e^{0.6}}$$    divide by $e^{0.6}$ (exact form)

$$P \approx 41.7$$    approximate form

✓ **D. You've just learned how to solve applications involving logistic, exponential, and logarithmic functions**

Under these conditions and at this altitude, the atmospheric pressure would be 41.7 cmHg.

**Now try Exercises 117 through 120 ▶**

## C EXERCISES

▶ **CONCEPTS AND VOCABULARY**

**Fill in each blank with the appropriate word or phrase. Carefully reread the section if needed.**

1. For $e^{-0.02x+1} = 10$, the solution process is most efficient if we apply a base _____ logarithm to both sides.

2. To solve $3 \ln x - \ln(x + 3) = 0$, we can combine terms using the _____ property, or add $\ln(x + 3)$ to both sides and use the _____ property.

3. Since logarithmic functions are not defined for all real numbers, we should check all "solutions" for _____ roots.

4. The statement $\log_e 10 = \dfrac{\log 10}{\log e}$ is an example of the _____ -of- _____ property.

5. Solve the equation here, giving a step-by-step discussion of the solution process:
   $\ln(4x + 3) + \ln(2) = 3.2$

6. Describe the difference between *evaluating* the equation below given $x = 9.7$ and *solving* the equation given $y = 9.7$: $y = 3 \log_2(x - 1.7) - 2.3$.

▶ **DEVELOPING YOUR SKILLS**

 **Solve each equation by applying fundamental properties. Round to thousandths.**

7. $\ln x = 3.4$        8. $\ln x = \frac{1}{2}$

9. $\log x = \frac{1}{4}$        10. $\log x = 1.6$

11. $e^x = 9.025$        12. $e^x = 0.343$

13. $10^x = 18.197$        14. $10^x = 0.024$

**Solve each equation. Write answers in exact form and in approximate form to four decimal places.**

15. $4e^{x-2} + 5 = 70$        16. $2 - 3e^{0.4x} = -7$

17. $10^{x+5} - 228 = -150$        18. $10^{2x} + 27 = 190$

19. $-150 = 290.8 - 190e^{-0.75x}$

20. $250e^{0.05x+1} + 175 = 1175$

Solve each equation. Write answers in exact form and in approximate form to four decimal places.

**21.** $3 \ln(x + 4) - 5 = 3$    **22.** $-15 = -8 \ln(3x) + 7$

**23.** $-1.5 = 2 \log(5 - x) - 4$

**24.** $-4 \log(2x) + 9 = 3.6$

**25.** $\frac{1}{2} \ln(2x + 5) + 3 = 3.2$

**26.** $\frac{3}{4} \ln(4x) - 6.9 = -5.1$

Use properties of logarithms to write each expression as a single term.

**27.** $\ln(2x) + \ln(x - 7)$    **28.** $\ln(x + 2) + \ln(3x)$

**29.** $\log(x + 1) + \log(x - 1)$

**30.** $\log(x - 3) + \log(x + 3)$

**31.** $\log_3 28 - \log_3 7$    **32.** $\log_6 30 - \log_6 10$

**33.** $\log x - \log(x + 1)$    **34.** $\log(x - 2) - \log x$

**35.** $\ln(x - 5) - \ln x$    **36.** $\ln(x + 3) - \ln(x - 1)$

**37.** $\ln(x^2 - 4) - \ln(x + 2)$

**38.** $\ln(x^2 - 25) - \ln(x + 5)$

**39.** $\log_2 7 + \log_2 6$    **40.** $\log_9 2 + \log_9 15$

**41.** $\log_5(x^2 - 2x) + \log_5 x^{-1}$

**42.** $\log_3(3x^2 + 5x) - \log_3 x$

Use the power property of logarithms to rewrite each term as the product of a constant and a logarithmic term.

**43.** $\log 8^{x+2}$    **44.** $\log 15^{x-3}$

**45.** $\ln 5^{2x-1}$    **46.** $\ln 10^{3x+2}$

**47.** $\log \sqrt{22}$    **48.** $\log \sqrt[3]{34}$

**49.** $\log_5 81$    **50.** $\log_7 121$

Use the properties of logarithms to write the following expressions as a sum or difference of simple logarithmic terms.

**51.** $\log(a^3 b)$    **52.** $\log(m^2 n)$

**53.** $\ln(x \sqrt[4]{y})$    **54.** $\ln(\sqrt[3]{pq})$

**55.** $\ln\left(\dfrac{x^2}{y}\right)$    **56.** $\ln\left(\dfrac{m^2}{n^3}\right)$

**57.** $\log\left(\sqrt{\dfrac{x - 2}{x}}\right)$    **58.** $\log\left(\sqrt[3]{\dfrac{3 - v}{2v}}\right)$

**59.** $\ln\left(\dfrac{7x\sqrt{3 - 4x}}{2(x - 1)^3}\right)$    **60.** $\ln\left(\dfrac{x^4\sqrt{x^2 - 4}}{\sqrt[3]{x^2 + 5}}\right)$

Evaluate each expression using the change-of-base formula and either base 10 or base $e$. Answer in exact form and in approximate form using nine decimal places, then verify the result using the original base.

**61.** $\log_7 60$    **62.** $\log_8 92$

**63.** $\log_5 152$    **64.** $\log_6 200$

**65.** $\log_3 1.73205$    **66.** $\log_2 1.41421$

**67.** $\log_{0.5} 0.125$    **68.** $\log_{0.2} 0.008$

Use the change-of-base formula to write an equivalent function, then evaluate the function as indicated (round to four decimal places). Investigate and discuss any patterns you notice in the output values, then determine the next input that will continue the pattern.

**69.** $f(x) = \log_3 x; f(5), f(15), f(45)$

**70.** $g(x) = \log_2 x; g(5), g(10), g(20)$

**71.** $h(x) = \log_9 x; h(2), h(4), h(8)$

**72.** $H(x) = \log_\pi x; H(\sqrt{2}), H(2), H(\sqrt{2^3})$

Solve each equation and check your answers.

**73.** $\log 4 + \log(x - 7) = 2$

**74.** $\log 5 + \log(x - 9) = 1$

**75.** $\log(2x - 5) - \log 78 = -1$

**76.** $\log(4 - 3x) - \log 145 = -2$

**77.** $\log(x - 15) - 2 = -\log x$

**78.** $\log x - 1 = -\log(x - 9)$

**79.** $\log(2x + 1) = 1 - \log x$

**80.** $\log(3x - 13) = 2 - \log x$

Solve each equation using the uniqueness property of logarithms.

**81.** $\log(5x + 2) = \log 2$

**82.** $\log(2x - 3) = \log 3$

**83.** $\log_4(x + 2) - \log_4 3 = \log_4(x - 1)$

**84.** $\log_3(x + 6) - \log_3 x = \log_3 5$

**85.** $\ln(8x - 4) = \ln 2 + \ln x$

**86.** $\ln(x - 1) + \ln 6 = \ln(3x)$

Solve each logarithmic or exponential equation using any appropriate method. Clearly identify any extraneous roots. If there are no solutions, so state.

**87.** $\log(2x - 1) + \log 5 = 1$

**88.** $\log(x - 7) + \log 3 = 2$

**89.** $\log_2(9) + \log_2(x + 3) = 3$

**90.** $\log_3(x - 4) + \log_3(7) = 2$

**91.** $\ln(x + 7) + \ln 9 = 2$

**92.** $\ln 5 + \ln(x - 2) = 1$

**93.** $\log(x + 8) + \log x = \log(x + 18)$

**94.** $\log(x + 14) - \log x = \log(x + 6)$

**95.** $\ln(2x + 1) = 3 + \ln 6$

**96.** $\ln 21 = 1 + \ln(x - 2)$

**97.** $\log(-x - 1) = \log(5x) - \log x$

**98.** $\log(1 - x) + \log x = \log(x + 4)$

**99.** $\ln(2t + 7) = \ln 3 - \ln(t + 1)$

**100.** $\ln 6 - \ln(5 - r) = \ln(r + 2)$

**101.** $\log(x - 1) - \log x = \log(x - 3)$

**102.** $\ln x + \ln(x - 2) = \ln 4$

**103.** $7^{x+2} = 231$       **104.** $6^{x+2} = 3589$

**105.** $5^{3x-2} = 128{,}965$     **106.** $9^{5x-3} = 78{,}462$

**107.** $2^{x+1} = 3^x$       **108.** $7^x = 4^{2x-1}$

**109.** $5^{2x+1} = 9^{x+1}$     **110.** $\left(\dfrac{1}{5}\right)^{x-1} = \left(\dfrac{1}{2}\right)^{3-x}$

**111.** $\dfrac{250}{1 + 4e^{-0.06x}} = 200$   **112.** $\dfrac{80}{1 + 15e^{-0.06x}} = 50$

## ▶ WORKING WITH FORMULAS

**113. Logistic growth:** $P(t) = \dfrac{C}{1 + ae^{-kt}}$

For populations that exhibit logistic growth, the population at time $t$ is modeled by the function shown, where $C$ is the carrying capacity of the population (the maximum population that can be supported over a long period of time), $k$ is the growth constant, and $a = \frac{C - P(0)}{P(0)}$. Solve the formula for $t$, then use the result to find the value of $t$ given $C = 450$, $a = 8$, $P = 400$, and $k = 0.075$.

**114. Forensics—estimating time of death:**

$$h = -3.9 \cdot \ln\left(\frac{T - T_R}{T_0 - T_R}\right)$$

Using the formula shown, a forensic expert can compute the approximate time of death for a person found recently expired, where $T$ is the body temperature when it was found, $T_R$ is the (constant) temperature of the room, $T_0$ is the body temperature at the time of death ($T_0 = 98.6°F$), and $h$ is the number of hours since death. If the body was discovered at 9:00 A.M. with a temperature of 86.2°F, in a room at 73°F, at approximately what time did the person expire? (Note this formula is a version of Newton's law of cooling.)

## ▶ APPLICATIONS

 **115. Stocking a lake:** A farmer wants to stock a private lake on his property with catfish. A specialist studies the area and depth of the lake, along with other factors, and determines it can support a maximum population of around 750 fish, with growth modeled by the function $P(t) = \dfrac{750}{1 + 24e^{-0.075t}}$, where $P(t)$ gives the current population after $t$ months.
(a) How many catfish did the farmer initially put in the lake? (b) How many months until the population reaches 300 fish?

**116. Increasing sales:** After expanding their area of operations, a manufacturer of small storage buildings believes the larger area can support sales of 40 units per month. After increasing the advertising budget and enlarging the sales force, sales are expected to grow according to the model $S(t) = \dfrac{40}{1 + 1.5e^{-0.08t}}$, where $S(t)$ is the expected number of sales after $t$ months. (a) How many sales were being made each month, prior to the expansion? (b) How many months until sales reach 25 units per month?

Use the *barometric equation* $H = (30T + 8000) \ln\left(\dfrac{P_0}{P}\right)$ for exercises 117 and 118. Recall that $P_0 = 76$ cmHg.

117. **Altitude and temperature:** A sophisticated spy plane is cruising at an altitude of 18,250 m. If the temperature at this altitude is $-75°C$, what is the barometric pressure?

118. **Altitude and temperature:** A large weather balloon is released and takes altitude, pressure, and temperature readings as it climbs, and radios the information back to Earth. What is the pressure reading at an altitude of 5000 m, given the temperature is $-18°C$?

Use *Newton's law of cooling* $T = T_R + (T_0 - T_R)e^{kh}$ to complete Exercises 119 and 120. Recall that water freezes at $32°F$ and use $k = -0.012$. Refer to Appendix I.A, page A-7 as needed.

119. **Making popsicles:** On a hot summer day, Sean and his friends mix some Kool-Aid® and decide to freeze it in an ice tray to make popsicles. If the water used for the Kool-Aid® was $75°F$ and the freezer has a temperature of $-20°F$, how long will they have to wait to enjoy the treat?

120. **Freezing time:** Suppose the current temperature in Esconabe, Michigan, was $47°F$ when a $5°F$ arctic cold front moved over the state. How long would it take a puddle of water to freeze over?

**Depreciation/appreciation:** As time passes, the value of certain items decrease (appliances, automobiles, etc.), while the value of other items increase (collectibles, real estate, etc.). The time $T$ in years for an item to reach a future value can be modeled by the formula $T = k \ln\left(\dfrac{V_n}{V_f}\right)$, where $V_n$ is the purchase price when new, $V_f$ is its future value, and $k$ is a constant that depends on the item.

121. **Automobile depreciation:** If a new car is purchased for $28,500, find its value 3 yr later if $k = 5$.

122. **Home appreciation:** If a new home in an "upscale" neighborhood is purchased for $130,000, find its value 12 yr later if $k = -16$.

**Drug absorption:** The time required for a certain percentage of a drug to be *absorbed* by the body depends on the drug's absorption rate. This can be modeled by the function $T(p) = \dfrac{-\ln p}{k}$, where $p$ represents the percent of the drug that *remains unabsorbed* (expressed as a decimal), $k$ is the absorption rate of the drug, and $T(p)$ represents the elapsed time.

123. For a drug with an absorption rate of 7.2%, (a) find the time required (to the nearest hour) for the body to *absorb* 35% of the drug, and (b) find the percent of this drug (to the nearest half percent) that remains unabsorbed after 24 hr.

124. For a drug with an absorption rate of 5.7%, (a) find the time required (to the nearest hour) for the body to *absorb* 50% of the drug, and (b) find the percent of this drug (to the nearest half percent) that remains unabsorbed after 24 hr.

**Spaceship velocity:** In space travel, the change in the velocity of a spaceship $V_s$ (in km/sec) depends on the mass of the ship $M_s$ (in tons), the mass of the fuel which has been burned $M_f$ (in tons) and the escape velocity of the exhaust $V_e$ (in km/sec). Disregarding frictional forces, these are related by the equation $V_s = V_e \ln\left(\dfrac{M_s}{M_s - M_f}\right)$.

125. For the Jupiter VII rocket, find the mass of the fuel $M_f$ that has been burned if $V_s = 6$ km/sec when $V_e = 8$ km/sec, and the ship's mass is 100 tons.

126. For the Neptune X satellite booster, find the mass of the ship $M_s$ if $M_f = 75$ tons of fuel has been burned when $V_s = 8$ km/sec and $V_e = 10$ km/sec.

**Learning curve:** The job performance of a new employee when learning a repetitive task (as on an assembly line) improves very quickly at first, then grows more slowly over time. This can be modeled by the function $P(t) = a + b \ln t$, where $a$ and $b$ are constants that depend on the type of task and the training of the employee.

127. The number of toy planes an employee can assemble from its component parts depends on the length of time the employee has been working. This output is modeled by $P(t) = 5.9 + 12.6 \ln t$, where $P(t)$ is the number of planes assembled daily after working $t$ days. (a) How many planes is an employee making after 5 days on the job? (b) How many days until the employee is able to assemble 34 planes per day?

128. The number of circuit boards an associate can assemble from its component parts depends on the length of time the associate has been working. This output is modeled by $B(t) = 1 + 2.3 \ln t$, where $B(t)$ is the number of boards assembled daily after working $t$ days. (a) How many boards is an employee completing after 9 days on the job? (b) How long will it take until the employee is able to complete 10 boards per day?

▶ **EXTENDING THE CONCEPT**

Use prime factors, properties of logs, and the values given to evaluate each expression without a calculator. Check each result using the change-of-base formula:

129. $\log_3 4 = 1.2619$ and $\log_3 5 = 1.4649$:

    **a.** $\log_3 20$   **b.** $\log_3 \dfrac{4}{5}$   **c.** $\log_3 25$

130. $\log_5 2 \approx 0.4307$ and $\log_5 3 \approx 0.6826$:

    **a.** $\log_5 \dfrac{9}{2}$   **b.** $\log_5 216$   **c.** $\log_5 \sqrt[3]{6}$

131. Match each equation with the most appropriate solution strategy, and justify/discuss why.

    **a.** $e^{x+1} = 25$    \_\_\_\_\_   apply base-10 logarithm to both sides

    **b.** $\log(2x + 3) = \log 53$    \_\_\_\_\_   rewrite and apply uniqueness property for exponentials

    **c.** $\log(x^2 - 3x) = 2$    \_\_\_\_\_   apply uniqueness property for logarithms

    **d.** $10^{2x} = 97$    \_\_\_\_\_   apply either base-10 or base-$e$ logarithm

    **e.** $2^{5x-3} = 32$    \_\_\_\_\_   apply base-$e$ logarithm

    **f.** $7^{x+2} = 23$    \_\_\_\_\_   write in exponential form

Solve the following equations. Note that equations in Exercises 132 and 133 are in quadratic form.

132. $2e^{2x} - 7e^x = 15$

133. $3e^{2x} - 4e^x - 7 = -3$

134. $\log_2(x + 5) = \log_4(21x + 1)$

135. Use the algebraic method to find the inverse function.

    **a.** $f(x) = 2^{x+1}$     **b.** $y = 2 \ln(x - 3)$

136. Show that $g(x) = f^{-1}(x)$ by composing the functions.

    **a.** $f(x) = 3^{x-2}$; $g(x) = \log_3 x + 2$

    **b.** $f(x) = e^{x-1}$; $g(x) = \ln x + 1$

137. Use properties of logarithms and/or exponents to show

    **a.** $y = 2^x$ is equivalent to $y = e^{x \ln 2}$.

    **b.** $y = b^x$ is equivalent to $y = e^{rx}$, where $r = \ln b$.

138. Verify that $\ln x = (\ln 10)(\log x)$, and discuss *why* they're equal. Then use the relationship to find the value of $\ln e$, $\ln 10$, and $\ln 2$.

139. Use test values for $p$ and $q$ to demonstrate that the following relationships are *false,* then state the correct property and use the same test value to verify the property.

    **a.** $\ln(pq) = \ln p \ln q$   **b.** $\ln\left(\dfrac{p}{q}\right) = \dfrac{\ln p}{\ln q}$

    **c.** $\ln p + \ln q = \ln(p + q)$

140. To understand the formula for the half-life of radioactive material, consider that for each time increment, a constant proportion of mass $m$ is lost. In symbols; $m(t + 1) - m(t) = -km(t)$. (a) Solve for $m(t + 1)$ and factor the right-hand side. (b) Evaluate the new equation for $t = 0, 1, 2$, and 3, to show that $m(t) = m(0)(1 - k)^t$. (c) For any half-life $h$, we have $m(h) = m(0)(1 - k)^h = \frac{1}{2}m(0)$. Solve for $1 - k$, raise both sides to the power $t$, and substitute to show $m(t) = m(0)(\frac{1}{2})^{\frac{t}{h}}$.

## Learning Objectives

*In Section D you will learn how to:*

☐ **A.** Calculate simple interest and compound interest

☐ **B.** Calculate interest compounded continuously

☐ **C.** Solve applications of annuities and amortization

☐ **D.** Solve applications of exponential growth and decay

### WORTHY OF NOTE

If a loan is kept for only a certain number of months, weeks, or days, the time *t* should be stated as a fractional part of a year so the time period for the rate (years) matches the time period over which the loan is repaid.

Would you pay $750,000 for a home worth only $250,000? Surprisingly, when a conventional mortgage is repaid over 30 years, this is not at all rare. Over time, the accumulated interest on the mortgage is easily more than two or three times the original value of the house. In this section we explore how interest is paid or charged, and look at other applications of exponential and logarithmic functions from business, finance, as well as the physical and social sciences.

## A. Simple and Compound Interest

**Simple interest** is an amount of interest that is computed only once during the lifetime of an investment (or loan). In the world of finance, the initial deposit or base amount is referred to as the **principal** *p,* the **interest rate** *r* is given as a percentage and stated as an annual rate, with the term of the investment or loan most often given as *time t* in years. Simple interest is merely an application of the basic percent equation, with the additional element of time coming into play: *interest = principal × rate × time,* or *I = prt.* To find the total amount *A* that has accumulated (for deposits) or is due (for loans) after *t* years, we merely add the accumulated interest to the initial principal: *A = p + prt.*

### Simple Interest Formula

If principal *p* is deposited or borrowed at interest rate *r* for a period of *t* years, the simple interest on this account will be

$$I = prt$$

The total amount *A* accumulated or due after this period will be:

$$A = p + prt \quad \text{or} \quad A = p(1 + rt)$$

**EXAMPLE 1** ▶ **Solving an Application of Simple Interest**

Many finance companies offer what have become known as *PayDay Loans*—a small $50 loan to help people get by until payday, usually no longer than 2 weeks. If the cost of this service is $12.50, determine the annual rate of interest charged by these companies.

**Solution** ▶ The interest charge is $12.50, the initial principal is $50.00, and the time period is 2 weeks or $\frac{2}{52} = \frac{1}{26}$ of a year. The simple interest formula yields

$$I = prt \qquad \text{simple interest formula}$$

$$12.50 = 50r\left(\frac{1}{26}\right) \qquad \text{substitute \$12.50 for } I, \text{\$50.00 for } p, \text{ and } \tfrac{1}{26} \text{ for } t$$

$$6.5 = r \qquad \text{solve for } r$$

The annual interest rate on these loans is a whopping 650%!

**Now try Exercises 7 through 16** ▶

### Compound Interest

Many financial institutions pay **compound interest** on deposits they receive, which is interest paid on previously accumulated interest. The most common compounding periods are yearly, semiannually (two times per year), quarterly (four times per year), monthly (12 times per year), and daily (365 times per year). Applications of compound interest typically involve exponential functions. For convenience, consider $1000 in principal, deposited at 8% for 3 yr. The simple interest calculation shows $240 in interest is earned and there will be $1240 in the account: $A = 1000[1 + (0.08)(3)] = \$1240$. If the interest is *compounded each year* $(t = 1)$ instead of once at the start of the 3-yr period, the interest calculation shows

$$A_1 = 1000(1 + 0.08) = 1080 \text{ in the account at the end of year 1,}$$
$$A_2 = 1080(1 + 0.08) = 1166.40 \text{ in the account at the end of year 2,}$$
$$A_3 = 1166.40(1 + 0.08) \approx 1259.71 \text{ in the account at the end of year 3.}$$

The account has earned an additional $19.71 interest. More importantly, notice that we're multiplying by $(1 + 0.08)$ each compounding period, meaning results can be computed more efficiently by simply applying the factor $(1 + 0.08)^t$ to the initial principal $p$. For example,

$$A_3 = 1000(1 + 0.08)^3 \approx \$1259.71.$$

In general, for interest compounded yearly the **accumulated value** is $A = p(1 + r)^t$. Notice that solving this equation for $p$ will tell us the amount we need to deposit *now,* in order to accumulate $A$ dollars in $t$ years: $p = \frac{A}{(1 + r)^t}$. This is called the **present value equation.**

### Interest Compounded Annually

If a principal $p$ is deposited at interest rate $r$ and compounded yearly for a period of $t$ yr, the *accumulated value* is

$$A = p(1 + r)^t$$

If an accumulated value $A$ is desired after $t$ yr, and the money is deposited at interest rate $r$ and compounded yearly, the *present value* is

$$p = \frac{A}{(1 + r)^t}$$

---

**EXAMPLE 2 ▶ Finding the Doubling Time of an Investment**

An initial deposit of $1000 is made into an account paying 6% compounded yearly. How long will it take for the money to double?

Solution ▶ Using the formula for interest compounded yearly we have

$$A = p(1 + r)^t \qquad \text{given}$$
$$2000 = 1000(1 + 0.06)^t \qquad \text{substitute 2000 for } A, \text{ 1000 for } p, \text{ and 0.06 for } r$$
$$2 = 1.06^t \qquad \text{isolate variable term}$$
$$\ln 2 = t \ln 1.06 \qquad \text{apply base-}e \text{ logarithms; power property}$$
$$\frac{\ln 2}{\ln 1.06} = t \qquad \text{solve for } t$$
$$11.9 \approx t \qquad \text{approximate form}$$

The money will double in just under 12 yr.

Now try Exercises 17 through 22 ▶

If interest is compounded monthly (12 times each year), the bank will divide the interest rate by 12 (the number of compoundings), but then pay you interest 12 times per year (interest is *compounded*). The net effect is an increased gain in the interest you earn, and the final compound interest formula takes this form:

$$\text{total amount} = \text{principal}\left(1 + \frac{\text{interest rate}}{\text{compoundings per year}}\right)^{\text{(years} \times \text{compoundings per year)}}$$

### Compounded Interest Formula

If principal $p$ is deposited at interest rate $r$ and compounded $n$ times per year for a period of $t$ yr, the *accumulated value* will be:

$$A = p\left(1 + \frac{r}{n}\right)^{nt}$$

**EXAMPLE 3** ▶ **Solving an Application of Compound Interest**

Macalyn won $150,000 in the Missouri lottery and decides to invest the money for retirement in 20 yr. Of all the options available here, which one will produce the most money for retirement?

   **a.** A certificate of deposit paying 5.4% compounded yearly.
   **b.** A money market certificate paying 5.35% compounded semiannually.
   **c.** A bank account paying 5.25% compounded quarterly.
   **d.** A bond issue paying 5.2% compounded daily.

**Solution** ▶

**a.** $A = \$150{,}000\left(1 + \dfrac{0.054}{1}\right)^{(20 \times 1)}$

    $\approx \$429{,}440.97$

**b.** $A = \$150{,}000\left(1 + \dfrac{0.0535}{2}\right)^{(20 \times 2)}$

    $\approx \$431{,}200.96$

**c.** $A = \$150{,}000\left(1 + \dfrac{0.0525}{4}\right)^{(20 \times 4)}$

    $\approx \$425{,}729.59$

**d.** $A = \$150{,}000\left(1 + \dfrac{0.052}{365}\right)^{(20 \times 365)}$

    $\approx \$424{,}351.12$

The best choice is (b), semiannual compounding at 5.35% for 20 yr.

☑ **A.** You've just learned how to calculate simple interest and compound interest

**Now try Exercises 23 through 30** ▶

## B.  Interest Compounded Continuously

It seems natural to wonder what happens to the interest accumulation as $n$ (the number of compounding periods) becomes very large. It appears the interest rate becomes very small (because we're dividing by $n$), but the exponent becomes very large (since we're multiplying by $n$). To see the result of this interplay more clearly, it will help to rewrite the compound interest formula $A = p\left(1 + \frac{r}{n}\right)^{nt}$ using the substitution $n = xr$. This gives $\frac{r}{n} = \frac{1}{x}$, and by direct substitution ($xr$ for $n$ and $\frac{1}{x}$ for $\frac{r}{n}$) we obtain the form

$$A = p\left[\left(1 + \frac{1}{x}\right)^x\right]^{rt}$$

by regrouping. This allows for a more careful study of the "denominator versus exponent" relationship using $\left(1 + \frac{1}{x}\right)^x$, *the same expression we used in Appendix I.A to define the number e* (also **see Appendix I.A Exercise 97**). Once again, note what happens as $x \to \infty$ (meaning the number of compounding periods increase without bound).

| $x$ | 1 | 10 | 100 | 1000 | 10,000 | 100,000 | 1,000,000 |
|---|---|---|---|---|---|---|---|
| $\left(1 + \dfrac{1}{x}\right)^x$ | 2 | 2.56374 | 2.70481 | 2.71692 | 2.71815 | 2.71827 | 2.71828 |

As before, we have, as $x \to \infty$, $(1 + \frac{1}{x})^x \to e$. The net result of this investigation is a formula for **interest compounded continuously,** derived by replacing $(1 + \frac{1}{x})^x$ with the number $e$ in the formula for compound interest, where

$$A = p\left[\left(1 + \frac{1}{x}\right)^x\right]^{rt} = pe^{rt}$$

### Interest Compounded Continuously

If a principal $p$ is deposited at interest rate $r$ and compounded continuously for a period of $t$ years, the *accumulated value* will be

$$A = pe^{rt}$$

**EXAMPLE 4** ▶ **Solving an Application of Interest Compounded Continuously**

Jaimin has $10,000 to invest and wants to have at least $25,000 in the account in 10 yr for his daughter's college education fund. If the account pays interest compounded continuously, what interest rate is required?

Solution ▶ In this case, $P = \$10,000$, $A = \$25,000$, and $t = 10$.

| | |
|---|---|
| $A = pe^{rt}$ | given |
| $25,000 = 10,000e^{10r}$ | substitute 25,000 for $A$, 10,000 for $p$, and 10 for $t$ |
| $2.5 = e^{10r}$ | isolate variable term |
| $\ln 2.5 = 10r \ln e$ | apply base-$e$ logarithms ($\ln e = 1$); power property |
| $\dfrac{\ln 2.5}{10} = r$ | solve for $r$ |
| $0.092 \approx r$ | approximate form |

Jaimin will need an interest rate of about 9.2% to meet his goal.

**Now try Exercises 31 through 40 ▶**

### GRAPHICAL SUPPORT

To check the result from Example 4, use $Y_1 = 10,000e^{10x}$ and $Y_2 = 25,000$, then look for their point of intersection. We need only set an appropriate window size to ensure the answer will appear in the viewing window. Since 25,000 is the goal, $y \in [0, 30,000]$ seems reasonable for $y$. Although 12% interest ($x = 0.12$) is too good to be true, $x \in [0, 0.12]$ leaves a nice frame for the $x$-values. Verify that the calculator's answer is equal to $\frac{\ln 2.5}{10}$.

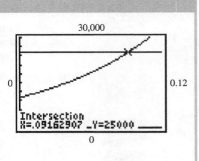

☑ **B.** You've just learned how to calculate interest compounded continuously

**WORTHY OF NOTE**

It is often assumed that the first payment into an annuity is made *at the end of a compounding period,* and hence earns no interest. This is why the first $100 deposit is not multiplied by the interest factor. These terms are actually the terms of a **geometric sequence.**

## C. Applications Involving Annuities and Amortization

Our previous calculations for simple and compound interest involved a single (lump) deposit (the principal) that accumulated interest over time. Many savings and investment plans involve a regular schedule of deposits (monthly, quarterly, or annual deposits) over the life of the investment. Such an investment plan is called an **annuity.**

Suppose that for 4 years, $100 is deposited annually into an account paying 8% compounded yearly. Using the compound interest formula we can track the accumulated value $A$ in the account:

$$A = 100 + 100(1.08)^1 + 100(1.08)^2 + 100(1.08)^3$$

To develop an annuity formula, we multiply the annuity equation by 1.08, then subtract the original equation. This leaves only the first and last terms, since the other (interior) terms add to zero:

$$1.08A = 100(1.08) + 100(1.08)^2 + 100(1.08)^3 + 100(1.08)^4 \quad \text{multiply by 1.08}$$
$$-A = -[100 + 100(1.08)^1 + 100(1.08)^2 + 100(1.08)^3] \quad \text{original equation}$$
$$1.08A - A = 100(1.08)^4 - 100 \quad \text{subtract ("interior terms" sum to zero)}$$
$$0.08A = 100[(1.08)^4 - 1] \quad \text{factor out 100}$$
$$A = \frac{100[(1.08)^4 - 1]}{0.08} \quad \text{solve for } A$$

This result can be generalized for any periodic payment $\mathcal{P}$, interest rate $r$, number of compounding periods $n$, and number of years $t$. This would give

$$A = \frac{\mathcal{P}\left[\left(1 + \dfrac{r}{n}\right)^{nt} - 1\right]}{\dfrac{r}{n}}$$

The formula can be made less formidable using $R = \frac{r}{n}$, where $R$ is the interest rate per compounding period.

---

**Accumulated Value of an Annuity**

If a periodic payment $\mathcal{P}$ is deposited $n$ times per year at an *annual interest rate r* with interest compounded $n$ times per year for $t$ years, the accumulated value is given by

$$A = \frac{\mathcal{P}}{R}[(1 + R)^{nt} - 1], \text{ where } R = \frac{r}{n}$$

This is also referred to as the **future value** of the account.

---

**EXAMPLE 5** ▶ **Solving an Application of Annuities**

Since he was a young child, Fitisemanu's parents have been depositing $50 each month into an annuity that pays 6% annually and is compounded monthly. If the account is now worth $9875, how long has it been open?

Solution ▶ In this case, $\mathcal{P} = 50, r = 0.06, n = 12, R = 0.005$, and $A = 9875$. The formula gives

$$A = \frac{\mathcal{P}}{R}[(1 + R)^{nt} - 1] \quad \text{future value formula}$$

$$9875 = \frac{50}{0.005}[(1.005)^{(12)(t)} - 1] \quad \text{substitute 9875 for } A, 50 \text{ for } \mathcal{P}, 0.005 \text{ for } R, \text{ and 12 for } n$$

$$1.9875 = 1.005^{12t} \quad \text{simplify and isolate variable term}$$

$$\ln(1.9875) = 12t(\ln 1.005) \quad \text{apply base-}e\text{ logarithms; power property}$$

$$\frac{\ln(1.9875)}{12\ln(1.005)} = t \quad \text{solve for } t \text{(exact form)}$$

$$11.5 \approx t \quad \text{approximate form}$$

The account has been open approximately 11.5 yr.

**Now try Exercises 41 through 44** ▶

The periodic payment required to meet a future goal or obligation can be computed by solving for $\mathcal{P}$ in the future value formula: $\mathcal{P} = \dfrac{AR}{\left[(1+R)^{nt} - 1\right]}$. In this form, $\mathcal{P}$ is referred to as a **sinking fund.**

**EXAMPLE 6** ▶ **Solving an Application of Sinking Funds**

Sheila is determined to stay out of debt and decides to save \$20,000 to pay cash for a new car in 4 yr. The best investment vehicle she can find pays 9% compounded monthly. If \$300 is the most she can invest each month, can she meet her "4-yr" goal?

**Solution** ▶ Here we have $\mathcal{P} = 300$, $A = 20{,}000$, $r = 0.09$, $n = 12$, and $R = 0.0075$. The sinking fund formula gives

$$\mathcal{P} = \frac{AR}{\left[(1+R)^{nt} - 1\right]} \quad \text{sinking fund}$$

$$300 = \frac{(20{,}000)(0.0075)}{(1.0075)^{12t} - 1} \quad \text{substitute 300 for } \mathcal{P}\text{, 20,000 for } A\text{, 0.0075 for } R\text{, and 12 for } n$$

$$300(1.0075^{12t} - 1) = 150 \quad \text{multiply in numerator, clear denominators}$$

$$1.0075^{12t} = 1.5 \quad \text{isolate variable term}$$

$$12t\ln(1.0075) = \ln 1.5 \quad \text{apply base-}e\text{ logarithms; power property}$$

$$t = \frac{\ln(1.5)}{12\ln(1.0075)} \quad \text{solve for } t \text{(exact form)}$$

$$\approx 4.5 \quad \text{approximate form}$$

No. She is close, but misses her original 4-yr goal.

**Now try Exercises 45 and 46** ▶

☑ **C.** You've just learned how to solve applications of annuities and amortization

For Example 6, we could have substituted 4 for $t$ and left $\mathcal{P}$ unknown, to see if a payment of \$300 per month would be sufficient. You can verify the result would be $\mathcal{P} \approx \$347.70$, which is what Sheila would need to invest to meet her 4-yr goal exactly.

For additional practice with the formulas for interest earned or paid, the *Working with Formulas* portion of this Exercise Set has been expanded. See **Exercises 47 through 54.**

## D. Applications Involving Exponential Growth and Decay

Closely related to interest compounded continuously are applications of **exponential growth** and **exponential decay**. If $Q$ (quantity) and $t$ (time) are variables, then $Q$ grows exponentially as a function of $t$ if $Q(t) = Q_0 e^{rt}$ for positive constants $Q_0$ and $r$. Careful studies have shown that population growth, whether it be humans, bats, or bacteria, can be modeled by these "base-$e$" exponential growth functions. If $Q(t) = Q_0 e^{-rt}$, then we say $Q$ decreases or **decays exponentially** over time. The constant $r$ determines how rapidly a quantity grows or decays and is known as the **growth rate** or **decay rate** constant.

**WORTHY OF NOTE**

Notice the formula for exponential growth is virtually identical to the formula for interest compounded continuously. In fact, both are based on the same principles. If we let $A(t)$ represent the amount in an account after $t$ years and $A_0$ represent the initial deposit (instead of $P$), we have: $A(t) = A_0 e^{rt}$ versus $Q(t) = Q_0 e^{rt}$ and the two cannot be distinguished.

**EXAMPLE 7** ▶ **Solving an Application of Exponential Growth**

Because fruit flies multiply very quickly, they are often used in a study of genetics. Given the necessary space and food supply, a certain population of fruit flies is known to double every 12 days. If there were 100 flies to begin, find (a) the growth rate $r$ and (b) the number of days until the population reaches 2000 flies.

Solution ▶ **a.** Using the formula for exponential growth with $Q_0 = 100$, $t = 12$, and $Q(t) = 200$, we can solve for the growth rate $r$.

$$Q(t) = Q_0 e^{rt}$$ exponential growth function
$$200 = 100e^{12r}$$ substitute 200 for $Q(t)$, 100 for $Q_0$, and 12 for $t$
$$2 = e^{12r}$$ isolate variable term
$$\ln 2 = 12r \ln e$$ apply base-$e$ logarithms; power property
$$\frac{\ln 2}{12} = r$$ solve for $r$ (exact form)
$$0.05776 \approx r$$ approximate form

The growth rate is approximately 5.78%.

**b.** To find the number of days until the fly population reaches 2000, we substitute 0.05776 for $r$ in the exponential growth function.

$$Q(t) = Q_0 e^{rt}$$ exponential growth function
$$2000 = 100e^{0.05776t}$$ substitute 2000 for $Q(t)$, 100 for $Q_0$, and 0.05776 for $r$
$$20 = e^{0.05776t}$$ isolate variable term
$$\ln 20 = 0.05776t \ln e$$ apply base-$e$ logarithms; power property
$$\frac{\ln 20}{0.05776} = t$$ solve for $t$ (exact form)
$$51.87 \approx t$$ approximate form

The fruit fly population will reach 2000 on day 51.

Now try Exercises 55 and 56 ▶

**WORTHY OF NOTE**

Many population growth models assume an unlimited supply of resources, nutrients, and room for growth. When this is not the case, a logistic growth model often results.

Perhaps the best-known examples of exponential decay involve radioactivity. Ever since the end of World War II, common citizens have been aware of the existence of **radioactive elements** and the power of atomic energy. Today, hundreds of additional applications have been found for these materials, from areas as diverse as biological research, radiology, medicine, and archeology. Radioactive elements decay of their own accord by emitting radiation. The rate of decay is measured using the **half-life** of the substance, which is the time required for a mass of radioactive material to decay until only one-half of its original mass remains. This half-life is used to find the rate of decay $r$, first mentioned in Appendix I.C. In general, if $h$ represents the half-life of the substance, one-half the initial amount remains when $t = h$.

$$Q(t) = Q_0 e^{-rt}$$ exponential decay function
$$\frac{1}{2} Q_0 = Q_0 e^{-rh}$$ substitute $\frac{1}{2}Q_0$ for $Q(t)$, $h$ for $t$
$$\frac{1}{2} = \frac{1}{e^{rh}}$$ divide by $Q_0$; rewrite expression
$$2 = e^{rh}$$ property of ratios
$$\ln 2 = rh \ln e$$ apply base-$e$ logarithms; power property
$$\frac{\ln 2}{h} = r$$ solve for $r$

### Radioactive Rate of Decay

If $h$ represents the half-life of a radioactive substance per unit time, the nominal rate of decay per a like unit of time is given by

$$r = \frac{\ln 2}{h}$$

The rate of decay for known radioactive elements varies greatly. For example, the element carbon-14 has a half-life of about 5730 yr, while the element lead-211 has a half-life of only about 3.5 min. Radioactive elements can be detected in extremely small amounts. If a drug is "labeled" (mixed with a radioactive element and injected into a living organism), its passage through the organism can be traced and information on the health of internal organs can be obtained.

**EXAMPLE 8** ▶ **Solving a Rate of Decay Application**

The radioactive element potassium-42 is often used in biological experiments, since it has a half-life of only about 12.4 hr. How much of a 2-g sample will remain after 18 hr and 45 min?

Solution ▶ To begin we must find the nominal rate of decay $r$ and use this value in the exponential decay function.

$$r = \frac{\ln 2}{h} \qquad \text{radioactive rate of decay}$$

$$r = \frac{\ln 2}{12.4} \qquad \text{substitute 12.4 for } h$$

$$r \approx 0.056 \qquad \text{result}$$

The rate of decay is approximately 5.6%. To determine how much of the sample remains after 18.75 hr, we use $r = 0.056$ in the decay function and evaluate it at $t = 18.75$.

$$Q(t) = Q_0 e^{-rt} \qquad \text{exponential decay function}$$

$$Q(18.75) = 2e^{(-0.056)(18.75)} \qquad \text{substitute 2 for } Q_0, 0.056 \text{ for } r, \text{ and } 18.75 \text{ for } t$$

$$Q(18.75) \approx 0.7 \qquad \text{evaluate}$$

☑ **D.** You've just learned how to solve applications of exponential growth and decay

After 18 hr and 45 min, only 0.7 g of potassium-42 will remain.

Now try Exercises 57 through 62 ▶

## TECHNOLOGY HIGHLIGHT

### Exploring Compound Interest

The graphing calculator is an excellent tool for exploring mathematical relationships, particularly when many variables work simultaneously to produce a single result. For example, the formula $A = P\left(1 + \frac{r}{n}\right)^{nt}$ has five different unknowns. In Example 2, we asked how long it would take $1000 to double if it were compounded yearly at 6% ($n = 1, r = 0.06$). What if we deposited $5000 instead of $1000? Compounded daily instead of quarterly? Or invested at 12% rather than 10%? There are many ways a graphing calculator can be used to answer such questions. In this exercise, we make use of the calculator's "alpha constants." Most graphing calculators can use any of the 26 letters of the English alphabet (and even a few other symbols) to store constant values. We can use them to write a formula

*—continued*

Figure AI.16    Figure AI.17    Figure AI.18

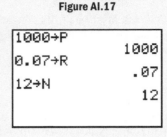

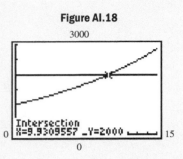

on the Y= screen, then change any constant on the home screen to see how other values are affected. On the TI-84 Plus, these alpha constants are shown in green and accessed by pressing the ALPHA key. Suppose we wanted to study the relationship between an interest rate $r$ and the time $t$ required for a deposit to double. Using $Y_1$ in place of $A$ as output variable, and $x$ in place of $t$, enter $A = P\left(1 + \frac{r}{n}\right)^{nt}$ as $Y_1$ on the Y= screen (Figure AI.16). Let's start with a deposit of $1000 at 7% interest compounded monthly. The keystrokes are: 1000 STO→ ALPHA 8 ENTER , 0.07 STO→ ALPHA × ENTER , and 12 STO→ ALPHA LOG ENTER (Figure AI.17). After setting an appropriate window size (perhaps Xmax = 15 and Ymax = 3000), and entering $Y_2 = 2000$ we can graph both functions and use the intersection of graphs method to find the doubling time. This produces the result in Figure AI.18, where we note it will take about 9.9 yr. Return to the home screen ( 2nd MODE ), change the interest rate to 10%, and graph the functions again. This time the point of intersection is just less than 7 yr. Experiment with other rates and compounding periods.

**Exercise 1:**  With $P = \$1000$, and $r = 0.08$, investigate the "doubling time" for interest compounded quarterly, monthly, daily, and hourly.

**Exercise 2:**  With $P = \$1000$, investigate "doubling time" for rates of 6%, 8%, 10%, and 12%, and $n = 4$, $n = 12$, and $n = 365$. Which had a more significant impact, more compounding periods, or a greater interest rate?

**Exercise 3:**  Will a larger principal cause the money to double faster? Investigate and respond.

# D EXERCISES

▶ CONCEPTS AND VOCABULARY

**Fill in each blank with the appropriate word or phrase. Carefully reread the section if needed.**

1. _____ interest is interest paid to you on previously accumulated interest.

2. The formula for interest compounded _____ is $A = pe^{rt}$, where $e$ is approximately _____.

3. Given constants $Q_0$ and $r$, and that $Q$ decays exponentially as a function of $t$, the equation model is $Q(t) =$ _____.

4. Investment plans calling for regularly scheduled deposits are called _____. The annuity formula gives the _____ value of the account.

5. Explain/Describe the difference between the future value and present value of an annuity. Include an example.

6. Describe/Explain how you would find the rate of growth $r$, given that a population of ants grew from 250 to 3000 in 6 weeks.

## ▶ DEVELOPING YOUR SKILLS

For simple interest accounts, the interest earned or due depends on the principal $p$, interest rate $r$, and the time $t$ in years according to the formula $I = prt$.

**7.** Find $p$ given $I = \$229.50$, $r = 6.25\%$, and $t = 9$ months.

**8.** Find $r$ given $I = \$1928.75$, $p = \$8500$, and $t = 3.75$ yr.

**9.** Larry came up a little short one month at bill-paying time and had to take out a title loan on his car at Check Casher's, Inc. He borrowed \$260, and 3 weeks later he paid off the note for \$297.50. What was the annual interest rate on this title loan? (*Hint:* How much *interest* was charged?)

**10.** Angela has \$750 in a passbook savings account that pays 2.5% simple interest. How long will it take the account balance to hit the \$1000 mark at this rate of interest, if she makes no further deposits? (*Hint:* How much *interest* will be paid?)

For simple interest accounts, the amount $A$ accumulated or due depends on the principal $p$, interest rate $r$, and the time $t$ in years according to the formula $A = p(1 + rt)$.

**11.** Find $p$ given $A = \$2500$, $r = 6.25\%$, and $t = 31$ months.

**12.** Find $r$ given $A = \$15,800$, $p = \$10,000$, and $t = 3.75$ yr.

**13.** Olivette Custom Auto Service borrowed \$120,000 at 4.75% simple interest to expand their facility from three service bays to four. If they repaid \$149,925, what was the term of the loan?

**14.** Healthy U sells nutritional supplements and borrows \$50,000 to expand their product line. When the note is due 3 yr later, they repay the lender \$62,500. If it was a simple interest note, what was the annual interest rate?

**15. Simple interest:** The owner of Paul's Pawn Shop loans Larry \$200.00 using his Toro riding mower as collateral. Thirteen weeks later Larry comes back to get his mower out of pawn and pays Paul \$240.00. What was the annual simple interest rate on this loan?

**16. Simple interest:** To open business in a new strip mall, Laurie's Custom Card Shoppe borrows \$50,000 from a group of investors at 4.55% simple interest. Business booms and blossoms, enabling Laurie to repay the loan fairly quickly. If Laurie repays \$62,500, how long did it take?

For accounts where interest is compounded annually, the amount $A$ accumulated or due depends on the principal $p$, interest rate $r$, and the time $t$ in years according to the formula $A = p(1 + r)^t$.

**17.** Find $t$ given $A = \$48,428$, $p = \$38,000$, and $r = 6.25\%$.

**18.** Find $p$ given $A = \$30,146$, $r = 5.3\%$, and $t = 7$ yr.

**19.** How long would it take \$1525 to triple if invested at 7.1%?

**20.** What interest rate will ensure a \$747.26 deposit will be worth \$1000 in 5 yr?

For accounts where interest is compounded annually, the principal $P$ needed to ensure an amount $A$ has been accumulated in the time period $t$ when deposited at interest rate $r$ is given by the formula $P = \frac{A}{(1 + r)^t}$.

**21.** The Stringers need to make a \$10,000 balloon payment in 5 yr. How much should be invested now at 5.75%, so that the money will be available?

**22.** Morgan is 8 yr old. If her mother wants to have \$25,000 for Morgan's first year of college (in 10 yr), how much should be invested now if the account pays a 6.375% fixed rate?

For compound interest accounts, the amount $A$ accumulated or due depends on the principal $p$, interest rate $r$, number of compoundings per year $n$, and the time $t$ in years according to the formula $A = p\left(1 + \frac{r}{n}\right)^{nt}$.

**23.** Find $t$ given $A = \$129,500$, $p = \$90,000$, and $r = 7.125\%$ compounded weekly.

**24.** Find $r$ given $A = \$95,375$, $p = \$65,750$, and $t = 15$ yr with interest compounded monthly.

**25.** How long would it take a \$5000 deposit to double, if invested at a 9.25% rate and compounded daily?

**26.** What principal should be deposited at 8.375% compounded monthly to ensure the account will be worth \$20,000 in 10 yr?

**27. Compound interest:** As a curiosity, David decides to invest \$10 in an account paying 10% interest compounded 10 times per year for 10 yr. Is that enough time for the \$10 to triple in value?

**28. Compound interest:** As a follow-up experiment (see Exercise 27), David invests \$10 in an account paying 12% interest compounded 10 times per year for 10 yr, and another \$10 in an account paying 10% interest compounded 12 times per year for 10 yr. Which produces the better investment—more compounding periods or a higher interest rate?

29. **Compound interest:** Due to demand, Donovan's Dairy (Wisconsin, USA) plans to double its size in 4 yr and will need $250,000 to begin development. If they invest $175,000 in an account that pays 8.75% compounded semiannually, (a) will there be sufficient funds to break ground in 4 yr? (b) If not, find the *minimum interest rate* that will allow the dairy to meet its 4-yr goal.

30. **Compound interest:** To celebrate the birth of a new daughter, Helyn invests 6000 Swiss francs in a college savings plan to pay for her daughter's first year of college in 18 yr. She estimates that 25,000 francs will be needed. If the account pays 7.2% compounded daily, (a) will she meet her investment goal? (b) If not, find the *minimum rate of interest* that will enable her to meet this 18-yr goal.

For accounts where interest is compounded continuously, the amount $A$ accumulated or due depends on the principal $p$, interest rate $r$, and the time $t$ in years according to the formula $A = pe^{rt}$.

31. Find $t$ given $A = \$2500$, $p = \$1750$, and $r = 4.5\%$.

32. Find $r$ given $A = \$325,000$, $p = \$250,000$, and $t = 10$ yr.

33. How long would it take $5000 to double if it is invested at 9.25%? Compare the result to Exercise 25.

34. What principal should be deposited at 8.375% to ensure the account will be worth $20,000 in 10 yr? Compare the result to Exercise 26.

35. **Interest compounded continuously:** Valance wants to build an addition to his home outside Madrid (Spain) so he can watch over and help his parents in their old age. He hopes to have 20,000 euros put aside for this purpose within 5 yr. If he invests 12,500 euros in an account paying 8.6% interest compounded continuously, (a) will he meet his investment goal? (b) If not, find the *minimum rate of interest* that will enable him to meet this 5-yr goal.

36. **Interest compounded continuously:** Minh-Ho just inherited her father's farm near Mito (Japan), which badly needs a new barn. The estimated cost of the barn is 8,465,000 yen and she would like to begin construction in 4 yr. If she invests 6,250,000 yen in an account paying 6.5% interest compounded continuously, (a) will she meet her investment goal? (b) If not, find the *minimum rate of interest* that will enable her to meet this 4-yr goal.

37. **Interest compounded continuously:** William and Mary buy a small cottage in Dovershire (England), where they hope to move after retiring in 7 yr. The cottage needs about 20,000 euros worth of improvements to make it the retirement home they desire. If they invest 12,000 euros in an account paying 5.5% interest compounded continuously, (a) will they have enough to make the repairs? (b) If not, find the *minimum amount they need to deposit* that will enable them to meet this goal in 7 yr.

38. **Interest compounded continuously:** After living in Oslo (Norway) for 20 years, Zirkcyt and Shybrt decide to move inland to help operate the family ski resort. They hope to make the move in 6 yr, after they have put aside 140,000 kroner. If they invest 85,000 kroner in an account paying 6.9% interest compounded continuously, (a) will they meet their 140,000 kroner goal? (b) If not, find the *minimum amount they need to deposit* that will enable them to meet this goal in 6 yr.

The length of time $T$ (in years) required for an initial principal $P$ to grow to an amount $A$ at a given interest rate $r$ is given by $T = \frac{1}{r} \ln(\frac{A}{P})$.

39. **Investment growth:** A small business is planning to build a new $350,000 facility in 8 yr. If they deposit $200,000 in an account that pays 5% interest compounded continuously, will they have enough for the new facility in 8 yr? If not, what amount should be invested on these terms to meet the goal?

40. **Investment growth:** After the twins were born, Sasan deposited $25,000 in an account paying 7.5% compounded continuously, with the goal of having $120,000 available for their college education 20 yr later. Will Sasan meet the 20-yr goal? If not, what amount should be invested on these terms to meet the goal?

Ordinary annuities: If a periodic payment $\mathcal{P}$ is deposited $n$ times per year, with annual interest rate $r$ also compounded $n$ times per year for $t$ years, the future value of the account is given by $A = \frac{\mathcal{P}[(1 + R)^{nt} - 1]}{R}$, where $R = \frac{r}{n}$ (if the rate is 9% compounded monthly, $R = \frac{0.09}{12} = 0.0075$).

41. **Saving for a rainy day:** How long would it take Jasmine to save $10,000 if she deposits $90/month at an annual rate of 7.75% compounded monthly?

42. **Saving for a sunny day:** What quarterly investment amount is required to ensure that Larry can save $4700 in 4 yr at an annual rate of 8.5% compounded quarterly?

**43. Saving for college:** At the birth of their first child, Latasha and Terrance opened an annuity account and have been depositing $50 per month in the account ever since. If the account is now worth $30,000 and the interest on the account is 6.2% compounded monthly, how old is the child?

**44. Saving for a bequest:** When Cherie (Brandon's first granddaughter) was born, he purchased an annuity account for her and stipulated that she should receive the funds (in trust, if necessary) upon his death. The quarterly annuity payments were $250 and interest on the account was 7.6% compounded quarterly. The account balance of $17,500 was recently given to Cherie. How much longer did Brandon live?

**45. Saving for a down payment:** Tae-Hon is tired of renting and decides that within the next 5 yr he must save $22,500 for the down payment on a home. He finds an investment company that offers 8.5% interest compounded monthly and begins depositing $250 each month in the account. (a) Is this monthly amount sufficient to help him meet his 5 yr goal? (b) If not, find the *minimum amount he needs to deposit each month* that will enable him to meet his goal in 5 yr.

**46. Saving to open a business:** Madeline feels trapped in her current job and decides to save $75,000 over the next 7 yr to open up a Harley Davidson franchise. To this end, she invests $145 every week in an account paying $7\frac{1}{2}$% interest compounded weekly. (a) Is this weekly amount sufficient to help her meet the seven-year goal? (b) If not, find the *minimum amount she needs to deposit each week* that will enable her to meet this goal in 7 yr?

► **WORKING WITH FORMULAS**

Solve for the indicated unknowns.

**47.** $A = p + prt$

    **a.** solve for $t$

    **b.** solve for $p$

**48.** $A = p(1 + r)^t$

    **a.** solve for $t$

    **b.** solve for $r$

**49.** $A = P\left(1 + \dfrac{r}{n}\right)^{nt}$

    **a.** solve for $r$

    **b.** solve for $t$

**50.** $A = pe^{rt}$

    **a.** solve for $p$

    **b.** solve for $r$

**51.** $Q(t) = Q_0 e^{rt}$

    **a.** solve for $Q_0$

    **b.** solve for $t$

**52.** $p = \dfrac{AR}{[(1 + R)^{nt} - 1]}$

    **a.** solve for $A$

    **b.** solve for $n$

**53. Amount of a mortgage payment:**

$$\mathcal{P} = \frac{AR}{1 - (1 + R)^{-nt}}$$

The mortgage payment required to pay off (or amortize) a loan is given by the formula shown, where $\mathcal{P}$ is the payment amount, $A$ is the original amount of the loan, $t$ is the time in years, $r$ is the annual interest rate, $n$ is the number of payments per year, and $R = \frac{r}{n}$. Find the *monthly payment* required to amortize a $125,000 home, if the interest rate is 5.5%/year and the home is financed over 30 yr.

**54. Total interest paid on a home mortgage:**

$$I = \left[\frac{prt}{1 - \left(\dfrac{1}{1 + 0.08\overline{3}r}\right)^{12t}}\right] - p$$

The total interest $I$ paid in $t$ years on a home mortgage of $p$ dollars is given by the formula shown, where $r$ is the interest rate on the loan (note that $0.08\overline{3} = \frac{1}{12}$). If the original mortgage was $198,000 at an interest rate of 6.5%, (a) how much interest has been paid in 10 yr? (b) Use a table of values to determine how many years it will take for the interest paid to exceed the amount of the original mortgage.

▶ APPLICATIONS

**55. Exponential growth:** As part of a lab experiment, Luamata needs to grow a culture of 200,000 bacteria, which are known to double in number in 12 hr. If he begins with 1000 bacteria, (a) find the growth rate $r$ and (b) find how many hours it takes for the culture to produce the 200,000 bacteria.

**56. Exponential growth:** After the wolf population was decimated due to overhunting, the rabbit population in the Boluhti Game Reserve began to double every 6 months. If there were an estimated 120 rabbits to begin, (a) find the growth rate $r$ and (b) find the number of months required for the population to reach 2500.

**57. Radioactive decay:** The radioactive element iodine-131 has a half-life of 8 days and is often used to help diagnose patients with thyroid problems. If a certain thyroid procedure requires 0.5 g and is scheduled to take place in 3 days, what is the minimum amount that must be on hand now (to the nearest hundredth of a gram)?

**58. Radioactive decay:** The radioactive element sodium-24 has a half-life of 15 hr and is used to help locate obstructions in blood flow. If the procedure requires 0.75 g and is scheduled to take place in 2 days (48 hr), what minimum amount must be on hand *now* (to the nearest hundredth of a gram)?

**59. Radioactive decay:** The radioactive element americium-241 has a half-life of 432 yr and although extremely small amounts are used (about 0.0002 g), it is the most vital component of standard household smoke detectors. How many years will it take a 10-g mass of americium-241 to decay to 2.7 g?

**60. Radioactive decay:** Carbon-14 is a radioactive compound that occurs naturally in all living organisms, with the amount in the organism constantly renewed. After death, no new carbon-14 is acquired and the amount in the organism begins to decay exponentially. If the half-life of carbon-14 is 5730 yr, how old is a mummy having only 30% of the normal amount of carbon-14?

**Carbon-14 dating: If the percentage $p$ of carbon-14 that remains in a fossil can be determined, the formula $T = -8267 \ln p$ can be used to estimate the number of years $T$ since the organism died.**

**61. Dating the Lascaux Cave Dwellers:** Bits of charcoal from Lascaux Cave (home of the prehistoric Lascaux Cave Paintings) were used to estimate that the fire had burned some 17,255 yr ago. What percent of the original amount of carbon-14 remained in the bits of charcoal?

**62. Dating Stonehenge:** Using organic fragments found near Stonehenge (England), scientists were able to determine that the organism that produced the fragments lived about 3925 yr ago. What percent of the original amount of carbon-14 remained in the organism?

▶ EXTENDING THE CONCEPT

**63.** Many claim that inheritance taxes are put in place simply to prevent a massive accumulation of wealth by a select few. Suppose that in 1890, your great-grandfather deposited $10,000 in an account paying 6.2% compounded continuously. If the account were to pass to you untaxed, what would it be worth in 2010? Do some research on the inheritance tax laws in your state. In particular, what amounts can be inherited untaxed (i.e., before the inheritance tax kicks in)?

**64.** In Appendix I.A, we noted that one important characteristic of exponential functions is their rate of growth is in constant proportion to the population at time $t$: $\frac{\Delta P}{\Delta t} = kP$. This rate of growth can also be applied to finance and biological models, as well as the growth of tumors, and is of great value in studying these applications. In Exercise 96 of Appendix I.A, we computed the value of $k$ for the Goldsboro model ($P = 1000 \cdot 2^t$) using the difference quotient. If we rewrite this model in terms of base $e$ ($P = 1000 \cdot e^{kt}$), the value of $k$ is given directly. The following sequence shows how this is done, and you are asked to supply the reason or justification for each step.

$$P = b^t \qquad \text{base-}b \text{ exponential}$$
$$\ln P = \ln b^t \qquad \rule{3cm}{0.4pt}$$
$$\ln P = t \ln b \qquad \rule{3cm}{0.4pt}$$
$$P = e^{t \ln b} \qquad \rule{3cm}{0.4pt}$$
$$P = e^{kt} \qquad k = \ln b$$

The last step shows the growth rate constant is equal to the natural log of the given base $b$: $k = \ln b$.

a. Use this result to verify the growth rate constant for Goldsboro is 0.6931472.

b. After the Great Oklahoma Land Run of 1890, the population of the state grew rapidly for the next 2 decades. For this time period, population growth could be approximated by $P = 260(1.10^t)$. Find the growth rate constant for this model, and use it to write the base-$e$ population equation. Use the TABLE feature of a graphing calculator to verify that the equations are equivalent.

65. If you have not already completed Exercise 30, please do so. For *this* exercise, *solve the compound interest equation for r* to find the exact rate of interest that will allow Helyn to meet her 18-yr goal.

 66. If you have not already completed Exercise 43, please do so. Suppose the final balance of the account was $35,100 with interest again being compounded monthly. For *this* exercise, use a graphing calculator to find $r$, the exact rate of interest the account would have been earning.

# SUMMARY AND CONCEPT REVIEW

## A  Exponential Functions

### KEY CONCEPTS

- An exponential function is defined as $f(x) = b^x$, where $b > 0$, $b \neq 1$, and $b$, $x$ are real numbers.
- The natural exponential function is $f(x) = e^x$, where $e \approx 2.71828182846$.
- For exponential functions, we have
  - one-to-one function
  - $y$-intercept $(0, 1)$
  - domain: $x \in \mathbb{R}$
  - range: $y \in (0, \infty)$
  - increasing if $b > 1$
  - decreasing if $0 < b < 1$
  - asymptotic to $x$-axis
- The graph of $y = b^{x \pm h} \pm k$ is a translation of the basic graph of $y = b^x$, horizontally $h$ units opposite the sign and vertically $k$ units in the same direction as the sign.
- If an equation can be written with like bases on each side, we solve it using the uniqueness property: If $b^m = b^n$, then $m = n$ (equal bases imply equal exponents).
- All previous properties of exponents also apply to exponential functions.

### EXERCISES

Graph each function using *transformations of the basic function,* then strategically plot a few points to check your work and round out the graph. Draw and label the asymptote.

1. $y = 2^x + 3$
2. $y = 2^{-x} - 1$
3. $y = -e^{x+1} - 2$

Solve using the uniqueness property.

4. $3^{2x-1} = 27$
5. $4^x = \frac{1}{16}$
6. $e^x \cdot e^{x+1} = e^6$

7. A ballast machine is purchased new for $142,000 by the AT & SF Railroad. The machine loses 15% of its value each year and must be replaced when its value drops below $20,000. How many years will the machine be in service?

## B  Logarithms and Logarithmic Functions

### KEY CONCEPTS

- A logarithm is an exponent. For $x$, $b > 0$, and $b \neq 1$, the expression $\log_b x$ represents the exponent that goes on base $b$ to obtain $x$: If $y = \log_b x$, then $b^y = x \Rightarrow b^{\log_b x} = x$ (by substitution).

- The equations $x = b^y$ and $y = \log_b x$ are equivalent. We say $x = b^y$ is the *exponential* form and $y = \log_b x$ is the *logarithmic* form of the equation.
- The value of $\log_b x$ can sometimes be determined by writing the expression in exponential form. If $b = 10$ or $b = e$, the value of $\log_b x$ can be found directly using a calculator.
- A logarithmic *function* is defined as $f(x) = \log_b x$, where $x, b > 0$, and $b \neq 1$.
  - $y = \log_{10} x = \log x$ is called a *common* logarithmic function.
  - $y = \log_e x = \ln x$ is called a *natural* logarithmic function.
- For $f(x) = \log_b x$ as defined we have
  - one-to-one function
  - $x$-intercept $(1, 0)$
  - domain: $x \in (0, \infty)$
  - range: $y \in \mathbb{R}$
  - increasing if $b > 1$
  - decreasing if $0 < b < 1$
  - asymptotic to $y$-axis
- The graph of $y = \log_b(x \pm h) \pm k$ is a translation of the graph of $y = \log_b x$, horizontally $h$ units opposite the sign and vertically $k$ units in the same direction as the sign.

## EXERCISES

Write each expression in *exponential* form.

**8.** $\log_3 9 = 2$    **9.** $\log_5 \frac{1}{125} = -3$    **10.** $\ln 43 \approx 3.7612$

Write each expression in *logarithmic* form.

**11.** $5^2 = 25$    **12.** $e^{-0.25} \approx 0.7788$    **13.** $3^4 = 81$

Find the value of each expression without using a calculator.

**14.** $\log_2 32$    **15.** $\ln\left(\frac{1}{e}\right)$    **16.** $\log_9 3$

Graph each function using *transformations of the basic function,* then strategically plot a few points to check your work and round out the graph. Draw and label the asymptote.

**17.** $f(x) = \log_2 x$    **18.** $f(x) = \log_2(x + 3)$    **19.** $f(x) = 2 + \ln(x - 1)$

Find the domain of the following functions.

**20.** $g(x) = \log \sqrt{2x + 3}$    **21.** $f(x) = \ln(x^2 - 6x)$

**22.** The magnitude of an earthquake is given by $M(I) = \log\dfrac{I}{I_0}$, where $I$ is the intensity and $I_0$ is the reference intensity. (a) Find $M(I)$ given $I = 62{,}000 I_0$ and (b) find the intensity $I$ given $M(I) = 7.3$.

## C  Properties of Logarithms; Solving Exponential/Logarithmic Equations

### KEY CONCEPTS

- The basic definition of a logarithm gives rise to the following properties: For any base $b > 0$, $b \neq 1$,
  1. $\log_b b = 1$ (since $b^1 = b$)
  2. $\log_b 1 = 0$ (since $b^0 = 1$)
  3. $\log_b b^x = x$ (since $b^x = b^x$)
  4. $b^{\log_b x} = x$
- Since a logarithm is an exponent, they have properties that parallel those of exponents.

| **Product Property** | **Quotient Property** | **Power Property** |
|:---:|:---:|:---:|
| like base and multiplication, add exponents: | like base and division, subtract exponents: | exponent raised to a power, multiply exponents: |
| $\log_b(MN) = \log_b M + \log_b N$ | $\log_b\left(\dfrac{M}{N}\right) = \log_b M - \log_b N$ | $\log_b M^p = p\log_b M$ |

- The logarithmic properties can be used to expand an expression: $\log(2x) = \log 2 + \log x$.
- The logarithmic properties can be used to contract an expression: $\ln(2x) - \ln(x + 3) = \ln\left(\dfrac{2x}{x + 3}\right)$.

- To evaluate logarithms with bases other than 10 or $e$, use the change-of-base formula:

$$\log_b M = \frac{\log M}{\log b} = \frac{\ln M}{\ln b}$$

- If an equation can be written with like bases on each side, we solve it using the uniqueness property: if $\log_b m = \log_b n$, then $m = n$ (equal bases imply equal arguments).
- If a single exponential or logarithmic term can be isolated on one side, then for any base $b$:

$$\text{If } b^x = k, \text{ then } x = \frac{\log k}{\log b} \qquad\qquad \text{If } \log_b x = k, \text{ then } x = b^k.$$

## EXERCISES

**23.** Solve each equation by applying fundamental properties.

    **a.** $\ln x = 32$     **b.** $\log x = 2.38$     **c.** $e^x = 9.8$     **d.** $10^x = \sqrt{7}$

**24.** Solve each equation. Write answers in exact form and in approximate form to four decimal places.

    **a.** $15 = 7 + 2e^{0.5x}$     **b.** $10^{0.2x} = 19$     **c.** $-2\log(3x) + 1 = -5$     **d.** $-2\ln x + 1 = 6.5$

**25.** Use the product or quotient property of logarithms to write each sum or difference as a single term.

    **a.** $\ln 7 + \ln 6$     **b.** $\log_9 2 + \log_9 15$     **c.** $\ln(x + 3) - \ln(x - 1)$     **d.** $\log x + \log(x + 1)$

**26.** Use the power property of logarithms to rewrite each term as a product.

    **a.** $\log_5 9^2$     **b.** $\log_7 4^2$     **c.** $\ln 5^{2x-1}$     **d.** $\ln 10^{3x+2}$

**27.** Use the properties of logarithms to write the following expressions as a sum or difference of simple logarithmic terms.

    **a.** $\ln(x\sqrt[4]{y})$     **b.** $\ln(\sqrt[3]{pq})$     **c.** $\log\left(\dfrac{\sqrt[3]{x^5 \cdot y^4}}{\sqrt{x^5 y^3}}\right)$     **d.** $\log\left(\dfrac{4\sqrt[3]{p^5 q^4}}{\sqrt{p^3 q^2}}\right)$

**28.** Evaluate using a change-of-base formula. Answer in exact form and approximate form to thousandths.

    **a.** $\log_6 45$     **b.** $\log_3 128$     **c.** $\ln_2 124$     **d.** $\ln_5 0.42$

Solve each equation.

**29.** $2^x = 7$                **30.** $3^{x+1} = 5$              **31.** $e^{x-2} = 3^x$

**32.** $\ln(x + 1) = 2$        **33.** $\log x + \log(x - 3) = 1$     **34.** $\log_{25}(x + 2) - \log_{25}(x - 3) = \frac{1}{2}$

**35.** The rate of decay for radioactive material is related to its half-life by the formula $R(h) = \frac{\ln 2}{h}$, where $h$ represents the half-life of the material and $R(h)$ is the rate of decay expressed as a decimal. The element radon-222 has a half-life of approximately 3.9 days. (a) Find its rate of decay to the nearest hundredth of a percent. (b) Find the half-life of thorium-234 if its rate of decay is 2.89% per day.

**36.** The *barometric equation* $H = (30T + 8000)\ln\left(\frac{P_0}{P}\right)$ relates the altitude $H$ to atmospheric pressure $P$, where $P_0 = 76$ cmHg. Find the atmospheric pressure at the summit of Mount Pico de Orizaba (Mexico), whose summit is at 5657 m. Assume the temperature at the summit is $T = 12°C$.

## D  Applications from Business, Finance, and Science

### KEY CONCEPTS

- Simple interest: $I = prt$; $p$ is the initial principal, $r$ is the interest rate per year, and $t$ is the time in years.
- Amount in an account after $t$ years: $A = p + prt$ or $A = p(1 + rt)$.
- Interest compounded $n$ times per year: $A = p\left(1 + \dfrac{r}{n}\right)^{nt}$; $p$ is the initial principal, $r$ is the interest rate per year, $t$ is the time in years, and $n$ is the times per year interest is compounded.
- Interest compounded continuously: $A = pe^{rt}$; $p$ is the initial principal, $r$ is the interest rate per year, and $t$ is the time in years.

- If a loan or savings plan calls for a regular schedule of deposits, the plan is called an annuity.
- For periodic payment $\mathcal{P}$, deposited or paid $n$ times per year, at annual interest rate $r$, with interest compounded or calculated $n$ times per year for $t$ years, and $R = \dfrac{r}{n}$:
  - The accumulated value of the account is $A = \dfrac{\mathcal{P}}{R}[(1+R)^{nt} - 1]$.
  - The payment required to meet a future goal is $\mathcal{P} = \dfrac{AR}{[(1+R)^{nt} - 1]}$.
  - The payment required to amortize an amount $A$ is $\mathcal{P} = \dfrac{AR}{1 - (1+R)^{-nt}}$.
  - The general formulas for exponential growth and decay are $Q(t) = Q_0 e^{rt}$ and $Q(t) = Q_0 e^{-rt}$, respectively.

## EXERCISES

Solve each application.

**37.** Jeffery borrows $600.00 from his dad, who decides it's best to charge him interest. Three months later Jeff repays the loan plus interest, a total of $627.75. What was the annual interest rate on the loan?

**38.** To save money for her first car, Cheryl invests the $7500 she inherited in an account paying 7.8% interest compounded monthly. She hopes to buy the car in 6 yr and needs $12,000. Is this possible?

**39.** To save up for the vacation of a lifetime, Al-Harwi decides to save $15,000 over the next 4 yr. For this purpose he invests $260 every month in an account paying $7\frac{1}{2}\%$ interest compounded monthly. (a) Is this monthly amount sufficient to meet the four-year goal? (b) If not, find the *minimum amount he needs to deposit each month* that will allow him to meet this goal in 4 yr.

**40.** Eighty prairie dogs are released in a wilderness area in an effort to repopulate the species. Five years later a statistical survey reveals the population has reached 1250 dogs. Assuming the growth was exponential, approximate the growth rate to the nearest tenth of a percent.

## MIXED REVIEW

**1.** Evaluate each expression using the change-of-base formula.
   **a.** $\log_2 30$
   **b.** $\log_{0.25} 8$
   **c.** $\log_8 2$

**2.** Solve each equation using the uniqueness property.
   **a.** $10^{4x-5} = 1000$
   **b.** $5^{3x-1} = \sqrt{5}$
   **c.** $2^x \cdot 2^{0.5x} = 64$

**3.** Use the power property of logarithms to rewrite each expression as a product.
   **a.** $\log_{10} 20^2$
   **b.** $\log 10^{0.05x}$
   **c.** $\ln 2^{x-3}$

Graph each of the following functions by shifting the basic function, then strategically plotting a few points to check your work and round out the graph. Graph and label the asymptote.

**4.** $y = -e^x + 15$
**5.** $y = 5 \cdot 2^{-x}$
**6.** $y = \ln(x+5) + 7$
**7.** $y = \log_2(-x) - 4$

**8.** Use the properties of logarithms to write the following expressions as a sum or difference of simple logarithmic terms.
   **a.** $\ln\left(\dfrac{x^3}{2y}\right)$
   **b.** $\log(10a\sqrt[3]{a^2 b})$
   **c.** $\log_2\left(\dfrac{8x^4\sqrt{x}}{3\sqrt{y}}\right)$

**9.** Write the following expressions in exponential form.
   **a.** $\log_5 625 = 4$
   **b.** $\ln 0.15x = 0.45$
   **c.** $\log(0.1 \times 10^8) = 7$

**10.** Write the following expressions in logarithmic form.
   **a.** $343^{1/3} = 7$
   **b.** $256^{3/4} = 64$
   **c.** $2^{-3} = \frac{1}{8}$

**11.** Find the domain of the following functions.
   **a.** $\log(2x^2 - 3x - 2)$
   **b.** $\ln|x^3 - 8|$

Solve the following equations. State answers in exact form.

**12.** $\log_5(4x + 7) = 0$     **13.** $10^{x-4} = 200$

**14.** $e^{x+1} = 3^x$

**15.** $\log_2(2x - 5) + \log_2(x - 2) = 4$

**16.** $\log(3x - 4) - \log(x - 2) = 1$

Solve each application.

**17.** The magnitude of an earthquake is given by

$M(I) = \log\left(\dfrac{I}{I_0}\right)$, where $I$ is the intensity of the quake

and $I_0$ is the reference intensity $2 \times 10^{11}$ (energy released from the smallest detectable quake). On October 23, 2004, the Niigata region of Japan was hit by an earthquake that registered 6.5 on the Richter scale. Find the intensity of this earthquake by solving the following equation for

$I: 6.5 = \log\left(\dfrac{I}{2 \times 10^{11}}\right)$.

**18.** Serene is planning to buy a house. She has $6500 to invest in a certificate of deposit that compounds interest quarterly at an annual rate of 4.4%. (a) Find how long it will take for this account to grow to the $12,500 she will need for a 10% down payment for a $125,000 house. Round to the nearest tenth of a year. (b) Suppose instead of investing an initial $6500, Serene deposits $500 a quarter in an account paying 4% each quarter. Find how long it will take for this account to grow to $12,500. Round to the nearest tenth of a year.

**19.** British artist Simon Thomas designs sculptures he calls hypercones. These sculptures involve rings of exponentially decreasing radii rotated through space. For one sculpture, the radii follow the model $r(n) = 2(0.8)^n$, where $n$

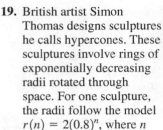

counts the rings (outer-most first) and $r(n)$ is radii in meters. Find the radii of the six largest rings in the sculpture. Round to the nearest hundredth of a meter.

Source: http://www.plus.maths.org/issue8/features/art/

**20.** Ms. Chan-Chiu works for MediaMax, a small business that helps other companies purchase advertising in publications. Her model for the benefits of advertising is $P(a) = 1000(1.07)^a$, where $P$ represents the number of potential customers reached when $a$ dollars (in thousands) are invested in advertising.

**a.** Use this model to predict (to the nearest thousand) how many potential customers will be reached when $50,000 is invested in advertising.

**b.** Use this model to determine how much money a company should expect to invest in advertising (to the nearest thousand), if it wants to reach 100,000 potential customers.

## PRACTICE TEST

**1.** Write the expression $\log_3 81 = 4$ in exponential form.

**2.** Write the expression $25^{1/2} = 5$ in logarithmic form.

**3.** Write the expression $\log_b\left(\dfrac{\sqrt{x^5 y^3}}{z}\right)$ as a sum or difference of logarithmic terms.

**4.** Write the expression $\log_b m + \left(\frac{3}{2}\right)\log_b n - \frac{1}{2}\log_b p$ as a single logarithm.

Solve for $x$ using the uniqueness property.

**5.** $5^{x-7} = 125$     **6.** $2 \cdot 4^{3x} = \dfrac{8^x}{16}$

Given $\log_a 3 \approx 0.48$ and $\log_a 5 \approx 1.72$, evaluate the following without the use of a calculator:

**7.** $\log_a 45$     **8.** $\log_a 0.6$

Graph using transformations of the parent function. Verify answers using a graphing calculator.

**9.** $g(x) = -2^{x-1} + 3$     **10.** $h(x) = \log_2(x - 2) + 1$

**11.** Use the change-of-base formula to evaluate. Verify results using a calculator.

**a.** $\log_3 100$     **b.** $\log_6 0.235$

**12.** State the domain and range of $f(x) = \ln(x - 2) - 3$. Then find its inverse, including the domain and range.

Solve each equation.

**13.** $3^{x-1} = 89$

**14.** $\log_5 x + \log_5(x + 4) = 1$

**15.** A copier is purchased new for $8000. The machine loses 18% of its value each year and must be replaced when its value drops below $3000. How many years will the machine be in service?

**16.** How long would it take $1000 to double if invested at 8% annual interest compounded daily?

**17.** The number of ounces of unrefined platinum drawn from a mine is modeled by $Q(t) = -2600 + 1900 \ln(t)$, where $Q(t)$ represents the number of ounces mined in $t$ months. How many months did it take for the number of ounces mined to exceed 3000?

**18.** Septashi can invest his savings in an account paying 7% compounded semi-annually, or in an account paying 6.8% compounded daily. Which is the better investment?

**19.** Jacob decides to save $4000 over the next 5 yr so that he can present his wife with a new diamond ring

for their 20th anniversary. He invests $50 every month in an account paying $8\frac{1}{4}$% interest compounded monthly. (a) Is this amount sufficient to meet the 5-yr goal? (b) If not, find the *minimum amount he needs to save monthly* that will enable him to meet this goal.

**20.** Chaucer is a typical Welsh Corgi puppy. During his first year of life, his weight very closely follows the model $W(t) = 6.79 \ln t - 11.97$, where $W(t)$ is his weight in pounds after $t$ weeks and $8 \le t \le 52$.
  **a.** How much will Chaucer weigh when he is 6 months old (to the nearest one-tenth pound)?
  **b.** To the nearest week, how old is Chaucer when he weighs 8 lb?

---

# CALCULATOR EXPLORATION AND DISCOVERY

## Investigating Logistic Equations

As we saw in Appendix I.C, logistics models have the form $P(t) = \dfrac{c}{1 + ae^{-bt}}$, where $a$, $b$, and $c$ are constants and $P(t)$ represents the population at time $t$. For populations modeled by a logistics curve (sometimes called an "S" curve) growth is very rapid at first (like an exponential function), but this growth begins to slow down and level off due to various factors. This *Calculator Exploration and Discovery* is designed to investigate the effects that $a$, $b$, and $c$ have on the resulting graph.

**Figure AI.19**

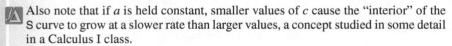

**I.** From our earlier observation, as $t$ becomes larger and larger, the term $ae^{-bt}$ becomes smaller and smaller (approaching 0) because it is a decreasing function: as $t \to \infty$, $ae^{-bt} \to 0$. If we allow that the term eventually becomes so small it can be disregarded, what remains is $P(t) = \dfrac{c}{1}$ or $c$. This is why $c$ is called the capacity constant and the population can get no larger than $c$. In Figure AI.19, the graph of $P(t) = \dfrac{1000}{1 + 50e^{-1x}}$ ($a = 50$, $b = 1$, and $c = 1000$) is shown using a lighter line, while the graph of $P(t) = \dfrac{750}{1 + 50e^{-1x}}$ ($a = 50$, $b = 1$, and $c = 750$), is given in bold. The window size is indicated in Figure AI.20.

Also note that if $a$ is held constant, smaller values of $c$ cause the "interior" of the S curve to grow at a slower rate than larger values, a concept studied in some detail in a Calculus I class.

**Figure AI.20**

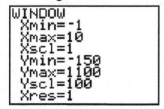

**II.** If $t = 0$, $ae^{-bt} = ae^0 = a$, and we note the ratio $P(0) = \dfrac{c}{1 + a}$ represents the *initial population*. This also means for constant values of $c$, larger values of $a$ make the ratio $\dfrac{c}{1 + a}$ smaller; while smaller values of $a$ make the ratio $\dfrac{c}{1 + a}$ larger. From this we conclude that $a$ primarily affects the initial population. For the screens shown next, $P(t) = \dfrac{1000}{1 + 50e^{-1x}}$ (from I) is graphed using a lighter line. For comparison, the graph of $P(t) = \dfrac{1000}{1 + 5e^{-1x}}$ ($a = 5$, $b = 1$, and $c = 1000$) is shown in bold in Figure AI.21, while the graph of

**Figure AI.21**

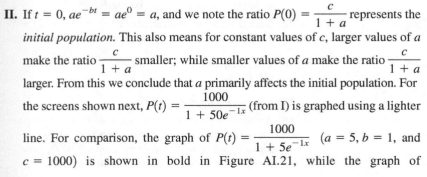

$P(t) = \dfrac{1000}{1 + 500e^{-1x}}$ ($a = 500$, $b = 1$, and $c = 1000$) is shown in bold in Figure AI.22.

Note that changes in $a$ appear to have no effect on the rate of growth in the interior of the S curve.

**III.** As for the value of $b$, we might expect that it affects the rate of growth in much the same way as the growth rate $r$ does for exponential functions $Q(t) = Q_0 e^{-rt}$. Sure enough, we note from the graphs shown that $b$ has no effect on the initial value or the eventual capacity, but causes the population to approach this capacity more quickly for larger values of $b$, and more slowly for smaller values of $b$. For the screens shown, $P(t) = \dfrac{1000}{1 + 50e^{-1x}}$ ($a = 50$, $b = 1$, and $c = 1000$) is graphed using a lighter line. For comparison, the graph of $P(t) = \dfrac{1000}{1 + 50e^{-1.2x}}$ ($a = 50$, $b = 1.2$, and $c = 1000$) is shown in bold in Figure AI.23, while the graph of $P(t) = \dfrac{1000}{1 + 50e^{-0.8x}}$ ($a = 50$, $b = 0.8$, and $c = 1000$) is shown in bold in Figure AI.24.

The following exercises are based on the population of an ant colony, modeled by the logistic function $P(t) = \dfrac{2500}{1 + 25e^{-0.5x}}$. Respond to Exercises 1 through 6 without the use of a calculator.

**Exercise 1:** Identify the values of $a$, $b$, and $c$ for this logistics curve.

**Exercise 2:** What was the approximate initial population of the colony?

**Exercise 3:** Which gives a larger initial population: (a) $c = 2500$ and $a = 25$ or (b) $c = 3000$ and $a = 15$?

**Exercise 4:** What is the maximum population capacity for this colony?

**Exercise 5:** Would the population of the colony surpass 2000 more quickly if $b = 0.6$ or if $b = 0.4$?

**Exercise 6:** Which causes a slower population growth: (a) $c = 2000$ and $a = 25$ or (b) $c = 3000$ and $a = 25$?

**Exercise 7:** Verify your responses to Exercises 2 through 6 using a graphing calculator.

**Figure AI.22**
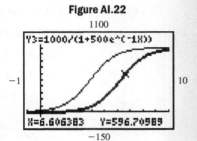

**Figure AI.23**
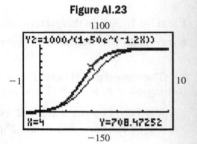

**Figure AI.24**
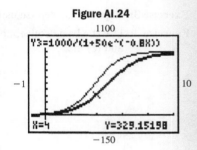

## STRENGTHENING CORE SKILLS

### Understanding Properties of Logarithms

To effectively use the properties of logarithms as a mathematical tool, a student must attain some degree of comfort and fluency in their application. Otherwise we are resigned to using them as a template or formula, leaving little room for growth or insight. This feature is divided into two parts. The first is designed to promote an understanding of the product and quotient properties of logarithms, which play a role in the solution of logarithmic and exponential equations.

We begin by looking at some logarithmic expressions that are obviously true:

$\log_2 2 = 1$      $\log_2 4 = 2$      $\log_2 8 = 3$      $\log_2 16 = 4$      $\log_2 32 = 5$      $\log_2 64 = 6$

Next, we view the same expressions with their value *understood mentally*, illustrated by the numbers in the background, rather than expressly written.

$\log_2 2$          $\log_2 4$          $\log_2 8$          $\log_2 16$          $\log_2 32$          $\log_2 64$

This will make the product and quotient properties of equality much easier to "see." Recall the product property states:

$\log_b M + \log_b N = \log_b(MN)$ and the quotient property states: $\log_b M - \log_b N = \log_b\left(\dfrac{M}{N}\right)$. Consider the following.

$$\log_2 4 + \log_2 8 = \log_2 32 \qquad\qquad \log_2 64 - \log_2 32 = \log_2 2$$

which is the same as saying          which is the same as saying

$$\log_2 4 + \log_2 8 = \log_2(4\cdot 8) \qquad\qquad \log_2 64 - \log_2 32 = \log_2(\tfrac{64}{32})$$

$$\text{(since } 4\cdot 8 = 32) \qquad\qquad\qquad\qquad \text{(since } \tfrac{64}{32} = 2)$$

$$\log_b M + \log_b N = \log_b(MN) \qquad\qquad \log_b M - \log_b N = \log_b\left(\dfrac{M}{N}\right)$$

**Exercise 1:** Repeat this exercise using logarithms of base 3 and various sums and differences.

**Exercise 2:** Use the basic concept behind these exercises to combine these expressions: (a) $\log(x) + \log(x + 3)$, (b) $\ln(x + 2) + \ln(x - 2)$, and (c) $\log(x) - \log(x + 3)$.

The second part is similar to the first, but highlights the power property: $\log_b M^x = x\log_b M$. For instance, knowing that $\log_2 64 = 6$, $\log_2 8 = 3$, and $\log_2 2 = 1$, consider the following:

$\log_2 8$ can be written as $\log_2 2^3$ (since $2^3 = 8$). Applying the power property gives $3\cdot\log_2 2 = 3$.

$\log_2 64$ can be written as $\log_2 2^6$ (since $2^6 = 64$). Applying the power property gives $6\cdot\log_2 2 = 6$.

$$\log_b M^x = x\log_b M$$

**Exercise 3:** Repeat this exercise using logarithms of base 3 and various powers.

**Exercise 4:** Use the basic concept behind these exercises to rewrite each expression as a product: (a) $\log 3^x$, (b) $\ln x^5$, and (c) $\ln 2^{3x-1}$.

# APPENDIX II

# Transformations of a Basic Graph

In previous coursework, you've likely noted the graph of <u>any</u> function from a given family maintains the same general shape. The graphs of $y = -2x^2 - 5x + 3$ and $y = x^2$ are both parabolas, the graphs of $y = \sqrt[3]{x}$ and $y = -\sqrt[3]{x-2} + 1$ are both "horizontal propellers," and so on for other functions. Once you're aware of the main features of a basic function, you can graph any function from that family using far fewer points, and analyze the graph more efficiently. As we study specific transformations of a graph, it's important to develop a *global view of the transformations*, as they can be applied to virtually any function (see Illustration 7).

## A. Vertical and Horizontal Shifts

We'll begin our review using the absolute value function family.

### Vertical Translations

If a constant $k$ is added to the output of a basic function $y = f(x)$, the result is a vertical shift since the output values are altered uniformly.

---

**ILLUSTRATION 1** ▶ **Graphing Vertical Translations**

Construct a table of values for $f(x) = |x|$, $g(x) = |x| + 1$, and $h(x) = |x| - 3$ and graph the functions on the same coordinate grid. Then discuss what you observe.

**Solution** ▶ A table of values for all three functions is given, with the corresponding graphs shown in the figure.

| $x$ | $f(x) = |x|$ | $g(x) = |x| + 1$ | $h(x) = |x| - 3$ |
|---|---|---|---|
| −3 | 3 | 4 | 0 |
| −2 | 2 | 3 | −1 |
| −1 | 1 | 2 | −2 |
| 0 | 0 | 1 | −3 |
| 1 | 1 | 2 | −2 |
| 2 | 2 | 3 | −1 |
| 3 | 3 | 4 | 0 |

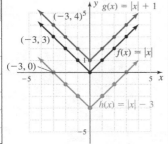

Note that outputs of $g(x)$ are one more than the outputs for $f(x)$, and that each point on the graph of $f$ has been shifted *upward 1 unit* to form the graph of $g$. Similarly, each point on the graph of $f$ has been shifted *downward 3 units* to form the graph of $h$ since $h(x) = f(x) - 3$.

---

We describe the transformations in Illustration 1 as a **vertical shift** or **vertical translation** of a basic graph. The graph of $g$ is the graph of $f$ *shifted up 1 unit*, and the graph of $h$ is the graph of $f$ *shifted down 3 units*. In general, we have the following:

---

**Vertical Translations of a Basic Graph**

Given $k > 0$ and any function whose graph is determined by $y = f(x)$,

1. The graph of $y = f(x) + k$ is the graph of $f(x)$ shifted upward $k$ units.
2. The graph of $y = f(x) - k$ is the graph of $f(x)$ shifted downward $k$ units.

---

## Horizontal Translations

The graph of a parent function can also be shifted left or right. This happens when we *alter the inputs to the basic function,* as opposed to adding or subtracting something to the basic function itself. For $Y_1 = x^2 + 2$ note that we first square inputs, then add 2, which results in a vertical shift. For $Y_2 = (x + 2)^2$, we add 2 to $x$ *prior to squaring* and since the input values are affected, we might anticipate the graph will shift along the $x$-axis—horizontally.

---

**ILLUSTRATION 2** ▶ **Graphing Horizontal Translations**

Construct a table of values for $f(x) = x^2$ and $g(x) = (x + 2)^2$, then graph the functions on the same grid and discuss what you observe.

**Solution** ▶ Both $f$ and $g$ belong to the quadratic family and their graphs are parabolas. A table of values is shown along with the corresponding graphs.

| $x$ | $f(x) = x^2$ | $g(x) = (x + 2)^2$ |
|-----|--------------|---------------------|
| $-3$ | 9 | 1 |
| $-2$ | 4 | 0 |
| $-1$ | 1 | 1 |
| 0 | 0 | 4 |
| 1 | 1 | 9 |
| 2 | 4 | 16 |
| 3 | 9 | 25 |

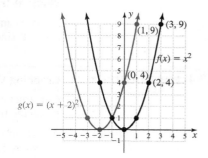

It is apparent the graphs of $g$ and $f$ are identical, but the graph of $g$ has been shifted horizontally 2 units left.

---

We describe the transformation in Illustration 2 as a **horizontal shift** or **horizontal translation** of a basic graph. The graph of $g$ is the graph of $f$, *shifted 2 units to the left.* Once again it seems reasonable that since *input* values were altered, the shift must be horizontal rather than vertical. From this example, we also learn the direction of the shift is **opposite the sign:** $y = (x + 2)^2$ is 2 units *to the left* of $y = x^2$. Although it may seem counterintuitive, the shift *opposite the sign* can be "seen" by locating the new $x$-intercept, which in this case is also the vertex. Substituting 0 for $y$ gives $0 = (x + 2)^2$ with $x = -2$, as shown in the graph. In general, we have

**A.** You've just reviewed how to perform vertical/horizontal shifts of a basic graph

### Horizontal Translations of a Basic Graph

Given $h > 0$ and any function whose graph is determined by $y = f(x)$,
1. The graph of $y = f(x + h)$ is the graph of $f(x)$ shifted *to the left* $h$ units.
2. The graph of $y = f(x - h)$ is the graph of $f(x)$ shifted *to the right* $h$ units.

## B. Vertical and Horizontal Reflections

The next transformation we investigate is called a **vertical reflection,** in which we compare the function $Y_1 = f(x)$ with the negative of the function: $Y_2 = -f(x)$.

### Vertical Reflections

**ILLUSTRATION 3** ▶ **Graphing Vertical Reflections**

Construct a table of values for $Y_1 = x^2$ and $Y_2 = -x^2$, then graph the functions on the same grid and discuss what you observe.

**Solution** ▶ A table of values is given for both functions, along with the corresponding graphs.

| $x$ | $Y_1 = x^2$ | $Y_2 = -x^2$ |
|---|---|---|
| $-2$ | 4 | $-4$ |
| $-1$ | 1 | $-1$ |
| 0 | 0 | 0 |
| 1 | 1 | $-1$ |
| 2 | 4 | $-4$ |

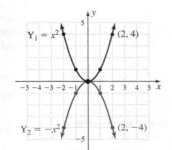

As you might have anticipated, the outputs for $f$ and $g$ differ only in sign. Each output is a **reflection** of the other, being an equal distance from the $x$-axis but on opposite sides.

The vertical reflection in Illustration 3 is called a **reflection across the $x$-axis.** In general,

### Vertical Reflections of a Basic Graph

For any function $y = f(x)$, the graph of $y = -f(x)$
is the graph of $f(x)$ reflected across the $x$-axis.

### Horizontal Reflections

It's also possible for a graph to be reflected horizontally *across the y-axis.* Just as we noted that $f(x)$ versus $-f(x)$ resulted in a vertical reflection, $f(x)$ versus $f(-x)$ results in a horizontal reflection.

**ILLUSTRATION 4** ▶ **Graphing a Horizontal Reflection**

Construct a table of values for $f(x) = \sqrt{x}$ and $g(x) = \sqrt{-x}$, then graph the functions on the same coordinate grid and discuss what you observe.

**Solution** ▶ A table of values is given here, along with the corresponding graphs.

| $x$ | $f(x) = \sqrt{x}$ | $g(x) = \sqrt{-x}$ |
|---|---|---|
| $-4$ | not real | 2 |
| $-2$ | not real | $\sqrt{2} \approx 1.41$ |
| $-1$ | not real | 1 |
| 0 | 0 | 0 |
| 1 | 1 | not real |
| 2 | $\sqrt{2} \approx 1.41$ | not real |
| 4 | 2 | not real |

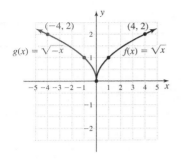

The graph of $g$ is the same as the graph of $f$, but it has been reflected across the $y$-axis. A study of the domain shows why—$f$ represents a real number only for nonnegative inputs, so its graph occurs to the right of the $y$-axis, while $g$ represents a real number for nonpositive inputs, so its graph occurs to the left.

The transformation in Illustration 4 is called a **horizontal reflection** of a basic graph. In general,

☑ **B.** You've just reviewed how to perform vertical/horizontal reflections of a basic graph

> **Horizontal Reflections of a Basic Graph**
>
> For any function $y = f(x)$, the graph of $y = f(-x)$
> is the graph of $f(x)$ reflected across the $y$-axis.

## C. Vertically Stretching/Compressing a Basic Graph

As the words "stretching" and "compressing" imply, the graph of a basic function can also become elongated or flattened after certain transformations are applied. However, even these transformations preserve the key characteristics of the graph.

**ILLUSTRATION 5** ▶ **Stretching and Compressing a Basic Graph**

Construct a table of values for $f(x) = x^2$, $g(x) = 3x^2$, and $h(x) = \frac{1}{3}x^2$, then graph the functions on the same grid and discuss what you observe.

**Solution** ▶ A table of values is given for all three functions, along with the corresponding graphs.

| $x$ | $f(x) = x^2$ | $g(x) = 3x^2$ | $h(x) = \frac{1}{3}x^2$ |
|---|---|---|---|
| $-3$ | 9 | 27 | 3 |
| $-2$ | 4 | 12 | $\frac{4}{3}$ |
| $-1$ | 1 | 3 | $\frac{1}{3}$ |
| 0 | 0 | 0 | 0 |
| 1 | 1 | 3 | $\frac{1}{3}$ |
| 2 | 4 | 12 | $\frac{4}{3}$ |
| 3 | 9 | 27 | 3 |

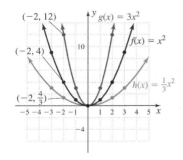

The outputs of $g$ are triple those of $f$, making these outputs farther from the $x$-axis and *stretching* $g$ upward (making the graph more narrow). The outputs of $h$ are one-third those of $f$, and the graph of $h$ is *compressed* downward, with its outputs closer to the $x$-axis (making the graph wider).

☑ **C.** You've just reviewed how to perform vertical stretches and compressions of a basic graph

The transformations in Illustration 5 are called **vertical stretches** or **compressions** of a basic graph. In general,

---

**Stretches and Compressions of a Basic Graph**

For any function $y = f(x)$, the graph of $y = af(x)$ is
  **1.** the graph of $f(x)$ stretched vertically if $|a| > 1$,
  **2.** the graph of $f(x)$ compressed vertically if $0 < |a| < 1$.

---

## D. Transformations of a General Function

If more than one transformation is applied to a basic graph, it's helpful to use the following sequence for graphing the new function.

---

**General Transformations of a Basic Graph**

Given a function $y = f(x)$, the graph of $y = af(x \pm h) \pm k$ can be obtained by applying the following sequence of transformations:
  **1.** horizontal shifts          **2.** reflections
  **3.** stretches or compressions    **4.** vertical shifts

---

We generally use a few characteristic points to track the transformations involved, then draw the transformed graph through the new location of these points.

---

**ILLUSTRATION 6** ▶ **Graphing Functions Using Transformations**

Use transformations of a parent function to sketch the graphs of
  **a.** $g(x) = -(x + 2)^2 + 3$      **b.** $h(x) = 2\sqrt[3]{x - 2} - 1$

Solution ▶   **a.** The graph of $g$ is a parabola, shifted left 2 units, reflected across the $x$-axis, and shifted up 3 units. This sequence of transformations in shown in Figures AII.1 through AII.3.

**Figure AII.1**                **Figure AII.2**                **Figure AII.3**

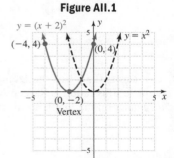

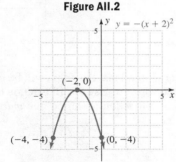

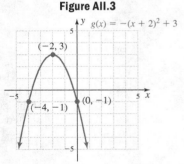

Shifted left 2 units              Reflected across the $x$-axis              Shifted up 3 units

**b.** The graph of $h$ is a cube root function, shifted right 2 units, stretched by a factor of 2, then shifted down 1 unit. This sequence is shown in Figures AII.4 through AII.6.

**Figure AII.4**

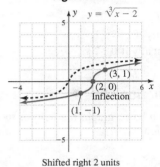

Shifted right 2 units

**Figure AII.5**

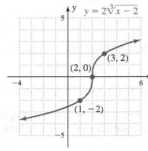

Stretched by a factor of 2

**Figure AII.6**

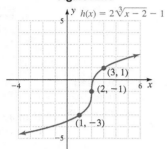

Shifted down 1 unit

It's important to note that the transformations can actually be applied to *any function,* even those that are new and unfamiliar. Consider the following pattern:

| Parent Function | Transformation of Parent Function |
|---|---|
| quadratic: $y = x^2$ | $y = -2(x - 3)^2 + 1$ |
| absolute value: $y = |x|$ | $y = -2|x - 3| + 1$ |
| cube root: $y = \sqrt[3]{x}$ | $y = -2\sqrt[3]{x - 3} + 1$ |
| general: $y = f(x)$ | $y = -2f(x - 3) + 1$ |

In each case, the transformation involves a horizontal shift right 3, a vertical reflection, a vertical stretch, and a vertical shift up 1. Since the shifts are the same regardless of the initial function, we can generalize the results to any function $f(x)$.

**General Function**          **Transformed Function**

$$y = f(x) \qquad\qquad y = af(x \pm h) \pm k$$

vertical reflections
vertical stretches and compressions

horizontal shift
$h$ units, opposite
direction of sign

vertical shift
$k$ units, same
direction as sign

Also bear in mind that the graph will be reflected across the $y$-axis (horizontally) if $x$ is replaced with $-x$. Use this illustration to complete Illustration 7. Remember— if the graph of a function is shifted, the *individual points* on the graph are likewise shifted.

**ILLUSTRATION 7** ▶ **Graphing Transformations of a General Function**

Given the graph of $f(x)$ shown in Figure AII.7, graph $g(x) = -f(x + 1) - 2$.

Solution ▶ For $g$, the graph of $f$ is (1) shifted horizontally 1 unit left, (2) reflected across the $x$-axis, and (3) shifted vertically 2 units down. The final result is shown in Figure AII.8.

**Figure AII.7**          **Figure AII.8**

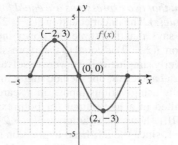

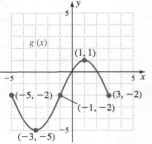

☑ **D.** You've just reviewed how to perform transformations on a general function $f(x)$

# Solving Equations Graphically

At the heart of understanding graphical solutions to an equation is this basic definition: *An equation is a statement that two expressions are equal for a certain input value(s).* The linear equation $3(x - 2) = x - 8$ literally says that for some unknown input $x$, the expression $3(x - 2)$ is equal to the expression $x - 8$. While overly simplistic, if we were to solve this equation by trial and error, our method might involve systematically using various inputs, in a search for one that resulted in a like output for both expressions. Table AIII.1 shows the solution to $3(x - 2) = x - 8$ is $x = -1$, since the left-hand expression is equal to

**Table AIII.1**

| Inputs | $3(x - 2)$ | $x - 8$ |
|--------|------------|---------|
| $-4$ | $-18$ | $-12$ |
| $-3$ | $-15$ | $-11$ |
| $-2$ | $-12$ | $-10$ |
| $-1$ | $-9$ | $-9$ |
| $0$ | $-6$ | $-8$ |
| $1$ | $-3$ | $-7$ |
| $2$ | $0$ | $-6$ |

the right-hand expression for this input. Note that we're actually treating each expression as the independent functions $Y_1 = 3(x - 2)$ and $Y_2 = x - 8$, and can actually view the solution method as *an attempt to find where the graphs of these two lines intersect.* This basic idea is very powerful and can be extended to expressions and equations of all kinds. With the help of graphing and calculating technology, we have the ability to solve some very sophisticated equations.

To solve the equation $2\sin\left(x - \dfrac{\pi}{6}\right) + 1 = 1.5$ graphically, we begin by assigning $Y_1$ to the left-hand expression, $Y_2$ to the right-hand expression, and carefully entering them on the $\boxed{\text{Y=}}$ screen (Figure AIII.1). The TI-84 Plus is programmed with a "standard window" for trigonometric functions, which is preset as shown in Figure AIII.2 (with the calculator in radian $\boxed{\text{MODE}}$), and accessed by pressing $\boxed{\text{ZOOM}}$ **7:ZTrig**. Note the range is $y \in [-4, 4]$, the $x$-axis is scaled in units of $\dfrac{\pi}{2} \approx 1.57$, and the independent variable has a domain of roughly $-2\pi$ to $2\pi$. This should be adequate for the equation at hand, and pressing $\boxed{\text{ENTER}}$ and $\boxed{\text{TRACE}}$ produces the graph shown

**Figure AIII.1**

```
Plot1 Plot2 Plot3
\Y1▪2sin(X-π/6)+
1
\Y2▪1.5
\Y3=
\Y4=
\Y5=
\Y6=
```

**Figure AIII.2**

```
WINDOW
 Xmin=-6.152285…
 Xmax=6.1522856…
 Xscl=1.5707963…
 Ymin=-4
 Ymax=4
 Yscl=1
 Xres=1
```

in Figure AIII.3. To have the calculator locate a point of intersection, we press $\boxed{\text{2nd}}$ $\boxed{\text{CALC}}$ and select option **5:intersect** by pressing the number 5 or using the down arrow $\boxed{\blacktriangledown}$ to access this option. We then press $\boxed{\text{ENTER}}$ *three* times: The first " $\boxed{\text{ENTER}}$ " selects the graph of $Y_1$, the second " $\boxed{\text{ENTER}}$ " selects the graph of $Y_2$, and the third " $\boxed{\text{ENTER}}$ " (the **"GUESS"** option) uses the $x$-value of the current cursor location

**Figure AIII.3**

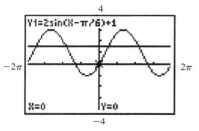

to begin its search for a point of intersection (this means we can help the calculator find a specific point of intersection if there is more than one showing). The calculator will "think" for a moment or two, then display $x$- and $y$-coordinates of the point of intersection at the bottom of the screen (Figure AIII.4). For $2\sin\left(x - \dfrac{\pi}{6}\right) + 1 = 1.5$, the calculator finds a solution of $x \approx 0.7763$ (Figure AIII.4). To find the next point of intersection to the right, recall that the $x$-axis is scaled in units of $\dfrac{\pi}{2}$, so we can repeat the preceding sequence of keystrokes, except that we'll enter $x = \pi$ (the point of intersection occurs at roughly the second tick-mark) at the "**GUESS**" option. The calculator then finds a second solution at $x \approx 3.4125$ (Figure AIII.5). Use these ideas to find points of intersection where $x < 0$.

**Figure AIII.4**

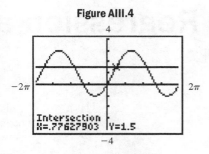

**Figure AIII.5**

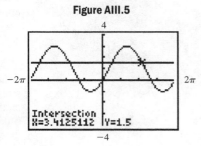

# Regression and Calculator Use

Collecting and analyzing data is a tremendously important mathematical endeavor, having applications throughout business, industry, science, and government. The link between classroom mathematics and real-world mathematics is called a **regression,** in which we attempt to find an equation that will act as a model for the raw data. In this appendix, we focus on linear and quadratic equation models.

## A. Scatter-Plots and Positive/Negative Association

You can hardly pick up a newspaper or magazine without noticing it contains a large volume of data presented in graphs, charts, and tables. In addition, there are many simple experiments or activities that enable you to collect your own data. We begin analyzing the collected data using a **scatter-plot,** which is simply a graph of all of the ordered pairs in a data set. Often, real data (sometimes called **raw data**) is not very "well behaved" and the points may be somewhat scattered—the reason for the name.

### Positive and Negative Associations

Earlier we noted that lines with positive slope rise from left to right, while lines with negative slope fall from left to right. We can extend this idea to the data from a scatter-plot. The data points in Illustration 1A seem to *rise* as you move from left to right, with larger input values generally resulting in larger outputs. In this case, we say there is a **positive association** between the variables. If the data seems to decrease or fall as you move left to right, we say there is a **negative association.**

---

**ILLUSTRATION 1A** ▶ **Drawing a Scatter-Plot and Observing Associations**

The ratio of the federal debt to the total population is known as the *per capita debt*. The per capita debt of the United States is shown in the table for the odd-numbered years from 1997 to 2007. Draw a scatter-plot of the data and state whether the association is positive or negative.

*Source:* Data from the Bureau of Public Debt at www.publicdebt.treas.gov

| Year | Per Capita Debt ($1000s) |
|------|--------------------------|
| 1997 | 20.0 |
| 1999 | 20.7 |
| 2001 | 20.5 |
| 2003 | 23.3 |
| 2005 | 27.6 |
| 2007 | 30.4 |

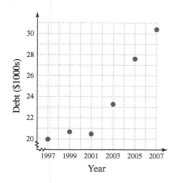

Solution ▶ Since the amount of debt depends on the year, *year* is the input *x* and *per capita debt* is the output *y*. Scale the *x*-axis from 1997 to 2007 and the *y*-axis from 20 to 30 to comfortably fit the data (the "squiggly lines," near the 20 and 1997 in the graph are used to show that some initial values have been skipped). The graph indicates a positive association between the variables, meaning the debt is generally *increasing* as time goes on.

---

**ILLUSTRATION 1B** ▶ **Drawing a Scatter-Plot and Observing Associations**

A cup of coffee is placed on a table and allowed to cool. The temperature of the coffee is measured every 10 min and the data are shown in the table. Draw the scatter-plot and state whether the association is positive or negative.

| Elapsed Time (minutes) | Temperature (°F) |
|---|---|
| 0 | 110 |
| 10 | 89 |
| 20 | 76 |
| 30 | 72 |
| 40 | 71 |

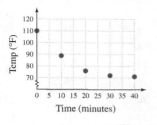

**Solution** ▶ Since temperature depends on cooling time, *time* is the input $x$ and *temperature* is the output $y$. Scale the $x$-axis from 0 to 40 and the $y$-axis from 70 to 110 to comfortably fit the data. As you see in the figure, there is a negative association between the variables, meaning the temperature *decreases* over time.

☑ **A.** You've just learned how to draw a scatter-plot and identify positive and negative associations

## B. Scatter-Plots and Linear/Nonlinear Associations

The data in Illustration 1A had a positive association, while the association in Illustration 1B was negative. But the data from these examples differ in another important way. In Illustration 1A, the data seem to cluster about an imaginary line. This indicates a linear equation model might be a good approximation for the data, and we say there is a **linear association** between the variables. The data in Illustration 1B could not accurately be modeled using a straight line, and we say the variables *time* and *cooling temperature* exhibit a **nonlinear association.**

---

**ILLUSTRATION 2** ▶ **Drawing a Scatter-Plot and Observing Associations**

A college professor tracked her annual salary for 2002 to 2009 and the data are shown in the table. Draw the scatter-plot and determine if there is a linear or nonlinear association between the variables. Also state whether the association is positive, negative, or cannot be determined.

| Year | Salary ($1000s) |
|---|---|
| 2002 | 30.5 |
| 2003 | 31 |
| 2004 | 32 |
| 2005 | 33.2 |
| 2006 | 35.5 |
| 2007 | 39.5 |
| 2008 | 45.5 |
| 2009 | 52 |

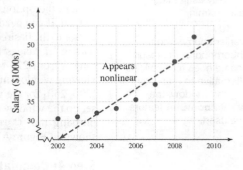

**Solution** ▶ Since salary earned depends on a given year, *year* is the input $x$ and *salary* is the output $y$. Scale the $x$-axis from 1996 to 2005, and the $y$-axis from 30 to 55 to comfortably fit the data. A line doesn't seem to model the data very well, and the association appears to be nonlinear. The data rises from left to right, indicating a positive association between the variables. This makes good sense, since we expect our salaries to increase over time.

☑ **B.** You've just learned how to use a scatter-plot to identify linear and nonlinear associations

## C.  Linear Regression and the Line of Best Fit

**Table AIV.1**

| Year ($x$) (1980→0) | Time ($y$) (sec) |
|---|---|
| 0 | 231 |
| 4 | 231 |
| 8 | 227 |
| 12 | 225 |
| 16 | 228 |
| 20 | 221 |
| 24 | 223 |

There is actually a sophisticated method for calculating the equation of a line that best fits a data set, called the **regression line.** The method minimizes the vertical distance between all data points and the line itself, making it the unique **line of best fit.** Most graphing calculators have the ability to perform this calculation quickly. The process involves these steps: (1) clearing old data; (2) entering new data; (3) displaying the data; (4) calculating the regression line; and (5) displaying and using the regression line. We'll illustrate by finding the regression line for the data shown in Table AIV.1, which gives the men's 400-m freestyle gold medal times (in seconds) for the 1980 through the 2004 Olympics, with 1980→0.

### Step 1: Clear Old Data

To prepare for the new data, we first clear out any old data. Press the [ STAT ] key and select option **4:ClrList.** This places the **ClrList** command on the home screen. We tell the calculator which lists to clear by pressing [ 2nd ] 1 to indicate List1 (L1), then enter a comma using the [ , ] key, and continue entering other lists we want to clear: [ 2nd ] 2 [ , ] [ 2nd ] 3 [ ENTER ] will clear List1 (L1), List2 (L2), and List3 (L3).

### Step 2: Enter New Data

Press the [ STAT ] key and select option **1:Edit.** Move the cursor to the first position of List1, and simply enter the data from the first column of Table AIV.1 in order: 0 [ ENTER ] 4 [ ENTER ] 8 [ ENTER ], and so on. Then use the right arrow [ ▶ ] to navigate to List2, and enter the data from the second column: 231 [ ENTER ] 231 [ ENTER ] 227 [ ENTER ], and so on. When finished, you should obtain the screen shown in Figure AIV.1.

**Figure AIV.1**

### Step 3: Display the Data

With the data held in these lists, we can now display the related ordered pairs on the coordinate grid. First press the [ Y= ] key and [ CLEAR ] any existing equations. Then press [ 2nd ] [ Y= ] to access the "**STATPLOTS**" screen. With the cursor on **1:Plot1,** press [ ENTER ] and be sure the options shown in Figure AIV.2 are highlighted. If you need to make any changes, navigate the cursor to the desired option and press [ ENTER ]. Note the data in L1 ranges from 0 to 24, while the data in L2 ranges from 221 to 231. This means an appropriate viewing window might be [0, 30] for the $x$-values, and [200, 250] for the $y$-values. Press the [ WINDOW ] key and set up the window accordingly. After you're finished, pressing the [ GRAPH ] key should produce the graph shown in Figure AIV.3.

**Figure AIV.2**

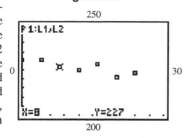

**Figure AIV.3**

### Step 4: Calculate the Regression Equation

To have the calculator compute the regression equation, press the [ STAT ] and [ ▶ ] keys to move the cursor over to the **CALC** options (see Figure AIV.4). Since it appears the data is best modeled by a linear equation, we choose option **4:LinReg (ax + b).** Pressing the number 4 places this option

**Figure AIV.4**

If the input variable is a unit of time, particularly the time in years, we often **scale the data** to avoid working with large numbers. For instance, if the data involved the cost of attending a major sporting event for the years 1980 to 2000, we would say 1980 corresponds to 0 and use input values of 0 to 20 (subtracting the smallest value from itself and all other values has the effect of scaling down the data). This is easily done on a graphing calculator. Simply enter the four-digit years in L1, then with the cursor in the header of L1—use the keystrokes `2nd` `1` **(L1)** `−` 1980 `ENTER` and the data in this list automatically adjusts.

on the home screen, and pressing `ENTER` computes the values of a and b (the calculator automatically uses the values in L1 and L2 unless instructed otherwise). Rounded to hundredths, the linear regression model is $y = -0.38x + 231.18$ (Figure AIV.5).

**Figure AIV.5**

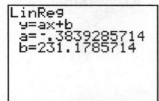

### Step 5: Display and Use the Results

Although graphing calculators have the ability to paste the regression equation directly into $Y_1$ on the `Y=` screen, for now we'll enter $Y_1 = -0.38x + 231.18$ by hand. Afterward, pressing the `GRAPH` key will plot the data points (if Plot1 is still active) and graph the line. Your display screen should now look like the one in Figure AIV.6. The regression line is the best estimator for the set of data as a whole, but there will still be some difference between the values it generates and the values from the set of raw data (the output in Figure AIV.6 shows the estimated time for the 1996 Olympics is 225.1 sec, while the actual time was 228 sec).

**Figure AIV.6**

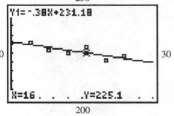

---

ILLUSTRATION 3 ▶  **Using Regression to Model Employee Performance**

Riverside Electronics reviews employee performance semiannually, and awards increases in their hourly rate of pay based on the review. The table shows Thomas' hourly wage for the last 4 yr (eight reviews). Find the regression equation for the data and use it to project his hourly wage for the year 2011, after his fourteenth review.

| Year (x) | Wage (y) |
|---|---|
| (2004) 1 | $9.58 |
| 2 | $9.75 |
| (2005) 3 | $10.54 |
| 4 | $11.41 |
| (2006) 5 | $11.60 |
| 6 | $11.91 |
| (2007) 7 | $12.11 |
| 8 | $13.02 |

Solution ▶

☑ **C. You've just learned how to use a linear regression to find the line of best fit**

Following the prescribed sequence produces the equation $y = 0.48x + 9.09$. For $x = 14$ we obtain $y = 0.48(14) + 9.09$ or a wage of $15.81. According to this model, Thomas will be earning $15.81 per hour in 2011.

## D. Quadratic Regression and the Parabola of Best Fit

Once the data have been entered, graphing calculators have the ability to find many different regression equations. The choice of regression depends on the context of the data, patterns formed by the scatter-plot, and/or some foreknowledge of how the data are related. Earlier we focused on linear regression equations. We now turn our attention to quadratic regression equations.

## ILLUSTRATION 4A ▶ Drawing a Scatter-Plot to Sketch a Best-Fit Curve

Since 1990, the number of *new* books published each year has been growing at a rate that can be approximated by a quadratic function. The table shows the number of books published in the United States for selected years. Draw a scatter-plot and sketch an estimated parabola of best fit by hand.

*Source: 1998, 2000, 2002, and 2004 Statistical Abstract of the United States.*

| Year (1990→0) | Books Published (1000s) |
|---|---|
| 0 | 46.7 |
| 2 | 49.2 |
| 3 | 49.8 |
| 4 | 51.7 |
| 5 | 62.0 |
| 6 | 68.2 |
| 7 | 65.8 |
| 9 | 102.0 |
| 10 | 122.1 |

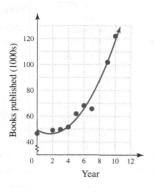

Solution ▶ Begin by drawing the scatter-plot, being sure to scale the axes appropriately. The data appear to form a quadratic pattern, and we sketch a parabola that seems to best fit the data (see graph).

The regression abilities of a graphing calculator can be used to find a **parabola of best fit** and the steps are identical to those for linear regression.

## ILLUSTRATION 4B ▶ Calculating a Nonlinear Regression Model from a Data Set

Use the data from Example 4A to calculate a quadratic regression equation, then display the data and graph. How well does the equation match the data?

Solution ▶ Begin by entering the data in L1 and L2 as shown in Figure AIV.7. Press [2nd] [Y=] to be sure that Plot 1 is still active and is using L1 and L2 with the desired point type. Set the window size to comfortably fit the data (see upcoming Figure AIV.9—window size is indicated along the perimeter). Finally, press [STAT] and the right arrow [▶] to overlay the **CALC** option. The quadratic regression option is number **5:QuadReg.** Pressing [5] places this option directly on the home screen. Lists L1 and L2 are the default lists, so pressing [ENTER] will have the calculator compute the regression equation for the data in L1 and L2. After "chewing on the data" for a short while, the calculator returns the regression equation in the form shown in Figure AIV.8. To maintain a higher degree of accuracy, we can actually paste the entire regression equation in $Y_1$.

**Figure AIV.7**

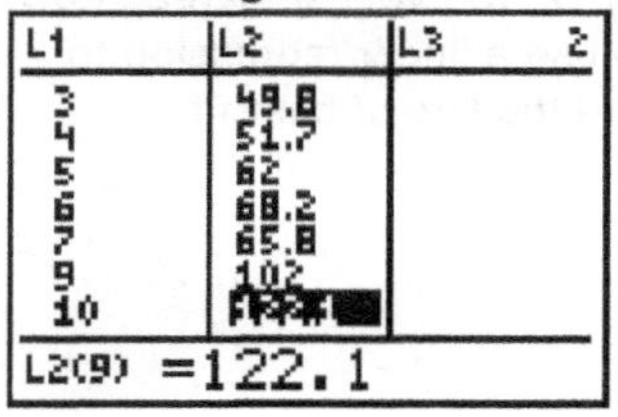

| L1 | L2 | L3 | 2 |
|---|---|---|---|
| 3 | 49.8 | | |
| 4 | 51.7 | | |
| 5 | 62 | | |
| 6 | 68.2 | | |
| 7 | 65.8 | | |
| 9 | 102 | | |
| 10 | 122.1 | | |

L2(9) =122.1

**Figure AIV.8**

```
QuadReg
 y=ax²+bx+c
 a=1.04386823
 b=-3.505801827
 c=49.41433895
```

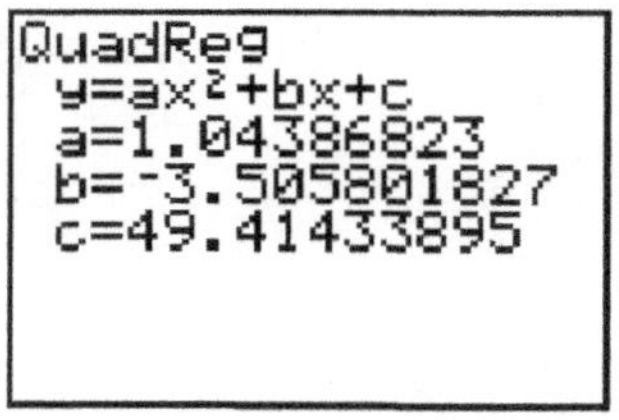

**WORTHY OF NOTE**

The TI-84 Plus can round all coefficients to any desired number of decimal places. For three decimal places, press [MODE] and change the **Float** setting to **"3."** Also, be aware that there are additional methods for pasting the equation in $Y_1$.

Recall the last operation using [2nd] [ENTER], and **QuadReg** should (re)appear. Then enter the function $Y_1$ after the QuadReg option by pressing [VARS] [▶] (**Y-Vars**) and [ENTER] (**1:Function**) and [ENTER] ($Y_1$). After pressing [ENTER] once again, the full equation is automatically pasted in $Y_1$. To compare this equation model with the data, simply press [GRAPH] and both the graph and plotted data will appear. The graph and data seem to match very well (Figure AIV.9).

**Figure AIV.9**

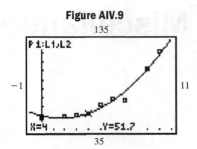

---

**ILLUSTRATION 4C** ▶  **Using a Regression Model to Predict Trends**

Use the equation from Example 4B to answer the following questions: According to the function model, how many new books were published in 1991? If this trend continues, how many new books will be published in 2011?

Solution ▶  Since the year 1990 corresponds to 0 in this data set, we use an input value of 1 for 1991, and an input of 21 for 2011. Accessing the table ( [2nd] [GRAPH] ) feature and inputting 1 and 21 gives the screen shown. Approximately 47,000 new books were published in 1991, and about 436,000 will be published in the year 2011.

☑ **D.** You just learned how to use quadratic regression to find the parabola of best fit

# Miscellaneous Algebra Review

### The Pythagorean Theorem

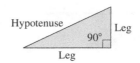

Recall a right triangle is one that has a 90° angle. The longest side (opposite the right angle) is called the **hypotenuse,** while the other two sides are simply called "legs." The **Pythagorean theorem** is a formula that says if you add the square of each leg, the result will be equal to the square of the hypotenuse. Furthermore, we note the converse of this theorem is also true.

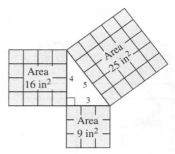

---

**Pythagorean Theorem**

1. For any right triangle with legs $a$, $b$ and hypotenuse $c$,
$$a^2 + b^2 = c^2$$
2. For any triangle with sides $a$, $b$, and $c$, if $a^2 + b^2 = c^2$, then the triangle is a right triangle.

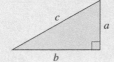

---

A geometric interpretation of the theorem is given in the figure, which shows $3^2 + 4^2 = 5^2$.

### The Distance Formula

**Figure AV.1**

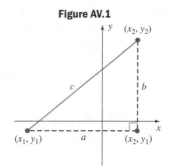

For any two points $(x_1, y_1)$ and $(x_2, y_2)$ not lying on a horizontal or vertical line, a right triangle can be formed as in Figure AV.1. Regardless of the triangle's orientation, the length of side $a$ (the horizontal segment or base of the triangle) will have length $|x_2 - x_1|$ units, with side $b$ (the vertical segment or height) having length $|y_2 - y_1|$ units. From the Pythagorean theorem, we see that $c^2 = a^2 + b^2$ corresponds to $c^2 = (|x_2 - x_1|)^2 + (|y_2 - y_1|)^2$. By taking the square root of both sides we obtain the length of the hypotenuse, *which is identical to the distance between these two points*: $c = \sqrt{(x_2 - x_1)^2 + (y_2 - y_1)^2}$. The result is called the **distance formula,** although it's most often written using $d$ for **d**istance, rather than $c$. Note the absolute value bars are dropped from the formula, since the square of any quantity is always nonnegative. This also means that *either* point can be used as the initial point in the computation.

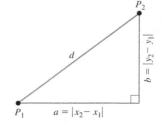

---

**The Distance Formula**

Given any two points $P_1 = (x_1, y_1)$ and $P_2 = (x_2, y_2)$, the straight line distance between them is
$$d = \sqrt{(x_2 - x_1)^2 + (y_2 - y_1)^2}$$

---

**ILLUSTRATION 1** ▶ **Determining if Three Points Form a Right Triangle**

Use the distance formula to determine if the following points are the vertices of a right triangle: $(-8, 1)$, $(-2, 9)$, and $(10, 0)$

**Solution ▶** We begin by finding the distance between each pair of points, then attempt to apply the Pythagorean theorem.

For $(x_1, y_1) = (-8, 1), (x_2, y_2) = (-2, 9)$:

$$d = \sqrt{(x_2 - x_1)^2 + (y_2 - y_1)^2}$$
$$= \sqrt{[-2 - (-8)]^2 + (9 - 1)^2}$$
$$= \sqrt{6^2 + 8^2}$$
$$= \sqrt{100} = 10$$

For $(x_2, y_2) = (-2, 9), (x_3, y_3) = (10, 0)$:

$$d = \sqrt{(x_3 - x_2)^2 + (y_3 - y_2)^2}$$
$$= \sqrt{[10 - (-2)]^2 + (0 - 9)^2}$$
$$= \sqrt{12^2 + (-9)^2}$$
$$= \sqrt{225} = 15$$

For $(x_1, y_1) = (-8, 1), (x_3, y_3) = (10, 0)$:

$$d = \sqrt{(x_3 - x_1)^2 + (y_3 - y_1)^2}$$
$$= \sqrt{[10 - (-8)]^2 + (0 - 1)^2}$$
$$= \sqrt{18^2 + (-1)^2}$$
$$= \sqrt{325} = 5\sqrt{13}$$

Using the unsimplified form, we clearly see that $a^2 + b^2 = c^2$ corresponds to $(\sqrt{100})^2 + (\sqrt{225})^2 = (\sqrt{325})^2$, a true statement. Yes, the triangle is a right triangle.

## Composition of Functions

The composition of functions is best understood by studying the "input/output" nature of a function. Consider $g(x) = x^2 - 3$. For $g(x)$ we might say, "inputs are squared, then decreased by three." In diagram form we have:

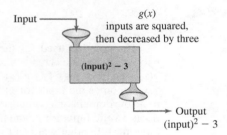

In many respects, a function box can be regarded as a very simple machine, running a simple program. It doesn't matter what the input is, this machine is going to *square the input then subtract three.*

**ILLUSTRATION 2 ▶ Evaluating a Function**

For $g(x) = x^2 - 3$, find

  **a.** $g(-5)$

  **b.** $g(5t)$

  **c.** $g(t - 4)$

**Solution ▶**  **a.**    $g(x) = x^2 - 3$    original function

input −5

$$g(-5) = (-5)^2 - 3 \quad \text{square input, then subtract 3}$$
$$= 25 - 3 \quad \text{simplify}$$
$$= 22 \quad \text{result}$$

    **b.**    $g(x) = x^2 - 3$    original function

input 5t

$$g(5t) = (5t)^2 - 3 \quad \text{square input, then subtract 3}$$
$$= 25t^2 - 3 \quad \text{result}$$

It's important to note that $t$ and $t - 4$ are two different, distinct values—the number represented by $t$, and a number four less than $t$. Examples would be 7 and 3, 12 and 8, as well as $-10$ and $-14$. There should be nothing awkward or unusual about evaluating $g(t)$ versus evaluating $g(t - 4)$ as in Illustration 2(c).

**c.** 

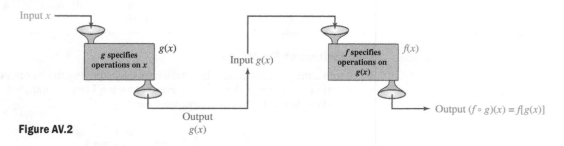

$$g(x) = x^2 - 3 \qquad \text{original function}$$

input $t - 4$

$$g(t - 4) = (t - 4)^2 - 3 \qquad \text{square input, then subtract 3}$$
$$= t^2 - 8t + 16 - 3 \qquad \text{expand binomial}$$
$$= t^2 - 8t + 13 \qquad \text{result}$$

When the input value is itself a function (rather than a single number or variable), this process is called the **composition of functions.** The evaluation method is exactly the same, we are simply using a function input. Using a general function $g(x)$ and a function diagram as before, we illustrate the process in Figure AV.2.

**Figure AV.2**

The notation used for the composition of $f$ with $g$ is an open dot "∘" placed between them, and is read, "$f$ composed with $g$." The notation $(f \circ g)(x)$ indicates that $g(x)$ is an input for $f$: $(f \circ g)(x) = f[g(x)]$. If the order is reversed, as in $(g \circ f)(x)$, then $f(x)$ becomes the input for $g$: $(g \circ f)(x) = g[f(x)]$. Figure AV.2 also helps us determine the domain of a composite function, in that the first function $g$ can operate only if $x$ is a valid input for $g$, and the second function $f$ can operate only if $g(x)$ is a valid input for $f$. In other words, $(f \circ g)(x)$ is defined for *all $x$ in the domain of $g$, such that $g(x)$ is in the domain of $f$.*

⚠ **CAUTION** ▶ Try not to confuse the new "open dot" notation for the *composition* of functions, with the multiplication dot used to indicate the *product* of two functions: $(f \cdot g)(x) = (fg)(x)$ or the product of $f$ with $g$; $(f \circ g)(x) = f[g(x)]$ or $f$ composed with $g$.

**The Composition of Functions**

Given two functions $f$ and $g$, the composition of $f$ with $g$ is defined by
$$(f \circ g)(x) = f[g(x)]$$
The domain of the composition is all $x$ in the domain of $g$ for which $g(x)$ is in the domain of $f$.

In Figure AV.3, these ideas are displayed using mapping notation, as we consider the simple case where $g(x) = x$ and $f(x) = \sqrt{x}$.

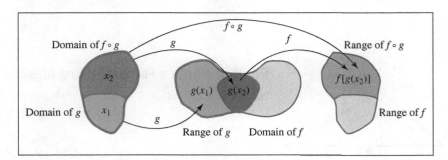

**Figure AV.3**

The domain of $g$ (all real numbers) is shown within the red border, with $g$ taking the negative inputs represented by $x_1$ (light red), to a like-colored portion of the range—the negative outputs $g(x_1)$. The nonnegative inputs represented by $x_2$ (dark red) are also mapped to a like-colored portion of the range—the nonnegative outputs $g(x_2)$. While the range of $g$ is also all real numbers, function $f$ can only use the nonnegative inputs represented by $g(x_2)$. This restricts the domain of $(f \circ g)(x)$ to only the inputs from $g$, where $g(x)$ is in the domain of $f$.

---

**ILLUSTRATION 3** ▶ **Finding a Composition of Functions**

Given $f(x) = \sqrt{x - 4}$ and $g(x) = 3x + 2$, find
a. $(f \circ g)(x)$
b. $(g \circ f)(x)$
Also determine the domain for each.

**Solution** ▶ **a.** $f(x) = \sqrt{x - 4}$ says "decrease inputs by 4, and take the square root of the result."

$$
\begin{aligned}
(f \circ g)(x) &= f[g(x)] && \text{$g(x)$ is an input for $f$}\\
&= \sqrt{g(x) - 4} && \text{decrease input by 4, and take the square root of the result}\\
&= \sqrt{(3x + 2) - 4} && \text{substitute $3x + 2$ for $g(x)$}\\
&= \sqrt{3x - 2} && \text{result}
\end{aligned}
$$

While $g$ is defined for all real numbers, $f$ is defined only for nonnegative numbers. Since $f[g(x)] = \sqrt{3x - 2}$, we need $3x - 2 \geq 0$, $x \geq \frac{2}{3}$. In interval notation, the domain of $(f \circ g)(x)$ is $x \in [\frac{2}{3}, \infty)$.

**b.** The function $g$ says "inputs are multiplied by 3, then increased by 2."

$$
\begin{aligned}
(g \circ f)(x) &= g[f(x)] && \text{$f(x)$ is an input for $g$}\\
&= 3f(x) + 2 && \text{multiply input by 3, then increase by 2}\\
&= 3\sqrt{x - 4} + 2 && \text{substitute $\sqrt{x - 4}$ for $f(x)$}
\end{aligned}
$$

For $g[f(x)]$, $g$ can accept any real number input, but $f$ can supply only those where $x \geq 4$. The domain of $(g \circ f)(x)$ is $x \in [4, \infty)$.

**WORTHY OF NOTE**

Illustration 3 shows that $(f \circ g)(x)$ is generally not equal to $(g \circ f)(x)$.

# Selected Proofs

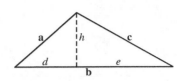

## Proof of Heron's Formula Using Algebra

Note that $\sqrt{a^2 - d^2} = h = \sqrt{c^2 - e^2}$. It follows that

$$\sqrt{a^2 - d^2} = \sqrt{c^2 - e^2}$$
$$a^2 - d^2 = c^2 - e^2$$
$$a^2 - (b - e)^2 = c^2 - e^2$$
$$a^2 - b^2 + 2be - e^2 = c^2 - e^2$$
$$a^2 - b^2 - c^2 = -2be$$
$$\frac{b^2 + c^2 - a^2}{2b} = e$$

This shows:

$$A = \frac{1}{2}bh$$

$$= \frac{1}{2}b\sqrt{c^2 - e^2}$$

$$= \frac{1}{2}b\sqrt{c^2 - \left(\frac{b^2 + c^2 - a^2}{2b}\right)^2}$$

$$= \frac{1}{2}b\sqrt{c^2 - \left(\frac{b^4 + 2b^2c^2 - 2a^2b^2 - 2a^2c^2 + a^4 + c^4}{4b^2}\right)}$$

$$= \frac{1}{2}b\sqrt{\frac{4b^2c^2}{4b^2} - \left(\frac{b^4 + 2b^2c^2 - 2a^2b^2 - 2a^2c^2 + a^4 + c^4}{4b^2}\right)}$$

$$= \frac{1}{2}b\sqrt{\frac{4b^2c^2 - b^4 - 2b^2c^2 + 2a^2b^2 + 2a^2c^2 - a^4 - c^4}{4b^2}}$$

$$= \frac{1}{4}\sqrt{2a^2b^2 + 2a^2c^2 + 2b^2c^2 - a^4 - b^4 - c^4}$$

$$= \frac{1}{4}\sqrt{[(a + b)^2 - c^2][c^2 - (a - b)^2]}$$

$$= \frac{1}{4}\sqrt{(a + b + c)(a + b - c)(c + a - b)(c - a + b)}$$

From this point, the conclusion of the proof is the same as the trigonometric development found on page 335.

## Proof that $\mathbf{u} \cdot \mathbf{v} = \text{comp}_\mathbf{v} \mathbf{u} \times |\mathbf{v}|$

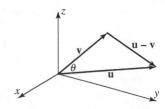

Consider the vectors in the figure shown, which form a triangle. Applying the Law of Cosines to this triangle yields:

$$|\mathbf{u} - \mathbf{v}|^2 = |\mathbf{u}|^2 + |\mathbf{v}|^2 - 2|\mathbf{u}||\mathbf{v}|\cos\theta$$

Using properties of the dot product (page 365), we can rewrite the left-hand side as follows:

$$|\mathbf{u} - \mathbf{v}|^2 = (\mathbf{u} - \mathbf{v}) \cdot (\mathbf{u} - \mathbf{v})$$

$$= \mathbf{u} \cdot \mathbf{u} - \mathbf{u} \cdot \mathbf{v} - \mathbf{v} \cdot \mathbf{u} + \mathbf{v} \cdot \mathbf{v}$$

$$= |\mathbf{u}|^2 - 2\,\mathbf{u} \cdot \mathbf{v} + |\mathbf{v}|^2$$

Substituting the last expression for $|\mathbf{u} - \mathbf{v}|^2$ from the Law of Cosines gives

$$|\mathbf{u}|^2 - 2\,\mathbf{u} \cdot \mathbf{v} + |\mathbf{v}|^2 = |\mathbf{u}|^2 + |\mathbf{v}|^2 - 2\,|\mathbf{u}||\mathbf{v}| \cos \theta$$

$$-2\,\mathbf{u} \cdot \mathbf{v} = -2\,|\mathbf{u}||\mathbf{v}| \cos \theta$$

$$\mathbf{u} \cdot \mathbf{v} = |\mathbf{u}||\mathbf{v}| \cos \theta$$

$$= |\mathbf{u}| \cos \theta \times |\mathbf{v}|.$$

Substituting $\text{comp}_\mathbf{v}\, \mathbf{u}$ for $|\mathbf{u}| \cos \theta$ completes the proof:

$$\mathbf{u} \cdot \mathbf{v} = \text{comp}_\mathbf{v}\, \mathbf{u} \times |\mathbf{v}|$$

## Proof of De Moivre's Theorem:
## $(\cos x + i \sin x)^n = \cos(nx) + i \sin(nx)$

For $n > 0$, we proceed using mathematical induction.

**1.** Show the statement is true for $n = 1$ (base case):

$$(\cos x + i \sin x)^1 = \cos(1x) + i \sin(1x)$$

$$\cos x + i \sin x = \cos x + i \sin x \quad \checkmark$$

**2.** Assume the statement is true for $n = k$ (induction hypothesis):

$$(\cos x + i \sin x)^k = \cos(kx) + i \sin(kx)$$

**3.** Show the statement is true for $n = k + 1$:

$$(\cos x + i \sin x)^{k+1} = (\cos x + i \sin x)^k (\cos x + i \sin x)^1$$

$$= [\cos(kx) + i \sin(kx)](\cos x + i \sin x) \qquad \text{induction hypothesis}$$

$$= \cos(kx)\cos x - \sin(kx)\sin x + i[\cos(kx)\sin x + \sin(kx)\cos x] \qquad \text{F-O-I-L}$$

$$= \cos[(k+1)x] + i \sin[(k+1)x] \quad \checkmark \qquad \text{sum/difference identities}$$

By the principle of mathematical induction, the statement is true for all positive integers. For $n < 0$ (the theorem is obviously true for $n = 0$), consider a positive integer $m$, where $n = -m$.

$$(\cos x + i \sin x)^n = (\cos x + i \sin x)^{-m}$$

$$= \frac{1}{(\cos x + i \sin x)^m} \qquad \text{negative exponent property}$$

$$= \frac{1}{\cos(mx) + i \sin(mx)} \qquad \text{DeMoivre's theorem for } n > 0$$

$$= \cos(mx) - i \sin(mx) \qquad \text{multiply numerator and denominator by } \cos(mx) - i\sin(mx) \text{ and simplify}$$

$$= \cos(-mx) + i \sin(-mx) \qquad \text{even/odd identities}$$

$$= \cos(nx) + i \sin(nx) \qquad n = -m$$

# Families of Polar Curves

## Circles and Spiral Curves

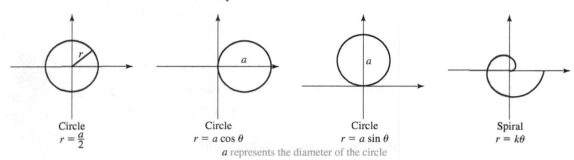

| Circle $r = \dfrac{a}{2}$ | Circle $r = a \cos \theta$ | Circle $r = a \sin \theta$ | Spiral $r = k\theta$ |

*a* represents the diameter of the circle

## Roses: $r = a \sin(n\theta)$ (illustrated here) and $r = a \cos(n\theta)$

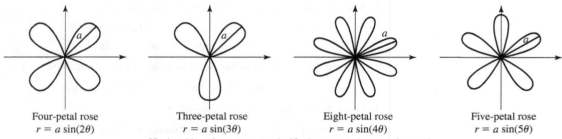

| Four-petal rose $r = a \sin(2\theta)$ | Three-petal rose $r = a \sin(3\theta)$ | Eight-petal rose $r = a \sin(4\theta)$ | Five-petal rose $r = a \sin(5\theta)$ |

If *n* is odd → there are *n* petals, if *n* is even → there are 2*n* petals.
|*a*| represents the maximum distance from the origin
(the radius of a circumscribed circle)

## Limaçons: $r = a + b \sin \theta$ (illustrated here) and $r = a + b \cos \theta$

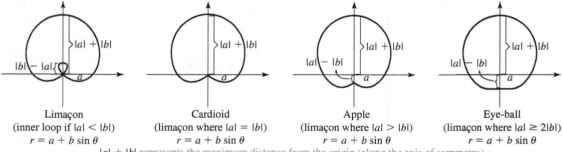

| Limaçon (inner loop if |*a*| < |*b*|) $r = a + b \sin \theta$ | Cardioid (limaçon where |*a*| = |*b*|) $r = a + b \sin \theta$ | Apple (limaçon where |*a*| > |*b*|) $r = a + b \sin \theta$ | Eye-ball (limaçon where |*a*| ≥ 2|*b*|) $r = a + b \sin \theta$ |

|*a*| + |*b*| represents the maximum distance from the origin (along the axis of symmetry)

# Lemniscates: $r^2 = a^2\sin(2\theta)$ and $r^2 = a^2\cos(2\theta)$

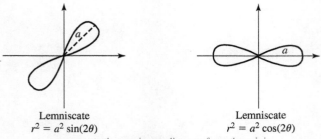

Lemniscate
$r^2 = a^2 \sin(2\theta)$

Lemniscate
$r^2 = a^2 \cos(2\theta)$

*a* represents the maximum distance from the origin
(the radius of a circumscribed circle)

# Student Answer Appendix

# Student Answer Appendix

## CHAPTER 1

### Exercises 1.1, pp. 7–10

**1.** Complementary; 180  **3.** coterminal; 360°  **5.** Answers will vary.
**7.** 77.5°; 30.8°  **9.** 53°  **11.** 42.5°  **13.** 67.555°  **15.** 285.0025°
**17.** 45.7625°  **19.** 20°15′00″  **21.** 67°18′25.2″  **23.** 275°19′48″
**25.** 5°27′9″  **27.** 77°15′  **29.** 90°49′36″  **31.** 0°56′08″
**33.** 47°59′59″  **35.** −645°, −285°, 435°, 795°
**37.** −765°, −405°, 315°, 675°  **39.** 65°  **41.** −130°  **43.** 80°
**45.** $5\sqrt{2}$ cm  **47.** 6 ft, 6 ft  **49.** 10 mm  **51.** $4\sqrt{2}$ yd, $4\sqrt{2}$ yd
**53.** $3\sqrt{3}$ mm, 6 mm  **55.** $\frac{7}{2}$ in., $\frac{7\sqrt{3}}{2}$ in.
**57.** $2\sqrt{3}$ cm, $4\sqrt{3}$ cm  **59.** $41\sqrt{2}$ ft ≈ 58 ft + 10 ft = 68 ft
**61.** 67.555°  **63.** $\frac{25\sqrt{3}}{2}$  **65. a.** 56°  **b.** 0.7 sec
**67.** 35°33′27″S, 58°3′18″W  **69.** No; 180°, 540°
**71. a.** 1000 m  **b.** 1000 m

**c.** 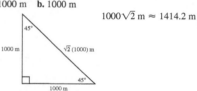   $1000\sqrt{2}$ m ≈ 1414.2 m

**73.** $50\sqrt{2}$ or about 10.7 mi apart  **75.** $\frac{\sqrt{91}}{3}$ in.

### Exercises 1.2, pp. 14–19

**1.** sides; acute; right; obtuse  **3.** capital; opposite; lowercase
**5.** Answers will vary.  **7.** b  **9.** d  **11.** g  **13.** e  **15.** 69°
**17.** 25°  **19.** $C = 25°$  **21.** $C = 65.5°$  **23.** $C = 38°10′$
**25.** $C = 43°21′51″$  **27.** $A = 27°, C = 60°$
**29.** $A = 102°, B = 14°, C = 64°$  **31.** $A = 51°, B = 53°, C = 76°$
**33.** $A = 26°, B = 82°$  **35.** $A = 61°, B = 83°, C = 36°$
**37.** $A = 41°, B = 98°, C = 41°$  **39.** $A = 60°, B = 90°, C = 30°$
**41.** $c = 85°; a = 121$ dm, $b = 89$ dm, $c = 144$ dm
**43.** $c = 38°; a = 7.4$ ft, $b = 4.7$ ft, $c = 4.7$ ft
**45.** $C = 15°; a = 2\sqrt{2}$ in., $b = \sqrt{3} + 1$ in., $c = \sqrt{3} - 1$ in.
**47.** No, $19 + 16 < 40$  **49.** 62.5 m  **51.** 30 m  **53.** 11 m  **55.** 9/5″
**57.** $\frac{4}{5}$ in  **59.** $x = 6$ m  **61.** $x = 6$ ft; 24 ft, 7 ft  **63.** $x = 2$; 1, 4, 3, 12
**65.** $h ≈ 7.06$ cm; $m ≈ 3.76$ cm; $n ≈ 13.24$ cm  **67.** 21 m  **69.** 555 ft
**71.** 18.8 cm  **73.** 960 mi  **75.** Answers will vary.  **77.** Answers will
vary.  **79.** 84°16′30″  **81.** 287°  **83.** $\frac{5}{\sqrt{2}}$ cm

### Mid-Chapter Check, pp. 19–20

**1.** 36.11°N, 115.08°W  **2.** $\frac{28\sqrt{3}}{3}$ in., $\frac{14\sqrt{3}}{3}$ in.  **3. a.** 378°, −342°
**b.** 253°, −467°  **4. a.** 51°  **b.** 16.3°  **c.** 35°44′21″  **d.** 90° − x
**5.** $B = 65°, C = 55°$  **6.** $3\sqrt{2} ≈ 4.24$ ft  **7.** $R = 21°, S = 111°, T = 48°$
**8.** 4.1 mm  **9.** $x = 6$ in.  **10.** 8.6 ft

### Reinforcing Basic Concepts, pp. 20–21

**Exercise 1:**  $2(\sqrt{6} - \sqrt{2})$ cm
**Exercise 2:**  $3(\sqrt{6} + \sqrt{2})″$

**Exercise 3:**  $\frac{20}{\sqrt{6} + \sqrt{2}}$ ft

**Exercise 4:**  $\frac{28}{\sqrt{6} - \sqrt{2}}$ m

**Exercise 5:**  1 mm
**Exercise 6:**  1 yd

### Exercises 1.3, pp. 28–31

**1.** origin; x-axis  **3.** $\cos\theta$; $\sin\theta$; $\tan\theta$; $\frac{r}{x}$; $\frac{r}{y}$; $\frac{x}{y}$

**5.** Answers will vary.

**7.**  $y = \frac{5}{4}x, [0, \infty),$ QI  **9.** $y = \sqrt{3}x, (-\infty, 0],$ QIII

**11.**  $y = -\frac{5}{3}x, [0, \infty),$ QIV  **13.** $y = -\frac{6}{5}x, (-\infty, 0],$ QII

**15.**  $(-2, -1), (-4, -2), \frac{1}{2}, 2$  **17.** $(1, 3), (2, 6), 3, \frac{1}{3}$

**19.** $(-2, 3), (-4, 6), -\frac{3}{2}, -\frac{2}{3}$  **21.** $(-3, -4), (-6, -8), \frac{4}{3}, \frac{3}{4}$

**23.** $(7, -2), (14, -4), -\frac{2}{7}, -\frac{7}{2}$

**25.** $\sin\theta = \frac{15}{17}, \csc\theta = \frac{17}{15}, \cos\theta = \frac{8}{17}, \sec\theta = \frac{17}{8}, \tan\theta = \frac{15}{8},$
$\cot\theta = \frac{8}{15}$

**27.** $\sin\theta = \frac{21}{29}, \csc\theta = \frac{29}{21}, \cos\theta = \frac{-20}{29},$
$\sec\theta = \frac{-29}{20}, \tan\theta = \frac{-21}{20}, \cot\theta = \frac{-20}{21}$

**29.** $\sin\theta = \frac{-\sqrt{2}}{2}, \csc\theta = \frac{-2}{\sqrt{2}}, \cos\theta = \frac{\sqrt{2}}{2},$
$\sec\theta = \frac{2}{\sqrt{2}}, \tan\theta = -1, \cot\theta = -1$

**31.** $\sin\theta = \frac{1}{2}, \csc\theta = 2, \cos\theta = \frac{\sqrt{3}}{2},$
$\sec\theta = \frac{2}{\sqrt{3}}, \tan\theta = \frac{1}{\sqrt{3}}, \cot\theta = \sqrt{3}$

**33.** $\sin\theta = \frac{4}{\sqrt{17}}, \csc\theta = \frac{\sqrt{17}}{4}, \cos\theta = \frac{1}{\sqrt{17}},$
$\sec\theta = \sqrt{17}, \tan\theta = 4, \cot\theta = \frac{1}{4}$

**35.** $\sin\theta = \frac{-2}{\sqrt{13}}, \csc\theta = \frac{-\sqrt{13}}{2}, \cos\theta = \frac{-3}{\sqrt{13}},$
$\sec\theta = \frac{-\sqrt{13}}{3}, \tan\theta = \frac{2}{3}, \cot\theta = \frac{3}{2}$

**37.** $\sin\theta = \frac{6}{\sqrt{61}}, \csc\theta = \frac{\sqrt{61}}{6}, \cos\theta = \frac{-5}{\sqrt{61}},$
$\sec\theta = \frac{-\sqrt{61}}{5}, \tan\theta = \frac{-6}{5}, \cot\theta = \frac{-5}{6}$

**39.** $\sin\theta = \frac{-2\sqrt{5}}{\sqrt{21}}, \csc\theta = -\frac{\sqrt{21}}{2\sqrt{5}}, \cos\theta = \frac{1}{\sqrt{21}},$
$\sec\theta = \sqrt{21}, \tan\theta = -2\sqrt{5}, \cot\theta = \frac{-1}{2\sqrt{5}}$

**41.**  QI/III;

$(4, 3)$: $\sin \theta = \dfrac{3}{5}$     $(-4, -3)$: $\sin \theta = -\dfrac{3}{5}$

$\cos \theta = \dfrac{4}{5}$          $\cos \theta = -\dfrac{4}{5}$

$\tan \theta = \dfrac{3}{4}$          $\tan \theta = \dfrac{3}{4}$

**43.**  QII/QIV;

$(-3, \sqrt{3})$: $\sin \theta = \dfrac{1}{2}$     $(3, -\sqrt{3})$: $\sin \theta = -\dfrac{1}{2}$

$\cos \theta = -\dfrac{\sqrt{3}}{2}$          $\cos \theta = \dfrac{\sqrt{3}}{2}$

$\tan \theta = -\dfrac{1}{\sqrt{3}}$          $\tan \theta = -\dfrac{1}{\sqrt{3}}$

**45.** QII    **47.** QII    **49.** positive    **51.** negative    **53.** negative

**55.** $x = 4$, $y = -3$, $r = 5$; QIV; $\sin \theta = \dfrac{-3}{5}$, $\csc \theta = \dfrac{-5}{3}$, $\cos \theta = \dfrac{4}{5}$,

$\sec \theta = \dfrac{5}{4}$, $\tan \theta = \dfrac{-3}{4}$, $\cot \theta = \dfrac{-4}{3}$

**57.** $x = -12$, $y = -35$, $r = 37$; QIII; $\sin \theta = \dfrac{-35}{37}$, $\csc \theta = \dfrac{-37}{35}$,

$\cos \theta = \dfrac{-12}{37}$, $\sec \theta = \dfrac{-37}{12}$, $\tan \theta = \dfrac{35}{12}$, $\cot \theta = \dfrac{12}{35}$

**59.** $x = 2\sqrt{2}$, $y = 1$, $r = 3$; QI; $\sin \theta = \dfrac{1}{3}$, $\csc \theta = 3$, $\cos \theta = \dfrac{2\sqrt{2}}{3}$,

$\sec \theta = \dfrac{3}{2\sqrt{2}}$, $\tan \theta = \dfrac{1}{2\sqrt{2}}$, $\cot \theta = 2\sqrt{2}$

**61.** $x = -\sqrt{15}$, $y = -7$, $r = 8$; QIII; $\sin \theta = \dfrac{-7}{8}$, $\csc \theta = \dfrac{-8}{7}$,

$\cos \theta = \dfrac{-\sqrt{15}}{8}$, $\sec \theta = -\dfrac{8}{\sqrt{15}}$, $\tan \theta = \dfrac{7}{\sqrt{15}}$, $\cot \theta = \dfrac{\sqrt{15}}{7}$

**63.** $x = 0$, $y = k$; $k > 0$; $r = |k|$;

$\sin 90° = \dfrac{k}{k}$, $\cos 90° = \dfrac{0}{k}$, $\tan 90° = \dfrac{k}{0}$,

$\sin 90° = 1$, $\cos 90° = 0$, $\tan 90°$ undefined

$\csc 90° = 1$, $\sec 90°$ undefined

$\cot 90° = 0$

**65.** $90°$    **67.** $270°$    **69.** $0°$    **71.** $180°$    **73.** QIV, negative

**75.** QIV, negative     **77.** QIV, negative

**79.** QI, positive    **81. a.** 3/5, **b.** 1, **c.** Answers will vary.

**83.** $-2/3$    **85.** 3/10    **87.** 6/7

**89.** $\sin \alpha = \dfrac{\sqrt{b^2 - a^2}}{b}$, $\tan \alpha = \dfrac{\sqrt{b^2 - a^2}}{a}$, $\sec \alpha = \dfrac{b}{a}$,

$\csc \alpha = \dfrac{b\sqrt{b^2 - a^2}}{b^2 - a^2}$, $\cot \alpha = \dfrac{a\sqrt{b^2 - a^2}}{b^2 - a^2}$

**91.** $\sin \theta = \dfrac{\sqrt{r_1^2 r_2^2 - (x_1 x_2 + y_1 y_2)^2}}{r_1 r_2}$,    **93. a.** $62.74°$

**b.** $94°23''$    **95.** $x = 17$, $A = 43°$, $B = 51°$, $C = 86°$

**97.** $-813°$, $-453°$, $267°$, $627°$

---

**Exercises 1.4, pp. 35–37**

**1.** $\sin \theta$; $\sec \theta$; $\cos \theta$    **3.** $\cos^2 \theta$; $1 + \cot^2 \theta = \csc^2 \theta$

**5.** $\dfrac{1 - \sin^2 \theta}{\sin \theta \sec \theta}$; Answers will vary.

**7.** Answers may vary;

$\tan \theta = \dfrac{\sec \theta}{\csc \theta}$, $\dfrac{\sin \theta}{\cos \theta} = \dfrac{\sec \theta}{\csc \theta}$, $\dfrac{1}{\cot \theta} = \dfrac{\sec \theta}{\csc \theta}$, $\dfrac{1}{\cot \theta} = \dfrac{\sin \theta}{\cos \theta}$

**9.** $1 = \sec^2 \theta - \tan^2 \theta$; $\tan^2 \theta = \sec^2 \theta - 1$;

$1 = (\sec \theta + \tan \theta)(\sec \theta - \tan \theta)$; $\tan \theta = \pm\sqrt{\sec^2 \theta - 1}$

**11.** $\sin \theta \cot \theta = \sin \theta \dfrac{\cos \theta}{\sin \theta} = \cos \theta$

**13.** $\sec^2 \theta \cot^2 \theta = \dfrac{1}{\cos^2 \theta} \dfrac{\cos^2 \theta}{\sin^2 \theta} = \dfrac{1}{\sin^2 \theta} = \csc^2 \theta$

**15.** $\cos \theta (\sec \theta - \cos \theta) = \cos \theta \sec \theta - \cos^2 \theta =$

$\cos \theta \dfrac{1}{\cos \theta} - \cos^2 \theta = 1 - \cos^2 \theta = \sin^2 \theta$

**17.** $\sin \theta (\csc \theta - \sin \theta) = 1 - \sin^2 \theta = \cos^2 \theta$

**19.** $\tan \theta (\csc \theta + \cot \theta) = \tan \theta \csc \theta + \tan \theta \cot \theta =$

$\dfrac{\sin \theta}{\cos \theta} \dfrac{1}{\sin \theta} + \dfrac{\sin \theta}{\cos \theta} \dfrac{\cos \theta}{\sin \theta} = \dfrac{1}{\cos \theta} + 1 = \sec \theta + 1$

**21.** $\tan^2 \theta \csc^2 \theta - \tan^2 \theta = \tan^2 \theta (\csc^2 \theta - 1) = 1$; $\tan^2 \theta (\cot^2 \theta) = 1$

**23.** $\dfrac{\sin \theta \cos \theta + \sin \theta}{\cos \theta + \cos^2 \theta} = \dfrac{\sin \theta (\cos \theta + 1)}{\cos \theta (1 + \cos \theta)} = \tan \theta$; $\dfrac{\sin \theta}{\cos \theta} = \tan \theta$

**25.** $\dfrac{1 + \sin \theta}{\cos \theta + \cos \theta \sin \theta} = \dfrac{(1)(1 + \sin \theta)}{(\cos \theta)(1 + \sin \theta)} = \dfrac{1}{\cos \theta} = \sec \theta$

**27.** $\dfrac{\sin \theta \tan \theta + \sin \theta}{\tan \theta + \tan^2 \theta} = \dfrac{\sin \theta (\tan \theta + 1)}{\tan \theta (1 + \tan \theta)} = \dfrac{\sin \theta}{\tan \theta} =$

$\dfrac{\sin \theta}{\sin \theta / \cos \theta} = \dfrac{\sin \theta \cos \theta}{\sin \theta} = \cos \theta$

**29.** $\dfrac{(\sin \theta + \cos \theta)^2}{\cos \theta} = \dfrac{\sin^2 \theta + 2 \sin \theta \cos \theta + \cos^2 \theta}{\cos \theta} =$

$\dfrac{\sin^2 \theta + \cos^2 \theta + 2 \sin \theta \cos \theta}{\cos \theta} = \dfrac{1 + 2 \sin \theta \cos \theta}{\cos \theta} =$

$\dfrac{1}{\cos \theta} + \dfrac{2 \sin \theta \cos \theta}{\cos \theta} = \sec \theta + 2 \sin \theta$

**31.** $(1 + \sin \theta)(1 - \sin \theta) = 1 - \sin^2 \theta = \cos^2 \theta$

**33.** $\dfrac{(\csc \theta - \cot \theta)(\csc \theta + \cot \theta)}{\tan \theta} = \dfrac{\csc^2 \theta - \cot^2 \theta}{\tan \theta} = \dfrac{1}{\tan \theta} = \cot \theta$

**35.** $\dfrac{\cos^2 \theta}{\sin \theta} + \dfrac{\sin \theta}{1} = \dfrac{\cos^2 \theta + \sin^2 \theta}{\sin \theta} = \dfrac{1}{\sin \theta} = \csc \theta$

**37.** $\dfrac{\tan \theta}{\csc \theta} - \dfrac{\sin \theta}{\cos \theta} = \dfrac{\tan \theta \cos \theta - \sin \theta \csc \theta}{\csc \theta \cos \theta} = \dfrac{\dfrac{\sin \theta}{\cos \theta} \cos \theta - 1}{\dfrac{1}{\sin \theta} \cos \theta} = \dfrac{\sin \theta - 1}{\cot \theta}$

**39.** $\dfrac{\sec \theta}{\sin \theta} - \dfrac{\csc \theta}{\sec \theta} = \dfrac{\sec^2 \theta - \sin \theta \csc \theta}{\sin \theta \sec \theta} = \dfrac{\sec^2 \theta - 1}{\sin \theta \dfrac{1}{\cos \theta}} = \dfrac{\tan^2 \theta}{\tan \theta} = \tan \theta$

**41.** $\dfrac{\sin \theta}{\pm\sqrt{1 - \sin^2 \theta}}$      **43.** $\pm\sqrt{\dfrac{1}{\cot^2 \theta} + 1}$

**45.** $\dfrac{\pm\sqrt{1 - \sin^2 \theta}}{\sin \theta}$

**47.** $\sin \theta = \dfrac{21}{29}$, $\tan \theta = -\dfrac{21}{20}$, $\sec \theta = -\dfrac{29}{20}$, $\csc \theta = \dfrac{29}{21}$, $\cot \theta = -\dfrac{20}{21}$

**49.** $\cos\theta = -\dfrac{8}{17}$, $\sin\theta = -\dfrac{15}{17}$, $\sec\theta = -\dfrac{17}{8}$, $\csc\theta = -\dfrac{17}{15}$, $\cot\theta = \dfrac{8}{15}$

**51.** $\cos\theta = \dfrac{x}{\sqrt{x^2+25}}$, $\sin\theta = \dfrac{5}{\sqrt{x^2+25}}$, $\tan\theta = \dfrac{5}{x}$,

$\sec\theta = \dfrac{\sqrt{x^2+25}}{x}$, $\csc\theta = \dfrac{\sqrt{x^2+25}}{5}$

**53.** $\cos\theta = -\dfrac{\sqrt{120}}{13} = -\dfrac{2\sqrt{30}}{13}$, $\tan\theta = \dfrac{7}{2\sqrt{30}}$, $\sec\theta = -\dfrac{13}{2\sqrt{30}}$,

$\csc\theta = -\dfrac{13}{7}$, $\cot\theta = \dfrac{2\sqrt{30}}{7}$

**55.** $\sin\theta = \dfrac{4\sqrt{2}}{9}$, $\cos\theta = -\dfrac{7}{9}$, $\tan\theta = -\dfrac{4\sqrt{2}}{7}$,

$\csc\theta = \dfrac{9}{4\sqrt{2}}$, $\cot\theta = -\dfrac{7}{4\sqrt{2}}$

**57.** $V = 2(1 - \cos^2\theta)$

**59.** $\cos^3\theta = (\cos\theta)(\cos^2\theta) = (\cos\theta)(1 - \sin^2\theta)$

**61.** $\tan\theta + \tan^3\theta = (\tan\theta)(1 + \tan^2\theta) = (\tan\theta)(\sec^2\theta)$

**63.** $\tan^2\theta \sec\theta - 4\tan^2\theta = (\tan^2\theta)(\sec\theta - 4)$
$= (\sec\theta - 4)(\tan^2\theta) = (\sec\theta - 4)(\sec^2 - 1)$
$= (\sec\theta - 4)(\sec\theta - 1)(\sec\theta + 1)$

**65.** $\cos^2\theta \sin\theta - \cos^2\theta = (\cos^2\theta)(\sin\theta - 1)$
$= (1 - \sin^2\theta)(\sin\theta - 1)$
$= (1 + \sin\theta)(1 - \sin\theta)(\sin\theta - 1)$
$= (1 + \sin\theta)(1 - \sin\theta)(-1)(1 - \sin\theta)$
$= (-1)(1 + \sin\theta)(1 - \sin\theta)^2$

**67.** $\tan\theta = \dfrac{1 + m_1 m_2}{m_2 - m_1}$    **69.** $\tan\theta = 1$

**71.** $-2\sin^4\theta + \sqrt{3}\sin^3\theta + 2\sin^2\theta - \sqrt{3}\sin\theta$
$= \sin\theta\,(-2\sin^3\theta + \sqrt{3}\sin^2\theta + 2\sin\theta - \sqrt{3})$
$= \sin\theta[(-2\sin^3\theta + \sqrt{3}\sin^2\theta) + (2\sin\theta - \sqrt{3})]$
$= \sin\theta\,[-\sin^2\theta\,(2\sin\theta - \sqrt{3}) + 1\,(2\sin\theta - \sqrt{3})]$
$= \sin\theta\,(1 - \sin^2\theta)(2\sin\theta - \sqrt{3})$
$= \sin\theta\,(\cos^2\theta)(2\sin\theta - \sqrt{3})$

**73.** $\dfrac{7\sqrt{2}}{2}$ in., $\dfrac{7\sqrt{2}}{2}$ in.

**75.** no, $17 + 22 < 40$

**77.** right and isosceles

## Summary and Concept Review, pp. 38–40

**1.** $42°56'11''$   **2.** $120°59'43''$   **3.** $147.61\overline{3}°$   **4.** $32°52'12''$
**5.** $207° + 360°k$; Answers will vary.   **6.** $-276°$, $-636°$, $-996°$
**7.** approx. 692.82 yd   **8.** $7\sqrt{2}$ cm   **9.** obtuse and isosceles
**10.** i and iii   **11.** $61°$   **12.** $A = 20°$, $B = 31°$, $C = 129°$
**13.** $10.5 \times 13.5 \times 16.875$   **14.** 57 ft   **15.** 3 in., 21 in.

**16.** $y = \dfrac{3}{5}x$, QI

**17.** $\cos\theta = -\dfrac{\sqrt{10}}{10}$, $\sin\theta = -\dfrac{3\sqrt{10}}{10}$, $\tan\theta = 3$, $\sec\theta = -\sqrt{10}$,

$\csc\theta = -\dfrac{\sqrt{10}}{3}$, $\cot\theta = \dfrac{1}{3}$

**18. a.** $\cos\theta = -\dfrac{12}{37}$, $\sin\theta = \dfrac{35}{37}$, $\tan\theta = -\dfrac{35}{12}$, $\sec\theta = -\dfrac{37}{12}$,

$\csc\theta = \dfrac{37}{35}$, $\cot\theta = -\dfrac{12}{35}$;

**b.** $\cos\theta = \dfrac{2\sqrt{13}}{13}$, $\sin\theta = -\dfrac{3\sqrt{13}}{13}$, $\tan\theta = -\dfrac{3}{2}$, $\sec\theta = \dfrac{\sqrt{13}}{2}$,

$\csc\theta = -\dfrac{\sqrt{13}}{3}$, $\cot\theta = -\dfrac{2}{3}$

**19. a.** $x = 4$, $y = -3$, $r = 5$; QIV; $\sin\theta = -\dfrac{3}{5}$,

$\tan\theta = -\dfrac{3}{4}$, $\sec\theta = \dfrac{5}{4}$, $\csc\theta = -\dfrac{5}{3}$, $\cot\theta = -\dfrac{4}{3}$

**b.** $x = 5$, $y = -12$, $r = 13$; QIV; $\cos\theta = \dfrac{5}{13}$,

$\sin\theta = -\dfrac{12}{13}$, $\sec\theta = \dfrac{13}{5}$, $\csc\theta = -\dfrac{13}{12}$, $\cot\theta = -\dfrac{5}{12}$

**20. a.** positive  **b.** positive   **21. a.** undefined  **b.** 0  **c.** 0  **d.** undefined

**22.** $\sin\theta(\csc\theta - \sin\theta) = \sin\theta\csc\theta - \sin\theta\sin\theta$
$$= \sin\theta\dfrac{1}{\sin\theta} - \sin^2\theta$$
$$= 1 - \sin^2\theta$$
$$= \cos^2\theta$$

**23.** $\dfrac{\tan^2\theta\csc\theta + \csc\theta}{\sec^2\theta} = \dfrac{\csc\theta(\tan^2\theta + 1)}{\sec^2\theta}$
$$= \dfrac{\csc\theta\sec^2\theta}{\sec^2\theta}$$
$$= \csc\theta$$

**24.** $\dfrac{(\sec\theta - \tan\theta)(\sec\theta + \tan\theta)}{\csc\theta}$
$$= \dfrac{\sec^2\theta + \sec\theta\tan\theta - \sec\theta\tan\theta - \tan^2\theta}{\csc\theta}$$
$$= \dfrac{\sec^2\theta - \tan^2\theta}{\csc\theta}$$
$$= \dfrac{1 + \tan^2\theta - \tan^2\theta}{\csc\theta}$$
$$= \dfrac{1}{\csc\theta}$$
$$= \sin\theta$$

**25.** $\dfrac{\sec^2\theta}{\csc\theta} - \sin\theta = \dfrac{\sec^2\theta - \sin\theta\csc\theta}{\csc\theta}$
$$= \dfrac{\sec^2\theta - 1}{\csc\theta}$$
$$= \dfrac{\tan^2\theta}{\csc\theta}$$

**26.** $\sin\theta = \dfrac{-35}{37}$, $\csc\theta = \dfrac{-37}{35}$, $\cot\theta = \dfrac{12}{35}$, $\tan\theta = \dfrac{35}{12}$, $\sec\theta = \dfrac{-37}{12}$

**27.** $\sin\theta = \dfrac{-4\sqrt{6}}{25}$, $\csc\theta = \dfrac{-25}{4\sqrt{6}}$, $\cot\theta = \dfrac{-23}{4\sqrt{6}}$, $\tan\theta = -\dfrac{4\sqrt{6}}{23}$,

$\cos\theta = \dfrac{23}{25}$

## Mixed Review, pp. 40–41

**1. a.** 15 cm; **b.** $10\sqrt{3}$   **3.** $(-16, 14)$, $(-8, 7)$
**5.** $220°48'50''$   **7.** $12\sqrt{2}$ in.; $60\sqrt{2} \approx 84.9$ in.

**9. a.** QI  **b.** QIV  **c.** QIII  **d.** QII   **11.** $86.915°$

**13.** $\sin\theta = \dfrac{-8}{17}$, $\sec\theta = \dfrac{17}{15}$, $\cos\theta = \dfrac{15}{17}$, $\csc\theta = \dfrac{-17}{8}$,

$\tan\theta = \dfrac{-8}{15}$, $\cot\theta = \dfrac{-15}{8}$

**15.** $\csc\theta\tan\theta - \cos\theta = \dfrac{1}{\sin\theta}\dfrac{\sin\theta}{\cos\theta} - \cos\theta$
$$= \dfrac{1}{\cos\theta} - \cos\theta = \dfrac{1 - \cos^2\theta}{\cos\theta} = \dfrac{\sin^2\theta}{\cos\theta}$$

**17.** $\cos\theta = -\dfrac{3\sqrt{13}}{13}$, $\sin\theta = \dfrac{2\sqrt{13}}{13}$, $\tan\theta = -\dfrac{2}{3}$, $\sec\theta = -\dfrac{\sqrt{13}}{3}$

$\cot\theta = -\dfrac{3}{2}$   **19.** $\tan\theta = \dfrac{\pm\sqrt{1 - \cos^2\theta}}{\cos\theta}$

## Practice Test, pp. 41–42

**1.** complement: 55°; supplement: 145°   **2.** $\dfrac{17\sqrt{2}}{2}$ cm

**3.** $30° + 360°k$; $k \in Z$   **4.** 100.755°; 48°12′45″

**5. a.** 430 mi   **b.** $215\sqrt{3} \approx 372$ mi   **6. a.** $C = 90°$; right   **b.** $C = 92°$;

obtuse   **7.** 67.5°   **8. a.** (0, 96), **b.** 55.4 mm

**9.** $a = 15$ yd, $c = 12$ yd, $d = 10$ yd   **10.** 66 m

**11. a.** $y = -\dfrac{9}{7}x$,   **b.** $(-14, 18)$

**12.** $\cos\beta = -\dfrac{7\sqrt{130}}{130}$, $\sin\beta = \dfrac{9\sqrt{130}}{130}$,

$\tan\beta = -\dfrac{9}{7}$, $\sec\beta = -\dfrac{\sqrt{130}}{7}$,

$\csc\beta = \dfrac{\sqrt{130}}{9}$, $\cot\beta = -\dfrac{7}{9}$

**13.** $\sec\theta = \dfrac{5}{2}$, $\sin\theta = \dfrac{-\sqrt{21}}{5}$,

$\tan\theta = \dfrac{-\sqrt{21}}{2}$, $\csc\theta = \dfrac{-5}{\sqrt{21}}$, $\cot\theta = \dfrac{-2}{\sqrt{21}}$

**14.** 0; 1; 0; undefined; 1; undefined

1; 0; undefined; 1; undefined; 0

0; $-1$; 0; undefined; $-1$; undefined

$-1$; 0; undefined; $-1$; undefined; 0

**15. a.** positive   **b.** negative   **c.** positive   **d.** negative

**16.** $\csc\theta\,(\tan\theta + \sin\theta) = \csc\theta\tan\theta + \csc\theta\sin\theta$

$= \dfrac{1}{\sin\theta}\dfrac{\sin\theta}{\cos\theta} + \dfrac{1}{\sin\theta}\sin\theta = \dfrac{1}{\cos\theta} + 1 = \sec\theta + 1$

**17.** $\dfrac{(\csc\theta - \cot\theta)(\csc\theta + \cot\theta)}{\sec\theta} = \dfrac{\csc^2\theta - \cot^2\theta}{\sec\theta} = \dfrac{1}{\sec\theta} = \cos\theta$

**18.** $\dfrac{\sin^3\theta - \cos^3\theta}{1 + \cos\theta\sin\theta} = \dfrac{(\sin\theta - \cos\theta)(\sin^2\theta + \sin\theta\cos\theta + \cos^2\theta)}{1 + \cos\theta\sin\theta}$

$= \dfrac{(\sin\theta - \cos\theta)(1 + \sin\theta\cos\theta)}{1 + \cos\theta\sin\theta} = \sin\theta - \cos\theta$

**19.** $\sin\theta = -\dfrac{55}{73}$, $\tan\theta = -\dfrac{55}{48}$, $\sec\theta = \dfrac{73}{48}$,

$\csc\theta = -\dfrac{73}{55}$, $\cot\theta = -\dfrac{48}{55}$

**20.** $\cot\theta = \dfrac{1}{\pm\sqrt{\sec^2\theta - 1}}$

## Strengthening Core Skills, pp. 43–44

**Exercise 1:** $\dfrac{1 + \sin\theta}{\cos\theta}$

**Exercise 2:** $1 + 2\sin\theta\cos\theta$

**Exercise 3:** $\cos\theta$

**Exercise 4:** $\dfrac{2\cos\theta}{1 - \cos^2\theta}$

**Exercise 5:** $\dfrac{1 - \cos\theta}{\sin\theta}$

**Exercise 6:** $2\cos^2\theta - 1$

**9. a.** $\dfrac{\sqrt{2}}{2}$  **b.** $\dfrac{\sqrt{2}}{2}$  **c.** 1  **11. a.** $\dfrac{4}{5}$  **b.** $\dfrac{3}{5}$  **c.** $\dfrac{3}{4}$

**13. a.** $\dfrac{5}{3}$  **b.** $\dfrac{5}{4}$  **c.** $\dfrac{3}{4}$

**15.** $\sin\theta = \frac{12}{13}$, $\csc\theta = \frac{13}{12}$, $\sec\theta = \frac{13}{5}$, $\tan\theta = \frac{12}{5}$, $\cot\theta = \frac{5}{12}$

**17.** $\cos\theta = \frac{13}{85}$, $\sec\theta = \frac{85}{13}$, $\cot\theta = \frac{13}{84}$, $\sin\theta = \frac{84}{85}$, $\csc\theta = \frac{85}{84}$

**19.** $\sin\theta = \frac{11}{5\sqrt{5}}$, $\tan\theta = \frac{11}{2}$, $\csc\theta = \frac{5\sqrt{5}}{11}$, $\cos\theta = \frac{2}{5\sqrt{5}}$, $\sec\theta = \frac{5\sqrt{5}}{2}$

**21.** $\cos\theta = \frac{\sqrt{5}}{5}$, $\sin\theta = \frac{2\sqrt{5}}{5}$, $\sec\theta = \sqrt{5}$, $\csc\theta = \frac{\sqrt{5}}{2}$, $\cot\theta = \frac{1}{2}$

**23.** $\cos\theta = \dfrac{t\sqrt{t^2+1}}{t^2+1}$, $\sin\theta = \dfrac{\sqrt{t^2+1}}{t^2+1}$, $\tan\theta = \dfrac{1}{t}$,

$\sec\theta = \dfrac{\sqrt{t^2+1}}{t}$, $\csc\theta = \sqrt{t^2+1}$

**25.** $(21, 20)$  **27.** $(\sqrt{5}, 2)$  **29.** $(6.5, 7.2)$  **31.** $(a, b)$  **33.** $(55, 48)$

**35.** $43°$  **37.** $21°$  **39.** $x = 10$  **41.** $x = 8$

**43.** $\dfrac{1}{2}, \dfrac{\sqrt{3}}{2}, \dfrac{\sqrt{3}}{3}, \dfrac{\sqrt{3}}{2}, \dfrac{1}{2}, \sqrt{3}, 2, \dfrac{2\sqrt{3}}{3}, \sqrt{3}$  **45.** $6 + 2\sqrt{3}$

**47.** $7 + 4\sqrt{3}$  **49.** $\dfrac{\sin\alpha}{\sin\beta} = \dfrac{\sin\alpha}{\cos\alpha} = \tan\alpha$

**51.** $\sec^2\alpha = \tan^2\alpha + 1 = \cot^2\beta + 1$

**53.** $\tan^2\alpha\,\sec^2\beta - \cot^2\beta = \tan^2\alpha\,\csc^2\alpha - \tan^2\alpha$

$= \tan^2\alpha(\csc^2\alpha - 1) = \tan^2\alpha\,\cot^2\alpha = 1$

**55.** 7.2 ft/sec

**57.** 3.75  **59.** 1.5  **61.** 0.8  **63. a.** $10\sqrt{3}$ cm  **b.** $\dfrac{\sqrt{3}}{3}$

**65.** $\cot u = \dfrac{x}{h}$

$x = h\cot u$

$\cot v = \dfrac{x - d}{h}$

$\cot v = \dfrac{h\cot u - d}{h}$

$h\cot v = h\cot u - d$

$d = h\cot u - h\cot v$

$h = \dfrac{d}{\cot u - \cot v}$

**67.** $\dfrac{\sin\theta}{\tan^2\theta} = \sin\theta\cot^2\theta = \sin\theta\,\dfrac{\cos^2\theta}{\sin^2\theta} = \dfrac{\cos^2\theta}{\sin\theta} = \cot\theta\cos\theta$

**69.** 14.4 m  **71.** $\dfrac{25}{29}$

## Exercises 2.2, pp. 57–60

**1.** $\theta = \tan^{-1}x$  **3.** Pythagorean; hypotenuse; $\tan^{-1}$; angle
**5.** To find the measure of all three angles and all three sides.

**7.**

| Angles | Sides |
|---|---|
| $A = 30°$ | $a = 98$ cm |
| $B = 60°$ | $b = 98\sqrt{3}$ cm |
| $C = 90°$ | $c = 196$ cm |

**9.**

| Angles | Sides |
|---|---|
| $A = 45°$ | $a = 9.9$ mm |
| $B = 45°$ | $b = 9.9$ mm |
| $C = 90°$ | $c = 9.9\sqrt{2}$ mm |

**11.**

| Angles | Sides |
|---|---|
| $A = 22°$ | $a = 14$ m |
| $B = 68°$ | $b \approx 34.65$ m |
| $C = 90°$ | $c \approx 37.37$ m |

verified

**13.**

| Angles | Sides |
|---|---|
| $A = 32°$ | $a = 5.6$ mi |
| $B = 58°$ | $b \approx 8.96$ mi |
| $C = 90°$ | $c \approx 10.57$ mi |

verified

**15.**

| Angles | Sides |
|---|---|
| $A = 65°$ | $a = 625$ mm |
| $B = 25°$ | $b \approx 291.44$ mm |
| $C = 90°$ | $c \approx 689.61$ mm |

verified

## CHAPTER 2

## Exercises 2.1, pp. 51–54

**1.** complementary; cotangent  **3.** opposite; hypotenuse

**5.** Answers will vary.  **7. a.** $\dfrac{2\sqrt{3}}{3}$  **b.** 2  **c.** $\sqrt{3}$

**17.** 0.4540    **19.** 0.8391    **21.** 1.3230    **23.** 0.9063
**25.** 27°    **27.** 40°    **29.** 40.9°    **31.** 65°    **33.** 44.7°    **35.** 20.2°
**37.** 18.4°    **39.** 46.2°    **41.** 61.6°    **43.** 21.98 mm    **45.** 3.04 mi
**47.** 177.48 furlongs    **49.** $\theta \approx 11.0°, \beta \approx 23.9°, \gamma \approx 145.1°$
**51.** approx. 386.0 Ω
**53. a.** 875 m    **b.** 1200 m
**c.** 1485 m; 36.1°

**55.** approx. 450 ft
**57. a.** approx. 20.2 cm for each side  **b.** approx. 35.3°

**59.** $\tan v = \dfrac{h}{d}$

$d = \dfrac{h}{\tan v}$

$\tan u = \dfrac{h - x}{d}$

$\tan u = \dfrac{h - x}{\dfrac{h}{\tan v}}$

$\tan u = \dfrac{(h - x)\tan v}{h}$

$h \tan u = h \tan v - x \tan v$

$h(\tan v - \tan u) = x \tan v$

$h = \dfrac{x \tan v}{\tan v - \tan u}$

$h \approx 253.45$ m

**61.** 132.715°    **63.** $4 + 2\sqrt{2}$

**65.** 0.75

## Mid-Chapter Check, pp. 60–61

**1.**  $\sin \theta = \dfrac{5}{13}, \tan \theta = \dfrac{5}{12}, \sec \theta = \dfrac{13}{12}, \csc \theta = \dfrac{13}{5}, \cot \theta = \dfrac{12}{5}$

**2.**  **a.** $\dfrac{4}{3}$  **b.** $\dfrac{5}{4}$  **c.** $\dfrac{5}{4}$  **d.** $\dfrac{4}{3}$

**3.**  $\dfrac{\cos \beta}{\cos \alpha} = \dfrac{\sin(90° - \beta)}{\cos \alpha} = \dfrac{\sin \alpha}{\cos \alpha} = \tan \alpha$

**4.**  **a.** 1.3270  **b.** 0.4756  **c.** 0.4756  **d.** 1

**5.**

| Angles | Sides |
|--------|-------|
| $A = 35°$ | $a \approx 16.80$ |
| $B = 55°$ | $b = 24$ |
| $C = 90°$ | $c \approx 29.30$ |

**6.**  $\cot 15° = 2 + \sqrt{3}$, since $\cot 15° = \tan(90 - 15)° = \tan 75°$

**7.**

| Angles | Sides |
|--------|-------|
| $A \approx 26.6°$ | $a = 7$ ft |
| $B \approx 63.4°$ | $b = 14$ ft |
| $C = 90°$ | $c \approx 15.7$ ft |

**8.**

| $\theta$ | $\sin \theta$ | $\cos \theta$ | $\tan \theta$ | $\csc \theta$ | $\sec \theta$ | $\cot \theta$ |
|---|---|---|---|---|---|---|
| 30° | $\dfrac{1}{2}$ | $\dfrac{\sqrt{3}}{2}$ | $\dfrac{\sqrt{3}}{3}$ | 2 | $\dfrac{2\sqrt{3}}{3}$ | $\sqrt{3}$ |
| 45° | $\dfrac{\sqrt{2}}{2}$ | $\dfrac{\sqrt{2}}{2}$ | 1 | $\sqrt{2}$ | $\sqrt{2}$ | 1 |
| 60° | $\dfrac{\sqrt{3}}{2}$ | $\dfrac{1}{2}$ | $\sqrt{3}$ | $\dfrac{2\sqrt{3}}{3}$ | 2 | $\dfrac{\sqrt{3}}{3}$ |

**9.** 53°    **10.** 343.2 in. or 28 ft, 7.2 in.

## Reinforcing Basic Concepts, pp. 61–62

**1.** 70.4 cm²    **2.** 441.3 mm²    **3.** 2161.7 in.²    **4.** 248.3 ft²

## Exercises 2.3, pp. 68–71

**1.** orientation; parallel    **3.** calculators; sine; cosine; tangent
**5.** Answers will vary.    **7.** 11 m    **9.** 14 m    **11.** 17 m    **13.** 25 ft
**15.** 29 ft    **17.** 33 ft    **19. a.** 63°, **b.** 27°    **21. a.** 49°, **b.** 41°
**23. a.** 23°31′, **b.** 66°29′    **25. a.** 15°32′49″, **b.** 74°27′11″
**27. a.** approx. 81.2 m  **b.** approx 27.1 sec
**29. a.** approx. 82.8 m  **b.** approx. 27.6 sec
**31. a.** approx. 85.1 m  **b.** approx. 28.4 sec    **33.** approx. 118.3 ft
**35.** approx. 300.6 m    **37.** approx. 481.1 m    **39.** 87 ft 9 in.
**41.** approx. 118.1 mph    **43. a.** approx. 250.0 yd   **b.** approx. 351.0 yd
**c.** approx. 23.1 yd    **45.** approx. 1815.2 ft; approx. 665.3 ft    **47.** S 85° W
**49.** $7\sqrt{3}$ in. and 21 in.

**51. a.** $\dfrac{-3\sqrt{10}}{10}$, **b.** $\dfrac{\sqrt{10}}{10}$

**53.** $\cos \alpha = \dfrac{\sqrt{21}}{5}, \tan \alpha = \dfrac{2\sqrt{21}}{21}, \csc \alpha = \dfrac{5}{2}, \sec \alpha = \dfrac{5\sqrt{21}}{21},$

$\cot \alpha = \dfrac{\sqrt{21}}{2}$

## Exercises 2.4, pp. 75–78

**1.** coterminal; reference; 80°    **3.** integers; 360°$k$

**5.** Answers will vary.

**7.** slope $= \sqrt{3}$, equation : $y = \sqrt{3} x$, $\sin 60° = \dfrac{\sqrt{3}}{2}$, $\cos 60° = \dfrac{1}{2}$,

$\tan 60° = \sqrt{3}$

**9.** 50°    **11.** 30°    **13.** 45°    **15.** 68°    **17.** 44.4°    **19.** 40°
**21.** 11.6°    **23.** 22.1°    **25.** 78°30′

**27.** $\sin \theta = -\dfrac{1}{2}; \cos \theta = \dfrac{\sqrt{3}}{2}, \tan \theta = -\dfrac{1}{\sqrt{3}}$

**29.** $\sin \theta = \dfrac{-\sqrt{2}}{2}; \cos \theta = \dfrac{\sqrt{2}}{2}, \tan \theta = -1$

**31.** $\sin \theta = \dfrac{-\sqrt{3}}{2}; \cos \theta = \dfrac{-1}{2}, \tan \theta = \sqrt{3}$

**33.** $\sin \theta = -\dfrac{1}{2}; \cos \theta = \dfrac{-\sqrt{3}}{2}, \tan \theta = \dfrac{1}{\sqrt{3}}$

**35.** $\sin \theta = \dfrac{-\sqrt{3}}{2}, \cos \theta = \dfrac{-1}{2}, \tan \theta = \sqrt{3}$

**37.** $\sin \theta = \dfrac{-\sqrt{3}}{2}, \cos \theta = -\dfrac{1}{2}, \tan \theta = \sqrt{3}$

**39.** $\sin \theta = \dfrac{-1}{2}, \cos \theta = \dfrac{-\sqrt{3}}{2}, \tan \theta = \dfrac{1}{\sqrt{3}}$

**41.** $\sin\theta = \dfrac{-1}{2}$, $\cos\theta = \dfrac{-\sqrt{3}}{2}$, $\tan\theta = \dfrac{1}{\sqrt{3}} = -1$

**43.** $52° + 360°k$    **45.** $87.5° + 360°k$    **47.** $225° + 360°k$

**49.** $-107° + 360°k$

**51.** $\dfrac{\sqrt{3}}{2}, \dfrac{-1}{2}, -\sqrt{3}$    **53.** $-\dfrac{1}{2}, \dfrac{\sqrt{3}}{2}, \dfrac{1}{\sqrt{3}}$

**55.** QIV; negative; $1°$; $-0.0175$; $0.0175$

**57.** QIV; negative; $59°$; $-1.6643$; $1.6643$

**59.** QIV; negative; $39°$; $-1.5890$; $1.5890$

**61.** QI; positive; $85°$; $0.0872$; $0.0872$

**63.** **a.** approx. $144.78$ units$^2$ **b.** $53°$ **c.** The parallelogram is a rectangle whose area is $A = ab$. **d.** $A = \dfrac{ab}{2}\sin\theta$

**65.** $\theta = 60° + 360°k$ and $\theta = 300° + 360°k$

**67.** $\theta = 240° + 360°k$ and $\theta = 300° + 360°k$

**69.** $\theta = 61.1° + 360°k$ and $\theta = 118.9° + 360°k$

**71.** $\theta = 113.0° + 360°k$ and $\theta = 293.0° + 360°k$

**73.** $1890°$; $90° + 360°k$

**75.** head first; $900°$

**77.** approx. $701.6°$

**79.** **a.** $30°, 60°$   **b.** $15°, 150°, 45°$    **c.** Answers will vary.

**81.** **a.** $12,960°$ **b.** $125.66$ in.   **c.** $15,080$ in.   **d.** $85.68$ mph

**83.** approx. $0.8391$; $40° + 50° = 90°$ and cofunction relationship

**85.**

| Angles | Sides |
|---|---|
| $A = 30°$ | $a = 18$ m |
| $B = 60°$ | $b = 18\sqrt{3}$ m |
| $C = 90°$ | $c = 36$ m |

**87.** $77°25'04''$; $167°25'04''$

## Summary and Concept Review, pp. 78–80

**1.** **a.** $\dfrac{2\sqrt{6}}{7}$   **b.** $\dfrac{5}{7}$    **2.** **a.** $\dfrac{5}{7}$   **b.** $\dfrac{2\sqrt{6}}{7}$

**3.** **a.** $\dfrac{2\sqrt{6}}{5}$   **b.** $\dfrac{5\sqrt{6}}{12}$    **4.** **a.** $\dfrac{7\sqrt{6}}{12}$   **b.** $\dfrac{7}{5}$

**5.** **a.** $\dfrac{7}{5}$   **b.** $\dfrac{7\sqrt{6}}{12}$    **6.** **a.** $\dfrac{5\sqrt{6}}{12}$   **b.** $\dfrac{2\sqrt{6}}{5}$

**7.** $\sin\theta = \dfrac{3\sqrt{10}}{10}$, $\cos\theta = \dfrac{\sqrt{10}}{10}$, $\csc\theta = \dfrac{\sqrt{10}}{3}$, $\sec\theta = \sqrt{10}$, $\cot\theta = \dfrac{1}{3}$

**8.** **a.** $\cot 32.6°$   **b.** $\cos(70°29'45'')$

**9.** **a.** $A \approx 0.80$   **b.** $A \approx 64.3°$

**10.**

| Angles | Sides |
|---|---|
| $A = 49°$ | $a = 89$ in. |
| $B = 41°$ | $b \approx 77.37$ in. |
| $C = 90°$ | $c = 117.93$ in. |

**11.**

| Angles | Sides |
|---|---|
| $A \approx 43.6°$ | $a = 20$ m |
| $B \approx 46.4°$ | $b = 21$ m |
| $C = 90°$ | $c = 29$ m |

**12.** approx. $5.18$ m   **13.** approx. $54.5°$ and $35.5°$   **14.** $473$ ft

**15.** N $31°$ E, N $31°$ W, S $31°$ E, S $31°$ W    **16.** approx. $1.5$ ft/sec

**17.** **a.** approx. $239.32$ m   **b.** approx. $240.68$ m apart   **18.** $28°, 19°, 30°$

**19.** $-\dfrac{1}{2}, -\dfrac{\sqrt{3}}{2}, \dfrac{\sqrt{3}}{3}$    **20.** **a.** $\dfrac{\sqrt{2}}{2}$   **b.** $-\dfrac{\sqrt{2}}{2}$   **c.** $-1$

**21.** **a.** $\theta = 135° + 180°k$ **b.** $\theta = 30° + 360°k$ or $\theta = 330° + 360°k$
**c.** $\theta \approx 76.0° + 180°k$   **d.** $\theta \approx -27.0° + 360°k$ or
$\theta \approx 207.0° + 360°k$

## Mixed Review , pp. 81–82

**1.** $\dfrac{6\sqrt{61}}{61}; \dfrac{5}{6}$   **3.** $\dfrac{\sqrt{3}}{2}, -\dfrac{1}{2}, -\sqrt{3}$   **5.** approx. $997$ m

**7.** $\sin\theta = \dfrac{77}{85}$, $\tan\theta = \dfrac{77}{36}$, $\sec\theta = \dfrac{85}{36}$, $\csc\theta = \dfrac{85}{77}$, $\cot\theta = \dfrac{36}{77}$

**9.** **a.** $-\dfrac{1}{2}$   **b.** $\dfrac{\sqrt{3}}{2}$   **c.** $-\dfrac{\sqrt{3}}{3}$   **11.** $20$ ft   **13.** $-630°$   **15.** $60°$

**17.**

| Angles | Sides |
|---|---|
| $A = 11.3°$ | $a \approx 12.1$ m |
| $B = 78.7°$ | $b = 60.5$ m |
| $C = 90°$ | $c \approx 61.7$ m |

**19.** $\sqrt{3}$

## Practice Test , pp. 82–84

**1.** $18.87$ cm   **2. a.** $45°$   **b.** $30°$

**3.** $\sin\theta = \dfrac{1}{4}$, $\cos\theta = \dfrac{\sqrt{15}}{4}$, $\tan\theta = \dfrac{\sqrt{15}}{15}$, $\sec\theta = \dfrac{4\sqrt{15}}{15}$, $\cot\theta = \sqrt{15}$

**4.**

| Angles | Sides |
|---|---|
| $A = 33°$ | $a \approx 8.2$ cm |
| $B = 57°$ | $b \approx 12.6$ cm |
| $C = 90°$ | $c = 15.0$ cm |

**5.**

| Angles | Sides |
|---|---|
| $A \approx 38.4°$ | $a = 138$ ft |
| $B = 90°$ | $b = 174$ ft |
| $C \approx 51.6°$ | $c \approx 222.1$ ft |

**6.** approx. $67.9$ ft

**7.**

| $\theta$ | $\sin\theta$ | $\cos\theta$ | $\tan\theta$ | $\csc\theta$ | $\sec\theta$ | $\cot\theta$ |
|---|---|---|---|---|---|---|
| $30°$ | $\dfrac{1}{2}$ | $\dfrac{\sqrt{3}}{2}$ | $\dfrac{\sqrt{3}}{3}$ | $2$ | $\dfrac{2\sqrt{3}}{3}$ | $\sqrt{3}$ |
| $45°$ | $\dfrac{\sqrt{2}}{2}$ | $\dfrac{\sqrt{2}}{2}$ | $1$ | $\sqrt{2}$ | $\sqrt{2}$ | $1$ |
| $60°$ | $\dfrac{\sqrt{3}}{2}$ | $\dfrac{1}{2}$ | $\sqrt{3}$ | $\dfrac{2\sqrt{3}}{3}$ | $2$ | $\dfrac{\sqrt{3}}{3}$ |
| $135°$ | $\dfrac{\sqrt{2}}{2}$ | $-\dfrac{\sqrt{2}}{2}$ | $-1$ | $\sqrt{2}$ | $-\sqrt{2}$ | $-1$ |
| $240°$ | $-\dfrac{\sqrt{3}}{2}$ | $-\dfrac{1}{2}$ | $\sqrt{3}$ | $\dfrac{2\sqrt{3}}{3}$ | $-2$ | $\dfrac{\sqrt{3}}{3}$ |
| $330°$ | $-\dfrac{1}{2}$ | $\dfrac{\sqrt{3}}{2}$ | $-\dfrac{\sqrt{3}}{3}$ | $-2$ | $\dfrac{2\sqrt{3}}{3}$ | $-\sqrt{3}$ |

**8.** **a.** $-\dfrac{4}{5}$   **b.** $-\dfrac{3}{5}$   **c.** $-\dfrac{4}{3}$   **9.** $47.7°$   **10.** $2 - \sqrt{3}$

**11.** about $67$ cm, $49.6°$   **12.** $57.9$ m   **13.** approx. $2.8$ mi.

**14.** $\theta = 150° + 360°k$ and $\theta = 210° + 360°k$

**15.** **a.** $\cot\alpha$   **b.** $\csc\alpha$   **c.** $\cos\alpha$   **d.** $\sin\alpha$   **e.** $\sec\alpha$
   **f.** $\tan\alpha$

**16.** $\theta \approx 65.9°$

**17.** $\sin \alpha(\sec \beta - \sin \alpha) = \sin \alpha(\csc \alpha - \sin \alpha) = \sin \alpha\left(\dfrac{1}{\sin \alpha} - \sin \alpha\right)$

$= 1 - \sin^2\alpha = \cos^2\alpha = \sin^2\beta$

**18. a.** about 39 ft       **b.** about 74 ft       **c.** about 4.8 mph

**19.** $\approx 0.53$; $\approx -0.53$; $\approx -0.53$       **20.** approx. 228 km

**21.** not possible, $a + c < b$

**23.** $\sin \beta = \dfrac{\sqrt{15}}{8}$, $\cos \beta = \dfrac{7}{8}$, $\tan \beta = \dfrac{\sqrt{15}}{7}$, $\csc \beta = \dfrac{8\sqrt{15}}{15}$,

$\sec \beta = \dfrac{8}{7}$, $\cot \beta = \dfrac{7\sqrt{15}}{15}$

**25.** $\dfrac{5\sqrt{3}}{3}$ in., $\dfrac{10\sqrt{3}}{3}$ in.

## Strengthening Core Skills, pp. 85–86

**Exercise 1:**

| $\theta$ | 0° | 30° | 45° | 60° | 90° |
|---|---|---|---|---|---|
| $\sin \theta$ | 0 | $\dfrac{1}{2}$ | $\dfrac{\sqrt{2}}{2}$ | $\dfrac{\sqrt{3}}{2}$ | 1 |
| $\cos \theta$ | 1 | $\dfrac{\sqrt{3}}{2}$ | $\dfrac{\sqrt{2}}{2}$ | $\dfrac{1}{2}$ | 0 |
| $\tan \theta$ | 0 | $\dfrac{\sqrt{3}}{3}$ | 1 | $\sqrt{3}$ | — |

| 120° | 135° | 150° | 180° | 210° | 225° |
|---|---|---|---|---|---|
| $\dfrac{\sqrt{3}}{2}$ | $\dfrac{\sqrt{2}}{2}$ | $\dfrac{1}{2}$ | 0 | $\dfrac{-1}{2}$ | $\dfrac{-\sqrt{2}}{2}$ |
| $\dfrac{-1}{2}$ | $\dfrac{-\sqrt{2}}{2}$ | $\dfrac{-\sqrt{3}}{2}$ | $-1$ | $\dfrac{-\sqrt{3}}{2}$ | $\dfrac{-\sqrt{2}}{2}$ |
| $-\sqrt{3}$ | $-1$ | $\dfrac{-\sqrt{3}}{3}$ | | $\dfrac{\sqrt{3}}{3}$ | |

**Exercise 2: a.** $\theta = 240°, 300°$  **b.** $\theta = 45°, 315°$  **c.** $\theta = 30°, 210°$
**d.** $\theta = 45°, 315°$

**Exercise 3: a.** no solution  **b.** $\theta \approx 70.5°, 289.5°$
**c.** $\theta \approx 166.0°, 346.0°$  **d.** $\theta \approx 113.6°, 246.4°$

## Cumulative Review Chapters 1–2, pp. 86–87

**1.**   hyp = 89; $\theta \approx 64°$; $90 - \theta = 26°$

**3.** $60.585°$       **5.** $\approx 114.3$ ft

**7.** $x = -9, y = 40, r = 41$, QII;

$\cos \theta = \dfrac{-9}{41}$, $\sin \theta = \dfrac{40}{41}$, $\tan \theta = \dfrac{40}{-9}$, $\sec \theta = \dfrac{41}{-9}$, $\csc \theta = \dfrac{41}{40}$,

$\cot \theta = \dfrac{-9}{40}$, $\theta \approx 102.7°$

**9.** $\cos(90 - \theta) = \sin \theta$

**11.** $260°, 620°, -460°, -820°$

**13.** $270°$

**15.** $\dfrac{\sqrt{2}}{2}$

**17.**

| Angles | Sides |
|---|---|
| $A \approx 47.7°$ | $a = 11$ m |
| $B \approx 42.3°$ | $b = 10$ m |
| $C = 90°$ | $c \approx 14.87$ m |

**19.** $-\dfrac{1}{2}, \dfrac{\sqrt{3}}{2}, -\dfrac{\sqrt{3}}{3}$

## CHAPTER 3

### Exercises 3.1, pp. 94–97

**1.** central; 5; $\pi$ **3.** $\pi$; 3; 4; 6; 1; 2 **5.** Answers will vary. **7.** 4 **9.** 1

**11.** $\dfrac{1}{2}$ **13.** 3 **15.** $\dfrac{11}{3}$ **17.** $\dfrac{16}{3}$ **19.** $-3$ **21.** $-2.4$ **23.** $-\dfrac{17}{4}$

**25.** $\dfrac{13\pi}{6}, \dfrac{25\pi}{6}, -\dfrac{11\pi}{6}, -\dfrac{23\pi}{6}$ **27.** $\dfrac{7\pi}{3}, \dfrac{13\pi}{3}, -\dfrac{5\pi}{3}, -\dfrac{11\pi}{3}$

**29.** $2\pi$ rad **31.** $\dfrac{\pi}{4}$ rad **33.** $\dfrac{7\pi}{6}$ rad **35.** $\dfrac{-2\pi}{3}$ rad

**37.** $\dfrac{2\pi}{9}$ **39.** $-\dfrac{61\pi}{36}$ **41.** $\dfrac{251\pi}{450}$ **43.** 0.4712 rad

**45.** 3.9776 rad **47.** $-0.9178$ rad **49.** 60° **51.** 30°

**53.** 120° **55.** 720° **57.** 165° **59.** 186.4°

**61.** 171.9° **63.** $-143.2°$ **65. a.** $b$ **b.** $e$ **c.** $c$

**67.** QII **69.** QI **71.** QIII

**73.** $18\sqrt{3} \approx 31.2$ ft-lb; $50\sqrt{3} \approx 86.6$ lb

**75.** 4 rad **77.** $91\pi$ rad **79.** 764° **81.** $\dfrac{5\pi}{8}$

**83.** $1' = \dfrac{\pi}{10,800} \approx 0.000291$, $1'' = \dfrac{\pi}{648,000} \approx 0.00000485$,

approx. 1.179 **85.** $-\dfrac{1}{2}, -\dfrac{\sqrt{3}}{2}, \dfrac{\sqrt{3}}{3}$ **87.** 75.4° **89. a.** 28° **b.** 42°

### Exercises 3.2, pp. 103–106

**1.** latitude; equator; longitude; Prime Meridian

**3.** $\omega = \dfrac{\theta}{t}$; $V = r\omega$; radians **5.** Answers will vary.

**7.** $s = 980$ m **9.** $\theta = 0.75$ rad **11.** $r \approx 1760$ yd

**13.** $s = \dfrac{8\pi}{3}$ mi **15.** $\theta = 0.2575$ rad **17.** $r \approx 9.4$ km

**19.** $\dfrac{\pi}{4}$ rad/sec **21.** $\dfrac{\pi}{4}$ rad/hr **23.** $\dfrac{\pi}{6}$ rad/day **25.** $\dfrac{7\pi}{12}$ rad/min

**27.** 40 in./sec **29.** 140.74 mph **31.** 31.42 mm/sec **33.** 6 kph

**35.** $\mathcal{A} = 115.6$ km$^2$ **37.** $\theta = 0.6$ rad **39.** $r \approx 3$ m

**41.** $\theta = 1.5$ rad; $s = 7.5$ cm; $r = 5$ cm; $\mathcal{A} = 18.75$ cm$^2$

**43.** $\theta = 4.3$ rad; $s = 43$ m; $r = 10$ m; $\mathcal{A} = 215$ m$^2$

**45.** $\theta = 3$ rad; $\mathcal{A} = 864$ mm$^2$; $s = 72$ mm; $r = 24$ mm

**47.** approx. 0.04206 **49.** 960.7 mi apart

**51. a.** $1.5\pi$ rad/sec **b.** about 15 mi/hr

**53. a.** $40\pi$ rad/min **b.** $\dfrac{\pi}{6}$ ft/sec $\approx 0.52$ ft/sec **c.** about 11.5 sec

**55. a.** $\approx 50.3$ m$^2$ **b.** $\approx 80°$ **c.** $\approx 17$ m

**57. a.** $\approx 50.3°$/day; $\approx 0.8788$ rad/day **b.** $\approx 0.0366$ rad/hr

**c.** $\approx 6.67$ mi/sec **59.** 34.9 m/hr **61. a.** approx. 3055.6 mi

**b.** approx. 9012.8 mi **c.** approx. 7 hr, 13 min **63.** 240°

**65.** $5\sqrt{2}$ in. **67.** $\dfrac{7\sqrt{30}}{30}$

### Mid-Chapter Check, p. 106

**1. a.** 36.11°N, 115.08°W **b.** 2495.7 mi. **2.** $\theta = 4.3$; $\mathcal{A} = 860$ cm$^2$

**3. a.** $\dfrac{7\pi}{6}$ **b.** $-\dfrac{3\pi}{4}$ **c.** $\dfrac{8\pi}{3}$ **4. a.** 229.18° **b.** $-134.07°$

**c.** 270° **5.** $\dfrac{17\pi}{6}, -\dfrac{7\pi}{6}$ **6. a.** $20\pi$ rad/min **b.** about 10.7 mph

**7. a.** 206 in² **b.** 115° **8. a.** QII **b.** QIII **c.** QI **d.** QIV
**9.** about 451 m **10.** 120 rad

## Reinforcing Basic Concepts, p. 107

**Exercise 1: a.** $(0.97, 0.24)$, $(0.97)^2 + (0.24)^2 \approx 1$,
$\cos t = 0.9689124217$, $\sin t = 0.2474039593$ **b.** $(0.88, 0.48)$,
$(0.88)^2 + (0.48)^2 \approx 1$, $\cos t = 0.8775825619$, $\sin t = 0.4794255386$
**c.** $(0.73, 0.68)$, $(0.73)^2 + (0.68)^2 \approx 1$, $\cos t = 0.73168886889$,
$\sin t = 0.68163876$ **d.** $(0.54, 0.84)$, $(0.54)^2 + (0.84)^2 \approx 1$,
$\cos t = 0.5403023059$, $\sin t = 0.8414709848$
**Exercise 2: a.** $(-0.5, 0.87)$, $(-0.5)^2 + (0.87)^2 \approx 1$,
$\cos t = -\frac{1}{2}$, $\sin t = \frac{\sqrt{3}}{2}$ **b.** $(-0.71, 0.71)$, $(-0.71)^2 + (0.71)^2 \approx 1$,
$\cos t = -\frac{\sqrt{2}}{2}$, $\sin t = \frac{\sqrt{2}}{2}$ **c.** $(-0.87, 0.5)$, $(-0.87)^2 + (0.5)^2 \approx 1$,
$\cos t = -\frac{\sqrt{3}}{2}$, $\sin t = \frac{1}{2}$ **d.** $(-1, 0)$, $(-1)^2 + (0)^2 = 1$, $\cos t = -1$,
$\sin t = 0$

## Exercises 3.3, pp. 114–117

**1.** $x$; $y$; origin **3.** $x$; $y$; $\frac{y}{x}$; $\sec \theta$; $\csc \theta$; $\cot \theta$ **5.** Answers will vary.

**7.** $(-0.6, -0.8)$ **9.** $\left(\frac{5}{13}, \frac{-12}{13}\right)$ **11.** $\left(\frac{\sqrt{11}}{6}, \frac{5}{6}\right)$

**13.** $\left(\frac{-\sqrt{11}}{4}, \frac{\sqrt{5}}{4}\right)$ **15.** $(-0.9769, -0.2137)$ **17.** $(-0.9928, 0.1198)$

**19.** $\left(\frac{-\sqrt{3}}{2}, \frac{-1}{2}\right), \left(\frac{\sqrt{3}}{2}, \frac{1}{2}\right), \left(\frac{\sqrt{3}}{2}, \frac{-1}{2}\right)$

**21.** $\left(\frac{-\sqrt{11}}{6}, \frac{-5}{6}\right), \left(\frac{-\sqrt{11}}{6}, \frac{5}{6}\right), \left(\frac{\sqrt{11}}{6}, \frac{5}{6}\right)$

**23.** $(-0.3325, 0.9431), (-0.3325, -0.9431), (0.3325, -0.9431)$
**25.** $(0.9937, 0.1121), (-0.9937, 0.1121), (-0.9937, -0.1121)$

**27.** $\left(\frac{1}{2}, \frac{\sqrt{3}}{2}\right)$ is on unit circle. **29.** $\frac{\pi}{4}; \left(\frac{-\sqrt{2}}{2}, \frac{-\sqrt{2}}{2}\right)$

**31.** $\frac{\pi}{6}; \left(\frac{-\sqrt{3}}{2}, \frac{-1}{2}\right)$ **33.** $\frac{\pi}{4}; \left(\frac{-\sqrt{2}}{2}, \frac{\sqrt{2}}{2}\right)$ **35.** $\frac{\pi}{6}; \left(\frac{\sqrt{3}}{2}, \frac{1}{2}\right)$

**37. a.** $\frac{\sqrt{2}}{2}$ **b.** $\frac{\sqrt{2}}{2}$ **c.** $\frac{-\sqrt{2}}{2}$ **d.** $\frac{-\sqrt{2}}{2}$ **e.** $\frac{\sqrt{2}}{2}$ **f.** $\frac{-\sqrt{2}}{2}$ **g.** $\frac{\sqrt{2}}{2}$

**h.** $\frac{-\sqrt{2}}{2}$ **39. a.** $-1$ **b.** $1$ **c.** $0$ **d.** $0$

**41. a.** $\pm\frac{8}{9}$ **b.** $\pm\frac{6}{11}$ **c.** $\pm\frac{6}{7}$

**43.** $(0.7660, 0.6428)$ **45.** $(-0.9336, -0.3584)$
**47.** $(-0.4161, 0.9093)$ **49.** $(0.2837, -0.9589)$
**51.** 193.2 cm, 51.8 cm **53.** 50 cm right and 86.6 cm above center of circle
**55.** Answers will vary. **57.** about 32 mph
**59. a.** $\theta = 3.7$ **b.** $\mathcal{A} = 46.25 \text{ cm}^2$ **61.** $\pi - 3$

## Exercises 3.4, pp. 121–125

**1.** length; equal; radian; $t$; $\theta$ **3.** $x$; $y$; $\frac{y}{x}$; $\sec t$; $\csc t$; $\cot t$

**5.**

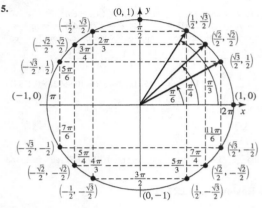

**7. a.** $\frac{\sqrt{3}}{2}$ **b.** $\frac{-\sqrt{3}}{2}$ **c.** $\frac{-\sqrt{3}}{2}$ **d.** $\frac{\sqrt{3}}{2}$ **e.** $\frac{\sqrt{3}}{2}$ **f.** $\frac{\sqrt{3}}{2}$

**g.** $\frac{-\sqrt{3}}{2}$ **h.** $\frac{\sqrt{3}}{2}$ **9. a.** 0 **b.** 0 **c.** undefined **d.** undefined

**11.** $\sin t = 0.6$, $\cos t = -0.8$, $\tan t = -0.75$, $\csc t = 1.\overline{6}$, $\sec t = -1.25$,
$\cot t = -1.\overline{3}$ **13.** $\sin t = -\frac{12}{13}$, $\cos t = -\frac{5}{13}$, $\tan t = \frac{12}{5}$, $\csc t = -\frac{13}{12}$,

$\sec t = -\frac{13}{5}$, $\cot t = \frac{5}{12}$ **15.** $\sin t = \frac{\sqrt{11}}{6}$, $\cos t = \frac{5}{6}$, $\tan t = \frac{\sqrt{11}}{5}$,

$\csc t = \frac{6\sqrt{11}}{11}$, $\sec t = \frac{6}{5}$, $\cot t = \frac{5\sqrt{11}}{11}$

**17.** $\sin t = \frac{\sqrt{21}}{5}$, $\cos t = \frac{-2}{5}$, $\tan t = \frac{-\sqrt{21}}{2}$, $\csc t = \frac{5\sqrt{21}}{21}$,

$\sec t = \frac{-5}{2}$, $\cot t = \frac{-2\sqrt{21}}{21}$ **19.** $\sin t = \frac{-2\sqrt{2}}{3}$, $\cos t = \frac{-1}{3}$,

$\tan t = 2\sqrt{2}$, $\csc t = \frac{-3\sqrt{2}}{4}$, $\sec t = -3$, $\cot t = \frac{\sqrt{2}}{4}$

**21.** $\sin t = \frac{\sqrt{3}}{2}$, $\cos t = \frac{1}{2}$, $\tan t = \sqrt{3}$, $\csc t = \frac{2\sqrt{3}}{3}$, $\sec t = 2$,

$\cot t = \frac{\sqrt{3}}{3}$ **23.** $\sin t = \frac{\sqrt{2}}{2}$, $\cos t = \frac{-\sqrt{2}}{2}$, $\tan t = -1$, $\csc t = \sqrt{2}$,

$\sec t = -\sqrt{2}$, $\cot t = -1$ **25.** QI, 0.7 **27.** QIV, 0.7 **29.** QI, 1

**31.** QII, 1.1 **33.** QII, −0.4 **35.** QIV, −3.1 **37.** $\frac{2\pi}{3}$ **39.** $\frac{7\pi}{6}$

**41.** $\frac{2\pi}{3}$ **43.** $\frac{\pi}{2}$ **45.** $\frac{3\pi}{4}, \frac{5\pi}{4}$ **47.** $\frac{\pi}{2}, \frac{3\pi}{2}$ **49.** $\frac{3\pi}{4}, \frac{5\pi}{4}$

**51.** $0, \pi$ **53.** 0.3273 **55.** 4.5695 **57.** 2.4608 **59.** 5.7510
**61.** 2.3416 **63.** 1.7832 **65.** 3.5416 **67. a.** $\left(\frac{3}{4}, \frac{4}{5}\right)$ **b.** $\left(\frac{-3}{4}, \frac{4}{5}\right)$

**69. a.** $-\frac{5\pi}{4}, -\frac{3\pi}{4}, -\frac{\pi}{4}, \frac{\pi}{4}, \frac{3\pi}{4}, \frac{5\pi}{4}, \frac{7\pi}{4}$

**b.** tangent: $(3k+1)\frac{\pi}{3}$; cotangent: $(6k+1)\frac{\pi}{6}$ **71. a.** 5 rad **b.** 30 rad

**73. a.** 5 dm **b.** $\approx 6.28$ dm **75. a.** 2.5 AU **b.** $\approx 6.28$ AU
**77.** yes **79.** range of $\sin t$ and $\cos t$ is $[-1, 1]$
**81. a.** $2t \approx 2.2$ **b.** QI **c.** $\cos t \approx 0.5$ **d.** No **83.** $\approx 537.6 \text{ in}^2$

**85.** $\cos \theta = -\frac{20}{29}$, $\tan \theta = -\frac{21}{20}$, $\csc \theta = \frac{29}{21}$, $\sec \theta = -\frac{29}{20}$, $\cot \theta = -\frac{20}{21}$

**87.** $\sin \theta = -\frac{1}{2}$, $\cos \theta = \frac{\sqrt{3}}{2}$, $\tan \theta = -\frac{\sqrt{3}}{3}$, $\csc \theta = -2$, $\sec \theta = \frac{2\sqrt{3}}{3}$,

$\cot \theta = -\sqrt{3}$

## Summary and Concept Review, pp. 125–127

**1.** 3 rad  **2.** 114.6°  **3.** −1.76  **4.** 120°

**5.** $\dfrac{7\pi}{6}$  **6.** $-\dfrac{19\pi}{5}, -\dfrac{9\pi}{5}, \dfrac{11\pi}{5}, \dfrac{21\pi}{5}$

**7.** approx. 4.97 units  **8.** $s = 25.5$ cm, $A = 191.25$ cm$^2$

**9.** $r \approx 41.74$ in., $A \approx 2003.48$ in$^2$  **10.** $\theta = 4.75$ rad, $s = 38$ m

**11. a.** approx. 9.4248 rad/sec  **b.** approx. 3.9 ft/sec  **c.** about 15.4 sec

**12.** $y = -\dfrac{6}{7}, \left(-\dfrac{\sqrt{13}}{7}, \dfrac{6}{7}\right), \left(-\dfrac{\sqrt{13}}{7}, -\dfrac{6}{7}\right),$ and $\left(\dfrac{\sqrt{13}}{7}, \dfrac{6}{7}\right)$

**13.** $\dfrac{\pi}{3}; \left(-\dfrac{1}{2}, \dfrac{\sqrt{3}}{2}\right)$  **14.** $-\dfrac{1}{2}$  **15.** 0.9004  **16.** (0.9602, −0.2794)

**17.** $\sin t = -\dfrac{\sqrt{7}}{4}$, $\csc t = -\dfrac{4}{\sqrt{7}}$, $\cos t = \dfrac{3}{4}$, $\sec t = \dfrac{4}{3}$,

$\tan t = -\dfrac{\sqrt{7}}{3}$, $\cot t = -\dfrac{3}{\sqrt{7}}$

**18.** $\dfrac{\pi}{3}$ and $\dfrac{2\pi}{3}$  **19.** $t \approx 2.44$  **20. a.** approx. 19.6667 rad  **b.** 25 rad

## Mixed Review , pp. 127–128

**1.** $t = \dfrac{\pi}{4}$ and $t = \dfrac{5\pi}{4}$

**3.** arc length: $\dfrac{28}{3}\pi \approx 29.3$ units; area: $\dfrac{112\pi}{3} \approx 117.3$ units$^2$

**5.** $x^2 + y^2 = 1$ is the unit circle.

$\left(\dfrac{-\sqrt{2}}{2}\right)^2 + \left(\dfrac{\sqrt{2}}{2}\right)^2 = \dfrac{2}{4} + \dfrac{2}{4} = 1$, $\sin \theta = \dfrac{\sqrt{2}}{2}$,

$\tan \theta = -1$, $\sec \theta = -\sqrt{2}$,

$\cos \theta = \dfrac{-\sqrt{2}}{2}$, $\csc \theta = \dfrac{2}{\sqrt{2}} = \sqrt{2}$, $\cot \theta = -1$

**7.** $-\dfrac{\sqrt{2}}{2}$  **9. a.** $-\dfrac{3\pi}{4}$  **b.** 4.5047  **11. a.** 420°  **b.** −28.6°

**13.** $-\dfrac{25\pi}{7}, -\dfrac{11\pi}{7}, \dfrac{17\pi}{7}, \dfrac{31\pi}{7}$  **15.** $\mathcal{A} = 22.45$ m$^2$

**17.** approx. 226.2 kph  **19.** (−0.3857, 0.9226)

## Practice Test , pp. 128–129

**1. a.** $\dfrac{\pi}{6}$  **b.** $\dfrac{\pi}{3}$

**2.**

| $t$ | $\sin t$ | $\cos t$ | $\tan t$ | $\csc t$ | $\sec t$ | $\cot t$ |
|---|---|---|---|---|---|---|
| 0 | 0 | 1 | 0 | undefined | 1 | undefined |
| $\dfrac{2\pi}{3}$ | $\dfrac{\sqrt{3}}{2}$ | $-\dfrac{1}{2}$ | $-\sqrt{3}$ | $\dfrac{2\sqrt{3}}{3}$ | $-2$ | $\dfrac{-\sqrt{3}}{3}$ |
| $\dfrac{7\pi}{6}$ | $-\dfrac{1}{2}$ | $-\dfrac{\sqrt{3}}{2}$ | $\dfrac{\sqrt{3}}{3}$ | $-2$ | $\dfrac{-2\sqrt{3}}{3}$ | $\sqrt{3}$ |
| $\dfrac{5\pi}{4}$ | $-\dfrac{\sqrt{2}}{2}$ | $-\dfrac{\sqrt{2}}{2}$ | 1 | $-\sqrt{2}$ | $-\sqrt{2}$ | 1 |
| $\dfrac{5\pi}{3}$ | $-\dfrac{\sqrt{3}}{2}$ | $\dfrac{1}{2}$ | $-\sqrt{3}$ | $\dfrac{-2\sqrt{3}}{3}$ | 2 | $\dfrac{-\sqrt{3}}{3}$ |
| $\dfrac{7\pi}{4}$ | $\dfrac{-\sqrt{2}}{2}$ | $\dfrac{\sqrt{2}}{2}$ | $-1$ | $-\sqrt{2}$ | $\sqrt{2}$ | $-1$ |
| $\dfrac{13\pi}{6}$ | $\dfrac{1}{2}$ | $\dfrac{\sqrt{3}}{2}$ | $\dfrac{\sqrt{3}}{3}$ | 2 | $\dfrac{2\sqrt{3}}{3}$ | $\sqrt{3}$ |

**3.** $\left(\dfrac{1}{3}\right)^2 + \left(-\dfrac{2\sqrt{2}}{3}\right)^2 = \dfrac{1}{9} + \dfrac{8}{9} = 1$; $\sin \theta = \dfrac{-2\sqrt{2}}{3}$, $\cos \theta = \dfrac{1}{3}$,

$\tan \theta = -2\sqrt{2}$, $\csc \theta = \dfrac{-3\sqrt{2}}{4}$, $\sec \theta = 3$, $\cot \theta = \dfrac{-\sqrt{2}}{4}$

**4. a.** $\approx 225.8$ ft or 225 ft 9.6 in.  **b.** $\dfrac{23\pi}{480} \approx 0.1505$ rad/sec

**c.** 11.29 ft/sec $\approx 7.7$ mph

**5. a.** $\dfrac{7\pi}{6}$  **b.** $\dfrac{11\pi}{6}$  **c.** $\dfrac{3\pi}{4}$

**6.** about 600.6 km

**7.** $\left(-\dfrac{20}{29}, \dfrac{21}{29}\right), \left(-\dfrac{20}{29}, -\dfrac{21}{29}\right), \left(\dfrac{20}{29}, -\dfrac{21}{29}\right)$

**8.** about 26.3 cm  **9. a.** $\approx 4$  **b.** $\approx 2.3$

**10. a.** $\dfrac{5\pi}{3}$  **b.** −1.2680  **c.** 0.0548  **11. a.** 532.3°  **b.** −270°

**c.** 2578.3°  **12. a.** 0.9 mph,  **b.** 10.7 mph  **13.** 120.3°  **14.** 3.5 ft$^2$

**15.** $t = \pi k, k \in \mathbb{Z}$  **16. a.** QI  **b.** QIV  **c.** QIII  **d.** QII

**17.** 10.2°  **18.** 50 min  **19.** (−0.6046, −0.7966)

**20.** $-\dfrac{41\pi}{9}, -\dfrac{23\pi}{9}, \dfrac{13\pi}{9}, \dfrac{31\pi}{9}$

## Strengthening Core Skills, p. 131

**1.** $\left(-\dfrac{1}{2}, \dfrac{\sqrt{3}}{2}\right)$, $\cos t = -\dfrac{1}{2}$, $\sin t = \dfrac{\sqrt{3}}{2}$  **2.** $t = \dfrac{5\pi}{6}$, negative since $x < 0$

**3.** QIV, negative since $y < 0$  **4.** QI, $\cos t = \dfrac{1}{2}$, $\sin t = \dfrac{\sqrt{3}}{2}$, $t = \dfrac{\pi}{3}$

## Cumulative Review Chapters 1–3, pp. 131–132

**1.** $t = \dfrac{7\pi}{6}, \dfrac{11\pi}{6}$  **3.** 22°37′21″  **5.** $A = 72°, B = 52°, C = 56°$

**7.** 1.0253  **9.** $\cos \theta = -\dfrac{5\sqrt{89}}{89}$, $\sin \theta = -\dfrac{8\sqrt{89}}{89}$, $\tan \theta = \dfrac{8}{5}$,

$\sec \theta = -\dfrac{\sqrt{89}}{5}$, $\csc \theta = -\dfrac{\sqrt{89}}{8}$, $\cot \theta = \dfrac{5}{8}$

**11.**

| Angles | Sides |
|---|---|
| $A = 30°$ | $a = 7$ ft |
| $B = 60°$ | $b \approx 12.12$ ft |
| $C = 90°$ | $c = 14$ ft |

**13. a.** $\dfrac{504\pi}{1 \text{ min}}$  **b.** $\approx 3$ mph

**15.** $\dfrac{\sin x \cos x + \cos x}{\sin x + \sin^2 x} = \dfrac{\cos x(\sin x + 1)}{\sin x\,(1 + \sin x)}$

$= \dfrac{\cos x}{\sin x}$

$= \cot x$

**17. a.** $S = 18$ m  **b.** $\mathcal{A} = 135$ m$^2$  **19.** −80°, −440°

**21.** approx. 1313 mi  **23.** QIV  **25. a.** 1  **b.** undefined
**c.** undefined  **d.** 0

# CHAPTER 4
## Exercises 4.1, pp. 145–150

**1.** increasing   **3.** $(-\infty, \infty)$; $[-1, 1]$   **5.** Answers will vary.

**7.**

| $t$ | $y = \cos t$ |
|---|---|
| $\pi$ | $-1$ |
| $\dfrac{7\pi}{6}$ | $\dfrac{\sqrt{3}}{2}$ |
| $\dfrac{5\pi}{4}$ | $\dfrac{\sqrt{2}}{2}$ |
| $\dfrac{4\pi}{3}$ | $-\dfrac{1}{2}$ |
| $\dfrac{3\pi}{2}$ | $0$ |
| $\dfrac{5\pi}{3}$ | $\dfrac{1}{2}$ |
| $\dfrac{7\pi}{4}$ | $\dfrac{\sqrt{2}}{2}$ |
| $\dfrac{11\pi}{6}$ | $\dfrac{\sqrt{3}}{2}$ |
| $2\pi$ | $1$ |

**9. a.** II   **b.** V   **c.** IV   **d.** I   **e.** III

**11.**    **13.**

**15.** $|A| = 3, P = 2\pi$   **17.** $|A| = 2, P = 2\pi$

**19.** $|A| = \frac{1}{2}, P = 2\pi$   **21.** $|A| = 1, P = \pi$

**23.** $|A| = 0.8, P = \pi$   **25.** $|A| = 4, P = 4\pi$

**27.** $|A| = 3, P = \frac{1}{2}$   **29.** $|A| = 4, P = \frac{6}{5}$

**31.** $|A| = 2, P = \frac{1}{128}$

**33.** $|A| = 2, P = \dfrac{\pi}{2}$, g   **35.** $|A| = 3, P = \pi$, f   **37.** $|A| = \frac{3}{4}, P = 5\pi$, b

**39.** $|A| = 4, P = \frac{1}{72}$, d   **41.** $y = -\frac{3}{4}\cos(8t)$

**43.** $y = 6\cos\left(\dfrac{2\pi}{3}t\right)$   **45.** $y = 3\sin(\frac{1}{5}t)$   **47.** $y = -\frac{3}{22}\sin(10\pi t)$

**49.** red: $y = -\cos x$; blue: $y = \sin x$; $x = \dfrac{3\pi}{4}, \dfrac{7\pi}{4}$

**51.** red: $y = -2\cos x$; blue: $y = 2\sin(3x)$;
$x = \dfrac{3\pi}{8}, \dfrac{3\pi}{4}, \dfrac{7\pi}{8}, \dfrac{11\pi}{8}, \dfrac{7\pi}{4}, \dfrac{15\pi}{8}$

**53.   a.** $100\pi \text{ cm}^2 \approx 314.2 \text{ cm}^2$   **b.** $200 \text{ cm}^2$; it is a square.

**c.**

| $n$ | $A$ |
|---|---|
| 10 | 293.89 |
| 20 | 309.02 |
| 30 | 311.87 |
| 100 | 313.95 |

The area of the polygon seems to be approaching the area of the circle.

**55. a.** 3 ft   **b.** 80 mi   **c.** $h = 1.5\cos\left(\dfrac{\pi}{40}x\right)$   **57. a.** $D = -4\cos\left(\dfrac{\pi}{12}t\right)$

**b.** $D \approx 3.86$   **c.** 72°   **59. a.** $D = 15\cos(\pi t)$   **b.** at center
**c.** Swimming leisurely. One complete cycle in 2 sec!   **61. a.** Graph a
**b.** 76 days   **c.** 96 days   **63. a.** 480 nm → blue   **b.** 620 nm → orange
**65.** $I = 30\sin(50\pi t)$, $I \approx 21.2$ amps

**67.** Since $m = -M$, 0;

| $t$ | $y$ |
|---|---|
| 0 | 3 |
| $\dfrac{\pi}{2}$ | 5 |
| $\pi$ | 3 |
| $\dfrac{3\pi}{2}$ | 1 |
| $2\pi$ | 3 |

avg. value $= 3$; shifted up 3 units;
avg. value $= 1$; amplitude is
"centered" on average value.

**69.** $g(t)$ has the shortest period;

**71.** about 3196 mi   **73.** $d = \dfrac{200\sqrt{3}}{3} \approx 115.5$ yd   **75.** about 282 ft 3 in.

## Exercises 4.2, pp. 160–165

**1.** $\pi$; $P = \dfrac{\pi}{|B|}$   **3.** odd; $-f(t)$; $-0.268$   **5. a.** Use reciprocals of standard
values.   **b.** Use reciprocals of given values.

**7.**    **9.**

**11.** 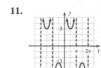 **13.**

**15.** $0, \dfrac{1}{\sqrt{3}}, 1, \sqrt{3},$ und.  **17.** 1.6, 0.8, 0.5, 1.4, 0.7, 1.2

**19. a.** $-1$  **b.** $\sqrt{3}$  **c.** $-1$  **d.** $\sqrt{3}$

**21. a.** $\dfrac{7\pi}{4}$  **b.** $\dfrac{7\pi}{6}$  **c.** $\dfrac{5\pi}{3}$  **d.** $\dfrac{3\pi}{4}$  **23.** und., $\sqrt{3}, 1, \dfrac{1}{\sqrt{3}}, 0$

**25.** $\dfrac{-13\pi}{24}, \dfrac{35\pi}{24}, \dfrac{59\pi}{24}$  **27.** $-1.6, 4.6, 7.8$  **29.** $\dfrac{\pi}{10} + \pi k, k \in Z$

**31.** $\dfrac{\pi}{12} + \pi k, k \in Z$

**33.**  **35.**

**37.** 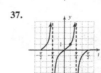 **39.**

**41.**  **43.**

**45.**  **47.**

**49.** $P = 4\pi,$ b  **51.** $P = \frac{1}{4},$ d  **53.** $y = 2\csc(5\pi t)$

**55.** $y = 3\tan\left(\dfrac{1}{2}t\right)$  **57.** $y = 2\cot\left(\dfrac{2\pi}{3}t\right)$  **59.** $\dfrac{\pi}{8}, \dfrac{3\pi}{8}$  **61.** about 137.8 ft

**63. a.** $20\pi$ cm $\approx 62.8$ cm  **b.** 80 cm; it is a square

**c.**

| n | P |
|---|---|
| 10 | 64.984 |
| 20 | 63.354 |
| 30 | 63.063 |
| 100 | 62.853 |

getting close to $20\pi$

**65.**

**a.** no; $\approx 35°$  **b.** 1.05  **c.** Angles will be greater than 68.2°; soft rubber on sandstone  **67. a.** 5.67 units  **b.** 86.5°  **c.** Yes. Range of $\tan\theta$ is $(-\infty, \infty)$.  **d.** The closer $\theta$ gets to 90°, the longer the line segment gets.

**69. a.** $A = 4 \cdot 4^2 \sin\dfrac{\pi}{4}\sec\dfrac{\pi}{4} = 64$ m$^2$  **b.** $A \approx 51.45$ m$^2$

**71.** $\sin 0.6662394325 = 0.6180339887 \approx \dfrac{-1 + \sqrt{5}}{2};\ \cos x = \tan x$ can be rewritten as $\sin^2 x = 1 - \sin x$, which can in turn be converted to $\sin^2(-x) = 1 + \sin(-x)$, which is the basis of the golden ratio.

**73.** $\sqrt{12}$ ft $\approx 3.46$ ft  **75.** $\theta$ in QII, $\theta_r = \dfrac{\pi}{6};\ -\cos\left(\dfrac{\pi}{6}\right) = \dfrac{-\sqrt{3}}{2}$

**77.** 328°

## Mid-Chapter Check, pp. 165–166

**1.** $y = \cot t; y = \cos t$  **2.** $P = 4,$ at $t = 1$ and $t = 3$  **3. a.** $\dfrac{1}{\sqrt{3}}$

**b.** $\dfrac{-\sqrt{2}}{2}$  **4. a.** $\approx 1.0353$  **b.** $\approx 2.2858$  **5.** $y = \cos t$ and $y = \sec t$

**6.** $t \in (-\infty, \infty); t \neq \dfrac{\pi}{2}k, k \in Z$

**7.** asymptotes: $x = -5, -3, -1, 1, 3, 5$  **8.** $|A| = 3, P = 4;$

**9. a.** QIV  **b.** $2\pi - 5.94 \approx 0.343$  **c.** $\sin t, \tan t$

**10. a.** $|A| = 6, P = \dfrac{3\pi}{4}$  **b.** $f(t) = -6\cos\left(\dfrac{8}{3}t\right)$  **c.** $f(\pi) = 3$

## Exercises 4.3, pp. 176–179

**1.** $y = A\sin(Bt + C) + D; y = A\cos(Bt + C) + D$

**3.** up; right  **5.** Answers will vary.

**7.**  **9.**

**11.** 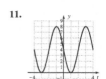 **13.**

**15.**  **17.**

**19.**  **21.**

**23.** $|A| = 120; P = 24;$ HS: 6 units right; VS: (none); PI: $6 \leq t < 30$
**25.** $|A| = 1; P = 12;$ HS: 2 units right; VS: (none); PI: $2 \leq t < 14$
**27.** $|A| = 1; P = 8;$ HS: $\frac{2}{3}$ unit right; VS: (none); PI: $\frac{2}{3} \leq t < \frac{26}{3}$
**29.** $|A| = 24.5; P = 20;$ HS: 2.5 units right; VS: 15.5 units up; PI: $2.5 \leq t < 22.5$  **31.** $|A| = 28; P = 12;$ HS: $\frac{5}{2}$ units right; VS: 92 units up; PI: $\frac{5}{2} \leq t < \frac{29}{2}$  **33.** $|A| = 2500; P = 8;$ HS: $\frac{1}{3}$ unit left; VS: 3150 units up; PI: $-\frac{1}{3} \leq t < \frac{23}{3}$

**35.** $y = 250 \sin\left(\frac{\pi}{12}t\right) + 350$      **37.** $y = 5 \sin\left(\frac{\pi}{50}t + \frac{\pi}{2}\right) + 13$

**39.** $y = 4 \sin\left(\frac{\pi}{180}t + \frac{\pi}{4}\right) + 7$

**41.**       **43.**

**45.**       **47.**

**49. a.** 2.5   **b.** $\frac{24}{\pi}$   **c.** $\frac{24}{\pi}$   **51. a.** 24 hr   **b.** 18°, 26°   **c.** $t = 3, t = 15$

**53. a.** 6 sec   **b.** 5.2 ft   **55. a.** 80 sec   **b.** approx. 15 sec.   **c.** 3 mi

**57. a.** Caracas: $\approx$ 11.4 hr, Tokyo: $\approx$ 9.9 hr   **b.** (i) Same # of hours on 79th day & 261st day (ii) Caracas: $\approx$ 81 days, Tokyo: $\approx$ 158 days

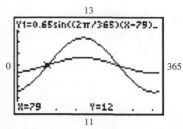

**59. a.** Adds 12 hr. The sinusoidal behavior is actually based on hours more/less than an average of 12 hr of light.   **b.** Means 12 hr of light and dark on March 20, day 79 (Solstice!).   **c.** Additional hours of deviation from average. In the north, the planet is tilted closer toward the Sun or farther from Sun, depending on date. Variations will be greater!

**61.** 12   **63.** 2.5 rad   **65. a.** $\approx$137.4 ft   **b.** $\approx$18.7 miles per hour

**67.**

## Exercises 4.4, pp. 185–190

**1.** $\sin(Bx + C)$; $A$   **3.** minimum; maximum

**5.** Answers will vary.   **7. a.** $|A| = 50, P = 24$   **b.** $\approx -25$
**c.** [1.6, 10.4]   **9. a.** $|A| = 200, P = 3$   **b.** $-175$   **c.** [1.75, 2.75]

**11.** $y = 40 \sin\left(\frac{\pi}{15}t\right) + 60$      **13.** $y = 8 \sin\left(\frac{\pi}{180}t\right) + 12$

**15.** $\frac{1}{4}$   **17.** $\frac{1}{\pi}$   **19.** $\frac{2}{3\pi}$

**21.** $P = \frac{2\pi}{B}, B = \frac{2\pi}{P}; f = \frac{1}{P}, P = \frac{1}{f}; B = \frac{2\pi}{1/f} = 2\pi f;$

$A \sin(Bt) = A \sin[(2\pi f)t]$   **23. a.** $P = 4$ sec, $f = \frac{1}{4}$ cycle/sec

**b.** $-4.24$ cm, moving away   **c.** $-4.24$ cm, moving toward

**d.** about 1.76 cm. avg. vel. $= 3.52$ cm/sec, greater, still gaining speed

**25.** $d(t) = 15 \cos\left(\frac{5\pi}{4}t\right)$   **27.** red $\rightarrow D_2$; blue $\rightarrow A\#_2$

**29.** $D_2: y = \sin[146.84 \, (2\pi t)]; P \approx 0.0068$ sec;
$G_3: y = \sin[392 \, (2\pi t)]; P \approx 0.00255$ sec

**31. a.** $y = 5 \sin\left(\frac{\pi}{12}t\right) + 34$

**b.** 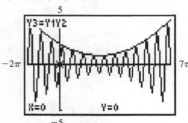   **c.** $\approx$ 1:30 A.M., 10:30 A.M.

**33. a.** $y = -6.4 \cos\left(\frac{\pi}{6}t\right) + 12.4$   **b.**

**c.** $\approx$ 134 days

**35. a.** $P = 11$ yr   **b.**

**c.** max $= 1200$, min $= 700$   **d.** about 2 yr

**37.** $P(t) = 250 \cos\left[\frac{2\pi}{11}(t - 2.75)\right] + 950; P(t) = 250 \sin\left(\frac{2\pi}{11}t\right) + 950$

**39.** $y = 5.2 \tan\left(\frac{\pi}{12}x\right); P = 12$; asymptotes at $x = 6 + 12k, k \in \mathbb{Z}$; using
$(3, 5.2), |A| = 5.2$; at $x = 2$, model gives $y \approx 3.002$; at $x = -2$, model
gives $y \approx -3.002$; answers will vary.   **41.** Answers will vary;
$y = 11.95 \tan \theta; P = 180°$; asymptotes at $\theta = 90° + 180°k$; $|A| = 11.95$
from $(30°, 6.9$ cm$)$; pen is $\approx$ 12 cm long.

**43. a.** $L(t) = 10 \csc\left(\frac{\pi}{6}t\right)$   **b.** 20 m   **45.** Answers will vary.

**47.** the dampening factor is quadratic, $f(x) \approx 0.02x^2 - 0.32x + 2.28$,
$Y_1 = \sin(3x), Y_2 = 0.02x^2 - 0.32x + 2.28, x \in [-2\pi, 7\pi], y \in [-5, 5]$

**49.** $t = \frac{\pi}{3}, \frac{2\pi}{3}, \frac{4\pi}{3}, \frac{5\pi}{3}$   **51.** $y = \sec\left(x - \frac{\pi}{3}\right)$

**53.** $2 \times \frac{1}{2}(24^2)\left(\frac{7\pi}{36}\right) = 112\pi$ in$^2$

## Summary and Concept Review, pp. 190–193

**1.** $|A| = 3, P = 2\pi$

**2.** $|A| = 1, P = \pi$

**3.** $|A| = 1.7, P = \dfrac{\pi}{2}$

**4.** $|A| = 2, P = \dfrac{1}{2}$

**5.** $|A| = 3, P = \dfrac{1}{199}$

**6.** $y = 0.75 \sin(6t)$    **7.** green; red

**8.** $P = 2\pi$

**9.** $y = 4 \csc(3\pi t)$    **10. a.** $\tan\left(\dfrac{7\pi}{4}\right) = -1$;    **b.** $\cot\left(\dfrac{\pi}{3}\right) = \dfrac{1}{\sqrt{3}}$

**11. a.** $\theta = \dfrac{2\pi}{3}$;    **b.** $\theta = \dfrac{2\pi}{3}$

**12.**

**13.**

**14.** $1.55 + k\pi$ radians; $k \in Z$    **15.** $3.5860$    **16.** $\approx 151.14$ m

**17. a.** $|A| = 240, P = 12$, HS: 3 units right, VS: 520 units up
**b.**

**18. a.** $|A| = 3.2, P = 8$, HS: 6 units left, VS: 6.4 units up
**b.**

**19.** $|A| = 125, P = 24$, HS: 3 units right, VS: 175 units up,

$y = 125 \cos\left[\dfrac{\pi}{12}(t - 3)\right] + 175$    **20.** $A = 75, P = \dfrac{3\pi}{8}$, HS: (none), VS:

105 units up,    $y = 75 \sin\left(\dfrac{16}{3}t\right) + 105$

**21.** $y = \sin[370(2\pi t)]$; $P \approx 0.0027$ sec

**22. a.** $P(t) = 0.91 \sin\left(\dfrac{\pi}{6}t\right) + 1.35$    **b.** Aug: 1.81 in.,

Dec: 0.44 in.    **23.** $y = 5.2 \tan\left(\dfrac{\pi}{12}x\right)$; period $= 12$; $A = 5.2$;

asymptotes $x = -6, x = 6$

## Mixed Review, p. 194

**1.** $f(t) = 10\sin(2t)$    **3. a.** $A = 10$    **b.** $D = 15$    **c.** $P = 6$

**d.** $f(4) = 20$    **5.** $y = -2\cot\left[\dfrac{3}{2}\left(x + \dfrac{\pi}{3}\right)\right]$, other solutions are possible.

**7.**

**9.**

**11.**

**13. a.** $P(t) = 1.63 \sin\left(\dfrac{\pi}{6}t\right) + 2.42$    **b.** July: 4.05 in.,  Dec: 1.01 in.

**15. a.** $\dfrac{1}{12}$    **b.** $\dfrac{4}{3\pi}$

**17.** $|A| = 5; P = \pi$;
HS: (none);
VS: 8 units down;
PI: $0 \le t < \pi$

**19.** $P = 4\pi$; no horizontal shift

## Practice Test, pp. 195–196

**1.**

| $t$ | $\sin t$ | $\cos t$ | $\tan t$ | $\csc t$ | $\sec t$ | $\cot t$ | $P(x, y)$ |
|---|---|---|---|---|---|---|---|
| $0$ | $0$ | $1$ | $0$ | — | $1$ | — | $(1, 0)$ |
| $\dfrac{\pi}{6}$ | $\dfrac{1}{2}$ | $\dfrac{\sqrt{3}}{2}$ | $\dfrac{\sqrt{3}}{3}$ | $2$ | $\dfrac{2\sqrt{3}}{3}$ | $\sqrt{3}$ | $\left(\dfrac{\sqrt{3}}{2}, \dfrac{1}{2}\right)$ |
| $\dfrac{\pi}{4}$ | $\dfrac{\sqrt{2}}{2}$ | $\dfrac{\sqrt{2}}{2}$ | $1$ | $\sqrt{2}$ | $\sqrt{2}$ | $1$ | $\left(\dfrac{\sqrt{2}}{2}, \dfrac{\sqrt{2}}{2}\right)$ |
| $\dfrac{\pi}{2}$ | $1$ | $0$ | — | $1$ | — | $0$ | $(0, 1)$ |
| $\dfrac{2\pi}{3}$ | $\dfrac{\sqrt{3}}{2}$ | $-\dfrac{1}{2}$ | $-\sqrt{3}$ | $\dfrac{2\sqrt{3}}{3}$ | $-2$ | $-\dfrac{\sqrt{3}}{3}$ | $\left(-\dfrac{1}{2}, \dfrac{\sqrt{3}}{2}\right)$ |
| $\dfrac{5\pi}{6}$ | $\dfrac{1}{2}$ | $-\dfrac{\sqrt{3}}{2}$ | $-\dfrac{\sqrt{3}}{3}$ | $2$ | $-\dfrac{2\sqrt{3}}{3}$ | $-\sqrt{3}$ | $\left(-\dfrac{\sqrt{3}}{2}, \dfrac{1}{2}\right)$ |
| $\dfrac{5\pi}{4}$ | $-\dfrac{\sqrt{2}}{2}$ | $-\dfrac{\sqrt{2}}{2}$ | $1$ | $-\sqrt{2}$ | $-\sqrt{2}$ | $1$ | $\left(-\dfrac{\sqrt{2}}{2}, -\dfrac{\sqrt{2}}{2}\right)$ |
| $\dfrac{4\pi}{3}$ | $-\dfrac{\sqrt{3}}{2}$ | $-\dfrac{1}{2}$ | $\sqrt{3}$ | $-\dfrac{2\sqrt{3}}{3}$ | $-2$ | $\dfrac{\sqrt{3}}{3}$ | $\left(-\dfrac{1}{2}, -\dfrac{\sqrt{3}}{2}\right)$ |
| $\dfrac{3\pi}{2}$ | $-1$ | $0$ | — | $-1$ | — | $0$ | $(0, -1)$ |

**2. a.** 0   **b.** 0   **c.** 1   **d.** $\dfrac{2\sqrt{3}}{3}$   **3. a.** $\dfrac{\pi}{3}$   **b.** $\dfrac{2\pi}{3}$   **c.** $\dfrac{4\pi}{3}$   **d.** $\dfrac{7\pi}{4}$

**4.** $|A| = 3, P = 10$    **5.** no amplitude, $P = \pi$

**6.** no amplitude, $P = \dfrac{\pi}{3}$    **7.** $|A| = 12, P = \dfrac{2\pi}{3}$, HS: $\dfrac{\pi}{6}$ right,
VS: 19 units up

**8.** $|A| = \dfrac{3}{4}, P = 4$, HS: 0,    **9.** no amplitude, $P = 3$, HS: $\dfrac{3}{2}$ right,
VS: $\dfrac{1}{2}$ unit down     VS: none

**10. a.** 6 or $6,000   **b.** January through July   **11.** $t \approx 1.11, t \approx 7.39$

**12.** $t \approx 4.6018$   **13. a.** $r(t) = 0.41 \sin\left[\dfrac{\pi}{6}(x + 2)\right] + 0.65$   **b.** January

**14.** $y = 5 \cos(6\pi t)$   **15.** $y = 7.5 \sin\left(\dfrac{\pi}{6}t - \dfrac{\pi}{2}\right) + 12.5$

**16.** $y = 2 \csc\left(\dfrac{\pi}{2}t\right) - 1$   **17.** a   **18.** c   **19.** b   **20.** d

### Strengthening Core Skills, pp. 197–198

**Exercise 1. a.** $h(t) = \sin\left(t + \dfrac{\pi}{2}\right) - 1$   **b.** $t = \dfrac{\pi}{4} + 2\pi k$

**Exercise 2. a.** $h(t) = \cos\left(t - \dfrac{\pi}{2}\right) - 1$   **b.** $t = -\dfrac{\pi}{6} + 2\pi k$

**Exercise 3. a.** $h(t) = 3 \sin\left(t + \dfrac{\pi}{2}\right) + 3$   **b.** $t = \left(\dfrac{3\pi}{2} + 0.7\right) + 2\pi k$

### Cumulative Review Chapters 1–4, pp. 198–199

**1.**

**3.** 73; approx. 41.1°, 48.9°

**5.** $\sin t = \dfrac{2\sqrt{2}}{3}, \cos t = -\dfrac{1}{3}, \tan t = -2\sqrt{2}, \csc t = \dfrac{3\sqrt{2}}{4}, \sec t = -3,$

$\cot t = -\dfrac{\sqrt{2}}{4}$   **7. a.** 35.7825°   **b.** approx 0.6245

**9.** $\left(\dfrac{13}{85}\right)^2 + \left(\dfrac{84}{85}\right)^2 = \dfrac{169}{7225} + \dfrac{7056}{7225} = 1, \left(-\dfrac{13}{85}, \dfrac{84}{85}\right),$

$\left(-\dfrac{13}{85}, -\dfrac{84}{85}\right), \left(\dfrac{13}{85}, -\dfrac{84}{85}\right)$   **11.** 26 m   **13.** $\sin t = -\dfrac{\sqrt{3}}{2}, \cos t = -\dfrac{1}{2},$

$\tan t = \sqrt{3}, \csc t = -\dfrac{2\sqrt{3}}{3}, \sec t = -2, \cot t = \dfrac{\sqrt{3}}{3}$   **15. a.** $\dfrac{\pi}{2}$ rad/sec

---

**b.** 22 in./sec   **17. a.** QIII   **b.** $4.22 - \pi \approx 1.08$   **c.** 1.8641

**19.** $y = \dfrac{3}{2} \sin\left(4t - \dfrac{\pi}{2}\right) + \dfrac{1}{2}$   **21.** false; $(\cos t)(\csc t) = \cot t$

**23.** $\sin t = -\dfrac{5}{13}, \cos t = \dfrac{12}{13}, \tan t = -\dfrac{5}{12}, \sec t = \dfrac{13}{12}, \cot t = -\dfrac{12}{5}$

**25. a.** $y = 5000 \sin\left(\dfrac{\pi}{3}x + \pi\right) + 9000$   **b.** $\approx$$4670   **c.** mid-October

## MODELING WITH TECHNOLOGY
### Modeling with Technology Exercises, pp. 207–210

**1.** $y = 25 \sin\left(\dfrac{\pi}{6}x\right) + 50$   **3.** $y = 2.25 \sin\left(\dfrac{\pi}{12}x + \dfrac{\pi}{4}\right) + 5.25$

**5.** $y = 503 \sin\left(\dfrac{\pi}{6}x + \dfrac{2\pi}{3}\right) + 782$

**7. a.** $T(x) = 19.6 \sin\left(\dfrac{\pi}{6}x + \dfrac{4\pi}{3}x\right) + 84.6$   **b.** about 94.4°F

**c.** beginning of May ($x \approx 5.1$) to end of August ($x \approx 8.9$)

**9. a.** $T(x) = 0.4 \sin\left(\dfrac{\pi}{12}x + \dfrac{13\pi}{12}\right) + 98.6$   **b.** at 11 A.M. and 11 P.M.

**c.** from $x = 1$ to $x = 9$, about 8 hr

**11.** $P = 12, B = \dfrac{\pi}{12}, C = \dfrac{\pi}{2}$; using (4, 3) gives $A = -3\sqrt{3}$, so

$f(x) = -3\sqrt{3} \tan\left(\dfrac{\pi}{12}x + \dfrac{\pi}{2}\right)$   **a.** $f(2.5) \approx 6.77$   **b.** $f(x) = 16$ for

$x \approx 1.20$   **13. a.** using (18, 10) gives $A \approx 4.14$; $H(d) = 4.14 \tan\left(\dfrac{\pi}{48}d\right)$

**b.** $\approx 12.2$ cm   **c.** $\approx 21.9$ mi

**15. a.** $y \approx 49.26 \sin(0.213x - 1.104) + 51.43$
**b.** $y \approx 49 \sin(0.203x - 0.963) + 51$   **c.** at day 31 $\approx 5.6$
**17. a.** $y \approx 5.88 \sin(0.523x - 0.521) + 16.00$
**b.** $y \approx 6 \sin(0.524x - 0.524) + 16$   **c.** at month 9 $\approx 0.12$
**19. a.** $T(m) \approx 15.328 \sin(0.461m - 1.610) + 85.244$

**b.**

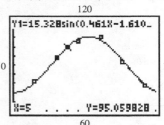

| Month | Temp. (°F) |
|---|---|
| 1 | 71 |
| 3 | 82 |
| 5 | 95 |
| 7 | 101 |
| 9 | 94 |
| 11 | 80 |

**c.** max difference is about 1°F in months 6 and 8
**21. a.** $f(x) \approx 49.659 \sin(0.214x - 0.689) + 48.328$   **b.** about 26.8%

**c.** $g(x) = 49.5 \sin\left(\dfrac{2\pi}{31}x - \dfrac{7\pi}{62}\right) + 49.5$; values for $A$, $B$, and $D$ are very

close; some variation in $C$.
**23. a.** Reno: $R(t) \approx 0.452 \sin(0.396t + 1.831) + 0.750$
**b.** The graphs intersect at $t \approx 2.6$ and $t \approx 10.5$. Reno gets more rainfall
than Cheyenne for about 4 months of the year: $2.6 + (12 - 10.5) = 4.1$

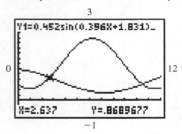

**25.** physical, $\dfrac{2\pi}{23}$; emotional, $\dfrac{\pi}{14}$; intellectual, $\dfrac{2\pi}{33}$; answers will vary.

# CHAPTER 5
## Exercises 5.1, pp. 216–219

**1.** identities; symmetry.   **3.** complicated; simplify; build.   **5.** Because we don't know if the equation is true.

**7.** $(1 + \sin x)[1 + \sin(-x)] = (1 + \sin x)(1 - \sin x) = 1 - \sin^2 x = \cos^2 x$

**9.** $\sin^2(-x) + \cos^2 x = (-\sin x)^2 + \cos^2 x = \sin^2 x + \cos^2 x = 1$

**11.** $\dfrac{1 - \sin(-x)}{\cos x + \cos(-x)\sin x} = \dfrac{1 + \sin x}{\cos x + \cos x \sin x} = \dfrac{1 + \sin x}{\cos x(1 + \sin x)}$

$= \dfrac{1}{\cos x} = \sec x$

**13.** $\cos^2 x \tan^2 x = \cos^2 x \dfrac{\sin^2 x}{\cos^2 x}$

$= \sin^2 x$

$= 1 - \cos^2 x$

**15.** $\tan x + \cot x = \dfrac{\sin x}{\cos x} + \dfrac{\cos x}{\sin x}$

$= \dfrac{\sin^2 x + \cos^2 x}{\cos x \sin x}$

$= \dfrac{1}{\cos x \sin x}$

$= \dfrac{1}{\cos x}\dfrac{1}{\sin x}$

$= \sec x \csc x$

**17.** $\csc x - \sin x = \dfrac{1}{\sin x} - \sin x$

$= \dfrac{1 - \sin^2 x}{\sin x}$

$= \dfrac{\cos^2 x}{\sin x}$

$= \dfrac{\cos x}{\sin x / \cos x}$

$= \dfrac{\cos x}{\tan x}$

**19.** $\sec \theta + \tan \theta = \dfrac{1}{\cos \theta} + \dfrac{\sin \theta}{\cos \theta}$

$= \dfrac{1 + \sin \theta}{\cos \theta}$

$= \dfrac{(1 + \sin \theta)(1 - \sin \theta)}{\cos \theta(1 - \sin \theta)}$

$= \dfrac{1 - \sin^2 \theta}{\cos \theta(1 - \sin \theta)}$

$= \dfrac{\cos^2 \theta}{\cos \theta(1 - \sin \theta)}$

$= \dfrac{\cos \theta}{1 - \sin \theta}$

**21.** $\dfrac{1 - \sin x}{\cos x} = \dfrac{(1 - \sin x)(1 + \sin x)}{\cos x(1 + \sin x)}$

$= \dfrac{1 - \sin^2 x}{\cos x(1 + \sin x)}$

$= \dfrac{\cos^2 x}{\cos x(1 + \sin x)}$

$= \dfrac{\cos x}{1 + \sin x}$

**23.** $\dfrac{\csc x}{\cos x} - \dfrac{\cos x}{\csc x} = \dfrac{\csc^2 x - \cos^2 x}{\cos x \csc x}$

$= \dfrac{\csc^2 x - (1 - \sin^2 x)}{\cos x \dfrac{1}{\sin x}}$

$= \dfrac{\csc^2 x - 1 + \sin^2 x}{\cot x}$

$= \dfrac{\cot^2 x + \sin^2 x}{\cot x}$

**25.** $\dfrac{\sin x}{1 + \sin x} - \dfrac{\sin x}{1 - \sin x} = \dfrac{\sin x(1 - \sin x) - \sin x(1 + \sin x)}{(1 + \sin x)(1 - \sin x)}$

$= \dfrac{\sin x - \sin^2 x - \sin x - \sin^2 x}{1 - \sin^2 x}$

$= \dfrac{-2 \sin^2 x}{\cos^2 x}$

$= -2 \tan^2 x$

**27.** $\dfrac{\cot x}{1 + \csc x} - \dfrac{\cot x}{1 - \csc x} = \dfrac{\cot x(1 - \csc x) - \cot x(1 + \csc x)}{(1 + \csc x)(1 - \csc x)}$

$= \dfrac{\cot x - \cot x \csc x - \cot x - \cot x \csc x}{1 - \csc^2 x}$

$= \dfrac{2 \cot x \csc x}{\cot^2 x}$

$= \dfrac{2 \csc x}{\cot x}$

$= \dfrac{2 \dfrac{1}{\sin x}}{\dfrac{\cos x}{\sin x}}$

$= \dfrac{2}{\cos x}$

$= 2 \sec x$

**29.** $\dfrac{\sec^2 x}{1 + \cot^2 x} = \dfrac{\sec^2 x}{\csc^2 x}$

$= \dfrac{\dfrac{1}{\cos^2 x}}{\dfrac{1}{\sin^2 x}}$

$= \dfrac{\sin^2 x}{\cos^2 x}$

$= \tan^2 x$

**31.** $\sin^2 x(\cot^2 x - \csc^2 x) = \sin^2 x \cot^2 x - \sin^2 x \csc^2 x$

$= \sin^2 x \dfrac{\cos^2 x}{\sin^2 x} - \sin^2 x \dfrac{1}{\sin^2 x}$

$= \cos^2 x - 1$

$= -\sin^2 x$

**33.** $\cos x \cot x + \sin x = \cos x \dfrac{\cos x}{\sin x} + \sin x$

$= \dfrac{\cos^2 x}{\sin x} + \sin x$

$= \dfrac{\cos^2 x + \sin^2 x}{\sin x}$

$= \dfrac{1}{\sin x}$

$= \csc x$

**35.** $\dfrac{\sec x}{\cot x + \tan x} = \dfrac{\dfrac{1}{\cos x}(\sin x)(\cos x)}{\left(\dfrac{\cos x}{\sin x} + \dfrac{\sin x}{\cos x}\right)(\sin x)(\cos x)}$

$= \dfrac{\sin x}{\cos^2 x + \sin^2 x}$

$= \dfrac{\sin x}{1}$

$= \sin x$

**37.** $\dfrac{\sin x - \csc x}{\csc x} = \dfrac{\sin x}{\csc x} - \dfrac{\csc x}{\csc x}$

$= \sin^2 x - 1$

$= -\cos^2 x$

**39.**
$$\frac{1}{\csc x - \sin x} = \frac{1}{(\csc x - \sin x)}\cdot\frac{\sin x}{\sin x}$$
$$= \frac{\sin x}{1 - \sin^2 x}$$
$$= \frac{\sin x}{\cos^2 x}$$
$$= \frac{\sin x}{\cos x}\cdot\frac{1}{\cos x}$$
$$= \tan x \sec x$$

**41.**
$$\frac{1 + \sin x}{1 - \sin x} = \frac{(1 + \sin x)}{(1 - \sin x)}\cdot\frac{(1 + \sin x)}{(1 + \sin x)}$$
$$= \frac{1 + 2\sin x + \sin^2 x}{1 - \sin^2 x}$$
$$= \frac{1 + 2\sin x + \sin^2 x}{\cos^2 x}$$
$$= \frac{1}{\cos^2 x} + 2\frac{\sin x}{\cos x}\cdot\frac{1}{\cos x} + \frac{\sin^2 x}{\cos^2 x}$$
$$= \sec^2 x + 2\tan x \sec x + \tan^2 x$$
$$= (\sec x + \tan x)^2$$
$$= (\tan x + \sec x)^2$$

**43.**
$$\frac{\cos x - \sin x}{1 - \tan x} = \frac{(\cos x - \sin x)}{(1 - \tan x)}\cdot\frac{(\cos x + \sin x)}{(\cos x + \sin x)}$$
$$= \frac{(\cos x - \sin x)(\cos x + \sin x)}{\cos x + \sin x - \sin x - \dfrac{\sin^2 x}{\cos x}}$$
$$= \frac{(\cos x - \sin x)(\cos x + \sin x)}{\cos x\left(1 - \dfrac{\sin^2 x}{\cos^2 x}\right)}$$
$$= \frac{(\cos x - \sin x)(\cos x + \sin x)}{\cos x(1 - \tan^2 x)}$$
$$= \frac{(\cos x - \sin x)(\cos x + \sin x)}{\cos x(1 - \tan x)(1 + \tan x)}$$
$$= \frac{\cancel{(\cos x - \sin x)}(\cos x + \sin x)}{\cancel{(\cos x - \sin x)}(1 + \tan x)}$$
$$= \frac{\cos x + \sin x}{1 + \tan x}$$

**45.**
$$\frac{\tan^2 x - \cot^2 x}{\tan x - \cot x} = \frac{(\tan x + \cot x)(\tan x - \cot x)}{(\tan x - \cot x)}$$
$$= \tan x + \cot x$$
$$= \frac{\sin x}{\cos x} + \frac{\cos x}{\sin x}$$
$$= \frac{\sin^2 x + \cos^2 x}{\cos x \sin x}$$
$$= \frac{1}{\cos x \sin x}$$
$$= \frac{1}{\cos x}\cdot\frac{1}{\sin x}$$
$$= \sec x \csc x$$
$$= \csc x \sec x$$

**47.**
$$\frac{\cot x}{\cot x + \tan x} = \frac{\dfrac{\cos x}{\sin x}}{\dfrac{\cos x}{\sin x} + \dfrac{\sin x}{\cos x}}\cdot\frac{(\cos x)(\sin x)}{(\cos x)(\sin x)}$$
$$= \frac{\cos^2 x}{\cos^2 x + \sin^2 x}$$
$$= \frac{\cos^2 x}{1}$$
$$= 1 - \sin^2 x$$

**49.**
$$\frac{\sec^4 x - \tan^4 x}{\sec^2 x + \tan^2 x} = \frac{(\sec^2 x - \tan^2 x)\cancel{(\sec^2 x + \tan^2 x)}}{\cancel{(\sec^2 x + \tan^2 x)}}$$
$$= \sec^2 x - \tan^2 x$$
$$= 1$$

**51.**
$$\frac{\cos^4 x - \sin^4 x}{\cos^2 x} = \frac{(\cos^2 x - \sin^2 x)(\cos^2 x + \sin^2 x)}{\cos^2 x}$$
$$= \frac{(\cos^2 x - \sin^2 x)(1)}{\cos^2 x}$$
$$= \frac{\cos^2 x}{\cos^2 x} - \frac{\sin^2 x}{\cos^2 x}$$
$$= 1 - \tan^2 x$$
$$= 1 - (\sec^2 x - 1)$$
$$= 1 - \sec^2 x + 1$$
$$= 2 - \sec^2 x$$

**53.**
$$(\sec x + \tan x)^2 = \sec^2 x + 2\sec x \tan x + \tan^2 x$$
$$= \frac{1}{\cos^2 x} + \frac{2\sin x}{\cos^2 x} + \frac{\sin^2 x}{\cos^2 x}$$
$$= \frac{1 + 2\sin x + \sin^2 x}{\cos^2 x}$$
$$= \frac{(1 + \sin x)^2}{\cos^2 x}$$
$$= \frac{(\sin x + 1)^2}{\cos^2 x}$$

**55.**
$$\frac{\cos x}{\sin x} + \frac{\sin x}{\cos x} + \frac{\csc x}{\sec x} = \frac{\cos^2 x \sec x + \sin^2 x \sec x + \csc x \sin x \cos x}{\sin x \cos x \sec x}$$
$$= \frac{\sec x(\cos^2 x + \sin^2 x) + (1)\cos x}{\sin x(1)}$$
$$= \frac{\sec x + \cos x}{\sin x}$$

**57.**
$$\frac{\sin^4 x - \cos^4 x}{\sin^3 x + \cos^3 x} = \frac{(\sin^2 x + \cos^2 x)(\sin^2 x - \cos^2 x)}{(\sin x + \cos x)(\sin^2 x - \sin x \cos x + \cos^2 x)}$$
$$= \frac{(1)\cancel{(\sin x + \cos x)}(\sin x - \cos x)}{\cancel{(\sin x + \cos x)}(\sin^2 x + \cos^2 x - \sin x \cos x)}$$
$$= \frac{\sin x - \cos x}{1 - \sin x \cos x}$$

**59.** Answers will vary.   **61.** Answers will vary.   **63.** Answers will vary.

**65. a.** $d^2 = (20 + x\cos\theta)^2 + (20 - x\sin\theta)^2$
$$= 400 + 40x\cos\theta + x^2\cos^2\theta + 400 - 40x\sin\theta + x^2\sin^2\theta$$
$$= 800 + 40x(\cos\theta - \sin\theta) + x^2(\cos^2\theta + \sin^2\theta)$$
$$= 800 + 40x(\cos\theta - \sin\theta) + x^2$$

**b.** $\approx 42.2$ ft

**67. a.** $h = \sqrt{\cot x + \tan x}$;
$$h \approx 3.76$$

**b.** $\cot x + \tan x = \dfrac{\cos x}{\sin x} + \dfrac{\sin x}{\cos x}$
$$= \frac{\cos^2 x + \sin^2 x}{\sin x \cos x}$$
$$= \frac{1}{\sin x \cos x}$$
$$= \csc x \sec x;$$
$$h = \sqrt{\csc x \sec x}$$
$$h \approx 3.76; \text{ yes}$$

**69.** $D^2 = 400 + 40x\cos\theta + x^2$
$$D \approx 40.5 \text{ ft}$$

**71.** $\sin\alpha = \cos\theta$   **73.** Answers will vary.

**75.** $(\sin^2 x + \cos^2 x)^2 = (1)^2 = 1$

**77.** about 1148 ft   **79.** $\sin\theta = \frac{-63}{65}$, $\csc\theta = \frac{65}{-63}$, $\cos\theta = \frac{-16}{65}$, $\sec\theta = \frac{65}{-16}$, $\tan\theta = \frac{63}{16}$, $\cot\theta = \frac{16}{63}$

**81.**

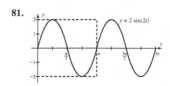

## Exercises 5.2, pp. 225–229

**1.** false; QII  **3.** repeat; opposite  **5.** Answers will vary.

**7.** $\dfrac{\sqrt{2}-\sqrt{6}}{4}$  **9.** $\dfrac{\sqrt{2}-\sqrt{6}}{4}$

**11. a.** $\cos(45°+30°)=\cos 45°\cos 30°-\sin 45°\sin 30°=\dfrac{\sqrt{6}-\sqrt{2}}{4}$

**b.** $\cos(120°-45°)=\cos 120°\cos 45°+\sin 120°\sin 45°=$
$\dfrac{-\sqrt{2}+\sqrt{6}}{4}=\dfrac{\sqrt{6}-\sqrt{2}}{4}$

**13.** $\cos(5\theta)$  **15.** $\dfrac{\sqrt{3}}{2}$  **17.** $\dfrac{-16}{65}$  **19.** $\sin 33°$  **21.** $\cot\left(\dfrac{\pi}{12}\right)$

**23.** $\cos\left(\dfrac{\pi}{3}+\theta\right)$  **25.** $\sin(8x)$  **27.** $\tan(3\theta)$  **29.** 1  **31.** $\sqrt{3}$

**33. a.** $\dfrac{-304}{425}$  **b.** $\dfrac{-304}{297}$  **35.** $\dfrac{\sqrt{6}+\sqrt{2}}{4}$  **37.** $\dfrac{\sqrt{6}+\sqrt{2}}{4}$

**39.** $-\dfrac{1}{\sqrt{3}}=-\dfrac{\sqrt{3}}{3}$  **41.** $-\sqrt{3}$

**43. a.** $\sin(45°-30°)=\sin 45°\cos 30°-\cos 45°\sin 30°=\dfrac{\sqrt{6}-\sqrt{2}}{4}$

**b.** $\sin(135°-120°)=\sin 135°\cos 120°-\cos 135°\sin 120°$
$$=\left(\dfrac{\sqrt{2}}{2}\right)\left(-\dfrac{1}{2}\right)-\left(\dfrac{-\sqrt{2}}{2}\right)\left(\dfrac{\sqrt{3}}{2}\right)$$
$$=\dfrac{-\sqrt{2}}{4}+\dfrac{\sqrt{6}}{4}$$
$$=\dfrac{\sqrt{6}-\sqrt{2}}{4}$$

**45.** $\dfrac{-\sqrt{2}-\sqrt{6}}{4}$  **47. a.** $\dfrac{319}{481}$  **b.** $\dfrac{480}{481}$  **c.** $-\dfrac{319}{360}$

**49. a.** $\dfrac{3416}{4505}$  **b.** $\dfrac{-1767}{4505}$  **c.** $\dfrac{3416}{2937}$

**51. a.** $\dfrac{12+5\sqrt{3}}{26}$  **b.** $\dfrac{12\sqrt{3}-5}{26}$  **c.** $\dfrac{12+5\sqrt{3}}{12\sqrt{3}-5}$

**53.** $(90°-\alpha)+\theta+(90°-\beta)=180°$  **a.** $\dfrac{247}{265}$  **b.** $\dfrac{96}{265}$  **c.** $\dfrac{247}{96}$

**55.** $\sin(\pi-\alpha)=\sin\pi\cos\alpha-\cos\pi\sin\alpha$
$$=0-(-1)\sin\alpha$$
$$=\sin\alpha$$

**57.** $\cos\left(x+\dfrac{\pi}{4}\right)=\cos x\cos\left(\dfrac{\pi}{4}\right)-\sin x\sin\left(\dfrac{\pi}{4}\right)=$
$\cos x\left(\dfrac{\sqrt{2}}{2}\right)-\sin x\left(\dfrac{\sqrt{2}}{2}\right)=\dfrac{\sqrt{2}}{2}(\cos x-\sin x)$

**59.** $\tan\left(x+\dfrac{\pi}{4}\right)=\dfrac{\tan x+\tan\left(\dfrac{\pi}{4}\right)}{1-\tan x\tan\left(\dfrac{\pi}{4}\right)}=\dfrac{\tan x+1}{1-\tan x}=\dfrac{1+\tan x}{1-\tan x}$

**61.** $\cos(\alpha+\beta)+\cos(\alpha-\beta)=$
$\cos\alpha\cos\beta-\sin\alpha\sin\beta+\cos\alpha\cos\beta+\sin\alpha\sin\beta=$
$2\cos\alpha\cos\beta$

**63.** $\cos(2t)=\cos(t+t)$
$$=\cos t\cos t-\sin t\sin t$$
$$=\cos^2 t-\sin^2 t$$

**65.** $\sin(3t)=\sin(2t+t)$
$$=\sin(2t)\cos t+\cos(2t)\sin t$$
$$=2\sin t\cos t\cos t+(\cos^2 t-\sin^2 t)\sin t$$
$$=2\sin t\cos^2 t+\sin t\cos^2 t-\sin^3 t$$
$$=3\sin t\cos^2 t-\sin^3 t$$
$$=3\sin t(1-\sin^2 t)-\sin^3 t$$
$$=3\sin t-3\sin^3 t-\sin^3 t$$
$$=-4\sin^3 t+3\sin t$$

**67.** $\cos\left(x-\dfrac{\pi}{4}\right)=\cos x\cos\left(\dfrac{\pi}{4}\right)+\sin x\sin\left(\dfrac{\pi}{4}\right)$
$$=\cos x\left(\dfrac{\sqrt{2}}{2}\right)+\sin x\left(\dfrac{\sqrt{2}}{2}\right)$$
$$=\dfrac{\sqrt{2}}{2}(\cos x+\sin x)$$

**69.** $F=\dfrac{Wk}{c}\dfrac{1-\sqrt{3}}{1+\sqrt{3}}$

**71.** $R=\dfrac{\cos s\cos t}{\overline{\omega}C\sin(s+t)}$
$$=\dfrac{\cos s\cos t}{\overline{\omega}C(\sin s\cos t+\cos s\sin t)}$$
$$=\dfrac{\cos s\cos t\dfrac{1}{\cos s\cos t}}{\overline{\omega}C(\sin s\cos t+\cos s\sin t)\dfrac{1}{\cos s\cos t}}$$
$$=\dfrac{1}{\overline{\omega}C\left(\dfrac{\sin s\,\cancel{\cos t}}{\cos s\,\cancel{\cos t}}+\dfrac{\cancel{\cos s}\sin t}{\cancel{\cos s}\cos t}\right)}$$
$$=\dfrac{1}{\overline{\omega}C(\tan s+\tan t)}$$

**73.** $\dfrac{A}{B}=\dfrac{\sin\theta\cos(90°-\theta)}{\cos\theta\sin(90°-\theta)}$
$$\dfrac{A}{B}=\dfrac{\sin\theta(\cos 90°\cos\theta+\sin 90°\sin\theta)}{\cos\theta(\sin 90°\cos\theta-\cos 90°\sin\theta)}$$
$$=\dfrac{\sin\theta(0+\sin\theta)}{\cos\theta(\cos\theta-0)}$$
$$=\dfrac{\sin^2\theta}{\cos^2\theta}$$
$$=\tan^2\theta$$

**75.** verified using sum identity for sine

**77.** $\dfrac{f(x+h)-f(x)}{h}=\dfrac{\sin(x+h)-\sin x}{h}$
$$=\dfrac{\sin x\cos h+\cos x\sin h-\sin x}{h}=\dfrac{\sin x\cos h-\sin x+\cos x\sin h}{h}$$
$$=\dfrac{\sin x(\cos h-1)+\cos x\sin h}{h}=\sin x\left(\dfrac{\cos h-1}{h}\right)+\cos x\left(\dfrac{\sin h}{h}\right)$$

**79.** $\dfrac{-\sqrt{2}}{2}$  **81.** $\dfrac{1}{2}$

**83.** $D=d$, so $D^2=d^2$, and
$$D^2=(\cos\alpha-\cos\beta)^2+(\sin\alpha-\sin\beta)^2$$
$$=\cos^2\alpha-2\cos\alpha\cos\beta+\cos^2\beta+\sin^2\alpha-$$
$$2\sin\alpha\sin\beta+\sin^2\beta$$
$$=2-2\cos\alpha\cos\beta-2\sin\alpha\sin\beta$$
$$d^2=\sin^2(\alpha-\beta)+[\cos(\alpha-\beta)-1]^2$$
$$=\sin^2(\alpha-\beta)+\cos^2(\alpha-\beta)-2\cos(\alpha-\beta)+1$$
$$=2-2\cos(\alpha-\beta)$$
$$D^2=d^2\text{ so}$$
$$2-2\cos\alpha\cos\beta-2\sin\alpha\sin\beta=2-2\cos(\alpha-\beta)$$
$$\dfrac{-2\cos\alpha\cos\beta-2\sin\alpha\sin\beta}{-2}=\dfrac{-2\cos(\alpha-\beta)}{-2}$$
$$\cos\alpha\cos\beta+\sin\alpha\sin\beta=\cos(\alpha-\beta)$$

**85.** $\sin t = \dfrac{3}{4}$, $\cos t = \dfrac{\sqrt{7}}{4}$, $\tan t = \dfrac{3}{\sqrt{7}}$

**87.**

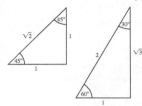

**89.**

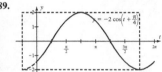

## Mid-Chapter Check, p. 230

**1.**
$$\cos^2 x - \cot^2 x = -\cos^2 x \cot^2 x$$
$$\cos^2 x - \frac{\cos^2 x}{\sin^2 x} =$$
$$\cos^2 x\left(1 - \frac{1}{\sin^2 x}\right) =$$
$$\cos^2 x(1 - \csc^2 x) =$$
$$\cos^2 x(-\cot^2 x) =$$
$$-\cos^2 x \cot^2 x =$$

**2.**
$$1 - \sin^4 t = (1 + \sin^2 t)\cos^2 t$$
$$(1 + \sin^2 t)(1 - \sin^2 t) =$$
$$(1 + \sin^2 t)\cos^2 t =$$

**3.**
$$\frac{2\sin x}{\sec x} - \frac{\cos x}{\csc x} = \cos x \sin x$$
$$\frac{2\sin x \csc x - \cos x \sec x}{\sec x \csc x} =$$
$$\frac{2(1) - 1}{\sec x \csc x} =$$
$$\frac{1}{\sec x \csc x} =$$
$$\cos x \sin x =$$

**4.**
$$\frac{1 - \cos t}{\cos t} + \frac{\sec t - 1}{\sec t} = \sec t - \cos t$$
$$\frac{(\sec t - 1) + (1 - \cos t)}{\cos t \sec t} =$$
$$\sec t - \cos t =$$

**5.**
$$1 + \sec^2 x = \tan^2 x$$
$$1 + \sec^2 0 = \tan^2 0$$
$$1 + 1^2 = 0^2$$
$$1 + 1 = 0$$
$$2 = 0 \text{ False}$$

**6.**
$$\cos^2 \frac{\pi}{6} = \sin^2 \frac{\pi}{6} - 1$$
$$\left(\frac{\sqrt{3}}{2}\right)^2 = \left(\frac{1}{2}\right)^2 - 1$$
$$\frac{3}{4} = \frac{1}{4} - 1$$
$$\frac{3}{4} = -\frac{3}{4}; \text{ false}$$

**7.** $\cos(4\alpha)$    **8.** $\sin\left(\dfrac{7\pi}{12}t\right)$    **9. a.** $\dfrac{56}{65}$    **b.** $\dfrac{63}{65}$    **c.** $-\dfrac{56}{33}$

**10. a.** $\dfrac{456}{5785}$    **b.** $\dfrac{-3193}{5785}$    **c.** $\dfrac{456}{5767}$

## Reinforcing Basic Concepts, p. 230

**Exercise 1.** For $\alpha$,
$$a \approx 34 \text{ mm}$$
$$b \approx 18.5 \text{ mm}$$
$$34^2 + 18.5^2 = h^2$$
$$\sqrt{1498.25} = h$$
$$38.7 \approx h$$
$$38.5 \text{ vs } 38.7; 0.5\%$$
For $\beta$
$$a \approx 34 \text{ mm}$$
$$b \approx 23.5 \text{ mm}$$
$$34^2 + 23.5^2 = h^2$$
$$\sqrt{1708.25} = h$$
$$41.3 \approx h$$
$$41.5 \text{ vs } 41.3; 0.4\%$$

**Exercise 2.** $\cos\alpha = \dfrac{34}{38.5}$; $\cos\beta = \dfrac{34}{41.5}$;
$$\sin\alpha = \frac{18.5}{38.5}; \sin\beta = \frac{23.5}{41.5};$$
$$\left(\frac{18.5}{38.5}\right)^2 + \left(\frac{34}{38.5}\right)^2 \approx 1; \left(\frac{34}{41.5}\right)^2 + \left(\frac{23.5}{41.5}\right)^2 \approx 1;$$
Their sum is very close to 1.

**Exercise 3.** yes, yes    **Exercise 4.** verified

## Exercises 5.3, pp. 235–239

**1.** sum; $\alpha = \beta$    **3.** $2x; x$    **5.** Answers will vary

**7.** $\sin(2\theta) = \dfrac{-120}{169}$, $\cos(2\theta) = \dfrac{119}{169}$, $\tan(2\theta) = \dfrac{-120}{119}$

**9.** $\sin(2\theta) = \dfrac{-720}{1681}$, $\cos(2\theta) = \dfrac{-1519}{1681}$, $\tan(2\theta) = \dfrac{720}{1519}$

**11.** $\sin(2\theta) = \dfrac{2184}{7225}$, $\cos(2\theta) = \dfrac{6887}{7225}$, $\tan(2\theta) = \dfrac{2184}{6887}$

**13.** $\sin(2\theta) = \dfrac{-5280}{5329}$, $\cos(2\theta) = \dfrac{721}{5329}$, $\tan(2\theta) = \dfrac{-5280}{721}$

**15.** $\sin(2\theta) = \dfrac{-24}{25}$, $\cos(2\theta) = \dfrac{7}{25}$, $\tan(2\theta) = \dfrac{-24}{7}$

**17.** $\sin\theta = \dfrac{4}{5}$, $\cos\theta = \dfrac{3}{5}$, $\tan\theta = \dfrac{4}{3}$

**19.** $\sin\theta = \dfrac{21}{29}$, $\cos\theta = \dfrac{20}{29}$, $\tan\theta = \dfrac{21}{20}$

**21.** $\sin(3\theta) = \sin(2\theta + \theta)$
$$= \sin(2\theta)\cos\theta + \cos(2\theta)\sin\theta$$
$$= (2\sin\theta\cos\theta)\cos\theta + (1 - 2\sin^2\theta)\sin\theta$$
$$= 2\sin\theta\cos^2\theta + \sin\theta - 2\sin^3\theta$$
$$= 2\sin\theta(1 - \sin^2\theta) + \sin\theta - 2\sin^3\theta$$
$$= 2\sin\theta - 2\sin^3\theta + \sin\theta - 2\sin^3\theta$$
$$= 3\sin\theta - 4\sin^3\theta$$

**23.** $\dfrac{1}{4}$    **25.** $\dfrac{\sqrt{2}}{2}$    **27.** 1    **29.** $4.5\sin(6x)$    **31.** $\dfrac{1}{8} - \dfrac{1}{8}\cos(4x)$

**33.** $\dfrac{9}{8} + \dfrac{3}{2}\cos(2x) + \dfrac{3}{8}\cos(4x)$

**35.** $\dfrac{5}{8} - \dfrac{7}{8}\cos(2x) + \dfrac{3}{8}\cos(4x) - \dfrac{1}{8}\cos(2x)\cos(4x)$

**37.** $\sin\theta = \dfrac{\sqrt{2 - \sqrt{2}}}{2}$, $\cos\theta = \dfrac{\sqrt{2 + \sqrt{2}}}{2}$, $\tan\theta = \sqrt{2} - 1$

**39.** $\sin\theta = \dfrac{\sqrt{2 - \sqrt{3}}}{2}$, $\cos\theta = \dfrac{\sqrt{2 + \sqrt{3}}}{2}$, $\tan\theta = 2 - \sqrt{3}$

**41.** $\sin\theta = \dfrac{\sqrt{2 + \sqrt{2}}}{2}$, $\cos\theta = \dfrac{\sqrt{2 - \sqrt{2}}}{2}$, $\tan\theta = \sqrt{2} + 1$

**43.** $\sin\theta = \dfrac{\sqrt{2 + \sqrt{2}}}{2}$, $\cos\theta = \dfrac{\sqrt{2 - \sqrt{2}}}{2}$, $\tan\theta = \sqrt{2} + 1$

**45.** $\dfrac{\sqrt{2 - \sqrt{2 + \sqrt{2}}}}{2}$    **47.** $\dfrac{\sqrt{2 - \sqrt{2 + \sqrt{3}}}}{2}$    **49.** $\cos 15°$

**51.** $\tan 2\theta$   **53.** $\tan x$

**55.** $\sin\left(\dfrac{\theta}{2}\right) = \dfrac{3}{\sqrt{13}}$, $\cos\left(\dfrac{\theta}{2}\right) = \dfrac{2}{\sqrt{13}}$, $\tan\left(\dfrac{\theta}{2}\right) = \dfrac{3}{2}$

**57.** $\sin\left(\dfrac{\theta}{2}\right) = \dfrac{3}{\sqrt{10}}$, $\cos\left(\dfrac{\theta}{2}\right) = \dfrac{1}{\sqrt{10}}$, $\tan\left(\dfrac{\theta}{2}\right) = 3$

**59.** $\sin\left(\dfrac{\theta}{2}\right) = \dfrac{7}{\sqrt{74}}$, $\cos\left(\dfrac{\theta}{2}\right) = \dfrac{5}{\sqrt{74}}$, $\tan\left(\dfrac{\theta}{2}\right) = \dfrac{7}{5}$

**61.** $\sin\left(\dfrac{\theta}{2}\right) = \dfrac{1}{\sqrt{226}}$, $\cos\left(\dfrac{\theta}{2}\right) = \dfrac{15}{\sqrt{226}}$, $\tan\left(\dfrac{\theta}{2}\right) = \dfrac{1}{15}$

**63.** $\sin\left(\dfrac{\theta}{2}\right) = \dfrac{5}{\sqrt{29}}$, $\cos\left(\dfrac{\theta}{2}\right) = \dfrac{-2}{\sqrt{29}}$, $\tan\left(\dfrac{\theta}{2}\right) = -\dfrac{5}{2}$

**65.**
$$\dfrac{2\sin x \cos x}{\cos^2 x - \sin^2 x} = \dfrac{\sin(2x)}{\cos(2x)}$$
$$= \tan(2x)$$

**67.**
$$(\sin x + \cos x)^2 = \sin^2 x + 2\sin x \cos x + \cos^2 x$$
$$= \sin^2 x + \cos^2 x + 2\sin x \cos x$$
$$= 1 + 2\sin x \cos x$$
$$= 1 + \sin(2x)$$

**69.**
$$\cos(8\theta) = \cos(2 \cdot 4\theta)$$
$$= \cos^2(4\theta) - \sin^2(4\theta)$$

**71.**
$$\dfrac{\cos(2\theta)}{\sin^2 \theta} = \dfrac{\cos^2\theta - \sin^2\theta}{\sin^2\theta}$$
$$= \dfrac{\cos^2\theta}{\sin^2\theta} - \dfrac{\sin^2\theta}{\sin^2\theta}$$
$$= \cot^2\theta - 1$$

**73.**
$$\tan(2\theta) = \dfrac{2\tan\theta}{1 - \tan^2\theta}$$
$$= \dfrac{(2\tan\theta)\dfrac{1}{\tan\theta}}{(1 - \tan^2\theta)\dfrac{1}{\tan\theta}}$$
$$= \dfrac{2}{\dfrac{1}{\tan\theta} - \tan\theta}$$
$$= \dfrac{2}{\cot\theta - \tan\theta}$$

**75.**
$$2\csc(2x) = \dfrac{2}{\sin(2x)}$$
$$= \dfrac{2}{2\sin x \cos x}$$
$$= \dfrac{1}{\sin x \cos x}$$
$$= \dfrac{\sin^2 x + \cos^2 x}{\sin x \cos x}$$
$$= \dfrac{\sin^2 x}{\sin x \cos x} + \dfrac{\cos^2 x}{\sin x \cos x}$$
$$= \dfrac{\sin x}{\cos x} + \dfrac{\cos x}{\sin x}$$
$$= \tan x + \cot x$$

**77.**
$$\cos^2\left(\dfrac{x}{2}\right) - \sin^2\left(\dfrac{x}{2}\right) = \cos\left(2 \cdot \dfrac{x}{2}\right)$$
$$= \cos x$$

**79.**
$$1 - 4\sin^2\theta + 4\sin^4\theta = (1 - 2\sin^2\theta)^2$$
$$= [\cos(2\theta)]^2$$
$$= \cos^2(2\theta)$$
$$= 1 - \sin^2(2\theta)$$

**81.**
$$\sin^2\alpha + (1 - \cos\alpha)^2 = \sin^2\alpha + 1 - 2\cos\alpha + \cos^2\alpha$$
$$= \sin^2\alpha + \cos^2\alpha + 1 - 2\cos\alpha = 1 + 1 - 2\cos\alpha = 2 - 2\cos\alpha$$
$$= 2(1 - \cos\alpha) = 4\left(\dfrac{1 - \cos\alpha}{2}\right) = 4\sin^2\left(\dfrac{\alpha}{2}\right) = \left[2\sin\left(\dfrac{\alpha}{2}\right)\right]^2$$

**83.**
$$\sin(2\alpha) = \sin(\alpha + \alpha)$$
$$= \sin\alpha\cos\alpha + \cos\alpha\sin\alpha$$
$$= \sin\alpha\cos\alpha + \sin\alpha\cos\alpha$$
$$= 2\sin\alpha\cos\alpha$$
$$\tan(\alpha + \beta) = \tan(\alpha + \alpha)$$
$$= \dfrac{\tan\alpha + \tan\alpha}{1 - \tan\alpha\tan\alpha}$$
$$= \tan(2\alpha) = \dfrac{2\tan\alpha}{1 - \tan^2\alpha}$$

**85. a.** $\mathcal{M} = \dfrac{2}{\sqrt{2 - \sqrt{3}}}$, $\mathcal{M} \approx 3.9$

**b.** $\mathcal{M} = \dfrac{2}{\sqrt{2 - \sqrt{2}}}$, $\mathcal{M} \approx 2.6$   **c.** $\theta = 60°$

**87.**
$$d(t) = \left|6\sin\left(\dfrac{\pi t}{60}\right)\right|$$
$$= \left|6\sin\left(\dfrac{1}{2} \cdot \dfrac{\pi t}{30}\right)\right|$$
$$= \left|6\left(\pm\sqrt{\dfrac{1 - \cos\left(\dfrac{\pi t}{30}\right)}{2}}\right)\right|$$
$$= 6\sqrt{\dfrac{1 - \cos\left(\dfrac{\pi t}{30}\right)}{2}}$$
$$= \sqrt{36\dfrac{1 - \cos\left(\dfrac{\pi t}{30}\right)}{2}}$$
$$= \sqrt{18\left[1 - \cos\left(\dfrac{\pi t}{30}\right)\right]}$$

**89. A.**
$$\sin(2\theta - 90°) + 1$$
$$= \sin(2\theta)\cos 90° - \cos(2\theta)\sin 90° + 1$$
$$= 0 - \cos(2\theta) + 1$$
$$= 1 - \cos(2\theta)$$
**B.**
$$2\sin^2\theta = \sin^2\theta + \sin^2\theta$$
$$= 1 - \cos^2\theta + \sin^2\theta$$
$$= 1 - (\cos^2\theta - \sin^2\theta)$$
$$= 1 - \cos(2\theta)$$
**C.**
$$1 + \sin^2\theta - \cos^2\theta = 1 - (\cos^2\theta - \sin^2\theta)$$
$$= 1 - \cos(2\theta)$$
**D.** $1 - \cos(2\theta) = 1 - \cos(2\theta)$

**91. a.** $\approx 0.9659$; $\approx 0.9659$

**b.**
$$\left(\dfrac{\sqrt{2 + \sqrt{3}}}{2}\right)^2 \overset{?}{=} \left(\dfrac{\sqrt{6} + \sqrt{2}}{4}\right)^2$$
$$\dfrac{2 + \sqrt{3}}{4} \overset{?}{=} \dfrac{6 + 2\sqrt{12} + 2}{16}$$
$$\dfrac{2 + \sqrt{3}}{4} \overset{?}{=} \dfrac{8 + 4\sqrt{3}}{16}$$
$$\dfrac{2 + \sqrt{3}}{4} = \dfrac{2 + \sqrt{3}}{4}$$

**93.**
$$\cos 15° = \dfrac{\sqrt{2 + \sqrt{3}}}{2}$$
$$\cos 7.5° = \dfrac{\sqrt{2 + \sqrt{2 + \sqrt{3}}}}{2}$$
$$\cos 3.75° = \dfrac{\sqrt{2 + \sqrt{2 + \sqrt{2 + \sqrt{3}}}}}{2} \approx 0.9979$$
$$\cos 1.875° = \dfrac{\sqrt{2 + \sqrt{2 + \sqrt{2 + \sqrt{2 + \sqrt{3}}}}}}{2} \approx 0.9995;$$

They are getting close to 1.

**95.** $\sin^2 x + \cos^2 x = 1$, $\tan^2 x + 1 = \sec^2 x$, $1 + \cot^2 x = \csc^2 x$

**97.** about 19.3 ft   **99.** $y = 26\sin\left[\dfrac{\pi}{6}(x - 4)\right] + 84$

## Exercises 5.4, pp. 243–245

**1.** product; sum; sum; difference

**3.** $\dfrac{1}{16}v^2\sin\theta\cos\theta$; range; air resistance   **5.** Answers will vary.

**7.** $\dfrac{1}{2}[\cos(12\theta) - \cos(4\theta)]$   **9.** $\sin 5t - \sin 2t$

**11.** $\cos(1540\pi t) + \cos(2418\pi t)$   **13.** $\sin(2x) + \sin(4y)$

**15.** $\dfrac{1 + \sqrt{3}}{2}$   **17.** $\dfrac{\sqrt{2}}{4}$   **19.** $2\cos\left(\dfrac{13}{2}h\right)\cos\left(\dfrac{5}{2}h\right)$

**21.** $2\cos x \sin\left(\dfrac{3}{8}x\right)$   **23.** $-2\sin(1072\pi t)\sin(375\pi t)$

**25.** $2\sin(3x + 3y)\cos(-2y)$   **27.** $\dfrac{\sqrt{6}}{2}$   **29.** $\dfrac{-\sqrt{2}}{2}$

**31.** $\dfrac{\sin m + \sin n}{\cos m + \cos n} = \dfrac{2\sin\left(\dfrac{m+n}{2}\right)\cos\left(\dfrac{m-n}{2}\right)}{2\cos\left(\dfrac{m+n}{2}\right)\cos\left(\dfrac{m-n}{2}\right)}$

$$= \dfrac{\sin\left(\dfrac{m+n}{2}\right)}{\cos\left(\dfrac{m+n}{2}\right)}$$

$$= \tan\left(\dfrac{m+n}{2}\right)$$

**33.** $\dfrac{2\sin 2t\cos t - \sin 3t}{\cos t} = \dfrac{2\left[\dfrac{1}{2}(\sin 3t + \sin t)\right] - \sin 3t}{\cos t}$

$$= \dfrac{\sin 3t + \sin t - \sin 3t}{\cos t}$$

$$= \dfrac{\sin t}{\cos t}$$

$$= \tan t$$

**35.** $\dfrac{2\cos 2t}{\sin 3t - \sin t} = \dfrac{2\cos 2t}{2\cos 2t \sin t}$

$$= \dfrac{1}{\sin t}$$

$$= \csc t$$

**37.** $\dfrac{\sin(120\pi t) + \sin(80\pi t)}{\cos(120\pi t) - \cos(80\pi t)} = \dfrac{2\sin(100\pi t)\cos(20\pi t)}{-2\sin(100\pi t)\sin(20\pi t)}$

$$= \dfrac{\cos(20\pi t)}{\sin(20\pi t)}$$

$$= -\cot(20\pi t)$$

**39.** $\dfrac{1}{2}[\cos(\alpha - \beta) - \cos(\alpha + \beta)] = \sin\alpha\sin\beta$

**41.** $-\dfrac{1}{4} = -\dfrac{1}{4}$, verified   **43.** $y(t) = 2\cos(2174\pi t)\cos(780\pi t)$

**45.** $\cos[2\pi(1209)t] + \cos[2\pi(941)t]$; the ✳ key

**47. a.** $288 - 144\sqrt{2}$ ft $\approx 84.3$ ft   **b.** $288 - 144\sqrt{2}$ ft $\approx 84.3$ ft

**49.** $y = 4\sin(1.1x)\cos(0.6t)$

**51.** $(\sin a \sin b)\sin c = \dfrac{1}{2}[\cos(a - b) - \cos(a + b)]\sin c$
$= \dfrac{1}{2}[\cos(a - b)(\sin c) - \cos(a + b)(\sin c)]$
$= \dfrac{1}{2}\{\dfrac{1}{2}[\sin(a - b - c) - \sin(a - b + c)] - \dfrac{1}{2}[\sin(a + b + c)$
$\quad - \sin(a + b - c)]\}$
$= \dfrac{1}{4}[\sin(a + b - c) + \sin(b + c - a) + \sin(c + a - b)$
$\quad - \sin(a + b + c)]$

**53.** $Y_1$ is increasing; $Y_2$ is defined on $(0, \pi)$.

**55.** $\left(\dfrac{16}{65}\right)^2 + \left(\dfrac{63}{65}\right)^2 = \dfrac{256}{4225} + \dfrac{3969}{4225} = \dfrac{4225}{4225} = 1,$

$\tan\theta = \dfrac{63}{16}; \sec\theta = \dfrac{65}{16}$

$1 + \left(\dfrac{63}{16}\right)^2 = \left(\dfrac{65}{16}\right)^2$

$1 + \dfrac{3969}{256} = \dfrac{4225}{256}$

$\dfrac{256}{256} + \dfrac{3969}{256} = \dfrac{4225}{256}$

**57.** $\dfrac{\sqrt{2} - \sqrt{6}}{4}$

## Summary and Concept Review, pp. 246–248

**1.** $\dfrac{\csc^2 x(1 - \cos^2 x)}{\tan^2 x} = \dfrac{\csc^2 x \sin^2 x}{\tan^2 x}$

$$= \dfrac{1}{\tan^2 x}$$

$$= \cot^2 x$$

**2.** $\dfrac{\cot x}{\sec x} - \dfrac{\csc x}{\tan x} = \cot x \dfrac{1}{\sec x} - \cot x \csc x$

$$= \cot x \cos x - \cot x \csc x$$

$$= \cot x(\cos x - \csc x)$$

**3.** $\dfrac{\sin^4 x - \cos^4 x}{\sin x \cos x} = \dfrac{(\sin^2 x - \cos^2 x)(\sin^2 x + \cos^2 x)}{\sin x \cos x}$

$$= \dfrac{(\sin^2 x - \cos^2 x)(1)}{\sin x \cos x}$$

$$= \dfrac{\sin x \sin x}{\sin x \cos x} - \dfrac{\cos x \cos x}{\sin x \cos x}$$

$$= \dfrac{\sin x}{\cos x} - \dfrac{\cos x}{\sin x}$$

$$= \tan x - \cot x$$

**4.** $\dfrac{(\sin x + \cos x)^2}{\sin x \cos x} = \dfrac{\sin^2 x + 2\sin x \cos x + \cos^2 x}{\sin x \cos x}$

$$= \dfrac{\sin^2 x + \cos^2 x}{\sin x \cos x} + \dfrac{2\sin x \cos x}{\sin x \cos x}$$

$$= \dfrac{1}{\sin x \cos x} + 2$$

$$= \csc x \sec x + 2$$

**5. a.** $\cos 75° = \dfrac{\sqrt{6} - \sqrt{2}}{4}$

**b.** $\tan\left(\dfrac{\pi}{12}\right) = \dfrac{\sqrt{3} - 1}{1 + \sqrt{3}} = \dfrac{(\sqrt{3} - 1)^2}{2} = 2 - \sqrt{3}$

**6. a.** $\tan 15° = \dfrac{\sqrt{3} - 1}{1 + \sqrt{3}} = \dfrac{(\sqrt{3} - 1)^2}{2} = 2 - \sqrt{3}$

**b.** $\sin\left(\dfrac{-\pi}{12}\right) = \dfrac{\sqrt{2} - \sqrt{6}}{4}$   **7. a.** $\cos 180° = -1$  **b.** $\sin 120° = \dfrac{\sqrt{3}}{2}$

**8. a.** $\cos x$   **b.** $\sin\left(\dfrac{5x}{8}\right)$   **9. a.** $\cos 1170° = \cos 90° = 0$

**b.** $\sin\left(\dfrac{57\pi}{4}\right) = \sin\left(\dfrac{\pi}{4}\right) = \dfrac{\sqrt{2}}{2}$   **10. a.** $\cos\left(\dfrac{x}{8}\right) = \sin\left(\dfrac{\pi}{2} - \dfrac{x}{8}\right)$

**b.** $\sin\left(x - \dfrac{\pi}{12}\right) = \cos\left(\dfrac{7\pi}{12} - x\right)$

**11.** $\tan(45° - 30°) = \dfrac{\tan 45° - \tan 30°}{1 + \tan 45° \tan 30°}$

$= \dfrac{1 - \dfrac{\sqrt{3}}{3}}{1 + 1 \cdot \dfrac{\sqrt{3}}{3}} = \dfrac{1 - \dfrac{\sqrt{3}}{3}}{1 + \dfrac{\sqrt{3}}{3}} = \dfrac{\dfrac{3 - \sqrt{3}}{3}}{\dfrac{3 + \sqrt{3}}{3}}$

$= \dfrac{3 - \sqrt{3}}{\cancel{3}} \cdot \dfrac{\cancel{3}}{3 + \sqrt{3}} = \dfrac{3 - \sqrt{3}}{3 + \sqrt{3}} = \dfrac{\cancel{\sqrt{3}}(\sqrt{3} - 1)}{\cancel{\sqrt{3}}(\sqrt{3} + 1)} = \dfrac{\sqrt{3} - 1}{\sqrt{3} + 1}$

$\tan(135° - 120°) = \dfrac{\tan 135° - \tan 120°}{1 + \tan 135° \tan 120°}$

$= \dfrac{-1 + \sqrt{3}}{1 + (-1)(-\sqrt{3})} = \dfrac{\sqrt{3} - 1}{1 + \sqrt{3}} = \dfrac{\sqrt{3} - 1}{\sqrt{3} + 1}$

**12.** $\cos\left(x + \dfrac{\pi}{6}\right) + \cos\left(x - \dfrac{\pi}{6}\right) = \sqrt{3}\cos x$

$= \cos x \cos\left(\dfrac{\pi}{6}\right) - \sin x \sin\left(\dfrac{\pi}{6}\right) + \cos x \cos\left(\dfrac{\pi}{6}\right) + \sin x \sin\left(\dfrac{\pi}{6}\right)$

$= 2\cos x \cos\left(\dfrac{\pi}{6}\right) + 0 = 2\cos x\left(\dfrac{\sqrt{3}}{2}\right) = \sqrt{3}\cos x$

**13. a.** $\sin(2\theta) = 2\left(\dfrac{-84}{85}\right)\left(\dfrac{13}{85}\right) = \dfrac{-2184}{7225}$

$\cos(2\theta) = \left(\dfrac{13}{85}\right)^2 - \left(\dfrac{84}{85}\right)^2 = \dfrac{-6887}{7225}$

$\tan(2\theta) = \dfrac{2184}{-7225}\left(\dfrac{7225}{-6887}\right) = \dfrac{2184}{6887}$

**b.** $\sin(2\theta) = 2\left(\dfrac{-20}{29}\right)\left(\dfrac{-21}{29}\right) = \dfrac{840}{841}$

$\cos(2\theta) = \left(\dfrac{-21}{29}\right)^2 - \left(\dfrac{-20}{29}\right)^2 = \dfrac{441 - 400}{841} = \dfrac{41}{841}$

$\tan(2\theta) = \dfrac{2\left(\dfrac{20}{21}\right)}{1 - \left(\dfrac{20}{21}\right)^2} = \dfrac{840}{41}$

**14. a.** $\sin\theta = \dfrac{21}{29}$, $\cos\theta = \dfrac{-20}{29}$, $\tan\theta = -\dfrac{21}{20}$,

**b.** $\sin\theta = \dfrac{7}{25}$ or $\sin\theta = \dfrac{24}{25}$, $\cos\theta = \dfrac{-24}{25}$ or $\cos\theta = \dfrac{-7}{25}$, $\tan\theta = \dfrac{-7}{24}$

or $\tan\theta = \dfrac{-24}{7}$　**15. a.** $\cos 45° = \dfrac{\sqrt{2}}{2}$　**b.** $\cos\left(\dfrac{\pi}{6}\right) = \dfrac{\sqrt{3}}{2}$

**16. a.** $\sin 67.5 = \sqrt{\dfrac{1 - \cos 135°}{2}} = \sqrt{\dfrac{1 + \dfrac{\sqrt{2}}{2}}{2}} = \sqrt{\dfrac{2 + \sqrt{2}}{4}}$

$= \dfrac{\sqrt{2 + \sqrt{2}}}{2}$

$\cos 67.5 = \sqrt{\dfrac{1 + \cos 135°}{2}} = \sqrt{\dfrac{1 - \dfrac{\sqrt{2}}{2}}{2}} = \sqrt{\dfrac{2 - \sqrt{2}}{4}}$

$= \dfrac{\sqrt{2 - \sqrt{2}}}{2}$

**b.** $\sin\left(\dfrac{5\pi}{8}\right) = \sqrt{\dfrac{1 - \cos\left(\dfrac{5\pi}{4}\right)}{2}} = \sqrt{\dfrac{1 + \dfrac{\sqrt{2}}{2}}{2}} = \sqrt{\dfrac{2 + \sqrt{2}}{4}}$

$= \dfrac{\sqrt{2 + \sqrt{2}}}{2}$

$\cos\left(\dfrac{5\pi}{8}\right) = -\sqrt{\dfrac{1 + \cos\left(\dfrac{5\pi}{4}\right)}{2}} = -\sqrt{\dfrac{1 - \dfrac{\sqrt{2}}{2}}{2}} = -\sqrt{\dfrac{2 - \sqrt{2}}{4}}$

$= -\dfrac{\sqrt{2 - \sqrt{2}}}{2}$

**17. a.** $\sin\left(\dfrac{\theta}{2}\right) = \sqrt{\dfrac{1 - 24/25}{2}} = \sqrt{\dfrac{25 - 24}{50}} = +\dfrac{1}{5\sqrt{2}}, \dfrac{\theta}{2}$ in QII

$\cos\left(\dfrac{\theta}{2}\right) = -\sqrt{\dfrac{1 + 24/25}{2}} = -\sqrt{\dfrac{25 + 24}{50}}$

$= -\sqrt{\dfrac{49}{50}} = \dfrac{-7}{5\sqrt{2}}, \dfrac{\theta}{2}$ in QII

**b.** $\sin\left(\dfrac{\theta}{2}\right) = -\sqrt{\dfrac{1 - 56/65}{2}} = -\sqrt{\dfrac{65 - 56}{130}}$

$= -\sqrt{\dfrac{9}{130}} = \dfrac{-3}{\sqrt{130}}, \dfrac{\theta}{2}$ in QIV

$\cos\left(\dfrac{\theta}{2}\right) = \sqrt{\dfrac{1 + 56/65}{2}} = \sqrt{\dfrac{65 + 56}{130}} = \sqrt{\dfrac{121}{130}} = +\dfrac{11}{\sqrt{130}}, \dfrac{\theta}{2}$ in QIV

**18. a.** $A = 12^2\sin\left(\dfrac{30°}{2}\right)\cos\left(\dfrac{30°}{2}\right) = 144\sqrt{\dfrac{1 - \cos 30°}{2}}\sqrt{\dfrac{1 + \cos 30°}{2}}$

$= 144\sqrt{\dfrac{1 - \dfrac{\sqrt{3}}{2}}{2}}\sqrt{\dfrac{1 + \dfrac{\sqrt{3}}{2}}{2}} = 144\sqrt{\dfrac{2 - \sqrt{3}}{4}}\sqrt{\dfrac{2 + \sqrt{3}}{4}}$

$= \dfrac{144\sqrt{4 - 3}}{4} = 36$ cm$^2$; yes

**19.** $\dfrac{1}{2}[\sin(-6t) - \sin(12t)]$　**20.** $\dfrac{1}{2}\left[\cos\left(-\dfrac{2\pi}{3}t\right) - \cos(2\pi t)\right]$

**21.** $2\cos(2t)\cos(-t)$　**22.** $2\cos\left(\dfrac{t}{8}\right)\sin\left(-\dfrac{5}{16}t\right)$

**23.** $-1 - \dfrac{\sqrt{3}}{2}$　**24.** $-\dfrac{\sqrt{2}}{2}$

**25.** $\dfrac{\cos(3\alpha) - \cos\alpha}{\cos(3\alpha) + \cos\alpha} = \dfrac{-2\sin(2\alpha)\sin\alpha}{2\cos(2\alpha)\cos\alpha}$

$= \dfrac{-2\sin^2\alpha}{\cos^2\alpha - \sin^2\alpha} = \dfrac{2\sin^2\alpha}{\sin^2\alpha - \cos^2\alpha}$

$= \dfrac{2\sin^2\alpha}{1 - 2\cos^2\alpha} = \dfrac{2\tan^2\alpha}{\sec^2\alpha - 2}$

## Mixed Review, pp. 248–249

**1.** $\sin(-\theta)\tan(-\theta) + \cos\theta = (-\sin\theta)(-\tan\theta) + \cos\theta$

$= \sin\theta\tan\theta + \cos\theta$

$= \dfrac{\sin^2\theta}{\cos\theta} + \cos\theta$

$= \dfrac{\sin^2\theta}{\cos\theta} + \dfrac{\cos^2\theta}{\cos\theta}$

$= \dfrac{1}{\cos\theta} = \sec\theta = \sec(-\theta)$

**3.** $\sqrt{3} + 2$　**5.** $\cos\left[2\left(\dfrac{\pi}{12}\right)\right] = \cos\left(\dfrac{\pi}{6}\right) = \dfrac{\sqrt{3}}{2}$

**7.** $\dfrac{1 - (\cos^2\theta - \sin^2\theta)}{\tan^2\theta} = \dfrac{1 - \cos(2\theta)}{\dfrac{1 - \cos(2\theta)}{1 + \cos(2\theta)}} = \cancel{1 - \cos(2\theta)}\cdot\dfrac{1 + \cos(2\theta)}{\cancel{1 - \cos(2\theta)}}$

$= 1 + \cos(2\theta)$

**9.** $\sin\left(\dfrac{x}{2}\right) = \dfrac{-2}{\sqrt{5}}$; $\cos\left(\dfrac{x}{2}\right) = \dfrac{1}{\sqrt{5}}$

**11.** $\sin(2\alpha) = \sin(\alpha + \alpha) = \sin\alpha\cos\alpha + \sin\alpha\cos\alpha$

$= 2\sin\alpha\cos\alpha$

$= \cos^2\alpha - \sin^2\alpha$

**13.** $\dfrac{-\sqrt{3}\sqrt{2 - \sqrt{2}}}{2}$　**15.** $\dfrac{1 + \sqrt{2}}{4}$

**17.** $\sin(\alpha + \beta)\sin(\alpha - \beta) = (\sin\alpha\cos\beta + \cos\alpha\sin\beta)$

$(\sin\alpha\cos\beta - \cos\alpha\sin\beta)$

$= \sin^2\alpha\cos^2\beta - \cos^2\alpha\sin^2\beta$

$= \sin^2\alpha(1 - \sin^2\beta) - (1 - \sin^2\alpha)\sin^2\beta$

$= \sin^2\alpha - \sin^2\alpha\sin^2\beta - \sin^2\beta + \sin^2\alpha\sin^2\beta$

$= \sin^2\alpha - \sin^2\beta$

**19.** $R = \dfrac{1}{16}v^2 \sin\theta \cos\theta = \dfrac{1}{2} \cdot \dfrac{1}{16}v^2(2)\sin\theta\cos\theta$

$$= \dfrac{1}{32}v^2 \sin(2\theta)$$

## Practice Test, p. 249

**1.**
$$\dfrac{(\csc x - \cot x)(\csc x + \cot x)}{\sec x} = \cos x$$
$$\dfrac{\csc^2 x + \csc x \cot x - \csc x \cot x - \cot^2 x}{\sec x} =$$
$$\dfrac{\csc^2 x - \cot^2 x}{\sec x} = \dfrac{(1 + \cot^2 x) - \cot^2 x}{\sec x} =$$
$$\dfrac{1}{\sec x} =$$
$$\cos x =$$

**2.**
$$\dfrac{\sin^3 x - \cos^3 x}{1 + \cos x \sin x} = \sin x - \cos x$$
$$\dfrac{(\sin x - \cos x)(\sin^2 x + \sin x \cos x + \cos^2 x)}{1 + \cos x \sin x} =$$
$$\dfrac{(\sin x - \cos x)(1 + \sin x \cos x)}{1 + \cos x \sin x} =$$
$$\sin x - \cos x =$$

**3.** $\sin\theta = \dfrac{-55}{73}, \sec\theta = \dfrac{73}{48}, \cot\theta = \dfrac{-48}{55}, \tan\theta = \dfrac{-55}{48},$
$\csc\theta = \dfrac{-73}{55}$

**4.** $\dfrac{\sqrt{3}-1}{\sqrt{3}+1}$   **5.** $\dfrac{\sqrt{2}}{2}$   **6.** $\dfrac{-\sqrt{2}}{2}$

**7.** $\sin\left(x + \dfrac{\pi}{4}\right) - \sin\left(x - \dfrac{\pi}{4}\right) = \sqrt{2}\cos x$

$\sin x \cos\left(\dfrac{\pi}{4}\right) + \cos x \sin\left(\dfrac{\pi}{4}\right) - \sin x \cos\left(\dfrac{\pi}{4}\right) + \cos x \sin\left(\dfrac{\pi}{4}\right) =$

$$\sin\left(\dfrac{\pi}{4}\right)\cos x + \sin\left(\dfrac{\pi}{4}\right)\cos x =$$
$$2\sin\left(\dfrac{\pi}{4}\right)\cos x =$$
$$2\dfrac{\sqrt{2}}{2}\cos x =$$
$$\sqrt{2}\cos x =$$

**8.** $\sin\theta = \dfrac{15}{17}, \cos\theta = \dfrac{8}{17}, \tan\theta = \dfrac{15}{8}$   **9.** $\dfrac{-\sqrt{3}}{2}$   **10.** $\dfrac{1}{\sqrt{37}}; \dfrac{6}{\sqrt{37}}$

**11.** $20\sqrt{2-\sqrt{2}}$   **12.** $\dfrac{\sqrt{6}-\sqrt{2}}{4} \approx 0.2588; \dfrac{\sqrt{6}+\sqrt{2}}{4} \approx 0.9659$

**13.**
$$\dfrac{\tan\theta + \cot\theta}{\sin\theta\cos\theta} = \csc^2\theta\sec^2\theta$$
$$\dfrac{\dfrac{\sin\theta}{\cos\theta} + \dfrac{\cos\theta}{\sin\theta}}{\sin\theta\cos\theta} =$$
$$\dfrac{\dfrac{\sin^2\theta + \cos^2\theta}{\sin\theta\cos\theta}}{\sin\theta\cos\theta} =$$
$$\dfrac{1}{\sin\theta\cos\theta}\dfrac{1}{\sin\theta\cos\theta} =$$
$$\dfrac{1}{\sin^2\theta}\dfrac{1}{\cos^2\theta} =$$
$$\csc^2\theta\sec^2\theta =$$

**14.** $-1(2\cos^4\theta - 3\cos^2\theta + 1) =$
$-1(\cos^2\theta - 1)(2\cos^2\theta - 1) =$
$(1 - \cos^2\theta)(2\cos^2\theta - 1) =$
$\sin^2\theta\cos^2(2\theta) =$

**15.** $\dfrac{3-\sqrt{3}}{3+\sqrt{3}}$ or $\dfrac{\sqrt{3}-1}{\sqrt{3}+1}$   **16.** $\dfrac{\sqrt{2}}{2}$

**17.** $x = -35, y = -12, r = 37$

$\sin(2\theta) = \dfrac{840}{1369}, \cos(2\theta) = \dfrac{1081}{1369}, \tan(2\theta) = \dfrac{840}{1081}$

**18.**
$$\dfrac{\csc^2 x - 2}{2\cot^2 x - \csc^2 x} = 1$$
$$\dfrac{1 + \cot^2 x - 2}{2\cot^2 x - (1 + \cot^2 x)} =$$
$$\dfrac{\cot^2 x - 1}{2\cot^2 x - 1 - \cot^2 x} =$$
$$\dfrac{\cot^2 x - 1}{\cot^2 x - 1} =$$
$$1 =$$

**19. a.** The "0" (zero) was pressed.   **b.** $y(t) = 2\cos(2277\pi t)\cos(395\pi t)$

**20.** $y_a + y_h = 2\sin\left(800\pi t - \dfrac{\pi}{2}\right)\cos\dfrac{\pi}{2} = 0$

## Strengthening Core Skills, pp. 250–251

**1.** $\sin^2 x + \cos^2 x = 1$
$$\dfrac{\sin^2 x}{\sin^2 x} + \dfrac{\cos^2 x}{\sin^2 x} = \dfrac{1}{\sin^2 x}$$
$$1 + \cot^2 x = \csc^2 x \checkmark$$
$$\sin^2 x + \cos^2 x = 1$$
$$\dfrac{\sin^2 x}{\cos^2 x} + \dfrac{\cos^2 x}{\cos^2 x} = \dfrac{1}{\cos^2 x}$$
$$\tan^2 x + 1 = \sec^2 x \checkmark$$

**2.** $\cos(\alpha + \beta) = \cos(\alpha + \alpha) = \cos\alpha\cos\alpha - \sin\alpha\sin\alpha$
$$= \cos^2\alpha - \sin^2\alpha$$
$$= \cos^2\alpha - (1 - \cos^2\alpha)$$
$$= 2\cos^2\alpha - 1$$
$$= \cos^2\alpha - \sin^2\alpha$$
$$= (1 - \sin^2\alpha) - \sin^2\alpha$$
$$= 1 - 2\sin^2\alpha$$

## Cumulative Review Chapters 1–5, p. 252

**1.**

| Angles | Sides |
|---|---|
| $\alpha = 30°$ | $a = 20$ m |
| $\beta = 60°$ | $b = 20\sqrt{3}$ m |
| $\gamma = 90°$ | $c = 40$ m |

**3.** $\sin^2 x + \cos^2 x = 1; 1 + \cot^2 x = \csc^2 x; \tan^2 x + 1 = \sec^2 x$

**5.** about 15.7 ft/sec

**7.**

**9.** $\cos^2\left(\dfrac{\alpha}{2}\right) = \dfrac{\sec\alpha + 2 + \cos\alpha}{2\sec\alpha + 2}$
$$= \dfrac{\sec\alpha + 2 + \cos\alpha}{2\sec\alpha + 2}\dfrac{\cos\alpha}{\cos\alpha}$$
$$= \dfrac{1 + 2\cos\alpha + \cos^2\alpha}{2 + 2\cos\alpha}$$
$$= \dfrac{(1 + \cos\alpha)(1 + \cos\alpha)}{2(1 + \cos\alpha)}$$
$$= \dfrac{(1 + \cos\alpha)}{2}; \text{ let } \alpha = 2\theta$$

**11.** $\sin(2x) = 2 \sin x \cos x$

$\cos(2x) = \cos^2 x - \sin^2 x = 2 \cos^2 x - 1 = 1 - 2 \sin^2 x$

**13.** $\sin 195° = \dfrac{\sqrt{2} - \sqrt{6}}{4}$

$\cos 195° = \dfrac{-\sqrt{2} - \sqrt{6}}{4}$

**15. a.** just over 15 hr   **b.** April 15 to September 1 or 2

**17.** $\cot x \left( \tan x - \dfrac{\sin x}{\cos^3 x} \right) = \tan^2 x$

$1 - \dfrac{\cos x}{\sin x} \dfrac{\sin x}{\cos^3 x} =$

$1 - \dfrac{1}{\cos^2 x} =$

$1 - \sec^2 x =$

$\tan^2 x =$

**19.** about 1034 km

**85.**   **87.**

**89.**     $D: x \in [0, \infty), R: y \in [-2, \infty)$;
$D: x \in [-2, \infty), R: y \in [0, \infty)$

**91.**     $D: x \in (0, \infty), R: y \in (-\infty, \infty)$;
$D: x \in (-\infty, \infty), R: y \in (0, \infty)$

**93.**    $D: x \in (-\infty, 4], R: y \in (-\infty, 4]$;
$D: x \in (-\infty, 4], R: y \in (-\infty, 4]$

# CHAPTER 6
## Exercises 6.1, pp. 262–266

**1.** second; one    **3.** $(-11, -2), (-5, 0), (1, 2), (19, 4)$    **5.** False, answers will vary.    **7.** one-to-one    **9.** one-to-one    **11.** not a function
**13.** one-to-one    **15.** not one-to-one, fails horizontal line test: $x = -3$ and $x = 3$ are paired with $y = 1$    **17.** not one-to-one, $y = 7$ is paired with $x = -2$ and $x = 2$    **19.** one-to-one    **21.** one-to-one
**23.** not one-to-one; $p(t) > 5$, corresponds to two $x$-values
**25.** one-to-one    **27.** one-to-one
**29.** $f^{-1}(x) = \{(1, -2), (4, -1), (5, 0), (9, 2), (15, 5)\}$
**31.** $v^{-1}(x) = \{(3, -4), (2, -3), (1, 0), (0, 5), (-1, 12), (-2, 21), (-3, 32)\}$
**33.** $f^{-1}(x) = x - 5$    **35.** $p^{-1}(x) = \dfrac{-5}{4}x$    **37.** $f^{-1}(x) = \dfrac{x - 3}{4}$
**39.** $Y_1^{-1} = x^3 + 4$    **41.** $f^{-1}(x) = x^3 + 2$    **43.** $f^{-1}(x) = \sqrt[3]{x - 1}$
**45.** $f^{-1}(x) = \dfrac{8}{x} - 2$    **47.** $f^{-1}(x) = \dfrac{x}{1 - x}$
**49. a.** $x \geq -5, y \geq 0$    **b.** $f^{-1}(x) = \sqrt{x} - 5, x \geq 0, y \geq -5$
**51. a.** $x > 3, y > 0$    **b.** $v^{-1}(x) = \sqrt{\dfrac{8}{x} + 3}, x > 0, y > 3$
**53. a.** $x \geq -4, y \geq -2$    **b.** $p^{-1}(x) = \sqrt{x + 2} - 4, x \geq -2, y \geq -4$
**55.** $(f \circ g)(x) = x, (g \circ f)(x) = x$    **57.** $(f \circ g)(x) = x, (g \circ f)(x) = x$
**59.** $(f \circ g)(x) = x, (g \circ f)(x) = x$    **61.** $(f \circ g)(x) = x, (g \circ f)(x) = x$
**63.** $f^{-1}(x) = \dfrac{x + 5}{3}$    **65.** $f^{-1}(x) = 2x + 5$    **67.** $f^{-1}(x) = 2x + 6$
**69.** $f^{-1}(x) = \sqrt[3]{x - 3}$    **71.** $f^{-1}(x) = \dfrac{x^3 - 1}{2}$    **73.** $f^{-1}(x) = 2\sqrt[3]{x} + 1$
**75.** $f^{-1}(x) = \dfrac{x^2 - 2}{3}, x \geq 0; y \in \left[-\dfrac{2}{3}, \infty\right)$
**77.** $p^{-1}(x) = \dfrac{x^2}{4} + 3, x \geq 0; y \in [3, \infty)$
**79.** $v^{-1}(x) = \sqrt{x - 3}, x \geq 3; y \in [0, \infty)$
**81.**     **83.**

**95. a.** 31.5 cm    **b.** The result is 80 cm. It gives the distance of the projector from the screen.    **97. a.** $-63.5°F$    **b.** $f^{-1}(x) = \dfrac{-2}{7}(x - 59)$; independent: temperature, dependent: altitude    **c.** 22,000 ft
**99. a.** 144 ft    **b.** $f^{-1}(x) = \dfrac{\sqrt{x}}{4}$, independent: distance fallen, dependent: time fallen    **c.** 7 sec    **101. a.** 28,260 ft³    **b.** $f^{-1}(x) = \sqrt[3]{\dfrac{3x}{\pi}}$, independent: volume, dependent: height    **c.** 9 ft    **103.** Answers will vary.    **105.** d

**107.** $\tan^2\theta - \sin^2\theta = \dfrac{\sin^2\theta}{\cos^2\theta} - \dfrac{\sin^2\theta \cos^2\theta}{\cos^2\theta}$
$= \dfrac{\sin^2\theta - \sin^2\theta \cos^2\theta}{\cos^2\theta}$
$= \dfrac{\sin^2\theta}{\cos^2\theta}(1 - \cos^2\theta)$
$= \tan^2\theta \sin^2\theta$

**109.** $y = 2\sin\left(x - \dfrac{\pi}{4}\right), y = 2\cos\left(x - \dfrac{3\pi}{4}\right)$

**111.** Yes: 3777 m > 3428 m

## Exercises 6.2, p. 277–282

**1.** horizontal; line; one; one    **3.** $[-1, 1]; \left[-\dfrac{\pi}{2}, \dfrac{\pi}{2}\right]$
**5.** $\cos^{-1}(\frac{1}{3})$    **7.** $0; \dfrac{1}{2}; -\dfrac{\pi}{6}; -\dfrac{\pi}{2}$    **9.** $\dfrac{\pi}{4}$    **11.** $\dfrac{\pi}{2}$
**13.** 1.0956, 62.8°    **15.** 0.3876, 22.2°    **17.** $\dfrac{\sqrt{2}}{2}$    **19.** $\dfrac{\pi}{3}$
**21.** 45°    **23.** 0.8205    **25.** $0; \dfrac{\sqrt{3}}{2}; 120°; \pi$    **27.** $\dfrac{\pi}{3}$    **29.** $\pi$
**31.** 1.4352; 82.2°    **33.** 0.7297; 41.8°    **35.** $\dfrac{\pi}{4}$    **37.** 0.5560
**39.** $-\dfrac{\sqrt{2}}{2}$    **41.** $\dfrac{3\pi}{4}$    **43.** $0; -\sqrt{3}; 30°; \sqrt{3}; \dfrac{\pi}{3}$
**45.** $-\dfrac{\pi}{6}$    **47.** $\dfrac{\pi}{3}$    **49.** $-1.1170, -64.0°$    **51.** 0.9441, 54.1°

**53.** $-\dfrac{\pi}{6}$　**55.** $\dfrac{\sqrt{3}}{3}$　**57.** $\sqrt{2}$　**59.** $-30°$

**61.** cannot evaluate $\tan\left(\dfrac{\pi}{2}\right)$

**63.** $\csc\dfrac{\pi}{4} = \sqrt{2} > 1$, not in domain of $\sin^{-1}x$

**65.** $\sin\theta = \dfrac{3}{5}, \cos\theta = \dfrac{4}{5}, \tan\theta = \dfrac{3}{4}$

**67.** $\sin\theta = \dfrac{\sqrt{x^2 - 36}}{x}, \cos\theta = \dfrac{6}{x}, \tan\theta = \dfrac{\sqrt{x^2 - 36}}{6}$

**69.** $\dfrac{24}{25}$ 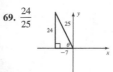　**71.** $\dfrac{\sqrt{5}}{3}$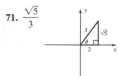

**73.** $\dfrac{\sqrt{25 - 9x^2}}{3x}$　**75.** $\sqrt{\dfrac{12}{12 + x^2}}$

**77.** $0; 2; 30°; -1; \pi$　**79.** $\dfrac{\pi}{6}$　**81.** $\dfrac{\pi}{6}$　**83.** $80.1°$　**85.** $67.8°$

**87. a.** $F_N \approx 2.13$ N; $F_N \approx 1.56$ N　**b.** $\theta \approx 63°$ for $F_N = 1$ N, $\theta \approx 24.9°$ for $F_N = 2$ N　**89.** $\approx 30°$

**91.** $\theta \approx 72.3°$; straight line distance; $\approx 157.5$ yd

**93. a.** $\alpha = \tan^{-1}\left(\dfrac{4}{x}\right), \beta = \tan^{-1}\left(\dfrac{1.5}{x}\right)$

**b.** $\theta = \tan^{-1}\left(\dfrac{4}{x}\right) - \tan^{-1}\left(\dfrac{1.5}{x}\right)$　**c.** $\theta \approx 27.0°$ at $x \approx 2.5$ ft

**95. a.** $\theta = \tan^{-1}\left(\dfrac{94}{x}\right) - \tan^{-1}\left(\dfrac{70}{x}\right)$　**b.** $\theta \approx 8.4°$ at $d \approx 81.1$ ft

**97. a.** $\theta \approx 15.5°$; $\theta \approx 0.2705$ rad　**b.** $\approx 29$ mi

**99. a.** $413.6$ ft away　**b.** $-503$ ft　**c.** $\approx 651.2$ ft

**101.** $\sin(2\theta) = \dfrac{84}{85}$

**103.** about 5 miles per hour

**105.** $\sin\theta = \dfrac{12}{13}, \cos\theta = \dfrac{5}{13}, \tan\theta = \dfrac{12}{5}$

## Mid-Chapter Check, p. 282–283

**1.** implicit, explicit

**2.** not one-to-one, $y = 5$ is paired with $x = -3$ and $x = -2$

**3.** $f^{-1}(x) = \{(-14, -3), (-8, -1), (10, 5), (-11, -2), (-2, 1)\}$

**4.** $f(x) = 2\sqrt[3]{x + 1} + 3$　　$(f \circ f^{-1})(x) = f[f^{-1}(x)]$

$y = 2\sqrt[3]{x + 1} + 3$　　　$= 2\sqrt[3]{\left(\dfrac{x - 3}{2}\right)^3 - 1 + 1} + 3$

$x = 2\sqrt[3]{y + 1} + 3$　　　$= 2\left(\dfrac{x - 3}{2}\right) + 3$

$\dfrac{x - 3}{2} = \sqrt[3]{y + 1}$　　　$= x - 3 + 3$

$\left(\dfrac{x - 3}{2}\right)^3 - 1 = y = f^{-1}(x)$　　$= x$ ✓

$(f^{-1} \circ f)(x) = f^{-1}[f(x)]$

$= \left(\dfrac{2\sqrt[3]{x + 1} + 3 - 3}{2}\right)^3 - 1$

$= (\sqrt[3]{x + 1})^3 - 1$

$= x + 1 - 1$

$= x$ ✓

**5. a.** $g(x)$ fails the horizontal line test　**b.** $D = [-3, \infty)$

**c.** $y = x - 1, D = [-2, \infty), R = [-3, \infty)$

**6.** The domain of $y = \sin x$ is restricted to $[-90°, 90]$ to create a one-to-one function.

**7. a.** $\sec^{-1}(\sqrt{2}) = \cos^{-1}\left(\dfrac{\sqrt{2}}{2}\right) = \dfrac{\pi}{4}$

**b.** $\csc^{-1}\left(\dfrac{2}{\sqrt{3}}\right) = \sin^{-1}\left(\dfrac{\sqrt{3}}{2}\right) = \dfrac{\pi}{3}$

**8. a.** $\dfrac{\pi}{6}$　**b.** $\cos\left(\dfrac{7\pi}{6}\right) = \cos\left(\dfrac{5\pi}{6}\right)$; $\cos^{-1}\left[\cos\left(\dfrac{5\pi}{6}\right)\right] = \left(\dfrac{5\pi}{6}\right)$

**9. a.** $0.9$　**b.** $1.2$

**10. a.** $\theta = \tan^{-1}\left(\dfrac{13}{84}\right), \cos\theta = \dfrac{84}{85}$

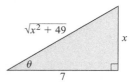

**b.** $\theta = \sin^{-1}\left(\dfrac{x}{\sqrt{x^2 + 49}}\right), \sec\theta = \dfrac{\sqrt{x^2 + 49}}{7}$

## Reinforcing Basic Concepts, p. 283–284

**Exercise 1: a.** $D = (-\infty, -1] \cup [1, \infty), R = \left[-\dfrac{\pi}{2}, 0\right) \cup \left(0, \dfrac{\pi}{2}\right]$

**b.** $D = [-1, 1], R = [0, \pi]$

**Exercise 2: a.** $D = (-\infty, \infty), R = (0, \pi)$

**b.** $D = [-1, 1], R = \left[-\dfrac{\pi}{2}, \dfrac{\pi}{2}\right]$

## Exercises 6.3, pp. 291–295

**1.** principal; $[0, 2\pi)$; real　**3.** $\dfrac{\pi}{4}; \dfrac{\pi}{4}; \dfrac{3\pi}{4}; \dfrac{\pi}{4} + 2\pi k; \dfrac{3\pi}{4} + 2\pi k$

**5.** Answers will vary.　**7. a.** QIV　**b.** 2 roots　**9. a.** QIV　**b.** 2 roots

**11.**

| $\theta$ | $\sin\theta$ | $\cos\theta$ | $\tan\theta$ |
|---|---|---|---|
| $0$ | $0$ | $1$ | $0$ |
| $\dfrac{\pi}{6}$ | $\dfrac{1}{2}$ | $\dfrac{\sqrt{3}}{2}$ | $\dfrac{\sqrt{3}}{3}$ |
| $\dfrac{\pi}{3}$ | $\dfrac{\sqrt{3}}{2}$ | $\dfrac{1}{2}$ | $\sqrt{3}$ |
| $\dfrac{\pi}{2}$ | $1$ | $0$ | und. |
| $\dfrac{2\pi}{3}$ | $\dfrac{\sqrt{3}}{2}$ | $-\dfrac{1}{2}$ | $-\sqrt{3}$ |
| $\dfrac{5\pi}{6}$ | $\dfrac{1}{2}$ | $-\dfrac{\sqrt{3}}{2}$ | $-\dfrac{\sqrt{3}}{3}$ |
| $\pi$ | $0$ | $-1$ | $0$ |
| $\dfrac{7\pi}{6}$ | $-\dfrac{1}{2}$ | $-\dfrac{\sqrt{3}}{2}$ | $\dfrac{\sqrt{3}}{3}$ |
| $\dfrac{4\pi}{3}$ | $-\dfrac{\sqrt{3}}{2}$ | $-\dfrac{1}{2}$ | $\sqrt{3}$ |

**13.** $\dfrac{\pi}{4}$　**15.** $-\dfrac{\pi}{4}$　**17.** $\dfrac{\pi}{6}$　**19.** $-\dfrac{\pi}{3}$　**21.** $\pi$　**23.** $\dfrac{\pi}{3}$　**25.** $\dfrac{\pi}{6}$　**27.** $\dfrac{5\pi}{6}$

**29.** $\dfrac{\pi}{6}, \dfrac{5\pi}{6}$　**31.** $\dfrac{2\pi}{3}, \dfrac{5\pi}{3}$　**33.** $\dfrac{3\pi}{4}, \dfrac{7\pi}{4}$　**35.** $\dfrac{\pi}{6}, \dfrac{5\pi}{6}, \dfrac{7\pi}{6}, \dfrac{11\pi}{6}$

**37.** $\dfrac{\pi}{3}, \dfrac{2\pi}{3}, \dfrac{4\pi}{3}, \dfrac{5\pi}{3}$　**39.** $\dfrac{\pi}{4}, \dfrac{3\pi}{4}, \dfrac{5\pi}{4}, \dfrac{7\pi}{4}$　**41.** $\dfrac{\pi}{2}, \dfrac{3\pi}{2}$

**43.** $\theta = 1.2310 + 2\pi k$ or $5.0522 + 2\pi k$

**45.** $x = \dfrac{\pi}{2} + \pi k$ or $\dfrac{\pi}{6} + 2\pi k$ or $\dfrac{5\pi}{6} + 2\pi k$

**47.** $x = \dfrac{2\pi}{3} + 2\pi k$ or $\dfrac{4\pi}{3} + 2\pi k$ or $1.4455 + 2\pi k$ or $4.8377 + 2\pi k$

**49.** $x = \dfrac{\pi}{6} + \pi k$ or $\dfrac{5\pi}{6} + \pi k$   **51.** $x = \dfrac{5\pi}{4} + 2\pi k$ or $\dfrac{7\pi}{4} + 2\pi k$

**53.** $x = \dfrac{3\pi}{4} + 2\pi k$ or $\dfrac{5\pi}{4} + 2\pi k$   **55.** $x = \dfrac{3\pi}{4} + \pi k$

**57.** $x = \dfrac{\pi}{3} + \pi k$ or $\dfrac{2\pi}{3} + \pi k$   **59.** $x = \dfrac{3\pi}{8} + \dfrac{\pi}{2}k$   **61.** $x = 3\pi + 6\pi k$

**63.** $x = \dfrac{\pi}{2} + \pi k$   **65.** $x = \dfrac{\pi}{6} + \dfrac{\pi}{3}k$ or $\dfrac{\pi}{12} + \pi k$ or $\dfrac{5\pi}{12} + \pi k$

**67. a.** $x \approx 1.2310$   **b.** $x \approx 1.2310 + 2\pi k$, $5.0522 + 2\pi k$

**69. a.** $x \approx 1.2094$   **b.** $x \approx 1.2094 + 2\pi k$, $5.0738 + 2\pi k$

**71. a.** $\theta \approx 0.3649$   **b.** $\theta \approx 0.3649 + \pi k$, $1.2059 + \pi k$

**73. a.** $\theta \approx 0.8861$   **b.** $\theta \approx 0.8861 + \pi k$, $2.2555 + \pi k$

**75.** $x = \dfrac{\pi}{6} + \pi k$ or $\dfrac{5\pi}{6} + \pi k$   **77.** $x = \dfrac{2\pi}{9} + \dfrac{4\pi}{3}k$ or $\dfrac{10\pi}{9} + \dfrac{4\pi}{3}k$

**79.** $\theta = \dfrac{\pi}{2}k$   **81.** $\theta \approx 0.3398 + 2\pi k$ or $2.8018 + 2\pi k$

**83.** $x \approx 0.7290$   **85.** $x \approx 2.6649$   **87.** $x \approx 0.4566$

**89.** 22.1° and 67.9°   **91.** 0°; the ramp is horizontal.

**93.** 30.7°; smaller   **95.** $\alpha = 35°$, $\beta \approx 25.5°$

**97.** $k \approx 1.36$, $\alpha \approx 20.6°$   **99. a.** 7 in.   **b.** $\approx 1.05$ in. and $\approx 5.24$ in.

**101.** 1.1547   **103.** $\dfrac{\pi}{2} + \pi k$, explanations will vary.

**105.** QIII: $\cos\theta = -\dfrac{5}{13}$, $\sec\theta = -\dfrac{13}{5}$, $\sin\theta = -\dfrac{12}{13}$, $\csc\theta = -\dfrac{13}{12}$, $\tan\theta = \dfrac{5}{12}$, $\cot\theta = \dfrac{12}{5}$

**107.** $\theta = \tan^{-1}\left(\dfrac{-12}{100}\right) \approx -6.8°$

**109.** $y = \sec\left(x - \dfrac{\pi}{4}\right)$, $y = \csc\left(x + \dfrac{\pi}{4}\right)$

### Exercises 6.4, pp. 302–306

**1.** $\sin^2 x + \cos^2 x = 1$; $1 + \tan^2 x = \sec^2 x$; $1 + \cot^2 x = \csc^2 x$

**3.** factor; grouping   **5.** Answers will vary.

**7.** $\dfrac{\pi}{12}, \dfrac{5\pi}{12}$   **9.** 0   **11.** 0.4456, 1.1252   **13.** $\dfrac{\pi}{4}, \dfrac{5\pi}{4}, \dfrac{\pi}{6}, \dfrac{5\pi}{6}$

**15.** $\dfrac{\pi}{4}, \dfrac{3\pi}{4}, \dfrac{5\pi}{4}, \dfrac{7\pi}{4}, 0.8411, 5.4421$   **17.** $\dfrac{\pi}{4}, \dfrac{3\pi}{4}, \dfrac{5\pi}{4}, \dfrac{7\pi}{4}$

**19.** $\dfrac{\pi}{6}, \dfrac{5\pi}{6}, 0.7297, 2.4119$   **21.** $\dfrac{2\pi}{3}$

**23.** $\dfrac{\pi}{9} + \dfrac{2\pi}{3}k, \dfrac{5\pi}{9} + \dfrac{2\pi}{3}k$; $k = 0, 1, 2$   **25.** $\dfrac{\pi}{4}, \dfrac{3\pi}{4}, \dfrac{5\pi}{4}, \dfrac{7\pi}{4}$

**27.** $P = 12$; $x = 3$; $x = 11$   **29.** $P = 24$; $x \approx 0.4909$, $x \approx 5.5091$

**31.** $\dfrac{\pi}{12}, \dfrac{17\pi}{12}$   **33.** 0.3747, 5.9085, 2.7669, 3.5163

**35.** $\dfrac{\pi}{2}\left(\dfrac{3\pi}{2}\text{ is extraneous}\right)$   **37.** $\dfrac{3\pi}{4}, \dfrac{7\pi}{4}$   **39.** $\dfrac{\pi}{12}, \dfrac{5\pi}{12}, \dfrac{13\pi}{12}, \dfrac{17\pi}{12}$

**41. I. a.** $\left(\dfrac{5}{2}, \dfrac{5}{2}\right)$   **b.** $D = \sqrt{12.5}$, $\theta = \dfrac{\pi}{4}$, $y = \dfrac{\sqrt{12.5} - x\cos\left(\dfrac{\pi}{4}\right)}{\sin\left(\dfrac{\pi}{4}\right)}$

**c.** verified

**II. a.** $(2, 4)$   **b.** $D = 2\sqrt{5}$, $\theta \approx 1.1071$, $y = \dfrac{2\sqrt{5} - x\cos 1.1071}{\sin 1.1071}$

**c.** verified

**III. a.** $(1, \sqrt{3})$   **b.** $D = 2$, $\theta = \dfrac{\pi}{3}$, $y = \dfrac{2 - x\cos\left(\dfrac{\pi}{3}\right)}{\sin\left(\dfrac{\pi}{3}\right)}$   **c.** verified

**43. a.** $2500\pi$ ft$^3 \approx 7853.98$ ft$^3$   **b.** $\approx 7824.09$ ft$^3$   **c.** $\theta \approx 78.5°$

**45. a.** $\approx 78.53$ m$^3$/sec   **b.** during the months of August, September, October, and November   **47. a.** $\approx \$3554.52$   **b.** during the months of May, June, July, and August   **49. a.** $\approx 12.67$ in.   **b.** during the months of April, May, June, July, and August   **51. a.** $\approx 8.39$ gal   **b.** approx. day 214 to day 333   **53. a.** 68 bpm   **b.** $\approx 176.2$ bpm   **c.** from about 4.6 min to 7.4 min

**55. a.** $y = 19\cos\left(\pi - \dfrac{\pi}{6}x\right) + 53$   **b.** $y = -21\sin\left(\dfrac{2\pi}{365}x\right) + 29$

**57. a.** $L \approx 25.5$ cm.   **b.** $\theta \approx 38.9°$ or $33.4°$, depending on what side you consider the base.

**59.** $\theta = \tan^{-1}\left(\dfrac{x}{6}\right)$, $\cos\theta = \dfrac{6}{\sqrt{x^2 + 6}}$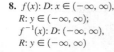

**61.** $\dfrac{\sqrt{6} + \sqrt{2}}{4}, \dfrac{\sqrt{6} - \sqrt{2}}{4}$   **63.** $\theta \approx 4.56°$

### Summary and Concept Review, pp. 306–309

**1.** no   **2.** no   **3.** yes   **4.** $f^{-1}(x) = \dfrac{x - 2}{-3}$   **5.** $f^{-1}(x) = \sqrt{x + 2}$

**6.** $f^{-1}(x) = x^2 + 1$; $x \geq 0$

**7.** $f(x)$: $D$: $x \in [-4, \infty)$;   **8.** $f(x)$: $D$: $x \in (-\infty, \infty)$;
$R$: $y \in [0, \infty)$;   $R$: $y \in (-\infty, \infty)$;
$f^{-1}(x)$: $D$: $x \in [0, \infty)$,   $f^{-1}(x)$: $D$: $(-\infty, \infty)$,
$R$: $y \in [-4, \infty)$   $R$: $y \in (-\infty, \infty)$

**9.** $f(x)$: $D$: $x \in (-\infty, \infty)$,
$R$: $y \in (0, \infty)$;
$f^{-1}(x)$: $D$: $x \in (0, \infty)$,
$R$: $y \in (-\infty, \infty)$

**10. a.** \$3.05   **b.** $f^{-1}(t) = \dfrac{t - 2}{0.15}$, $f^{-1}(3.05) = 7$   **c.** 12 days

**11.** $\dfrac{\pi}{4}$ or 45°   **12.** $\dfrac{\pi}{6}$ or 30°

**13.** $\dfrac{5\pi}{6}$ or 150°   **14.** 1.3431 or 77.0°   **15.** 1.0956 or 62.8°

**16.** 0.5054 or 29.0°   **17.** $\dfrac{1}{2}$   **18.** $\dfrac{\pi}{4}$   **19.** undefined

**20.** 1.0245   **21.** 60°   **22.** $\dfrac{3\pi}{4}$   **23.** $\sin\theta = \dfrac{35}{37}$

**24.** $\tan\theta = \dfrac{\sqrt{49 - 9x^2}}{3x}$   **25.** $\cot\theta = \dfrac{9}{x}$   **26.** $\theta = \cos^{-1}\left(\dfrac{x}{5}\right)$

**27.** $\theta = \sec^{-1}\left(\dfrac{x}{7\sqrt{3}}\right)$   **28.** $\theta = \sin^{-1}\left(\dfrac{x}{4}\right) + \dfrac{\pi}{6}$

**29. a.** $\dfrac{\pi}{4}$   **b.** $\dfrac{\pi}{4}, \dfrac{3\pi}{4}$   **c.** $x = \dfrac{\pi}{4} + 2\pi k$ or $\dfrac{3\pi}{4} + 2\pi k$, $k \in \mathbb{Z}$

**30. a.** $\dfrac{2\pi}{3}$   **b.** $\dfrac{2\pi}{3}, \dfrac{4\pi}{3}$   **c.** $\dfrac{2\pi}{3} + 2\pi k$ or $\dfrac{4\pi}{3} + 2\pi k$, $k \in \mathbb{Z}$

**31. a.** $-\dfrac{\pi}{3}$   **b.** $\dfrac{2\pi}{3}, \dfrac{5\pi}{3}$   **c.** $\dfrac{2\pi}{3} + \pi k$, $k \in \mathbb{Z}$

**32. a.** $\approx 1.1102$   **b.** $\approx 1.1102, 5.1729$   **c.** $\approx 1.1102 + 2\pi k$ or $5.1729 + 2\pi k$, $k \in \mathbb{Z}$   **33. a.** $\approx 0.3376$   **b.** $\approx 0.3376, 1.2332, 3.4792, 4.3748$   **c.** $\approx 0.3376 + \pi k$ or $1.2332 + \pi k$, $k \in \mathbb{Z}$   **34. a.** $\approx 0.3614$   **b.** $\approx 0.3614, 2.7802$   **c.** $\approx 0.3614 + 2\pi k$ or $2.7802 + 2\pi k$, $k \in \mathbb{Z}$

**35.** $\theta \approx 1.1547$   **36.** $x = \dfrac{\pi}{12}, \dfrac{5\pi}{12}$   **37.** $x \approx 0.7297, 2.4119$; $x = \dfrac{\pi}{6}, \dfrac{5\pi}{6}$

**38.** $x = \dfrac{\pi}{6}, \dfrac{5\pi}{6}, \dfrac{11\pi}{6}$   **39.** $x = \dfrac{\pi}{2}$   **40.** $P = 12$; $x \approx 2.6931$, $x \approx 9.3069$

**41.** $P = 6; x = 0, x = \dfrac{9}{2}$    **42. a.** $\approx 43(1000) = \$43,000$
**b.** April through August

### Mixed Review, pp. 309–310

**1. a.** $f^{-1}(x) = \sqrt{\dfrac{1}{x} - 2}$   **b.** $D: x > 0, R: y > -2$   **c.** verified

**3.** $x = \dfrac{7\pi}{6}, \dfrac{11\pi}{6}$   **5.** 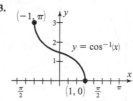    $\tan\theta = \dfrac{x}{\sqrt{100 - x^2}}$

**7.** $x \approx 0.4103; x \approx 4.9230$   **9. a.** $x \in [1, \infty), y \in [2, \infty);$
**b.** $g^{-1}(x) = (x - 2)^2 + 1, x \in [2, \infty), y \in [1, \infty);$   **c.** Answers will vary.

**11.** $\dfrac{3\pi}{4}$ or $135°$   **13.** $\dfrac{\pi}{3}$ or $60°$   **15.** $\theta = \csc^{-1}\left(\dfrac{x}{2\sqrt{2}}\right) + \dfrac{\pi}{4}$

**17.** $\theta \approx 15.7°$   **19.** $\theta = \dfrac{7\pi}{6} + 2\pi k, \dfrac{11\pi}{6} + 2\pi k; k \in \mathbb{Z}$

### Practice Test, pp. 310–311

**1.** $f(x) = x^3$ is a one-to-one function, $f(x) = x^2$ is not.

**2. a.** $A \approx 39.27$ cm$^2$   **b.** $A^{-1}(t) = \dfrac{2t}{r^2}$; we obtain $t = \dfrac{\pi}{4}$

**3.**     **4.** $y \approx 1.2310$

$D: x \in [-1, 1], R: y \in [0, \pi]$

**5.** $y = 30°$   **6.** $f(x) = \dfrac{1}{2}$   **7.** $y = 30°$

**8.** $y = 0.8523$ rad or $y = 48.8°$   **9.** $y = 78.5°$ or $\dfrac{157\pi}{360}$ rad

**10.** $y = \dfrac{7\pi}{24}$ rad or $52.5°$

**11.**     **12.**

$\cos\theta = \dfrac{33}{65}$     $\cot\theta = \dfrac{x}{5}$

**13. a.** $\cos^{-1}\left(\dfrac{-\sqrt{2}}{2}\right) = \dfrac{3\pi}{4}$   **b.** $x = \dfrac{3\pi}{4}, \dfrac{5\pi}{4}$

**c.** $x = \dfrac{3\pi}{4} + 2\pi k$ or $\dfrac{5\pi}{4} + 2\pi k, k \in \mathbb{Z}$

**14. a.** $\dfrac{\pi}{6}$   **b.** $x = \dfrac{\pi}{6}, \dfrac{11\pi}{6}$   **c.** $x = \dfrac{\pi}{6} + 2\pi k$ or $\dfrac{11\pi}{6} + 2\pi k, k \in \mathbb{Z}$

**15. a.** $x \approx 0.1922$   **b.** $x \approx 0.1922, 1.3786, 3.3338, 4.5202$
**c.** $x \approx 0.1922 + \pi k$ or $1.3786 + \pi k, k \in \mathbb{Z}$
**16. a.** $x \approx 0.9204$   **b.** $x \approx 0.9204, 2.2212, 4.0620, 5.3628$
**c.** $x \approx 0.9204 + \pi k$ or $2.2212 + \pi k, k \in \mathbb{Z}$
**17.** $x \approx -1.6875, -0.3413, 1.1321, 2.8967$
**18.** $x \approx 0.9671, 2.6110, 3.4538$   **19.** $x = 0, \pi, \dfrac{7\pi}{6}, \dfrac{11\pi}{6}$

**20.** $x = \dfrac{7\pi}{12}, \dfrac{11\pi}{12}, \dfrac{19\pi}{12}, \dfrac{23\pi}{12}$   **21.** $x = \dfrac{\pi}{2}, \dfrac{3\pi}{2}; x \approx 3.3090, 6.1157$

**22.** $x = \dfrac{5\pi}{6}, \dfrac{11\pi}{6}$   **23. a.** 6 or \$6,000   **b.** January through July

**24.** $x \in \mathbb{R}, y \in [-3, \infty)$; graph of $f$ is a parabola (hence not one-to-one); $x \in [2, \infty); f^{-1}(x) = \sqrt{x + 3} + 2, x \in [-3, \infty), y \in [2, \infty)$.
**25.** $-\dfrac{1}{2}$

### Strengthening Core Skills, pp. 312–313

**Exercise 1:** $x \in (0.6025, 2.5391)$
**Exercise 2:** $x \in [0, 0.7945] \cup [4.4415, 2\pi]$
**Exercise 3:** $x \in [0, 2.6154] \cup [9.3847, 12]$
**Exercise 4:** $x \in (67.3927, 202.6073)$

### Cumulative Review Chapters, 1–6, pp. 313–314

**1.** $\sin\theta = \dfrac{84}{85}$, $\csc\theta = \dfrac{85}{84}$, $\cos\theta = \dfrac{-13}{85}$, $\sec\theta = \dfrac{-85}{13}$, $\tan\theta = \dfrac{-84}{13}$,
$\cot\theta = \dfrac{-13}{84}$   **3. a.** $56.335°$   **b.** $0.9832$   **5.** about 474 ft

**7.** $x = \dfrac{\pi}{2}, \dfrac{3\pi}{2}, 2\pi + \sin^{-1}\left(-\dfrac{1}{6}\right) \approx 6.1157,$
$\pi - \sin^{-1}\left(-\dfrac{1}{6}\right) \approx 3.3090$   **9.** 50.89 km/hr   **11.** $\dfrac{\sqrt{3}}{2}$
**13. a.** $Y_1 = 48.778\sin(0.213x - 1.106) + 51.642$   **b.** about 83.2%

**15.** $x \in (1, 5)$   **17.** $\dfrac{99}{101}$

**19.** $\dfrac{\cos x + 1}{\tan^2 x} = \dfrac{\cos x}{\sec x - 1}$
$= \dfrac{\cos x(\sec x + 1)}{(\sec x - 1)(\sec x + 1)}$
$= \dfrac{1 + \cos x}{\sec^2 x - 1}$
$= \dfrac{1 + \cos x}{\tan^2 x}$

## CHAPTER 7
### Exercises 7.1, pp. 324–329

**1.** ambiguous  **3.** I; II  **5.** Answers will vary.  **7.** $a \approx 8.98$
**9.** $C \approx 49.2°$  **11.** $C \approx 21.4°$  **13.** $\angle C = 78°$, $b \approx 109.5$ cm,
$c \approx 119.2$ cm  **15.** $\angle C = 90°$, $a = 10$ in., $c = 20$ in.
**17.**                    **19.** $\angle C = 90°$, $a = 15$ mi, $b = 15$ mi

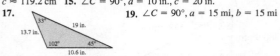

**21.** $\angle A = 57°$, $b \approx 49.5$ km, $c \approx 17.1$ km

**23.**                    **25. a.** 10 cm  **b.** 0  **c.** 2  **d.** 1

**27.** not possible  **29.** $B = 60°$, $C = 90°$, $b = 12.9\sqrt{3}$ mi
**31.** $A \approx 39°$, $B \approx 82°$, $a \approx 42.6$ mi or $A \approx 23°$, $B \approx 98°$, $a \approx 26.4$ mi
**33.** $A \approx 39°$, $B \approx 82°$, $a \approx 42.6$ ft or $A \approx 23°$, $B \approx 98°$, $a \approx 26.4$ ft
**35.** not possible  **37.** $A \approx 80.0°$, $B \approx 38.0°$, $b \approx 1.8 \times 10^{25}$ mi
**39.** $A_1 \approx 19.3°$, $A_2 \approx 160.7°$, $48° + 160.7° > 180°$; no second solution
possible  **41.** $C_1 \approx 71.3°$, $C_2 \approx 108.7°$, $57° + 108.7° < 180°$; two
solutions possible  **43.** not possible, $\sin A > 1$  **45.** $\dfrac{\sqrt{2}}{2}$

**47.** 34.6 million miles or 119.7 million miles  **49. a.** No  **b.** $\approx 3.9$ mi
**51.** $V \leftrightarrow S = 41.7$ km, $V \leftrightarrow P = 80.8$ km
**53. a.** No  **b.** about 201.5 ft  **c.** $\approx 15$ sec
**55.** Two triangles

| Angles | Sides | | Angles | Sides |
|---|---|---|---|---|
| $A_1 \approx 41.1°$ | $a = 12$ cm | | $A_2 \approx 138.9°$ | $a = 12$ cm |
| $B = 26°$ | $b = 8$ cm | | $B = 26°$ | $b = 8$ cm |
| $C_1 \approx 112.9°$ | $c_1 \approx 16.8$ cm | | $C_2 \approx 15.1°$ | $c_2 \approx 4.8$ cm |

**57.**

| Angles | Sides |
|---|---|
| $A_1 \approx 47.0°$ | $a = 9$ cm |
| $B_1 \approx 109.0°$ | $b_1 \approx 11.6$ cm |
| $C \approx 24°$ | $c = 5$ cm |

| Angles | Sides |
|---|---|
| $A_2 \approx 133.0°$ | $a = 9$ cm |
| $B_2 \approx 23.0°$ | $b_2 \approx 4.8$ cm |
| $C \approx 24°$ | $c = 5$ cm |

**59.** $a \approx 33.7$ ft, $c \approx 22.3$ ft  **61.** Rhymes to Tarryson: 61.7 km, Sexton to Tarryson: 52.6 km  **63.** $\approx 3.2$ mi  **65.** $h \approx 161.9$ yd
**67.** angle = 90°; sides ≈ 9.8 cm, 11 cm; diameter ≈ 11 cm; it is a right triangle.  **69. a.** about 3187 m  **b.** about 2613 m  **c.** about 2368 m
**71.**

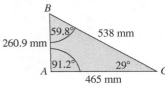

$\sqrt{3} = \dfrac{\sin 60°}{\sin 30°}$; $\sqrt{2} = \dfrac{\sin 90°}{\sin 45°}$

**73.** $A = 19°$, $B = 31°$, $C = 130°$, $a = 45$ cm, $b \approx 71.2$ cm, $c \approx 105.8$ cm

**75.** $\approx 12,564$ mph

**77.**
$$\tan^2 x - \sin^2 x = \tan^2 x \sin^2 x$$
$$\frac{\sin^2 x}{\cos^2 x} - \sin^2 x =$$
$$\frac{\sin^2 x}{\cos^2 x} - \frac{\sin^2 x \cos^2 x}{\cos^2 x} =$$
$$\frac{\sin^2 x - \sin^2 x \cos^2 x}{\cos^2 x} =$$
$$\frac{\sin^2 x (1 - \cos^2 x)}{\cos^2 x} =$$
$$\frac{\sin^2 x \sin^2 x}{\cos^2 x} =$$
$$\sin^2 x \frac{\sin^2 x}{\cos^2 x} =$$
$$\sin^2 x \tan^2 x =$$

**79.** $x = \dfrac{\pi}{6}, \dfrac{5\pi}{6}$  **81.** $y = 2\tan\left(\dfrac{1}{2}x - \dfrac{\pi}{2}\right)$

### Exercises 7.2, pp. 337–342

**1.** cosines  **3.** Pythagorean  **5.** $B \approx 33.1°$, $C \approx 129.9°$, $a \approx 19.8$ m; law of sines  **7.** yes  **9.** no  **11.** yes  **13.** verified  **15.** $B \approx 41.4°$
**17.** $a \approx 7.24$  **19.** $A \approx 41.6°$  **21.** $A \approx 120.4°$, $B \approx 21.6°$, $c \approx 53.5$ cm
**23.** $A \approx 23.8°$, $C \approx 126.2°$, $b \approx 16$ mi
**25.**

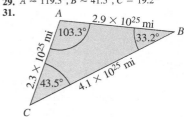

**27.** $A \approx 137.9°$, $B \approx 15.6°$, $C \approx 26.5°$
**29.** $A \approx 119.3°$, $B \approx 41.5°$, $C \approx 19.2°$
**31.**

**33.** $A \approx 139.7°$, $B \approx 23.7°$, $C \approx 16.6°$
**35.** $C \approx 86.3°$  **37.** about 1688 mi
**39.** It cannot be constructed (available length ≈ 10,703.6 ft).
**41.** $P \approx 27.7°$; heading 297.7°  **43.** 1678.2 mi
**45.** $P \approx 22.4$ cm, $A = 135°$, $B \approx 23.2°$, $C \approx 21.8°$
**47.** $A \approx 20.6°$, $B \approx 15.3°$, $C \approx 144.1°$  **49.** 58.78 cm
**51.** $a = 13$    $A \approx 133.2°$   **53.** 33.7°; 150 ft$^2$
   $b = 5$     $B \approx 16.3°$
   $c = \sqrt{82}$  $C \approx 30.5°$

**55. a.** $0.65 = 65\%$ **b.** \$1,950,000  **57.** about 483,529 km$^2$
**59.** $387 + 502 = 889 < 902$  **61.** (1) $a^2 = b^2 + c^2 - 2bc \cos A$
(2) $b^2 = a^2 + c^2 - 2ac \cos B$, use substitution for $a^2$ and
(2) becomes $b^2 = (b^2 + c^2 - 2bc \cos A) + c^2 - 2ac \cos B$.
Then $0 = 2c^2 - 2bc \cos A - 2ac \cos B$, $2bc \cos A + 2ac \cos B = 2c^2$, $b \cos A + a \cos B = c$.
**63.** $\theta = \dfrac{\pi}{6}$  **65.** Divide by $\cos x$: $\tan^2 x + 1 = \sec^2 x$; divide by $\sin x$:
$1 + \cot^2 x = \csc^2 x$  **67.** $\sin 75° = \dfrac{\sqrt{6} + \sqrt{2}}{4}$

### Mid-Chapter Check, p. 342–343

**1.** $\sin B = \dfrac{b \sin A}{a}$  **2.** $\cos B = \dfrac{a^2 + c^2 - b^2}{2ac}$
**3.** $a \approx 129$ m, $B \approx 86.5°$, $C \approx 62.5°$
**4.** $A \approx 42.3°$, $B \approx 81.5°$, $C \approx 56.2°$
**5.** $A = 44°$    $a = 2.1$ km  **6.** $A \approx 18.5°$    $a = 70$ yd
   $B \approx 68.1°$  $b \approx 2.8$ km      $B \approx 134.5°$  $b \approx 157.1$ yd
   $C \approx 67.9°$  $c = 2.8$ km      $C = 27°$     $c = 100$ yd
or
   $A = 44°$    $a = 2.1$ km
   $B \approx 23.9°$  $b \approx 1.2$ km
   $C \approx 112.1°$  $c = 2.8$ km
**7.** about 60.7 ft  **8.** 169 m  **9.** $\alpha \approx 49.6°$; $\beta \approx 92.2°$; $\gamma \approx 38.2°$
**10.** 9.4 mi

### Reinforcing Basic Concepts, pp. 343

**1.**

| Angles | Sides |
|---|---|
| $A = 35°$ | $a = 11.6$ cm |
| $B \approx 81.5°$ | $a = 20$ cm |
| $C \approx 63.5°$ | $c = 18$ cm |

Very close.

**2.** For $\angle A = 35°$, $a \approx 10.3$
For $\angle A = 50°$, $a \approx 14.2$
For $\angle A = 70°$, $a \approx 19.1$;
yes, very close

### Exercises 7.3, pp. 355–359

**1.** scalar  **3.** directed; line  **5.** Answers will vary.
**7.**     **9.**     **11.**

**13.**  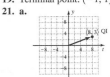   **15.**

**17.** Terminal point: $(5, -1)$, length: $\sqrt{53}$
**19.** Terminal point: $(-1, 1)$, length: $\sqrt{34}$
**21. a.**  **23. a.**

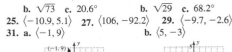

**b.** $\sqrt{73}$  **c.** 20.6°       **b.** $\sqrt{29}$  **c.** 68.2°
**25.** $\langle -10.9, 5.1 \rangle$  **27.** $\langle 106, -92.2 \rangle$  **29.** $\langle -9.7, -2.6 \rangle$
**31. a.** $\langle -1, 9 \rangle$       **b.** $\langle 5, -3 \rangle$

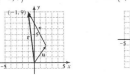

**c.** $\langle -0.5, 15 \rangle$

**d.** $\langle 8, -9 \rangle$

**33. a.** $\langle 8, 4 \rangle$

**b.** $\langle 6, -8 \rangle$

**c.** $\langle 15.5, 5 \rangle$

**d.** $\langle 5, -14 \rangle$

**35. a.** $\langle -3, 6 \rangle$

**b.** $\langle -5, -2 \rangle$

**c.** $\langle -6.5, 10 \rangle$

**d.** $\langle -6, -6 \rangle$

**37.** True   **39.** False   **41.** True

**43.** $\mathbf{u} + \mathbf{v} = \langle 8, 6 \rangle$
$\mathbf{u} - \mathbf{v} = \langle -6, 2 \rangle$

**45.** $\mathbf{u} + \mathbf{v} = \langle -9, -6 \rangle$
$\mathbf{u} - \mathbf{v} = \langle 7, 0 \rangle$

**47.** $\mathbf{u} + \mathbf{v} = \langle -3, -6 \rangle$
$\mathbf{u} - \mathbf{v} = \langle -7, 0 \rangle$

**49.** $\mathbf{u} = 8\mathbf{i} + 15\mathbf{j}$
$|\mathbf{u}| = 17$

**51.** $\mathbf{p} = -3.2\mathbf{i} - 5.7\mathbf{j}$
$|\mathbf{p}| \approx 6.54$

**53. a.**

**b.** $\mathbf{v} = \langle -11.5, -3.3 \rangle$
**c.** $\mathbf{v} = -11.5\mathbf{i}, -3.3\mathbf{j}$

**55. a.**

**b.** $\mathbf{w} = \langle 2.5, 9.2 \rangle$
**c.** $\mathbf{w} = 2.5\mathbf{i} + 9.2\mathbf{j}$

**57. a.** $\mathbf{p} = -2\mathbf{i} + 2\mathbf{j}; |\mathbf{p}| = 2\sqrt{2}, \theta = 135°$
**b.** $\mathbf{q} = 6\mathbf{i} - 8\mathbf{j}; |\mathbf{q}| = 10, \theta = 306.9°$
**c.** $\mathbf{r} = -2\mathbf{i} + 1.5\mathbf{j}; |\mathbf{r}| = 2.5, \theta = 143.1°$
**d.** $\mathbf{s} = 10\mathbf{i} - 13\mathbf{j}; |\mathbf{s}| \approx 16.4, \theta = 307.6°$
**59. a.** $\mathbf{p} = 2\sqrt{2}\mathbf{i} + 2\mathbf{j}; |\mathbf{p}| \approx 3.5, \theta \approx 35.3°$
**b.** $\mathbf{q} = 8\sqrt{2}\mathbf{i} + 12\mathbf{j}; |\mathbf{q}| \approx 16.5, \theta \approx 46.7°$
**c.** $\mathbf{r} = 5.5\sqrt{2}\mathbf{i} + 6.5\mathbf{j}; |\mathbf{r}| \approx 10.1, \theta \approx 39.9°$
**d.** $\mathbf{s} = 11\sqrt{2}\mathbf{i} + 17\mathbf{j}; |\mathbf{s}| \approx 23.0, \theta \approx 47.5°$
**61. a.** $\mathbf{p} = 8\mathbf{i} + 4\mathbf{j}; |\mathbf{p}| \approx 8.9, \theta \approx 26.6°$
**b.** $\mathbf{q} = 16\mathbf{i} + 4\mathbf{j}; |\mathbf{q}| \approx 16.5, \theta \approx 14.0°$
**c.** $\mathbf{r} = 18\mathbf{i} + 8\mathbf{j}; |\mathbf{r}| \approx 19.7, \theta \approx 24.0°$
**d.** $\mathbf{s} = 20\mathbf{i} + 4\mathbf{j}; |\mathbf{s}| \approx 20.4, \theta \approx 11.3°$

**63.** $\left\langle \dfrac{7}{25}, \dfrac{24}{25} \right\rangle$, verified   **65.** $\left\langle \dfrac{-20}{29}, \dfrac{21}{29} \right\rangle$, verified

**67.** $\dfrac{20}{29}\mathbf{i} - \dfrac{21}{29}\mathbf{j}$, verified   **69.** $\dfrac{7}{25}\mathbf{i} + \dfrac{24}{25}\mathbf{j}$, verified

**71.** $\left\langle -\dfrac{13}{\sqrt{178}}, \dfrac{3}{\sqrt{178}} \right\rangle$, verified   **73.** $\dfrac{6}{\sqrt{157}}\mathbf{i} + \dfrac{11}{\sqrt{157}}\mathbf{j}$, verified

**75.** $\approx 4.48 \left\langle \dfrac{5}{\sqrt{29}}, \dfrac{2}{\sqrt{29}} \right\rangle \approx \langle 4.16, 1.66 \rangle$

**77.** $\approx 5.83 \left\langle \dfrac{8}{\sqrt{73}}, \dfrac{-3}{\sqrt{73}} \right\rangle \approx \langle 5.46, -2.05 \rangle$   **79.** $\approx 14.4$   **81.** $\approx 24.3°$

**83.** hor. comp. $\approx 79.9$ ft/sec; vert. comp. $\approx 60.2$ ft/sec
**85.** heading $68.2°$ at $266.7$ mph   **87.** $\approx (82.10$ cm, $22.00$ cm$)$
**89.** $1\langle a, b \rangle = \langle 1a, 1b \rangle = \langle a, b \rangle$
**91.** $\langle a, b \rangle - \langle c, d \rangle = \langle a - c, b - d \rangle = \langle a + (-c), b + (-d) \rangle$
$= \langle a, b \rangle + \langle -c, -d \rangle = \langle a, b \rangle + -1\langle c, d \rangle = \mathbf{u} + (-1\mathbf{v})$
**93.** $(ck)\mathbf{u} = \langle cka, ckb \rangle = c\langle ka, kb \rangle = c(k\mathbf{u})$
$c(k\mathbf{u}) = \langle cka, ckb \rangle = \langle kca, kcb \rangle = k\langle ca, cb \rangle = k(c\mathbf{u})$
**95.** $\mathbf{u} + (-\mathbf{u}) = \langle a, b \rangle + \langle -a, -b \rangle = \langle a - a, b - b \rangle = \langle 0, 0 \rangle$
**97.** $(c + k)\mathbf{u} = (c + k)\langle a, b \rangle = \langle (c + k)a, (c + k)b \rangle =$
$\langle ca + ka, cb + kb \rangle = \langle ca, cb \rangle + \langle ka, kb \rangle = c\mathbf{u} + k\mathbf{u}$
**99.** $\langle 1, 3 \rangle + \langle 3, 3 \rangle + \langle 4, -1 \rangle + \langle 2, -4 \rangle + \langle -4, -3 \rangle + \langle -6, 2 \rangle = \langle 0, 0 \rangle$
**101.** Answers will vary, one possibility: $0°, 81.4°, -34°$.

**103.** $2 \sec^2\theta = \dfrac{1}{1 + \sin \theta} + \dfrac{1}{1 - \sin \theta}$

$= \dfrac{1 - \sin \theta}{(1 + \sin \theta)(1 - \sin \theta)} + \dfrac{1 + \sin \theta}{(1 - \sin \theta)(1 + \sin \theta)}$

$= \dfrac{2}{1 - \sin^2\theta}$

$= \dfrac{2}{\cos^2\theta}$

$= 2 \sec^2\theta$

**105.** $\sin x = \dfrac{5}{13}$, $\csc x = \dfrac{13}{5}$, $\cos x = \dfrac{12}{13}$, $\sec x = \dfrac{13}{12}$, $\tan x = \dfrac{5}{12}$,

$\cot x = \dfrac{12}{5}$   **107. a.** $y = 2 \sin\left( x + \dfrac{\pi}{4} \right)$

**b.** $y = 2 \cos\left( x - \dfrac{\pi}{4} \right)$

## Exercises 7.4, pp. 369–373
**1.** equilibrium; zero   **3.** orthogonal   **5.** Answers will vary.
**7.** $\langle 6, 8 \rangle$   **9.** $\langle -5, 10 \rangle$   **11.** $-6\mathbf{i} - 8\mathbf{j}$   **13.** $-2.2\mathbf{i} + 0.4\mathbf{j}$
**15.** $\langle -11.48, -9.16 \rangle$   **17.** $\langle -24, -27 \rangle$   **19.** $|\mathbf{F}_3| \approx 3336.8; \theta \approx 268.5°$
**21.** 37.16 kg   **23.** 644.49 lb   **25.** 2606.74 kg   **27.** approx. 286.79 lb
**29.** approx. 43.8°   **31.** 1125 N-m   **33.** approx. 957.0 ft   **35.** approx.
64,951.90 ft-lb   **37.** approx. 451.72 lb   **39.** approx. 2819.08 N-m
**41.** 800 ft-lb   **43.** 118 ft-lb   **45.** verified   **47.** verified   **49. a.** 29

**b.** 45°   **51. a.** 0   **b.** 90°   **53. a.** 1   **b.** 89.4°   **55.** yes   **57.** no
**59.** yes   **61.** 3.68   **63.** −4   **65.** 3.17   **67. a.** $\langle 3.73, 1.40 \rangle$
**b.** $u_1 = \langle 3.73, 1.40 \rangle, u_2 = \langle -1.73, 4.60 \rangle$   **69. a.** $\langle -0.65, 0.11 \rangle$
**b.** $u_1 = \langle -0.65, 0.11 \rangle, u_2 = \langle -1.35, -8.11 \rangle$   **71. a.** $10.54i + 1.76j$
**b.** $u_1 = 10.54i + 1.76j, u_2 = -0.54i + 3.24j$   **73. a.** projectile is about
375 ft away, and 505.52 ft high   **b.** approx. 1.27 sec and 12.26 sec
**75. a.** projectile is about 424.26 ft away, and 280.26 ft high   **b.** approx.
2.44 sec and 6.40 sec   **77.** about 74.84 ft; $t \approx 3.9 - 1.2 = 2.7$ sec
**79.** $w \cdot (u + v) = \langle e, f \rangle \cdot \langle a + c, b + d \rangle$
$\qquad = e(a + c) + f(b + d) = ea + ec + fb + fd$
$\qquad = (ea + fb) + (ec + fd)$
$\qquad = \langle e, f \rangle \cdot \langle a, b \rangle + \langle e, f \rangle \cdot \langle c, d \rangle$
$\qquad = w \cdot u + w \cdot v$
**81.** $0 \cdot u = \langle 0, 0 \rangle \cdot \langle a, b \rangle = 0(a) + 0(b) = 0$
$\qquad u \cdot 0 = \langle a, b \rangle \cdot \langle 0, 0 \rangle = a(0) + b(0) = 0$
**83.** $\theta \approx 56.9°$; answers will vary.

**85.**

| Angles | Sides |
|---|---|
| $A \approx 25.1°$ | $a \approx 25.98$ cm |
| $B \approx 34.9°$ | $b = 53$ cm |
| $C = 120°$ | $c = 35$ cm |

**87.**

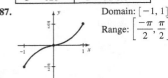

Domain: $[-1, 1]$
Range: $\left[ \dfrac{-\pi}{2}, \dfrac{\pi}{2} \right]$

**89.** $\sin 15° = \dfrac{1}{2}\sqrt{2 - \sqrt{3}}, \cos 75° = \dfrac{1}{2}\sqrt{2 - \sqrt{3}}$; they are identical.

## Summary and Concept Review pp. 373–376

**1.**

| Angles | Sides |
|---|---|
| $A = 36°$ | $a \approx 205.35$ cm |
| $B = 21°$ | $b \approx 125.20$ cm |
| $C = 123°$ | $c = 293$ cm |

**2.**

| Angles | Sides |
|---|---|
| $A = 28°$ | $a \approx 140.59$ yd |
| $B = 10°$ | $b = 52$ yd |
| $C = 142°$ | $c \approx 184.36$ yd |

**3.** approx. 41.84 ft

**4.** approx. 20.2° and 159.8°

**5.**

| Angles | Sides | Angles | Sides |
|---|---|---|---|
| $A = 35°$ | $a = 67$ cm | $A = 35°$ | $a = 67$ cm |
| $B_1 \approx 64.0°$ | $b = 105$ cm | $B_2 \approx 116.0°$ | $b = 105$ cm |
| $C_1 \approx 81.0°$ | $c_1 \approx 115.37$ cm | $C_2 \approx 29.0°$ | $c_2 \approx 56.63$ cm |

**6.** no; 36°   **7.** approx. 36.9°   **8.** approx. 385.5 m
**9.** 133.2°, 30.1°, and 16.7°   **10.** 85,570.7 m²
**11.**

**12.** $-8i + 3j; |u| \approx 8.54; \theta \approx 159.4°$
**13.** horiz. comp. $\approx 11.08$, vertical comp. $\approx 14.18$
**14.** $\langle -4, -2 \rangle; |2u + v| \approx 4.47, \theta \approx 206.6°$   **15.** $\dfrac{7}{\sqrt{193}}i + \dfrac{12}{\sqrt{193}}j$
**16.** QII; since the $x$-component is negative and the $y$-component is positive.
**17.** $\frac{1}{6}$ mi   **18.** approx. 19.7°   **19.** $\langle -25, -123 \rangle$   **20.** approx. −0.87
**21.** 4   **22.** $p \cdot q = -6; \theta \approx 97.9°$   **23.** 4340 ft-lb   **24.** approx. 417.81 lb
**25.** approx. 8156.77 ft-lb   **26. a.** $x \approx 269.97$ ft; $y \approx 285.74$ ft
**b.** approx. 0.74 sec

## Mixed Review pp. 376–377

**1.**

| Angles | Sides |
|---|---|
| $A = 41°$ | $a \approx 13.44$ in. |
| $B = 27°$ | $b \approx 9.30$ in. |
| $C = 112°$ | $c = 19$ in. |

Area $\approx 57.9$ in²

**3.** $x \approx 16.09, y \approx 13.50$   **5.** approx. 176.15 ft   **7.** approx. 793.70 mph;
heading 28.2°
**9.** One solution possible since side $a >$ side $b$

| Angles | Sides |
|---|---|
| $A = 31°$ | $a = 36$ m |
| $B \approx 20.1°$ | $b = 24$ m |
| $C \approx 128.9°$ | $c \approx 54.4$ m |

**11.** No; barely touches ("tangent") at 30°
**13. a.** 3865 mi   **b.** 2384 mi

**15.** $\approx 13.1°$   **17.** $comp_v u \approx -0.87, proj_v u \approx \dfrac{-38}{53}i + \dfrac{26}{53}j$

**19.** $(2, -1)$

## Practice Test pp. 377–379

**1.** 6.58 mi   **2.** 137.18 ft
**3.**

| Angles | Sides (in.) | Angles | Sides (in.) |
|---|---|---|---|
| $A_1 \approx 58.8°$ | $a = 15$ | $A_2 \approx 121.2°$ | $a = 15$ |
| $B = 20°$ | $b = 6$ | $B = 20°$ | $b = 6$ |
| $C_1 \approx 101.2°$ | $c_1 \approx 17.21$ | $C_2 \approx 38.8°$ | $c_2 \approx 11.0$ |

**4. a.** No   **b.** 2.66 mi   **5. a.** No   **b.** 1   **c.** 8.43 sec
**6. a.** 2.30 mi   **b.** 7516.5 ft   **7.** $A \approx 438, 795$ mi², $P \approx 61.7°$,
$B \approx 61.2°$, $M \approx 57.1°$   **8.** speed $\approx 73.36$ mph, bearing $\approx 47.8°$
**9.** $\theta \approx 36.5°$   **10.** 63.48 cm to the right and 130.05 cm down from the
initial point on the ceiling   **11.** $|F_3| \approx 212.94$ N, $\theta \approx 251.2°$
**12. a.** $\theta \approx 42.5°$   **b.** $proj_v u = \langle -2.4, 7.2 \rangle$
**c.** $u_1 = \langle -2.4, 7.2 \rangle, u_2 = \langle -6.6, -2.2 \rangle$

**13.** 104.53 ft; 3.27 sec   **14.** $C = \cos^{-1}\left( \dfrac{c^2 - a^2 - b^2}{-2ab} \right)$

**15. a.** $\langle -20, 6 \rangle$   **b.** $2\sqrt{109}$   **16.** $\dfrac{5}{\sqrt{61}}i + \dfrac{6}{\sqrt{61}}j$   **17.** $\langle -6.6, 4.6 \rangle$

**18. a.** $W = px \cos 15°$   **b.** approx. 1545 ft-lb

**19. a.** approx. 61.3°   **b.** 47 ft-lb   **20.** $\approx 2,414,300$ mi²

## Strengthening Core Skills p. 380

**Exercise 1:**   664.46 lb, 640.86 lb   **Exercise 2:**   106.07 lb, 106.07 lb
**Exercise 3:**   yes

## Cumulative Review Chapters 1–7, pp. 381–382

**1.** $20\sqrt{3}, 40, 60°, 90°$   **3.** $t = \dfrac{\cos^{-1}\left( \dfrac{D}{A} \right) - C}{B}$

**5.** QIV, $\sin \theta = \dfrac{-3}{5}; \cos \theta = \dfrac{4}{5}; \tan \theta = \dfrac{-3}{4}; \csc \theta = -\dfrac{5}{3}; \sec \theta = \dfrac{5}{4};$
$\cot \theta = -\dfrac{4}{3}$

**7. a.** $\sin(2\alpha) = 2 \sin \alpha \cos \alpha$   **b.** $\sin\left( \dfrac{\alpha}{2} \right) = \pm\sqrt{\dfrac{1 - \cos \alpha}{2}}$

**c.** $\sin(\alpha + \beta) = \sin \alpha \cos \beta + \cos \alpha \sin \beta$

**9.** $\cos 19° \approx 0.94, \quad \cos 125° \approx -0.58$

**11.** $D(t) = 5.704 \sin(0.511t - 1.835) + 12.189$
**a.** about 14.7 hr   **b.** $t \approx 4.6$ to $t \approx 8.7$, approx. April 18 to August 22

**13.** $\dfrac{2\cos^2\theta}{\csc^2\theta} + \dfrac{2\sin^2\theta}{\sec^2\theta} = \dfrac{2\cos^2\theta \sec^2\theta + 2\sin^2\theta \csc^2\theta}{\csc^2\theta \sec^2\theta} = 4\sin^2\theta \cos^2\theta$
$\qquad = (2 \sin \theta \cos \theta)^2 = \sin^2(2\theta)$
**15.** $\angle A = 37°, a \approx 33$ cm; $\angle B \approx 34.4°, b = 31$ cm; $\angle C \approx 108.6°$,
$c = 52$ cm   **17.** about 422.5 lb   **19.** $\theta \approx 70°$

# CHAPTER 8
## Exercises 8.1, pp. 390–394

**1.** $3 - 2i$   **3.** $2; 3\sqrt{2}$   **5.** (b) is correct.   **7. a.** $4i$   **b.** $7i$   **c.** $3\sqrt{3}$
**d.** $6\sqrt{2}$   **9. a.** $-3i\sqrt{2}$   **b.** $-5i\sqrt{2}$   **c.** $15i$   **d.** $6i$   **11. a.** $i\sqrt{19}$
**b.** $i\sqrt{31}$   **c.** $\dfrac{2\sqrt{3}}{5}i$   **d.** $\dfrac{3\sqrt{2}}{8}i$   **13. a.** $1 + i; a = 1, b = 1$
**b.** $2 + \sqrt{3}i; a = 2, b = \sqrt{3}$   **15. a.** $4 + 2i; a = 4, b = 2$
**b.** $2 - \sqrt{2}i; a = 2, b = -\sqrt{2}$   **17. a.** $5 + 0i; a = 5, b = 0$
**b.** $0 + 3i; a = 0, b = 3$   **19. a.** $18i; a = 0, b = 18$
**b.** $\dfrac{\sqrt{2}}{2}i; a = 0, b = \dfrac{\sqrt{2}}{2}$   **21. a.** $4 + 5\sqrt{2}i; a = 4, b = 5\sqrt{2}$
**b.** $-5 + 3\sqrt{3}i; a = -5, b = 3\sqrt{3}$

**23. a.** $\dfrac{7}{4} + \dfrac{7\sqrt{2}}{8}i; a = \dfrac{7}{4}, b = \dfrac{7\sqrt{2}}{8}$   **b.** $\dfrac{1}{2} + \dfrac{\sqrt{10}}{2}i; a = \dfrac{1}{2}, b = \dfrac{\sqrt{10}}{2}$
**25. a.** $19 + i$   **b.** $2 - 4i$   **c.** $9 + 10\sqrt{3}i$   **27. a.** $-3 + 2i$   **b.** $8$

**c.** $2 - 8i$   **29. a.** $2.7 + 0.2i$   **b.** $15 + \dfrac{1}{12}i$   **c.** $-2 - \dfrac{1}{8}i$

**31. a.** $15$   **b.** $16$   **33. a.** $-21 - 35i$   **b.** $-42 - 18i$
**35. a.** $-12 - 5i$   **b.** $1 + 5i$   **37. a.** $4 - 5i; 41$   **b.** $3 + i\sqrt{2}; 11$
**39. a.** $-7i; 49$   **b.** $\frac{1}{2} + \frac{2}{3}i; \frac{25}{36}$   **41. a.** $41$   **b.** $74$   **43. a.** $11$   **b.** $\frac{17}{36}$
**45. a.** $-5 + 12i$   **b.** $-7 - 24i$   **47. a.** $-21 - 20i$   **b.** $7 + 6\sqrt{2}i$
**49.** no   **51.** yes   **53.** yes   **55.** yes   **57.** yes   **59.** Answers will vary.

**61. a.** $1$   **b.** $-1$   **c.** $-i$   **d.** $i$   **63. a.** $\dfrac{2}{7}i$   **b.** $\dfrac{-4}{5}i$

**65. a.** $\dfrac{21}{13} - \dfrac{14}{13}i$   **b.** $\dfrac{-10}{13} - \dfrac{15}{13}i$   **67. a.** $1 - \dfrac{3}{4}i$   **b.** $-1 - \dfrac{2}{3}i$

**69. a.** $\sqrt{13}$   **b.** $5$   **c.** $\sqrt{11}$   **71.** $A + B = 10$   $AB = 40$
**73.** $7 - 5i\,\Omega$   **75.** $25 + 5i$ V   **77.** $\frac{7}{4} + i\,\Omega$   **79. a.** $(x + 6i)(x - 6i)$
**b.** $(m + i\sqrt{3})(m - i\sqrt{3})$   **c.** $(n + 2i\sqrt{3})(n - 2i\sqrt{3})$
**d.** $(2x + 7i)(2x - 7i)$   **81.** $-8 - 6i$   **83.** $\theta = 62.7°$

**85.** $\dfrac{\cos^2\theta}{1 - \sin\theta} = \dfrac{1 - \sin^2\theta}{1 - \sin\theta}$

$= \dfrac{(1 + \sin\theta)(1 - \sin\theta)}{1 - \sin\theta}$

$= 1 + \sin\theta$

**87.**

| Angles | Sides |
|---|---|
| $A = 32°$ | $a \approx 138.4$ m |
| $B \approx 106.8°$ | $b = 250$ m |
| $C \approx 41.2°$ | $c = 172$ m |

## Exercises 8.2, pp. 403–406

**1.** modulus; argument   **3.** multiply; add
**5.** $2(\cos 240° + i\sin 240°)$, $z$ is in QIII
**7.** $z_2 = z_1 + z_3$            **9.** $z_2 = z_1 + z_3$

**11.** $2\sqrt{2}(\cos 225° + i\sin 225°)$   **13.** $10(\cos 210° + i\sin 210°)$

**15.** $6\left[\cos\left(\dfrac{3\pi}{4}\right) + i\sin\left(\dfrac{3\pi}{4}\right)\right]$   **17.** $8\left[\cos\left(\dfrac{11\pi}{6}\right) + i\sin\left(\dfrac{11\pi}{6}\right)\right]$

**19.** $10\,\text{cis}\left[\tan^{-1}\left(\dfrac{6}{8}\right)\right]$; $10\,\text{cis}\,36.9°$

**21.** $13\,\text{cis}\left[180° + \tan^{-1}\left(\dfrac{12}{5}\right)\right]$; $13\,\text{cis}\,247.4°$

**23.** $18.5\,\text{cis}\left[\tan^{-1}\left(\dfrac{17.5}{6}\right)\right]$; $18.5\,\text{cis}\,1.2405$

**25.** $2\sqrt{34}\,\text{cis}\left[\pi + \tan^{-1}\left(-\dfrac{5}{3}\right)\right]$; $2\sqrt{34}\,\text{cis}\,2.1112$

**27.** $r = 2, \theta = \dfrac{\pi}{4}$

$z = 2\,\text{cis}\left(\dfrac{\pi}{4}\right)$

$= \sqrt{2} + \sqrt{2}i$

**29.** $r = 4\sqrt{3}, \theta = \dfrac{\pi}{3}$

$z = 4\sqrt{3}\,\text{cis}\left(\dfrac{\pi}{3}\right)$

$= 2\sqrt{3} + 6i$

**31.** $r = 17, \theta = \tan^{-1}\left(\dfrac{15}{8}\right)$

$z = 17\,\text{cis}\left[\tan^{-1}\left(\dfrac{15}{8}\right)\right]$

$= 17\left(\dfrac{8}{17} + \dfrac{15}{17}i\right) = 8 + 15i$

**33.** $r = 6, \theta = \pi - \tan^{-1}\left(\dfrac{5}{\sqrt{11}}\right)$

$z = 6\,\text{cis}\left[\pi - \tan^{-1}\dfrac{5}{\sqrt{11}}\right]$

$= 6\left(-\dfrac{\sqrt{11}}{6} + \dfrac{5}{6}i\right) = -\sqrt{11} + 5i$

**35.** $r_1 = 2\sqrt{2}$,   $r_2 = 3\sqrt{2}$,   $\theta_1 = 135°$,   $\theta_2 = 45°$;
$z = z_1z_2 = -12 + 0i \Rightarrow r = 12$,   $\theta = 180°$;
$r_1r_2 = 2\sqrt{2}(3\sqrt{2}) = 12\checkmark$
$\theta_1 + \theta_2 = 135° + 45° = 180°\checkmark$

**37.** $r_1 = 2, r_2 = 2, \theta_1 = 30°, \theta_2 = 60°$;
$z = \dfrac{z_1}{z_2} = \dfrac{\sqrt{3}}{2} - \dfrac{1}{2}i \Rightarrow r = 1, \theta = -30°; \dfrac{r_1}{r_2} = \dfrac{2}{2} = 1\checkmark$
$\theta_1 - \theta_2 = 30° - 60° = -30°\checkmark$

**39.** $z_1z_2 = -24 + 0i, \dfrac{z_1}{z_2} = -\dfrac{4}{3} + \dfrac{4\sqrt{3}}{3}i$

**41.** $z_1z_2 = 21\sqrt{3} - 21i, \dfrac{z_1}{z_2} = \dfrac{\sqrt{3}}{7} + \dfrac{1}{7}i$

**43.** $z_1z_2 = -10.84 + 12.04i, \dfrac{z_1}{z_2} = -1.55 - 4.76i$

**45.** $z_1z_2 = 0 + 40i, \dfrac{z_1}{z_2} = \dfrac{5\sqrt{3}}{4} + \dfrac{5}{4}i$

**47.** $z_1z_2 = -10 - 10\sqrt{3}i, \dfrac{z_1}{z_2} = \dfrac{-5}{2} + 0i$

**49.** $z_1z_2 = -2.93 + 8.5i, \dfrac{z_1}{z_2} = 2.29 + 3.28i$

**51.** verified; verified, $u^2 + v^2 + w^2 = uv + uw + vw$
$(1 + 4\sqrt{3}i) + (97 + 20\sqrt{3}i) + (-39 + 60\sqrt{3}i)$
$= (17 + 12\sqrt{3}i) + (-3 + 16\sqrt{3}i) + (45 + 56\sqrt{3}i),$
$59 + 84\sqrt{3}i = 59 + 84\sqrt{3}i$

**53. a.** $V(t) = 170\sin(120\pi t)$

**b.**

| t | V(t) |
|---|------|
| 0 | 0 |
| 0.001 | 62.6 |
| 0.002 | 116.4 |
| 0.003 | 153.8 |
| 0.004 | 169.7 |
| 0.005 | 161.7 |
| 0.006 | 131.0 |
| 0.007 | 81.9 |
| 0.008 | 21.3 |

**c.** $t \approx 0.00257$ sec

**55. a.** 17 cis 28.1°  **b.** 51 V  **57. a.** 8.60 cis 324.5°  **b.** 15.48 V

**59. a.** 13 cis 22.6°  **b.** 22.1 V

**61.** $I = 2$ cis 30°; $Z = 5\sqrt{2}$ cis 45°; $V = 10\sqrt{2}$ cis 75°

**63.** $I = \sqrt{13}$ cis 326.3°; $Z = \dfrac{17}{4}$ cis 61.9°; $V = \dfrac{17\sqrt{13}}{4}$ cis 28.2°

**65.** $V = 4$ cis 60°; $Z = 4\sqrt{2}$ cis 315°; $I = \dfrac{\sqrt{2}}{2}$ cis 105°

**67.** $V = 5$ cis 306.9°; $Z = 8.5$ cis 61.9°; $I = \dfrac{10}{17}$ cis 245°

**69.** $\dfrac{\sqrt{65} \text{ cis } 29.7°}{4}$  **71.** verified

**73.** $z_2 = \dfrac{24}{5} - \dfrac{7}{5}i, z_3 = -\dfrac{24}{5} + \dfrac{7}{5}i$  **75.** $\dfrac{5\pi}{24}, \dfrac{13\pi}{24}, \dfrac{29\pi}{24}, \dfrac{37\pi}{24}$

**77. a.** $\dfrac{1 + \cos\alpha}{1 - \cos\alpha} = \left(\dfrac{1 + \cos\alpha}{1 - \cos\alpha}\right)\dfrac{\sec\alpha}{\sec\alpha} = \dfrac{\sec\alpha + 1}{\sec\alpha - 1}$

**79.** approx. 2.70 mi

## Exercises 8.3, pp. 411–414

**1.** $r^5[\cos(5\theta) + i\sin(5\theta)]$; De Moivre's  **3.** complex

**5.** $z_5 = 2$ cis 366° = 2 cis 6°, $z_6 = 2$ cis 438° = 2 cis 78°, $z_7 = 2$ cis 510° = 2 cis 150°; Answers will vary.

**7.** $r = 3\sqrt{2}; n = 4; \theta = 45°; -324$  **9.** $r = 2; n = 3; \theta = 120°; 8$

**11.** $r = 1; n = 5; \theta = -60°; \dfrac{1}{2} + \dfrac{\sqrt{3}}{2}i$  **13.** $r = 1; n = 6; \theta = -45°; i$

**15.** $r = 4; n = 3; \theta = 330°; -64i$

**17.** $r = \dfrac{\sqrt{2}}{2}; n = 5; \theta = 135°; \dfrac{1}{8} - \dfrac{1}{8}i$

**19.** verified  **21.** verified  **23.** verified  **25.** verified

**27.** $r = 1; n = 5; \theta = 0°$; roots: 1, $0.3090 \pm 0.9511i$, $-0.8090 \pm 0.5878i$

**29.** $r = 243; n = 5; \theta = 0°$; roots: 3, $0.9271 \pm 2.8532i$, $-2.4271 \pm 1.7634i$

**31.** $r = 27; n = 3; \theta = 270°$; roots: $3i$, $\dfrac{-3\sqrt{3}}{2} - \dfrac{3}{2}i, \dfrac{3\sqrt{3}}{2} - \dfrac{3}{2}i$

**33.** $2, 0.6180 \pm 1.9021i, -1.6180 \pm 1.1756i$

**35.** $\dfrac{3\sqrt{3}}{2} + \dfrac{3}{2}i, -\dfrac{3\sqrt{3}}{2} + \dfrac{3}{2}i, -3i$

**37.** $1.1346 + 0.1797i, 0.1797 + 1.1346i, -1.0235 + 0.5215i,$ $-0.8123 - 0.8123i, 0.5215 - 1.0235i$

**39.** $x = 1, -\dfrac{1}{2} \pm \dfrac{\sqrt{3}}{2}i$. These are the same results as in Example 3.

**41.** $r = 16; n = 4; \theta = 120°$; roots: $\sqrt{3} + i, -1 + \sqrt{3}i, -\sqrt{3} - i, 1 - \sqrt{3}i$

**43.** $r = 7\sqrt{2}; n = 4; \theta = 225°$; roots: $0.9855 + 1.4749i, -1.4749 +$ $0.9855i, -0.9855 - 1.4749i, 1.4749i - 0.9855i$

**45.** $D = -4, z_0 = 8^{\frac{1}{8}}$cis 45°, $z_1 = 8^{\frac{1}{8}}$cis 165°, $z_2 = 8^{\frac{1}{8}}$cis 285°, $z_0 = 8^{\frac{1}{8}}$cis 75°, $z_1 = 8^{\frac{1}{8}}$cis 195°, $z_2 = 8^{\frac{1}{8}}$cis 315°  **47.** verified

**49. a.** numerator: $-117 + 44j$, denominator: $-21 + 72j$  **b.** $1 + \dfrac{4}{3}j$

**c.** verified  **51.** Answers will vary.  **53.** $-7 - 24i$

**55.** $z \approx -2.7320, z \approx 0.7320, z = 2$.
Note: Using sum and difference identities, all three solutions can actually be given in exact form: $-1 - \sqrt{3}, -1 + \sqrt{3}, 2$.

**57. a.** $I = 4 + i$,  **b.** $(3 - 2i)(4 + i) =$ $12 + 3i - 8i - 2i^2 = 12 - 5i + 2 = 14 - 5i$✓

**59.** $\dfrac{\tan^2 x}{\sec x + 1} = \dfrac{1 - \cos x}{\cos x}, \dfrac{\sec^2 x - 1}{\sec x + 1} = \dfrac{(\sec x + 1)(\sec x - 1)}{\sec x + 1} =$ $\sec x - 1 = \dfrac{1}{\cos x} - \dfrac{\cos x}{\cos x} = \dfrac{1 - \cos x}{\cos x}$

**61.**

| Angles | Sides |
|--------|-------|
| $A = 30°$ | $a = 2\sqrt{3}$ |
| $B = 60°$ | $b = 6$ |
| $C = 90°$ | $c = 4\sqrt{3}$ |

## Mid-Chapter Check, p. 414

**1.** sum 4, product 13; both yield real numbers.  **2.** $i$

**3.** $(1 + 2i)^2 - 2(1 + 2i) + 5 = 0$
$1 + 4i + 4i^2 - 2 - 4i + 5 = 0$
$1 + (-4) - 2 + 5 = 0$
$0 = 0$

**4. a.** QII, 8 cis 120°  **b.** QIII, 15 cis 216.9°

**5. a.** $3 + 3i$  **b.** $3 - \sqrt{3}i$  **6.** $z_1 z_2 = 20$ cis 210°

**7.** $\dfrac{z_1}{z_2} = \dfrac{3\sqrt{2}}{10}$ cis $\left(\dfrac{7\pi}{12}\right)$  **8.** $128 - 128i$  **9.** 2 cis $(36° + 72°k)$

**10.** $z_0 = 9, z_1 = -\dfrac{9}{2} + \dfrac{9\sqrt{3}}{2}i, z_2 = -\dfrac{9}{2} - \dfrac{9\sqrt{3}}{2}i$

## Reinforcing Basic Concepts, p. 415

**Exercise 1:**  The product yields a new complex number rotated 180° counterclockwise, 270° counterclockwise, or 360° counterclockwise (for $i^4$ the result would be coterminal), all on a central circle of radius $|z|$.

**Exercise 2:**  verified; $-3 + 2i, -2 - 3i, 3 - 2i$

**Exercise 3:**  **a.** $|z| = 1, \theta = 45°$

**b.** $-\sqrt{2} + \sqrt{2}i, -2, -\sqrt{2} - \sqrt{2}i, -2i, \sqrt{2} - \sqrt{2}i, 2, \sqrt{2} + \sqrt{2}i$

**Exercise 4:**  **a.** any point on the unit circle  **b.** $-\dfrac{1}{2} + \dfrac{\sqrt{3}}{2}i$

**c.** $-\sqrt{3} - i, \sqrt{3} - i$

## Exercises 8.4, pp. 428–431

**1.** polar  **3.** II; IV  **5.** To plot the point $(r, \theta)$ start at the origin or pole and move $|r|$ units out along the polar axis. Then move counterclockwise an angle measure of $\theta$. You should be $r$ units straight out from the pole in a direction of $\theta$ from the positive polar axis. If $r$ is negative, final resting place for the point $(r, \theta)$ will be 180° from $\theta$.

**7.**   **9.**   **11.**

**13.**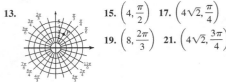

**15.** $\left(4, \dfrac{\pi}{2}\right)$  **17.** $\left(4\sqrt{2}, \dfrac{\pi}{4}\right)$  **19.** $\left(8, \dfrac{2\pi}{3}\right)$  **21.** $\left(4\sqrt{2}, \dfrac{3\pi}{4}\right)$

**23.** $\left(3\sqrt{2}, \dfrac{-5\pi}{4}\right), \left(-3\sqrt{2}, \dfrac{7\pi}{4}\right), \left(3\sqrt{2}, \dfrac{11\pi}{4}\right), \left(-3\sqrt{2}, \dfrac{-\pi}{4}\right)$

**25.** $\left(2, \dfrac{5\pi}{6}\right), \left(2, \dfrac{-7\pi}{6}\right), \left(2, \dfrac{17\pi}{6}\right), \left(-2, \dfrac{-\pi}{6}\right)$  **27.** $C$  **29.** $C$  **31.** $D$

**33.** $B$  **35.** $D$  **37.** $(8, 180°)$ or $(8, \pi)$  **39.** $(4\sqrt{2}, 45°)$ or $\left(4\sqrt{2}, \dfrac{\pi}{4}\right)$

**41.** $(10, 45°)$ or $\left(10, \dfrac{\pi}{4}\right)$  **43.** $(13, 247.4°)$ or $(13, 4.3176)$

**45.** $(4\sqrt{2}, 4\sqrt{2})$  **47.** $(-2\sqrt{2}, 2\sqrt{2})$  **49.** $(\sqrt{3}, 1)$  **51.** $\left(\dfrac{5\sqrt{2}}{2}, \dfrac{5\sqrt{2}}{2}\right)$

**53.** $r = 5$  **55.** $r^2 \sin 2\theta = 6$  **57.** $\tan \theta = 3r\cos\theta + 1$ or $r = \dfrac{\tan\theta - 1}{3\cos\theta}$

**59.** $r^2 = \cos 2\theta$  **61.** $x^2 + y^2 = 6x$  **63.** $x = 2$  **65.** $x^2 + y^2 = x - 1$

**67.** $y = -\dfrac{1}{2}x^2 + \dfrac{1}{2}$

**69.** 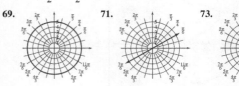  **71.**  **73.**

**75.**   **77.**  **79.**

**81.** 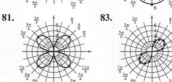  **83.**  **85.**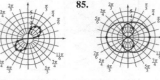

**87.** 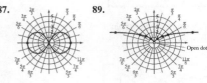  **89.**  Open dot

**91.**

**93.** $\left(\dfrac{4\sqrt{3} + 3\sqrt{2}}{2}, \dfrac{4 + 3\sqrt{2}}{2}\right)$; $(3\sqrt{2}, 3\sqrt{2})$; $(4\sqrt{3}, 4)$; yes

$M = \left(\dfrac{3\sqrt{2} + 4\sqrt{3}}{2}, \dfrac{3\sqrt{2} + 4}{2}\right)$

**95.** $r = 4 + 4\cos\theta$  **97.** $r = 4\cos(5\theta)$

**99.** $r^2 = 16\cos(2\theta)$  **101.** $r = 4\sin\theta$

**103.** a; this is a circle through $(6, 0°)$ symmetric about the polar axis

**105.** g; this is a circle through $\left(6, \dfrac{\pi}{2}\right)$ symmetric about $\theta = \dfrac{\pi}{2}$.

**107.** f; this is a limaçon symmetric about $\theta = \dfrac{\pi}{2}$ with an inner loop. Thus $a < b$.

**109.** b; this is a cardioid symmetric about $\theta = \dfrac{\pi}{2}$ through $\left(6, \dfrac{3\pi}{2}\right)$.

**111.** $r^2 = 7200^2 \sin(2\theta)$  **113.** $r = 15\cos(5\theta)$ or $r = 15\sin(5\theta)$

**115.** $\pi$; $\pi$; $\pi$; Answers will vary.

**117.** Consider $r = a\sqrt{\cos(2\theta)}$ and $r = -a\sqrt{\cos(2\theta)}$; both satisfy $r^2 = a^2\cos(2\theta)$. Thus, $(r, \theta)$ and $(-r, \theta)$ will both be on the curve. The same is true with $a\sqrt{\sin(2\theta)}$ and $-a\sqrt{\sin(2\theta)}$.  **119.** $9\pi$ units$^2$

**121.** $\dfrac{1 + \sin x}{\cos x} = \dfrac{(1 + \sin x)(1 - \sin x)}{\cos x(1 - \sin x)}$

$= \dfrac{1 - \sin^2 x}{\cos x(1 - \sin x)}$

$= \dfrac{\cos^2 x}{\cos x(1 - \sin x)}$

$= \dfrac{\cos x}{1 - \sin x}$

**123.** $|z_1| = \sqrt{226} < \sqrt{250} = |z_2|$  **125.** $L \approx 115.0$ m

## Exercises 8.5, pp. 439–443

**1.** parameter  **3.** direction  **5.** Answers will vary.

**7. a.** parabola with vertex at $(2, -1)$  **9. a.** parabola

**b.** $y = x^2 - 4x + 3$  **b.** $y = x \pm 2\sqrt{x} + 1$

**11. a.** power function with $p = -2$  **13. a.** ellipse

**b.** $y = \dfrac{25}{x^2}, x \neq 0$  **b.** $\dfrac{x^2}{16} + \dfrac{y^2}{9} = 1$

**15. a.** Lissajous figure  **17.**

**b.** $y = 6\cos\left[\dfrac{1}{2}\sin^{-1}\left(\dfrac{x}{4}\right)\right]$

**19.** $x = t, y = 3t - 2$; $x = \dfrac{1}{3}t, y = t - 2$; $x = \cos t, y = 3\cos t - 2$

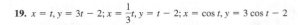

**21.** $x = t, y = (t + 3)^2 + 1; x = t - 3, y = t^2 + 1; x = \tan t - 3,$
$y = \sec^2 t, t \neq \dfrac{(2k + 1)\pi}{2}, k \in \mathbb{Z}$

**23.** $x = t, y = \tan^2(t - 2) + 1, t \neq \pi k + \dfrac{\pi}{2} + 2, k \in \mathbb{Z}; x = t + 2,$
$y = \sec^2 t, t \neq \left(k + \dfrac{1}{2}\right)\pi, k \in \mathbb{Z}; x = \tan^{-1} t + 2, y = t^2 + 1$

**25.** verified

**27. a.**

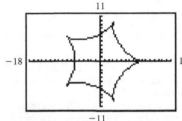

**b.** $x$-intercepts: $t = 0, x = 10, y = 0$ and $t = \pi, x = -6, y = 0$;
$y$-intercepts: $t \approx 1.757, x = 0, y \approx 6.5$ and
$t \approx 4.527, x = 0, y \approx -6.5$; minimum $x$-value is $-8.1$; maximum
$x$-value is 10; minimum $y$-value is $-9.5$; the maximum $y$-value
is 9.5

**29. a.**

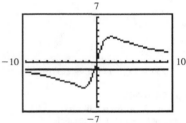

**b.** $x$-intercepts none, $y$-intercepts none; no minimum or maximum
$x$-values; minimum $y$-value is $-4$ and maximum $y$-value is 4

**31. a.**

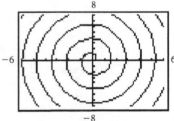

**b.** $x$-intercepts: $t = 0, x = 2, y = 0$ and $t \approx 4.493, x \approx -9.2, y = 0$;
infinitely many others; $y$-intercepts: $t \approx 2.798, x = 0, y \approx 5.9$ and
$t \approx 6.121, x = 0, y \approx -12.4$; infinitely many others; no minimum
or maximum values for $x$ or $y$

**33. a.**

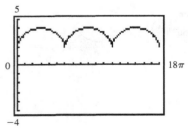

**b.** no $x$-intercepts; $y$-intercept is $t = 0, x = 0, y = 2$; no minimum or
maximum $x$-values; minimum $y$-value is 2; maximum $y$-value is 4

**35. a.**

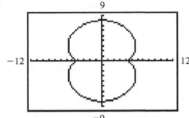

**b.** $x$-intercepts: $t = 0, x = 4, y = 0$ and $t = \pi, x = -4, y = 0$;
$y$-intercepts: $t = \dfrac{\pi}{2}, x = 0, y = 8$ and $t = \dfrac{3\pi}{2}, x = 0, y = -8$;
minimum and maximum $x$-values are approx. $\pm 5.657$; minimum
and maximum $y$-values are $\pm 8$

**37.**

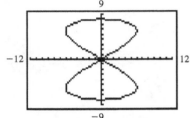

width 12 and length 16; including the endpoint $t = 2\pi$, the graph crosses
itself two times from 0 to $2\pi$.

**39.**

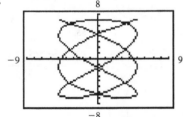

width 10 and length 14; including the endpoint $t = 2\pi$, the graph crosses
itself nine times from 0 to $2\pi$.

**41.**

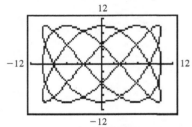

width 20 and length 20; including the endpoint $t = 4\pi$, the graph crosses
itself 23 times from 0 to $4\pi$.

**43.** The maximum value (as the graph swells to a peak) is at
$(x, y) = \left(a, \dfrac{b}{2}\right)$. The minimum value (as the graph dips to the valley)
is at $(x, y) = \left(-a, \dfrac{-b}{2}\right)$.

**45. a.** The curve is approaching $y = 2$ as $t$ approaches $\dfrac{3\pi}{2}$, but $\cot\left(\dfrac{3\pi}{2}\right)$ is
undefined, and the trig form seems to indicate a hole at
$t = \dfrac{3\pi}{2}, x = 0, y = 2$. The algebraic form does not have this
problem and shows a maximum defined at $t = 0, x = 0, y = 2$.

**b.** As $|t| \to \infty$, $y(t) \to 0$    **c.** The maximum value occurs at $(0, 2k)$.

**47. a.** Yes   **b.** Yes   **c.** $\approx 0.82$ ft    **49.** No, the kick is short.

**51.** The electron is moving left and downward.

**53.** $\left(t, \dfrac{6t}{17} - \dfrac{6}{17}, \dfrac{13t}{17} + \dfrac{21}{17}\right)$    **55.** Inconsistent, no solutions

**57.** $x = 1.22475^t$
$y = 0.25t^2 - 2t$

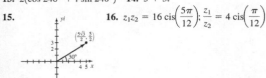

The parametric equations fit the data very well.

**59.** Answers will vary.    **61.** 13.1 mph. at heading 327.8°

**63.** $\cos 105° = \dfrac{\sqrt{2} - \sqrt{6}}{4}$    **65.** No triangles are possible.

## Summary and Concept Review, pp. 444–446

**1.** $6\sqrt{2}i$   **2.** $24\sqrt{3}i$   **3.** $-2 + \sqrt{2}i$   **4.** $3\sqrt{2}i$   **5.** $i$   **6.** $21 + 20i$
**7.** $-2 + i$   **8.** $-5 + 7i$   **9.** 13   **10.** $-20 - 12i$
**11.** $(5i)^2 - 9 = -34$      $(-5i)^2 - 9 = -34$
       $25i^2 - 9 = -34$        $25i^2 - 9 = -34$
     $-25 - 9 = -34$✓     $-25 - 9 = -34$✓
**12.**   $(2 + i\sqrt{5})^2 - 4(2 + i\sqrt{5}) + 9 = 0$
    $4 + 4i\sqrt{5} + 5i^2 - 8 - 4i\sqrt{5} + 9 = 0$
                    $5 + (-5) = 0$✓
    $(2 - i\sqrt{5})^2 - 4(2 - i\sqrt{5}) + 9 = 0$
    $4 - 4i\sqrt{5} + 5i^2 - 8 + 4i\sqrt{5} + 9 = 0$
                    $5 + (-5) = 0$✓
**13.** $2(\cos 240° + i \sin 240°)$    **14.** $3 + 3i$

**15.**

**16.** $z_1 z_2 = 16 \operatorname{cis}\left(\dfrac{5\pi}{12}\right); \dfrac{z_1}{z_2} = 4 \operatorname{cis}\left(\dfrac{\pi}{12}\right)$

**17.** $2\sqrt{3} + 2j$   **18.** $|Z| \approx 10.44$; $\theta \approx 16.7°$, $10.44 \operatorname{cis} 16.7°$

**19.** $-16 - 16\sqrt{3}i$   **20.** verified   **21.** $\dfrac{5\sqrt{3}}{2} + \dfrac{5}{2}i, -\dfrac{5\sqrt{3}}{2} + \dfrac{5}{2}i, -5i$

**22.** $6, -3 \pm 3i\sqrt{3}$   **23.** $2 - 2i, -2 \pm 2i$   **24.** $1 \pm 2i, -1 \pm 2i$
**25.** verified

**26.**      **27.**      **28.**

**29.**

**30.** $y = -2(x + 4)^2 + 3$   **31.** $y = (-1 \pm \sqrt{x})^2$   **32.** $\dfrac{x^2}{9} + \dfrac{y^2}{16} = 1$

**33.** Answers will vary.    **34.** $x \in [-4, 4]$: $y \in [-8, 8]$

## Mixed Review, pp. 446–447

**1. a.** $8i\sqrt{2}$   **b.** $-3 - 4i$   **c.** $\dfrac{3}{2} + \dfrac{3}{2}i$   **d.** 7   **3. b.** $x = -i, x = 7i$
**5.** $-4096$   **7.** $Z \approx 13.33(\cos 25.8° + i \sin 25.8°)$, $V_{RLC} \approx 86.6$ V

**9. a.** $\left(-\dfrac{7}{4}, \dfrac{7\sqrt{3}}{4}\right)$
   **b.** $(2\sqrt{2}, 2\sqrt{2})$

**11.** $r = 5 \sin(7\theta)$   **13.** $\dfrac{x^2}{9} + \dfrac{y^2}{16} = 1$   **15.** verified   **17.** $x^2 + y^2 = 9$

**19.** $1, i, -1, -i, \pm\dfrac{\sqrt{2}}{2} \pm \dfrac{\sqrt{2}}{2}i$

## Practice Test, p. 448

**1.** $-\dfrac{4}{3} \pm \dfrac{i\sqrt{5}}{3}$   **2.** $-i$   **3. a.** 1   **b.** $i\sqrt{3}$   **c.** 1   **4.** $-\dfrac{3}{2} + \dfrac{3}{2}i$   **5.** 34
**6.** $(2 - 3i)^2 - 4(2 - 3i) + 13 = 0$
    $-5 - 12i - 8 + 12i + 13 = 0$
                      $0 = 0$✓

**7.** $2 \operatorname{cis}\left(\dfrac{\pi}{24}\right)$   **8.** $48\sqrt{2} \operatorname{cis} 75°$; verified

**9.** $Z \approx 18.6 \operatorname{cis} 14.6°$, $V_{RLC} \approx 46.5$ V   **10.** $-8 - 8\sqrt{3}i$   **11.** verified

**12.** $\dfrac{5\sqrt{3}}{2} + \dfrac{5}{2}i, -\dfrac{5\sqrt{3}}{2} + \dfrac{5}{2}i, -5i$
**13.** $2.3039 \pm 1.5192i, -2.3039 \pm 1.5192i$

**14.**      **15.**     **16.**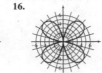

**17.** ellipse; $\dfrac{x^2}{16} + \dfrac{y^2}{25} = 1$

**18.** parabola; $x = (y - 5)^2 + 1$

**19.** max: $y = 8$; min: $y = 0$; $P = 8\pi$

**20.** The ball is 0.43 ft above the ground at $x = 165$ ft, and will likely go into the goal.

## Strengthening Core Skills, pp. 449–451

**Exercise 1:** $\cos(\alpha - \beta) = \cos \alpha \cos \beta + \sin \alpha \sin \beta$;

$\sin(\alpha - \beta) = \cos \alpha \sin \beta - \sin \alpha \cos \beta$

**Exercise 2: a.** $z_1 z_2 = \text{cis } 525°$

**b.** $z_1 = -\dfrac{\sqrt{2}}{2} - \dfrac{\sqrt{2}}{2}i, z_2 = \dfrac{1}{2} - \dfrac{\sqrt{3}}{2}i, z_1 z_2 = \dfrac{-\sqrt{2} - \sqrt{6}}{4} + \dfrac{\sqrt{6} - \sqrt{2}}{4}i$

**c.** $\cos 525° = \dfrac{-\sqrt{2} - \sqrt{6}}{4}, \sin 525° = \dfrac{\sqrt{6} - \sqrt{2}}{4}$    **d.** verified

**e.** verified    **Exercise 3:** $-\dfrac{\sqrt{3}}{2} + \dfrac{3}{2}i$    **Exercise 4:** $8i$

**Exercise 5:** $-80.21 - 11.27i$

## Cumulative Review Chapters 1–8, pp. 451–452

**1.** $\dfrac{5\pi}{6} + k\pi, k \in \mathbb{Z}$

**3.** $x = 1 + 6k; k \in \mathbb{Z}$
$x = 3 + 6k; k \in \mathbb{Z}$

**5.** $h \approx 2307$ m

**7.** $\sin(2t) = \dfrac{-120}{169}$,

$\cos(2t) = \dfrac{119}{169}$

**9.**                   **11.** $61.9°$    **13.** $A \approx 75.2 \text{ m}^2$

**15.** $\theta = 0, \dfrac{\pi}{2}, \pi, \dfrac{3\pi}{2}$    **17.** $\alpha = 392°, \beta \approx 7.0001$    **19.** $A \approx 39.3 \text{ ft}^2$

**21.** about 128 yd    **23.** $2\cos^2\theta - 1, 1 - 2\sin^2\theta$    **25.** $\sin\left(\dfrac{\pi}{24}\right)$

**27.** No, it is not detected.    **29.** $z^4 = -8 + 8\sqrt{3}i$

**25.** left 1, down 3

**27.** up 1

**29.** right 2

**31.** down 2

**33.** e  **35.** a  **37.** b  **39.** 2.718282  **41.** 7.389056  **43.** 4.481689
**45.** 4.113250

**47.**

**49.**

**51.**

**53.** 3  **55.** $\frac{3}{2}$  **57.** $-\frac{1}{3}$  **59.** 4  **61.** $-3$  **63.** 3  **65.** 2  **67.** $-2$
**69.** 2  **71.** 3
**73. a.** 1732, 3000, 5196, 9000  **d.**
**b.** yes  **c.** as $t \to \infty, P \to \infty$

**75.** No, they will have to wait about 10 min.  **77. a.** $100,000  **b.** 3 yr
**79. a.** $\approx$ $86,806  **b.** 3 yr  **81. a.** $40 million  **b.** 7 yr  **83.** 32%
transparent  **85.** 17% transparent  **87.** $\approx$ $32,578  **89. a.** 8 g

**b.** 48 min  **91.** $\frac{1}{5}$  **93.** 75  **95.** $9.5 \times 10^{-7}$; answers will vary

**97. a.** $\frac{\Delta y}{\Delta x}$ = 0.3842, 0.056, 0.011, 0.003; the rate of growth seems to
be approaching zero  **b.** 16,608  **c.** Yes, the secant lines are becoming
virtually horizontal.

## Exercises AI-B, pp. A-22–A-26

**1.** $\log_b x$; $b$; $b$; greater  **3.** (1, 0); 0  **5.** 5; answers will vary  **7.** $2^3 = 8$
**9.** $7^{-1} = \frac{1}{7}$  **11.** $9^0 = 1$  **13.** $8^{\frac{1}{3}} = 2$  **15.** $2^1 = 2$  **17.** $7^2 = 49$
**19.** $10^2 = 100$  **21.** $e^4 \approx 54.598$  **23.** $\log_4 64 = 3$  **25.** $\log_3 \frac{1}{9} = -2$
**27.** $0 = \log_e 1$  **29.** $\log_{\frac{1}{3}} 27 = -3$  **31.** $\log 1000 = 3$  **33.** $\log \frac{1}{100} = -2$
**35.** $\log_4 8 = \frac{3}{2}$  **37.** $\log_4 \frac{1}{8} = \frac{-3}{2}$  **39.** 1  **41.** 2  **43.** 1  **45.** $\frac{1}{2}$

**47.** $-2$  **49.** $-2$  **51.** 1.6990  **53.** 0.4700  **55.** 5.4161  **57.** 0.7841
**59.** shift up 3

**61.** shift right 2, up 3

**63.** shift left 1

**65.** reflect across $x$-axis, shift left 1

## APPENDIX I
### Exercises AI-A, pp. A-9–A-13

**1.** $b^x$; $b$; $b$; $x$  **3.** $a$; 1  **5.** False; for $|b| < 1$ and $x_2 > x_1$, $b^{x_2} < b^{x_1}$, so
function is decreasing  **7.** 40,000; 5000; 20,000; 27,589.162  **9.** 500;
1.581; 2.321; 221.168  **11.** 10,000; 1975.309; 1487.206; 1316.872
**13.** increasing

increasing

**15.** decreasing

decreasing

**17.** up 2

**19.** left 3

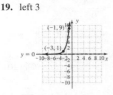

**21.** reflect across $y$-axis

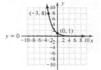

**23.** reflect across $y$-axis, up 3

**67.** II  **69.** VI  **71.** V  **73.** $x \in (-\infty, -1) \cup (3, \infty)$  **75.** $x \in (\frac{3}{2}, \infty)$
**77.** $x \in (-3, 3)$  **79.** pH $\approx 4.1$; acid  **81. a.** $\approx 4.7$  **b.** $\approx 4.9$
**83.** about 3.2 times  **85. a.** $\approx 2.4$  **b.** $\approx 1.2$  **87. a.** 20 dB  **b.** 120 dB
**89.** about 3162 times  **91.** 6,194 m  **93. a.** about 5434 m
**b.** 4000 m  **95. a.** 2225 items  **b.** 2732 items  **c.** $117,000
**d.** verified  **97. a.** about 58.6 cfm  **b.** about 1605 ft$^2$  **99. a.** 95%
**b.** 67%  **c.** 39%  **101.** $\approx 4.3$; acid  **103.** Answers will vary.  **a.** 0 dB
**b.** 90 dB  **c.** 15 dB  **d.** 120 dB  **e.** 100 dB  **f.** 140 dB  **105. a.** $\dfrac{-2}{3}$
**b.** $\dfrac{-3}{2}$  **c.** $\dfrac{-5}{2}$

## Mid-Chapter Check, p. A-26

**1. a.** $\frac{2}{3} = \log_{27}9$  **b.** $\frac{5}{4} = \log_{81}243$  **2. a.** $8^{\frac{5}{3}} = 32$  **b.** $1296^{0.25} = 6$
**3. a.** $x = 5$  **b.** $b = \frac{5}{4}$  **4. a.** $x = 3$  **b.** $b = 5$  **5. a.** $71,191.41
**b.** 6 yr  **6.** $F(x) = 4 \cdot 5^{x-3} + 2$  **7. a.** $129°$  **b.** 5 min
**8. a.** $4 = \log_3 81$, verified  **b.** $4 \approx \ln 54.598$, verified  **9. a.** $27^{\frac{2}{3}} = 9$,
verified  **b.** $e^{1.4} \approx 4.0552$, verified  **10.** $\approx 7.9$ times more intense

## Reinforcing Basic Concepts, pp. A-26–A-27

**Exercise 1:** about 158 times      **Exercise 4:** about 398 times
**Exercise 2:** about 501 times      **Exercise 5:** about 39,811 times
**Exercise 3:** about 12,589 times

## Exercises AI-C, pp. A-39–A-43

**1.** $e$  **3.** extraneous  **5.** 2.316566275  **7.** $x \approx 29.964$  **9.** $x \approx 1.778$
**11.** $x \approx 2.200$  **13.** $x \approx 1.260$  **15.** $x = \ln\frac{65}{4} + 2, x \approx 4.7881$
**17.** $x = \log(78) - 5, x \approx -3.1079$  **19.** $x = -\dfrac{\ln 2.32}{0.75}, x \approx -1.1221$
**21.** $x = e^{\frac{2}{3}} - 4, x \approx 10.3919$  **23.** $x = 5 - 10^{1.25}, x \approx -12.7828$
**25.** $x = \dfrac{e^{0.4} - 5}{2}, x \approx -1.7541$  **27.** $\ln(2x^2 - 14x)$  **29.** $\log(x^2 - 1)$
**31.** $\log_3 4$  **33.** $\log\left(\dfrac{x}{x+1}\right)$  **35.** $\ln\left(\dfrac{x-5}{x}\right)$  **37.** $\ln(x - 2)$  **39.** $\log_2 42$
**41.** $\log_5(x - 2)$  **43.** $(x + 2)\log 8$  **45.** $(2x - 1)\ln 5$  **47.** $\frac{1}{2}\log 22$
**49.** $4\log_5 3$  **51.** $3\log a + \log b$  **53.** $\ln x + \frac{1}{4}\ln y$  **55.** $2\ln x - \ln y$
**57.** $\frac{1}{2}[\log(x - 2) - \log x]$
**59.** $\ln 7 + \ln x + \frac{1}{2}\ln(3 - 4x) - \ln 2 - 3\ln(x - 1)$
**61.** $\dfrac{\ln 60}{\ln 7}$; 2.104076884  **63.** $\dfrac{\ln 152}{\ln 5}$; 3.121512475
**65.** $\dfrac{\log 1.73205}{\log 3}$; 0.499999576  **67.** $\dfrac{\log 0.125}{\log 0.5}$; 3
**69.** $f(x) = \dfrac{\log(x)}{\log(3)}$; $f(5) \approx 1.4650$; $f(15) \approx 2.4650$; $f(45) \approx 3.4650$;
outputs increase by 1; $f(3^3 \cdot 5) = 4.465$
**71.** $h(x) = \dfrac{\log(x)}{\log(9)}$; $h(2) \approx 0.3155$; $h(4) \approx 0.6309$; $h(8) \approx 0.9464$;
outputs are multiples of 0.3155; $h(2^4) = 4(0.3155) \approx 1.2619$
**73.** $x = 32$  **75.** $x = 6.4$  **77.** $x = 20$, $-5$ is extraneous
**79.** $x = 2$, $-\frac{5}{2}$ is extraneous  **81.** $x = 0$  **83.** $x = \frac{5}{2}$  **85.** $x = \frac{2}{3}$
**87.** $x = \frac{3}{2}$  **89.** $x = \frac{-19}{9}$  **91.** $x = \dfrac{e^2 - 63}{9}$
**93.** $x = 2$; $-9$ is extraneous  **95.** $x = 3e^3 - \frac{1}{2}$; $x \approx 59.75661077$
**97.** no solution  **99.** $t = -\frac{1}{2}$; $-4$ is extraneous
**101.** $x = 2 + \sqrt{3}$, $x = 2 - \sqrt{3}$ is extraneous
**103.** $x = \dfrac{\ln 231}{\ln 7} - 2$; $x \approx 0.7968$  **105.** $x = \dfrac{\ln 128,965}{3\ln 5} + \dfrac{2}{3}$; $x \approx 3.1038$
**107.** $x = \dfrac{\ln 2}{\ln 3 - \ln 2}$; $x \approx 1.7095$  **109.** $x = \dfrac{\ln 9 - \ln 5}{2\ln 5 - \ln 9}$; $x \approx 0.5753$
**111.** $x \approx 46.2$  **113.** $t = \dfrac{\ln\left(\frac{c}{p} - 1\right)}{-k}$, $t \approx 55.45$

**115. a.** 30 fish  **b.** about 37 months  **117.** about 3.2 cmHg
**119.** about 50.2 min  **121.** $15,641  **123.** 6 hr, 18.0%
**125.** $M_f = 52.76$ tons  **127. a.** 26 planes  **b.** 9 days
**129. a.** $\log_3 4 + \log_3 5 = 2.7268$  **b.** $\log_3 4 - \log_3 5 = -0.203$
**c.** $2\log_3 5 = 2.9298$  **131. a.** d  **b. e. c. b  d. f  e. a  f. c**
**133.** $x = 0.69314718$  **135. a.** $(f \circ g)(x) = 3^{(\log_3 x + 2) - 2} = 3^{\log_3 x} = x$;
$(g \circ f)(x) = \log_3(3^{x-2}) + 2 = x - 2 + 2 = x$
**b.** $(f \circ g)(x) = e^{(\ln x + 1) - 1} = e^{\ln x} = x$;
$(g \circ f)(x) = \ln e^{x-1} + 1 = x - 1 + 1 = x$
**137. a.** $y = e^{x\ln 2} = e^{\ln 2^x} = 2^x$;
$y = 2^x \Rightarrow \ln y = x\ln 2$, $e^{\ln y} = e^{x\ln 2} \Rightarrow y = e^{x\ln 2}$
**b.** $y = b^x$, $\ln y = x\ln b$, $e^{\ln y} = e^{x\ln b}$, $y = e^{xr}$ for $r = \ln b$
**139.** Answers will vary.

## Exercises AI-D, pp. A-52–A-57

**1.** Compound  **3.** $Q_0 e^{-rt}$  **5.** Answers will vary.  **7.** $4896  **9.** 250%
**11.** $2152.47  **13.** 5.25 yr  **15.** 80%  **17.** 4 yr  **19.** 16 yr
**21.** $7561.33  **23.** about 5 yr  **25.** 7.5 yr  **27.** no  **29. a.** no
**b.** 9.12%  **31.** 7.9 yr  **33.** 7.5 yr  **35. a.** no  **b.** 9.4%  **37. a.** no
**b.** approx 13,609 euros  **39.** No; $234,612.01  **41.** about 7 yr
**43.** 23 yr  **45. a.** no  **b.** $302.25  **47. a.** $t = \dfrac{A - P}{pr}$  **b.** $p = \dfrac{A}{1 + rt}$

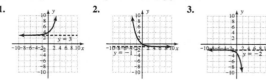

**49. a.** $r = n\left(\sqrt[nt]{\dfrac{A}{p}} - 1\right)$  **b.** $t = \dfrac{\ln\left(\dfrac{A}{p}\right)}{n\ln\left(1 + \dfrac{r}{n}\right)}$  **51. a.** $Q_0 = \dfrac{Q(t)}{e^{rt}}$
**b.** $t = \dfrac{\ln\left(\dfrac{Q(t)}{Q_0}\right)}{r}$  **53.** $709.74  **55. a.** 5.78%  **b.** 91.67 hr  **57.** 0.65 g
**59.** 816 yr  **61.** about 12.4%  **63.** $17,027,502.21  **65.** 7.93%

## Summary and Concept Review, pp. A-57–A-60

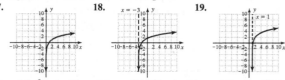

**4.** 2  **5.** $-2$  **6.** $\frac{5}{2}$  **7.** 12.1 yr  **8.** $3^2 = 9$  **9.** $5^{-3} = \frac{1}{125}$
**10.** $e^{3.7612} \approx 43$  **11.** $\log_5 25 = 2$  **12.** $\ln 0.7788 \approx -0.25$
**13.** $\log_3 81 = 4$  **14.** 5  **15.** $-1$  **16.** $\frac{1}{2}$

**17.**    **18.**    **19.**

**20.** $x \in (-\frac{3}{2}, \infty)$  **21.** $x \in (-\infty, 0) \cup (6, \infty)$  **22. a.** 4.79  **b.** $10^{7.3}I_0$
**23. a.** $x = e^{32}$  **b.** $x = 10^{2.38}$  **c.** $x = \ln 9.8$  **d.** $x = \frac{1}{2}\log 7$
**24. a.** $x = \dfrac{\ln 4}{0.5}$, $x \approx 2.7726$  **b.** $x = \dfrac{\ln 19}{0.2}$, $x \approx 6.3938$
**c.** $x = \dfrac{10^3}{3}$, $x \approx 33.3333$  **d.** $x = e^{-2.75}$, $x \approx 0.0639$  **25. a.** $\ln 42$
**b.** $\log_9 30$  **c.** $\ln\left(\frac{x+3}{x-1}\right)$  **d.** $\log(x^2 + x)$  **26. a.** $2\log_5 9$  **b.** $2\log_7 4$
**c.** $(2x - 1)\ln 5$  **d.** $(3x + 2)\ln 10$  **27. a.** $\ln x + \frac{1}{4}\ln y$
**b.** $\frac{1}{3}\ln p + \ln q$  **c.** $\frac{5}{3}\log x + \frac{4}{3}\log y - \frac{5}{2}\log x - \frac{3}{2}\log y$
**d.** $\log 4 + \frac{5}{3}\log p + \frac{4}{3}\log q - \frac{3}{2}\log p - \log q$  **28. a.** $\dfrac{\log 45}{\log 6} \approx 2.215$
**b.** $\dfrac{\log 128}{\log 3} \approx 4.417$  **c.** $\dfrac{\ln 124}{\ln 2} \approx 6.954$  **d.** $\dfrac{\ln 0.42}{\ln 5} \approx -0.539$
**29.** $x = \dfrac{\ln 7}{\ln 2}$  **30.** $x = \dfrac{\ln 5}{\ln 3} - 1$  **31.** $x = \dfrac{2}{1 - \ln 3}$  **32.** $x \approx 6.389$

**33.** $x = 5$; $-2$ is extraneous   **34.** $x = 4.25$   **35. a.** 17.77%

**b.** 23.98 days   **36.** 38.6 cmHg   **37.** 18.5%   **38.** Almost, she needs

$42.15 more.   **39. a.** no   **b.** $268.93   **40.** 55.0%

## Mixed Review, pp. A-60–A-61

**1. a.** $\dfrac{\log 30}{\log 2} \approx 4.9069$   **b.** $-1.5$   **c.** $\frac{1}{3}$   **3. a.** $2\log_{10}20$   **b.** $0.05x$
**c.** $(x - 3)\ln 2$

**5.**    **7.**   **9. a.** $5^4 = 625$

**b.** $e^{0.45} = 0.15x$   **c.** $10^7 = 0.1 \times 10^8$   **11. a.** $(-\infty, -\frac{1}{2}) \cup (2, \infty)$

**b.** $(-\infty, 2) \cup (2, \infty)$   **13.** $6 + \log 2$   **15.** $\frac{9}{4} + \frac{\sqrt{129}}{4}$

**17.** $I \approx 6.3 \times 10^{17}$   **19.** 1.6 m, 1.28 m, 1.02 m, 0.82 m, 0.66 m, 0.52 m

## Practice Test, pp. A-61–A-62

**1.** $3^4 = 81$   **2.** $\log_{25}5 = \frac{1}{2}$   **3.** $\frac{5}{2}\log_b x + 3\log_b y - \log_b z$
**4.** $\log_b \dfrac{m\sqrt{n^3}}{\sqrt{p}}$   **5.** $x = 10$   **6.** $x = \dfrac{-5}{3}$   **7.** 2.68   **8.** $-1.24$

**9.**    **10.**   **11. a.** 4.19   **b.** $-0.81$

**12.** $D = (2, \infty)$, $R = (-\infty, \infty)$;
$f^{-1}(x) = e^{x+3} + 2$, $D = (-\infty, \infty)$, $R = (2, \infty)$

**13.** $x = 1 + \dfrac{\ln 89}{\ln 3}$   **14.** $x = 1, x = -5$ is extraneous   **15.** $\approx 5$ yr

**16.** $\approx 8.7$ yr   **17.** 19.1 months   **18.** 7% compounded semi-annually
**19. a.** no   **b.** $54.09   **20. a.** 10.2 lb   **b.** 19 weeks

## Strengthening Core Skills, pp. A-63–A-64

**Exercise 1:** Answers will vary.
**Exercise 2: a.** $\log(x^2 + 3x)$   **b.** $\ln(x^2 - 4)$   **c.** $\log\frac{x}{x+3}$
**Exercise 3:** Answers will vary.
**Exercise 4: a.** $x\log 3$   **b.** $5\ln x$   **c.** $(3x - 1)\ln 2$

# INDEX

## ▼ Fundamental Identities

### Reciprocal Identities

$$\sec\theta = \frac{1}{\cos\theta}$$

$$\csc\theta = \frac{1}{\sin\theta}$$

$$\cot\theta = \frac{1}{\tan\theta}$$

### Ratio Identities

$$\tan\theta = \frac{\sin\theta}{\cos\theta}$$

$$\cot\theta = \frac{\cos\theta}{\sin\theta}$$

### Pythagorean Identities

$$\sin^2\theta + \cos^2\theta = 1$$

$$\tan^2\theta + 1 = \sec^2\theta$$

$$1 + \cot^2\theta = \csc^2\theta$$

### Identities due to Symmetry

$$\sin(-\theta) = -\sin\theta$$

$$\cos(-\theta) = \cos\theta$$

$$\tan(-\theta) = -\tan\theta$$

## ▼ Cofunction Identities

$$\sin\left(\frac{\pi}{2} - \theta\right) = \cos\theta \qquad \cos\left(\frac{\pi}{2} - \theta\right) = \sin\theta$$

$$\tan\left(\frac{\pi}{2} - \theta\right) = \cot\theta \qquad \cot\left(\frac{\pi}{2} - \theta\right) = \tan\theta$$

$$\sec\left(\frac{\pi}{2} - \theta\right) = \csc\theta \qquad \csc\left(\frac{\pi}{2} - \theta\right) = \sec\theta$$

## ▼ Sum and Difference Identities

$$\cos(\alpha \pm \beta) = \cos\alpha\cos\beta \mp \sin\alpha\sin\beta$$

$$\sin(\alpha \pm \beta) = \sin\alpha\cos\beta \pm \cos\alpha\sin\beta$$

$$\tan(\alpha \pm \beta) = \frac{\tan\alpha \pm \tan\beta}{1 \mp \tan\alpha\tan\beta}$$

## ▼ Double-Angle Identities

$$\sin(2\alpha) = 2\sin\alpha\cos\alpha$$

$$\cos(2\alpha) = \cos^2\alpha - \sin^2\alpha$$

$$= 2\cos^2\alpha - 1$$

$$= 1 - 2\sin^2\alpha$$

## ▼ Half-Angle Identities

$$\sin\left(\frac{\theta}{2}\right) = \pm\sqrt{\frac{1 - \cos\theta}{2}}$$

$$\cos\left(\frac{\theta}{2}\right) = \pm\sqrt{\frac{1 + \cos\theta}{2}}$$

$$\tan\left(\frac{\theta}{2}\right) = \frac{1 - \cos\theta}{\sin\theta}$$

$$= \frac{\sin\theta}{1 + \cos\theta}$$

## ▼ Power Reduction Identities

$$\sin^2\theta = \frac{1 - \cos 2\theta}{2}$$

$$\cos^2\theta = \frac{1 + \cos 2\theta}{2}$$

$$\tan^2\theta = \frac{1 - \cos 2\theta}{1 + \cos 2\theta}$$

## ▼ Product-to-Sum Identities

$$\sin\alpha\cos\beta = \frac{1}{2}[\sin(\alpha + \beta) + \sin(\alpha - \beta)]$$

$$\cos\alpha\sin\beta = \frac{1}{2}[\sin(\alpha + \beta) - \sin(\alpha - \beta)]$$

$$\cos\alpha\cos\beta = \frac{1}{2}[\cos(\alpha + \beta) + \cos(\alpha - \beta)]$$

$$\sin\alpha\sin\beta = \frac{1}{2}[\cos(\alpha - \beta) - \cos(\alpha + \beta)]$$

## ▼ Sum-to-Product Identities

$$\sin\alpha + \sin\beta = 2\sin\left(\frac{\alpha + \beta}{2}\right)\cos\left(\frac{\alpha - \beta}{2}\right)$$

$$\sin\alpha - \sin\beta = 2\cos\left(\frac{\alpha + \beta}{2}\right)\sin\left(\frac{\alpha - \beta}{2}\right)$$

$$\cos\alpha + \cos\beta = 2\cos\left(\frac{\alpha + \beta}{2}\right)\cos\left(\frac{\alpha - \beta}{2}\right)$$

$$\cos\alpha - \cos\beta = -2\sin\left(\frac{\alpha + \beta}{2}\right)\sin\left(\frac{\alpha - \beta}{2}\right)$$

## ▼ Law of Sines

$$\frac{\sin A}{a} = \frac{\sin B}{b} = \frac{\sin C}{c}$$

## ▼ Area of a Triangle

$$\text{Area} = \frac{1}{2}bc\sin A$$

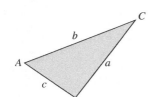

## ▼ Law of Cosines

$$a^2 = b^2 + c^2 - 2bc\cos A$$

$$b^2 = a^2 + c^2 - 2ac\cos B$$

$$c^2 = a^2 + b^2 - 2ab\cos C$$

## ▼ Special Triangles and Special Angles

| $\theta$ | $\sin\theta$ | $\cos\theta$ | $\tan\theta$ | $\csc\theta$ | $\sec\theta$ | $\cot\theta$ |
|---|---|---|---|---|---|---|
| $0° = 0$ | 0 | 1 | 0 | — | 1 | — |
| $30° = \dfrac{\pi}{6}$ | $\dfrac{1}{2}$ | $\dfrac{\sqrt{3}}{2}$ | $\dfrac{1}{\sqrt{3}}$ | 2 | $\dfrac{2}{\sqrt{3}}$ | $\sqrt{3}$ |
| $45° = \dfrac{\pi}{4}$ | $\dfrac{\sqrt{2}}{2}$ | $\dfrac{\sqrt{2}}{2}$ | 1 | $\sqrt{2}$ | $\sqrt{2}$ | 1 |
| $60° = \dfrac{\pi}{3}$ | $\dfrac{\sqrt{3}}{2}$ | $\dfrac{1}{2}$ | $\sqrt{3}$ | $\dfrac{2}{\sqrt{3}}$ | 2 | $\dfrac{1}{\sqrt{3}}$ |
| $90° = \dfrac{\pi}{2}$ | 1 | 0 | — | 1 | — | 0 |

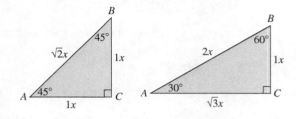

## ▼ Degree and Radian Conversions

degrees to radians: multiply by $\dfrac{\pi}{180°}$ (degrees cancel)

radians to degrees: multiply by $\dfrac{180°}{\pi}$ (radians cancel)

## ▼ Triangle Classifications

### By Angle Measure

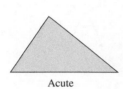

Acute

Right

Obtuse

### By Side Length

Equilateral

Isoceles

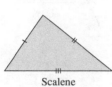

Scalene

## ▼ Trigonometry and the Coordinate Plane

For $P(x, y)$ a point on the terminal side of an angle $\theta$ in standard position:

$\cos\theta = \dfrac{x}{r}$

$\sin\theta = \dfrac{y}{r}$

$\tan\theta = \dfrac{y}{x}, x \neq 0$

$\sec\theta = \dfrac{r}{x}, x \neq 0$

$\csc\theta = \dfrac{r}{y}, y \neq 0$

$\cot\theta = \dfrac{x}{y}, y \neq 0$

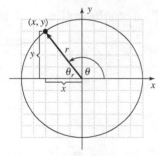

## ▼ Right Triangle Trigonometry

For right $\triangle ABC$ with indicated sides **adj**acent and **opp**osite to acute angle $\theta$:

$\cos\theta = \dfrac{\text{adj}}{\text{hyp}}$

$\sin\theta = \dfrac{\text{opp}}{\text{hyp}}$

$\tan\theta = \dfrac{\text{opp}}{\text{adj}}$

$\sec\theta = \dfrac{\text{hyp}}{\text{adj}}$

$\csc\theta = \dfrac{\text{hyp}}{\text{opp}}$

$\cot\theta = \dfrac{\text{adj}}{\text{opp}}$

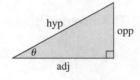

## ▼ Trigonometric Functions of a Real Number

For any real number $t$ and point $P(x, y)$ on the unit circle associated with $t$:

$\cos t = x$

$\sin t = y$

$\tan t = \dfrac{y}{x}; x \neq 0$

$\sec t = \dfrac{1}{x}; x \neq 0$

$\csc t = \dfrac{1}{y}; y \neq 0$

$\cot t = \dfrac{x}{y}; y \neq 0$

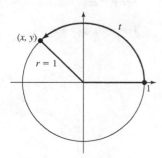

## ▼ Special Constants

$\pi \approx 3.1416$    $\dfrac{\pi}{2} \approx 1.5708$    $\dfrac{\pi}{3} \approx 1.0472$    $\dfrac{\pi}{4} \approx 0.7854$    $\dfrac{\pi}{6} \approx 0.5236$    $\dfrac{\pi}{12} \approx 0.2618$

$e \approx 2.7183$    $\sqrt{2} \approx 1.4142$    $\sqrt{3} \approx 1.7321$    $\dfrac{\sqrt{2}}{2} \approx 0.7071$    $\dfrac{\sqrt{3}}{2} \approx 0.8660$    $\dfrac{\sqrt{3}}{3} \approx 0.5774$

## ▼ Arcs and Sectors

For a circle of radius $r$ and angle $\theta$ in radians:

arc length: $s = r\theta$

area of sector: $A = \dfrac{1}{2}r^2\theta$

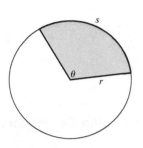

## ▼ Graphs of the Trigonometric Functions

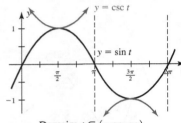

Domain: $t \in (-\infty, \infty)$
Range: $\sin t \in [-1, 1]$

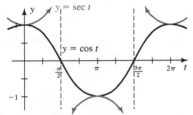

Domain: $t \in (-\infty, \infty)$
Range: $\cos t \in [-1, 1]$

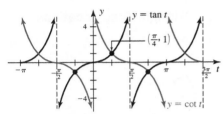

Domain: $t \neq \dfrac{\pi}{2}(2k + 1); k \in \mathbb{Z}$
Range: $\tan t \in \mathbb{R}$

## ▼ Transformations of Basic Trig Graphs

**Given Function**

$y = f(x)$

**Transformation of $y = f(x)$**

$$y = Af\left[B\left(x \pm \dfrac{C}{B}\right)\right] \pm D$$

north/south reflections;
vertical stretches and compressions

horizontal shift, opposite
direction of sign

vertical shift, same
direction as sign

For $y = A\sin\left[B\left(x \pm \dfrac{C}{B}\right)\right] \pm D$ we have: amplitude: $|A|$, period: $\dfrac{2\pi}{B}$, horizontal shift: $\dfrac{C}{B}$, vertical shift: $D$

## ▼ The Inverse Trigonometric Functions

For $y = \sin t$ with $t \in \left[-\dfrac{\pi}{2}, \dfrac{\pi}{2}\right]$ and $y \in [1, 1]$, the inverse function is $y = \sin^{-1}t$, where $t \in [1, 1]$ and $y \in \left[-\dfrac{\pi}{2}, \dfrac{\pi}{2}\right]$.

For $y = \cos t$ with $t \in [0, \pi]$ and $y \in [1, 1]$, the inverse function is $y = \cos^{-1}t$, where $t \in [1, 1]$ and $y \in [0, \pi]$.

For $y = \tan t$ with $t \in \left(-\dfrac{\pi}{2}, \dfrac{\pi}{2}\right)$ and $y \in \mathbb{R}$, the inverse function is $y = \tan^{-1}t$, where $t \in \mathbb{R}$ and $y \in \left(-\dfrac{\pi}{2}, \dfrac{\pi}{2}\right)$.

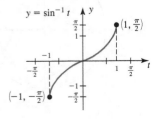

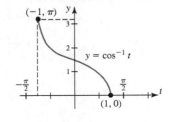

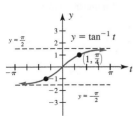

## ▼ Commonly used, small case Greek letters

| | | | | | | | | | |
|---|---|---|---|---|---|---|---|---|---|
| $\alpha$ | alpha | $\beta$ | beta | $\gamma$ | gamma | $\delta$ | delta | $\epsilon$ | epsilon |
| $\zeta$ | zeta | $\theta$ | theta | $\lambda$ | lambda | $\mu$ | mu | $\pi$ | pi |
| $\rho$ | rho | $\sigma$ | sigma | $\phi$ | phi | $\psi$ | psi | $\omega$ | omega |

## ▼ Complex Numbers $z = a + bi$

**Absolute Value**

$$|z| = \sqrt{a^2 + b^2}$$

distance from $(0, 0)$ to $(a, b)$

**Trigonometric Form**

$$z = r(\cos\theta + i\sin\theta)$$

where $r = |z|$

**Products and Quotients**

$$z_1 z_2 = r_1 r_2[\cos(\theta_1 + \theta_2) + i\sin(\theta_1 + \theta_2)]$$
$$\frac{z_1}{z_2} = \frac{r_1}{r_2}[\cos(\theta_1 - \theta_2) + i\sin(\theta_1 - \theta_2)]$$

**Powers and DeMoivres Theorem**

$z^n = r^n(\cos n\theta + i\sin n\theta)$ for positive integers $n$

**Roots and the $n$th Roots Theorem**

$$\sqrt[n]{z} = \sqrt[n]{r}\left(\cos\frac{\theta + 2\pi k}{n} + i\sin\frac{\theta + 2\pi k}{n}\right) \text{ for } k = 0, 1, 2, ..., n-1$$

## ▼ Vectors and the Dot Product

- For a position vector, $\mathbf{v} = \langle a, b\rangle$ and angle $\theta$ as shown, $a = |\mathbf{v}|\cos\theta$ and $b = |\mathbf{v}|\sin\theta$, where $\theta_r = \tan^{-1}\left|\frac{b}{a}\right|$ and $|\mathbf{v}| = \sqrt{a^2 + b^2}$.

- For any nonzero vector $\mathbf{v} = \langle a, b\rangle = a\mathbf{i} + b\mathbf{j}$, the vector $\mathbf{u} = \dfrac{\mathbf{v}}{|\mathbf{v}|}$ is a unit vector in the same direction as $\mathbf{v}$.

- Given the vectors $\mathbf{u} = \langle a, b\rangle$ and $\mathbf{v} = \langle c, d\rangle$, their dot product is denoted $\mathbf{u} \cdot \mathbf{v}$ and is defined as: $\mathbf{u} \cdot \mathbf{v} = \langle a, b\rangle \cdot \langle c, d\rangle = ac + bd$.

- Given the nonzero vectors $\mathbf{u}$ and $\mathbf{v}$ and angle $\theta$ between them, $\cos\theta = \dfrac{\mathbf{u}}{|\mathbf{u}|} \cdot \dfrac{\mathbf{v}}{|\mathbf{v}|}$.

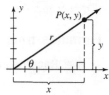

## ▼ Polar Coordinates

$P(x, y)$ in rectangular coordinates can be represented as $P(r, \theta)$ in polar coordinates:

$$x = r\cos\theta \qquad y = r\sin\theta \qquad r = \sqrt{x^2 + y^2} \qquad \theta_r = \tan^{-1}\left|\frac{y}{x}\right|, x \neq 0$$

## ▼ Logarithms and Logarithmic Properties

$$y = \log_b x \Leftrightarrow b^y = x \qquad\qquad \log_b b = 1 \qquad\qquad \log_b 1 = 0$$

$$\log_b b^x = x \qquad\qquad b^{\log_b x} = x \qquad\qquad \log_c x = \frac{\log_b x}{\log_b c}$$

$$\log_b MN = \log_b M + \log_b N \qquad \log_b \frac{M}{N} = \log_b M - \log_b N \qquad \log_b M^P = P \cdot \log_b M$$

## ▼ Applications of Exponentials and Logarithms

$A \to$ amount accumulated   $P \to$ initial deposit, $\mathcal{P} \to$ periodic payment   $n \to$ compounding periods/year

$r \to$ interest rate per year   $R \to$ interest rate per time period$\left(\dfrac{r}{n}\right)$   $t \to$ time in years

**Interest Compounded $n$ Times per Year**

$$A = P\left(1 + \frac{r}{n}\right)^{nt}$$

**Interest Compounded Continuously**

$$A = Pe^{rt}$$

**Accumulated Value of an Annuity**

$$A = \frac{\mathcal{P}}{R}[(1 + R)^{nt} - 1]$$

**Payments Required to Accumulate Amount $A$**

$$\mathcal{P} = \frac{AR}{(1 + R)^{nt} - 1}$$

# Topics from Algebra

## ▼ Special Products

$$(a + b)^2 = a^2 + 2ab + b^2$$
$$(a + b)^3 = a^3 + 3a^2 b + 3ab^2 + b^3$$
$$(x + c)(x + d) = x^2 + (c + d)x + cd$$

$$(a - b)^2 = a^2 - 2ab + b^2$$
$$(a - b)^3 = a^3 - 3a^2 b + 3ab^2 - b^3$$
$$(ax + c)(bx + d) = abx^2 + (ad + bc)x + cd$$

## ▼ Special Factorizations

$$a^2 + 2ab + b^2 = (a + b)^2$$
$$x^2 + (c + d)x + cd = (x + c)(x + d)$$
$$a^2 - b^2 = (a + b)(a - b)$$
$$a^3 - b^3 = (a - b)(a^2 + ab + b^2)$$

$$a^2 - 2ab + b^2 = (a - b)^2$$
$$abx^2 + (ad + bc)x + cd = (ax + c)(bx + d)$$
$$a^2 + b^2 \text{ is prime over the real numbers}$$
$$a^3 + b^3 = (a + b)(a^2 - ab + b^2)$$

## ▼ Formulas from Plane Geometry: $P \rightarrow$ perimeter, $C \rightarrow$ circumference, $A \rightarrow$ area

### Rectangle
$$P = 2l + 2w$$
$$A = lw$$

### Square
$$P = 4s$$
$$A = s^2$$

### Regular Polygon
$$P = ns$$
$$A = \frac{a}{2}P$$

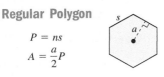

### Parallelogram
$$A = bh$$

### Trapezoid
$$A = \frac{h}{2}(a + b)$$

### Triangle
$$A = \frac{1}{2}bh$$

### Triangle
Sum of angles
$$A + B + C = 180°$$

### Right Triangle
Pythagorean Theorem
$$a^2 + b^2 = c^2$$

### Circle
$$A = \pi r^2$$
$$C = 2\pi r = \pi d$$

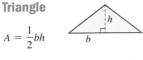

### Ellipse
$$A = \pi ab$$
$$C \approx \sqrt{2(a^2 + b^2)}$$

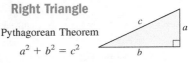

### Right Parabolic Segment
$$A = \frac{2}{3}ab$$

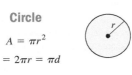

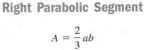

## ▼ Formulas from Solid Geometry: $S \rightarrow$ surface area, $V \rightarrow$ volume

### Rectangular Solid
$$V = lwh$$
$$S = lw + lh + wh$$

### Cube
$$V = s^3$$
$$S = 6s^2$$

### Right Circular Cylinder
$$V = \pi r^2 h$$
$$S = 2\pi r(r + h)$$

### Right Circular Cone
$$V = \frac{1}{3}\pi r^2 h$$
$$S = \pi r(r + \sqrt{r^2 + h^2})$$

### Right Square Pyramid
$$V = \frac{1}{3}s^2 h$$
$$S = s^2 + s\sqrt{s^2 + 4h^2}$$

### Sphere
$$V = \frac{4}{3}\pi r^3$$
$$S = 4\pi r^2$$

## ▼ Formulas from Analytical Geometry: $P_1 \rightarrow (x_1, y_1)$, $P_2 \rightarrow (x_2, y_2)$

### Distance between $P_1$ and $P_2$
$$d = \sqrt{(x_2 - x_1)^2 + (y_2 - y_1)^2}$$

### Slope of Line Containing $P_1$ and $P_2$
$$m = \frac{\Delta y}{\Delta x} = \frac{y_2 - y_1}{x_2 - x_1}$$

### Equation of Line Containing $P_1$ and $P_2$
Point-Slope Form
$$y - y_1 = m(x - x_1)$$

### Equation of Line Containing $P_1$ and $P_2$
Slope-Intercept Form (slope $m$, $y$-intercept $b$)
$$y = mx + b, \text{ where } b = y_1 - mx_1$$

### Parallel Lines
Slopes Are Equal: $m_1 = m_2$

### Perpendicular Lines
Slopes Have a Product of $-1$: $m_1 = -\dfrac{1}{m_2}$ or $m_1 m_2 = -1$

### Intersecting Lines
Slopes Are Unequal: $m_1 \neq m_2$

### Dependent (Coincident) Lines
Slopes and $y$-Intercepts Are Equal: $m_1 = m_2$, $b_1 = b_2$

# Credits

## Student Answer Appendix 641